D1543845

Frequently Used Symbols and Formulas

A Key to the Icons Appearing in the Exercise Sets

Concept reinforcement exercises, indicated by purple exercise numbers, provide basic practice with the new concepts and vocabulary.

1 Following most examples, students are directed to TRY EXERCISES . These selected exercises are identified with a color block around the exercise numbers.

Aha! Exercises labeled Aha! can often be solved quickly with the proper insight.

Calculator exercises are designed to be worked using a scientific or graphing calculator.

Graphing calculator exercises are designed to be worked using a graphing calculator and often provide practice for concepts discussed in the Technology Connections.

Writing exercises are designed to be answered using one or more complete sentences.

Symbols

$=$	Is equal to
$\approx$	Is approximately equal to
$>$	Is greater than
$<$	Is less than
$\geq$	Is greater than or equal to
$\leq$	Is less than or equal to
$\in$	Is an element of
$\subseteq$	Is a subset of
$|x|$	The absolute value of x
$\{x \mid x \ldots\}$	The set of all x such that $x\ldots$
$-x$	The opposite of x
$\sqrt{x}$	The square root of x
$\sqrt[n]{x}$	The nth root of x
LCM	Least Common Multiple
LCD	Least Common Denominator
π	Pi
i	$\sqrt{-1}$
$f(x)$	f of x, or f at x
$f^{-1}(x)$	f inverse of x
$(f \circ g)(x)$	$f(g(x))$
e	Approximately 2.7
Σ	Summation
$n!$	Factorial notation

Formulas

$m = \dfrac{y_2 - y_1}{x_2 - x_1}$	Slope of a line
$y = mx + b$	Slope–intercept form of a linear equation
$y - y_1 = m(x - x_1)$	Point–slope form of a linear equation
$(A + B)(A - B) = A^2 - B^2$	Product of the sum and difference of the same two terms
$\left.\begin{array}{l}(A + B)^2 = A^2 + 2AB + B^2, \\ (A - B)^2 = A^2 - 2AB + B^2\end{array}\right\}$	Square of a binomial
$d = rt$	Formula for distance traveled
$\dfrac{1}{a} \cdot t + \dfrac{1}{b} \cdot t = 1$	Work principle
$s = 16t^2$	Free-fall distance
$y = kx$	Direct variation
$y = \dfrac{k}{x}$	Inverse variation
$x = \dfrac{-b \pm \sqrt{b^2 - 4ac}}{2a}$	Quadratic formula
$P(t) = P_0 e^{kt}, \ k > 0$	Exponential growth
$P(t) = P_0 e^{-kt}, \ k > 0$	Exponential decay
$d = \sqrt{(x_2 - x_1)^2 + (y_2 - y_1)^2}$	Distance formula
$\dbinom{n}{r} = \dfrac{n!}{(n - r)! \, r!}$	$\dbinom{n}{r}$ notation

Intermediate Algebra

CONCEPTS AND APPLICATIONS

BITTINGER

ELLENBOGEN

JOHNSON

Custom Edition for Miami Dade College

Taken from:
Elementary & Intermediate Algebra, Fifth Edition by Marvin L. Bittinger, David J. Ellenbogen
and Barbara L. Johnson

Learning Solutions

New York   Boston   San Francisco
London   Toronto   Sydney   Tokyo   Singapore   Madrid
Mexico City   Munich   Paris   Cape Town   Hong Kong   Montreal

Cover Art: Illustration by Kristen Kiley

Taken from:

Elementary & Intermediate Algebra, Fifth Edition
by Marvin L. Bittinger, David J. Ellenbogen and Barbara L. Johnson
Copyright © 2010, 2006, 2002, 1998, 1994 by Pearson Education, Inc.
Published by Prentice Hall
Upper Saddle River, New Jersey 07458

Pearson Learning Solutions, 501 Boylston Street, Suite 900, Boston, MA 02116
A Pearson Education Company
www.pearsoned.com

Printed in the United States of America

4 5 6 7 8 9 10 V382 15 14 13 12 11

000200010270578222

MT

ISBN 10: 0-558-76673-0
ISBN 13: 978-0-558-76673-3

Contents

3 Polynomials and Factoring 151

4   Rational Expressions and Equations   229

9   Quadratic Functions and Equations   563

Equations, Inequalities, and Problem Solving

DEBORAH ELIAS
EVENT COORDINATOR
Houston, Texas

As an event planner, I am constantly using math. Calculations range from figuring the tax and gratuity percentage to add to the final bill to finding dimensions of linens to fit a table properly. For every client, I also determine a budget with income and expenses.

AN APPLICATION

Event promoters use the formula

$$p = \frac{1.2x}{s}$$

to determine a ticket price p for an event with x dollars of expenses and s anticipated ticket sales. Grand Events expects expenses for an upcoming concert to be $80,000 and anticipates selling 4000 tickets. What should the ticket price be?

Source: *The Indianapolis Star*, 2/27/03

This problem appears as Example 1 in Section 1.3.

1

Solving equations and inequalities is a recurring theme in much of mathematics. In this chapter, we will study some of the principles used to solve equations and inequalities. We will then use equations and inequalities to solve applied problems.

1.1   Solving Equations

Equations and Solutions   •   The Addition Principle   •   The Multiplication Principle   •
Selecting the Correct Approach

Solving equations is essential for problem solving in algebra. In this section, we study two of the most important principles used for this task.

Equations and Solutions

We have already seen that an equation is a number sentence stating that the expressions on either side of the equals sign represent the same number. Some equations, like $3 + 2 = 5$ or $2x + 6 = 2(x + 3)$, are *always* true and some, like $3 + 2 = 6$ or $x + 2 = x + 3$, are *never* true. In this text, we will concentrate on equations like $x + 6 = 13$ or $7x = 141$ that are *sometimes* true, depending on the replacement value for the variable.

> **Solution of an Equation**
>
> Any replacement for the variable that makes an equation true is called a *solution* of the equation. To *solve* an equation means to find all of its solutions.

To determine whether a number is a solution, we substitute that number for the variable throughout the equation. If the values on both sides of the equals sign are the same, then the number that was substituted is a solution.

EXAMPLE   1   Determine whether 7 is a solution of $x + 6 = 13$.

SOLUTION   We have

$$\frac{x + 6 = 13}{7 + 6 \mid 13}$$
$$13 \overset{?}{=} 13 \quad \text{TRUE}$$

Writing the equation
Substituting 7 for x
$13 = 13$ is a true statement.

Since the left-hand side and the right-hand side are the same, 7 is a solution.

> *CAUTION!*   Note that in Example 1, the solution is 7, not 13.

EXAMPLE 2 Determine whether $\frac{2}{3}$ is a solution of $156x = 117$.

SOLUTION We have

$$156x = 117 \qquad \text{Writing the equation}$$

$$156\left(\frac{2}{3}\right) \mid 117 \qquad \text{Substituting } \frac{2}{3} \text{ for } x$$

$$104 \overset{?}{=} 117 \quad \text{FALSE} \qquad \text{The statement } 104 = 117 \text{ is false.}$$

Since the left-hand side and the right-hand side differ, $\frac{2}{3}$ is not a solution.

The Addition Principle

Consider the equation

$$x = 7.$$

We can easily see that the solution of this equation is 7. Replacing x with 7, we get

$$7 = 7, \quad \text{which is true.}$$

Now consider the equation

$$x + 6 = 13.$$

In Example 1, we found that the solution of $x + 6 = 13$ is also 7. Although the solution of $x = 7$ may seem more obvious, because $x + 6 = 13$ and $x = 7$ have identical solutions, the equations are said to be **equivalent**.

STUDENT NOTES

Be sure to remember the difference between an expression and an equation. For example, $5a - 10$ and $5(a - 2)$ are *equivalent expressions* because they represent the same value for all replacements for a. The *equations* $5a = 10$ and $a = 2$ are *equivalent* because they have the same solution, 2.

> **Equivalent Equations**
>
> Equations with the same solutions are called *equivalent equations*.

There are principles that enable us to begin with one equation and end up with an equivalent equation, like $x = 7$, for which the solution is obvious. One such principle concerns addition. The equation $a = b$ says that a and b stand for the same number. Suppose this is true, and some number c is added to a. We get the same result if we add c to b, because a and b are the same number.

> **The Addition Principle**
>
> For any real numbers a, b, and c,
>
> $$a = b \quad \text{is equivalent to} \quad a + c = b + c.$$

To visualize the addition principle, consider a balance similar to one a jeweler might use. When the two sides of a balance hold equal weight, the balance is level. If weight is then added or removed, equally, on both sides, the balance will remain level.

When using the addition principle, we often say that we "add the same number to both sides of an equation." We can also "subtract the same number from both sides," since subtraction can be regarded as the addition of an opposite.

EXAMPLE 3

Solve: $x + 5 = -7$.

SOLUTION We can add any number we like to both sides. Since -5 is the opposite, or additive inverse, of 5, we add -5 to each side:

$$x + 5 = -7$$
$$x + 5 - 5 = -7 - 5 \qquad \text{Using the addition principle: adding } -5 \text{ to both sides or subtracting 5 from both sides}$$
$$x + 0 = -12 \qquad \text{Simplifying; } x + 5 - 5 = x + 5 + (-5) = x + 0$$
$$x = -12. \qquad \text{Using the identity property of 0}$$

The equation $x = -12$ is equivalent to the equation $x + 5 = -7$ by the addition principle, so the solution of $x = -12$ is the solution of $x + 5 = -7$.

It is obvious that the solution of $x = -12$ is the number -12. To check the answer in the original equation, we substitute.

Check:
$$\frac{x + 5 = -7}{-12 + 5 \,\,|\,\, -7}$$
$$-7 \overset{?}{=} -7 \quad \text{TRUE} \qquad -7 = -7 \text{ is true.}$$

The solution of the original equation is -12.

TRY EXERCISE 11

In Example 3, note that because we added the *opposite*, or *additive inverse*, of 5, the left side of the equation simplified to x plus the *additive identity*, 0, or simply x. These steps effectively replaced the 5 on the left with a 0. To solve $x + a = b$ for x, we add $-a$ to (or subtract a from) both sides.

EXAMPLE 4

Solve: $-6.5 = y - 8.4$.

SOLUTION The variable is on the right side this time. We can isolate y by adding 8.4 to each side:

$$-6.5 = y - 8.4 \qquad y - 8.4 \text{ can be regarded as } y + (-8.4).$$
$$-6.5 + 8.4 = y - 8.4 + 8.4 \qquad \text{Using the addition principle: Adding 8.4 to both sides "eliminates" } -8.4 \text{ on the right side.}$$
$$1.9 = y. \qquad y - 8.4 + 8.4 = y + (-8.4) + 8.4 = y + 0 = y$$

STUDENT NOTES ⎯⎯⎯⎯

We can also think of "undoing" operations in order to isolate a variable. In Example 4, we began with $y - 8.4$ on the right side. To undo the subtraction, we *add* 8.4.

Check:
$$\frac{-6.5 = y - 8.4}{-6.5 \,\,|\,\, 1.9 - 8.4}$$
$$-6.5 \overset{?}{=} -6.5 \qquad \text{TRUE} \qquad -6.5 = -6.5 \text{ is true.}$$

The solution is 1.9.

TRY EXERCISE 15

Note that the equations $a = b$ and $b = a$ have the same meaning. Thus, $-6.5 = y - 8.4$ could have been rewritten as $y - 8.4 = -6.5$.

The Multiplication Principle

A second principle for solving equations concerns multiplying. Suppose a and b are equal. If a and b are multiplied by some number c, then ac and bc will also be equal.

The Multiplication Principle

For any real numbers a, b, and c, with $c \neq 0$,

$$a = b \quad \text{is equivalent to} \quad a \cdot c = b \cdot c.$$

EXAMPLE 5

Solve: $\frac{5}{4}x = 10$.

SOLUTION   We can multiply both sides by any nonzero number we like. Since $\frac{4}{5}$ is the reciprocal of $\frac{5}{4}$, we decide to multiply both sides by $\frac{4}{5}$:

$$\frac{5}{4}x = 10$$

$$\frac{4}{5} \cdot \frac{5}{4}x = \frac{4}{5} \cdot 10 \qquad \text{Using the multiplication principle: Multiplying both sides by } \frac{4}{5} \text{ "eliminates" the } \frac{5}{4} \text{ on the left.}$$

$$1 \cdot x = 8 \qquad \text{Simplifying}$$

$$x = 8. \qquad \text{Using the identity property of 1}$$

Check:
$$\frac{5}{4}x = 10$$

$$\begin{array}{c|c} \frac{5}{4} \cdot 8 & 10 \\ \frac{40}{4} & \end{array} \qquad \text{Think of 8 as } \frac{8}{1}.$$

$$10 \overset{?}{=} 10 \quad \text{TRUE} \qquad 10 = 10 \text{ is true.}$$

The solution is 8.

TRY EXERCISE 49

In Example 5, to get x alone, we multiplied by the *reciprocal*, or *multiplicative inverse* of $\frac{5}{4}$. We then simplified the left-hand side to x times the *multiplicative identity*, 1, or simply x. These steps effectively replaced the $\frac{5}{4}$ on the left with 1.

Because division is the same as multiplying by a reciprocal, the multiplication principle also tells us that we can "divide both sides by the same nonzero number." That is,

$$\text{if } a = b, \text{ then} \quad \frac{1}{c} \cdot a = \frac{1}{c} \cdot b \quad \text{and} \quad \frac{a}{c} = \frac{b}{c} \quad (\text{provided } c \neq 0).$$

In a product like $3x$, the multiplier 3 is called the **coefficient**. *When the coefficient of the variable is an integer or a decimal, it is usually easiest to solve an equation by dividing on both sides. When the coefficient is in fraction notation, it is usually easiest to multiply by the reciprocal.*

EXAMPLE 6

Solve: **(a)** $-4x = 9$; **(b)** $-x = 5$; **(c)** $\frac{2y}{9} = \frac{8}{3}$.

SOLUTION

a) In $-4x = 9$, the coefficient of x is an integer, so we *divide* on both sides:

$$\frac{-4x}{-4} = \frac{9}{-4} \qquad \text{Using the multiplication principle: Dividing both sides by } -4 \text{ is the same as multiplying by } -\frac{1}{4}.$$

$$1 \cdot x = -\frac{9}{4} \qquad \text{Simplifying}$$

$$x = -\frac{9}{4}. \qquad \text{Using the identity property of 1}$$

STUDENT NOTES ———

In Example 6(a), we can think of undoing the multiplication $-4 \cdot x$ by *dividing* by -4.

Check: $\dfrac{-4x = 9}{-4\left(-\frac{9}{4}\right) \mid 9}$

$9 \overset{?}{=} 9$ TRUE $\quad 9 = 9$ is true.

The solution is $-\frac{9}{4}$.

b) To solve an equation like $-x = 5$, remember that when an expression is multiplied or divided by -1, its sign is changed. Here we divide both sides by -1 to change the sign of $-x$:

$-x = 5$ Note that $-x = -1 \cdot x$.

$\dfrac{-x}{-1} = \dfrac{5}{-1}$ Dividing both sides by -1. (Multiplying by -1 would also work. Note that the reciprocal of -1 is -1.)

$x = -5.$ Note that $\dfrac{-x}{-1}$ is the same as $\dfrac{x}{1}$.

Check: $\dfrac{-x = 5}{-(-5) \mid 5}$

$5 \overset{?}{=} 5$ TRUE $\quad 5 = 5$ is true.

The solution is -5.

c) To solve an equation like $\dfrac{2y}{9} = \dfrac{8}{3}$, we rewrite the left-hand side as $\dfrac{2}{9} \cdot y$ and then use the multiplication principle, multiplying by the reciprocal of $\dfrac{2}{9}$:

$\dfrac{2y}{9} = \dfrac{8}{3}$

$\dfrac{2}{9} \cdot y = \dfrac{8}{3}$ Rewriting $\dfrac{2y}{9}$ as $\dfrac{2}{9} \cdot y$

$\dfrac{9}{2} \cdot \dfrac{2}{9} \cdot y = \dfrac{9}{2} \cdot \dfrac{8}{3}$ Multiplying both sides by $\dfrac{9}{2}$

$1y = \dfrac{3 \cdot \cancel{3} \cdot \cancel{2} \cdot 4}{\cancel{2} \cdot \cancel{3}}$ Removing a factor equal to 1: $\dfrac{3 \cdot 2}{2 \cdot 3} = 1$

$y = 12.$

Check: $\dfrac{2y}{9} = \dfrac{8}{3}$

$\dfrac{\dfrac{2 \cdot 12}{9}}{\dfrac{24}{9}} \Bigg| \dfrac{8}{3}$

$\dfrac{8}{3} \overset{?}{=} \dfrac{8}{3}$ TRUE $\quad \dfrac{8}{3} = \dfrac{8}{3}$ is true.

The solution is 12.

TRY EXERCISE 35

Selecting the Correct Approach

It is important that you be able to determine which principle should be used to solve a particular equation.

EXAMPLE 7

Solve: **(a)** $-\frac{2}{3} + x = \frac{5}{2}$; **(b)** $12.6 = 3t$.

SOLUTION

a) To undo addition of $-\frac{2}{3}$, we subtract $-\frac{2}{3}$ from both sides. Subtracting $-\frac{2}{3}$ is the same as adding $\frac{2}{3}$.

$$-\frac{2}{3} + x = \frac{5}{2}$$

$$-\frac{2}{3} + x + \frac{2}{3} = \frac{5}{2} + \frac{2}{3} \qquad \text{Using the addition principle}$$

$$x = \frac{5}{2} + \frac{2}{3}$$

$$x = \frac{5}{2} \cdot \frac{3}{3} + \frac{2}{3} \cdot \frac{2}{2} \qquad \text{Finding a common denominator}$$

$$x = \frac{15}{6} + \frac{4}{6}$$

$$x = \frac{19}{6}$$

Check:

$$\frac{-\frac{2}{3} + x = \frac{5}{2}}{\begin{array}{c|c} -\frac{2}{3} + \frac{19}{6} & \frac{5}{2} \\ -\frac{4}{6} + \frac{19}{6} & \\ \frac{15}{6} & \\ \frac{5 \cdot 3}{2 \cdot 3} & \\ \frac{5}{2} \overset{?}{=} \frac{5}{2} & \text{TRUE} \end{array}}$$

$-\frac{2}{3} \cdot \frac{2}{2} = -\frac{4}{6}$

Removing a factor equal to 1: $\frac{3}{3} = 1$

$\frac{5}{2} = \frac{5}{2}$ is true.

The solution is $\frac{19}{6}$.

b) To undo multiplication by 3, we either divide both sides by 3 or multiply both sides by $\frac{1}{3}$:

$$12.6 = 3t$$

$$\frac{12.6}{3} = \frac{3t}{3} \qquad \text{Using the multiplication principle}$$

$$4.2 = t. \qquad \text{Simplifying}$$

Check:

$$\frac{12.6 = 3t}{\begin{array}{c|c} 12.6 & 3(4.2) \\ 12.6 \overset{?}{=} 12.6 & \text{TRUE} \end{array}}$$

$12.6 = 12.6$ is true.

The solution is 4.2.

TRY EXERCISES 59 and 67

STUDY SKILLS ——————

Seeking Help?

A variety of resources are available to help make studying easier and more enjoyable.

- **Textbook supplements.** See the preface for a description of the supplements for this textbook: the *Student's Solutions Manual*, a complete set of videos on DVD, MathXL tutorial exercises on CD, and complete online courses in MathXL and MyMathLab.

- **Your college or university.** Your own college or university probably has resources to enhance your math learning: a learning lab or tutoring center, study skills workshops or group tutoring sessions tailored for the course you are taking, or a bulletin board or network where you can locate the names of experienced private tutors.

- **Your instructor.** Find out your instructor's office hours and make it a point to visit when you need additional help. Many instructors also welcome student e-mail.

1.1   EXERCISE SET

 For Extra Help — **MyMathLab** | Math XL PRACTICE | WATCH | DOWNLOAD

Concept Reinforcement *For each of Exercises 1–6, match the statement with the most appropriate choice from the column on the right.*

1. ____ The equations $x + 3 = 7$ and $6x = 24$

2. ____ The expressions $3(x - 2)$ and $3x - 6$

3. ____ A replacement that makes an equation true

4. ____ The role of 9 in $9ab$

5. ____ The principle used to solve $\frac{2}{3} \cdot x = -4$

6. ____ The principle used to solve $\frac{2}{3} + x = -4$

a) Coefficient

b) Equivalent expressions

c) Equivalent equations

d) The multiplication principle

e) The addition principle

f) Solution

For each of Exercises 7–10, match the equation with the step, from the column on the right, that would be used to solve the equation.

7. $6x = 30$ **a)** Add 6 to both sides.

8. $x + 6 = 30$ **b)** Subtract 6 from both sides.

9. $\frac{1}{6}x = 30$ **c)** Multiply both sides by 6.

10. $x - 6 = 30$ **d)** Divide both sides by 6.

To the student and the instructor: The **TRY EXERCISES** *for examples are indicated by a shaded block on the exercise number. Complete step-by-step solutions for these exercises appear online at www.pearsonhighered.com/ bittingerellenbogen.*

Solve using the addition principle. Don't forget to check!

11. $x + 10 = 21$ **12.** $t + 9 = 47$

13. $y + 7 = -18$ **14.** $x + 12 = -7$

15. $-6 = y + 25$ **16.** $-5 = x + 8$

17. $x - 18 = 23$ **18.** $x - 19 = 16$

19. $12 = -7 + y$ **20.** $15 = -8 + z$

21. $-5 + t = -11$ **22.** $-6 + y = -21$

23. $r + \frac{1}{3} = \frac{8}{3}$ **24.** $t + \frac{3}{8} = \frac{5}{8}$

25. $x - \frac{3}{5} = -\frac{7}{10}$ **26.** $x - \frac{2}{3} = -\frac{5}{6}$

27. $x - \frac{5}{6} = \frac{7}{8}$ **28.** $y - \frac{3}{4} = \frac{5}{6}$

29. $-\frac{1}{5} + z = -\frac{1}{4}$ **30.** $-\frac{2}{3} + y = -\frac{3}{4}$

31. $m - 2.8 = 6.3$ **32.** $y - 5.3 = 8.7$

33. $-9.7 = -4.7 + y$ **34.** $-7.8 = 2.8 + x$

Solve using the multiplication principle. Don't forget to check!

35. $8a = 56$ **36.** $6x = 72$

37. $84 = 7x$ **38.** $45 = 9t$

39. $-x = 38$ **40.** $100 = -x$

Aha! **41.** $-t = -8$ **42.** $-68 = -r$

43. $-7x = 49$ **44.** $-4x = 36$

45. $-1.3a = -10.4$ **46.** $-3.4t = -20.4$

47. $\frac{y}{8} = 11$ **48.** $\frac{a}{4} = 13$

49. $\frac{4}{5}x = 16$ **50.** $\frac{3}{4}x = 27$

51. $\frac{-x}{6} = 9$ **52.** $\frac{-t}{4} = 8$

53. $\frac{1}{9} = \frac{z}{-5}$ **54.** $\frac{2}{7} = \frac{x}{-3}$

Aha! **55.** $-\frac{3}{5}r = -\frac{3}{5}$ **56.** $-\frac{2}{5}y = -\frac{4}{15}$

57. $\frac{-3r}{2} = -\frac{27}{4}$ **58.** $\frac{5x}{7} = -\frac{10}{14}$

Solve. The icon ▤ indicates an exercise designed to give practice using a calculator.

59. $4.5 + t = -3.1$ **60.** $\frac{3}{4}x = 18$

61. $-8.2x = 20.5$ **62.** $t - 7.4 = -12.9$

63. $x - 4 = -19$ **64.** $y - 6 = -14$

65. $t - 3 = -8$ **66.** $t - 9 = -8$

67. $-12x = 14$ **68.** $-15x = 20$

69. $48 = -\frac{3}{8}y$ **70.** $14 = t + 27$

71. $a - \frac{1}{6} = -\frac{2}{3}$ **72.** $-\frac{x}{6} = \frac{2}{9}$

73. $-24 = \frac{8x}{5}$ **74.** $\frac{1}{5} + y = -\frac{3}{10}$

75. $-\frac{4}{3}t = -12$ **76.** $\frac{17}{35} = -x$

▤ **77.** $-483.297 = -794.053 + t$

▤ **78.** $-0.2344x = 2028.732$

79. When solving an equation, how do you determine what number to add, subtract, multiply, or divide by on both sides of that equation?

80. What is the difference between equivalent expressions and equivalent equations?

Skill Review

To prepare for Section 1.2, review the rules for order of operations.

Simplify.

81. $3 \cdot 4 - 18$

82. $14 - 2(7 - 1)$

83. $16 \div (2 - 3 \cdot 2) + 5$

84. $12 - 5 \cdot 2^3 + 4 \cdot 3$

Synthesis

85. To solve $-3.5 = 14t$, Anita adds 3.5 to both sides. Will this form an equivalent equation? Will it help solve the equation? Explain.

86. Explain why it is not necessary to state a subtraction principle: For any real numbers a, b, and c, $a = b$ is equivalent to $a - c = b - c$.

Solve for x. Assume a, c, m ≠ 0.

87. $mx = 11.6m$

88. $x - 4 + a = a$

89. $cx + 5c = 7c$

90. $c \cdot \dfrac{21}{a} = \dfrac{7cx}{2a}$

91. $7 + |x| = 30$

92. $ax - 3a = 5a$

93. If $t - 3590 = 1820$, find $t + 3590$.

94. If $n + 268 = 124$, find $n - 268$.

95. Lydia makes a calculation and gets an answer of 22.5. On the last step, she multiplies by 0.3 when she should have divided by 0.3. What should the correct answer be?

96. Are the equations $x = 5$ and $x^2 = 25$ equivalent? Why or why not?

1.2 Using the Principles Together

Applying Both Principles • Combining Like Terms • Clearing Fractions and Decimals • Contradictions and Identities

An important strategy for solving new problems is to find a way to make a new problem look like a problem that we already know how to solve. This is precisely the approach taken in this section. You will find that the last steps of the examples in this section are nearly identical to the steps used for solving the equations of Section 1.1. What is new in this section appears in the early steps of each example.

Applying Both Principles

The addition and multiplication principles, along with the laws, are our tools for solving equations. In this section, we will find that the sequence and manner in which these tools are used is especially important.

EXAMPLE 1   Solve: $5 + 3x = 17$.

SOLUTION   Were we to evaluate $5 + 3x$, the rules for the order of operations direct us to *first* multiply by 3 and *then* add 5. Because of this, we can isolate $3x$ and then x by reversing these operations: We first subtract 5 from both sides and then divide both sides by 3. Our goal is an equivalent equation of the form $x = a$.

$$5 + 3x = 17$$

$$5 + 3x - 5 = 17 - 5 \qquad \text{Using the addition principle: subtracting 5 from both sides (adding } -5\text{)}$$

$$5 + (-5) + 3x = 12 \qquad \text{Using a commutative law. Try to perform this step mentally.}$$

Isolate the x-term.

$$3x = 12 \qquad \text{Simplifying}$$

$$\frac{3x}{3} = \frac{12}{3} \qquad \text{Using the multiplication principle: dividing both sides by 3 (multiplying by } \tfrac{1}{3}\text{)}$$

Isolate x.

$$x = 4 \qquad \text{Simplifying}$$

Check:

$$\begin{array}{c|c} 5 + 3x = 17 \\ \hline 5 + 3 \cdot 4 & 17 \\ 5 + 12 & \\ 17 \stackrel{?}{=} 17 & \text{TRUE} \end{array}$$

We use the rules for order of operations: Find the product, $3 \cdot 4$, and then add.

The solution is 4.

TRY EXERCISE 7

EXAMPLE 2

Solve: $\frac{4}{3}x - 7 = 1$.

SOLUTION   In $\frac{4}{3}x - 7$, we multiply first and then subtract. To reverse these steps, we first add 7 and then either divide by $\frac{4}{3}$ or multiply by $\frac{3}{4}$.

$$\frac{4}{3}x - 7 = 1$$

$$\frac{4}{3}x - 7 + 7 = 1 + 7 \qquad \text{Adding 7 to both sides}$$

$$\frac{4}{3}x = 8$$

$$\frac{3}{4} \cdot \frac{4}{3}x = \frac{3}{4} \cdot 8 \qquad \text{Multiplying both sides by } \frac{3}{4}$$

$$\left.\begin{array}{l} 1 \cdot x = \dfrac{3 \cdot \cancel{4} \cdot 2}{\cancel{4}} \\[2mm] x = 6 \end{array}\right\} \quad \text{Simplifying}$$

Check:
$$\begin{array}{c|c} \frac{4}{3}x - 7 = 1 \\ \hline \frac{4}{3} \cdot 6 - 7 & 1 \\ 8 - 7 & \\ 1 \overset{?}{=} 1 & \text{TRUE} \end{array}$$

The solution is 6.

TRY EXERCISE 27

STUDY SKILLS ─────

Use the Answer Section Carefully

When using the answers listed at the back of this book, try not to "work backward" from the answer. If you frequently require two or more attempts to answer an exercise correctly, you probably need to work more carefully and/or reread the section preceding the exercise set. Remember that on quizzes and tests you have only one attempt per problem and no answer section to consult.

EXAMPLE 3

Solve: $45 - t = 13$.

SOLUTION   We have

$$45 - t = 13$$

$$45 - t - 45 = 13 - 45 \qquad \text{Subtracting 45 from both sides}$$

$$\left.\begin{array}{l} 45 + (-t) + (-45) = 13 - 45 \\ 45 + (-45) + (-t) = 13 - 45 \end{array}\right\} \quad \text{Try to do these steps mentally.}$$

$$-t = -32 \qquad \text{Try to go directly to this step.}$$

$$(-1)(-t) = (-1)(-32) \qquad \begin{array}{l}\text{Multiplying both sides by } -1 \\ \text{(Dividing by } -1 \text{ would also} \\ \text{work.)}\end{array}$$

$$t = 32.$$

Check:
$$\begin{array}{c|c} 45 - t = 13 \\ \hline 45 - 32 & 13 \\ 13 \overset{?}{=} 13 & \text{TRUE} \end{array}$$

The solution is 32.

TRY EXERCISE 19

As our skills improve, certain steps can be streamlined.

EXAMPLE 4

Solve: $16.3 - 7.2y = -8.18$.

SOLUTION   We have

$$16.3 - 7.2y = -8.18$$
$$16.3 - 7.2y - 16.3 = -8.18 - 16.3 \qquad \text{Subtracting 16.3 from both sides}$$
$$-7.2y = -24.48 \qquad \text{Simplifying}$$
$$\frac{-7.2y}{-7.2} = \frac{-24.48}{-7.2} \qquad \text{Dividing both sides by } -7.2$$
$$y = 3.4. \qquad \text{Simplifying}$$

Check:
$$\begin{array}{c|c} 16.3 - 7.2y = -8.18 \\ \hline 16.3 - 7.2(3.4) & -8.18 \\ 16.3 - 24.48 & \\ -8.18 \overset{?}{=} -8.18 & \text{TRUE} \end{array}$$

The solution is 3.4.

> TRY EXERCISE 23

Combining Like Terms

If like terms appear on the same side of an equation, we combine them and then solve. Should like terms appear on both sides of an equation, we can use the addition principle to rewrite all like terms on one side.

EXAMPLE 5

Solve.

a) $3x + 4x = -14$ **b)** $-x + 5 = -8x + 6$

c) $6x + 5 - 7x = 10 - 4x + 7$ **d)** $2 - 5(x + 5) = 3(x - 2) - 1$

SOLUTION

a) $3x + 4x = -14$

$$7x = -14 \qquad \text{Combining like terms}$$
$$\frac{7x}{7} = \frac{-14}{7} \qquad \text{Dividing both sides by 7}$$
$$x = -2 \qquad \text{Simplifying}$$

The check is left to the student. The solution is -2.

b) To solve $-x + 5 = -8x + 6$, we must first write only variable terms on one side and only constant terms on the other. This can be done by subtracting 5 from both sides, to get all constant terms on the right, and adding $8x$ to both sides, to get all variable terms on the left.

$$-x + 5 = -8x + 6$$

Isolate variable terms on one side and constant terms on the other side.

$$-x + 8x + 5 = -8x + 8x + 6 \qquad \text{Adding } 8x \text{ to both sides}$$
$$7x + 5 = 6 \qquad \text{Simplifying}$$
$$7x + 5 - 5 = 6 - 5 \qquad \text{Subtracting 5 from both sides}$$
$$7x = 1 \qquad \text{Combining like terms}$$
$$\frac{7x}{7} = \frac{1}{7} \qquad \text{Dividing both sides by 7}$$
$$x = \frac{1}{7}$$

The check is left to the student. The solution is $\frac{1}{7}$.

TECHNOLOGY CONNECTION

Most graphing calculators have a TABLE feature that lists the value of a variable expression for different choices of x. For example, to evaluate $6x + 5 - 7x$ for $x = 0, 1, 2, \ldots$, we first use $\boxed{Y=}$ to enter $6x + 5 - 7x$ as y_1. We then use $\boxed{2ND}$ $\boxed{TBLSET}$ to specify TblStart = 0, ΔTbl = 1, and select AUTO twice. By pressing $\boxed{2ND}$ $\boxed{TABLE}$, we can generate a table in which the value of $6x + 5 - 7x$ is listed for values of x starting at 0 and increasing by ones.

X	Y1	
0	5	
1	4	
2	3	
3	2	
4	1	
5	0	
6	−1	
X = 0		

1. Create the above table on your graphing calculator. Scroll up and down to extend the table.
2. Enter $10 - 4x + 7$ as y_2. Your table should now have three columns.
3. For what x-value is y_1 the same as y_2? Compare this with the solution of Example 5(c). Is this a reliable way to solve equations? Why or why not?

c)
$$6x + 5 - 7x = 10 - 4x + 7$$

$-x + 5 = 17 - 4x$	Combining like terms within each side
$-x + 5 + 4x = 17 - 4x + 4x$	Adding $4x$ to both sides
$5 + 3x = 17$	Simplifying. This is identical to Example 1.
$3x = 12$	Subtracting 5 from both sides
$\dfrac{3x}{3} = \dfrac{12}{3}$	Dividing both sides by 3
$x = 4$	

Check:

$$\begin{array}{c|c} \multicolumn{2}{c}{6x + 5 - 7x = 10 - 4x + 7} \\ \hline 6 \cdot 4 + 5 - 7 \cdot 4 & 10 - 4 \cdot 4 + 7 \\ 24 + 5 - 28 & 10 - 16 + 7 \\ 1 \stackrel{?}{=} 1 & \text{TRUE} \end{array}$$

The student can confirm that 4 checks and is the solution.

d)
$$2 - 5(x + 5) = 3(x - 2) - 1$$

$2 - 5x - 25 = 3x - 6 - 1$	Using the distributive law. This is now similar to part (c) above.
$-5x - 23 = 3x - 7$	Combining like terms on each side
$\left.\begin{array}{l} -5x - 23 + 7 = 3x \\ -23 + 7 = 3x + 5x \end{array}\right\}$	Adding 7 and $5x$ to both sides. This isolates the x-terms on one side and the constant terms on the other.
$-16 = 8x$	Simplifying
$\dfrac{-16}{8} = \dfrac{8x}{8}$	Dividing both sides by 8
$-2 = x$	This is equivalent to $x = -2$.

The student can confirm that -2 checks and is the solution.

> **TRY EXERCISE** 39

Clearing Fractions and Decimals

Equations are generally easier to solve when they do not contain fractions or decimals. The multiplication principle can be used to "clear" fractions or decimals, as shown here.

Clearing Fractions	Clearing Decimals
$\frac{1}{2}x + 5 = \frac{3}{4}$	$2.3x + 7 = 5.4$
$4\left(\frac{1}{2}x + 5\right) = 4 \cdot \frac{3}{4}$	$10(2.3x + 7) = 10 \cdot 5.4$
$2x + 20 = 3$	$23x + 70 = 54$

In each case, the resulting equation is equivalent to the original equation, but easier to solve.

The easiest way to clear an equation of fractions is to multiply *both sides* of the equation by the smallest, or *least*, common denominator of the fractions in the equation.

EXAMPLE 6   Solve: (a) $\frac{2}{3}x - \frac{1}{6} = 2x$; (b) $\frac{2}{5}(3x + 2) = 8$.

SOLUTION

a) We multiply both sides by 6, the least common denominator of $\frac{2}{3}$ and $\frac{1}{6}$.

$$6\left(\frac{2}{3}x - \frac{1}{6}\right) = 6 \cdot 2x \qquad \text{Multiplying both sides by 6}$$

$$6 \cdot \frac{2}{3}x - 6 \cdot \frac{1}{6} = 6 \cdot 2x \longleftarrow \boxed{\textit{CAUTION!} \quad \text{Be sure the distributive law is used to multiply } \textit{all} \text{ the terms by 6.}}$$

$$4x - 1 = 12x \qquad \text{Simplifying. Note that the fractions are cleared: } 6 \cdot \frac{2}{3} = 4, 6 \cdot \frac{1}{6} = 1, \text{ and } 6 \cdot 2 = 12.$$

$$-1 = 8x \qquad \text{Subtracting } 4x \text{ from both sides}$$

$$\frac{-1}{8} = \frac{8x}{8} \qquad \text{Dividing both sides by 8}$$

$$-\frac{1}{8} = x$$

The student can confirm that $-\frac{1}{8}$ checks and is the solution.

b) To solve $\frac{2}{5}(3x + 2) = 8$, we can multiply both sides by $\frac{5}{2}$ (or divide by $\frac{2}{5}$) to "undo" the multiplication by $\frac{2}{5}$ on the left side.

$$\frac{5}{2} \cdot \frac{2}{5}(3x + 2) = \frac{5}{2} \cdot 8 \qquad \text{Multiplying both sides by } \frac{5}{2}$$

$$3x + 2 = 20 \qquad \text{Simplifying; } \frac{5}{2} \cdot \frac{2}{5} = 1 \text{ and } \frac{5}{2} \cdot \frac{8}{1} = 20$$

$$3x = 18 \qquad \text{Subtracting 2 from both sides}$$

$$x = 6 \qquad \text{Dividing both sides by 3}$$

The student can confirm that 6 checks and is the solution.

TRY EXERCISE 69

To clear an equation of decimals, we count the greatest number of decimal places in any one number. If the greatest number of decimal places is 1, we multiply both sides by 10; if it is 2, we multiply by 100; and so on. This procedure is the same as multiplying by the least common denominator after converting the decimals to fractions.

EXAMPLE 7   Solve: $16.3 - 7.2y = -8.18$.

SOLUTION   The greatest number of decimal places in any one number is *two*. Multiplying by 100 will clear all decimals.

$$100(16.3 - 7.2y) = 100(-8.18) \qquad \text{Multiplying both sides by 100}$$

$$100(16.3) - 100(7.2y) = 100(-8.18) \qquad \text{Using the distributive law}$$

$$1630 - 720y = -818 \qquad \text{Simplifying}$$

$$-720y = -818 - 1630 \qquad \text{Subtracting 1630 from both sides}$$

$$-720y = -2448 \qquad \text{Combining like terms}$$

$$y = \frac{-2448}{-720} \qquad \text{Dividing both sides by } -720$$

$$y = 3.4$$

STUDENT NOTES ———

Compare the steps of Examples 4 and 7. Note that although the two approaches differ, they yield the same solution. Whenever you can use two approaches to solve a problem, try to do so, both as a check and as a valuable learning experience.

In Example 4, the same solution was found without clearing decimals. Finding the same answer in two ways is a good check. The solution is 3.4.

TRY EXERCISE 75

> **An Equation-Solving Procedure**
> 1. Use the multiplication principle to clear any fractions or decimals. (This is optional, but can ease computations. See Examples 6 and 7.)
> 2. If necessary, use the distributive law to remove parentheses. Then combine like terms on each side. (See Example 5.)
> 3. Use the addition principle, as needed, to isolate all variable terms on one side. Then combine like terms. (See Examples 1–7.)
> 4. Multiply or divide to solve for the variable, using the multiplication principle. (See Examples 1–7.)
> 5. Check all possible solutions in the original equation. (See Examples 1–4.)

Contradictions and Identities

All of the equations we have examined so far had a solution. Equations that are true for some values (solutions), but not for others, are called **conditional equations**. Equations that have no solution, such as $x + 1 = x + 2$, are called **contradictions**. If, when solving an equation, we obtain an equation that is false for any value of x, the equation has no solution.

EXAMPLE 8   Solve: $3x - 5 = 3(x - 2) + 4$.

SOLUTION

$$3x - 5 = 3(x - 2) + 4$$
$$3x - 5 = 3x - 6 + 4 \qquad \text{Using the distributive law}$$
$$3x - 5 = 3x - 2 \qquad \text{Combining like terms}$$
$$-3x + 3x - 5 = -3x + 3x - 2 \qquad \text{Using the addition principle}$$
$$-5 = -2$$

Since the original equation is equivalent to $-5 = -2$, which is false regardless of the choice of x, the original equation has no solution. There is no solution of $3x - 5 = 3(x - 2) + 4$. The equation is a contradiction. It is *never* true.

TRY EXERCISE 45

Some equations, like $x + 1 = x + 1$, are true for all replacements. Such an equation is called an **identity**.

EXAMPLE 9   Solve: $2x + 7 = 7(x + 1) - 5x$.

SOLUTION

$$2x + 7 = 7(x + 1) - 5x$$
$$2x + 7 = 7x + 7 - 5x \qquad \text{Using the distributive law}$$
$$2x + 7 = 2x + 7 \qquad \text{Combining like terms}$$

The equation $2x + 7 = 2x + 7$ is true regardless of the replacement for x, so all real numbers are solutions. Note that $2x + 7 = 2x + 7$ is equivalent to $2x = 2x$, $7 = 7$, or $0 = 0$. All real numbers are solutions and the equation is an identity.

TRY EXERCISE 33

1.2 EXERCISE SET

For Extra Help
MyMathLab Math XL PRACTICE WATCH DOWNLOAD

Concept Reinforcement   *In each of Exercises 1–6, match the equation with an equivalent equation from the column on the right that could be the next step in finding a solution.*

1. ____ $3x - 1 = 7$
2. ____ $4x + 5x = 12$
3. ____ $6(x - 1) = 2$
4. ____ $7x = 9$
5. ____ $4x = 3 - 2x$
6. ____ $8x - 5 = 6 - 2x$

a) $6x - 6 = 2$
b) $4x + 2x = 3$
c) $3x = 7 + 1$
d) $8x + 2x = 6 + 5$
e) $9x = 12$
f) $x = \frac{9}{7}$

Solve and check. Label any contradictions or identities.

7. $2x + 9 = 25$
8. $3x - 11 = 13$
9. $6z + 5 = 47$
10. $5z + 2 = 57$
11. $7t - 8 = 27$
12. $6x - 5 = 2$
13. $3x - 9 = 1$
14. $5x - 9 = 41$
15. $8z + 2 = -54$
16. $4x + 3 = -21$
17. $-37 = 9t + 8$
18. $-39 = 1 + 5t$
19. $12 - t = 16$
20. $9 - t = 21$
21. $-6z - 18 = -132$
22. $-7x - 24 = -129$
23. $5.3 + 1.2n = 1.94$
24. $6.4 - 2.5n = 2.2$
25. $32 - 7x = 11$
26. $27 - 6x = 99$
27. $\frac{3}{5}t - 1 = 8$
28. $\frac{2}{3}t - 1 = 5$

29. $6 + \frac{7}{2}x = -15$
30. $6 + \frac{5}{4}x = -4$
31. $-\frac{4a}{5} - 8 = 2$
32. $-\frac{8a}{7} - 2 = 4$
33. $4x = x + 3x$
34. $-3z + 8z = 45$
35. $4x - 6 = 6x$
36. $5x - x = x + 3x$
37. $2 - 5y = 26 - y$
38. $6x - 5 = 7 + 2x$
39. $7(2a - 1) = 21$
40. $5(3 - 3t) = 30$
Aha! 41. $11 = 11(x + 1)$
42. $9 = 3(5x - 2)$
43. $2(3 + 4m) - 6 = 48$
44. $3(5 + 3m) - 8 = 7$
45. $3(x + 4) = 3(x - 1)$
46. $5(x - 7) = 3(x - 2) + 2x$
47. $2r + 8 = 6r + 10$
48. $3b - 2 = 7b + 4$
49. $6x + 3 = 2x + 3$
50. $5y + 3 = 2y + 15$
51. $5 - 2x = 3x - 7x + 25$
52. $10 - 3x = x - 2x + 40$
53. $7 + 3x - 6 = 3x + 5 - x$
54. $5 + 4x - 7 = 4x - 2 - x$
55. $4y - 4 + y + 24 = 6y + 20 - 4y$
56. $5y - 10 + y = 7y + 18 - 5y$
57. $4 + 7x = 7(x + 1)$
58. $3(t + 2) + t = 2(3 + 2t)$
59. $19 - 3(2x - 1) = 7$

60. $5(d + 4) = 7(d - 2)$

61. $7(5x - 2) = 6(6x - 1)$

62. $5(t + 1) + 8 = 3(t - 2) + 6$

63. $2(3t + 1) - 5 = t - (t + 2)$

64. $4x - (x + 6) = 5(3x - 1) + 8$

65. $2(7 - x) - 20 = 7x - 3(2 + 3x)$

66. $5(x - 7) = 3(x - 2) + 2x$

67. $19 - (2x + 3) = 2(x + 3) + x$

68. $13 - (2c + 2) = 2(c + 2) + 3c$

Clear fractions or decimals, solve, and check.

69. $\frac{2}{3} + \frac{1}{4}t = 2$

70. $-\frac{5}{6} + x = -\frac{1}{2} - \frac{2}{3}$

71. $\frac{2}{3} + 4t = 6t - \frac{2}{15}$

72. $\frac{1}{2} + 4m = 3m - \frac{5}{2}$

73. $\frac{1}{3}x + \frac{2}{5} = \frac{4}{5} + \frac{3}{5}x - \frac{2}{3}$

74. $1 - \frac{2}{3}y = \frac{9}{5} - \frac{1}{5}y + \frac{3}{5}$

75. $2.1x + 45.2 = 3.2 - 8.4x$

76. $0.91 - 0.2z = 1.23 - 0.6z$

77. $0.76 + 0.21t = 0.96t - 0.49$

78. $1.7t + 8 - 1.62t = 0.4t - 0.32 + 8$

79. $\frac{2}{5}x - \frac{3}{2}x = \frac{3}{4}x + 3$

80. $\frac{5}{16}y + \frac{3}{8}y = 2 + \frac{1}{4}y$

81. $\frac{1}{3}(2x - 1) = 7$

82. $\frac{1}{5}(4x - 1) = 7$

83. $\frac{3}{4}(3t - 4) = 15$

84. $\frac{3}{2}(2x + 5) = -\frac{15}{2}$

85. $\frac{1}{6}\left(\frac{3}{4}x - 2\right) = -\frac{1}{5}$

86. $\frac{2}{3}\left(\frac{7}{8} - 4x\right) - \frac{5}{8} = \frac{3}{8}$

87. $0.7(3x + 6) = 1.1 - (x - 3)$

88. $0.9(2x - 8) = 4 - (x + 5)$

89. $a + (a - 3) = (a + 2) - (a + 1)$

90. $0.8 - 4(b - 1) = 0.2 + 3(4 - b)$

91. Tyla solves $45 - t = 13$ (Example 3) by adding $t - 13$ to both sides. Is this approach preferable to the one used in Example 3? Why or why not?

92. Why must the rules for the order of operations be understood before solving the equations in this section?

Skill Review

To prepare for Section 1.3, review evaluating algebraic expressions.

Evaluate.

93. $3 - 5a$, for $a = 2$

94. $12 \div 4 \cdot t$, for $t = 5$

95. $7x - 2x$, for $x = -3$

96. $t(8 - 3t)$, for $t = -2$

Synthesis

97. What procedure would you use to solve an equation like $0.23x + \frac{17}{3} = -0.8 + \frac{3}{4}x$? Could your procedure be streamlined? If so, how?

98. Dave is determined to solve $3x + 4 = -11$ by first using the multiplication principle to "eliminate" the 3. How should he proceed and why?

Solve. Label any contradictions or identities.

99. $8.43x - 2.5(3.2 - 0.7x) = -3.455x + 9.04$

100. $0.008 + 9.62x - 42.8 = 0.944x + 0.0083 - x$

101. $-2[3(x - 2) + 4] = 4(5 - x) - 2x$

102. $0 = t - (-6) - (-7t)$

103. $2x(x + 5) - 3(x^2 + 2x - 1) = 9 - 5x - x^2$

104. $x(x - 4) = 3x(x + 1) - 2(x^2 + x - 5)$

105. $9 - 3x = 2(5 - 2x) - (1 - 5x)$

Aha! **106.** $[7 - 2(8 \div (-2))]x = 0$

107. $\dfrac{x}{14} - \dfrac{5x + 2}{49} = \dfrac{3x - 4}{7}$

108. $\dfrac{5x + 3}{4} + \dfrac{25}{12} = \dfrac{5 + 2x}{3}$

109. $2\{9 - 3[-2x - 4]\} = 12x + 42$

110. $-9t + 2 = 2 - 9t - 5(8 \div 4(1 + 3^4))$

COLLABORATIVE CORNER

Step-by-Step Solutions

Focus: Solving linear equations

Time: 20 minutes

Group size: 3

In general, there is more than one correct sequence of steps for solving an equation. This makes it important that you write your steps clearly and logically so that others can follow your approach.

ACTIVITY

1. Each group member should select a different one of the following equations and, on a fresh sheet of paper, perform the first step of the solution.

$$4 - 3(x - 3) = 7x + 6(2 - x)$$
$$5 - 7[x - 2(x - 6)] = 3x + 4(2x - 7) + 9$$
$$4x - 7[2 + 3(x - 5) + x] = 4 - 9(-3x - 19)$$

2. Pass the papers around so that the second and third steps of each solution are performed by the other two group members. Before writing, make sure that the previous step is correct. If a mistake is discovered, return the problem to the person who made the mistake for repairs. Continue passing the problems around until all equations have been solved.

3. Each group should reach a consensus on what the three solutions are and then compare their answers to those of other groups.

1.3   Formulas

Evaluating Formulas   ■   Solving for a Variable

Many applications of mathematics involve relationships among two or more quantities. An equation that represents such a relationship will use two or more letters and is known as a **formula**. Most of the letters in this book are variables, but some are constants. For example, c in $E = mc^2$ represents the speed of light.

Evaluating Formulas

EXAMPLE 1   *Event promotion.*   Event promoters use the formula

$$p = \frac{1.2x}{s}$$

to determine a ticket price p for an event with x dollars of expenses and s anticipated ticket sales. Grand Events expects expenses for an upcoming concert to be $80,000 and anticipates selling 4000 tickets. What should the ticket price be?

Source: *The Indianapolis Star, 2/27/03*

SOLUTION   We substitute 80,000 for x and 4000 for s in the formula and calculate p:

$$p = \frac{1.2x}{s} = \frac{1.2(80,000)}{4000} = 24.$$

The ticket price should be \$24.

TRY EXERCISE ▶ 1

Solving for a Variable

In the Northeast, the formula $B = 30a$ is used to determine the minimum furnace output B, in British thermal units (Btu's), for a well-insulated home with a square feet of flooring. Suppose that a contractor has an extra furnace and wants to determine the size of the largest (well-insulated) house in which it can be used. The contractor can substitute the amount of the furnace's output in Btu's—say, 63,000—for B, and then solve for a:

$$63,000 = 30a \qquad \text{Replacing } B \text{ with } 63,000$$
$$2100 = a. \qquad \text{Dividing both sides by 30}$$

The home should have no more than 2100 ft² of flooring.

Were these calculations to be performed for a variety of furnaces, the contractor would find it easier to first solve $B = 30a$ for a, and *then* substitute values for B. Solving for a variable can be done in much the same way that we solved equations in Sections 1.1 and 1.2.

EXAMPLE 2

Solve for a: $B = 30a$.

SOLUTION   We have

$$B = 30a \qquad \text{We want this letter alone.}$$
$$\frac{B}{30} = a. \qquad \text{Dividing both sides by 30}$$

The equation $a = B/30$ gives a quick, easy way to determine the floor area of the largest (well-insulated) house that a furnace supplying B Btu's could heat.

TRY EXERCISE ▶ 9

To see how solving a formula is just like solving an equation, compare the following. In (A), we solve as usual; in (B), we show steps but do not simplify; and in (C), we *cannot* simplify because a, b, and c are unknown.

A. $5x + 2 = 12$
$5x = 12 - 2$
$5x = 10$
$x = \dfrac{10}{5} = 2$

B. $5x + 2 = 12$
$5x = 12 - 2$
$x = \dfrac{12 - 2}{5}$

C. $ax + b = c$
$ax = c - b$
$x = \dfrac{c - b}{a}$

TECHNOLOGY CONNECTION

Suppose that after calculating $63,000 \div 30$, we wish to find $72,000 \div 30$. Pressing **2ND** **ENTRY** gives the following.

```
63000/30
                2100
63000/30█
```

Moving the cursor left, we can change 63,000 to 72,000 and press **ENTER**.

```
63000/30
                2100
72000/30
                2400
```

1. Verify the work above and then use **2ND** **ENTRY** to find $72,000 \div 90$.

EXAMPLE 3

Circumference of a circle. The formula $C = 2\pi r$ gives the *circumference C* of a circle with radius r. Solve for r.

SOLUTION The **circumference** is the distance around a circle.

| Given a radius r, we can use this equation to find a circle's circumference C. |
| Given a circle's circumference C, we can use this equation to find the radius r. |

$$C = 2\pi r \qquad \text{We want this variable alone.}$$
$$\frac{C}{2\pi} = \frac{2\pi r}{2\pi} \qquad \text{Dividing both sides by } 2\pi$$
$$\frac{C}{2\pi} = r$$

TRY EXERCISE 13

EXAMPLE 4

Solve for y: $3x - 4y = 10$.

SOLUTION There is one term that contains y, so we begin by isolating that term on one side of the equation.

$$3x - 4y = 10 \qquad \text{We want this variable alone.}$$
$$-4y = 10 - 3x \qquad \text{Subtracting } 3x \text{ from both sides}$$
$$-\tfrac{1}{4}(-4y) = -\tfrac{1}{4}(10 - 3x) \qquad \text{Multiplying both sides by } -\tfrac{1}{4}$$
$$y = -\tfrac{10}{4} + \tfrac{3}{4}x \qquad \text{Multiplying using the distributive law}$$
$$y = -\tfrac{5}{2} + \tfrac{3}{4}x \qquad \text{Simplifying the fraction}$$

TRY EXERCISE 33

EXAMPLE 5

Nutrition. The number of calories K needed each day by a moderately active woman who weighs w pounds, is h inches tall, and is a years old, can be estimated using the formula

$$K = 917 + 6(w + h - a).^*$$

STUDY SKILLS

Pace Yourself

Most instructors agree that it is better for a student to study for one hour four days in a week, than to study once a week for four hours. Of course, the total weekly study time will vary from student to student. It is common to expect an average of two hours of homework for each hour of class time.

Solve for w.

SOLUTION We reverse the order in which the operations occur on the right side:

$$\text{We want } w \text{ alone.}$$
$$K = 917 + 6(w + h - a)$$
$$K - 917 = 6(w + h - a) \qquad \text{Subtracting 917 from both sides}$$
$$\frac{K - 917}{6} = w + h - a \qquad \text{Dividing both sides by 6}$$
$$\frac{K - 917}{6} + a - h = w. \qquad \text{Adding } a \text{ and subtracting } h \text{ on both sides}$$

This formula can be used to estimate a woman's weight, if we know her age, height, and caloric needs.

TRY EXERCISE 43

---

*Based on information from M. Parker (ed.), *She Does Math!* (Washington, D.C.: Mathematical Association of America, 1995), p. 96.

The above steps are similar to those used in Section 1.2 to solve equations. We use the addition and multiplication principles just as before. An important difference that we will see in the next example is that we will sometimes need to factor.

To Solve a Formula for a Given Variable

1. If the variable for which you are solving appears in a fraction, use the multiplication principle to clear fractions.
2. Isolate the term(s), with the variable for which you are solving on one side of the equation.
3. If two or more terms contain the variable for which you are solving, factor the variable out.
4. Multiply or divide to solve for the variable in question.

We can also solve for a letter that represents a constant.

EXAMPLE 6

Surface area of a right circular cylinder. The formula $A = 2\pi rh + 2\pi r^2$ gives the surface area A of a right circular cylinder of height h and radius r. Solve for π.

SOLUTION   We have

$$A = 2\pi rh + 2\pi r^2 \qquad \text{We want this letter alone.}$$

$$A = \pi(2rh + 2r^2) \qquad \text{Factoring}$$

$$\frac{A}{2rh + 2r^2} = \pi. \qquad \text{Dividing both sides by } 2rh + 2r^2,\ \text{or multiplying both sides by } 1/(2rh + 2r^2)$$

We can also write this as

$$\pi = \frac{A}{2rh + 2r^2}.$$

▸ TRY EXERCISE 47

CAUTION!   Had we performed the following steps in Example 6, we would *not* have solved for π:

$$A = 2\pi rh + 2\pi r^2 \qquad \text{We want } \pi \text{ alone.}$$

$$A - 2\pi r^2 = 2\pi rh \qquad \text{Subtracting } 2\pi r^2 \text{ from both sides}$$

Two occurrences of π

$$\frac{A - 2\pi r^2}{2rh} = \pi. \qquad \text{Dividing both sides by } 2rh$$

The mathematics of each step is correct, but because π occurs on both sides of the formula, *we have not solved the formula for π*. Remember that the letter being solved for should be alone on one side of the equation, with no occurrence of that letter on the other side!

1.3   EXERCISE SET

For Extra Help
MyMathLab
Math XL PRACTICE   WATCH   DOWNLOAD

1. *Outdoor concerts.*   The formula $d = 344t$ can be used to determine how far d, in meters, sound travels through room-temperature air in t seconds. At a large concert, fans near the back of the crowd experienced a 0.9-sec time lag between the time each word was pronounced on stage (as shown on large video monitors) and the time the sound reached their ears. How far were these fans from the stage?

2. *Furnace output.*   Contractors in the Northeast use the formula $B = 30a$ to determine the minimum furnace output B, in British thermal units (Btu's), for a well-insulated house with a square feet of flooring. Determine the minimum furnace output for an 1800-ft^2 house that is well insulated.
   Source: U.S. Department of Energy

3. *College enrollment.*   At many colleges, the number of "full-time-equivalent" students f is given by
$$f = \frac{n}{15},$$
   where n is the total number of credits for which students have enrolled in a given semester. Determine the number of full-time-equivalent students on a campus in which students registered for a total of 21,345 credits.

4. *Distance from a storm.*   The formula $M = \frac{1}{5}t$ can be used to determine how far M, in miles, you are from lightning when its thunder takes t seconds to reach your ears. If it takes 10 sec for the sound of thunder to reach you after you have seen the lightning, how far away is the storm?

5. *Federal funds rate.*   The Federal Reserve Board sets a target f for the federal funds rate, that is, the interest rate that banks charge each other for overnight borrowing of Federal funds. This target rate can be estimated by
$$f = 8.5 + 1.4(I - U),$$

where I is the core inflation rate over the previous 12 months and U is the seasonally adjusted unemployment rate. If core inflation is 0.025 and unemployment is 0.044, what should the federal funds rate be?
Source: Greg Mankiw, Harvard University, www.gregmankiw .blogspot.com/2006/06/what-would-alan-do.html

6. *Calorie density.*   The calorie density D, in calories per ounce, of a food that contains c calories and weighs w ounces is given by
$$D = \frac{c}{w}.^*$$
Eight ounces of fat-free milk contains 84 calories. Find the calorie density of fat-free milk.

7. *Absorption of ibuprofen.*   When 400 mg of the painkiller ibuprofen is swallowed, the number of milligrams n in the bloodstream t hours later (for $0 \le t \le 6$) is estimated by
$$n = 0.5t^4 + 3.45t^3 - 96.65t^2 + 347.7t.$$
How many milligrams of ibuprofen remain in the blood 1 hr after 400 mg has been swallowed?

8. *Size of a league schedule.*   When all n teams in a league play every other team twice, a total of N games are played, where
$$N = n^2 - n.$$
If a soccer league has 7 teams and all teams play each other twice, how many games are played?

In Exercises 9–48, solve each formula for the indicated letter.

9. $A = bh$, for b
   (Area of parallelogram with base b and height h)

10. $A = bh$, for h

11. $d = rt$, for r
    (A distance formula, where d is distance, r is speed, and t is time)

Source: Nutrition Action Healthletter, March 2000, p. 9. Center for Science in the Public Interest, Suite 300; 1875 Connecticut Ave NW, Washington, D.C. 20008.

12. $d = rt$, for t

13. $I = Prt$, for P
(Simple-interest formula, where I is interest, P is principal, r is interest rate, and t is time)

14. $I = Prt$, for t

15. $H = 65 - m$, for m
(To determine the number of heating degree days H for a day with m degrees Fahrenheit as the average temperature)

16. $d = h - 64$, for h
(To determine how many inches d above average an h-inch-tall woman is)

17. $P = 2l + 2w$, for l
(Perimeter of a rectangle of length l and width w)

18. $P = 2l + 2w$, for w

19. $A = \pi r^2$, for π
(Area of a circle with radius r)

20. $A = \pi r^2$, for r^2

21. $A = \frac{1}{2}bh$, for h
(Area of a triangle with base b and height h)

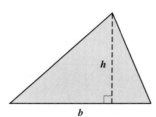

22. $A = \frac{1}{2}bh$, for b

23. $E = mc^2$, for c^2
(A relativity formula from physics)

24. $E = mc^2$, for m

25. $Q = \dfrac{c + d}{2}$, for d **26.** $Q = \dfrac{p - q}{2}$, for p

27. $A = \dfrac{a + b + c}{3}$, for b **28.** $A = \dfrac{a + b + c}{3}$, for c

29. $w = \dfrac{r}{f}$, for r
(To compute the wavelength w of a musical note with frequency f and speed of sound r)

30. $M = \dfrac{A}{s}$, for A
(To compute the Mach number M for speed A and speed of sound s)

31. $F = \dfrac{9}{5}C + 32$, for C
(To convert the Celsius temperature C to the Fahrenheit temperature F)

32. $M = \dfrac{5}{9}n + 18$, for n

33. $2x - y = 1$, for y

34. $3x - y = 7$, for y

35. $2x + 5y = 10$, for y

36. $3x + 2y = 12$, for y

37. $4x - 3y = 6$, for y

38. $5x - 4y = 8$, for y

39. $9x + 8y = 4$, for y

40. $x + 10y = 2$, for y

41. $3x - 5y = 8$, for y

42. $7x - 6y = 7$, for y

43. $z = 13 + 2(x + y)$, for x

44. $A = 115 + \dfrac{1}{2}(p + s)$, for s

45. $t = 27 - \dfrac{1}{4}(w - l)$, for l

46. $m = 19 - 5(x - n)$, for n

47. $A = at + bt$, for t

48. $S = rx + sx$, for x

49. *Area of a trapezoid.* The formula
$$A = \tfrac{1}{2}ah + \tfrac{1}{2}bh$$
can be used to find the area A of a trapezoid with bases a and b and height h. Solve for h. (*Hint*: First clear fractions.)

50. *Compounding interest.* The formula

$$A = P + Prt$$

is used to find the amount A in an account when simple interest is added to an investment of P dollars (see Exercise 13). Solve for P.

51. *Chess rating.* The formula

$$R = r + \frac{400(W - L)}{N}$$

is used to establish a chess player's rating R after that player has played N games, won W of them, and lost L of them. Here r is the average rating of the opponents. Solve for L.
Source: The U.S. Chess Federation

52. *Angle measure.* The angle measure S of a sector of a circle is given by

$$S = \frac{360A}{\pi r^2},$$

where r is the radius, A is the area of the sector, and S is in degrees. Solve for r^2.

53. Naomi has a formula that allows her to convert Celsius temperatures to Fahrenheit temperatures. She needs a formula for converting Fahrenheit temperatures to Celsius temperatures. What advice can you give her?

54. Under what circumstances would it be useful to solve $d = rt$ for r? (See Exercise 11.)

Skill Review

Review simplifying expressions.

Perform the indicated operations.

55. $-2 + 5 - (-4) - 17$

56. $-98 \div \frac{1}{2}$

Aha! **57.** $4.2(-11.75)(0)$

58. $(-2)^5$

Simplify.

59. $20 \div (-4) \cdot 2 - 3$

60. $5|8 - (2 - 7)|$

Synthesis

61. The equations

$$P = 2l + 2w \quad \text{and} \quad w = \frac{P}{2} - l$$

are equivalent formulas involving the perimeter P, length l, and width w of a rectangle. Devise a problem for which the second of the two formulas would be more useful.

62. While solving $2A = ah + bh$ for h, Lea writes $\frac{2A - ah}{b} = h$. What is her mistake?

63. The Harris–Benedict formula gives the number of calories K needed each day by a moderately active man who weighs w kilograms, is h centimeters tall, and is a years old as

$$K = 21.235w + 7.75h - 10.54a + 102.3.$$

If Janos is moderately active, weighs 80 kg, is 190 cm tall, and needs to consume 2852 calories a day, how old is he?

64. *Altitude and temperature.* Air temperature drops about 1° Celsius (C) for each 100-m rise above ground level, up to 12 km. If the ground level temperature is t°C, find a formula for the temperature T at an elevation of h meters.
Source: *A Sourcebook of School Mathematics*, Mathematical Association of America, 1980

65. *Surface area of a cube.* The surface area A of a cube with side s is given by

$$A = 6s^2.$$

If a cube's surface area is 54 in², find the volume of the cube.

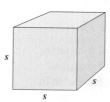

66. *Weight of a fish.* An ancient fisherman's formula for estimating the weight of a fish is

$$w = \frac{lg^2}{800},$$

where w is the weight, in pounds, l is the length, in inches, and g is the girth (distance around the midsection), in inches. Estimate the girth of a 700-lb yellow tuna that is 8 ft long.

67. *Dosage size.* Clark's rule for determining the size of a particular child's medicine dosage c is

$$c = \frac{w}{a} \cdot d,$$

where w is the child's weight, in pounds, and d is the usual adult dosage for an adult weighing a pounds. Solve for a.

Source: Olsen, June Looby, et al., *Medical Dosage Calculations.* Redwood City, CA: Addison-Wesley, 1995

Solve each formula for the given letter.

68. $\frac{y}{z} \div \frac{z}{t} = 1$, for y

69. $ac = bc + d$, for c

70. $qt = r(s + t)$, for t

71. $3a = c - a(b + d)$, for a

72. *Furnace output.* The formula

$$B = 50a$$

is used in New England to estimate the minimum furnace output B, in Btu's, for an old, poorly insulated house with a square feet of flooring. Find an equation for determining the number of Btu's saved by insulating an old house. (*Hint:* See Exercise 2.)

73. Revise the formula in Exercise 63 so that a man's weight in pounds (2.2046 lb = 1 kg) and his height in inches (0.3937 in. = 1 cm) are used.

74. Revise the formula in Example 5 so that a woman's weight in kilograms (2.2046 lb = 1 kg) and her height in centimeters (0.3937 in. = 1 cm) are used.

1.4   Applications with Percent

Converting Between Percent Notation and Decimal Notation • Solving Percent Problems

Percent problems arise so frequently in everyday life that most often we are not even aware of them. In this section, we will solve some real-world percent problems. Before doing so, however, we need to review a few basics.

Converting Between Percent Notation and Decimal Notation

Nutritionists recommend that no more than 30% of the calories in a person's diet come from fat. This means that of every 100 calories consumed, no more than 30 should come from fat. Thus, 30% is a ratio of 30 to 100.

Calories consumed

Calories from fat 30%

The percent symbol % means "per hundred." We can regard the percent symbol as part of a name for a number. For example,

$$30\% \quad \text{is defined to mean} \quad \frac{30}{100}, \quad \text{or} \quad 30 \times \frac{1}{100}, \quad \text{or} \quad 30 \times 0.01.$$

Percent Notation

$$n\% \quad \text{means} \quad \frac{n}{100}, \quad \text{or} \quad n \times \frac{1}{100}, \quad \text{or} \quad n \times 0.01.$$

EXAMPLE 1 Convert to decimal notation: **(a)** 78%; **(b)** 1.3%.

SOLUTION

a) $78\% = 78 \times 0.01$ Replacing % with $\times 0.01$

$\quad\quad = 0.78$

b) $1.3\% = 1.3 \times 0.01$ Replacing % with $\times 0.01$

$\quad\quad = 0.013$

TRY EXERCISE 19

As shown above, multiplication by 0.01 simply moves the decimal point two places to the left.

To convert from percent notation to decimal notation, move the decimal point two places to the left and drop the percent symbol.

EXAMPLE 2 Convert the percent notation in the following sentence to decimal notation: Only 20% of teenagers get 8 hr of sleep a night.

Source: National Sleep Foundation

SOLUTION

$\quad 20\% = 20.0\%$ 0.20.0 $20\% = 0.20$, or simply 0.2

Move the decimal point two places to the left.

TRY EXERCISE 11

The procedure used in Examples 1 and 2 can be reversed:

$\quad 0.38 = 38 \times 0.01$

$\quad\quad = 38\%.$ Replacing $\times 0.01$ with %

To convert from decimal notation to percent notation, move the decimal point two places to the right and write a percent symbol.

EXAMPLE 3 Convert to percent notation: **(a)** 1.27; **(b)** $\frac{1}{4}$; **(c)** 0.3.

SOLUTION

a) We first move the decimal point two places to the right: 1.27.

and then write a % symbol: 127%   This is the same as multiplying 1.27 by 100 and writing %.

b) Note that $\frac{1}{4} = 0.25$. We move the decimal point two places to the right: 0.25.

and then write a % symbol: 25%   Multiplying by 100 and writing %

c) We first move the decimal point two places to the right (recall that $0.3 = 0.30$):   0.30.

and then write a % symbol: 30%   Multiplying by 100 and writing %

TRY EXERCISE 33

Solving Percent Problems

In solving percent problems, we first *translate* the problem to an equation. Then we *solve* the equation using the techniques discussed in Sections 1.1–1.3. The key words in the translation are as follows.

> ## Key Words in Percent Translations
> "**Of**" translates to " $\cdot$ " or " $\times$ ".   "**Is**" or "**Was**" translates to " $=$ ".
> "**What**" translates to a variable.   "**%**" translates to " $\times \frac{1}{100}$ " or " $\times 0.01$ ".

EXAMPLE 4

STUDENT NOTES

A way of checking answers is by estimating as follows:

$$11\% \times 49 \approx 10\% \times 50$$
$$= 0.10 \times 50 = 5.$$

Since 5 is close to 5.39, our answer is reasonable.

What is 11% of 49?

SOLUTION

Translate: What is 11% of 49?

$$a = 0.11 \cdot 49 \qquad \text{"of" means multiply;}$$
$$11\% = 0.11$$
$$a = 5.39$$

Thus, 5.39 is 11% of 49. The answer is 5.39.

TRY EXERCISE 51

EXAMPLE 5

3 is 16 percent of what?

SOLUTION

Translate: 3 is 16 percent of what?

$$3 = 0.16 \cdot y$$

$$\frac{3}{0.16} = y \qquad \text{Dividing both sides by } 0.16$$

$$18.75 = y$$

Thus, 3 is 16 percent of 18.75. The answer is 18.75.

TRY EXERCISE 47

EXAMPLE 6

What percent of $50 is $34?

SOLUTION

Translate: What percent of $50 is $34?

$$n \cdot 50 = 34$$

$$n = \frac{34}{50} \qquad \text{Dividing both sides by } 50$$

$$n = 0.68 = 68\% \qquad \text{Converting to percent notation}$$

Thus, $34 is 68% of $50. The answer is 68%.

TRY EXERCISE 43

Examples 4–6 represent the three basic types of percent problems. Note that in all the problems, the following quantities are present:

- a percent, expressed in decimal notation in the translation,
- a base amount, indicated by "of" in the problem, and
- a percentage of the base, found by multiplying the base times the percent.

EXAMPLE 7

STUDENT NOTES —————

Always look for connections between examples. Here you should look for similarities between Examples 4 and 7 as well as between Examples 5 and 8 and between Examples 6 and 9.

Discount stores. In 2006, there were 300 million people in the United States, and 62.2% of them lived within 5 mi of a Wal-Mart store. How many lived within 5 mi of a Wal-Mart store?

Source: *The Wall Street Journal, 9/25/06*

SOLUTION We first reword and then translate. We let a = the number of people in the United States, in millions, who live within 5 mi of a Wal-Mart store.

Rewording: What is 62.2% of 300?

Translating: a = 0.622 × 300

The letter is by itself. To solve the equation, we need only multiply:

$$a = 0.622 \times 300 = 186.6.$$

Since 186.6 million is 62.2% of 300 million, we have found that in 2006 about 186.6 million people in the United States lived within 5 mi of a Wal-Mart store.

TRY EXERCISE 65

EXAMPLE 8

College enrollment. About 1.6 million students who graduated from high school in 2006 were attending college in the fall of 2006. This was 66% of all 2006 high school graduates. How many students graduated from high school in 2006?

Source: U.S. Bureau of Labor Statistics

SOLUTION Before translating the problem to mathematics, we reword and let S represent the total number of students, in millions, who graduated from high school in 2006.

Rewording: 1.6 is 66% of S.

Translating: 1.6 = 0.66 · S

$$\frac{1.6}{0.66} = S \qquad \text{Dividing both sides by 0.66}$$

$$2.4 \approx S \qquad \text{The symbol} \approx \text{means } \textit{is approximately equal to.}$$

About 2.4 million students graduated from high school in 2006.

TRY EXERCISE 67

EXAMPLE 9

Automobile prices. Recently, Harken Motors reduced the price of a Flex Fuel 2007 Chevy Impala from the manufacturer's suggested retail price (MSRP) of $20,830 to $18,955.

a) What percent of the MSRP does the sale price represent?

b) What is the percent of discount?

SOLUTION

a) We reword and translate, using n for the unknown percent.

Rewording: What percent of 20,830 is 18,955?

Translating: n · 20,830 = 18,955

$$n = \frac{18,955}{20,830} \qquad \text{Dividing both sides by 20,830}$$

$$n \approx 0.91 = 91\% \qquad \text{Converting to percent notation}$$

The sale price is about 91% of the MSRP.

b) Since the original price of $20,830 represents 100% of the MSRP, the sale price represents a discount of $(100 - 91)\%$, or 9%.

Alternatively, we could find the amount of discount and then calculate the percent of discount:

Amount of discount: $\$20,830 - \$18,955 = \$1875$.

Rewording: What percent of 20,830 is 1875?

Translating: $n \quad \cdot \quad 20,830 \quad = \quad 1875$

$$n = \frac{1875}{20,830}$$ Dividing both sides by 20,830

$$n \approx 0.09 = 9\%$$ Converting to percent notation

Again we find that the percent of discount is 9%.

 TRY EXERCISE 69

1.4 EXERCISE SET

Concept Reinforcement *In each of Exercises 1–10, match the question with the most appropriate translation from the column on the right. Some choices are used more than once.*

1. _____ What percent of 57 is 23?

2. _____ What percent of 23 is 57?

3. _____ 23 is 57% of what number?

4. _____ 57 is 23% of what number?

5. _____ 57 is what percent of 23?

6. _____ 23 is what percent of 57?

7. _____ What is 23% of 57?

8. _____ What is 57% of 23?

9. _____ 23% of what number is 57?

10. _____ 57% of what number is 23?

a) $a = (0.57)23$

b) $57 = 0.23y$

c) $n \cdot 23 = 57$

d) $n \cdot 57 = 23$

e) $23 = 0.57y$

f) $a = (0.23)57$

Convert the percent notation in each sentence to decimal notation.

11. *Energy use.* Heating accounts for 49% of all household energy use.
Source: Chevron

12. *Energy use.* Water heating accounts for 15% of all household energy use.
Source: Chevron

13. *Drinking water.* Only 1% of the water on Earth is suitable for drinking.
Source: www.drinktap.org

Drinking water, 1%

14. *Dehydration.* A 2% drop in water content of the body can affect one's ability to study mathematics.
Source: High Performance Nutrition

15. *College tuition.* Tuition and fees at two-year public colleges increased 4.1 percent in 2006.
Source: College Board 2006 tuition survey

16. *Plant species.* Trees make up about 3.5% of all plant species found in the United States.
Source: South Dakota Project Learning Tree

17. *Women in the workforce.* Women comprise 20% of all database administrators.
Source: U.S. Census Bureau

18. *Women in the workforce.* Women comprise 60% of all accountants and auditors.
Source: U.S. Census Bureau

Convert to decimal notation.

19. 6.25%

20. 8.375%

21. 0.2%

22. 0.8%

23. 175%

24. 250%

Convert the decimal notation in each sentence to percent notation.

25. *NASCAR fans.* Auto racing is the seventh most popular sport in the United States, with 0.38 of the adult population saying they are NASCAR fans.
Source: ESPN Sports poll

26. *Baseball fans.* Baseball is the second most popular sport in the United States, with 0.61 of the adult population saying they are baseball fans.
Source: ESPN Sports poll

27. *Food security.* The USDA defines food security as access to enough nutritious food for a healthy life. In 2005, 0.039 of U.S. households had very low food security.
Source: USDA

28. *Poverty rate.* In 2005, 0.199 of Americans age 65 and older were under the poverty level.
Source: www.census.gov

29. *Music downloads.* In 2006, 0.45 of Americans downloaded music.
Source: Solutions Research Group

30. *Music downloads.* In 2006, 0.23 of Americans paid to download a song.
Source: Solutions Research Group

31. *Composition of the sun.* The sun is 0.7 hydrogen.

32. *Jupiter's atmosphere.* The atmosphere of Jupiter is 0.1 helium.

Convert to percent notation.

33. 0.0009

34. 0.0056

35. 1.06

36. 1.08

37. 1.8

38. 2.4

39. $\frac{3}{5}$

40. $\frac{3}{4}$

41. $\frac{8}{25}$

42. $\frac{5}{8}$

Solve.

43. What percent of 76 is 19?

44. What percent of 125 is 30?

45. What percent of 150 is 39?

46. What percent of 360 is 270?

47. 14 is 30% of what number?

48. 54 is 24% of what number?

49. 0.3 is 12% of what number?

50. 7 is 175% of what number?

51. What number is 1% of one million?

52. What number is 35% of 240?

53. What percent of 60 is 75?

Aha! 54. What percent of 70 is 70?

55. What is 2% of 40?

56. What is 40% of 2?

Aha! **57.** 25 is what percent of 50?

58. 0.8 is 2% of what number?

59. What percent of 69 is 23?

60. What percent of 40 is 9?

Riding bicycles. *There are 57 million Americans who ride a bicycle at least occasionally. The following circle graph shows the reasons people ride. In each of Exercises 61–64, determine the number of Americans who ride a bicycle for the given reason.*

Reasons people rode bicycles, 2003

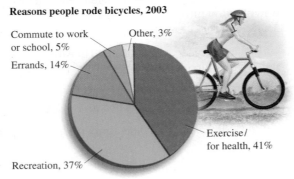

Other, 3%
Commute to work or school, 5%
Errands, 14%
Exercise/ for health, 41%
Recreation, 37%

Sources: U.S. Census Bureau; Bureau of Transportation Statistics

61. Commute to school or work

62. Run errands

63. Exercise for health

64. Recreation

65. *College graduation.* To obtain his bachelor's degree in nursing, Cody must complete 125 credit hours of instruction. If he has completed 60% of his requirement, how many credits did Cody complete?

66. *College graduation.* To obtain her bachelor's degree in journalism, Addy must complete 125 credit hours of instruction. If 20% of Addy's credit hours remain to be completed, how many credits does she still need to take?

67. *Batting average.* In the 2007 season, Magglio Ordonez of the Detroit Tigers had 216 hits. His batting average was 0.363, the highest in major league baseball for that season. This means that of the total number of at bats, 36.3% were hits. How many at bats did he have?
Source: ESPN

68. *Pass completions.* At one point in a recent season, Peyton Manning of the Indianapolis Colts had completed 357 passes. This was 62.5% of his attempts. How many attempts did he make?
Source: National Football League

69. *Tipping.* Trent left a $4 tip for a meal that cost $25.
a) What percent of the cost of the meal was the tip?
b) What was the total cost of the meal including the tip?

70. *Tipping.* Selena left a $12.76 tip for a meal that cost $58.
a) What percent of the cost of the meal was the tip?
b) What was the total cost of the meal including the tip?

71. *Crude oil imports.* In April 2007, crude oil imports to the United States averaged 10.2 million barrels per day. Of this total, 3.4 million came from Canada and Mexico. What percent of crude oil imports came from Canada and Mexico? What percent came from the rest of the world?
Source: Energy Information Administration

72. *Alternative-fuel vehicles.* Of the 550,000 alternative-fuel vehicles produced in the United States in 2004, 150,000 were E85 flexible-fuel vehicles. What percent of alternative-fuel vehicles used E85? What percent used other alternative fuels?
Source: Energy Information Administration

73. *Student loans.* Glenn takes out a subsidized federal Stafford loan for $2400. After a year, Glenn decides to pay off the interest, which is 7% of $2400. How much will he pay?

74. *Student loans.* To finance her community college education, LaTonya takes out a Stafford loan for $3500. After a year, LaTonya decides to pay off the interest, which is 8% of $3500. How much will she pay?

75. *Infant health.* In a study of 300 pregnant women with "good-to-excellent" diets, 95% had babies in good or excellent health. How many women in this group had babies in good or excellent health?

76. *Infant health.* In a study of 300 pregnant women with "poor" diets, 8% had babies in good or excellent health. How many women in this group had babies in good or excellent health?

77. *Cost of self-employment.* Because of additional taxes and fewer benefits, it has been estimated that a self-employed person must earn 20% more than a non–self-employed person performing the same task(s). If Tia earns $16 an hour working for Village Copy, how much would she need to earn on her own for a comparable income?

78. Refer to Exercise 77. Rik earns $18 an hour working for Round Edge stairbuilders. How much would Rik need to earn on his own for a comparable income?

79. *Budget overruns.* The Indianapolis Central Library expansion, begun in 2002, was expected to cost $103 million. By 2006, library officials estimated the cost would be $45 million over budget. By what percent did the actual cost exceed the initial estimate?
Source: *The Indianapolis Star*, 5/23/06

80. *Fastest swimmer.* In 1990, Tom Jager of the United States set a world record by swimming 50 m at a rate of 2.29 m/s. Previously, the fastest swimming rate on record was 2.26 m/s, set in 1975 by David Holmes Edgar, also of the United States. Calculate the percentage by which the rate increased.
Source: *Guinness Book of World Records* 1975 and 1998

81. A bill at Officeland totaled $47.70. How much did the merchandise cost if the sales tax is 6%?

82. Marta's checkbook shows that she wrote a check for $987 for building materials. What was the price of the materials if the sales tax is 5%?

83. *Deducting sales tax.* A tax-exempt school group received a bill of $157.41 for educational software. The bill incorrectly included sales tax of 6%. How much should the school group pay?

84. *Deducting sales tax.* A tax-exempt charity received a bill of $145.90 for a sump pump. The bill incorrectly included sales tax of 5%. How much does the charity owe?

Additional Exercises

85. A tax-exempt hospital received a bill of $1310.75 for linens. The bill incorrectly included sales tax of 7%. How much does the hospital owe?

86. A tax-exempt district attorney received a bill of $1012.30 for office supplies. The bill incorrectly included sales tax of 6%. How much does the attorney owe?

87. A tax-exempt court clerk received a bill of $956.75 for a filing cabinet. The bill incorrectly included sales tax of 7.5%. How much does the clerk owe?

88. A tax-exempt food bank received a bill of $242.65 for food storage bags. The bill incorrectly included sales tax of 5.5%. How much does the food bank owe?

89. Miles paid $74.88, including 4% sales tax, for an out-of-state purchase of books. In order to calculate the amount of sales tax he owes in his state, he must first find the price of the books without sales tax. How much did the books cost before sales tax?

90. Max paid $4601, including 7% sales tax, for an out-of-state purchase of a car. In order to calculate the amount of sales tax he owes in his state, he must first find the price of the car without sales tax. How much did the car cost before sales tax?

91. Becky purchased two sweaters for $132.06, including 6.5% sales tax. How much did the sweaters cost before tax?

92. Clay purchased a winter coat for $71.74, including 5.5% sales tax. How much did the coat cost before tax?

93. A tax-exempt school was received a bill of $138.33 for repairs to a window. The bill incorrectly included sales tax of 6%. How much should the school pay?

94. A tax-exempt emergency response unit received a bill of $1911.84 for a mobile radio unit. The bill incorrectly included sales tax of 5%. How much should the unit pay?

95. Brandon purchased 5 identical books to give as employee gifts. He paid a total of $100.17, including 6% sales tax. How much did each book cost before tax?

96. Kristy purchased 2 identical outfits for her twin nieces. She paid a total of $78.75, including 5% sales tax. How much did each outfit cost before tax?

97. At the grocery store, Destinee used a coupon entitling her to two bottles of shampoo for the price of one. She was not charged for the second bottle of shampoo, but she was incorrectly charged 5% sales tax on the price of both bottles. If her bill was $3.85, how much did one bottle of shampoo cost?

98. At a discount store, Jinney used a coupon entitling her to two 5×7 prints of a photograph for the price of one. She was not charged for the second photograph, but she was incorrectly charged 6% sales tax on the price of both photographs. If her bill was $0.84, how much did one photograph cost?

99. Melanie wants to claim sales tax paid on her income tax return. She spent $4960.80 during the year, including 6% sales tax. How much sales tax did she pay?

100. The Tea Chest needs to send the sales tax it has collected to the state. The total sales, including 4% sales tax, are $7115.68. How much in sales tax does the store need to send to the state?

101. *Body fat.* One author of this text exercises regularly at a local YMCA that recently offered a body-fat percentage test to its members. The device used measures the passage of a very low voltage of electricity through the body. The author's body-fat percentage was found to be 16.5% and he weighs 191 lb. What part, in pounds, of his body weight is fat?

102. *Areas of Alaska and Arizona.* The area of Arizona is 19% of the area of Alaska. The area of Alaska is 586,400 mi^2. What is the area of Arizona?

103. *Direct mail.* Only 2.15% of mailed ads lead to a sale or a response from customers. In 2006, businesses sent out 114 billion pieces of direct mail (catalogs, coupons, and so on). How many pieces of mail led to a response from customers?
Sources: Direct Marketing Association; U.S. Postal Service

104. *Kissing and colds.* In a medical study, it was determined that if 800 people kiss someone else who has a cold, only 56 will actually catch the cold. What percent is this?

105. *Calorie content.* Pepperidge Farm Light Style 7 Grain Bread® has 140 calories in a 3-slice serving. This is 15% less than the number of calories in a serving of regular bread. How many calories are in a serving of regular bread?

106. *Fat content.* Peek Freans Shortbread Reduced Fat Cookies® contain 35 calories of fat in each serving. This is 40% less than the fat content in the leading imported shortbread cookie. How many calories of fat are in a serving of the leading shortbread cookie?

107. Campus Bookbuyers pays $30 for a book and sells it for $60. Is this a 100% markup or a 50% markup? Explain.

108. If Julian leaves a $12 tip for a $90 dinner, is he being generous, stingy, or neither? Explain.

Skill Review

To prepare for Section 1.5, review translating to algebraic expressions and equations.

Translate to an algebraic expression or equation.

109. Twice the length plus twice the width

110. 5% of $180

111. 5 fewer than the number of points Tino scored

112. 15 plus the product of 1.5 and x

113. The product of 10 and half of a

114. 10 more than three times a number

115. The width is 2 in. less than the length.

116. A number is four times as large as a second number.

Synthesis

117. How is the use of statistics in the following misleading?
   a) A business explaining new restrictions on sick leave cited a recent survey indicating that 40% of all sick days were taken on Monday or Friday.
   b) An advertisement urging summer installation of a security system quoted FBI statistics stating that over 26% of home burglaries occur between Memorial Day and Labor Day.

118. Erin is returning a tent that she bought during a 25%-off storewide sale that has ended. She is offered store credit for 125% of what she paid (not to be used on sale items). Is this fair to Erin? Why or why not?

119. The community of Bardville has 1332 left-handed females. If 48% of the community is female and 15% of all females are left-handed, how many people are in the community?

120. It has been determined that at the age of 10, a girl has reached 84.4% of her final adult height. Dana is 4 ft 8 in. at the age of 10. What will her final adult height be?

121. It has been determined that at the age of 15, a boy has reached 96.1% of his final adult height. Jaraan is 6 ft 4 in. at the age of 15. What will his final adult height be?

122. *Dropout rate.* Between 2002 and 2004, the high school dropout rate in the United States decreased from 105 to 103 per thousand. Calculate the percent by which the dropout rate decreased and use that percentage to estimate dropout rates for the United States in 2005 and in 2006.
Source: www.childrendsdatabank.org

123. *Photography.* A 6-in. by 8-in. photo is framed using a mat meant for a 5-in. by 7-in. photo. What percentage of the photo will be hidden by the mat?

124. Would it be better to receive a 5% raise and then, a year later, an 8% raise or the other way around? Why?

125. Jorge is in the 30% tax bracket. This means that 30¢ of each dollar earned goes to taxes. Which would cost him the least: contributing $50 that is tax-deductible or contributing $40 that is not tax-deductible? Explain.

Discount Problems

126. Alex purchased a digital picture frame when it was on sale at 20% off. If he paid $68 for the frame, what was its original price?

127. Ryan purchased a camera when it was on sale at 30% off. If he paid $224 for the camera, what was its original price?

128. Lauren took a 25% pay cut when she changed jobs. If she makes $11.70 an hour on her new job, what was the hourly salary for her previous job?

129. Megan took a 15% pay cut when she changed jobs. If she makes $30,600 a year on her new job, what was the annual salary for her previous job?

130. The value of Karen's retirement account decreased by 40% to $87,000. How much was her retirement account worth before the decrease?

131. The value of Bradley's retirement account decreased by 35% to $26,000. How much was his retirement account worth before the decrease?

132. Dan had a coupon for 12% off his first meal at a new restaurant. If he was charged $11 for the meal, what was the original cost of the meal?

133. Raena had a coupon for 17% off for a haircut. If she was charged $13.28 for the haircut, what was the original price of the haircut?

Answers to Discount Problems

126. $85

127. $320

128. $15.60

129. $36,000

130. $145,000

131. $40,000

132. $12.50

133. $16.00

1.5 Problem Solving

Five Steps for Problem Solving • Applying the Five Steps

Probably the most important use of algebra is as a tool for problem solving. In this section, we develop a problem-solving approach that is used throughout the remainder of the text.

Five Steps for Problem Solving

In Section 1.4, we solved several real-world problems. To solve them, we first *familiarized* ourselves with percent notation. We then *translated* each problem into an equation, *solved* the equation, *checked* the solution, and *stated* the answer.

Five Steps for Problem Solving in Algebra

1. *Familiarize* yourself with the problem.
2. *Translate* to mathematical language. (This often means writing an equation.)
3. *Carry out* some mathematical manipulation. (This often means *solving* an equation.)
4. *Check* your possible answer in the original problem.
5. *State* the answer clearly, using a complete English sentence.

Of the five steps, the most important is probably the first one: becoming familiar with the problem. Here are some hints for familiarization.

To Become Familiar with a Problem

1. Read the problem carefully. Try to visualize the problem.
2. Reread the problem, perhaps aloud. Make sure you understand all important words and any symbols or abbreviations.
3. List the information given and the question(s) to be answered. Choose a variable (or variables) to represent the unknown and specify exactly what the variable represents. For example, let L = length in centimeters, d = distance in miles, and so on.
4. Look for similarities between the problem and other problems you have already solved. Ask yourself what type of problem this is.
5. Find more information. Look up a formula in a book, at a library, or online. Consult a reference librarian or an expert in the field.
6. Make a table that uses all the information you have available. Look for patterns that may help in the translation.
7. Make a drawing and label it with known and unknown information, using specific units if given.
8. Think of a possible answer and check the guess. Note the manner in which the guess is checked.

Applying the Five Steps

EXAMPLE 1

Bicycling.   After finishing college, Nico spent a week touring Tuscany, Italy, by bicycle. He biked 260 km from Pisa through Siena to Florence. At Siena, he had biked three times as far from Pisa as he would then bike to Florence. How far had he biked, and how far did he have left to go?

SOLUTION

1. **Familiarize.** It is often helpful to make a drawing. In this case, we can use a map of Nico's trip.

   To gain familiarity, let's suppose that Nico has 50 km to go. Then he would have traveled three times 50 km, or 150 km, already. Since 50 km + 150 km = 200 km and 200 km < 260 km, we see that our guess is too small. Rather than guess again, we let

   d = the distance, in kilometers, from Siena to Florence

   and

   $3d$ = the distance, in kilometers, from Siena to Pisa.

   (We could also let x = the distance to Pisa; then the distance to Florence would be $\frac{1}{3}x$.)

2. **Translate.** The lengths of the two parts of the trip must add up to 260 km. This leads to our translation.

Rewording:	Distance to Florence	plus	distance to Pisa	is	260 km
Translating:	d	$+$	$3d$	$=$	260

3. **Carry out.** We solve the equation:

   $d + 3d = 260$

   $\quad 4d = 260$ Combining like terms

   $\quad\ \ d = 65.$ Dividing both sides by 4

4. **Check.** As predicted in the *Familiarize* step, d is greater than 50 km. If $d = 65$ km, then $3d = 195$ km. Since 65 km + 195 km = 260 km, we have a check.

5. **State.** At Siena, Nico had biked 195 km and had 65 km left to go to arrive in Florence.

   TRY EXERCISE 9

   Before we solve the next problem, we need to learn some additional terminology regarding integers.
   The following are examples of **consecutive integers:** 16, 17, 18, 19, 20; and −31, −30, −29, −28. Note that consecutive integers can be represented in the form $x, x + 1, x + 2$, and so on.

The following are examples of **consecutive even integers:** 16, 18, 20, 22, 24; and $-52, -50, -48, -46$. Note that consecutive even integers can be represented in the form $x, x + 2, x + 4$, and so on.

The following are examples of **consecutive odd integers:** 21, 23, 25, 27, 29; and $-71, -69, -67, -65$. Note that consecutive odd integers can be also represented in the form $x, x + 2, x + 4$, and so on.

EXAMPLE 2

Interstate mile markers. U.S. interstate highways post numbered markers at every mile to indicate location in case of an emergency. The sum of two consecutive mile markers on I-70 in Kansas is 559. Find the numbers on the markers.

Source: Federal Highway Administration, Ed Rotalewski

STUDY SKILLS

Set Reasonable Expectations

Do not be surprised if your success rate drops some as you work through the exercises in this section. *This is normal.* Your success rate will increase as you gain experience with these types of problems and use some of the study skills already listed.

x	$x + 1$	**Sum of x and $x + 1$**
114	115	229
252	253	505
302	303	605

SOLUTION

1. **Familiarize.** The numbers on the mile markers are consecutive positive integers. Thus if we let $x =$ the smaller number, then $x + 1 =$ the larger number.

   To become familiar with the problem, we can make a table, as shown at left. First, we guess a value for x; then we find $x + 1$. Finally, we add the two numbers and check the sum.

   From the table, we see that the first marker will be between 252 and 302. We could continue guessing and solve the problem this way, but let's work on developing our algebra skills.

2. **Translate.** We reword the problem and translate as follows.

   Rewording: First integer plus second integer is 559.

   Translating: $x + (x + 1) = 559$

3. **Carry out.** We solve the equation:

$$x + (x + 1) = 559$$
$$2x + 1 = 559 \qquad \text{Using an associative law and combining like terms}$$
$$2x = 558 \qquad \text{Subtracting 1 from both sides}$$
$$x = 279. \qquad \text{Dividing both sides by 2}$$

   If x is 279, then $x + 1$ is 280.

4. **Check.** Our possible answers are 279 and 280. These are consecutive positive integers and $279 + 280 = 559$, so the answers check.

5. **State.** The mile markers are 279 and 280.

TRY EXERCISE 13

EXAMPLE 3

Color printers. Egads Computer Corporation rents a Xerox Phaser 8400 Color Laser Printer for $300 a month. A new art gallery is leasing a printer for a 2-month advertising campaign. The ink and paper for the brochures will cost an additional 21.5¢ per copy. If the gallery allots a budget of $3000, how many brochures can they print?

Source: egadscomputer.com

SOLUTION

1. **Familiarize.** Suppose that the art gallery prints 20,000 brochures. Then the cost is the monthly charges plus ink and paper cost, or

2($300) plus cost per brochure times number of brochures
$600 + $0.215 · 20,000,

which is $4900. Our guess of 20,000 is too large, but we have familiarized ourselves with the way in which a calculation is made. Note that we convert 21.5¢ to $0.215 so that all information is in the same unit, dollars. We let $c =$ the number of brochures that can be printed for $3000.

2. **Translate.** We reword the problem and translate as follows.

Rewording: Monthly cost plus ink and paper cost is $3000.

Translating: 2($300) + ($0.215)c = $3000

3. **Carry out.** We solve the equation:

$$2(300) + 0.215c = 3000$$
$$600 + 0.215c = 3000$$
$$0.215c = 2400 \quad \text{Subtracting 600 from both sides}$$
$$c = \frac{2400}{0.215} \quad \text{Dividing both sides by 0.215}$$
$$c \approx 11{,}162. \quad \text{We round } \textit{down} \text{ to avoid going over the budget.}$$

4. **Check.** We check in the original problem. The cost for 11,162 brochures is 11,162($0.215) = $2399.83. The rental for 2 months is 2($300) = $600. The total cost is then $2399.83 + $600 = $2999.83, which is just under the amount that was allotted. Our answer is less than 20,000, as we expected from the *Familiarize* step.

5. **State.** The art gallery can make 11,162 brochures with the rental allotment of $3000.

TRY EXERCISE 37

STUDENT NOTES ⎯⎯⎯⎯

For most students, the most challenging step is step (2), "Translate."

EXAMPLE 4

Perimeter of NBA court. The perimeter of an NBA basketball court is 288 ft. The length is 44 ft longer than the width. Find the dimensions of the court.

Source: National Basketball Association

SOLUTION

1. **Familiarize.** Recall that the perimeter of a rectangle is twice the length plus twice the width. Suppose the court were 30 ft wide. The length would then be 30 + 44, or 74 ft, and the perimeter would be 2 · 30 ft + 2 · 74 ft, or 208 ft. This shows that in order for the perimeter to be 288 ft, the width must exceed 30 ft. Instead of guessing again, we let $w =$ the width of the court, in feet.

Since the court is "44 ft longer than it is wide," we let $w + 44$ = the length of the court, in feet.

2. **Translate.** To translate, we use $w + 44$ as the length and 288 as the perimeter. To double the length, $w + 44$, parentheses are essential.

Rewording: Twice the length   plus   twice the width   is   288 ft.

Translating: $2(w + 44)$ $+$ $2w$ $=$ 288

3. **Carry out.** We solve the equation:

$$2(w + 44) + 2w = 288$$
$$2w + 88 + 2w = 288 \qquad \text{Using the distributive law}$$
$$4w + 88 = 288 \qquad \text{Combining like terms}$$
$$4w = 200$$
$$w = 50.$$

The dimensions appear to be $w = 50$ ft, and $l = w + 44 = 94$ ft.

4. **Check.** If the width is 50 ft and the length is 94 ft, then the court is 44 ft longer than it is wide. The perimeter is $2(50 \text{ ft}) + 2(94 \text{ ft}) = 100 \text{ ft} + 188 \text{ ft}$, or 288 ft, as specified. We have a check.

5. **State.** An NBA court is 50 ft wide and 94 ft long.   TRY EXERCISE 25

CAUTION!   Always be sure to answer the original problem completely. For instance, in Example 1 we needed to find *two* numbers: the distances from *each* city to Siena. Similarly, in Example 4 we needed to find two dimensions, not just the width. Be sure to label each answer with the proper unit.

EXAMPLE 5

Selling at an auction.   Jared is selling his collection of Transformers at an auction. He wants to be left with $1150 after paying a seller's premium of 8% on the final bid (hammer price) for the collection. What must the hammer price be in order for him to clear $1150?

SOLUTION

1. **Familiarize.** Suppose the collection sells for $1200. The 8% seller's premium can be determined by finding 8% of $1200:

$$8\% \text{ of } \$1200 = 0.08(\$1200) = \$96.$$

Subtracting this premium from $1200 would leave Jared with

$$\$1200 - \$96 = \$1104.$$

This shows that in order for Jared to clear $1150, the collection must sell for more than $1200. We let $x =$ the hammer price, in dollars. Jared then must pay a seller's premium of $0.08x$.

2. **Translate.** We reword the problem and translate as follows.

Rewording: Hammer price   less   seller's premium   is   amount remaining.

Translating: x $-$ $0.08x$ $=$ $\$1150$

3. **Carry out.** We solve the equation:

$$x - 0.08x = 1150$$
$$1x - 0.08x = 1150$$
$$0.92x = 1150 \qquad \text{Combining like terms. Had we noted that after the premium has been paid, 92\% remains, we could have begun with this equation.}$$
$$x = \frac{1150}{0.92} \qquad \text{Dividing both sides by 0.92}$$
$$x = 1250.$$

4. **Check.** To check, we first find 8% of $1250:

$$8\% \text{ of } \$1250 = 0.08(\$1250) = \$100. \qquad \text{This is the premium.}$$

Next, we subtract the premium to find the remaining amount:

$$\$1250 - \$100 = \$1150.$$

Since, after Jared pays the seller's premium, he is left with $1150, our answer checks. Note that the $1250 hammer price is greater than $1200, as predicted in the *Familiarize* step.

5. **State.** Jared's collection must sell for $1250 in order for him to be left with $1150.

TRY EXERCISE ▶ 7

EXAMPLE 6

Cross section of a roof.   In a triangular gable end of a roof, the angle of the peak is twice as large as the angle on the back side of the house. The measure of the angle on the front side is 20° greater than the angle on the back side. How large are the angles?

SOLUTION

1. **Familiarize.** We make a drawing. In this case, the measure of the back angle is x, the measure of the front angle is $x + 20$, and the measure of the peak angle is $2x$.

2. **Translate.** To translate, we need to recall that the sum of the measures of the angles in a triangle is $180°$.

Rewording: Measure of back angle $+$ measure of front angle $+$ measure of peak angle is $180°$.

Translating: $x + (x + 20) + 2x = 180$

3. **Carry out.** We solve:

$$x + (x + 20) + 2x = 180$$
$$4x + 20 = 180$$
$$4x = 160$$
$$x = 40.$$

The measures for the angles appear to be:

Back angle: $x = 40°,$

Front angle: $x + 20 = 40 + 20 = 60°,$

Peak angle: $2x = 2(40) = 80°.$

4. **Check.** Consider $40°, 60°,$ and $80°,$ as listed above. The measure of the front angle is $20°$ greater than the measure of the back angle, the measure of the peak angle is twice the measure of the back angle, and the sum is $180°$. These numbers check.

5. **State.** The measures of the angles are $40°, 60°,$ and $80°$. **TRY EXERCISE** 31

We close this section with some tips to aid you in problem solving.

Problem-Solving Tips

1. The more problems you solve, the more your skills will improve.
2. Look for patterns when solving problems. Each time you study an example or solve an exercise, you may observe a pattern for problems found later.
3. Clearly define variables before translating to an equation.
4. Consider the dimensions of the variables and constants in the equation. The variables that represent length should all be in the same unit, those that represent money should all be in dollars or all in cents, and so on.
5. Make sure that units appear in the answer whenever appropriate and that you completely answer the original problem.

1.5 EXERCISE SET

For Extra Help **MyMathLab**

Solve. Even though you might find the answer quickly in some other way, practice using the five-step problem-solving process in order to build the skill of problem solving.

1. Three less than twice a number is 19. What is the number?

2. Two fewer than ten times a number is 78. What is the number?

3. Five times the sum of 3 and twice some number is 70. What is the number?

4. Twice the sum of 4 and three times some number is 34. What is the number?

5. *Price of an iPod.*   Kyle paid $120 for an iPod nano during a 20%-off sale. What was the regular price?

6. *Price of sneakers.*   Amy paid $102 for a pair of New Balance 1122 running shoes during a 15%-off sale. What was the regular price?

7. *Price of a calculator.*   Kayla paid $137.80, including 6% tax, for her graphing calculator. How much did the calculator itself cost?

8. *Price of a printer.*   Laura paid $219.45, including 5% tax, for an all-in-one color printer. How much did the printer itself cost?

9. *Unicycling.*   In 2005, Ken Looi of New Zealand set a record by covering 235.3 mi in 24 hr on his unicycle. After 8 hr, he was approximately twice as far from the finish line as he was from the start. How far had he traveled?
Source: *Guinness World Records* 2007

10. *Sled-dog racing.*   The Iditarod sled-dog race extends for 1049 mi from Anchorage to Nome. If a musher is twice as far from Anchorage as from Nome, how many miles has the musher traveled?

11. *Indy Car racing.*   In April 2008, Danica Patrick won the Indy Japan 300 with a time of 01:51:02.6739 for the 300-mi race. At one point, Patrick was 20 mi closer to the finish than to the start. How far had Patrick traveled at that point?

12. *NASCAR racing.*   In June 2007, Carl Edwards won the Michigan 400 with a time of 2:42:5 for the 400-mi race. At one point, Edwards was 80 mi closer to the finish than to the start. How far had Edwards traveled at that point?

13. *Apartment numbers.*   The apartments in Erica's apartment house are consecutively numbered on each floor. The sum of her number and her next-door neighbor's number is 2409. What are the two numbers?

14. *Apartment numbers.*   The apartments in Brian's apartment house are numbered consecutively on each floor. The sum of his number and his next-door neighbor's number is 1419. What are the two numbers?

15. *Street addresses.*   The houses on the west side of Lincoln Avenue are consecutive odd numbers. Sam and Colleen are next-door neighbors and the sum of their house numbers is 572. Find their house numbers.

16. *Street addresses.*   The houses on the south side of Elm Street are consecutive even numbers. Wanda and Larry are next-door neighbors and the sum of their house numbers is 794. Find their house numbers.

17. The sum of three consecutive page numbers is 99. Find the numbers.

18. The sum of three consecutive page numbers is 60. Find the numbers.

19. *Longest marriage.*   As half of the world's longest-married couple, the woman was 2 yr younger than her husband. Together, their ages totaled 204 yr. How old were the man and the woman?
Source: *Guinness World Records* 2007

20. *Oldest bride.*   The world's oldest bride was 19 yr older than her groom. Together, their ages totaled 185 yr. How old were the bride and the groom?
Source: *Guinness World Records* 2007

21. *e-mail.*   In 2006, approximately 125 billion e-mail messages were sent each day. The number of spam messages was about four times the number of non-spam messages. How many of each type of message were sent each day in 2006?
Source: Ferris Research

22. *Home remodeling.*   In 2005, Americans spent a total of $26 billion to remodel bathrooms and kitchens. They spent $5 billion more on kitchens than on bathrooms. How much was spent on each?
Source: Joint Center for Housing Studies, Harvard University

23. *Page numbers.*   The sum of the page numbers on the facing pages of a book is 281. What are the page numbers?

24. *Perimeter of a triangle.*   The perimeter of a triangle is 195 mm. If the lengths of the sides are consecutive odd integers, find the length of each side.

25. *Hancock Building dimensions.* The top of the John Hancock Building in Chicago is a rectangle whose length is 60 ft more than the width. The perimeter is 520 ft. Find the width and the length of the rectangle. Find the area of the rectangle.

26. *Dimensions of a state.* The perimeter of the state of Wyoming is 1280 mi. The width is 90 mi less than the length. Find the width and the length.

27. A rectangular community garden is to be enclosed with 92 m of fencing. In order to allow for compost storage, the garden must be 4 m longer than it is wide. Determine the dimensions of the garden.

28. *Perimeter of a high school basketball court.* The perimeter of a standard high school basketball court is 268 ft. The length is 34 ft longer than the width. Find the dimensions of the court.
Source: Indiana High School Athletic Association

29. *Two-by-four.* The perimeter of a cross section of a "two-by-four" piece of lumber is $10\frac{1}{2}$ in. The length is twice the width. Find the actual dimensions of the cross section of a two-by-four.

$P = 10\frac{1}{2}$ in.

30. *Standard billboard sign.* A standard rectangular highway billboard sign has a perimeter of 124 ft. The length is 6 ft more than three times the width. Find the dimensions of the sign.

31. *Angles of a triangle.* The second angle of an architect's triangle is three times as large as the first. The third angle is 30° more than the first. Find the measure of each angle.

32. *Angles of a triangle.* The second angle of a triangular garden is four times as large as the first. The third angle is 45° less than the sum of the other two angles. Find the measure of each angle.

33. *Angles of a triangle.* The second angle of a triangular kite is four times as large as the first. The third angle is 5° more than the sum of the other two angles. Find the measure of the second angle.

34. *Angles of a triangle.* The second angle of a triangular building lot is three times as large as the first. The third angle is 10° more than the sum of the other two angles. Find the measure of the third angle.

35. *Rocket sections.* A rocket is divided into three sections: the payload and navigation section in the top, the fuel section in the middle, and the rocket engine section in the bottom. The top section is one-sixth the length of the bottom section. The middle section is one-half the length of the bottom section. The total length is 240 ft. Find the length of each section.

36. *Gourmet sandwiches.* Jenny, Demi, and Drew buy an 18-in. long gourmet sandwich and take it back to their apartment. Since they have different appetites, Jenny cuts the sandwich so that Demi gets half of what Jenny gets and Drew gets three-fourths of what Jenny gets. Find the length of each person's sandwich.

37. *Taxi rates.* In Chicago, a taxi ride costs $2.25 plus $1.80 for each mile traveled. Debbie has budgeted $18 for a taxi ride (excluding tip). How far can she travel on her $18 budget?
Source: City of Chicago

38. *Taxi fares.* In New York City, taxis charge $2.50 plus $2.00 per mile for off-peak fares. How far can Ralph travel for $17.50 (assuming an off-peak fare)?
Source: New York City Taxi and Limousine Commission

39. *Truck rentals.* Truck-Rite Rentals rents trucks at a daily rate of $49.95 plus 39¢ per mile. Concert Productions has budgeted $100 for renting a truck to haul equipment to an upcoming concert. How far can they travel in one day and stay within their budget?

40. *Truck rentals.* Fine Line Trucks rents an 18-ft truck for $42 plus 35¢ per mile. Judy needs a truck for one day to deliver a shipment of plants. How far can she drive and stay within a budget of $70?

41. *Complementary angles.* The sum of the measures of two *complementary* angles is 90°. If one angle measures 15° more than twice the measure of its complement, find the measure of each angle.

Complementary angles

42. *Complementary angles.* Two angles are complementary. (See Exercise 41.) The measure of one angle is $1\frac{1}{2}$ times the measure of the other. Find the measure of each angle.

43. *Supplementary angles.* The sum of the measures of two *supplementary* angles is 180°. If the measure of one angle is $3\frac{1}{2}$ times the measure of the other, find the measure of each angle.

Supplementary angles

44. *Supplementary angles.* Two angles are supplementary. (See Exercise 43.) If one angle measures 45° less than twice the measure of its supplement, find the measure of each angle.

45. *Copier paper.* The perimeter of standard-size copier paper is 99 cm. The width is 6.3 cm less than the length. Find the length and the width.

46. *Stock prices.* Sarah's investment in Jet Blue stock grew 28% to $448. How much did she originally invest?

47. *Savings interest.* Janeka invested money in a savings account at a rate of 6% simple interest. After 1 yr, she has $6996 in the account. How much did Janeka originally invest?

48. *Credit cards.* The balance in Will's Mastercard® account grew 2%, to $870, in one month. What was his balance at the beginning of the month?

49. *Scrabble®.* In a single game on October 12, 2006, Michael Cresta and Wayne Yorra set three North American Scrabble records: the most points in one game by one player, the most total points in the game, and the most points on a single turn. Cresta scored 340 points more than Yorra, and together they scored 1320 points. What was the winning score?
Source: www.slate.com

50. *Color printers.* The art gallery in Example 3 decides to raise its budget to $5000 for the 2-month period. How many brochures can they print for $5000?

51. *Selling a home.* The Brannons are planning to sell their home. If they want to be left with $117,500 after paying 6% of the selling price to a realtor as a commission, for how much must they sell the house?

52. *Budget overruns.* The massive roadworks project in Boston known as The Big Dig cost approximately $14.6 billion. This cost was 484% more than the original estimate. What was the original estimate of the cost of The Big Dig?
Sources: Taxpayers for Common Sense; www.msnbc.cmsn.com

53. *Cricket chirps and temperature.* The equation $T = \frac{1}{4}N + 40$ can be used to determine the temperature T, in degrees Fahrenheit, given the number of times N a cricket chirps per minute. Determine the number of chirps per minute for a temperature of 80°F.

54. *Race time.* The equation $R = -0.028t + 20.8$ can be used to predict the world record in the 200-m dash, where R is the record in seconds and t is the number of years since 1920. In what year will the record be 18.0 sec?

55. Sean claims he can solve most of the problems in this section by guessing. Is there anything wrong with this approach? Why or why not?

56. When solving Exercise 20, Beth used a to represent the bride's age and Ben used a to represent the groom's age. Is one of these approaches preferable to the other? Why or why not?

Skill Review

To prepare for Section 1.6, review inequalities.

Write a true sentence using either $<$ or $>$.

57. $-8 \ \blacksquare \ 1$ **58.** $-2 \ \blacksquare \ -5$

59. $\frac{1}{2} \ \blacksquare \ 0$ **60.** $-3 \ \blacksquare \ -1$

Write a second inequality with the same meaning.

61. $x \geq -4$ **62.** $x < 5$

63. $5 > y$ **64.** $-10 \leq t$

Synthesis

65. Write a problem for a classmate to solve. Devise it so that the problem can be translated to the equation $x + (x + 2) + (x + 4) = 375$.

66. Write a problem for a classmate to solve. Devise it so that the solution is "Audrey can drive the rental truck for 50 mi without exceeding her budget."

67. *Discounted dinners.* Kate's "Dining Card" entitles her to $10 off the price of a meal after a 15% tip has been added to the cost of the meal. If, after the discount, the bill is $32.55, how much did the meal originally cost?

68. *Test scores.* Pam scored 78 on a test that had 4 fill-in questions worth 7 points each and 24 multiple-choice questions worth 3 points each. She had one fill-in question wrong. How many multiple-choice questions did Pam get right?

69. *Gettysburg Address.* Abraham Lincoln's 1863 Gettysburg Address refers to the year 1776 as "four *score* and seven years ago." Determine what a score is.

70. One number is 25% of another. The larger number is 12 more than the smaller. What are the numbers?

71. A storekeeper goes to the bank to get $10 worth of change. She requests twice as many quarters as half dollars, twice as many dimes as quarters, three times as many nickels as dimes, and no pennies or dollars. How many of each coin did the storekeeper get?

72. *Perimeter of a rectangle.* The width of a rectangle is three fourths of the length. The perimeter of the rectangle becomes 50 cm when the length and the width are each increased by 2 cm. Find the length and the width.

73. *Discounts.* In exchange for opening a new credit account, Macy's Department Stores® subtracts 10% from all purchases made the day the account is established. Julio is opening an account and has a coupon for which he receives 10% off the first day's reduced price of a camera. If Julio's final price is $77.75, what was the price of the camera before the two discounts?

74. *Sharing fruit.*   Apples are collected in a basket for six people. One third, one fourth, one eighth, and one fifth of the apples are given to four people, respectively. The fifth person gets ten apples, and one apple remains for the sixth person. Find the original number of apples in the basket.

75. *eBay purchases.*   An eBay seller charges $9.99 for the first DVD purchased and $6.99 for all others. For shipping and handling, he charges the full shipping fee of $3 for the first DVD, one half of the shipping charge for the second item, and one third of the shipping charge per item for all remaining items. The total cost of a shipment (excluding tax) was $45.45. How many DVDs were in the shipment?

76. *Winning percentage.*   In a basketball league, the Falcons won 15 of their first 20 games. In order to win 60% of the total number of games, how many more games will they have to play, assuming they win only half of the remaining games?

77. *Taxi fares.*   In New York City, a taxi ride costs $2.50 plus 40¢ per $\frac{1}{5}$ mile and 40¢ per minute stopped in traffic. Due to traffic, Glenda's taxi took 20 min to complete what is usually a 10-min drive. If she is charged $18.50 for the ride, how far did Glenda travel?
Source: New York City Taxi and Limousine Commission

78. *Test scores.*   Ella has an average score of 82 on three tests. Her average score on the first two tests is 85. What was the score on the third test?

79. A school purchases a piano and must choose between paying $2000 at the time of purchase or $2150 at the end of one year. Which option should the school select and why?

80. Annette claims the following problem has no solution: "The sum of the page numbers on facing pages is 191. Find the page numbers." Is she correct? Why or why not?
Aha!

81. The perimeter of a rectangle is 101.74 cm. If the length is 4.25 cm longer than the width, find the dimensions of the rectangle.

82. The second side of a triangle is 3.25 cm longer than the first side. The third side is 4.35 cm longer than the second side. If the perimeter of the triangle is 26.87 cm, find the length of each side.

1.6   Solving Inequalities

Solutions of Inequalities   ▪   Graphs of Inequalities   ▪   Set-Builder and Interval Notation   ▪
Solving Inequalities Using the Addition Principle   ▪   Solving Inequalities Using the Multiplication Principle   ▪
Using the Principles Together

Many real-world situations translate to *inequalities*. For example, a student might need to register for *at least* 12 credits; an elevator might be designed to hold *at most* 2000 pounds; a tax credit might be allowable for families with incomes of *less than* $25,000; and so on. Before solving applications of this type, we must adapt our equation-solving principles to the solving of inequalities.

Solutions of Inequalities

Recall from Section 1.4 that an inequality is a number sentence containing $>$ (is greater than), $<$ (is less than), $\geq$ (is greater than or equal to), or $\leq$ (is less than or equal to). Inequalities like

$$-7 > x, \quad t < 5, \quad 5x - 2 \geq 9, \quad \text{and} \quad -3y + 8 \leq -7$$

are true for some replacements of the variable and false for others.

   Any value for the variable that makes an inequality true is called a **solution**. The set of all solutions is called the **solution set**. When all solutions of an inequality are found, we say that we have **solved** the inequality.

EXAMPLE **1**

Determine whether the given number is a solution of $x < 2$: **(a)** -3; **(b)** 2.

SOLUTION

a) Since $-3 < 2$ is true, -3 is a solution.

b) Since $2 < 2$ is false, 2 is not a solution.

TRY EXERCISE 9

EXAMPLE **2**

Determine whether the given number is a solution of $y \geq 6$: **(a)** 6; **(b)** -4.

SOLUTION

a) Since $6 \geq 6$ is true, 6 is a solution.

b) Since $-4 \geq 6$ is false, -4 is not a solution.

TRY EXERCISE 11

Graphs of Inequalities

Because the solutions of inequalities like $x < 2$ are too numerous to list, it is helpful to make a drawing that represents all the solutions. The **graph** of an inequality is such a drawing. Graphs of inequalities in one variable can be drawn on the number line by shading all points that are solutions. Parentheses are used to indicate endpoints that are *not* solutions and brackets to indicate endpoints that *are* solutions.*

EXAMPLE **3**

Graph each inequality: **(a)** $x < 2$; **(b)** $y \geq -3$; **(c)** $-2 < x \leq 3$.

SOLUTION

a) The solutions of $x < 2$ are those numbers less than 2. They are shown on the graph by shading all points to the left of 2. The parenthesis at 2 and the shading to its left indicate that 2 is *not* part of the graph, but numbers like 1.2 and 1.99 are.

b) The solutions of $y \geq -3$ are shown on the number line by shading the point for -3 and all points to the right of -3. The bracket at -3 indicates that -3 *is* part of the graph.

STUDENT NOTES —————

Note that $-2 < x < 3$ means $-2 < x$ and $x < 3$. Because of this, statements like $2 < x < 1$ make no sense—no number is both greater than 2 and less than 1.

c) The inequality $-2 < x \leq 3$ is read "-2 is less than x *and* x is less than or equal to 3," or "x is greater than -2 *and* less than or equal to 3." To be a solution of $-2 < x \leq 3$, a number must be a solution of both $-2 < x$ and $x \leq 3$. The number 1 is a solution, as are -0.5, 1.9, and 3. The parenthesis indicates that -2 is *not* a solution, whereas the bracket indicates that 3 *is* a solution. The other solutions are shaded.

TRY EXERCISE 17

*An alternative notation uses open dots to indicate endpoints that are not solutions and closed dots to indicate endpoints that are solutions. Using this notation, the solutions of $x < 2$ are graphed as and the solutions of $y \geq -3$ are graphed as .

Set–Builder and Interval Notation

To write the solution set of $x < 3$, we can use **set-builder notation:**

$$\{x | x < 3\}.$$

This is read "The set of all x such that x is less than 3."

Another way to write solutions of an inequality in one variable is to use **interval notation**. Interval notation uses parentheses, ( ), and brackets, [ ].

If a and b are real numbers with $a < b$, we define the **open interval (a, b)** as the set of all numbers x for which $a < x < b$. Using set-builder notation, we write

$$(a, b) = \{x | a < x < b\}. \qquad \text{Parentheses are used to exclude endpoints.}$$

Its graph excludes the endpoints:

$$(a, b)$$
$$\xleftarrow{\qquad \underset{a}{(} \qquad\qquad \underset{b}{)} \qquad} \qquad \{x | a < x < b\}$$

> **CAUTION!** Do not confuse the *interval* (a, b) with the *ordered pair* (a, b). The context in which the notation appears should make the meaning clear.

The **closed interval $[a, b]$** is defined as the set of all numbers x for which $a \le x \le b$. Thus,

$$[a, b] = \{x | a \le x \le b\}. \qquad \text{Brackets are used to include endpoints.}$$

Its graph includes the endpoints:

$$[a, b]$$
$$\xleftarrow{\qquad \underset{a}{[} \qquad\qquad \underset{b}{]} \qquad} \qquad \{x | a \le x \le b\}$$

STUDENT NOTES

You may have noticed which inequality signs in set-builder notation correspond to brackets and which correspond to parentheses. The relationship could be written informally as

$$\le \quad \ge \qquad [\ ]$$
$$< \quad > \qquad (\ ).$$

There are two kinds of **half-open intervals**, defined as follows:

1. $(a, b] = \{x | a < x \le b\}$. This is open on the left. Its graph is as follows:

$$(a, b]$$
$$\xleftarrow{\qquad \underset{a}{(} \qquad\qquad \underset{b}{]} \qquad} \qquad \{x | a < x \le b\}$$

2. $[a, b) = \{x | a \le x < b\}$. This is open on the right. Its graph is as follows:

$$[a, b)$$
$$\xleftarrow{\qquad \underset{a}{[} \qquad\qquad \underset{b}{)} \qquad} \qquad \{x | a \le x < b\}$$

We use the symbols ∞ and $-\infty$ to represent positive infinity and negative infinity, respectively. Thus the notation (a, ∞) represents the set of all real numbers greater than a, and $(-\infty, a)$ represents the set of all real numbers less than a.

$$(a, \infty)$$
$$\xleftarrow{\qquad \underset{a}{(} \qquad\qquad\qquad} \rightarrow \qquad \{x | x > a\}$$

$$(-\infty, a)$$
$$\leftarrow \xrightarrow{\qquad\qquad \underset{a}{)} \qquad} \qquad \{x | x < a\}$$

The notation $[a, \infty)$ or $(-\infty, a]$ is used when we want to include the endpoint a.

EXAMPLE 4 Graph $y \ge -2$ on a number line and write the solution set using both set-builder and interval notations.

SOLUTION Using set-builder notation, we write the solution set as $\{y | y \ge -2\}$.

Using interval notation, we write $[-2, \infty)$.

To graph the solution, we shade all numbers to the right of -2 and use a bracket to indicate that -2 is also a solution.

$$\xleftarrow{\ \underset{-7}{+}\ \underset{-6}{+}\ \underset{-5}{+}\ \underset{-4}{+}\ \underset{-3}{+}\ \underset{-2}{[}\ \underset{-1}{\ }\ \underset{0}{\ }\ \underset{1}{\ }\ \underset{2}{\ }\ \underset{3}{\ }\ \underset{4}{\ }\ \underset{5}{\ }\ \underset{6}{\ }\ \underset{7}{\ }\ }\rightarrow$$

TRY EXERCISE 27

Solving Inequalities Using the Addition Principle

Consider a balance similar to one that appears in Section 1.1. When one side of the balance holds more weight than the other, the balance tips in that direction. If equal amounts of weight are then added to or subtracted from both sides of the balance, the balance remains tipped in the same direction.

The balance illustrates the idea that when a number, such as 2, is added to (or subtracted from) both sides of a true inequality, such as $3 < 7$, we get another true inequality:

$$3 + 2 < 7 + 2, \quad or \quad 5 < 9.$$

Similarly, if we add -4 to both sides of $x + 4 < 10$, we get an *equivalent* inequality:

$$x + 4 + (-4) < 10 + (-4), \quad or \quad x < 6.$$

We say that $x + 4 < 10$ and $x < 6$ are **equivalent**, which means that both inequalities have the same solution set.

The Addition Principle for Inequalities

For any real numbers a, b, and c:

$a < b$ is equivalent to $a + c < b + c$;

$a \leq b$ is equivalent to $a + c \leq b + c$;

$a > b$ is equivalent to $a + c > b + c$;

$a \geq b$ is equivalent to $a + c \geq b + c$.

As with equations, our goal is to isolate the variable on one side.

EXAMPLE 5

Solve $x + 2 > 8$ and then graph the solution.

SOLUTION   We use the addition principle, subtracting 2 from both sides:

$$x + 2 - 2 > 8 - 2 \qquad \text{Subtracting 2 from, or adding } -2 \text{ to, both sides}$$
$$x > 6.$$

From the inequality $x > 6$, we can determine the solutions easily. Any number greater than 6 makes $x > 6$ true and is a solution of that inequality as well as the inequality $x + 2 > 8$. Using set-builder notation, the solution set is $\{x | x > 6\}$. Using interval notation, the solution set is $(6, \infty)$. The graph is as follows:

Because most inequalities have an infinite number of solutions, we cannot possibly check them all. A partial check can be made using one of the possible solutions. For this example, we can substitute any number greater than 6—say, 6.1—into the original inequality:

$$\frac{x + 2 > 8}{6.1 + 2 \mid 8}$$
$$8.1 \overset{?}{>} 8 \quad \text{TRUE} \qquad 8.1 > 8 \text{ is a true statement.}$$

Since $8.1 > 8$ is true, 6.1 is a solution. Any number greater than 6 is a solution.

> TRY EXERCISE ▸ 43

EXAMPLE 6

TECHNOLOGY CONNECTION

As a partial check of Example 5, we can let $y_1 = 3x - 1$ and $y_2 = 2x - 5$. We set TblStart $= -5$ and ΔTbl $= 1$ in the TBLSET menu to get the following table. By scrolling up or down, you can note that for $x \le -4$, we have $y_1 \le y_2$.

X	Y1	Y2
−5	−16	−15
−4	−13	−13
−3	−10	−11
−2	−7	−9
−1	−4	−7
0	−1	−5
1	2	−3

X = −5

Solve $3x - 1 \le 2x - 5$ and then graph the solution.

SOLUTION   We have

$$
\begin{aligned}
3x - 1 &\le 2x - 5 \\
3x - 1 + 1 &\le 2x - 5 + 1 && \text{Adding 1 to both sides} \\
3x &\le 2x - 4 && \text{Simplifying} \\
3x - 2x &\le 2x - 4 - 2x && \text{Subtracting } 2x \text{ from both sides} \\
x &\le -4. && \text{Simplifying}
\end{aligned}
$$

The graph is as follows:

The student should check that any number less than or equal to -4 is a solution. The solution set is $\{x \mid x \le -4\}$, or $(-\infty, -4]$.

> TRY EXERCISE ▸ 47

Solving Inequalities Using the Multiplication Principle

There is a multiplication principle for inequalities similar to that for equations, but it must be modified when multiplying both sides by a negative number. Consider the true inequality

$$3 < 7.$$

If we multiply both sides by a *positive* number—say, 2—we get another true inequality:

$$3 \cdot 2 < 7 \cdot 2, \quad \text{or} \quad 6 < 14. \qquad \text{TRUE}$$

If we multiply both sides by a negative number—say, -2—we get a *false* inequality:

$$3 \cdot (-2) < 7 \cdot (-2), \quad \text{or} \quad -6 < -14. \qquad \text{FALSE}$$

The fact that $6 < 14$ is true, but $-6 < -14$ is false, stems from the fact that the negative numbers, in a sense, *mirror* the positive numbers. Whereas 14 is to the *right* of 6, the number -14 is to the *left* of -6. Thus if we reverse the inequality symbol in $-6 < -14$, we get a true inequality:

$$-6 > -14. \qquad \text{TRUE}$$

> ### The Multiplication Principle for Inequalities
>
> For any real numbers a and b, and for any *positive* number c:
>
> $$a < b \quad \text{is equivalent to} \quad ac < bc, \quad \text{and}$$
> $$a > b \quad \text{is equivalent to} \quad ac > bc.$$
>
> For any real numbers a and b, and for any *negative* number c:
>
> $$a < b \quad \text{is equivalent to} \quad ac > bc, \quad \text{and}$$
> $$a > b \quad \text{is equivalent to} \quad ac < bc.$$
>
> Similar statements hold for $\leq$ and $\geq$.

CAUTION! When multiplying or dividing both sides of an inequality by a negative number, don't forget to reverse the inequality symbol!

EXAMPLE 7 Solve and graph each inequality: **(a)** $\frac{1}{4}x < 7$; **(b)** $-2y \leq 18$.

SOLUTION

a) $\quad \frac{1}{4}x < 7$

$\quad 4 \cdot \frac{1}{4}x < 4 \cdot 7 \qquad$ Multiplying both sides by 4, the reciprocal of $\frac{1}{4}$

$\qquad\qquad\qquad\qquad$ The symbol stays the same, since 4 is positive.

$\quad\quad x < 28 \qquad$ Simplifying

The solution set is $\{x \mid x < 28\}$, or $(-\infty, 28)$. The graph is shown at left.

b) $\quad -2y \leq 18$

$\quad \dfrac{-2y}{-2} \geq \dfrac{18}{-2} \qquad$ Multiplying both sides by $-\frac{1}{2}$, or dividing both sides by -2

$\qquad\qquad\qquad\qquad$ *At this step*, we reverse the inequality, because $-\frac{1}{2}$ is negative.

$\quad\quad y \geq -9 \qquad$ Simplifying

As a partial check, we substitute a number greater than -9, say -8, into the original inequality:

$$\frac{-2y \leq 18}{-2(-8) \mid 18}$$
$$16 \overset{?}{\leq} 18 \quad \text{TRUE} \qquad 16 \leq 18 \text{ is a true statement.}$$

The solution set is $\{y \mid y \geq -9\}$, or $[-9, \infty)$. The graph is shown at left.

▶ TRY EXERCISE 59

Using the Principles Together

We use the addition and multiplication principles together to solve inequalities much as we did when solving equations.

EXAMPLE 8 Solve: **(a)** $6 - 5y > 7$; **(b)** $2x - 9 < 7x + 1$.

SOLUTION

a) $\qquad 6 - 5y > 7$

$\quad -6 + 6 - 5y > -6 + 7 \qquad$ Adding -6 to both sides

$\qquad\qquad -5y > 1 \qquad$ Simplifying

$$-\tfrac{1}{5} \cdot (-5y) < -\tfrac{1}{5} \cdot 1 \qquad \text{Multiplying both sides by } -\tfrac{1}{5}, \text{ or dividing both sides by } -5$$

Remember to reverse the inequality symbol!

$$y < -\tfrac{1}{5} \qquad \text{Simplifying}$$

As a partial check, we substitute a number smaller than $-\tfrac{1}{5}$, say -1, into the original inequality:

$$\begin{array}{c|c} 6 - 5y > 7 \\ \hline 6 - 5(-1) & 7 \\ 6 - (-5) & \\ \end{array}$$

$$11 \overset{?}{>} 7 \quad \text{TRUE} \qquad 11 > 7 \text{ is a true statement.}$$

The solution set is $\{y \mid y < -\tfrac{1}{5}\}$, or $\left(-\infty, -\tfrac{1}{5}\right)$. We show the graph in the margin for reference.

b)
$$2x - 9 < 7x + 1$$
$$2x - 9 - 1 < 7x + 1 - 1 \qquad \text{Subtracting 1 from both sides}$$
$$2x - 10 < 7x \qquad \text{Simplifying}$$
$$2x - 10 - 2x < 7x - 2x \qquad \text{Subtracting } 2x \text{ from both sides}$$
$$-10 < 5x \qquad \text{Simplifying}$$
$$\frac{-10}{5} < \frac{5x}{5} \qquad \text{Dividing both sides by 5}$$
$$-2 < x \qquad \text{Simplifying}$$

The solution set is $\{x \mid -2 < x\}$, or $\{x \mid x > -2\}$, or $(-2, \infty)$.

> **TRY EXERCISE** 69

All of the equation-solving techniques used in Sections 1.1 and 1.2 can be used with inequalities provided we remember to reverse the inequality symbol when multiplying or dividing both sides by a negative number.

EXAMPLE 9 Solve: **(a)** $16.3 - 7.2p \le -8.18$; **(b)** $3(x - 9) - 1 \le 2 - 5(x + 6)$.

SOLUTION

a) The greatest number of decimal places in any one number is *two*. Multiplying both sides by 100 will clear decimals. Then we proceed as before.

$$16.3 - 7.2p \le -8.18$$
$$100(16.3 - 7.2p) \le 100(-8.18) \qquad \text{Multiplying both sides by 100}$$
$$100(16.3) - 100(7.2p) \le 100(-8.18) \qquad \text{Using the distributive law}$$
$$1630 - 720p \le -818 \qquad \text{Simplifying}$$
$$-720p \le -818 - 1630 \qquad \text{Subtracting 1630 from both sides}$$
$$-720p \le -2448 \qquad \text{Simplifying; } -818 - 1630 = -2448$$
$$p \ge \frac{-2448}{-720} \qquad \text{Dividing both sides by } -720$$

Remember to reverse the symbol!

$$p \ge 3.4$$

The solution set is $\{p \mid p \ge 3.4\}$, or $[3.4, \infty)$.

b) $3(x - 9) - 1 \leq 2 - 5(x + 6)$

$3x - 27 - 1 \leq 2 - 5x - 30$ Using the distributive law to remove parentheses

$3x - 28 \leq -5x - 28$ Simplifying

$3x - 28 + 28 \leq -5x - 28 + 28$ Adding 28 to both sides

$3x \leq -5x$

$3x + 5x \leq -5x + 5x$ Adding $5x$ to both sides

$8x \leq 0$

$x \leq 0$ Dividing both sides by 8

The solution set is $\{x \mid x \leq 0\}$, or $(-\infty, 0]$.

TRY EXERCISE 83

1.6   EXERCISE SET

For Extra Help   MyMathLab   Math XL PRACTICE   WATCH   DOWNLOAD

Concept Reinforcement *Insert the symbol* $<, >, \leq, or \geq$ *to make each pair of inequalities equivalent.*

1. $-5x \leq 30;$ $x \ \blacksquare \ -6$

2. $-7t \geq 56;$ $t \ \blacksquare \ -8$

3. $-2t > -14;$ $t \ \blacksquare \ 7$

4. $-3x < -15;$ $x \ \blacksquare \ 5$

Classify each pair of inequalities as "equivalent" or "not equivalent."

5. $x < -2;$ $-2 > x$

6. $t > -1;$ $-1 < t$

7. $-4x - 1 \leq 15;$
$-4x \leq 16$

8. $-2t + 3 \geq 11;$
$-2t \geq 14$

Determine whether each number is a solution of the given inequality.

9. $x > -4$

a) 4   **b)** -6 **c)** -4

10. $t < 3$

a) -3 **b)** 3   **c)** $2\frac{19}{20}$

11. $y \leq 19$

a) 18.99   **b)** 19.01   **c)** 19

12. $n \geq -4$

a) 0   **b)** -4.1 **c)** -3.9

13. $c \geq -7$

a) 0   **b)** -5.4 **c)** 7.1

14. $a > 6$

a) 6   **b)** -6.7 **c)** 0

15. $z < -3$

a) 0   **b)** $-3\frac{1}{3}$ **c)** 1

16. $m \leq -2$

a) $-1\frac{9}{10}$ **b)** 0   **c)** $-2\frac{1}{3}$

Graph on a number line.

17. $y < 2$ **18.** $x \leq 7$

19. $x \geq -1$ **20.** $t > -2$

21. $0 \leq t$ **22.** $1 \leq m$

23. $-5 \leq x < 2$

24. $-3 < x \leq 5$

25. $-4 < x < 0$

26. $0 \leq x \leq 5$

Graph each inequality, and write the solution set using both set-builder notation and interval notation.

27. $y < 6$ **28.** $x > 4$

29. $x \geq -4$ **30.** $t \leq 6$

31. $t > -3$ **32.** $y < -3$

33. $x \leq -7$ **34.** $x \geq -6$

Describe each graph using set-builder notation and interval notation.

35.
36.
37.
38.
39.
40.
41.
42.

Solve using the addition principle. Graph and write set-builder notation and interval notation for each answer.

43. $y + 6 > 9$

44. $x + 8 \leq -10$

45. $n - 6 < 11$

46. $n - 4 > -3$

47. $2x \leq x - 9$

48. $3x \leq 2x + 7$

49. $y + \frac{1}{3} \leq \frac{5}{6}$

50. $x + \frac{1}{4} \leq \frac{1}{2}$

51. $t - \frac{1}{8} > \frac{1}{2}$

52. $y - \frac{1}{3} > \frac{1}{4}$

53. $-9x + 17 > 17 - 8x$

54. $-8n + 12 > 12 - 7n$

Aha! **55.** $-23 < -t$

56. $19 < -x$

57. $10 - y \leq -12$

58. $3 - y \geq -6$

Solve using the multiplication principle. Graph and write set-builder notation and interval notation for each answer.

59. $4x < 28$

60. $3x \geq 24$

61. $-24 > 8t$

62. $-16x < -64$

63. $1.8 \geq -1.2n$

64. $9 \leq -2.5a$

65. $-2y \leq \frac{1}{5}$

66. $-2x \geq \frac{1}{5}$

67. $-\frac{8}{5} > 2x$

68. $-\frac{5}{8} < -10y$

Solve using the addition and multiplication principles.

69. $2 + 3x < 20$

70. $7 + 4y < 31$

71. $4t - 5 \leq 23$

72. $15x - 7 \leq -7$

73. $39 > 3 - 9x$

74. $5 > 5 - 7y$

75. $5 - 6y > 25$

76. $8 - 2y > 9$

77. $-3 < 8x + 7 - 7x$

78. $-5 < 9x + 8 - 8x$

79. $6 - 4y > 6 - 3y$

80. $7 - 8y > 5 - 7y$

81. $7 - 9y \leq 4 - 7y$

82. $6 - 13y \leq 4 - 12y$

83. $2.1x + 43.2 > 1.2 - 8.4x$

84. $0.96y - 0.79 \leq 0.21y + 0.46$

85. $1.7t + 8 - 1.62t < 0.4t - 0.32 + 8$

86. $0.7n - 15 + n \geq 2n - 8 - 0.4n$

87. $\frac{x}{3} + 4 \leq 1$

88. $\frac{2}{3} - \frac{x}{5} < \frac{4}{15}$

89. $3 < 5 - \frac{t}{7}$

90. $2 > 9 - \frac{x}{5}$

91. $4(2y - 3) \leq -44$

92. $3(2y - 3) > 21$

93. $8(2t + 1) > 4(7t + 7)$

94. $3(t - 2) \geq 9(t + 2)$

95. $3(r - 6) + 2 < 4(r + 2) - 21$

96. $5(t + 3) + 9 \geq 3(t - 2) - 10$

97. $\frac{4}{5}(3x + 4) \leq 20$

98. $\frac{2}{3}(2x - 1) \geq 10$

99. $\frac{2}{3}\left(\frac{7}{8} - 4x\right) - \frac{5}{8} < \frac{3}{8}$

100. $\frac{3}{4}\left(3x - \frac{1}{2}\right) - \frac{2}{3} < \frac{1}{3}$

101. Are the inequalities $x > -3$ and $x \geq -2$ equivalent? Why or why not?

102. Are the inequalities $t < -7$ and $t \leq -8$ equivalent? Why or why not?

Skill Review

Review simplifying expressions.

Simplify.

103. $5x - 2(3 - 6x)$

104. $8m - n - 3(2m + 5n)$

105. $x - 2[4y + 3(8 - x) - 1]$

106. $5 - 3t - 4[6 + 5(2t - 1) + t]$

107. $3[5(2a - b) + 1] - 5[4 - (a - b)]$

108. $9x - 2\{4 - 5[6 - 2(x + 1) - x]\}$

Synthesis

109. Explain how it is possible for the graph of an inequality to consist of just one number. (*Hint*: See Example 3c.)

110. The statements of the addition and multiplication principles begin with *conditions* set for the variables. Explain the conditions given for each principle.

Solve.

Aha! **111.** $x < x + 1$

112. $6[4 - 2(6 + 3t)] > 5[3(7 - t) - 4(8 + 2t)] - 20$

113. $27 - 4[2(4x - 3) + 7] \geq 2[4 - 2(3 - x)] - 3$

Solve for x.

114. $\frac{1}{2}(2x + 2b) > \frac{1}{3}(21 + 3b)$

115. $-(x + 5) \geq 4a - 5$

116. $y < ax + b$ (Assume $a < 0$.)

117. $y < ax + b$ (Assume $a > 0$.)

118. Graph the solutions of $|x| < 3$ on a number line.

Aha! **119.** Determine the solution set of $|x| > -3$.

120. Determine the solution set of $|x| < 0$.

CONNECTING the CONCEPTS

The procedure for solving inequalities is very similar to that used to solve equations. There are, however, two important differences.

- The multiplication principle for inequalities differs from the multiplication principle for equations: When we multiply or divide on both sides of an inequality by a *negative* number, we must *reverse* the direction of the inequality.

- The solution set of an equation like those we solved in this chapter typically consists of one number. The solution set of an inequality typically consists of a set of numbers and is written using set-builder notation.

Compare the following solutions.

Solve: $2 - 3x = x + 10$.

SOLUTION

$$2 - 3x = x + 10$$
$$-3x = x + 8 \quad \text{Subtracting 2 from both sides}$$
$$-4x = 8 \quad \text{Subtracting } x \text{ from both sides}$$
$$x = -2 \quad \text{Dividing both sides by } -4$$

The solution is -2.

Solve: $2 - 3x > x + 10$.

SOLUTION

$$2 - 3x > x + 10$$
$$-3x > x + 8 \quad \text{Subtracting 2 from both sides}$$
$$-4x > 8 \quad \text{Subtracting } x \text{ from both sides}$$
$$x < -2 \quad \text{Dividing both sides by } -4 \text{ and reversing the direction of the inequality symbol}$$

The solution is $\{x | x < -2\}$, or $(-\infty, -2)$.

MIXED REVIEW

Solve.

1. $x - 6 = 15$
2. $x - 6 \leq 15$
3. $3x = -18$
4. $3x > -18$
5. $-3x > -18$
6. $5x + 2 = 17$
7. $7 - 3x = 8$
8. $4y - 7 < 5$
9. $3 - t \geq 19$
10. $2 + 3n = 5n - 9$
11. $3 - 5a > a + 9$
12. $1.2x - 3.4 < 0.4x + 5.2$
13. $\frac{2}{3}(x + 5) \geq -4$

14. $\frac{n}{5} - 6 = 15$
15. $0.5x - 2.7 = 3x + 7.9$
16. $5(6 - t) = -45$
17. $8 - \frac{y}{3} \leq 7$
18. $\frac{1}{3}x - \frac{5}{6} = \frac{3}{2} - \frac{1}{6}x$
19. $-15 > 7 - 5x$
20. $10 \geq -2(a - 5)$

1.7   Solving Applications with Inequalities

Translating to Inequalities   •   Solving Problems

The five steps for problem solving can be used for problems involving inequalities.

Translating to Inequalities

Before solving problems that involve inequalities, we list some important phrases to look for. Sample translations are listed as well.

STUDY SKILLS

Avoiding Temptation

Maximize the effectiveness of your study time by choosing the right location. For example, sit in a comfortable chair in a well-lit location, but stay away from a coffee shop where friends may stop by. Once you begin studying, let the answering machine answer the phone, shut off any cell phones, and do not check e-mail.

Important Words	Sample Sentence	Translation
is at least	Ming walks at least 2 mi a day.	$m \geq 2$
is at most	At most, 5 students dropped the course.	$n \leq 5$
cannot exceed	The width cannot exceed 40 ft.	$w \leq 40$
must exceed	The speed must exceed 15 mph.	$s > 15$
is less than	Kamal's weight is less than 120 lb.	$w < 120$
is more than	Boston is more than 200 mi away.	$d > 200$
is between	The film was between 90 and 100 min long.	$90 < t < 100$
minimum	Ned drank a minimum of 5 glasses of water a day.	$w \geq 5$
maximum	The maximum penalty is $100.	$p \leq 100$
no more than	Alan weighs no more than 90 lb.	$w \leq 90$
no less than	Mallory scored no less than 8.3.	$s \geq 8.3$

The following phrases deserve special attention.

Translating "at least" and "at most"

The quantity x is at least some amount q: $x \geq q$.

(If x is *at least* q, it cannot be less than q.)

The quantity x is at most some amount q: $x \leq q$.

(If x is *at most* q, it cannot be more than q.)

Solving Problems

EXAMPLE 1

Catering costs. To cater a party, Curtis' Barbeque charges a $50 setup fee plus $15 per person. The cost of Hotel Pharmacy's end-of-season softball party cannot exceed $450. How many people can attend the party?

SOLUTION

1. **Familiarize.** Suppose that 20 people were to attend the party. The cost would then be $50 + $15 · 20, or $350. This shows that more than 20 people could attend without exceeding $450. Instead of making another guess, we let n = the number of people in attendance.

2. **Translate.** The cost of the party will be $50 for the setup fee plus $15 times the number of people attending. We can reword as follows:

	the cost of		
Rewording: The setup fee	plus	the meals	cannot exceed	$450.
↓	↓	↓	↓	↓
Translating: 50	+	15 · n	≤	450

3. **Carry out.** We solve for n:

$$50 + 15n \leq 450$$
$$15n \leq 400 \qquad \text{Subtracting 50 from both sides}$$
$$n \leq \frac{400}{15} \qquad \text{Dividing both sides by 15}$$
$$n \leq 26\frac{2}{3}. \qquad \text{Simplifying}$$

4. **Check.** Although the solution set of the inequality is all numbers less than or equal to $26\frac{2}{3}$, since n represents the number of people in attendance, we round *down* to 26. If 26 people attend, the cost will be $50 + $15 · 26, or $440, and if 27 attend, the cost will exceed $450.

5. **State.** At most 26 people can attend the party.

▶ TRY EXERCISE 23

CAUTION! Solutions of problems should always be checked using the original wording of the problem. In some cases, answers might need to be whole numbers or integers or rounded off in a particular direction.

Some applications with inequalities involve *averages*, or *means*. You are already familiar with the concept of averages from grades in courses that you have taken.

> ### Average, or Mean
> To find the **average**, or **mean**, of a set of numbers, add the numbers and then divide by the number of addends.

EXAMPLE 2

Financial aid. Full-time students in a health-care education program can receive financial aid and employee benefits from Covenant Health System by working at Covenant while attending school and also agreeing to work there after graduation. Students who work an average of at least 16 hr per week receive extra pay and part-time employee benefits. For the first three weeks of September, Dina worked 20 hr, 12 hr, and 14 hr. How many hours must she work during the fourth week in order to average at least 16 hr per week for the month?

Source: Covenant Health Systems

SOLUTION

1. **Familiarize.** Suppose Dina works 10 hr during the fourth week. Her average for the month would be

$$\frac{20\text{ hr} + 12\text{ hr} + 14\text{ hr} + 10\text{ hr}}{4} = 14\text{ hr.}$$ There are 4 addends, so we divide by 4.

This shows that Dina must work more than 10 hr during the fourth week, if she is to average at least 16 hr of work per week. We let x represent the number of hours Dina works during the fourth week.

2. **Translate.** We reword the problem and translate as follows:

   Rewording: The average number of hours worked — should be at least — 16 hr.

   Translating: $\dfrac{20 + 12 + 14 + x}{4} \geq 16$

3. **Carry out.** Because of the fraction, it is convenient to use the multiplication principle first:

$$\frac{20 + 12 + 14 + x}{4} \geq 16$$

$$4\left(\frac{20 + 12 + 14 + x}{4}\right) \geq 4 \cdot 16 \qquad \text{Multiplying both sides by 4}$$

$$20 + 12 + 14 + x \geq 64$$

$$46 + x \geq 64 \qquad \text{Simplifying}$$

$$x \geq 18. \qquad \text{Subtracting 46 from both sides}$$

4. **Check.** As a partial check, we show that if Dina works 18 hr, she will average at least 16 hr per week:

$$\frac{20 + 12 + 14 + 18}{4} = \frac{64}{4} = 16. \qquad \text{Note that 16 is at least 16.}$$

5. **State.** Dina will average at least 16 hr of work per week for September if she works at least 18 hr during the fourth week.

TRY EXERCISE 27

Translating for Success

1. *Consecutive integers.* The sum of two consecutive even integers is 102. Find the integers.

2. *Salary increase.* After Susanna earned a 5% raise, her new salary was $25,750. What was her former salary?

3. *Dimensions of a rectangle.* The length of a rectangle is 6 in. more than the width. The perimeter of the rectangle is 102 in. Find the length and the width.

4. *Population.* The population of Kelling Point is decreasing at a rate of 5% per year. The current population is 25,750. What was the population the previous year?

5. *Reading assignment.* Quinn has 6 days to complete a 150-page reading assignment. How many pages must he read the first day so that he has no more than 102 pages left to read on the 5 remaining days?

Translate each word problem to an equation or an inequality and select a correct translation from A–O.

A. $0.05(25,750) = x$

B. $x + 2x = 102$

C. $2x + 2(x + 6) = 102$

D. $150 - x \leq 102$

E. $x - 0.05x = 25,750$

F. $x + (x + 2) = 102$

G. $x + (x + 6) > 102$

H. $x + 5x = 150$

I. $x + 0.05x = 25,750$

J. $x + (2x + 6) = 102$

K. $x + (x + 1) = 102$

L. $102 + x > 150$

M. $0.05x = 25,750$

N. $102 + 5x > 150$

O. $x + (x + 6) = 102$

Answers on page A-1

An additional, animated version of this activity appears in MyMathLab. To use MyMathLab, you need a course ID and a student access code. Contact your instructor for more information.

6. *Numerical relationship.* One number is 6 more than twice another. The sum of the numbers is 102. Find the numbers.

7. *DVD collections.* Together Mindy and Ken have 102 DVDs. If Ken has 6 more DVDs than Mindy, how many does each have?

8. *Sales commissions.* Kirk earns a commission of 5% on his sales. One year he earned commissions totaling $25,750. What were his total sales for the year?

9. *Fencing.* Jess has 102 ft of fencing that he plans to use to enclose two dog runs. The perimeter of one run is to be twice the perimeter of the other. Into what lengths should the fencing be cut?

10. *Quiz scores.* Lupe has a total of 102 points on the first 6 quizzes in her sociology class. How many total points must she earn on the 5 remaining quizzes in order to have more than 150 points for the semester?

1.7 EXERCISE SET

For Extra Help

Concept Reinforcement *In each of Exercises 1–8, match the sentence with one of the following:*

$$a < b; \quad a \le b; \quad b < a; \quad b \le a.$$

1. a is at least b.

2. a exceeds b.

3. a is at most b.

4. a is exceeded by b.

5. b is no more than a.

6. b is no less than a.

7. b is less than a.

8. b is more than a.

Translate to an inequality.

9. A number is less than 10.

10. A number is greater than or equal to 4.

11. The temperature is at most $-3°C$.

12. The average credit-card debt is more than $8000.

13. To rent a car, a driver must have a minimum of 5 yr driving experience.

14. The Barringdean Shopping Center is no more than 20 mi away.

15. The age of the Mayan altar exceeds 1200 yr.

16. The maximum safe exposure limit of formaldehyde is 2 parts per million.

17. Tania earns between $12 and $15 an hour.

18. Leslie's test score was at least 85.

19. Wind speeds were greater than 50 mph.

20. The costs of production of that software cannot exceed $12,500.

21. A room at Pine Tree Bed and Breakfast costs no more than $120 a night.

22. The cost of gasoline was at most $4 per gallon.

Use an inequality and the five-step process to solve each problem.

23. *Furnace repairs.* RJ's Plumbing and Heating charges $55 plus $40 per hour for emergency service. Gary remembers being billed over $150 for an emergency call. How long was RJ's there?

24. *College tuition.* Karen's financial aid stipulates that her tuition not exceed $1000. If her local community college charges a $35 registration fee plus $375 per course, what is the greatest number of courses for which Karen can register?

25. *Graduate school.* An unconditional acceptance into the Master of Business Administration (MBA) program at Arkansas State University will be given to students whose GMAT score plus 200 times the undergraduate grade point average is at least 950. Robbin's GMAT score was 500. What must her grade point average be in order to be unconditionally accepted into the program?
Source: graduateschool.astate.edu

26. *Car payments.* As a rule of thumb, debt payments (other than mortgages) should be less than 8% of a consumer's monthly gross income. Oliver makes $54,000 a year and has a $100 student-loan payment every month. What size car payment can he afford?
Source: money.cnn.com

27. *Quiz average.* Rod's quiz grades are 73, 75, 89, and 91. What scores on a fifth quiz will make his average quiz grade at least 85?

28. *Nutrition.* Following the guidelines of the U.S. Department of Agriculture, Dale tries to eat at least 5 half-cup servings of vegetables each day. For the first six days of one week, she had 4, 6, 7, 4, 6, and 4 servings. How many servings of vegetables should Dale eat on Saturday, in order to average at least 5 servings per day for the week?

29. *College course load.* To remain on financial aid, Millie needs to complete an average of at least 7 credits per quarter each year. In the first three quarters of 2008, Millie completed 5, 7, and 8 credits. How many credits of course work must Millie complete in the fourth quarter if she is to remain on financial aid?

30. *Music lessons.* Band members at Colchester Middle School are expected to average at least 20 min of practice time per day. One week Monroe practiced 15 min, 28 min, 30 min, 0 min, 15 min, and 25 min. How long must he practice on the seventh day if he is to meet expectations?

31. *Baseball.* In order to qualify for a batting title, a major league baseball player must average at least 3.1 plate appearances per game. For the first nine games of the season, a player had 5, 1, 4, 2, 3, 4, 4, 3, and 2 plate appearances. How many plate appearances must the player have in the tenth game in order to average at least 3.1 per game?
Source: Major League Baseball

32. *Education.* The Mecklenberg County Public Schools stipulate that a standard school day will average at least $5\frac{1}{2}$ hr, excluding meal breaks. For the first four days of one school week, bad weather resulted in school days of 4 hr, $6\frac{1}{2}$ hr, $3\frac{1}{2}$ hr, and $6\frac{1}{2}$ hr. How long must the Friday school day be in order to average at least $5\frac{1}{2}$ hr for the week?
Source: www.meck.k12.va.us

33. *Perimeter of a triangle.* One side of a triangle is 2 cm shorter than the base. The other side is 3 cm longer than the base. What lengths of the base will allow the perimeter to be greater than 19 cm?

34. *Perimeter of a sign.* The perimeter of a rectangular sign is not to exceed 50 ft. The length is to be twice the width. What widths will meet these conditions?

35. *Well drilling.* All Seasons Well Drilling offers two plans. Under the "pay-as-you-go" plan, they charge $500 plus $8 a foot for a well of any depth. Under their "guaranteed-water" plan, they charge a flat fee of $4000 for a well that is guaranteed to provide adequate water for a household. For what depths would it save a customer money to use the pay-as-you-go plan?

36. *Cost of road service.* Rick's Automotive charges $50 plus $15 for each (15-min) unit of time when making a road call. Twin City Repair charges $70 plus $10 for each unit of time. Under what circumstances would it be more economical for a motorist to call Rick's?

37. *Insurance-covered repairs.* Most insurance companies will replace a vehicle if an estimated repair exceeds 80% of the "blue-book" value of the vehicle. Michele's insurance company paid $8500 for repairs to her Subaru after an accident. What can be concluded about the blue-book value of the car?

38. *Insurance-covered repairs.* Following an accident, Jeff's Ford pickup was replaced by his insurance company because the damage was so extensive. Before the damage, the blue-book value of the truck was $21,000. How much would it have cost to repair the truck? (See Exercise 37.)

39. *Sizes of packages.* The U.S. Postal Service defines a "package" as a parcel for which the sum of the length and the girth is less than 84 in. (Length is the longest side of a package and girth is the distance around the other two sides of the package.) A box has a fixed girth of 29 in. Determine (in terms of an inequality) those lengths for which the box is considered a "package."

40. *Sizes of envelopes.* Rhetoric Advertising is a direct-mail company. It determines that for a particular campaign, it can use any envelope with a fixed width of $3\frac{1}{2}$ in. and an area of at least $17\frac{1}{2}$ in^2. Determine (in terms of an inequality) those lengths that will satisfy the company constraints.

41. *Body temperature.* A person is considered to be feverish when his or her temperature is higher than 98.6°F. The formula $F = \frac{9}{5}C + 32$ can be used to convert Celsius temperatures C to Fahrenheit temperatures F. For which Celsius temperatures is a person considered feverish?

42. *Gold temperatures.* Gold stays solid at Fahrenheit temperatures below 1945.4°. Determine (in terms of an inequality) those Celsius temperatures for which gold stays solid. Use the formula given in Exercise 41.

43. *Area of a triangular sign.* Zoning laws in Harrington prohibit displaying signs with areas exceeding 12 ft^2. If Flo's Marina is ordering a triangular sign with an 8-ft base, how tall can the sign be?

44. *Area of a triangular flag.* As part of an outdoor education course, Trisha needs to make a bright-colored triangular flag with an area of at least 3 ft^2. What heights can the triangle be if the base is $1\frac{1}{2}$ ft?

45. *Fat content in foods.* Reduced Fat Skippy® peanut butter contains 12 g of fat per serving. In order for a food to be labeled "reduced fat," it must have at least 25% less fat than the regular item. What can you conclude about the number of grams of fat in a serving of the regular Skippy peanut butter?
Source: Best Foods

46. *Fat content in foods.* Reduced Fat Chips Ahoy!® cookies contain 5 g of fat per serving. What can you conclude about the number of grams of fat in regular Chips Ahoy! cookies (see Exercise 45)?
Source: Nabisco Brands, Inc.

47. *Weight gain.* In the last weeks before the yearly Topsfield Weigh In, heavyweight pumpkins gain about 26 lb per day. Charlotte's heaviest pumpkin weighs 532 lb on September 5. For what dates will its weight exceed 818 lb?
Source: Based on a story in the *Burlington Free Press*

48. *Pond depth.* On July 1, Garrett's Pond was 25 ft deep. Since that date, the water level has dropped $\frac{2}{3}$ ft per week. For what dates will the water level not exceed 21 ft?

49. *Cell-phone budget.* Liam has budgeted $60 a month for his cell phone. For his service, he pays a monthly fee of $39.95, plus taxes of $6.65, plus 10¢ for each text message sent or received. How many text messages can he send or receive and not exceed his budget?

50. *Banquet costs.* The women's volleyball team can spend at most $700 for its awards banquet at a local restaurant. If the restaurant charges a $100 setup fee plus $24 per person, at most how many can attend?

51. *World records in the mile run.* The formula
$$R = -0.0065t + 4.3259$$
can be used to predict the world record, in minutes, for the 1-mi run t years after 1900. Determine (in terms of an inequality) those years for which the world record will be less than 3.6 min.
Source: Based on information from Information Please Database 2007, Pearson Education, Inc.

52. *Women's records in the women's 1500-m run.* The formula
$$R = -0.0026t + 4.0807$$
can be used to predict the world record, in minutes, for the 1500-m run t years after 1900. Determine (in terms of an inequality) those years for which the world record will be less than 3.8 min.
Source: Based on information from *Track and Field*

53. *Toll charges.* The equation

$$y = 0.06x + 0.50$$

can be used to determine the approximate cost y, in dollars, of driving x miles on the Pennsylvania Turnpike. For what mileages x will the cost be at most $14?

54. *Price of a movie ticket.* The average price of a movie ticket can be estimated by the equation

$$P = 0.169Y - 333.04,$$

where Y is the year and P is the average price, in dollars. For what years will the average price of a movie ticket be at least $7? (Include the year in which the $7 ticket first occurs.)
Source: National Association of Theatre Owners

55. If f represents Fran's age and t represents Todd's age, write a sentence that would translate to $t + 3 < f$.

56. Explain how the meanings of "Five more than a number" and "Five is more than a number" differ.

Skill Review

Review operations with real numbers.

Simplify.

57. $-2 + (-5) - 7$

58. $\dfrac{1}{2} \div \left(-\dfrac{3}{4}\right)$

59. $3 \cdot (-10) \cdot (-1) \cdot (-2)$

60. $-6.3 + (-4.8)$

61. $(3 - 7) - (4 - 8)$

62. $3 - 2 + 5 \cdot 10 \div 5^2 \cdot 2$

63. $\dfrac{-2 - (-6)}{8 - 10}$

64. $\dfrac{1 - (-7)}{-3 - 5}$

Synthesis

65. Write a problem for a classmate to solve. Devise the problem so the answer is "At most 18 passengers can go on the boat." Design the problem so that at least one number in the solution must be rounded down.

66. Write a problem for a classmate to solve. Devise the problem so the answer is "The Rothmans can drive 90 mi without exceeding their truck rental budget."

67. *Ski wax.* Green ski wax works best between 5° and 15° Fahrenheit. Determine those Celsius temperatures for which green ski wax works best. (See Exercise 41.)

68. *Parking fees.* Mack's Parking Garage charges $4.00 for the first hour and $2.50 for each additional hour. For how long has a car been parked when the charge exceeds $16.50?

Aha! **69.** The area of a square can be no more than 64 cm^2. What lengths of a side will allow this?

Aha! **70.** The sum of two consecutive odd integers is less than 100. What is the largest pair of such integers?

71. *Nutritional standards.* In order for a food to be labeled "lowfat," it must have fewer than 3 g of fat per serving. Reduced-fat tortilla chips contain 60% less fat than regular nacho cheese tortilla chips, but still cannot be labeled lowfat. What can you conclude about the fat content of a serving of nacho cheese tortilla chips?

72. *Parking fees.* When asked how much the parking charge is for a certain car (see Exercise 68), Mack replies, "between 14 and 24 dollars." For how long has the car been parked?

73. *Frequent buyer bonus.* Alice's Books allows customers to select one free book for every 10 books purchased. The price of that book cannot exceed the average cost of the 10 books. Neoma has bought 9 books whose average cost is $12 per book. How much should her tenth book cost if she wants to select a $15 book for free?

74. *Grading.* After 9 quizzes, Blythe's average is 84. Is it possible for Blythe to improve her average by two points with the next quiz? Why or why not?

75. *Discount card.* Barnes & Noble offers a member card for $25 a year. This card entitles a customer to a 40% discount off list price on hardcover bestsellers, a 20% discount on adult hardcovers, and a 10% discount on other purchases. Describe two sets of circumstances for which an individual would save money by becoming a member.
Source: Barnes & Noble

Study Summary

KEY TERMS AND CONCEPTS	EXAMPLES

SECTION 1.1: SOLVING EQUATIONS

Equivalent equations share the same solution.

$3x - 1 = 10$, $3x = 11$, and $x = \dfrac{11}{3}$ are equivalent equations.

The Addition Principle for Equations

   $a = b$ is equivalent to
   $a + c = b + c$.

$$x + 5 = -2 \quad \text{is equivalent to}$$
$$x + 5 + (-5) = -2 + (-5) \quad \text{and to}$$
$$x = -7.$$

The Multiplication Principle for Equations

   $a = b$ is equivalent to $ac = bc$,
   for $c \neq 0$.

$$-\tfrac{1}{3}x = 7 \quad \text{is equivalent to}$$
$$(-3)\left(-\tfrac{1}{3}x\right) = (-3)(7) \quad \text{and to}$$
$$x = -21.$$

SECTION 1.2: USING THE PRINCIPLES TOGETHER

We can **clear fractions** by multiplying both sides of an equation by the least common multiple of the denominators in the equation.

Solve: $\tfrac{1}{2}x - \tfrac{1}{3} = \tfrac{1}{6}x + \tfrac{2}{3}$.

$6\left(\tfrac{1}{2}x - \tfrac{1}{3}\right) = 6\left(\tfrac{1}{6}x + \tfrac{2}{3}\right)$	Multiplying by 6, the least common denominator
$6 \cdot \tfrac{1}{2}x - 6 \cdot \tfrac{1}{3} = 6 \cdot \tfrac{1}{6}x + 6 \cdot \tfrac{2}{3}$	Using the distributive law
$3x - 2 = x + 4$	Simplifying
$2x = 6$	Subtracting x from and adding 2 to both sides
$x = 3$	

We can **clear decimals** by multiplying both sides by a power of 10. If there is at most one decimal place in any one number, multiply by 10. If there are at most two decimal places, multiply by 100, and so on.

Solve: $3.6t - 1.5 = 2 - 0.8t$.

$10(3.6t - 1.5) = 10(2 - 0.8t)$	Multiplying both sides by 10 because the greatest number of decimal places is 1.
$36t - 15 = 20 - 8t$	Using the distributive law
$44t = 35$	Adding $8t$ and 15 to both sides
$t = \dfrac{35}{44}$	Dividing both sides by 44

SECTION 1.3: FORMULAS

A **formula** uses letters to show a relationship among two or more quantities. Formulas can be solved for a given letter using the addition and multiplication principles.

Solve: $x = \tfrac{2}{5}y + 7$ *for y.*

$x = \tfrac{2}{5}y + 7$	We are solving for y.
$x - 7 = \tfrac{2}{5}y$	Isolating the term containing y
$\tfrac{5}{2}(x - 7) = \tfrac{5}{2} \cdot \tfrac{2}{5}y$	Multiplying both sides by $\tfrac{5}{2}$
$\tfrac{5}{2}x - \tfrac{5}{2} \cdot 7 = 1 \cdot y$	Using the distributive law
$\tfrac{5}{2}x - \tfrac{35}{2} = y$	We have solved for y.

SECTION 1.4: APPLICATIONS WITH PERCENT

Percent Notation

n% means $\dfrac{n}{100}$, or $n \times \dfrac{1}{100}$, or $n \times 0.01$

$31\% = 0.31$; $\frac{1}{8} = 0.125 = 12.5\%$;

$2.9\% = 0.029$; $2.94 = 294\%$

Key Words in Percent Translations

"Of" translates to " $\cdot$ " or "$\times$"

"What" translates to a variable

"Is" or "Was" translates to "$=$"

"%" translates to "$\times \frac{1}{100}$" or "$\times 0.01$"

$\underline{\text{What percent}} \quad \text{of} \quad 60 \quad \text{is} \quad 7.2?$

$\quad\quad n \quad\quad\quad\quad \cdot \quad 60 \quad = \quad 7.2$

$$n = \frac{7.2}{60}$$

$$n = 0.12$$

Thus, 7.2 is 12% of 60.

SECTION 1.5: PROBLEM SOLVING

Five Steps for Problem Solving in Algebra

1. *Familiarize* yourself with the problem.
2. *Translate* to mathematical language. (This often means writing an equation.)
3. *Carry out* some mathematical manipulation. (This often means *solving* an equation.)
4. *Check* your possible answer in the original problem.
5. *State* the answer clearly.

The perimeter of a rectangle is 70 cm. The width is 5 cm longer than half the length. Find the length and the width.

1. **Familiarize.** Look up, if necessary, the formula for the perimeter of a rectangle:

$$P = 2l + 2w.$$

We are looking for two values, the length and the width. We can describe the width in terms of the length:

$$w = \tfrac{1}{2}l + 5.$$

2. **Translate.**

Rewording: Twice the length plus twice the width is the perimeter.

Translating: $2l$ $+$ $2\left(\tfrac{1}{2}l + 5\right)$ $=$ 70

3. **Carry out.** Solve the equation:

$$2l + 2\left(\tfrac{1}{2}l + 5\right) = 70$$
$$2l + l + 10 = 70 \quad \text{Using the distributive law}$$
$$3l + 10 = 70 \quad \text{Combining like terms}$$
$$3l = 60 \quad \text{Subtracting 10 from both sides}$$
$$l = 20. \quad \text{Dividing both sides by 3}$$

If $l = 20$, then $w = \tfrac{1}{2}l + 5 = \tfrac{1}{2} \cdot 20 + 5 = 10 + 5 = 15$.

4. **Check.** The width should be 5 cm longer than half the length. Since half the length is 10 cm, and 15 cm is 5 cm longer, this statement checks. The perimeter should be 70 cm. Since $2l + 2w = 2(20) + 2(15) = 40 + 30 = 70$, this statement also checks.

5. **State.** The length is 20 cm and the width is 15 cm.

SECTION 1.6: SOLVING INEQUALITIES

An **inequality** is any sentence containing $<$, $>$, $\leq$, $\geq$, or $\neq$. Solution sets of inequalities can be **graphed** and written in **set-builder notation** or **interval notation**.

Interval Notation	Set-builder Notation	Graph
(a, b)	$\{x \mid a < x < b\}$	
$[a, b]$	$\{x \mid a \leq x \leq b\}$	
$[a, b)$	$\{x \mid a \leq x < b\}$	
$(a, b]$	$\{x \mid a < x \leq b\}$	
(a, ∞)	$\{x \mid a < x\}$	
$(-\infty, a)$	$\{x \mid x < a\}$	

The Addition Principle for Inequalities

For any real numbers a, b, and c,

$a < b$ is equivalent to $a + c < b + c$;

$a > b$ is equivalent to $a + c > b + c$.

Similar statements hold for $\leq$ and $\geq$.

$x + 3 \leq 5$ is equivalent to

$x + 3 - 3 \leq 5 - 3$ and to

$x \leq 2$.

The Multiplication Principle for Inequalities

For any real numbers a and b, and for any *positive* number c,

$a < b$ is equivalent to $ac < bc$;

$a > b$ is equivalent to $ac > bc$.

For any real numbers a and b, and for any *negative* number c,

$a < b$ is equivalent to $ac > bc$;

$a > b$ is equivalent to $ac < bc$.

Similar statements hold for $\leq$ and $\geq$.

$3x > 9$ is equivalent to

$\frac{1}{3} \cdot 3x > \frac{1}{3} \cdot 9$ The inequality symbol does not change because $\frac{1}{3}$ is positive.

$x > 3$.

$-3x > 9$ is equivalent to

$-\frac{1}{3} \cdot -3x < -\frac{1}{3} \cdot 9$ The inequality symbol is reversed because $-\frac{1}{3}$ is negative.

$x < -3$.

SECTION 1.7: SOLVING APPLICATIONS WITH INEQUALITIES

Many real-world problems can be solved by translating the problem to an inequality and applying the five-step problem-solving strategy.

Translate to an inequality.

The test score must exceed 85.	$s > 85$
At most 15 volunteers greeted visitors.	$v \leq 15$
Ona makes no more than $100 a week.	$w \leq 100$
Herbs need at least 4 hrs of sun a day.	$h \geq 4$

Review Exercises: Chapter 1

Concept Reinforcement *Classify each statement as either true or false.*

1. $5x - 4 = 2x$ and $3x = 4$ are equivalent equations. [1.1]

2. $5 - 2t < 9$ and $t > 6$ are equivalent inequalities. [1.6]

3. Some equations have no solution. [1.1]

4. Consecutive odd integers are 2 units apart. [1.5]

5. For any number a, $a \le a$. [1.6]

6. The addition principle is always used before the multiplication principle. [1.2]

7. A 10% discount results in a sale price that is 90% of the original price. [1.4]

8. Often it is impossible to list all solutions of an inequality number by number. [1.6]

Solve. Label any contradictions or identities.

9. $x + 9 = -16$ [1.1]

10. $-8x = -56$ [1.1]

11. $-\dfrac{x}{5} = 13$ [1.1]

12. $-8 = n - 11$ [1.1]

13. $\frac{2}{5}t = -8$ [1.1]

14. $x - 0.1 = 1.01$ [1.1]

15. $-\frac{2}{3} + x = -\frac{1}{6}$ [1.1]

16. $4y + 11 = 5$ [1.2]

17. $5 - x = 13$ [1.2]

18. $3t + 7 = t - 1$ [1.2]

19. $7x - 6 = 25x$ [1.2]

20. $\frac{1}{4}x - \frac{5}{8} = \frac{3}{8}$ [1.2]

21. $14y = 23y - 17 - 9y$ [1.2]

22. $0.22y - 0.6 = 0.12y + 3 - 0.8y$ [1.2]

23. $\frac{1}{4}x - \frac{1}{8}x = 3 - \frac{1}{16}x$ [1.2]

24. $6(4 - n) = 18$ [1.2]

25. $4(5x - 7) = -56$ [1.2]

26. $8(x - 2) = 4(x - 4)$ [1.2]

27. $3(x - 4) + 2 = x + 2(x - 5)$ [1.2]

Solve each formula for the given letter. [1.3]

28. $C = \pi d$, for d

29. $V = \dfrac{1}{3}Bh$, for B

30. $5x - 2y = 10$, for y

31. $tx = ax + b$, for x

32. Find decimal notation: 1.2%. [1.4]

33. Find percent notation: $\frac{11}{25}$. [1.4]

34. What percent of 60 is 42? [1.4]

35. 49 is 35% of what number? [1.4]

Determine whether each number is a solution of $x \le -5$. [1.6]

36. -3

37. -7

38. 4

Graph on a number line. [1.6]

39. $5x - 6 < 2x + 3$

40. $-2 < x \le 5$

41. $t > 0$

Solve. Write the answers in set-builder notation and interval notation. [1.6]

42. $t + \frac{2}{3} \ge \frac{1}{6}$

43. $9x \ge 63$

44. $2 + 6y > 20$

45. $7 - 3y \ge 27 + 2y$

46. $3x + 5 < 2x - 6$

47. $-4y < 28$

48. $3 - 4x < 27$

49. $4 - 8x < 13 + 3x$

50. $13 \le -\frac{2}{3}t + 5$

51. $7 \le 1 - \frac{3}{4}x$

Solve.

52. In 2006, U.S. retailers lost a record $41.6 billion due to theft and fraud. Of this amount, $20 billion was due to employee theft. What percent of the total loss was employee theft? [1.4]
Source: www.wwaytv3.com

53. An 18-ft beam is cut into two pieces. One piece is 2 ft longer than the other. How long are the pieces? [1.5]

54. In 2004, a total of 103,000 students from China and Japan enrolled in U.S. colleges and universities. The number of Japanese students was 10,000 more than half the number of Chinese students. How many Chinese students and how many Japanese students enrolled in the United States? [1.5]
Source: Institute of International Education

55. The sum of two consecutive odd integers is 116. Find the integers. [1.5]

56. The perimeter of a rectangle is 56 cm. The width is 6 cm less than the length. Find the width and the length. [1.5]

57. After a 25% reduction, a picnic table is on sale for $120. What was the regular price? [1.4]

58. From 2000 to 2006, the number of U.S. wireless-phone subscribers increased by 114 percent to 233 million. How many subscribers were there in 2000? [1.4]
Source: Cellular Telecommunications and Internet Association

59. The measure of the second angle of a triangle is 50° more than that of the first. The measure of the third angle is 10° less than twice the first. Find the measures of the angles. [1.5]

60. The U.S. Centers for Disease Control recommends that for a typical 2000-calorie daily diet, no more than 65 g of fat be consumed. In the first three days of a four-day vacation, Teresa consumed 55 g, 80 g, and 70 g of fat. Determine how many grams of fat Teresa can consume on the fourth day if she is to average no more than 65 g of fat per day. [1.7]

61. *Blueprints.* To make copies of blueprints, Vantage Reprographics charges a $6 setup fee plus $4 per copy. Myra can spend no more than $65 for the copying. What number of copies will allow her to stay within budget? [1.7]

Synthesis

62. How does the multiplication principle for equations differ from the multiplication principle for inequalities? [1.1], [1.6]

63. Explain how checking the solutions of an equation differs from checking the solutions of an inequality. [1.1], [1.6]

64. A study of sixth- and seventh-graders in Boston revealed that, on average, the students spent 3 hr 20 min per day watching TV or playing video and computer games. This represents 108% more than the average time spent reading or doing homework. How much time each day was spent, on average, reading or doing homework? [1.4]
Source: Harvard School of Public Health

65. In June 2007, a team of Brazilian scientists exploring the Amazon measured its length as 65 mi longer than the Nile. If the combined length of both rivers is 8385 mi, how long is each river? [1.5]
Source: news.nationalgeographic.com

66. Kent purchased a book online at 25% off the retail price. The shipping charges were $4.95. If the amount due was $16.95, what was the retail price of the book? [1.4], [1.5]

Solve.

67. $2|n| + 4 = 50$ [1.2]

68. $|3n| = 60$ [1.1]

69. $y = 2a - ab + 3$, for a [1.3]

70. The Maryland Heart Center gives the following steps to calculate the number of fat grams needed daily by a moderately active woman. Write the steps as one formula relating the number of fat grams F to a woman's weight w, in pounds. [1.3]

1. Calculate the total number of calories per day.
___ pounds $\times$ 12 calories = ___ total calories per day

2. Take the total number of calories and multiply by 30 percent.
___ calories per day $\times$ 0.30 = ___ calories from fat per day.

3. Take the number of calories from fat per day and divide by 9 (there are 9 calories per gram of fat).
___ calories from fat per day divided by 9 = ___ fat grams per day

Test: Chapter 1

Solve. Label any contradictions or identities.

1. $t + 7 = 16$ **2.** $t - 3 = 12$

3. $6x = -18$ **4.** $-\frac{4}{7}x = -28$

5. $3t + 7 = 2t - 5$ **6.** $\frac{1}{2}x - \frac{3}{5} = \frac{2}{5}$

7. $8 - y = 16$

8. $4.2x + 3.5 = 1.2 - 2.5x$

9. $4(x + 2) = 36$

10. $\frac{5}{6}(3x + 1) = 20$

11. $13t - (5 - 2t) = 5(3t - 1)$

Solve. Write the answers in set-builder notation and interval notation.

12. $x + 6 > 1$ **13.** $14x + 9 > 13x - 4$

14. $-5y \geq 65$ **15.** $4y \leq -30$

16. $4n + 3 < -17$ **17.** $3 - 5x > 38$

18. $\frac{1}{2}t - \frac{1}{4} \leq \frac{3}{4}t$ **19.** $5 - 9x \geq 19 + 5x$

Solve each formula for the given letter.

20. $A = 2\pi rh$, for r **21.** $w = \dfrac{P + l}{2}$, for l

22. Find decimal notation: 230%.

23. Find percent notation: 0.003.

24. What number is 18.5% of 80?

25. What percent of 75 is 33?

Graph on a number line.

26. $y < 4$ **27.** $-2 \leq x \leq 2$

Solve.

28. The perimeter of a rectangular calculator is 36 cm. The length is 4 cm greater than the width. Find the width and the length.

29. In 1948, Earl Shaffer became the first person to hike all 2100 mi of the Appalachian trail—from Springer Mountain, Georgia, to Mt. Katahdin, Maine. Shaffer repeated the feat 50 years later, and at age 79 became the oldest person to hike the entire trail. When Shaffer stood atop Big Walker Mountain, Virginia, he was three times as far from the northern end of the trail as from the southern end. At that point, how far was he from each end of the trail?

30. The perimeter of a triangle is 249 mm. If the sides are consecutive odd integers, find the length of each side.

31. By lowering the temperature of their electric hot-water heater from 140°F to 120°F, the Kellys' average electric bill dropped by 7% to $60.45. What was their electric bill before they lowered the temperature of their hot water?

32. *Mass transit.* Local light rail service in Denver, Colorado, costs $1.50 per trip (one way). A monthly pass costs $54. Gail is a student at Community College of Denver. Express as an inequality the number of trips per month that Gail should make if the pass is to save her money.
Source: rtd-denver.com

Synthesis

Solve.

33. $c = \dfrac{2cd}{a - d}$, for d

34. $3|w| - 8 = 37$

35. Translate to an inequality.

A plant marked "partial sun" needs at least 4 hr but no more than 6 hr of sun each day.
Source: www.yardsmarts.com

36. A concert promoter had a certain number of tickets to give away. Five people got the tickets. The first got one third of the tickets, the second got one fourth of the tickets, and the third got one fifth of the tickets. The fourth person got eight tickets, and there were five tickets left for the fifth person. Find the total number of tickets given away.

Cumulative Review: Chapter 1

Simplify.

1. $18 + (-30)$

2. $\frac{1}{2} - \left(-\frac{1}{4}\right)$

3. $-1.2(3.5)$

4. $-5 \div \left(-\frac{1}{2}\right)$

5. $150 - 10^2 \div 25 \cdot 4$

6. $(150 - 10^2) \div (25 \cdot 4)$

Remove parentheses and simplify.

7. $5x - (3x - 1)$

8. $2(t + 6) - 12t$

9. $3[4n - 5(2n - 1)] - 3(n - 7)$

10. Graph on a number line: $-\frac{5}{2}$.

11. Find the absolute value: $|27|$.

12. Factor: $12x + 18y + 30z$.

Solve.

13. $12 = -2x$ [1.1]

14. $4x - 7 = 3x + 9$ [1.1]

15. $\frac{2}{3}t + 7 = 13$ [1.2]

16. $9(2a - 1) = 4$ [1.2]

17. $12 - 3(5x - 1) = x - 1$ [1.2]

18. $3(x + 1) - 2 = 8 - 5(x + 7)$ [1.2]

Solve each formula for the given letter. [1.3]

19. $\frac{1}{2}x = 2yz$, for z

20. $4x - 9y = 1$, for y

21. $an = p - rn$, for n

22. Find decimal notation: 183%. [1.4]

23. Find percent notation: $\frac{3}{8}$. [1.4]

24. Graph on a number line: $t > -\frac{5}{2}$. [1.6]

Solve. Write the answer in set-builder notation and interval notation. [1.6]

25. $4t + 10 \leq 2$

26. $8 - t > 5$

27. $4 < 10 - \dfrac{x}{5}$

28. $4(2n - 3) \leq 2(5n - 8)$

Solve.

29. The total attendance at NCAA basketball games during the 2006–2007 school year was 33 million. This was 31.25% less than the total attendance at NCAA football games during that year. What was the total attendance at NCAA football games during the 2006–2007 school year? [1.4]
Source: NCAA

30. On an average weekday, a full-time college student spends a total of 7.1 hr in educational activities and in leisure activities. The average student spends 0.7 hr more in leisure activities than in educational activities. On an average weekday, how many hours does a full-time college student spend on educational activities? [1.5]
Source: U.S. Bureau of Labor Statistics

31. The wavelength w, in meters per cycle, of a musical note is given by

$$w = \frac{r}{f},$$

where r is the speed of the sound, in meters per second, and f is the frequency, in cycles per second. The speed of sound in air is 344 m/sec. What is the wavelength of a note whose frequency in air is 24 cycles per second? [1.3]

32. A 24-ft ribbon is cut into two pieces. One piece is 6 ft longer than the other. How long are the pieces? [1.5]

33. Juanita has budgeted an average of $65 a month for entertainment. For the first five months of the year, she has spent $88, $15, $125, $50, and $60. How much can Juanita spend in the sixth month without exceeding her average budget? [1.7]

34. In 2006, about 17 million Americans had diabetes. The U.S. Centers for Disease Control predicts that by 2050, 50 million Americans may have the disease. By what percent would the number of Americans with diabetes increase? [1.4]

35. The second angle of a triangle is twice as large as the first. The third angle is 5° more than four times the first. Find the measure of the largest angle. [1.5]

36. The length of a rectangular frame is 53 cm. For what widths would the perimeter be greater than 160 cm? [1.7]

Synthesis

37. Simplify: $t - \{t - [3t - (2t - t) - t] - 4t\} - t.$

38. Solve: $3|n| + 10 = 25.$ [1.2]

39. Lindy sold her Fender acoustic guitar on eBay using i-soldit.com. The i-soldit location she used charges 35% of the first $500 of the selling price and 20% of the amount over $500. After these charges were deducted from the selling price, she received $745. For how much did her guitar sell? [1.4], [1.5]

Source: Based on information in *The Wall Street Journal*, 9/11/07

Introduction to Graphing

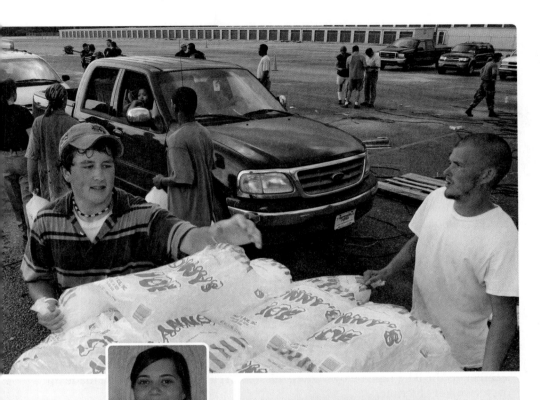

2.1
Reading Graphs, Plotting Points, and Scaling Graphs

2.2
Graphing Linear Equations

2.3
Graphing and Intercepts

2.4
Rates

2.5
Slope

2.6
Slope–Intercept Form

CONNECTING THE CONCEPTS

2.7
Point–Slope Form

CONNECTING THE CONCEPTS

STUDY SUMMARY
REVIEW EXERCISES
CHAPTER TEST
CUMULATIVE REVIEW

HEATHER HUTH
DIRECTOR OF VOLUNTEERS
New Orleans, Louisiana

We average about 750 volunteers a month who come to Beacon of Hope to help us clean New Orleans' neighborhoods. We service 22 neighborhoods, so I use math to figure out how many volunteers to send to each location, the quantity of supplies each will need, and how much time is required to complete the task.

AN APPLICATION

An increasing number of college students are donating time and energy in volunteer service. The number of college students volunteering grew from 2.7 million in 2002 to 3.3 million in 2005. Graph the given data and estimate the number of college students who volunteered in 2004, and then predict the number of college students who will volunteer in 2010.

Source: Corporation for National and Community Service

This problem appears as Example 7 in Section 2.7.

We now begin our study of graphing. First we will examine graphs as they commonly appear in newspapers or magazines and develop some terminology. Following that, we will graph certain equations and study the connection between rate and slope. We will also learn how graphs can be used as a problem-solving tool in many applications.

Our work in this chapter centers on equations that contain two variables.

2.1 Reading Graphs, Plotting Points, and Scaling Graphs

Problem Solving with Bar, Circle, and Line Graphs • Points and Ordered Pairs • Numbering the Axes Appropriately

Today's print and electronic media make almost constant use of graphs. In this section, we consider problem solving with bar graphs, line graphs, and circle graphs. Then we examine graphs that use a coordinate system.

Problem Solving with Bar, Circle, and Line Graphs

A *bar graph* is a convenient way of showing comparisons. In every bar graph, certain categories, such as levels of education in the example below, are paired with certain numbers.

EXAMPLE 1

STUDY SKILLS ————

To Err Is Human

Most students who are successful in this course work in pencil. We all make mistakes and by using pencil and eraser we are more willing to admit to ourselves that something needs to be rewritten. Try working with a pencil and eraser if you aren't doing so already.

Lifetime earnings. Getting a college degree usually means delaying the start of a career. As the bar graph below shows, this loss in earnings is more than made up over a worker's lifetime.

Source: U.S. Census Bureau

a) Keagan plans to get an associate's degree. How much can he expect to make in his lifetime?

b) Isabella would like to make at least $2 million in her lifetime. What level of education should she pursue?

SOLUTION

a) Since level of education is shown on the horizontal scale, we go to the top of the bar above the label "associate's degree." Then we move horizontally from the top of the bar to the vertical scale, which shows earnings. We read there that Keagan can expect to make about $1.6 million in his lifetime.

b) By moving up the vertical scale to $2 million and then moving horizontally, we see that the first bar to reach a height of $2 million or higher corresponds to a bachelor's degree. Thus Isabella should pursue a bachelor's, master's, doctoral, or professional degree in order to make at least $2 million in her lifetime.

TRY EXERCISE 5

Circle graphs, or pie charts, are often used to show what percent of the whole each particular item in a group represents.

EXAMPLE 2   Student aid.   The circle graph below shows the sources for student aid in 2006 and the percentage of aid students received from each source. In that year, the total amount of aid distributed was $134.8 billion. About 5,387,000 students received a federal Pell grant. What was the average amount of the aid per recipient?

Source: Trends in Student Aid 2006, www.collegeboard.com

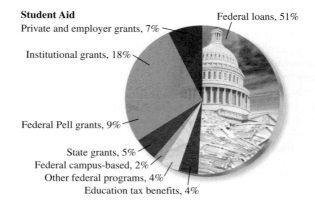

Student Aid
Private and employer grants, 7%
Institutional grants, 18%
Federal loans, 51%
Federal Pell grants, 9%
State grants, 5%
Federal campus-based, 2%
Other federal programs, 4%
Education tax benefits, 4%

SOLUTION

1. **Familiarize.** The problem involves percents, so if we were unsure of how to solve percent problems, we might review Section 1.4.

   The solution of this problem will involve two steps. We are told the total amount of student aid distributed. In order to find the average amount of a Pell grant, we must first calculate the total of all Pell grants and then divide by the number of students.

   We let g = the average amount of a Pell grant in 2006.

2. **Translate.** From the circle graph, we see that federal Pell grants were 9% of the total amount of aid. The total amount distributed was $134.8 billion, or $134,800,000,000, so we have

Find the value of all Pell grants.

$$\text{the value of all Pell grants} = 0.09(134,800,000,000)$$
$$= 12,132,000,000.$$

Then we reword the problem and translate as follows:

Calculate the average amount of a Pell grant.

Rewording: The average amount of a Pell grant   is   the value of all Pell grants   divided by   the number of recipients.

Translating: g =   12,132,000,000   ÷   5,387,000

3. **Carry out.** We solve the equation:

$$g = 12,132,000,000 \div 5,387,000$$
$$\approx 2252. \quad \text{Rounding to the nearest dollar}$$

4. **Check.** If each student received $2252, the total amount of aid distributed through Pell grants would be $2252 · 5,387,000, or $12,131,524,000. Since this is approximately 9% of the total student aid for 2006, our answer checks.

5. **State.** In 2006, the average Pell grant was $2252.

TRY EXERCISE ▶ 9

EXAMPLE 3

Exercise and pulse rate. The following *line graph* shows the relationship between a person's resting pulse rate and months of regular exercise.* Note that the symbol ⌇ is used to indicate that counting on the vertical scale begins at 50.

a) How many months of regular exercise are required to lower the pulse rate as much as possible?

b) How many months of regular exercise are needed to achieve a pulse rate of 65 beats per minute?

SOLUTION

a) The lowest point on the graph occurs above the number 6. Thus, after 6 months of regular exercise, the pulse rate is lowered as much as possible.

b) To determine how many months of exercise are needed to lower a person's resting pulse rate to 65, we locate 65 midway between 60 and 70 on the vertical scale. From that location, we move right until the line is reached. At that point, we move down to the horizontal scale and read the number of months required, as shown.

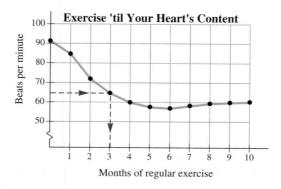

The pulse rate is 65 beats per minute after 3 months of regular exercise.

TRY EXERCISE ▶ 17

*Data from *Body Clock* by Dr. Martin Hughes (New York: Facts on File, Inc.), p. 60.

TECHNOLOGY CONNECTION

The portion of the coordinate plane shown by a graphing calculator is called a **viewing window**. We indicate the **dimensions** of the window by setting a minimum x-value, a maximum x-value, a minimum y-value, and a maximum y-value. The **scale** by which we count must also be chosen. Window settings are often abbreviated in the form [L, R, B, T], with the letters representing **L**eft, **R**ight, **B**ottom, and **T**op endpoints. The window [−10, 10, −10, 10] is called the **standard viewing window**. On most graphing calculators, a standard viewing window can be set up using an option in the ZOOM menu.

To set up a [−100, 100, −5, 5] window, we press (WINDOW) and use the following settings. A scale of 10 for the x-axis is large enough for the marks on the x-axis to be distinct.

```
WINDOW
 Xmin=-100
 Xmax=100
 Xscl=10
 Ymin=-5
 Ymax=5
 Yscl=1
 Xres=1
```

When (GRAPH) is pressed, a graph extending from −100 to 100 along the x-axis (counted by 10's) and from −5 to 5 along the y-axis appears. When the arrow keys are pressed, a cursor can be

(continued)

moved, its coordinates appearing at the bottom of the window.

X = 31.914894   Y = .96774194
Xscl = 10

Set up the following viewing windows, choosing an appropriate scale for each axis. Then move the cursor and practice reading coordinates.

1. $[-10, 10, -10, 10]$
2. $[-5, 5, 0, 100]$
3. $[-1, 1, -0.1, 0.1]$

Points and Ordered Pairs

The line graph in Example 3 contains a collection of points. Each point pairs up a number of months of exercise with a pulse rate. To create such a graph, we **graph**, or **plot**, pairs of numbers on a plane. This is done using two perpendicular number lines called **axes** (pronounced "ak-sēz"; singular, **axis**). The point at which the axes cross is called the **origin**. Arrows on the axes indicate the positive directions.

Consider the pair $(3, 4)$. The numbers in such a pair are called **coordinates**. The **first coordinate** in this case is 3 and the **second coordinate** is 4.* To plot, or graph, $(3, 4)$, we start at the origin, move horizontally to the 3, move up vertically 4 units, and then make a "dot." Thus, $(3, 4)$ is located above 3 on the first axis and to the right of 4 on the second axis.

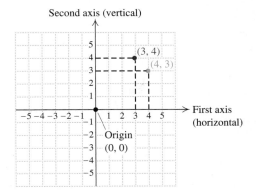

The point $(4, 3)$ is also plotted in the figure above. Note that $(3, 4)$ and $(4, 3)$ are different points. For this reason, coordinate pairs are called **ordered pairs**—the order in which the numbers appear is important.

EXAMPLE 4   Plot the point $(-3, 4)$.

SOLUTION   The first number, -3, is negative. Starting at the origin, we move 3 units in the negative horizontal direction (3 units to the left). The second number, 4, is positive, so we move 4 units in the positive vertical direction (up). The point $(-3, 4)$ is above -3 on the first axis and to the left of 4 on the second axis.

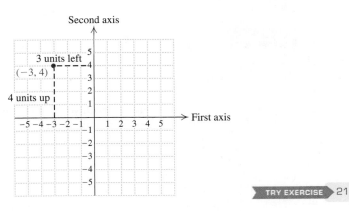

TRY EXERCISE   21

---

*The first coordinate is called the *abscissa* and the second coordinate is called the *ordinate*. The plane is called the *Cartesian coordinate plane* after the French mathematician René Descartes (1595–1650).

To find the coordinates of a point, we see how far to the right or left of the origin the point is and how far above or below the origin it is. Note that the coordinates of the origin itself are $(0, 0)$.

EXAMPLE 5

Find the coordinates of points A, B, C, D, E, F, and G.

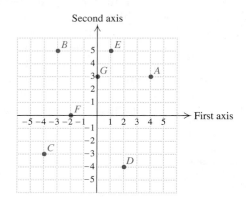

STUDENT NOTES

It is important that you remember that the first coordinate of an ordered pair is always represented on the horizontal axis. It is better to go slowly and plot points correctly than to go quickly and require more than one attempt.

SOLUTION Point A is 4 units to the right of the origin and 3 units above the origin. Its coordinates are $(4, 3)$. The coordinates of the other points are as follows:

B: $(-3, 5)$; C: $(-4, -3)$; D: $(2, -4)$;
E: $(1, 5)$; F: $(-2, 0)$; G: $(0, 3)$.

> TRY EXERCISE 27

The variables x and y are commonly used when graphing on a plane. Coordinates of ordered pairs are often labeled

$(x\text{-coordinate}, y\text{-coordinate})$.

The first, or horizontal, axis is labeled the x-axis, and the second, or vertical, axis is labeled the y-axis.

Numbering the Axes Appropriately

In Examples 4 and 5, each square on the grid shown is 1 unit long and 1 unit high: The **scale** of both the x-axis and the y-axis is 1. Often it is necessary to use a different scale on one or both of the axes.

EXAMPLE 6

Use a grid 10 squares wide and 10 squares high to plot $(-34, 450)$, $(48, 95)$, and $(10, -200)$.

SOLUTION Since x-coordinates vary from a low of -34 to a high of 48, the 10 horizontal squares must span $48 - (-34)$, or 82 units. Because 82 is not a multiple of 10, we round *up* to the next multiple of 10, which is 90. Dividing 90 by 10, we find that if each square is 9 units wide (has a scale of 9), we could represent all the x-values. However, since it is more convenient to count by 10's, we will instead use a scale of 10. Starting at 0, we count backward to -40 and forward to 60.

This is how we will arrange the x-axis.

There is more than one correct way to cover the values from -34 to 48 using 10 increments. For instance, we could have counted from -60 to 90, using a scale

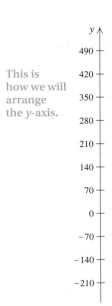

This is how we will arrange the y-axis.

of 15. In general, we try to use the smallest range and scale that will cover the given coordinates. Scales that are multiples of 2, 5, or 10 are especially convenient. It is essential that the numbering always begin at the origin.

Since we must be able to show y-values from -200 to 450, the 10 vertical squares must span $450 - (-200)$, or 650 units. For convenience, we round 650 *up* to 700 and then divide by 10: $700 \div 10 = 70$. Using 70 as the scale, we count *down* from 0 until we pass -200 and *up* from 0 until we pass 450, as shown at left.

Next, we combine our work with the x-values and the y-values to draw a graph in which the x-axis extends from -40 to 60 with a scale of 10 and the y-axis extends from -210 to 490 with a scale of 70. To correctly locate the axes on the grid, the two 0's must coincide where the axes cross. Finally, once the graph has been numbered, we plot the points as shown below.

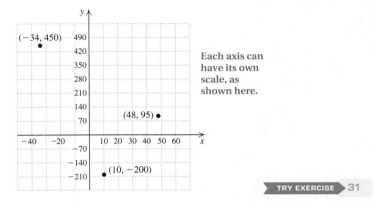

Each axis can have its own scale, as shown here.

TRY EXERCISE 31

The horizontal and vertical axes divide the plane into four regions, or **quadrants**, as indicated by Roman numerals in the following figure. Note that the point $(-4, 5)$ is in the second quadrant and the point $(5, -5)$ is in the fourth quadrant. The points $(3, 0)$ and $(0, 1)$ are on the axes and are not considered to be in any quadrant.

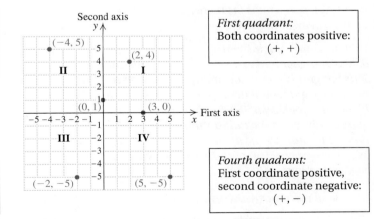

Second quadrant:
First coordinate negative, second coordinate positive: $(-, +)$

First quadrant:
Both coordinates positive: $(+, +)$

Third quadrant:
Both coordinates negative: $(-, -)$

Fourth quadrant:
First coordinate positive, second coordinate negative: $(+, -)$

2.1   EXERCISE SET

For Extra Help   MyMathLab   Math XL PRACTICE   WATCH   DOWNLOAD

🔖 ***Concept Reinforcement*** *In each of Exercises 1–4, match the set of coordinates with the graph on the right that would be the best for plotting the points.*

1. ____ $(-9, 3), (-2, -1), (4, 5)$

2. ____ $(-2, -1), (1, 5), (7, 3)$

3. ____ $(-2, -9), (2, 1), (4, -6)$

4. ____ $(-2, -1), (-9, 3), (-4, -6)$

a)

b)

c)

d)
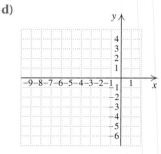

The ▸ TRY EXERCISES ▸ *for examples are indicated by a shaded block* ▢ *on the exercise number. Complete step-by-step solutions for these exercises appear online at www.pearsonhighered.com/bittingerellenbogen.*

Driving under the influence.   A blood-alcohol level of 0.08% or higher makes driving illegal in the United States. This bar graph shows how many drinks a person of a certain weight would need to consume in 1 hr to achieve a blood-alcohol level of 0.08%. Note that a 12-oz beer, a 5-oz glass of wine, or a cocktail containing $1\frac{1}{2}$ oz of distilled liquor all count as one drink.
Source: Adapted from soberup.com and vsa.vassar.edu/~source/drugs/alcohol.html

Friends Don't Let Friends Drive Drunk

5. Approximately how many drinks would a 100-lb person have consumed in 1 hr to reach a blood-alcohol level of 0.08%?

6. Approximately how many drinks would a 160-lb person have consumed in 1 hr to reach a blood-alcohol level of 0.08%?

7. What can you conclude about the weight of someone who has consumed 3 drinks in 1 hr without reaching a blood-alcohol level of 0.08%?

8. What can you conclude about the weight of someone who has consumed 4 drinks in 1 hr without reaching a blood-alcohol level of 0.08%?

Student aid.   Use the information in Example 2 to answer Exercises 9–12.

9. In 2006, there were 13,334,170 full-time equivalent students in U.S. colleges and universities. What was the average federal loan per full-time equivalent student?

10. In 2006, there were 13,334,170 full-time equivalent students in U.S. colleges and universities. What was the average education tax benefit received per full-time equivalent student?

11. Approximately 8.6% of campus-based federal student aid is given to students in two-year public institutions. How much campus-based aid did students at two-year public institutions receive in 2006?

12. Approximately 17.7% of Pell grant dollars is given to students in for-profit institutions. How much did students in for-profit institutions receive in Pell grants in 2006?

Sorting solid waste. Use the following pie chart to answer Exercises 13–16.

Sorting Solid Waste

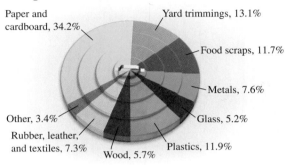

Paper and cardboard, 34.2%
Yard trimmings, 13.1%
Food scraps, 11.7%
Metals, 7.6%
Glass, 5.2%
Plastics, 11.9%
Wood, 5.7%
Rubber, leather, and textiles, 7.3%
Other, 3.4%

Source: Environmental Protection Agency

13. In 2005, Americans generated 245 million tons of waste. How much of the waste was plastic?

14. In 2005, the average American generated 4.5 lb of waste per day. How much of that was paper and cardboard?

15. Americans are recycling about 25.3% of all glass that is in the waste stream. How much glass did Americans recycle in 2005? (See Exercise 13.)

16. Americans are recycling about 61.9% of all yard trimmings. What amount of yard trimmings did the average American recycle per day in 2005? (Use the information in Exercise 14.)

Home video spending. The line graph below shows U.S. consumer spending on home-video movies.

Home Video Spending

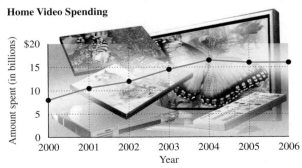

Amount spent (in billions) / Year
$20, 15, 10, 5, 0
2000 2001 2002 2003 2004 2005 2006

Source: Adams Media Research

17. Approximately how much was spent on home videos in 2002?

18. Approximately how much was spent on home videos in 2006?

19. In what year was approximately $10.5 billion spent on home videos?

20. In what year was approximately $14.5 billion spent on home videos?

Plot each group of points.

21. $(1, 2), (-2, 3), (4, -1), (-5, -3), (4, 0), (0, -2)$

22. $(-2, -4), (4, -3), (5, 4), (-1, 0), (-4, 4), (0, 5)$

23. $(4, 4), (-2, 4), (5, -3), (-5, -5), (0, 4), (0, -4), (-4, 0), (0, 0)$

24. $(2, 5), (-1, 3), (3, -2), (-2, -4), (0, 0), (0, -5), (5, 0), (-5, 0)$

25. *Text messaging.* Listed below are estimates of the number of text messages sent in the United States. Make a line graph of the data.

Year	Monthly Text Messages (in millions)
2000	12
2001	34
2002	931
2003	1221
2004	2862
2005	7253
2006	8000 (estimated)

Source: CSCA

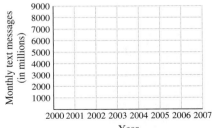

Monthly text messages (in millions)
9000 8000 7000 6000 5000 4000 3000 2000 1000
2000 2001 2002 2003 2004 2005 2006 2007
Year

26. *Ozone layer.* Listed below are estimates of the ozone level. Make a line graph of the data, listing years on the horizontal scale.

Year	Ozone Level (in Dobson Units)
2000	287.1
2001	288.2
2002	285.8
2003	285.0
2004	281.2
2005	283.5

Source: johnstonsarchive.net

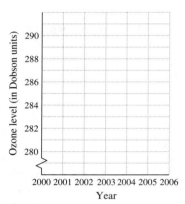

In Exercises 27–30, find the coordinates of points A, B, C, D, and E.

27.

28.

29.

30.

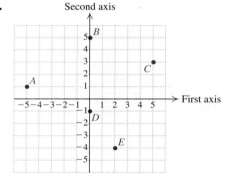

In Exercises 31–40, use a grid 10 squares wide and 10 squares high to plot the given coordinates. Choose your scale carefully. Scales may vary.

31. $(-75, 5), (-18, -2), (9, -4)$

32. $(-13, 3), (48, -1), (62, -4)$

33. $(-1, 83), (-5, -14), (5, 37)$

34. $(2, -79), (4, -25), (-4, 12)$

35. $(-10, -4), (-16, 7), (3, 15)$

36. $(5, -16), (-7, -4), (12, 3)$

37. $(-100, -5), (350, 20), (800, 37)$

38. $(750, -8), (-150, 17), (400, 32)$

39. $(-83, 491), (-124, -95), (54, -238)$

40. $(738, -89), (-49, -6), (-165, 53)$

In which quadrant is each point located?

41. $(7, -2)$ **42.** $(-1, -4)$ **43.** $(-4, -3)$

44. $(1, -5)$ **45.** $(2, 1)$ **46.** $(-4, 6)$

47. $(-4.9, 8.3)$ **48.** $(7.5, 2.9)$

49. In which quadrants are the first coordinates positive?

50. In which quadrants are the second coordinates negative?

51. In which quadrants do both coordinates have the same sign?

52. In which quadrants do the first and second coordinates have opposite signs?

53. The following graph was included in a mailing sent by Agway® to their oil customers in 2000. What information is missing from the graph and why is the graph misleading?

Source: Energy Research Center, Inc. *3/1/99–2/29/00

54. What do all points plotted on the vertical axis of a graph have in common?

Skill Review

To prepare for Section 2.2, review solving for a variable (Section 1.3).

Solve for y. [1.3]

55. $5y = 2x$

56. $2y = -3x$

57. $x - y = 8$

58. $2x + 5y = 10$

59. $2x + 3y = 5$

60. $5x - 8y = 1$

Synthesis

61. In an article about consumer spending on home videos (see the graph used for Exercise 17), the *Wall Street Journal* (9/2/06) stated that "the movie industry has hit a wall." To what were they referring?

62. Describe what the result would be if the first and second coordinates of every point in the following graph of an arrow were interchanged.

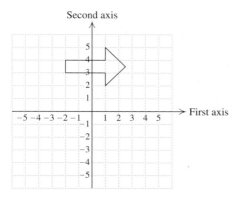

63. In which quadrant(s) could a point be located if its coordinates are opposites of each other?

64. In which quadrant(s) could a point be located if its coordinates are reciprocals of each other?

65. The points $(-1, 1)$, $(4, 1)$, and $(4, -5)$ are three vertices of a rectangle. Find the coordinates of the fourth vertex.

66. The pairs $(-2, -3)$, $(-1, 2)$, and $(4, -3)$ can serve as three (of four) vertices for three different parallelograms. Find the fourth vertex of each parallelogram.

67. Graph eight points such that the sum of the coordinates in each pair is 7. Answers may vary.

68. Find the perimeter of a rectangle if three of its vertices are $(5, -2)$, $(-3, -2)$, and $(-3, 3)$.

69. Find the area of a triangle whose vertices have coordinates $(0, 9)$, $(0, -4)$, and $(5, -4)$.

Coordinates on the globe. *Coordinates can also be used to describe the location on a sphere:* 0° *latitude is the equator and* 0° *longitude is a line from the North Pole to the South Pole through France and Algeria. In the figure shown here, hurricane Clara is at a point about 260 mi northwest of Bermuda near latitude* 36.0° *North, longitude* 69.0° *West.*

70. Approximate the latitude and the longitude of Bermuda.

71. Approximate the latitude and the longitude of Lake Okeechobee.

72. The graph accompanying Example 3 flattens out. Why do you think this occurs?

73. In the *Star Trek* science-fiction series, a three-dimensional coordinate system is used to locate objects in space. If the center of a planet is used as the origin, how many "quadrants" will exist? Why? If possible, sketch a three-dimensional coordinate system and label each "quadrant."

COLLABORATIVE CORNER

You Sank My Battleship!

Focus: Graphing points; logical questioning

Time: 15–25 minutes

Group size: 3–5

Materials: Graph paper

In the game Battleship®, a player places a miniature ship on a grid that only that player can see. An opponent guesses at coordinates that might "hit" the "hidden" ship. The following activity is similar to this game.

ACTIVITY

1. Using only integers from −10 to 10 (inclusive), one group member should secretly record the coordinates of a point on a slip of paper. (This point is the hidden "battleship.")

2. The other group members can then ask up to 10 "yes/no" questions in an effort to determine the coordinates of the secret point. Be sure to phrase each question mathematically (for example, "Is the x-coordinate negative?")

3. The group member who selected the point should answer each question. On the basis of the answer given, another group member should cross out the points no longer under consideration. All group members should check that this is done correctly.

4. If the hidden point has not been determined after 10 questions have been answered, the secret coordinates should be revealed to all group members.

5. Repeat parts (1)–(4) until each group member has had the opportunity to select the hidden point and answer questions.

2.2 Graphing Linear Equations

Solutions of Equations • Graphing Linear Equations • Applications

We have seen how bar, line, and circle graphs can represent information. Now we begin to learn how graphs can be used to represent solutions of equations.

Solutions of Equations

When an equation contains two variables, solutions are ordered pairs in which each number in the pair replaces a letter in the equation. Unless stated otherwise, the first number in each pair replaces the variable that occurs first alphabetically.

EXAMPLE 1   Determine whether each of the following pairs is a solution of $4b - 3a = 22$: **(a)** $(2, 7)$; **(b)** $(1, 6)$.

SOLUTION

a) We substitute 2 for a and 7 for b (alphabetical order of variables):

$$\begin{array}{c|c} 4b - 3a = 22 & \\ \hline 4(7) - 3(2) & 22 \\ 28 - 6 & \\ 22 \overset{?}{=} 22 & \text{TRUE} \end{array}$$

Since $22 = 22$ is *true*, the pair $(2, 7)$ *is* a solution.

b) In this case, we replace a with 1 and b with 6:

$$\begin{array}{c|c} 4b - 3a = 22 & \\ \hline 4(6) - 3(1) & 22 \\ 24 - 3 & \\ 21 \overset{?}{=} 22 & \text{FALSE} \qquad 21 \neq 22 \end{array}$$

Since $21 = 22$ is *false*, the pair $(1, 6)$ is *not* a solution.   TRY EXERCISE ▸ 7

EXAMPLE 2   Show that the pairs $(3, 7)$, $(0, 1)$, and $(-3, -5)$ are solutions of $y = 2x + 1$. Then graph the three points to determine another pair that is a solution.

SOLUTION   To show that a pair is a solution, we substitute, replacing x with the first coordinate and y with the second coordinate of each pair:

$$\begin{array}{c|c} y = 2x + 1 & \\ \hline 7 & 2 \cdot 3 + 1 \\ & 6 + 1 \\ 7 \overset{?}{=} 7 & \text{TRUE} \end{array} \qquad \begin{array}{c|c} y = 2x + 1 & \\ \hline 1 & 2 \cdot 0 + 1 \\ & 0 + 1 \\ 1 \overset{?}{=} 1 & \text{TRUE} \end{array} \qquad \begin{array}{c|c} y = 2x + 1 & \\ \hline -5 & 2(-3) + 1 \\ & -6 + 1 \\ -5 \overset{?}{=} -5 & \text{TRUE} \end{array}$$

In each of the three cases, the substitution results in a true equation. Thus the pairs $(3, 7)$, $(0, 1)$, and $(-3, -5)$ are all solutions. We graph them as shown at left.

Note that the three points appear to "line up." Will other points that line up with these points also represent solutions of $y = 2x + 1$? To find out, we use a ruler and draw a line passing through $(-3, -5)$, $(0, 1)$, and $(3, 7)$.

The line appears to pass through $(2, 5)$. Let's check to see if this pair is a solution of $y = 2x + 1$:

$$\begin{array}{c|c} y = 2x + 1 & \\ \hline 5 & 2 \cdot 2 + 1 \\ & 4 + 1 \\ 5 \overset{?}{=} 5 & \text{TRUE} \end{array}$$

We see that $(2, 5)$ *is* a solution. You should perform a similar check for at least one other point that appears to be on the line.   TRY EXERCISE ▸ 13

Example 2 leads us to suspect that *any* point on the line passing through $(3, 7)$, $(0, 1)$, and $(-3, -5)$ represents a solution of $y = 2x + 1$. In fact, every solution of $y = 2x + 1$ is represented by a point on this line and every point on this line represents a solution. The line is called the **graph** of the equation.

Graphing Linear Equations

Equations like $y = 2x + 1$ or $4b - 3a = 22$ are said to be **linear** because the graph of each equation is a line. In general, any equation that can be written in the form $y = mx + b$ or $Ax + By = C$ (where $m, b, A, B,$ and C are constants and A and B are not both 0) is linear.

To *graph* an equation is to make a drawing that represents its solutions. Linear equations can be graphed as follows.

> **To Graph a Linear Equation**
> 1. Select a value for one coordinate and calculate the corresponding value of the other coordinate. Form an ordered pair. This pair is one solution of the equation.
> 2. Repeat step (1) to find a second ordered pair. A third ordered pair should be found to use as a check.
> 3. Plot the ordered pairs and draw a straight line passing through the points. The line represents all solutions of the equation.

EXAMPLE 3   Graph: $y = -3x + 1$.

SOLUTION   Since $y = -3x + 1$ is in the form $y = mx + b$, the equation is linear and the graph is a straight line. We select a convenient value for x, compute y, and form an ordered pair. Then we repeat the process for other choices of x.

If $x = 2$,   then $y = -3 \cdot 2 + 1 = -5$,   and $(2, -5)$ is a solution.

If $x = 0$,   then $y = -3 \cdot 0 + 1 = 1$,   and $(0, 1)$ is a solution.

If $x = -1$,   then $y = -3(-1) + 1 = 4$,   and $(-1, 4)$ is a solution.

Results are often listed in a table, as shown below. The points corresponding to each pair are then plotted.

$$y = -3x + 1$$

x	y	(x, y)
2	-5	$(2, -5)$
0	1	$(0, 1)$
-1	4	$(-1, 4)$

Calculate ordered pairs.

Plot the points.

(1) Choose x.
(2) Compute y.
(3) Form the pair (x, y).
(4) Plot the points.

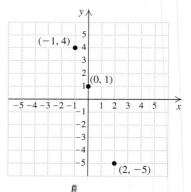

Note that all three points line up. If they didn't, we would know that we had made a mistake, because the equation is linear. When only two points are plotted, an error is more difficult to detect.

Draw the graph.

Finally, we use a ruler or other straight-edge to draw a line. We add arrowheads to the ends of the line to indicate that it extends indefinitely beyond the edge of the grid drawn. Every point on the line represents a solution of $y = -3x + 1$.

TRY EXERCISE 21

EXAMPLE   4

Graph: $y = 2x - 3$.

SOLUTION   We select some convenient x-values and compute y-values.

If $x = 0$,   then $y = 2 \cdot 0 - 3 = -3$,   and $(0, -3)$ is a solution.

If $x = 1$,   then $y = 2 \cdot 1 - 3 = -1$,   and $(1, -1)$ is a solution.

If $x = 4$,   then $y = 2 \cdot 4 - 3 = 5$,   and $(4, 5)$ is a solution.

$y = 2x - 3$

x	y	(x, y)
0	-3	$(0, -3)$
1	-1	$(1, -1)$
4	5	$(4, 5)$

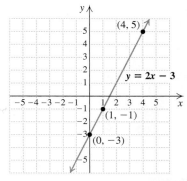

TRY EXERCISE   27

EXAMPLE   5

Graph: $4x + 2y = 12$.

SOLUTION   To form ordered pairs, we can replace either variable with a number and then calculate the other coordinate:

If $y = 0$, we have $4x + 2 \cdot 0 = 12$
$$4x = 12$$
$$x = 3,$$

so $(3, 0)$ is a solution.

If $x = 0$, we have $4 \cdot 0 + 2y = 12$
$$2y = 12$$
$$y = 6,$$

so $(0, 6)$ is a solution.

If $y = 2$, we have $4x + 2 \cdot 2 = 12$
$$4x + 4 = 12$$
$$4x = 8$$
$$x = 2,$$

so $(2, 2)$ is a solution.

$4x + 2y = 12$

x	y	(x, y)
3	0	$(3, 0)$
0	6	$(0, 6)$
2	2	$(2, 2)$

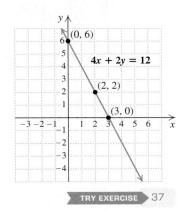

TRY EXERCISE   37

Note that in Examples 3 and 4 the variable y is isolated on one side of the equation. This generally simplifies calculations, so it is important to be able to solve for y before graphing.

EXAMPLE 6

Graph $3y = 2x$ by first solving for y.

SOLUTION   To isolate y, we divide both sides by 3, or multiply both sides by $\frac{1}{3}$:

$$3y = 2x$$

$$\frac{1}{3} \cdot 3y = \frac{1}{3} \cdot 2x \qquad \text{Using the multiplication principle to multiply both sides by } \frac{1}{3}$$

$$\left.\begin{array}{l} 1y = \frac{2}{3} \cdot x \\ y = \frac{2}{3}x. \end{array}\right\} \quad \text{Simplifying}$$

Because all the equations above are equivalent, we can use $y = \frac{2}{3}x$ to draw the graph of $3y = 2x$.

To graph $y = \frac{2}{3}x$, we can select x-values that are multiples of 3. This will allow us to avoid fractions when the corresponding y-values are computed.

$$\left.\begin{array}{l} \text{If } x = 3, \quad \text{then } y = \frac{2}{3} \cdot 3 = 2. \\ \text{If } x = -3, \quad \text{then } y = \frac{2}{3}(-3) = -2. \\ \text{If } x = 6, \quad \text{then } y = \frac{2}{3} \cdot 6 = 4. \end{array}\right\} \quad \begin{array}{l} \text{Note that when multiples of 3 are} \\ \text{substituted for } x, \text{ the } y\text{-coordinates} \\ \text{are not fractions.} \end{array}$$

The following table lists these solutions. Next, we plot the points and see that they form a line. Finally, we draw and label the line.

$$3y = 2x, \text{ or } y = \frac{2}{3}x$$

x	y	(x, y)
3	2	$(3, 2)$
-3	-2	$(-3, -2)$
6	4	$(6, 4)$

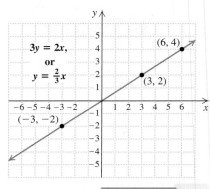

TRY EXERCISE 41

EXAMPLE 7

Graph $x + 5y = -10$ by first solving for y.

SOLUTION   We have

$$x + 5y = -10$$

$$5y = -x - 10 \qquad \text{Adding } -x \text{ to both sides}$$

$$y = \frac{1}{5}(-x - 10) \qquad \text{Multiplying both sides by } \frac{1}{5}$$

$$y = -\frac{1}{5}x - 2. \qquad \text{Using the distributive law}$$

> **CAUTION!** It is very important to multiply *both* $-x$ and -10 by $\frac{1}{5}$.

Thus, $x + 5y = -10$ is equivalent to $y = -\frac{1}{5}x - 2$. It is important to note that if we now choose x-values that are multiples of 5, we can avoid fractions when calculating the corresponding y-values.

$$\text{If } x = 5, \quad \text{then } y = -\frac{1}{5} \cdot 5 - 2 = -1 - 2 = -3.$$

$$\text{If } x = 0, \quad \text{then } y = -\frac{1}{5} \cdot 0 - 2 = 0 - 2 = -2.$$

$$\text{If } x = -5, \quad \text{then } y = -\frac{1}{5}(-5) - 2 = 1 - 2 = -1.$$

$$x + 5y = -10, \text{ or } y = -\frac{1}{5}x - 2$$

x	y	(x, y)
5	−3	(5, −3)
0	−2	(0, −2)
−5	−1	(−5, −1)

TRY EXERCISE   45

Applications

Linear equations appear in many real-life situations.

EXAMPLE 8   *Fuel efficiency.*   A typical tractor-trailer will move 18 tons of air per mile at 55 mph. Air resistance increases with speed, causing fuel efficiency to decrease at higher speeds. At highway speeds, a certain truck's fuel efficiency t, in miles per gallon (mpg), can be given by

$$t = -0.1s + 13.1,$$

where s is the speed of the truck, in miles per hour (mph). Graph the equation and then use the graph to estimate the fuel efficiency at 66 mph.

Source: Based on data from Kenworth Truck Co.

SOLUTION   We graph $t = -0.1s + 13.1$ by first selecting values for s and then calculating the associated values t. Since the equation is true for highway speeds, we use $s \geq 50$.

If $s = 50$,   then $t = -0.1(50) + 13.1 = 8.1$.
If $s = 60$,   then $t = -0.1(60) + 13.1 = 7.1$.
If $s = 70$,   then $t = -0.1(70) + 13.1 = 6.1$.

s	t
50	8.1
60	7.1
70	6.1

Because we are *selecting* values for s and *calculating* values for t, we represent s on the horizontal axis and t on the vertical axis. Counting by 5's horizontally, beginning at 50, and by 0.5 vertically, beginning at 4, will allow us to plot all three pairs, as shown below.

Since the three points line up, our calculations are probably correct. We draw a line, beginning at (50, 8.1). To estimate the fuel efficiency at 66 mph, we locate the point on the line that is above 66 and then find the value on the t-axis that corresponds to that point, as shown at left. The fuel efficiency at 66 mph is about 6.5 mpg.

TRY EXERCISE 49

> *CAUTION!*   When the coordinates of a point are read from a graph, as in Example 8, values should not be considered exact.

Many equations in two variables have graphs that are not straight lines. Three such graphs are shown below. As before, each graph represents the solutions of the given equation. Graphing calculators are especially helpful when drawing these *nonlinear* graphs. Nonlinear graphs are studied later in this text and in more advanced courses.

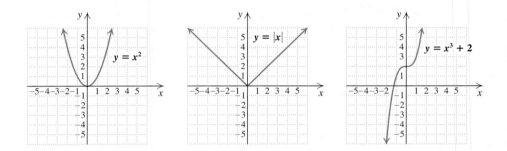

TECHNOLOGY CONNECTION

Most graphing calculators require that y be alone on one side before the equation is entered. For example, to graph $5y + 4x = 13$, we would first solve for y. The student can check that solving for y yields the equation $y = -\frac{4}{5}x + \frac{13}{5}$.

We press $\boxed{Y=}$, enter $-\frac{4}{5}x + \frac{13}{5}$ as Y1, and press $\boxed{GRAPH}$. The graph is shown here in the standard viewing window $[-10, 10, -10, 10]$.

Using a graphing calculator, graph each of the following. Select the "standard" $[-10, 10, -10, 10]$ window.

1. $y = -5x + 6.5$ **2.** $y = 3x + 4.5$
3. $7y - 4x = 22$ **4.** $5y + 11x = -20$
5. $2y - x^2 = 0$ **6.** $y + x^2 = 8$

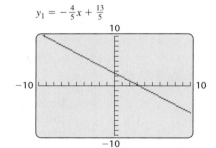

2.2 EXERCISE SET

For Extra Help MyMathLab   Math XL PRACTICE   WATCH   DOWNLOAD

Concept Reinforcement *Classify each statement as either true or false.*

1. A linear equation in two variables has at most one solution.

2. Every solution of $y = 3x - 7$ is an ordered pair.

3. The graph of $y = 3x - 7$ represents all solutions of the equation.

4. If a point is on the graph of $y = 3x - 7$, the corresponding ordered pair is a solution of the equation.

5. To find a solution of $y = 3x - 7$, we can choose any value for x and calculate the corresponding value for y.

6. The graph of every equation is a straight line.

Determine whether each equation has the given ordered pair as a solution.

7. $y = 4x - 7$; $(2, 1)$

8. $y = 5x + 8$; $(0, 8)$

9. $3y + 4x = 19$; $(5, 1)$

10. $5x - 3y = 15$; $(0, 5)$

11. $4m - 5n = 7$; $(3, -1)$

12. $3q - 2p = -8$; $(1, -2)$

In Exercises 13–20, an equation and two ordered pairs are given. Show that each pair is a solution of the equation. Then graph the two pairs to determine another solution. Answers may vary.

13. $y = x + 3$; $(-1, 2), (4, 7)$

14. $y = x - 2$; $(3, 1), (-2, -4)$

15. $y = \frac{1}{2}x + 3$; $(4, 5), (-2, 2)$

16. $y = \frac{1}{2}x - 1$; $(6, 2), (0, -1)$

17. $y + 3x = 7$; $(2, 1), (4, -5)$

18. $2y + x = 5$; $(-1, 3), (7, -1)$

19. $4x - 2y = 10$; $(0, -5), (4, 3)$

20. $6x - 3y = 3$; $(1, 1), (-1, -3)$

Graph each equation.

21. $y = x + 1$

22. $y = x - 1$

23. $y = -x$

24. $y = x$

25. $y = 2x$

26. $y = -3x$

27. $y = 2x + 2$

28. $y = 3x - 2$

29. $y = -\frac{1}{2}x$

30. $y = \frac{1}{4}x$

31. $y = \frac{1}{3}x - 4$

32. $y = \frac{1}{2}x + 1$

33. $x + y = 4$

34. $x + y = -5$

35. $x - y = -2$

36. $y - x = 3$

37. $x + 2y = -6$

38. $x + 2y = 8$

39. $y = -\frac{2}{3}x + 4$

40. $y = \frac{3}{2}x + 1$

41. $4x = 3y$

42. $2x = 5y$

43. $5x - y = 0$

44. $3x - 5y = 0$

45. $6x - 3y = 9$

46. $8x - 4y = 12$

47. $6y + 2x = 8$

48. $8y + 2x = -4$

49. *Student aid.* The average award a of federal student financial assistance per student is approximated by

$$a = 0.08t + 2.5,$$

where a is in thousands of dollars and t is the number of years since 1994. Graph the equation and use the graph to estimate the average amount of federal student aid per student in 2010.
Source: Based on data from U.S. Department of Education, Office of Postsecondary Education

50. *Value of a color copier.* The value of Dupliographic's color copier is given by

$$v = -0.68t + 3.4,$$

where v is the value, in thousands of dollars, t years from the date of purchase. Graph the equation and use the graph to estimate the value of the copier after $2\frac{1}{2}$ yr.

51. *FedEx mailing costs.* Recently, the cost c, in dollars, of shipping a FedEx Priority Overnight package weighing 1 lb or more a distance of 1001 to 1400 mi was given by

$$c = 3.1w + 29.07,$$

where w is the package's weight, in pounds. Graph the equation and use the graph to estimate the cost of shipping a $6\frac{1}{2}$-lb package.
Source: Based on data from FedEx.com

52. *Increasing life expectancy.* A smoker is 15 times more likely to die of lung cancer than a nonsmoker. An ex-smoker who stopped smoking t years ago is

w times more likely to die of lung cancer than a nonsmoker, where

$$w = 15 - t.$$

Graph the equation and use the graph to estimate how much more likely it is for Sandy to die of lung cancer than Polly, if Polly never smoked and Sandy quit $2\frac{1}{2}$ yr ago.
Source: Data from *Body Clock* by Dr. Martin Hughes, p. 60. New York: Facts on File, Inc.

53. *Scrapbook pricing.*   The price p, in dollars, of an 8-in. by 8-in. assembled scrapbook is given by

$$p = 3.5n + 9,$$

where n is the number of pages in the scrapbook. Graph the equation and use the graph to estimate the price of a scrapbook containing 25 pages.
Source: www.scrapbooksplease.com

54. *Value of computer software.*   The value v of a shopkeeper's inventory software program, in hundreds of dollars, is given by

$$v = -\frac{3}{4}t + 6,$$

where t is the number of years since the shopkeeper first bought the program. Graph the equation and use the graph to estimate what the program is worth 4 yr after it was first purchased.

55. *Bottled water.*   The number of gallons of bottled water w consumed by the average American in one year is given by

$$w = 1.6t + 16.7,$$

where t is the number of years since 2000. Graph the equation and use the graph to predict the number of gallons consumed by the average American in 2010.
Source: Based on data from Beverage Marketing Corporation

56. *Record temperature drop.*   On January 22, 1943, the temperature T, in degrees Fahrenheit, in Spearfish, South Dakota, could be approximated by

$$T = -2m + 54,$$

where m is the number of minutes since 9:00 A.M. that morning. Graph the equation and use the graph to estimate the temperature at 9:15 A.M.
Source: Based on information from the National Oceanic Atmospheric Administration

57. *Cost of college.*   The cost T, in hundreds of dollars, of tuition and fees at many community colleges can be approximated by

$$T = \frac{5}{4}c + 2,$$

where c is the number of credits for which a student registers. Graph the equation and use the graph to

estimate the cost of tuition and fees when a student registers for 4 three-credit courses.

Bartonville Community College
Ferndell Hall

Tuition $125 / credit
Fees
Registration $85
Transcripts $55
Computer $45
Activities $15
Activities include: Math team, fencing, drama club

58. *Cost of college.*   The cost C, in thousands of dollars, of a year at a private four-year college (all expenses) can be approximated by

$$C = \frac{13}{10}t + 21,$$

where t is the number of years since 1995. Graph the equation and use the graph to predict the cost of a year at a private four-year college in 2012.
Source: Based on information in *Statistical Abstract of the United States,* 2007

59. The equations $3x + 4y = 8$ and $y = -\frac{3}{4}x + 2$ are equivalent. Which equation would be easier to graph and why?

60. Suppose that a linear equation is graphed by plotting three points and that the three points line up with each other. Does this *guarantee* that the equation is being correctly graphed? Why or why not?

Skill Review

Review solving equations and formulas (Sections 1.2 and 1.3).

Solve and check. [1.2]

61. $5x + 3 \cdot 0 = 12$

62. $3 \cdot 0 - 8y = 6$

63. $5x + 3(2 - x) = 12$

64. $3(y - 5) - 8y = 6$

Solve. [1.3]

65. $A = \dfrac{T + Q}{2}$, for Q

66. $pq + p = w$, for p

67. $Ax + By = C$, for y

68. $\dfrac{y - k}{m} = x - h$, for y

Synthesis

69. Janice consistently makes the mistake of plotting the x-coordinate of an ordered pair using the y-axis, and the y-coordinate using the x-axis. How will Janice's incorrect graph compare with the appropriate graph?

70. Explain how the graph in Example 8 can be used to determine the speed for which the fuel efficiency is 6 mpg.

71. *Bicycling.* Long Beach Island in New Jersey is a long, narrow, flat island. For exercise, Laura routinely bikes to the northern tip of the island and back. Because of the steady wind, she uses one gear going north and another for her return. Laura's bike has 21 gears and the sum of the two gears used on her ride is always 24. Write and graph an equation that represents the different pairings of gears that Laura uses. Note that there are no fraction gears on a bicycle.

In Exercises 72–75, try to find an equation for the graph shown.

72.

73.

74.

75.

76. Translate to an equation:

d dimes and n nickels total $1.75.

Then graph the equation and use the graph to determine three different combinations of dimes and nickels that total $1.75 (see also Exercise 90).

77. Translate to an equation:

d $25 dinners and l $5 lunches total $225.

Then graph the equation and use the graph to determine three different combinations of lunches and dinners that total $225 (see also Exercise 90).

Use the suggested x-values $-3, -2, -1, 0, 1, 2,$ and 3 to graph each equation.

78. $y = |x|$

Aha! **79.** $y = -|x|$

Aha! **80.** $y = |x| - 2$

81. $y = x^2$

82. $y = x^2 + 1$

For Exercises 83–88, use a graphing calculator to graph the equation. Use a $[-10, 10, -10, 10]$ window.

83. $y = -2.8x + 3.5$

84. $y = 4.5x + 2.1$

85. $y = 2.8x - 3.5$

86. $y = -4.5x - 2.1$

87. $y = x^2 + 4x + 1$

88. $y = -x^2 + 4x - 7$

89. Example 8 discusses fuel efficiency. If fuel costs $3.50 a gallon, how much money will a truck driver save on a 500-mi trip by driving at 55 mph instead of 70 mph? How many gallons of fuel will be saved?

90. Study the graph of Exercises 76 and 77. Does *every* point on the graph represent a solution of the associated problem? Why or why not?

2.3 Graphing and Intercepts

Intercepts   •   Using Intercepts to Graph   •   Graphing Horizontal or Vertical Lines

Unless a line is horizontal or vertical, it will cross both axes. Often, finding the points where the axes are crossed gives us a quick way of graphing linear equations.

Intercepts

In Example 5 of Section 2.2, we graphed $4x + 2y = 12$ by plotting the points $(3, 0)$, $(0, 6)$, and $(2, 2)$ and then drawing the line.

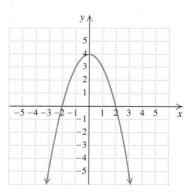

- The point at which a graph crosses the y-axis is called the **y-intercept**. In the figure above, the y-intercept is $(0, 6)$. The x-coordinate of a y-intercept is always 0.

- The point at which a graph crosses the x-axis is called the **x-intercept**. In the figure above, the x-intercept is $(3, 0)$. The y-coordinate of an x-intercept is always 0.

It is possible for the graph of a curve to have more than one y-intercept or more than one x-intercept.

EXAMPLE 1   For the graph shown below, **(a)** give the coordinates of any x-intercepts and **(b)** give the coordinates of any y-intercepts.

SOLUTION

a) The x-intercepts are the points at which the graph crosses the x-axis. For the graph shown, the x-intercepts are $(-2, 0)$ and $(2, 0)$.

b) The y-intercept is the point at which the graph crosses the y-axis. For the graph shown, the y-intercept is $(0, 4)$.

> TRY EXERCISE ▶ 7

Using Intercepts to Graph

It is important to know how to locate a graph's intercepts from the equation being graphed.

To Find Intercepts

To find the y-intercept(s) of an equation's graph, replace x with 0 and solve for y.

To find the x-intercept(s) of an equation's graph, replace y with 0 and solve for x.

EXAMPLE 2

Find the y-intercept and the x-intercept of the graph of $2x + 4y = 20$.

SOLUTION   To find the y-intercept, we let $x = 0$ and solve for y:

$$2 \cdot 0 + 4y = 20 \qquad \text{Replacing } x \text{ with } 0$$
$$4y = 20$$
$$y = 5.$$

Thus the y-intercept is $(0, 5)$.

To find the x-intercept, we let $y = 0$ and solve for x:

$$2x + 4 \cdot 0 = 20 \qquad \text{Replacing } y \text{ with } 0$$
$$2x = 20$$
$$x = 10.$$

Thus the x-intercept is $(10, 0)$.

> TRY EXERCISE ▶ 15

Since two points are sufficient to graph a line, intercepts can be used to graph linear equations.

EXAMPLE 3

Graph $2x + 4y = 20$ using intercepts.

SOLUTION   In Example 2, we showed that the y-intercept is $(0, 5)$ and the x-intercept is $(10, 0)$. Before drawing a line, we plot a third point as a check. We substitute any convenient value for x and solve for y.

If we let $x = 5$, then

$$2 \cdot 5 + 4y = 20 \qquad \text{Substituting 5 for } x$$
$$10 + 4y = 20$$
$$4y = 10 \qquad \text{Subtracting 10 from both sides}$$
$$y = \tfrac{10}{4}, \text{ or } 2\tfrac{1}{2}. \qquad \text{Solving for } y$$

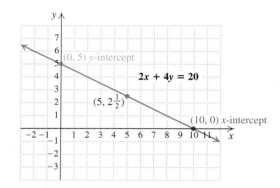

The point $\left(5, 2\tfrac{1}{2}\right)$ appears to line up with the intercepts, so our work is probably correct. To finish, we draw and label the line.

TRY EXERCISE 25

Note that when we solved for the y-intercept, we replaced x with 0 and simplified $2x + 4y = 20$ to $4y = 20$. Thus, to find the y-intercept, we can momentarily ignore the x-term and solve the remaining equation.

In a similar manner, when we solved for the x-intercept, we simplified $2x + 4y = 20$ to $2x = 20$. Thus, to find the x-intercept, we can momentarily ignore the y-term and then solve this remaining equation.

EXAMPLE 4

Graph $3x - 2y = 60$ using intercepts.

SOLUTION   To find the y-intercept, we let $x = 0$. This amounts to temporarily ignoring the x-term and then solving:

$$-2y = 60 \qquad \text{For } x = 0, \text{ we have } 3 \cdot 0 - 2y, \text{ or simply } -2y.$$
$$y = -30.$$

The y-intercept is $(0, -30)$.

To find the x-intercept, we let $y = 0$. This amounts to temporarily disregarding the y-term and then solving:

$$3x = 60 \qquad \text{For } y = 0, \text{ we have } 3x - 2 \cdot 0, \text{ or simply } 3x.$$
$$x = 20.$$

The x-intercept is $(20, 0)$.

To find a third point, we can replace x with 4 and solve for y:

$$3 \cdot 4 - 2y = 60 \qquad \text{Numbers other than 4 can be used for } x.$$
$$12 - 2y = 60$$
$$-2y = 48$$
$$y = -24. \qquad \text{This means that } (4, -24) \text{ is on the graph.}$$

In order for us to graph all three points, the y-axis of our graph must go down to at least -30 and the x-axis must go up to at least 20. Using a scale of 5 units per square allows us to display both intercepts and $(4, -24)$, as well as the origin.

The point $(4, -24)$ appears to line up with the intercepts, so we draw and label the line, as shown at left.

TRY EXERCISE ▶ 45

TECHNOLOGY CONNECTION

When an equation has been entered into a graphing calculator, we may not be able to see both intercepts. For example, if $y = -0.8x + 17$ is graphed in the window $[-10, 10, -10, 10]$, neither intercept is visible.

$y_1 = -0.8x + 17$

To better view the intercepts, we can change the window dimensions or we can zoom out. The ZOOM feature allows us to reduce or magnify a graph or a portion

$y_1 = -0.8x + 17$

of a graph. Before zooming, the ZOOM *factors* must be set in the memory of the ZOOM key. If we zoom out with factors set at 5, both intercepts are visible but the axes are heavily drawn, as shown in the preceding figure.

This suggests that the *scales* of the axes should be changed. To do this, we use the WINDOW menu and set Xscl to 5 and Yscl to 5. The resulting graph has tick marks 5 units apart and clearly shows both intercepts. Other choices for Xscl and Yscl can also be made.

$y_1 = -0.8x + 17$

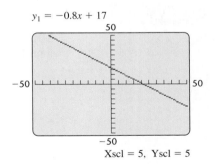

Xscl = 5, Yscl = 5

Graph each equation so that both intercepts can be easily viewed. Zoom or adjust the window settings so that tick marks can be clearly seen on both axes.

1. $y = -0.72x - 15$
2. $y - 2.13x = 27$
3. $5x + 6y = 84$
4. $2x - 7y = 150$
5. $19x - 17y = 200$
6. $6x + 5y = 159$

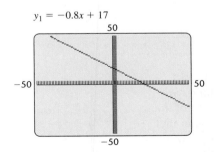

Graphing Horizontal or Vertical Lines

The equations graphed in Examples 3 and 4 are both in the form $Ax + By = C$. We have already stated that any equation in the form $Ax + By = C$ is linear, provided A and B are not both zero. What if A or B (but not both) is zero? We will find that when A is zero, there is no x-term and the graph is a horizontal line. We will also find that when B is zero, there is no y-term and the graph is a vertical line.

EXAMPLE 5

Graph: $y = 3$.

SOLUTION   We can regard the equation $y = 3$ as $0 \cdot x + y = 3$. No matter what number we choose for x, we find that y must be 3 if the equation is to be solved. Consider the following table.

STUDENT NOTES

Many students draw horizontal lines when they should be drawing vertical lines and vice versa. To avoid this mistake, first locate the correct number on the axis whose label is given. Thus, to graph $x = 2$, we locate 2 on the x-axis and then draw a line perpendicular to that axis at that point. Note that the graph of $x = 2$ on a plane is a line, whereas the graph of $x = 2$ on a number line is a point.

Choose any number for x. $\longrightarrow$

$y = 3$

x	y	(x, y)
-2	3	$(-2, 3)$
0	3	$(0, 3)$
4	3	$(4, 3)$

y must be 3.

All pairs will have 3 as the y-coordinate.

When we plot the ordered pairs $(-2, 3)$, $(0, 3)$, and $(4, 3)$ and connect the points, we obtain a horizontal line. Any ordered pair of the form $(x, 3)$ is a solution, so the line is parallel to the x-axis with y-intercept $(0, 3)$. Note that the graph of $y = 3$ has no x-intercept.

TRY EXERCISE 53

EXAMPLE 6

Graph: $x = -4$.

SOLUTION   We can regard the equation $x = -4$ as $x + 0 \cdot y = -4$. We make up a table with all -4's in the x-column.

$x = -4$

x must be -4. $\longrightarrow$

x	y	(x, y)
-4	-5	$(-4, -5)$
-4	1	$(-4, 1)$
-4	3	$(-4, 3)$

Any number can be used for y.

All pairs will have -4 as the x-coordinate.

When we plot the ordered pairs $(-4, -5)$, $(-4, 1)$, and $(-4, 3)$ and connect them, we obtain a vertical line. Any ordered pair of the form $(-4, y)$ is a solution. The line is parallel to the y-axis with x-intercept $(-4, 0)$. Note that the graph of $x = -4$ has no y-intercept.

TRY EXERCISE 55

Linear Equations in One Variable

The graph of $y = b$ is a horizontal line, with y-intercept $(0, b)$.

The graph of $x = a$ is a vertical line, with x-intercept $(a, 0)$.

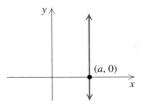

EXAMPLE 7 Write an equation for each graph.

a)

b)

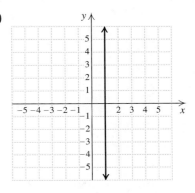

SOLUTION

a) Note that every point on the horizontal line passing through $(0, -2)$ has -2 as the y-coordinate. Thus the equation of the line is $y = -2$.

b) Note that every point on the vertical line passing through $(1, 0)$ has 1 as the x-coordinate. Thus the equation of the line is $x = 1$. **TRY EXERCISE** 71

2.3 EXERCISE SET

For Extra Help MyMathLab | Math XL PRACTICE WATCH DOWNLOAD

Concept Reinforcement *In each of Exercises 1–6, match the phrase with the most appropriate choice from the column on the right.*

1. ____ A vertical line
2. ____ A horizontal line
3. ____ A y-intercept
4. ____ An x-intercept
5. ____ A third point as a check
6. ____ Use a scale of 10 units per square.

a) $2x + 5y = 100$
b) $(3, -2)$
c) $(1, 0)$
d) $(0, 2)$
e) $y = 3$
f) $x = -4$

For Exercises 7–14, list **(a)** *the coordinates of the y-intercept and* **(b)** *the coordinates of all x-intercepts.*

7.

8.

9.

10.

11.

12.

13.

14.

For Exercises 15–24, list (**a**) *the coordinates of any y-intercept and* (**b**) *the coordinates of any x-intercept. Do not graph.*

15. $3x + 5y = 15$

16. $2x + 7y = 14$

17. $9x - 2y = 36$

18. $10x - 3y = 60$

19. $-4x + 5y = 80$

20. $-5x + 6y = 100$

Aha! **21.** $x = 12$

22. $y = 10$

23. $y = -9$

24. $x = -5$

Find the intercepts. Then graph.

25. $3x + 5y = 15$

26. $2x + y = 6$

27. $x + 2y = 4$

28. $2x + 5y = 10$

29. $-x + 2y = 8$

30. $-x + 3y = 9$

31. $3x + y = 9$

32. $2x - y = 8$

33. $y = 2x - 6$

34. $y = -3x + 6$

35. $5x - 10 = 5y$

36. $3x - 9 = 3y$

37. $2x - 5y = 10$

38. $2x - 3y = 6$

39. $6x + 2y = 12$

40. $4x + 5y = 20$

41. $4x + 3y = 16$

42. $3x + 2y = 8$

43. $2x + 4y = 1$

44. $3x - 6y = 1$

45. $5x - 3y = 180$

46. $10x + 7y = 210$

47. $y = -30 + 3x$

48. $y = -40 + 5x$

49. $-4x = 20y + 80$

50. $60 = 20x - 3y$

51. $y - 3x = 0$

52. $x + 2y = 0$

Graph.

53. $y = 1$

54. $y = 4$

55. $x = 3$

56. $x = 6$

57. $y = -2$

58. $y = -4$

59. $x = -1$

60. $x = -6$

61. $y = -15$

62. $x = 20$

63. $y = 0$

64. $y = \frac{3}{2}$

65. $x = -\frac{5}{2}$

66. $x = 0$

67. $-4x = -100$

68. $12y = -360$

69. $35 + 7y = 0$

70. $-3x - 24 = 0$

Write an equation for each graph.

71.

72.

73.

74.

75.

76.

87. Write an equation for the x-axis.

88. Write an equation of the line parallel to the x-axis and passing through $(3, 5)$.

89. Write an equation of the line parallel to the y-axis and passing through $(-2, 7)$.

90. Find the coordinates of the point of intersection of the graphs of $y = x$ and $y = 6$.

91. Find the coordinates of the point of intersection of the graphs of the equations $x = -3$ and $y = 4$.

92. Write an equation of the line shown in Exercise 7.

93. Write an equation of the line shown in Exercise 10.

94. Find the value of C such that the graph of $3x + C = 5y$ has an x-intercept of $(-4, 0)$.

95. Find the value of C such that the graph of $4x = C - 3y$ has a y-intercept of $(0, -8)$.

96. For A and B nonzero, the graphs of $Ax + D = C$ and $By + D = C$ will be parallel to an axis. Explain why.

97. Find the x-intercept of the graph of $Ax + D = C$.

In Exercises 98–103, find the intercepts of each equation algebraically. Then adjust the window and scale so that the intercepts can be checked graphically with no further window adjustments.

98. $3x + 2y = 50$

99. $2x - 7y = 80$

100. $y = 1.3x - 15$

101. $y = 0.2x - 9$

102. $25x - 20y = 1$

103. $50x + 25y = 1$

77. Explain in your own words why the graph of $y = 8$ is a horizontal line.

78. Explain in your own words why the graph of $x = -4$ is a vertical line.

Skill Review

Review translating to algebraic expressions.

Translate to an algebraic expression.

79. 7 less than d

80. 5 more than w

81. The sum of 7 and four times a number

82. The product of 3 and a number

83. Twice the sum of two numbers

84. Half of the sum of two numbers

Synthesis

85. Describe what the graph of $x + y = C$ will look like for any choice of C.

86. If the graph of a linear equation has one point that is both the x- and the y-intercepts, what is that point? Why?

2.4 Rates

Rates of Change • Visualizing Rates

Rates of Change

Because graphs make use of two axes, they allow us to visualize how two quantities change with respect to each other. A number accompanied by units is used to represent this type of change and is referred to as a *rate*.

> **Rate**
>
> A *rate* is a ratio that indicates how two quantities change with respect to each other.

Rates occur often in everyday life:

A business whose customer base grows by 1500 customers over a period of 2 yr has an average *growth rate* of $\frac{1500}{2}$, or 750, customers per year.

A vehicle traveling 260 mi in 4 hr is moving at a *rate* of $\frac{260}{4}$, or 65, mph (miles per hour).

A class of 25 students pays a total of $93.75 to visit a museum. The *rate* is $\frac{\$93.75}{25}$, or $3.75, per student.

> *CAUTION!* To calculate a rate, it is important to keep track of the units being used.

EXAMPLE 1 On January 3, Alisha rented a Ford Focus with a full tank of gas and 9312 mi on the odometer. On January 7, she returned the car with 9630 mi on the odometer.* If the rental agency charged Alisha $108 for the rental and needed 12 gal of gas to fill up the gas tank, find the following rates.

a) The car's rate of gas consumption, in miles per gallon

b) The average cost of the rental, in dollars per day

c) The car's rate of travel, in miles per day

SOLUTION

a) The rate of gas consumption, in miles per gallon, is found by dividing the number of miles traveled by the number of gallons used for that amount of driving:

$$\text{Rate, in miles per gallon} = \frac{9630 \text{ mi} - 9312 \text{ mi}}{12 \text{ gal}} \qquad \text{The word "per" indicates division.}$$

$$= \frac{318 \text{ mi}}{12 \text{ gal}}$$

$$= 26.5 \text{ mi/gal} \qquad \text{Dividing}$$

$$= 26.5 \text{ miles per gallon.}$$

*For all problems concerning rentals, assume that the pickup time was later in the day than the return time so that no late fees were applied.

b) The average cost of the rental, in dollars per day, is found by dividing the cost of the rental by the number of days:

$$\text{Rate, in dollars per day} = \frac{108 \text{ dollars}}{4 \text{ days}} \qquad \text{From January 3 to January 7 is } 7 - 3 = 4 \text{ days.}$$

$$= 27 \text{ dollars/day}$$

$$= \$27 \text{ per day.}$$

c) The car's rate of travel, in miles per day, is found by dividing the number of miles traveled by the number of days:

$$\text{Rate, in miles per day} = \frac{318 \text{ mi}}{4 \text{ days}} \qquad \begin{array}{l} 9630 \text{ mi} - 9312 \text{ mi} = 318 \text{ mi;} \\ \text{From January 3 to January 7} \\ \text{is } 7 - 3 = 4 \text{ days.} \end{array}$$

$$= 79.5 \text{ mi/day}$$

$$= 79.5 \text{ mi per day.} \qquad \boxed{\text{TRY EXERCISE} \quad 7}$$

> **CAUTION!**   Units are a vital part of real-world problems. They must be considered in the translation of a problem and included in the answer to a problem.

Many problems involve a rate of travel, or *speed*. The **speed** of an object is found by dividing the distance traveled by the time required to travel that distance.

EXAMPLE   2

Transportation.   An Atlantic City Express bus makes regular trips between Paramus and Atlantic City, New Jersey. At 6:00 P.M., the bus is at mileage marker 40 on the Garden State Parkway, and at 8:00 P.M. it is at marker 170. Find the average speed of the bus.

SOLUTION   Speed is the distance traveled divided by the time spent traveling:

$$\text{Bus speed} = \frac{\text{Distance traveled}}{\text{Time spent traveling}}$$

$$= \frac{\text{Change in mileage}}{\text{Change in time}}$$

$$= \frac{130 \text{ mi}}{2 \text{ hr}} \qquad \begin{array}{l} 170 \text{ mi} - 40 \text{ mi} = 130 \text{ mi;} \\ 8\!:\!00 \text{ P.M.} - 6\!:\!00 \text{ P.M.} = 2 \text{ hr} \end{array}$$

$$= 65 \frac{\text{mi}}{\text{hr}}$$

$$= 65 \text{ miles per hour.} \qquad \begin{array}{l} \text{This } \textit{average} \text{ speed does not} \\ \text{indicate by how much the bus speed} \\ \text{may vary along the route.} \end{array}$$

$$\boxed{\text{TRY EXERCISE} \quad 13}$$

Visualizing Rates

Graphs allow us to visualize a rate of change. As a rule, the quantity listed in the numerator appears on the vertical axis and the quantity listed in the denominator appears on the horizontal axis.

EXAMPLE 3   *Recycling.*   Between 1991 and 2006, the amount of paper recycled in the United States increased at a rate of approximately 1.5 million tons per year. In 1991, approximately 31 million tons of paper was recycled. Draw a graph to represent this information.

Source: Based on information from American Forest and Paper Association

SOLUTION   To label the axes, note that the rate is given as 1.5 million tons per year, or

$$1.5 \text{ million } \frac{\text{tons}}{\text{yr}}. \quad \begin{array}{l} \longleftarrow \text{Numerator: vertical axis} \\ \longleftarrow \text{Denominator: horizontal axis} \end{array}$$

We list *Amount of paper recycled (in millions of tons)* on the vertical axis and *Year* on the horizontal axis. (See the figure on the left below.)

Next, we select a scale for each axis that allows us to plot the given information. If we count by increments of 10 million on the vertical axis, we can show 31 million tons for 1991 and increasing amounts for later years. On the horizontal axis, we count by increments of 2 years to make certain that both 1991 and 2006 are included. (See the figure in the middle below.)

Label the axes.

Select the scale.

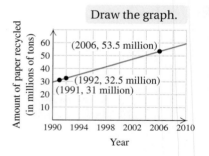
Draw the graph.

We now plot the point corresponding to (1991, 31 million). Then, to display the rate of growth, we move from that point to a second point that represents 1.5 million more tons 1 year later.

(1991,	31 million)	Beginning point
(1991 + 1,	31 million + 1.5 million)	1.5 million more tons, 1 year later
(1992,	32.5 million)	A second point on the graph

Similarly, we can find the coordinates for 2006. Since 2006 is 15 years after 1991, we add 15 to the year and 15(1.5 million) = 22.5 million to the amount.

(1991,	31 million)	Beginning point
(1991 + 15,	31 million + 22.5 million)	15(1.5) million more tons, 15 years later
(2006,	53.5 million)	A third point on the graph

After plotting the three points, we draw a line through them, as shown in the figure on the right above. This gives us the graph.   **TRY EXERCISE** 19

EXAMPLE 4   *Banking.*   Nadia prepared the following graph from data collected on a recent day at a branch bank.

a) What rate can be determined from the graph?

b) What is that rate?

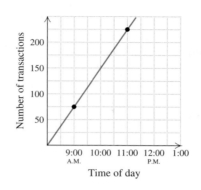

SOLUTION

a) Because the vertical axis shows the number of transactions and the horizontal axis lists the time in hour-long increments, we can find the rate *Number of transactions per hour.*

b) The points (9:00, 75) and (11:00, 225) are both on the graph. This tells us that in the 2 hours between 9:00 and 11:00, there were $225 - 75 = 150$ transactions. Thus the rate is

$$\frac{225 \text{ transactions} - 75 \text{ transactions}}{11:00 - 9:00} = \frac{150 \text{ transactions}}{2 \text{ hours}}$$

$$= 75 \text{ transactions per hour.}$$

Note that this is an *average* rate.

TRY EXERCISE ▸ 29

2.4 EXERCISE SET

For Extra Help
MyMathLab

Concept Reinforcement *For Exercises 1–6, fill in the missing units for each rate.*

1. If Eva biked 100 miles in 5 hours, her average rate was 20 _____.

2. If it took Lauren 18 hours to read 6 chapters, her average rate was 3 _____.

3. If Denny's ticket cost $300 for a 150-mile flight, his average rate was 2 _____.

4. If Geoff planted 36 petunias along a 12-ft sidewalk, his average rate was 3 _____.

5. If Christi ran 8 errands in 40 minutes, her average rate was 5 _____.

6. If Ben made 8 cakes using 20 cups of flour, his average rate was $2\frac{1}{2}$ _____.

Solve. For Exercises 7–14, round answers to the nearest cent.

7. *Car rentals.* Late on June 5, Gaya rented a Ford Focus with a full tank of gas and 13,741 mi on the odometer. On June 8, she returned the car with 14,131 mi on the odometer. The rental agency charged Gaya $118 for the rental and needed 13 gal of gas to fill up the tank.

   a) Find the car's rate of gas consumption, in miles per gallon.
   b) Find the average cost of the rental, in dollars per day.
   c) Find the average rate of travel, in miles per day.
   d) Find the rental rate, in cents per mile.

8. *SUV rentals.*   On February 10, Oscar rented a Chevy Trailblazer with a full tank of gas and 13,091 mi on the odometer. On February 12, he returned the vehicle with 13,322 mi on the odometer. The rental agency charged $92 for the rental and needed 14 gal of gas to fill the tank.

   a) Find the SUV's rate of gas consumption, in miles per gallon.

   b) Find the average cost of the rental, in dollars per day.

   c) Find the average rate of travel, in miles per day.

   d) Find the rental rate, in cents per mile.

9. *Bicycle rentals.*   At 9:00, Jodi rented a mountain bike from The Bike Rack. She returned the bicycle at 11:00, after cycling 14 mi. Jodi paid $15 for the rental.

   a) Find Jodi's average speed, in miles per hour.

   b) Find the rental rate, in dollars per hour.

   c) Find the rental rate, in dollars per mile.

10. *Bicycle rentals.*   At 2:00, Braden rented a mountain bike from The Slick Rock Cyclery. He returned the bike at 5:00, after cycling 18 mi. Braden paid $12 for the rental.

   a) Find Braden's average speed, in miles per hour.

   b) Find the rental rate, in dollars per hour.

   c) Find the rental rate, in dollars per mile.

11. *Proofreading.*   Sergei began proofreading at 9:00 A.M., starting at the top of page 93. He worked until 2:00 P.M. that day and finished page 195. He billed the publishers $110 for the day's work.

   a) Find the rate of pay, in dollars per hour.

   b) Find the average proofreading rate, in number of pages per hour.

   c) Find the rate of pay, in dollars per page.

12. *Temporary help.*   A typist for Kelly Services reports to 3E's Properties for work at 10:00 A.M. and leaves at 6:00 P.M. after having typed from the end of page 8 to the end of page 50 of a proposal. 3E's pays $120 for the typist's services.

   a) Find the rate of pay, in dollars per hour.

   b) Find the average typing rate, in number of pages per hour.

   c) Find the rate of pay, in dollars per page.

13. *National debt.*   The U.S. federal budget debt was $5770 billion in 2001 and $8612 billion in 2006. Find the rate at which the debt was increasing.
Source: U.S. Office of Management and Budget

14. *Four-year-college tuition.*   The average tuition at a public four-year college was $3983 in 2001 and $5948 in 2005. Find the rate at which tuition was increasing.
Source: U.S. National Center for Education Statistics

15. *Elevators.*   At 2:38, Lara entered an elevator on the 34th floor of the Regency Hotel. At 2:40, she stepped off at the 5th floor.

   a) Find the elevator's average rate of travel, in number of floors per minute.

   b) Find the elevator's average rate of travel, in seconds per floor.

16. *Snow removal.*   By 1:00 P.M., Olivia had already shoveled 2 driveways, and by 6:00 P.M. that day, the number was up to 7.

   a) Find Olivia's average shoveling rate, in number of driveways per hour.

   b) Find Olivia's average shoveling rate, in hours per driveway.

17. *Mountaineering.*   The fastest ascent of Mt. Everest was accomplished by the Sherpa guide Pemba Dorje of Nepal in 2004. Pemba Dorje climbed from base camp, elevation 17,552 ft, to the summit, elevation 29,028 ft, in 8 hr 10 min.
Source: *Guinness Book of World Records* 2006 Edition

   a) Find Pemba Dorje's average rate of ascent, in feet per minute.

   b) Find Pemba Dorje's average rate of ascent, in minutes per foot.

18. *Mountaineering.* As part of an ill-fated expedition to climb Mt. Everest in 1996, author Jon Krakauer departed "The Balcony," elevation 27,600 ft, at 7:00 A.M. and reached the summit, elevation 29,028 ft, at 1:25 P.M.
Source: Krakauer, Jon, *Into Thin Air, the Illustrated Edition.* New York: Random House, 1998

a) Find Krakauer's average rate of ascent, in feet per minute.

b) Find Krakauer's average rate of ascent, in minutes per foot.

In Exercises 19–28, draw a linear graph to represent the given information. Be sure to label and number the axes appropriately (see Example 3).

19. *Landfills.* In 2006, 35,700,000 tons of paper was deposited in landfills in the United States, and this figure was decreasing by 700,000 tons per year.
Source: Based on data from American Forest and Paper Association

20. *Health insurance.* In 2005, the average cost for health insurance for a family was about $11,000 and the figure was rising at a rate of about $1100 per year.
Source: Based on data from Kaiser/HRET Survey of Health Benefits

21. *Prescription drug sales.* In 2006, there were sales of approximately $11 billion of asthma drug products in the United States, and the figure was increasing at a rate of about $1.2 billion per year.
Source: *The Wall Street Journal,* 6/28/2007

22. *Violent crimes.* In 2004, there were approximately 21.1 violent crimes per 1000 population in the United States, and the figure was dropping at a rate of about 1.2 crimes per 1000 per year.
Source: U.S. Bureau of Justice Statistics

23. *Train travel.* At 3:00 P.M., the Boston–Washington Metroliner had traveled 230 mi and was cruising at a rate of 90 miles per hour.

24. *Plane travel.* At 4:00 P.M., the Seattle–Los Angeles shuttle had traveled 400 mi and was cruising at a rate of 300 miles per hour.

25. *Wages.* By 2:00 P.M., Diane had earned $50. She continued earning money at a rate of $15 per hour.

26. *Wages.* By 3:00 P.M., Arnie had earned $70. He continued earning money at a rate of $12 per hour.

27. *Telephone bills.* Roberta's phone bill was already $7.50 when she made a call for which she was charged at a rate of $0.10 per minute.

28. *Telephone bills.* At 3:00 P.M., Larry's phone bill was $6.50 and increasing at a rate of 7¢ per minute.

In Exercises 29–38, use the graph provided to calculate a rate of change in which the units of the horizontal axis are used in the denominator.

29. *Call center.* The following graph shows data from a technical assistance call center. At what rate are calls being handled?

30. *Hairdresser.* Eve's Custom Cuts has a graph displaying data from a recent day of work. At what rate does Eve work?

31. *Train travel.* The following graph shows data from a recent train ride from Chicago to St. Louis. At what rate did the train travel?

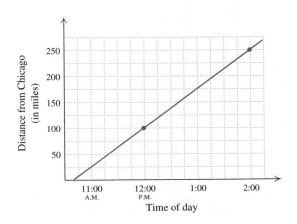

32. *Train travel.*   The following graph shows data from a recent train ride from Denver to Kansas City. At what rate did the train travel?

33. *Cost of a telephone call.*   The following graph shows data from a recent phone call between the United States and the Netherlands. At what rate was the customer being billed?

34. *Cost of a telephone call.*   The following graph shows data from a recent phone call between the United States and South Korea. At what rate was the customer being billed?

35. *Population.*   The following graph shows data regarding the population of Youngstown,

Ohio. At what rate was the population changing?

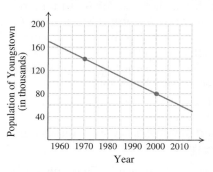

36. *Depreciation of an office machine.*   Data regarding the value of a particular color copier is represented in the following graph. At what rate is the value changing?

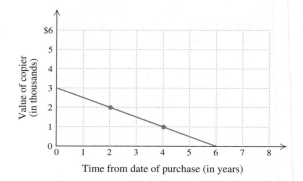

37. *Gas mileage.*   The following graph shows data for a 2008 Toyota Prius driven on interstate highways. At what rate was the vehicle consuming gas?
Source: www.fueleconomy.gov

38. *Gas mileage.*   The following graph shows data for a 2008 Chevy Malibu driven on city streets. At what rate was the vehicle consuming gas?
Source: Chevrolet

In each of Exercises 39–44, match the description with the most appropriate graph from the choices below. Scales are intentionally omitted. Assume that of the three sports listed, swimming is the slowest and biking is the fastest.

39. ____ Robin trains for triathlons by running, biking, and then swimming every Saturday.

40. ____ Gene trains for triathlons by biking, running, and then swimming every Sunday.

41. ____ Shirley trains for triathlons by swimming, biking, and then running every Sunday.

42. ____ Evan trains for triathlons by swimming, running, and then biking every Saturday.

43. ____ Angie trains for triathlons by biking, swimming, and then running every Sunday.

44. ____ Mick trains for triathlons by running, swimming, and then biking every Saturday.

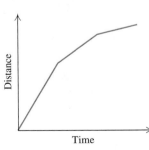

45. What does a negative rate of travel indicate? Explain.

46. Explain how to convert from kilometers per hour to meters per second.

Skill Review

To prepare for Section 2.5, review subtraction and order of operations.

Simplify.

47. $-2 - (-7)$

48. $-9 - (-3)$

49. $\dfrac{5 - (-4)}{-2 - 7}$

50. $\dfrac{8 - (-4)}{2 - 11}$

51. $\dfrac{-4 - 8}{11 - 2}$

52. $\dfrac{-5 - (-3)}{4 - 6}$

53. $\dfrac{-6 - (-6)}{-2 - 7}$

54. $\dfrac{-3 - 5}{-1 - (-1)}$

Synthesis

55. How would the graphs of Jon's and Jenny's total earnings compare in each of the following situations?

   a) Jon earns twice as much per hour as Jenny.
   b) Jon and Jenny earn the same hourly rate, but Jenny received a bonus for a cost-saving suggestion.
   c) Jon is paid by the hour, and Jenny is paid a weekly salary.

56. Write an exercise similar to those in Exercises 7–18 for a classmate to solve. Design the problem so that the solution is "The motorcycle's rate of gas consumption was 65 miles per gallon."

57. *Aviation.* A Boeing 737 climbs from sea level to a cruising altitude of 31,500 ft at a rate of 6300 ft/min. After cruising for 3 min, the jet is forced to land, descending at a rate of 3500 ft/min. Represent the flight with a graph in which altitude is measured on the vertical axis and time on the horizontal axis.

58. *Wages with commissions.* Each salesperson at Mike's Bikes is paid $140 a week plus 13% of all sales up to $2000, and then 20% on any sales in excess of $2000. Draw a graph in which sales are measured on the horizontal axis and wages on the vertical axis. Then use the graph to estimate the wages paid when a salesperson sells $2700 in merchandise in one week.

59. *Taxi fares.* The driver of a New York City Yellow Cab recently charged $2 plus 50¢ for each fifth of a mile traveled. Draw a graph that could be used to determine the cost of a fare.

60. *Gas mileage.* Suppose that a Kawasaki motorcycle travels three times as far as a Chevy Malibu on the same amount of gas (see Exercise 38). Draw a graph that reflects this information.

61. *Aviation.* Tim's F-16 jet is moving forward at a deck speed of 95 mph aboard an aircraft carrier that is traveling 39 mph in the same direction. How fast is the jet traveling, in minutes per mile, with respect to the sea?

62. *Navigation.* In 3 sec, Penny walks 24 ft, to the bow (front) of a tugboat. The boat is cruising at a rate of 5 ft/sec. What is Penny's rate of travel with respect to land?

63. *Running.* Anne ran from the 4-km mark to the 7-km mark of a 10-km race in 15.5 min. At this rate, how long would it take Anne to run a 5-mi race?

64. *Running.* Jerod ran from the 2-mi marker to the finish line of a 5-mi race in 25 min. At this rate, how long would it take Jerod to run a 10-km race?

65. Alex picks apples twice as fast as Ryan. By 4:30, Ryan had already picked 4 bushels of apples. Fifty minutes later, his total reached $5\frac{1}{2}$ bushels. Find Alex's picking rate. Give your answer in number of bushels per hour.

66. At 3:00 P.M., Catanya and Chad had already made 46 candles. By 5:00 P.M., the total reached 100 candles. Assuming a constant production rate, at what time did they make their 82nd candle?

COLLABORATIVE CORNER

Determining Depreciation Rates

Focus: Modeling, graphing, and rates

Time: 30 minutes

Group size: 3

Materials: Graph paper and straightedges

From the minute a new car is driven out of the dealership, it *depreciates*, or drops in value with the passing of time. The N.A.D.A. Official Used Car Guide is a periodic listing of the trade-in values of used cars. The data below are taken from two such reports from 2007.

ACTIVITY

1. Each group member should select a different one of the cars listed in the table below as his or her own. Assuming that the values are dropping linearly, each student should draw a line representing the trade-in value of his or her car. Draw all three lines on the same graph. Let the horizontal axis represent the time, in months, since January 2007, and let the vertical axis represent the trade-in value of each car. Decide as a group how many months or dollars each square should represent. Make the drawings as neat as possible.

2. At what *rate* is each car depreciating and how are the different rates illustrated in the graph of part (1)?

3. If one of the three cars had to be sold in January 2009, which one would your group sell and why? Compare answers with other groups.

Car	Trade-in Value in January 2007	Trade-in Value in June 2007
2005 Mustang V6 Coupe	$13,625	$13,125
2005 Nissan Sentra SE-R	$11,825	$11,000
2005 Volkswagen Jetta Sedan GL	$12,600	$11,425

2.5 Slope

Rate and Slope • Horizontal and Vertical Lines • Applications

In Section 2.4, we introduced *rate* as a method of measuring how two quantities change with respect to each other. In this section, we will discuss how rate can be related to the slope of a line.

Rate and Slope

Automated digitization machines use robotic arms to carefully turn pages of books so that they can take pictures of each page. Suppose that a large university library purchased a DL-1500 and an APT 1200. The DL-1500 digitizes 3 volumes of an encyclopedia every 2 hr. The APT 1200 digitizes 6 volumes of an encyclopedia every 5 hr. The following tables list the number of books digitized after various amounts of time for each machine.

Source: Based on information from Kirtas and 4DigitalBooks

DL-1500	
Hours Elapsed	**Books Digitized**
0	0
2	3
4	6
6	9
8	12

APT 1200	
Hours Elapsed	**Books Digitized**
0	0
5	6
10	12
15	18
20	24

We now graph the pairs of numbers listed in the tables, using the horizontal axis for the number of hours elapsed and the vertical axis for the number of books digitized.

DL-1500

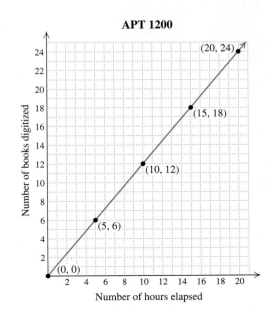

APT 1200

By comparing the number of books digitized by each machine over a specified period of time, we can compare the two rates. For example, the DL-1500 digitizes 3 books every 2 hr, so its *rate* is $3 \div 2 = \frac{3}{2}$ books per hour. Since the APT 1200 digitizes 6 books every 5 hr, its rate is $6 \div 5 = \frac{6}{5}$ books per hour. Note that the rate of the DL-1500 is greater so its graph is steeper.

The rates $\frac{3}{2}$ and $\frac{6}{5}$ can also be found using the coordinates of any two points that are on the line. For example, we can use the points $(6, 9)$ and $(8, 12)$ to find the digitization rate for the DL-1500. To do so, remember that these coordinates tell us that after 6 hr, 9 books have been digitized, and after 8 hr, 12 books have been digitized. In the 2 hr between the 6-hr and 8-hr points, $12 - 9$, or 3, books were digitized. Thus we have

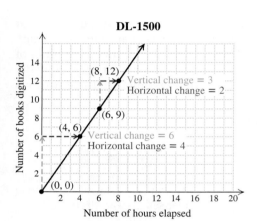

$$\text{DL-1500 digitization rate} = \frac{\text{change in number of books digitized}}{\text{corresponding change in time}}$$

$$= \frac{12 - 9 \text{ books}}{8 - 6 \text{ hr}}$$

$$= \frac{3 \text{ books}}{2 \text{ hr}} = \frac{3}{2} \text{ books per hour.}$$

Because the line is straight, the same rate is found using *any* pair of points on the line. For example, using $(0, 0)$ and $(4, 6)$, we have

$$\text{DL-1500 digitization rate} = \frac{6 - 0 \text{ books}}{4 - 0 \text{ hr}} = \frac{6 \text{ books}}{4 \text{ hr}} = \frac{3}{2} \text{ books per hour.}$$

Note that the rate is always the vertical change divided by the corresponding horizontal change.

EXAMPLE 1 Use the graph of book digitization by the APT 1200 to find the rate at which books are digitized.

SOLUTION We can use any two points on the line, such as $(15, 18)$ and $(20, 24)$:

$$\text{APT 1200 digitization rate} = \frac{\text{change in number of books digitized}}{\text{corresponding change in time}}$$

$$= \frac{24 - 18 \text{ books}}{20 - 15 \text{ hr}}$$

$$= \frac{6 \text{ books}}{5 \text{ hr}}$$

$$= \frac{6}{5} \text{ books per hour.}$$

As a check, we can use another pair of points, like $(0, 0)$ and $(10, 12)$:

$$\text{APT 1200 digitization rate} = \frac{12 - 0 \text{ books}}{10 - 0 \text{ hr}}$$

$$= \frac{12 \text{ books}}{10 \text{ hr}}$$

$$= \frac{6}{5} \text{ books per hour.}$$

TRY EXERCISE 11

When the axes of a graph are simply labeled x and y, the ratio of vertical change to horizontal change is the rate at which y is changing with respect to x. This ratio is a measure of a line's slant, or **slope**.

Consider a line passing through $(2, 3)$ and $(6, 5)$, as shown below. We find the ratio of vertical change, or *rise*, to horizontal change, or *run*, as follows:

$$\text{Ratio of vertical change to horizontal change} = \frac{\text{change in } y}{\text{change in } x} = \frac{\text{rise}}{\text{run}}$$

$$= \frac{5 - 3}{6 - 2}$$

$$= \frac{2}{4}, \text{ or } \frac{1}{2}.$$

Note that these calculations can be performed without viewing a graph.

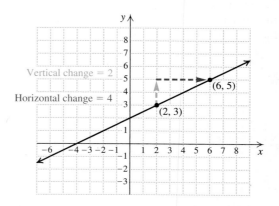

Thus the y-coordinates of points on this line increase at a rate of 2 units for every 4-unit increase in x, which is 1 unit for every 2-unit increase in x, or $\frac{1}{2}$ unit for every 1-unit increase in x. The slope of the line is $\frac{1}{2}$.

In the box below, the *subscripts* 1 and 2 are used to distinguish two arbitrary points, point 1 and point 2, from each other. The slightly lowered 1's and 2's are not exponents but are used to denote x-values (or y-values) that may differ from each other.

Slope

The *slope* of the line containing points (x_1, y_1) and (x_2, y_2) is given by

$$m = \frac{\text{change in } y}{\text{change in } x} = \frac{\text{rise}}{\text{run}} = \frac{y_2 - y_1}{x_2 - x_1}.$$

EXAMPLE **2**   Graph the line containing the points $(-4, 3)$ and $(2, -6)$ and find the slope.

SOLUTION   The graph is shown below. From $(-4, 3)$ to $(2, -6)$, the change in y, or rise, is $-6 - 3$, or -9. The change in x, or run, is $2 - (-4)$, or 6. Thus,

$$\text{Slope} = \frac{\text{change in } y}{\text{change in } x}$$

$$= \frac{\text{rise}}{\text{run}}$$

$$= \frac{-6 - 3}{2 - (-4)}$$

$$= \frac{-9}{6}$$

$$= -\frac{9}{6}, \text{ or } -\frac{3}{2}.$$

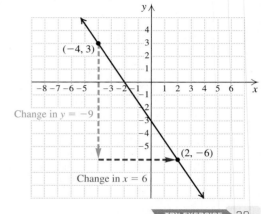

STUDENT NOTES ────────

You may wonder which point should be regarded as (x_1, y_1) and which should be (x_2, y_2). To see that the math works out the same either way, perform both calculations on your own.

TRY EXERCISE   39

CAUTION!   When we use the formula

$$m = \frac{y_2 - y_1}{x_2 - x_1},$$

it makes no difference which point is considered (x_1, y_1). What matters is that we subtract the y-coordinates in the same order that we subtract the x-coordinates.

To illustrate, we reverse *both* of the subtractions in Example 2. The slope is still $-\frac{3}{2}$:

$$\text{Slope} = \frac{\text{change in } y}{\text{change in } x} = \frac{3 - (-6)}{-4 - 2} = \frac{9}{-6} = -\frac{3}{2}.$$

As shown in the graphs below, a line with positive slope slants up from left to right, and a line with negative slope slants down from left to right. The larger the absolute value of the slope, the steeper the line.

$m = \frac{3}{7}$

$m = 2, \text{ or } \frac{2}{1}$

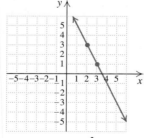

$m = -2, \text{ or } \frac{-2}{1}$

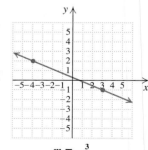

$m = -\frac{3}{7}$

Horizontal and Vertical Lines

What about the slope of a horizontal line or a vertical line?

EXAMPLE 3

Find the slope of the line $y = 4$.

SOLUTION Consider the points $(2, 4)$ and $(-3, 4)$, which are on the line. The change in y, or the rise, is $4 - 4$, or 0. The change in x, or the run, is $-3 - 2$, or -5. Thus,

$$m = \frac{4 - 4}{-3 - 2}$$

$$= \frac{0}{-5}$$

$$= 0.$$

Any two points on a horizontal line have the same y-coordinate. Thus the change in y is 0, so the slope is 0.

TRY EXERCISE 55

A horizontal line has slope 0.

EXAMPLE 4

Find the slope of the line $x = -3$.

SOLUTION Consider the points $(-3, 4)$ and $(-3, -2)$, which are on the line. The change in y, or the rise, is $-2 - 4$, or -6. The change in x, or the run, is $-3 - (-3)$, or 0. Thus,

$$m = \frac{-2 - 4}{-3 - (-3)}$$

$$= \frac{-6}{0}. \quad \text{(undefined)}$$

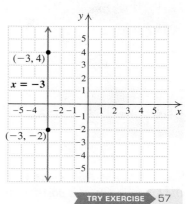

Since division by 0 is not defined, the slope of this line is not defined. The answer to a problem of this type is "The slope of this line is undefined."

TRY EXERCISE 57

The slope of a vertical line is undefined.

Applications

We have seen that slope has many real-world applications, ranging from car speed to production rate. Some applications use slope to measure steepness. For example, numbers like 2%, 3%, and 6% are often used to represent the **grade** of a road, a measure of a road's steepness. That is, since $3\% = \frac{3}{100}$, a 3% grade means that for every horizontal distance of 100 ft, the road rises or drops 3 ft. The concept of grade also occurs in skiing or snowboarding, where a 7% grade is considered very tame, but a 70% grade is considered steep.

EXAMPLE 5

Skiing. Among the steepest skiable terrain in North America, the Headwall on Mount Washington, in New Hampshire, drops 720 ft over a horizontal distance of 900 ft. Find the grade of the Headwall.

SOLUTION The grade of the Headwall is its slope, expressed as a percent:

$$m = \frac{720}{900}$$
$$= \frac{8}{10}$$
$$= 80\%.$$

Grade is slope expressed as a percent.

 TRY EXERCISE 63

Carpenters use slope when designing stairs, ramps, or roof pitches. Another application occurs in the engineering of a dam—the force or strength of a river depends on how much the river drops over a specified distance.

2.5 EXERCISE SET

For Extra Help

🥄 **Concept Reinforcement** *State whether each of the following rates is positive, negative, or zero.*

1. The rate at which a teenager's height changes

2. The rate at which an elderly person's height changes

3. The rate at which a pond's water level changes during a drought

4. The rate at which a pond's water level changes during the rainy season

5. The rate at which a runner's distance from the starting point changes during a race

6. The rate at which a runner's distance from the finish line changes during a race

7. The rate at which the number of U.S. senators changes

8. The rate at which the number of people in attendance at a basketball game changes in the moments before the opening tipoff

9. The rate at which the number of people in attendance at a basketball game changes in the moments after the final buzzer sounds

10. The rate at which a person's I.Q. changes during his or her sleep

11. *Blogging.* Find the rate at which a career blogger is paid.

Source: Based on information from Wired

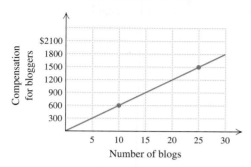

12. *Fitness.* Find the rate at which a runner burns calories.

13. *Cell-phone prices.* Find the rate of change in the average price of a new cell phone.

Source: Based on information from Market Reporter at PriceGrabber.com 2006

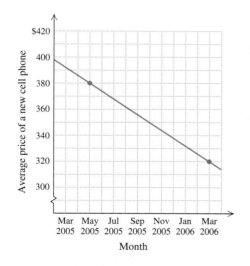

14. *Retail sales.* Find the rate of change in the percentage of department stores' share of total retail sales.

Source: Based on information from the National Retail Federation

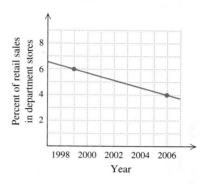

15. *College admission tests.* Find the rate of change in SAT verbal scores with respect to family income.

Source: Based on 2004–2005 data from the National Center for Education Statistics

16. *Long-term care.* Find the rate of change in Medicaid spending on long-term care.

Source: Based on data from Thomson Medstat, prepared by AARP Public Policy Institute

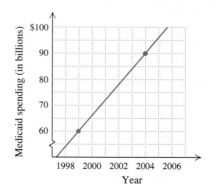

17. *Meteorology.* Find the rate of change in the temperature in Spearfish, Montana, on January 22, 1943, as shown below.
Source: National Oceanic Atmospheric Administration

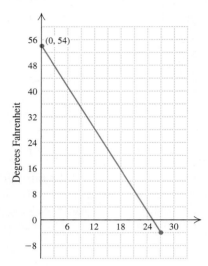

Number of minutes after 9 A.M.

18. Find the rate of change in the number of union-represented Ford employees.
Source: Ford Motor Co.

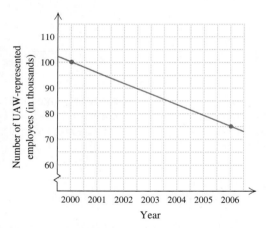

Find the slope, if it is defined, of each line. If the slope is undefined, state this.

19.

20.

21.

22.

23.

24.

25.

26.

27.

28.

29.

30.

31.

32.

36.

33.

37.

34.

38.

35.

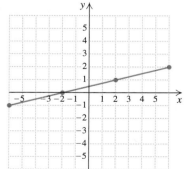

Find the slope of the line containing each given pair of points. If the slope is undefined, state this.

39. $(1, 3)$ and $(5, 8)$ **40.** $(1, 8)$ and $(6, 9)$

41. $(-2, 4)$ and $(3, 0)$ **42.** $(-4, 2)$ and $(2, -3)$

43. $(-4, 0)$ and $(5, 6)$ **44.** $(3, 0)$ and $(6, 9)$

45. $(0, 7)$ and $(-3, 10)$ **46.** $(0, 9)$ and $(-5, 0)$

47. $(-2, 3)$ and $(-6, 5)$ **48.** $(-1, 4)$ and $(5, -8)$

Aha! **49.** $\left(-2, \frac{1}{2}\right)$ and $\left(-5, \frac{1}{2}\right)$

50. $(-5, -1)$ and $(2, -3)$

51. $(5, -4)$ and $(2, -7)$

52. $(-10, 3)$ and $(-10, 4)$

53. $(6, -4)$ and $(6, 5)$

54. $(5, -2)$ and $(-4, -2)$

Find the slope of each line whose equation is given. If the slope is undefined, state this.

55. $y = 5$　　　　　　　**56.** $y = 13$

57. $x = -8$　　　　　　**58.** $x = 18$

59. $x = 9$　　　　　　　**60.** $x = -7$

61. $y = -10$　　　　　　**62.** $y = -4$

63. *Surveying.*　Lick Skillet Road, near Boulder, Colorado, climbs 792 ft over a horizontal distance of 5280 ft. What is the grade of the road?

64. *Navigation.*　Capital Rapids drops 54 ft vertically over a horizontal distance of 1080 ft. What is the slope of the rapids?

65. *Construction.*　Part of New Valley rises 28 ft over a horizontal distance of 80 ft, and is too steep to build on. What is the slope of the land?

66. *Engineering.*　At one point, Yellowstone's Beartooth Highway rises 315 ft over a horizontal distance of 4500 ft. Find the grade of the road.

67. *Carpentry.*　Find the slope (or pitch) of the roof.

68. *Exercise.*　Find the slope (or grade) of the treadmill.

69. *Bicycling.*　To qualify as a rated climb on the Tour de France, a grade must average at least 4%. The ascent of Dooley Mountain, Oregon, part of the Elkhorn Classic, begins at 3500 ft and climbs to 5400 ft over a horizontal distance of 37,000 ft. What is the grade of the road? Would it qualify as a rated climb if it were part of the Tour de France?
Source: barkercityherald.com

70. *Construction.*　Public buildings regularly include steps with 7-in. risers and 11-in. treads. Find the grade of such a stairway.

71. Explain why the order in which coordinates are subtracted to find slope does not matter so long as y-coordinates and x-coordinates are subtracted in the same order.

72. If one line has a slope of -3 and another has a slope of 2, which line is steeper? Why?

Skill Review

To prepare for Section 2.6, review solving a formula for a variable and graphing linear equations (Sections 1.3 and 2.2).

Solve. [1.3]

73. $ax + by = c$, for y　　**74.** $rx - mn = p$, for r

75. $ax - by = c$, for y　　**76.** $rs + nt = q$, for t

Graph. [1.2]

77. $8x + 6y = 24$　　　　**78.** $3y = 4$

Synthesis

79. The points $(-4, -3)$, $(1, 4)$, $(4, 2)$, and $(-1, -5)$ are vertices of a quadrilateral. Use slopes to explain why the quadrilateral is a parallelogram.

80. Which is steeper and why: a ski slope that is 50° or one with a grade of 100%?

81. The plans below are for a skateboard "Fun Box". For the ramps labeled A, find the slope or grade.
Source: www.heckler.com

82. A line passes through $(4, -7)$ and never enters the first quadrant. What numbers could the line have for its slope?

83. A line passes through $(2, 5)$ and never enters the second quadrant. What numbers could the line have for its slope?

84. *Architecture.* Architects often use the equation $x + y = 18$ to determine the height y, in inches, of the riser of a step when the tread is x inches wide. Express the slope of stairs designed with this equation without using the variable y.

In Exercises 85 and 86, the slope of the line is $-\frac{2}{3}$, but the numbering on one axis is missing. How many units should each tick mark on that unnumbered axis represent?

85.

86.

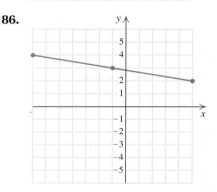

2.6 Slope–Intercept Form

Using the y-intercept and the Slope to Graph a Line • Equations in Slope–Intercept Form • Graphing and Slope–Intercept Form • Parallel and Perpendicular Lines

If we know the slope and the y-intercept of a line, it is possible to graph the line. In this section, we will discover that a line's slope and y-intercept can be determined directly from the line's equation, provided the equation is written in a certain form.

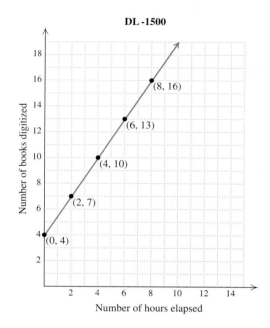

Using the y-intercept and the Slope to Graph a Line

Let's modify the book-digitization situation that first appeared in Section 2.5. Suppose that as the information technologist arrives, 4 books had already been digitized by the DL-1500. If the rate of $\frac{3}{2}$ books per hour remains in effect, the table and graph shown here can be made.

DL-1500	
Hours Elapsed	**Books Digitized**
0	4
2	7
4	10
6	13
8	16

To confirm that the digitization rate is still $\frac{3}{2}$, we calculate the slope. Recall that

$$\text{Slope} = \frac{\text{change in } y}{\text{change in } x} = \frac{\text{rise}}{\text{run}} = \frac{y_2 - y_1}{x_2 - x_1},$$

where (x_1, y_1) and (x_2, y_2) are any two points on the graphed line. Here we select $(0, 4)$ and $(2, 7)$:

$$\text{Slope} = \frac{\text{change in } y}{\text{change in } x} = \frac{7 - 4}{2 - 0} = \frac{3}{2}.$$

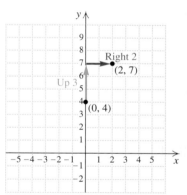

Knowing that the slope is $\frac{3}{2}$, we could have drawn the graph by plotting $(0, 4)$ and from there moving *up* 3 units and *to the right* 2 units. This would have located the point $(2, 7)$. Using $(0, 4)$ and $(2, 7)$, we can then draw the line. This is the method used in the next example.

EXAMPLE 1

Draw a line that has slope $\frac{1}{4}$ and y-intercept $(0, 2)$.

SOLUTION   We plot $(0, 2)$ and from there move *up* 1 unit and *to the right* 4 units. This locates the point $(4, 3)$. We plot $(4, 3)$ and draw a line passing through $(0, 2)$ and $(4, 3)$, as shown on the right below.

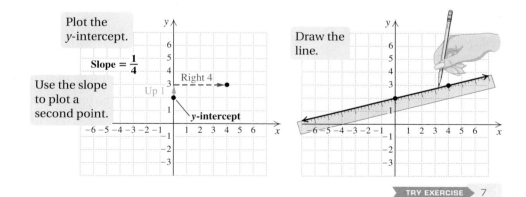

TRY EXERCISE 7

Equations in Slope–Intercept Form

It is possible to read the slope and the y-intercept of a line directly from its equation. Recall from Section 2.3 that to find the y-intercept of an equation's graph, we replace x with 0 and solve the resulting equation for y. For example, to find the y-intercept of the graph of $y = 2x + 3$, we replace x with 0 and solve as follows:

$$y = 2x + 3$$
$$= 2 \cdot 0 + 3 = 0 + 3 = 3. \qquad \text{The } y\text{-intercept is } (0, 3).$$

The y-intercept of the graph of $y = 2x + 3$ is $(0, 3)$. It can be similarly shown that the graph of $y = mx + b$ has the y-intercept $(0, b)$.

To calculate the slope of the graph of $y = 2x + 3$, we need two ordered pairs that are solutions of the equation. The y-intercept $(0, 3)$ is one pair; a second pair, $(1, 5)$, can be found by substituting 1 for x. We then have

$$\text{Slope} = \frac{\text{change in } y}{\text{change in } x} = \frac{5 - 3}{1 - 0} = \frac{2}{1} = 2.$$

Note that the slope, 2, is also the x-coefficient in $y = 2x + 3$. It can be similarly shown that the graph of any equation of the form $y = mx + b$ has slope m (see Exercise 79).

STUDENT NOTES

An equation for a given line can be written in many different forms. Note that in the slope–intercept form, the equation is solved for y.

The Slope–Intercept Equation

The equation $y = mx + b$ is called the *slope–intercept equation*. The equation represents a line of slope m with y-intercept $(0, b)$.

The equation of any nonvertical line can be written in this form.

EXAMPLE 2 Find the slope and the y-intercept of each line whose equation is given.

a) $y = \frac{4}{5}x - 8$ **b)** $2x + y = 5$ **c)** $3x - 4y = 7$

SOLUTION

a) We rewrite $y = \frac{4}{5}x - 8$ as $y = \frac{4}{5}x + (-8)$. Now we simply read the slope and the y-intercept from the equation:

$$y = \frac{4}{5}x + (-8).$$

The slope is $\frac{4}{5}$. The y-intercept is $(0, -8)$.

b) We first solve for y to find an equivalent equation in the form $y = mx + b$:

$$2x + y = 5$$
$$y = -2x + 5. \qquad \text{Adding } -2x \text{ to both sides}$$

The slope is -2. The y-intercept is $(0, 5)$.

c) We rewrite the equation in the form $y = mx + b$:

$$3x - 4y = 7$$
$$-4y = -3x + 7 \qquad \text{Adding } -3x \text{ to both sides}$$
$$y = -\frac{1}{4}(-3x + 7) \qquad \text{Multiplying both sides by } -\frac{1}{4}$$
$$y = \frac{3}{4}x - \frac{7}{4}. \qquad \text{Using the distributive law}$$

The slope is $\frac{3}{4}$. The y-intercept is $\left(0, -\frac{7}{4}\right)$.

TRY EXERCISE 19

EXAMPLE 3

A line has slope $-\frac{12}{5}$ and y-intercept $(0, 11)$. Find an equation of the line.

SOLUTION We use the slope–intercept equation, substituting $-\frac{12}{5}$ for m and 11 for b:

$$y = mx + b = -\frac{12}{5}x + 11.$$

The desired equation is $y = -\frac{12}{5}x + 11$.

TRY EXERCISE 35

EXAMPLE 4

Threatened species. A threatened species is a species that is likely to become endangered in the future. Determine an equation for the graph of threatened species in the Blue Mountains.

Source: Based on information from Sustainable Blue Mountains

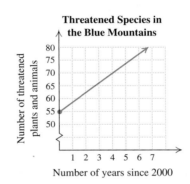

SOLUTION To write an equation for a line, we can use slope–intercept form, provided the slope and the y-intercept are known. From the graph, we see that $(0, 55)$ is the y-intercept. Looking closely, we see that the line passes through $(4, 70)$. We can either count squares on the graph or use the formula to calculate the slope:

$$m = \frac{\text{change in } y}{\text{change in } x} = \frac{70 - 55}{4 - 0} = \frac{15}{4}.$$

The desired equation is

$$y = \frac{15}{4}x + 55, \qquad \text{Using } \tfrac{15}{4} \text{ for } m \text{ and } 55 \text{ for } b$$

where y is the number of threatened species in the Blue Mountains x years after 2000.

TRY EXERCISE 43

Graphing and Slope–Intercept Form

In Example 1, we drew a graph, knowing only the slope and the y-intercept. In Example 2, we determined the slope and the y-intercept of a line by examining its equation. We now combine the two procedures to develop a quick way to graph a linear equation.

EXAMPLE 5

Graph: **(a)** $y = \frac{3}{4}x + 5$; **(b)** $2x + 3y = 3$.

SOLUTION

a) From the equation $y = \frac{3}{4}x + 5$, we see that the slope of the graph is $\frac{3}{4}$ and the y-intercept is $(0, 5)$. We plot $(0, 5)$ and then consider the slope, $\frac{3}{4}$. Starting at $(0, 5)$, we plot a second point by moving *up* 3 units (since the numerator is *positive* and corresponds to the change in y) and *to the right* 4 units (since the denominator is *positive* and corresponds to the change in x). We reach a new point, $(4, 8)$.

STUDENT NOTES ———————

Remember that

$$\frac{3}{4} = \frac{-3}{-4}.$$

Similarly,

$$-\frac{3}{4} = \frac{-3}{4} = \frac{3}{-4}.$$

Also note that

$$2 = \frac{2}{1} \quad \text{and} \quad -2 = \frac{-2}{1}.$$

Since $\frac{3}{4} = \frac{-3}{-4}$, we can again start at the y-intercept, $(0, 5)$, but move *down* 3 units (since the numerator is *negative* and corresponds to the change in y) and *to the left* 4 units (since the denominator is *negative* and corresponds to the change in x). We reach another point, $(-4, 2)$. Once two or three points have been plotted, the line representing all solutions of $y = \frac{3}{4}x + 5$ can be drawn.

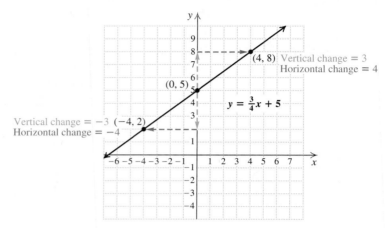

STUDENT NOTES ———————

The signs of the numerator and the denominator of the slope indicate whether to move up, down, left, or right. Compare the following slopes.

$$\frac{1}{2} \begin{array}{l} \leftarrow 1 \text{ unit up} \\ \leftarrow 2 \text{ units right} \end{array}$$

$$\frac{-1}{-2} \begin{array}{l} \leftarrow 1 \text{ unit down} \\ \leftarrow 2 \text{ units left} \end{array}$$

$$\frac{-1}{2} \begin{array}{l} \leftarrow 1 \text{ unit down} \\ \leftarrow 2 \text{ units right} \end{array}$$

$$\frac{1}{-2} \begin{array}{l} \leftarrow 1 \text{ unit up} \\ \leftarrow 2 \text{ units left} \end{array}$$

b) To graph $2x + 3y = 3$, we first rewrite it in slope–intercept form:

$$\begin{aligned} 2x + 3y &= 3 \\ 3y &= -2x + 3 &\quad &\text{Adding } -2x \text{ to both sides} \\ y &= \tfrac{1}{3}(-2x + 3) &\quad &\text{Multiplying both sides by } \tfrac{1}{3} \\ y &= -\tfrac{2}{3}x + 1. &\quad &\text{Using the distributive law} \end{aligned}$$

To graph $y = -\frac{2}{3}x + 1$, we first plot the y-intercept, $(0, 1)$. We can think of the slope as $\frac{-2}{3}$. Starting at $(0, 1)$ and using the slope, we find a second point by moving *down* 2 units (since the numerator is *negative*) and *to the right* 3 units (since the denominator is *positive*). We plot the new point, $(3, -1)$. In a similar manner, we can move from the point $(3, -1)$ to locate a third point, $(6, -3)$. The line can then be drawn.

Since $-\frac{2}{3} = \frac{2}{-3}$, an alternative approach is to again plot $(0, 1)$, but this time move *up* 2 units (since the numerator is *positive*) and *to the left* 3 units (since the denominator is *negative*). This leads to another point on the graph, $(-3, 3)$.

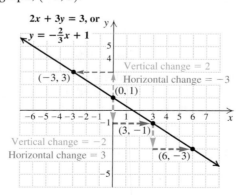

It is important to be able to use both $\frac{2}{-3}$ and $\frac{-2}{3}$ to draw the graph.

TRY EXERCISE 47

Slope–intercept form allows us to quickly determine the slope of a line by simply inspecting its equation. This can be especially helpful when attempting to decide whether two lines are parallel or perpendicular.

TECHNOLOGY CONNECTION

Using a standard $[-10, 10, -10, 10]$ window, graph the equations $y_1 = \frac{2}{3}x + 1$, $y_2 = \frac{3}{8}x + 1$, $y_3 = \frac{2}{3}x + 5$, and $y_4 = \frac{3}{8}x + 5$. If you can, use your graphing calculator in the MODE that graphs equations *simultaneously*. Once all lines have been drawn, try to decide which equation corresponds to each line. After matching equations with lines, you can check your matches by using TRACE and the up and down arrow keys to move from one line to the

next. The number of the equation will appear in a corner of the screen.

1. Graph $y_1 = -\frac{3}{4}x - 2$, $y_2 = -\frac{1}{5}x - 2$, $y_3 = -\frac{3}{4}x - 5$, and $y_4 = -\frac{1}{5}x - 5$ using the SIMULTANEOUS mode. Then match each line with the corresponding equation. Check using TRACE.

Parallel and Perpendicular Lines

Two lines are parallel if they lie in the same plane and do not intersect no matter how far they are extended. If two lines are vertical, they are parallel. How can we tell if nonvertical lines are parallel? The answer is simple: We look at their slopes.

> ### Slope and Parallel Lines
>
> Two lines are parallel if they have the same slope or if both lines are vertical.

EXAMPLE 6 Determine whether the graphs of $y = -3x + 4$ and $6x + 2y = -10$ are parallel.

SOLUTION   We compare the slopes of the two lines to determine whether the graphs are parallel.

One of the two equations given is in slope–intercept form:

$$y = -3x + 4. \qquad \text{The slope is } -3 \text{ and the } y\text{-intercept is } (0, 4).$$

To find the slope of the other line, we need to rewrite the other equation in slope–intercept form:

$$6x + 2y = -10$$
$$2y = -6x - 10 \qquad \text{Adding } -6x \text{ to both sides}$$
$$y = -3x - 5. \qquad \text{The slope is } -3 \text{ and the } y\text{-intercept is } (0, -5).$$

Since both lines have slope -3 but different y-intercepts, the graphs are parallel. There is no need for us to actually graph either equation. **TRY EXERCISE 63**

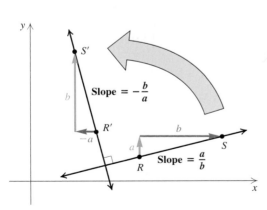

Two lines are perpendicular if they intersect at a right angle. If one line is vertical and another is horizontal, they are perpendicular. There are other instances in which two lines are perpendicular.

Consider a line $\overleftrightarrow{RS}$ as shown at left, with slope a/b. Then think of rotating the figure 90° to get a line $\overleftrightarrow{R'S'}$ perpendicular to $\overleftrightarrow{RS}$. For the new line, the rise and the run are interchanged, but the run is now negative. Thus the slope of the new line is $-b/a$. Let's multiply the slopes:

$$\frac{a}{b}\left(-\frac{b}{a}\right) = -1.$$

This can help us determine which lines are perpendicular.

> **Slope and Perpendicular Lines**
>
> Two lines are perpendicular if the product of their slopes is -1 or if one line is vertical and the other line is horizontal.

Thus, if one line has slope m ($m \neq 0$), the slope of a line perpendicular to it is $-1/m$. That is, we take the reciprocal of m ($m \neq 0$) and change the sign.

EXAMPLE **7**   Determine whether the graphs of $2x + y = 8$ and $y = \frac{1}{2}x + 7$ are perpendicular.

SOLUTION   One of the two equations given is in slope–intercept form:

$$y = \tfrac{1}{2}x + 7. \qquad \text{The slope is } \tfrac{1}{2}.$$

To find the slope of the other line, we rewrite the other equation in slope–intercept form:

$$2x + y = 8$$
$$y = -2x + 8. \qquad \text{Adding } -2x \text{ to both sides}$$

The slope of the line is -2.

The lines are perpendicular if the product of their slopes is -1. Since

$$\frac{1}{2}(-2) = -1,$$

the graphs are perpendicular.   **TRY EXERCISE** 69

EXAMPLE **8**   Write a slope–intercept equation for the line whose graph is described.

a) Parallel to the graph of $2x - 3y = 7$, with y-intercept $(0, -1)$
b) Perpendicular to the graph of $2x - 3y = 7$, with y-intercept $(0, -1)$

SOLUTION   We begin by determining the slope of the line represented by $2x - 3y = 7$:

$$2x - 3y = 7$$
$$-3y = -2x + 7 \qquad \text{Adding } -2x \text{ to both sides}$$
$$y = \tfrac{2}{3}x - \tfrac{7}{3}. \qquad \text{Dividing both sides by } -3$$

The slope is $\frac{2}{3}$.

a) A line parallel to the graph of $2x - 3y = 7$ has a slope of $\frac{2}{3}$. Since the y-intercept is $(0, -1)$, the slope–intercept equation is

$$y = \tfrac{2}{3}x - 1. \qquad \text{Substituting in } y = mx + b$$

b) A line perpendicular to the graph of $2x - 3y = 7$ has a slope that is the opposite of the reciprocal of $\frac{2}{3}$, or $-\frac{3}{2}$. Since the y-intercept is $(0, -1)$, the slope–intercept equation is

$$y = -\tfrac{3}{2}x - 1. \qquad \text{Substituting in } y = mx + b$$

                          TRY EXERCISE 75

2.6 EXERCISE SET

For Extra Help

Concept Reinforcement *In each of Exercises 1–6, match the phrase with the most appropriate choice from the column on the right.*

1. ____ The slope of the graph of $y = 3x - 2$ a) $\left(0, \frac{3}{4}\right)$

2. ____ The slope of the graph of $y = 2x - 3$ b) 2

3. ____ The slope of the graph of $y = \frac{2}{3}x + 3$ c) $(0, -3)$

4. ____ The y-intercept of the graph of $y = 2x - 3$ d) $\frac{2}{3}$

5. ____ The y-intercept of the graph of $y = 3x - 2$ e) $(0, -2)$

6. ____ The y-intercept of the graph of $y = \frac{2}{3}x + \frac{3}{4}$ f) 3

Draw a line that has the given slope and y-intercept.

7. Slope $\frac{2}{3}$; y-intercept $(0, 1)$

8. Slope $\frac{3}{5}$; y-intercept $(0, -1)$

9. Slope $\frac{5}{3}$; y-intercept $(0, -2)$

10. Slope $\frac{1}{2}$; y-intercept $(0, 0)$

11. Slope $-\frac{1}{3}$; y-intercept $(0, 5)$

12. Slope $-\frac{4}{5}$; y-intercept $(0, 6)$

13. Slope 2; y-intercept $(0, 0)$

14. Slope -2; y-intercept $(0, -3)$

15. Slope -3; y-intercept $(0, 2)$

16. Slope 3; y-intercept $(0, 4)$

Aha! 17. Slope 0; y-intercept $(0, -5)$

18. Slope 0; y-intercept $(0, 1)$

Find the slope and the y-intercept of each line whose equation is given.

19. $y = -\frac{2}{7}x + 5$

20. $y = -\frac{3}{8}x + 4$

21. $y = \frac{1}{3}x + 7$

22. $y = \frac{4}{5}x + 1$

23. $y = \frac{9}{5}x - 4$

24. $y = -\frac{9}{10}x - 5$

25. $-3x + y = 7$

26. $-4x + y = 7$

27. $4x + 2y = 8$

28. $3x + 4y = 12$

Aha! 29. $y = 3$

30. $y - 3 = 5$

31. $2x - 5y = -8$

32. $12x - 6y = 9$

33. $9x - 8y = 0$

34. $7x = 5y$

Find the slope–intercept equation for the line with the indicated slope and y-intercept.

35. Slope 5; y-intercept $(0, 7)$

36. Slope -4; y-intercept $\left(0, -\frac{3}{5}\right)$

37. Slope $\frac{7}{8}$; y-intercept $(0, -1)$

38. Slope $\frac{5}{7}$; y-intercept $(0, 4)$

39. Slope $-\frac{5}{3}$; y-intercept $(0, -8)$

40. Slope $\frac{3}{4}$; y-intercept $(0, -35)$

Aha! 41. Slope 0; y-intercept $\left(0, \frac{1}{3}\right)$

42. Slope 7; y-intercept $(0, 0)$

Determine an equation for each graph shown.

43.

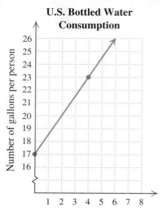

U.S. Bottled Water Consumption

Based on information from the International Bottled Water Association

44.

Cost of an Overseas Calling-Card Telephone Call

Source: www.pennytalk.com

45.

Jobs in Health Care and Social Assistance

Source: U.S. Bureau of Labor Statistics

46.

Average Hourly Earnings in Accommodations and Food Services

Source: U.S. Bureau of Labor Statistics

Graph.

47. $y = \frac{2}{3}x + 2$ **48.** $y = -\frac{2}{3}x - 3$

49. $y = -\frac{2}{3}x + 3$ **50.** $y = \frac{2}{3}x - 2$

51. $y = \frac{3}{2}x + 3$ **52.** $y = \frac{3}{2}x - 2$

53. $y = -\frac{4}{3}x + 3$ **54.** $y = -\frac{3}{2}x - 2$

55. $2x + y = 1$ **56.** $3x + y = 2$

57. $3x + y = 0$ **58.** $2x + y = 0$

59. $4x + 5y = 15$ **60.** $2x + 3y = 9$

61. $x - 4y = 12$ **62.** $x + 5y = 20$

Determine whether each pair of equations represents parallel lines.

63. $y = \frac{3}{4}x + 6,$ **64.** $y = \frac{1}{3}x - 2,$
$\quad\; y = \frac{3}{4}x - 2$ $\quad\; y = -\frac{1}{3}x + 1$

65. $y = 2x - 5,$ **66.** $y = -3x + 1,$
$\quad\; 4x + 2y = 9$ $\quad\; 6x + 2y = 8$

67. $3x + 4y = 8,$ **68.** $3x = 5y - 2,$
$\quad\; 7 - 12y = 9x$ $\quad\; 10y = 4 - 6x$

Determine whether each pair of equations represents perpendicular lines.

69. $y = 4x - 5,$ **70.** $2x - 5y = -3,$
$\quad\; 4y = 8 - x$ $\quad\; 2x + 5y = 4$

71. $x - 2y = 5,$ **72.** $y = -x + 7,$
$\quad\; 2x + 4y = 8$ $\quad\; y - x = 3$

73. $2x + 3y = 1$,
$3x - 2y = 1$

74. $y = 5 - 3x$,
$3x - y = 8$

Write a slope–intercept equation of the line whose graph is described.

75. Parallel to the graph of $y = 5x - 7$; y-intercept $(0, 11)$

76. Parallel to the graph of $2x - y = 1$; y-intercept $(0, -3)$

77. Perpendicular to the graph of $2x + y = 0$; y-intercept $(0, 0)$

78. Perpendicular to the graph of $y = \frac{1}{3}x + 7$; y-intercept $(0, 5)$

Aha! **79.** Parallel to the graph of $y = x$; y-intercept $(0, 3)$

Aha! **80.** Perpendicular to the graph of $y = x$; y-intercept $(0, 0)$

81. Perpendicular to the graph of $x + y = 3$; y-intercept $(0, -4)$

82. Parallel to the graph of $3x + 2y = 5$; y-intercept $(0, -1)$

83. Can a horizontal line be graphed using the method of Example 5? Why or why not?

84. If two lines are perpendicular, does it follow that the lines have slopes that are negative reciprocals of each other? Why or why not?

Skill Review

To prepare for Section 2.7, review solving a formula for a variable and subtracting real numbers (Section 1.3).

Solve. [1.3]

85. $y - k = m(x - h)$, for y

86. $y - 9 = -2(x + 4)$, for y

Simplify.

87. $-10 - (-3)$

88. $8 - (-5)$

89. $-4 - 5$

90. $-6 - 5$

Synthesis

91. Explain how it is possible for an incorrect graph to be drawn, even after plotting three points that line up.

92. Which would you prefer, and why: graphing an equation of the form $y = mx + b$ or graphing an equation of the form $Ax + By = C$?

93. Show that the slope of the line given by $y = mx + b$ is m. (*Hint*: Substitute both 0 and 1 for x to find two pairs of coordinates. Then use the formula, Slope = change in y/change in x.)

94. Write an equation of the line with the same slope as the line given by $5x + 2y = 8$ and the same y-intercept as the line given by $3x - 7y = 10$.

95. Write an equation of the line parallel to the line given by $2x - 6y = 10$ and having the same y-intercept as the line given by $9x + 6y = 18$.

96. Write an equation of the line parallel to the line given by $3x - 2y = 8$ and having the same y-intercept as the line given by $2y + 3x = -4$.

97. Write an equation of the line perpendicular to the line given by $3x - 5y = 8$ and having the same y-intercept as the line given by $2x + 4y = 12$.

98. Write an equation of the line perpendicular to the line given by $2x + 3y = 7$ and having the same y-intercept as the line given by $5x + 2y = 10$.

99. Write an equation of the line perpendicular to the line given by $3x - 2y = 9$ and having the same y-intercept as the line given by $2x + 5y = 0$.

100. Write an equation of the line perpendicular to the line given by $2x + 5y = 6$ that passes through $(2, 6)$. (*Hint*: Draw a graph.)

CONNECTING the CONCEPTS

If any two points are plotted on a plane, there is only one line that will go through both points. Thus, if we know that the graph of an equation is a straight line, we need only find two points that are on that line. Then we can plot those points and draw the line that goes through them.

The different graphing methods discussed in this chapter present efficient ways of finding two points that are on the graph of the equation. Following is a general strategy for graphing linear equations.

1. Make sure that the equation is linear. Linear equations can always be written in the form $Ax + By = C$. (A or B may be 0.)
2. Graph the line. Use substitution to find two points on the line, or use a more efficient method based on the form of the equation.
3. Check the graph by finding another point that should be on the line and determining whether it does actually fall on the line.

Form of Equation	Graph
$x = a$	Draw a vertical line through $(a, 0)$.
$y = b$	Draw a horizontal line through $(0, b)$.
$y = mx + b$	Plot the y-intercept $(0, b)$. Start at the y-intercept and count off the rise and run using the slope m to find another point. Draw a line through the two points.
$Ax + By = C$	Determine the x- and y-intercepts $(a, 0)$ and $(0, b)$. Draw a line through the two points.

MIXED REVIEW

For each equation, (a) determine whether it is linear and (b) if it is linear, graph the line.

1. $x = 3$
2. $y = -2$
3. $y = \frac{1}{2}x + 3$
4. $4x + 3y = 12$
5. $y - 5 = x$
6. $x + y = -2$
7. $3xy = 6$
8. $2x = 3y$
9. $3 - y = 4$
10. $y = x^2 - 4$
11. $2y = 9x - 10$
12. $x + 8 = 7$
13. $2x - 6 = 3y$
14. $y - 2x = 4$
15. $2y - x = 4$
16. $y = \frac{1}{x}$
17. $x - 2y = 0$
18. $y = 4 - x$
19. $y = 4 + x$
20. $4x - 5y = 20$

2.7 Point–Slope Form

Writing Equations in Point–Slope Form • Graphing and Point–Slope Form •
Estimations and Predictions Using Two Points

There are many applications in which a slope—or a rate of change—and an ordered pair are known. When the ordered pair is the y-intercept, an equation in slope–intercept form can be easily produced. When the ordered pair represents a point other than the y-intercept, a different form, known as *point–slope form*, is more convenient.

Writing Equations in Point–Slope Form

Consider a line with slope 2 passing through the point $(4, 1)$, as shown in the figure. In order for a point (x, y) to be on the line, the coordinates x and y must be solutions of the slope equation

$$\frac{y - 1}{x - 4} = 2. \qquad \text{If } (x, y) \text{ is not on the line, this equation will not be true.}$$

Take a moment to examine this equation. Pairs like $(5, 3)$ and $(3, -1)$ are on the line and are solutions, since

$$\frac{3 - 1}{5 - 4} = 2 \quad \text{and} \quad \frac{-1 - 1}{3 - 4} = 2.$$

When $x \neq 4$, then $x - 4 \neq 0$, and we can multiply on both sides of the slope equation by $x - 4$:

$$(x - 4) \cdot \frac{y - 1}{x - 4} = 2(x - 4)$$

$$y - 1 = 2(x - 4). \qquad \text{Removing a factor equal to 1: } \frac{x - 4}{x - 4} = 1$$

Every point on the line is a solution of this equation.

This is considered **point–slope form** for the line shown in the figure at left. A point–slope equation can be written any time a line's slope and a point on the line are known.

> ### The Point–Slope Equation
>
> The equation $y - y_1 = m(x - x_1)$ is called the *point–slope equation* for the line with slope m that contains the point (x_1, y_1).

Point–slope form is especially useful in more advanced mathematics courses, where problems similar to the following often arise.

EXAMPLE 1 Write a point–slope equation for the line with slope $\frac{1}{5}$ that contains the point $(7, 2)$.

SOLUTION We substitute $\frac{1}{5}$ for m, 7 for x_1, and 2 for y_1:

$$y - y_1 = m(x - x_1) \qquad \text{Using the point–slope equation}$$
$$y - 2 = \tfrac{1}{5}(x - 7). \qquad \text{Substituting}$$

TRY EXERCISE ▶ 13

EXAMPLE 2

Write a point–slope equation for the line with slope $-\frac{4}{3}$ that contains the point $(1, -6)$.

SOLUTION   We substitute $-\frac{4}{3}$ for m, 1 for x_1, and -6 for y_1:

$$y - y_1 = m(x - x_1) \qquad \text{Using the point–slope equation}$$
$$y - (-6) = -\frac{4}{3}(x - 1). \qquad \text{Substituting}$$

> TRY EXERCISE 19

EXAMPLE 3

Write the slope–intercept equation for the line with slope 2 that contains the point $(3, 1)$.

SOLUTION   There are two parts to this solution. First, we write an equation in point–slope form:

$$y - y_1 = m(x - x_1)$$
$$y - 1 = 2(x - 3). \qquad \text{Substituting} \qquad \boxed{\text{Write in point–slope form.}}$$

Next, we find an equivalent equation of the form $y = mx + b$:

$$y - 1 = 2(x - 3)$$
$$y - 1 = 2x - 6 \qquad \text{Using the distributive law} \qquad \boxed{\text{Write in slope–intercept form.}}$$
$$y = 2x - 5. \qquad \text{Adding 1 to both sides to get slope–intercept form}$$

> TRY EXERCISE 27

STUDENT NOTES

There are several forms in which a line's equation can be written. For instance, as shown in Example 3, $y - 1 = 2(x - 3), y - 1 = 2x - 6$, and $y = 2x - 5$ all are equations for the same line.

EXAMPLE 4

Consider the line given by the equation $8y = 7x - 24$.

a) Write the slope–intercept equation for a parallel line passing through $(-1, 2)$.

b) Write the slope–intercept equation for a perpendicular line passing through $(-1, 2)$.

SOLUTION   Both parts (a) and (b) require us to find the slope of the line given by $8y = 7x - 24$. To do so, we solve for y to find slope–intercept form:

$$8y = 7x - 24$$
$$y = \frac{7}{8}x - 3. \qquad \text{Multiplying both sides by } \frac{1}{8}$$
$$\text{The slope is } \frac{7}{8}.$$

a) The slope of any parallel line will be $\frac{7}{8}$. The point–slope equation yields

$$y - 2 = \frac{7}{8}[x - (-1)] \qquad \text{Substituting } \frac{7}{8} \text{ for the slope and } (-1, 2) \text{ for the point}$$
$$y - 2 = \frac{7}{8}[x + 1]$$
$$y = \frac{7}{8}x + \frac{7}{8} + 2 \qquad \text{Using the distributive law and adding 2 to both sides}$$
$$y = \frac{7}{8}x + \frac{23}{8}.$$

b) The slope of a perpendicular line is given by the opposite of the reciprocal of $\frac{7}{8}$, or $-\frac{8}{7}$. The point–slope equation yields

$$y - 2 = -\frac{8}{7}[x - (-1)] \qquad \text{Substituting } -\frac{8}{7} \text{ for the slope and } (-1, 2) \text{ for the point}$$
$$y - 2 = -\frac{8}{7}[x + 1]$$
$$y = -\frac{8}{7}x - \frac{8}{7} + 2 \qquad \text{Using the distributive law and adding 2 to both sides}$$
$$y = -\frac{8}{7}x + \frac{6}{7}.$$

> TRY EXERCISE 39

TECHNOLOGY CONNECTION

To check that the graphs of $y = \frac{7}{8}x - 3$ and $y = -\frac{8}{7}x + \frac{6}{7}$ are perpendicular, we use the ZSQUARE option of the ZOOM menu to create a "squared" window. This corrects for distortion that would result from the units on the axes being of different lengths.

1. Show that the graphs of $y = \frac{3}{4}x + 2$ and $y = -\frac{4}{3}x - 1$ appear to be perpendicular.

2. Show that the graphs of $y = -\frac{2}{5}x - 4$ and $y = \frac{5}{2}x + 3$ appear to be perpendicular.

3. To see that this type of check is not foolproof, graph

$$y = \frac{31}{40}x + 2$$

and $y = -\frac{40}{30}x - 1$.

Are the lines perpendicular? Why or why not?

Graphing and Point–Slope Form

When we know a line's slope and a point that is on the line, we can draw the graph, much as we did in Section 2.6. For example, the information given in the statement of Example 3 is sufficient for drawing a graph.

EXAMPLE 5 Graph the line with slope 2 that passes through $(3, 1)$.

SOLUTION We plot $(3, 1)$, move *up* 2 and *to the right* 1 $\left(\text{since } 2 = \frac{2}{1}\right)$, and draw the line.

Plot the point.

Use the slope to plot a second point.

Draw the line.

TRY EXERCISE 55

EXAMPLE 6 Graph: $y - 2 = 3(x - 4)$.

SOLUTION Since $y - 2 = 3(x - 4)$ is in point–slope form, we know that the line has slope 3, or $\frac{3}{1}$, and passes through the point $(4, 2)$. We plot $(4, 2)$ and then find a second point by moving *up* 3 units and *to the right* 1 unit. The line can then be drawn, as shown below.

TRY EXERCISE 65

EXAMPLE 7 Graph: $y + 4 = -\frac{5}{2}(x + 3)$.

SOLUTION Once we have written the equation in point–slope form, $y - y_1 = m(x - x_1)$, we can proceed much as we did in Example 6. To find an equivalent equation in point–slope form, we subtract opposites instead of adding:

$$y + 4 = -\frac{5}{2}(x + 3)$$
$$y - (-4) = -\frac{5}{2}(x - (-3)).$$

Subtracting a negative instead of adding a positive. This is now in point–slope form.

From this last equation, $y - (-4) = -\frac{5}{2}(x - (-3))$, we see that the line passes through $(-3, -4)$ and has slope $-\frac{5}{2}$, or $\frac{5}{-2}$.

TRY EXERCISE 61

Estimations and Predictions Using Two Points

We can estimate real-life quantities that are not already known by using two points with known coordinates. When the unknown point is located *between* the two points, this process is called **interpolation**. If a graph passing through the known points is *extended* to predict future values, the process is called **extrapolation**. In statistics, methods exist for using a set of several points to interpolate or extrapolate values using curves other than lines.

EXAMPLE 8

Student volunteers. An increasing number of college students are donating time and energy in volunteer service. The number of college-student volunteers grew from 2.7 million in 2002 to 3.3 million in 2005.

Source: Corporation for National and Community Service

a) Graph the line passing through the given data points, letting $x =$ the number of years since 2000.

b) Determine an equation for the line and estimate the number of college students who volunteered in 2004.

c) Predict the number of college students who will volunteer in 2010.

SOLUTION

a) We first draw and label a horizontal axis to display the year and a vertical axis to display the number of college-student volunteers, in millions. Next, we number the axes, choosing scales that will include both the given values and the values to be estimated.

Since $x =$ the number of years since 2000, we plot the points $(2, 2.7)$ and $(5, 3.3)$ and draw a line passing through both points.

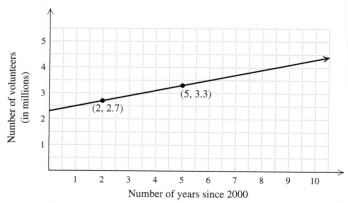

b) To find an equation for the line, we first calculate its slope:

$$m = \frac{\text{change in } y}{\text{change in } x} = \frac{3.3 - 2.7}{5 - 2} = \frac{0.6}{3} = 0.2.$$

The number of college-student volunteers increased at a rate of 0.2 million students per year. We can use either of the given points to write a point–slope equation for the line. Let's use $(2, 2.7)$ and then write an equivalent equation in slope–intercept form:

$y - 2.7 = 0.2(x - 2)$ This is a point–slope equation.

$y - 2.7 = 0.2x - 0.4$ Using the distributive law

$y = 0.2x + 2.3.$ Adding 2.7 to both sides. This is slope–intercept form.

To estimate the number of college-student volunteers in 2004, we substitute 4 for x in the slope–intercept equation:

$y = 0.2 \cdot 4 + 2.3 = 3.1.$

As the graph confirms, in 2004 there were about 3.1 million college-student volunteers.

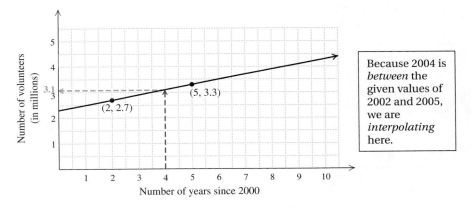

Because 2004 is *between* the given values of 2002 and 2005, we are *interpolating* here.

c) To predict the number of college-student volunteers in 2010, we again substitute for x in the slope–intercept equation:

$y = 0.2 \cdot 10 + 2.3 = 4.3.$ 2010 is 10 yr after 2000.

As we can see from the graph, if the trend continues, there will be about 4.3 million college-student volunteers in 2010.

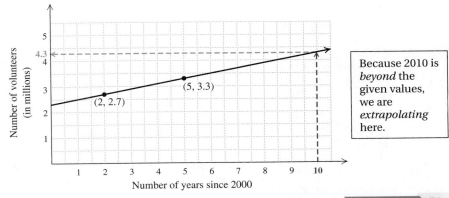

Because 2010 is *beyond* the given values, we are *extrapolating* here.

TRY EXERCISE 71

Visualizing for Success

Match each equation with its graph.

1. $y = x + 4$

2. $y = 2x$

3. $y = 3$

4. $x = 3$

5. $y = -\frac{1}{2}x$

6. $2x - 3y = 6$

7. $y = -3x - 2$

8. $3x + 2y = 6$

9. $y - 3 = 2(x - 1)$

10. $y + 2 = \frac{1}{2}(x + 1)$

Answers on page A-4

An additional, animated version of this activity appears in MyMathLab. To use MyMathLab, you need a course ID and a student access code. Contact your instructor for more information.

2.7 EXERCISE SET

For Extra Help
MyMathLab

Concept Reinforcement *In each of Exercises 1–8, match the given information about a line with the appropriate equation from the column on the right.*

1. ____ Slope 5; includes (2, 3)

2. ____ Slope 5; includes (3, 2)

3. ____ Slope −5; includes (2, 3)

4. ____ Slope −5; includes (3, 2)

5. ____ Slope −5; includes (−2, −3)

6. ____ Slope 5; includes (−2, −3)

7. ____ Slope −5; includes (−3, −2)

8. ____ Slope 5; includes (−3, −2)

a) $y + 3 = 5(x + 2)$

b) $y - 2 = 5(x - 3)$

c) $y + 2 = 5(x + 3)$

d) $y - 3 = -5(x - 2)$

e) $y + 3 = -5(x + 2)$

f) $y + 2 = -5(x + 3)$

g) $y - 3 = 5(x - 2)$

h) $y - 2 = -5(x - 3)$

In each of Exercises 9–12, match the graph with the appropriate equation from the column on the right.

9.
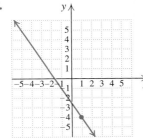

a) $y - 4 = -\frac{3}{2}(x + 1)$

b) $y - 4 = \frac{3}{2}(x + 1)$

c) $y + 4 = -\frac{3}{2}(x - 1)$

d) $y + 4 = \frac{3}{2}(x - 1)$

10.

11.

12.
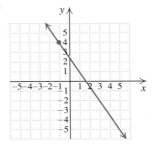

Write a point–slope equation for the line with the given slope that contains the given point.

13. $m = 3$; $(1, 6)$

14. $m = 2$; $(3, 7)$

15. $m = \frac{3}{5}$; $(2, 8)$

16. $m = \frac{2}{3}$; $(4, 1)$

17. $m = -4$; $(3, 1)$

18. $m = -5$; $(6, 2)$

19. $m = \frac{3}{2}$; $(5, -4)$

20. $m = -\frac{4}{3}$; $(7, -1)$

21. $m = -\frac{5}{4}$; $(-2, 6)$

22. $m = \frac{7}{2}$; $(-3, 4)$

23. $m = -2$; $(-4, -1)$

24. $m = -3$; $(-2, -5)$

25. $m = 1$; $(-2, 8)$

26. $m = -1$; $(-3, 6)$

Write the slope–intercept equation for the line with the given slope that contains the given point.

27. $m = 4$; $(3, 5)$

28. $m = 3$; $(6, 2)$

29. $m = \frac{7}{4}$; $(4, -2)$

30. $m = \frac{8}{3}$; $(3, -4)$

31. $m = -2$; $(-3, 7)$

32. $m = -3$; $(-2, 1)$

33. $m = -4$; $(-2, -1)$

34. $m = -5$; $(-1, -4)$

35. $m = \frac{2}{3}$; $(5, 6)$

36. $m = \frac{3}{2}$; $(7, 4)$

Aha! 37. $m = -\frac{5}{6}$; $(0, 4)$

38. $m = -\frac{3}{4}$; $(0, 5)$

Write an equation of the line containing the specified point and parallel to the indicated line.

39. $(2, 5)$, $x - 2y = 3$

40. $(1, 4)$, $3x + y = 5$

Aha! **41.** $(0, -5)$, $y = 4x + 3$

42. $(0, 2)$, $y = x - 11$

43. $(-2, -3)$, $2x + 3y = -7$

44. $(-7, 0)$, $5x + 2y = 6$

45. $(5, -4)$, $x = 2$

46. $(-3, 6)$, $y = 7$

Write an equation of the line containing the specified point and perpendicular to the indicated line.

47. $(3, 1)$, $2x - 3y = 4$

48. $(6, 0)$, $5x + 4y = 1$

49. $(-4, 2)$, $x + y = 6$

50. $(-2, -5)$, $x - 2y = 3$

Aha! **51.** $(0, 6)$, $2x - 5 = y$

52. $(0, -7)$, $4x + 3 = y$

53. $(-3, 7)$, $y = 5$

54. $(4, -2)$, $x = 1$

55. Graph the line with slope $\frac{4}{3}$ that passes through the point $(1, 2)$.

56. Graph the line with slope $\frac{2}{5}$ that passes through the point $(3, 4)$.

57. Graph the line with slope $-\frac{3}{4}$ that passes through the point $(2, 5)$.

58. Graph the line with slope $-\frac{3}{2}$ that passes through the point $(1, 4)$.

Graph.

59. $y - 5 = \frac{1}{3}(x - 2)$

60. $y - 2 = \frac{1}{2}(x - 1)$

61. $y - 1 = -\frac{1}{4}(x - 3)$

62. $y - 1 = -\frac{1}{2}(x - 3)$

63. $y + 2 = \frac{2}{3}(x - 1)$

64. $y - 1 = \frac{3}{4}(x + 5)$

65. $y + 4 = 3(x + 1)$

66. $y + 3 = 2(x + 1)$

67. $y - 4 = -2(x + 1)$

68. $y + 3 = -1(x - 4)$

69. $y + 1 = -\frac{3}{5}(x - 2)$

70. $y - 2 = -\frac{2}{3}(x + 1)$

In Exercises 71–78, graph the given data and determine an equation for the related line (as in Example 8). Then use the equation to answer parts (a) and (b).

71. *Birth rate among teenagers.* The birth rate among teenagers, measured in births per 1000 females age 15–19, fell steadily from 62.1 in 1991 to 41.1 in 2007.
Source: National Center for Health Statistics

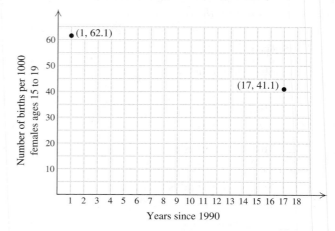

a) Calculate the birth rate among teenagers in 1999.
b) Predict the birth rate among teenagers in 2008.

72. *Food-stamp program participation.* Participation in the U.S. food-stamp program grew from approximately 17.1 million people in 2000 to approximately 23 million in 2004.
Source: U.S. Department of Agriculture

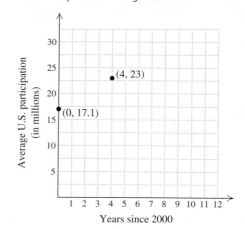

a) Calculate the number of participants in 2001.
b) Predict the number of participants in 2010.

73. *Cigarette smoking.* The percentage of people age 25–44 who smoke has changed from 14.2% in 2001 to 10.8% in 2004.
Source: Office on Smoking and Health, National Center for Chronic Disease Prevention and Health Promotion
a) Calculate the percentage of people age 25–44 who smoked in 2002.
b) Predict the percentage of people age 25–44 who will smoke in 2010.

74. *Cigarette smoking.* The percentage of people age 18–24 who smoke has dropped from 5.2% in 2001 to 3.4% in 2004.
Source: Office on Smoking and Health, National Center for Chronic Disease Prevention and Health Promotion

a) Calculate the percentage of people age 18–24 who smoked in 2003.

b) Estimate the percentage of people age 18–24 who smoked in 2008.

75. *College enrollment.* U.S. college enrollment has grown from approximately 14.3 million in 1995 to 17.4 million in 2005.
Source: National Center for Education Statistics

a) Calculate the U.S. college enrollment for 2002.

b) Predict the U.S. college enrollment for 2010.

76. *High school enrollment.* U.S. high school enrollment has changed from approximately 13.7 million in 1995 to 16.3 million in 2005.
Source: National Center for Education Statistics

a) Calculate the U.S. high school enrollment for 2002.

b) Predict the U.S. high school enrollment for 2010.

77. *Aging population.* The number of U.S. residents over the age of 65 was approximately 31 million in 1990 and 36.3 million in 2004.
Source: U.S. Census Bureau

Aha! **a)** Calculate the number of U.S. residents over the age of 65 in 1997.

b) Predict the number of U.S. residents over the age of 65 in 2010.

78. *Urban population.* The percentage of the U.S. population that resides in metropolitan areas increased from about 78% in 1980 to about 83% in 2006.

a) Calculate the percentage of the U.S. population residing in metropolitan areas in 1992.

b) Predict the percentage of the U.S. population residing in metropolitan areas in 2012.

Write the slope–intercept equation for the line containing the given pair of points.

79. $(2, 3)$ and $(4, 1)$

80 $(6, 8)$ and $(3, 5)$

81. $(-3, 1)$ and $(3, 5)$

82. $(-3, 4)$ and $(3, 1)$

83. $(5, 0)$ and $(0, -2)$

84. $(-2, 0)$ and $(0, 3)$

85. $(-4, -1)$ and $(1, 9)$

86. $(-3, 5)$ and $(-1, -3)$

87. Can equations for horizontal or vertical lines be written in point–slope form? Why or why not?

88. Describe a situation in which it is easier to graph the equation of a line in point–slope form than in slope–intercept form.

Skill Review

Simplify.

89. $(-5)^3$

90. $(-2)^6$

91. -2^6

92. $3 \cdot 2^4 - 5 \cdot 2^3$

93. $2 - (3 - 2^2) + 10 \div 2 \cdot 5$

94. $(5 - 7)^2(3 - 2 \cdot 2)$

Synthesis

95. Describe a procedure that can be used to write the slope–intercept equation for any nonvertical line passing through two given points.

96. Any nonvertical line has many equations in point–slope form, but only one in slope–intercept form. Why is this?

Graph.

Aha! **97.** $y - 3 = 0(x - 52)$

98. $y + 4 = 0(x + 93)$

Write the slope–intercept equation for each line shown.

99.

100.

101.

102.

Aha! **103.** Write an equation of the line parallel to the line given by $y = 3 - 4x$ that passes through $(0, 7)$.

104. Write the slope–intercept equation of the line that has the same y-intercept as the line $x - 3y = 6$ and contains the point $(5, -1)$.

105. Write the slope–intercept equation of the line that contains the point $(-1, 5)$ and is parallel to the line passing through $(2, 7)$ and $(-1, -3)$.

106. Write the slope–intercept equation of the line that has x-intercept $(-2, 0)$ and is parallel to $4x - 8y = 12$.

Another form of a linear equation is the double-intercept *form:* $\dfrac{x}{a} + \dfrac{y}{b} = 1$. *From this form, we can read the* x-intercept $(a, 0)$ *and the* y-intercept $(0, b)$ *directly.*

107. Find the x-intercept and the y-intercept of the graph of the line given by $\dfrac{x}{2} + \dfrac{y}{5} = 1$.

108. Find the x-intercept and the y-intercept of the graph of the line given by $\dfrac{x}{10} - \dfrac{y}{3} = 1$.

109. Write the equation $4y - 3x = 12$ in double-intercept form and find the intercepts.

110. Write the equation $6x + 5y = 30$ in double-intercept form and find the intercepts.

111. Why is slope–intercept form more useful than point–slope form when using a graphing calculator? How can point–slope form be modified so that it is more easily used with graphing calculators?

CONNECTING the CONCEPTS

Any line can be described by a number of equivalent equations. We write the equation in the form that is most useful for us. For example, all four of the equations below describe the given line.

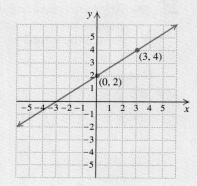

$2x - 3y = -6;$
$y = \frac{2}{3}x + 2;$
$y - 4 = \frac{2}{3}(x - 3);$
$2x + 6 = 3y$

Form of a Linear Equation	Example	Uses
Standard form: $Ax + By = C$	$2x - 3y = -6$	Finding x- and y-intercepts; Graphing using intercepts
Slope–intercept form: $y = mx + b$	$y = \frac{2}{3}x + 2$	Finding slope and y-intercept; Graphing using slope and y-intercept; Writing an equation given slope and y-intercept
Point–slope form: $y - y_1 = m(x - x_1)$	$y - 4 = \frac{2}{3}(x - 3)$	Finding slope and a point on the line; Graphing using slope and a point on the line; Writing an equation given slope and a point on the line

MIXED REVIEW

Tell whether each equation is in standard form, slope–intercept form, point–slope form, or none of these.

1. $y = -\frac{1}{2}x - 7$
2. $5x - 8y = 10$
3. $x = y + 2$
4. $\frac{1}{2}x + \frac{1}{3}y = 5$
5. $y - 2 = 5(x + 1)$
6. $3y + 7 = x$

Write each equation in standard form.

7. $2x = 5y + 10$
8. $x = y + 2$
9. $y = 2x + 7$

10. $y = -\frac{1}{2}x + 3$
11. $y - 2 = 3(x + 7)$
12. $x - 7 = 11$

Write each equation in slope–intercept form.

13. $2x - 7y = 8$
14. $y + 5 = -(x + 3)$
15. $8x = y + 3$
16. $6x + 10y = 30$
17. $9y = 5 - 8x$
18. $x - y = 3x + y$
19. $2 - 3y = 5y + 6$
20. $3(x - 4) = 6(y - 2)$

Study Summary

KEY TERMS AND CONCEPTS	EXAMPLES

SECTION 2.1: READING GRAPHS, PLOTTING POINTS, AND SCALING GRAPHS

Ordered pairs, like $(-3, 2)$ or $(4, 3)$, can be **plotted** or **graphed** using a **coordinate system** that uses two **axes**, which are most often labeled x and y. The axes intersect at the **origin**, $(0, 0)$, and divide a plane into four **quadrants**.

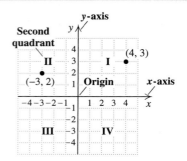

SECTION 2.2: GRAPHING LINEAR EQUATIONS

To **graph** an equation means to make a drawing that represents all of its solutions.

A **linear equation**, such as $y = 2x - 7$ or $2x + 3y = 12$, has a graph that is a straight line.

Any linear equation can be graphed by finding two ordered pairs that are solutions of the equation, plotting the corresponding points, and drawing a line through those points. Plotting a third point serves as a check.

x	y	(x, y)
1	2	$(1, 2)$
0	-1	$(0, -1)$
-1	-4	$(-1, -4)$

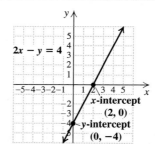

SECTION 2.3: GRAPHING AND INTERCEPTS

Intercepts
To find a y-intercept $(0, b)$, let $x = 0$ and solve for y.

To find an x-intercept $(a, 0)$, let $y = 0$ and solve for x.

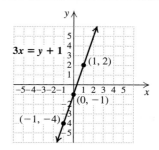

Horizontal Lines
The slope of a horizontal line is 0.
The graph of $y = b$ is a horizontal line, with y-intercept $(0, b)$.

Vertical Lines
The slope of a vertical line is undefined.
The graph of $x = a$ is a vertical line, with x-intercept $(a, 0)$.

SECTION 2.4: RATES

A **rate** is a ratio that indicates how two quantities change with respect to each other.

Lara had $1500 in her savings account at the beginning of February, and $2400 at the beginning of May. Find the rate at which Lara is saving.

$$\text{Savings rate} = \frac{\text{Amount saved}}{\text{Number of months}}$$

$$= \frac{\$2400 - \$1500}{3 \text{ months}}$$

$$= \frac{\$900}{3 \text{ months}} = \$300 \text{ per month}$$

SECTION 2.5: SLOPE

Slope

$$\text{Slope} = m = \frac{\text{change in } y}{\text{change in } x}$$

$$= \frac{\text{rise}}{\text{run}} = \frac{y_2 - y_1}{x_2 - x_1}$$

The slope of the line containing the points $(-1, -4)$ and $(2, -6)$ is

$$m = \frac{-6 - (-4)}{2 - (-1)} = \frac{-2}{3} = -\frac{2}{3}.$$

A line with positive slope slants up from left to right.

A line with negative slope slants down from left to right.

The slope of a horizontal line is 0.

The slope of a vertical line is undefined.

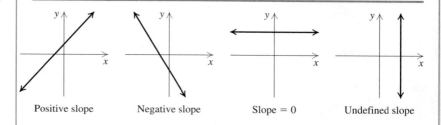

Positive slope   Negative slope   Slope = 0   Undefined slope

SECTION 2.6: SLOPE–INTERCEPT FORM

Slope–Intercept Form

$$y = mx + b$$

The slope of the line is m.
The y-intercept of the line is $(0, b)$.

For the line given by $y = \frac{2}{3}x - 8$:

The slope is $\frac{2}{3}$ and the y-intercept is $(0, -8)$.

To graph a line written in slope–intercept form, plot the y-intercept and count off the slope.

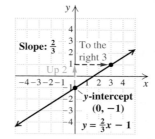

Parallel and Perpendicular Lines

Two lines are parallel if they have the same slope or if both are vertical.

Determine whether the graphs of $y = \frac{2}{3}x - 5$ *and* $3y - 2x = 7$ *are parallel.*

$$y = \frac{2}{3}x - 5 \qquad 3y - 2x = 7$$

The slope is $\frac{2}{3}$. $\qquad 3y = 2x + 7$

$$y = \frac{2}{3}x + \frac{7}{3}$$

The slope is $\frac{2}{3}$.

Since the slopes are the same, the graphs are parallel.

Two lines are perpendicular if the product of their slopes is -1 or if one line is vertical and the other line is horizontal.

Determine whether the graphs of $y = \frac{2}{3}x - 5$ and $2y + 3x = 1$ are perpendicular.

$$y = \frac{2}{3}x - 5 \qquad\qquad 2y + 3x = 1$$
The slope is $\frac{2}{3}$.
$$2y = -3x + 1$$
$$y = -\frac{3}{2}x + \frac{1}{2}$$
The slope is $-\frac{3}{2}$.

Since $\frac{2}{3}\left(-\frac{3}{2}\right) = -1$, the graphs are perpendicular.

SECTION 2.7: POINT–SLOPE FORM

Point–Slope Form
$$y - y_1 = m(x - x_1)$$
The slope of the line is m.
The line passes through (x_1, y_1).

Write a point–slope equation for the line with slope -2 that contains the point $(3, -5)$.
$$y - y_1 = m(x - x_1)$$
$$y - (-5) = -2(x - 3)$$

Review Exercises: Chapter 2

Concept Reinforcement   *Classify each statement as either true or false.*

1. Not every ordered pair lies in one of the four quadrants. [2.1]

2. The equation of a vertical line cannot be written in slope–intercept form. [2.6]

3. Equations for lines written in slope–intercept form appear in the form $Ax + By = C$. [2.6]

4. Every horizontal line has an x-intercept. [2.3]

5. A line's slope is a measure of rate. [2.5]

6. A positive rate of ascent means that an airplane is flying increasingly higher above the earth. [2.4]

7. Any two points on a line can be used to determine the line's slope. [2.5]

8. Knowing a line's slope is enough to write the equation of the line. [2.6]

9. Knowing two points on a line is enough to write the equation of the line. [2.7]

10. Parallel lines that are not vertical have the same slope. [2.6]

The following circle graph shows the percentage of online searches done in July 2006 that were performed by a particular search engine. [2.1]
Source: NetRatings for SearchEngineWatch.com

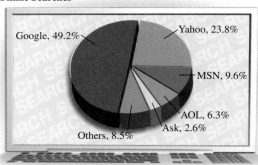

Online Searches

11. There were 5.6 billion searches done by home and business Internet users in July 2006. How many searches were done using Yahoo?

12. About 55% of the online searches done by Waterworks Graphics are image searches. In July 2006, Waterworks employees did 4200 online searches. If their search engine use is typical, how many image searches did they do using Google?

Plot each point. [2.1]

13. $(5, -1)$ **14.** $(2, 3)$ **15.** $(-4, 0)$

In which quadrant is each point located? [2.1]

16. $(-8, -7)$ **17.** $(15.3, -13.8)$ **18.** $\left(-\frac{1}{2}, \frac{1}{10}\right)$

Find the coordinates of each point in the figure. [2.1]

19. A **20.** B **21.** C

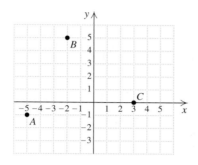

22. Use a grid 10 squares wide and 10 squares high to plot $(-65, -2), (-10, 6)$, and $(25, 7)$. Choose the scale carefully. [2.1]

23. Determine whether the equation $y = 2x + 7$ has *each* ordered pair as a solution: **(a)** $(3, 1)$; **(b)** $(-3, 1)$. [2.2]

24. Show that the ordered pairs $(0, -3)$ and $(2, 1)$ are solutions of the equation $2x - y = 3$. Then use the graph of the two points to determine another solution. Answers may vary. [2.2]

Graph.

25. $y = x - 5$ [2.2]   **26.** $y = -\frac{1}{4}x$ [2.2]

27. $y = -x + 4$ [2.2]   **28.** $4x + y = 3$ [2.2]

29. $4x + 5 = 3$ [2.3]   **30.** $5x - 2y = 10$ [2.3]

31. *TV viewing.* The average number of daily viewers v, in millions, of ABC's soap opera "General Hospital" is given by $v = -\frac{1}{4}t + 9$, where t is the number of years since 2000. Graph the equation and use the graph to predict the average number of daily viewers of "General Hospital" in 2008. [2.2]
Source: Nielsen Media Research

32. At 4:00 P.M., Jesse's Honda Civic was at mile marker 17 of Interstate 290 in Chicago. At 4:45 P.M., Jesse was at mile marker 23. [2.4]

 a) Find Jesse's driving rate, in number of miles per minute.

 b) Find Jesse's driving rate, in number of minutes per mile.

33. *Gas mileage.* The following graph shows data for a Ford Explorer driven on city streets. At what rate was the vehicle consuming gas? [2.4]

Find the slope of each line. [2.5]

34.

35.

36.

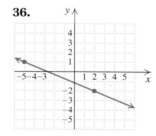

Find the slope of the line containing the given pair of points. If it is undefined, state this. [2.5]

37. $(-2, 5)$ and $(3, -1)$

38. $(6, 5)$ and $(-2, 5)$

39. $(-3, 0)$ and $(-3, 5)$

40. $(-8.3, 4.6)$ and $(-9.9, 1.4)$

41. *Architecture.* To meet federal standards, a wheelchair ramp cannot rise more than 1 ft over a horizontal distance of 12 ft. Express this slope as a grade. [2.5]

42. Find the x-intercept and the y-intercept of the line given by $5x - 8y = 80$. [2.3]

43. Find the slope and the y-intercept of the line given by $3x + 5y = 45$. [2.6]

Determine whether each pair of lines is parallel, perpendicular, or neither. [2.6]

44. $y + 5 = -x$,
$x - y = 2$

45. $3x - 5 = 7y$,
$7y - 3x = 7$

46. Write the slope–intercept equation of the line with slope $\frac{3}{8}$ and y-intercept $(0, 7)$. [2.6]

47. Write a point–slope equation for the line with slope $-\frac{1}{3}$ that contains the point $(-2, 9)$. [2.7]

48. The average tuition at a public two-year college was $1359 in 2001 and $1847 in 2005. Graph the data and determine an equation for the related line. Then **(a)** calculate the average tuition at a public two-year college in 2004 and **(b)** predict the average tuition at a public two-year college in 2012. [2.7]
Source: U.S. National Center for Education Statistics

49. Write the slope–intercept equation for the line with slope 5 that contains the point $(3, -10)$. [2.7]

50. Write the slope–intercept equation for the line that is perpendicular to the line $3x - 5y = 9$ and that contains the point $(2, -5)$ [2.7]

Graph.

51. $y = \frac{2}{3}x - 5$ [2.6]

52. $2x + y = 4$ [2.3]

53. $y = 6$ [2.3]

54. $x = -2$ [2.3]

55. $y + 2 = -\frac{1}{2}(x - 3)$ [2.7]

Synthesis

56. Can two perpendicular lines share the same y-intercept? Why or why not? [2.3]

57. Is it possible for a graph to have only one intercept? Why or why not? [2.3]

58. Find the value of m in $y = mx + 3$ such that $(-2, 5)$ is on the graph. [2.2]

59. Find the value of b in $y = -5x + b$ such that $(3, 4)$ is on the graph. [2.2]

60. Find the area and the perimeter of a rectangle for which $(-2, 2)$, $(7, 2)$, and $(7, -3)$ are three of the vertices. [2.1]

61. Find three solutions of $y = 4 - |x|$. [2.2]

Test: Chapter 2

Step-by-step test solutions are found on the video CD in the front of this book.

Volunteering. *The following pie chart shows the types of organizations in which college students volunteer.*
Source: Corporation for National and Community Service

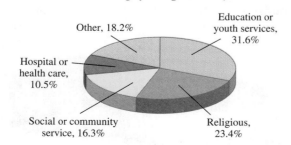

Volunteering by College Students, 2005

Other, 18.2%
Education or youth services, 31.6%
Hospital or health care, 10.5%
Social or community service, 16.3%
Religious, 23.4%

1. At Rolling Hills College, 25% of the 1200 students volunteer. If their choice of organizations is typical, how many students will volunteer in education or youth services?

2. At Valley University, $\frac{1}{3}$ of the 3900 students volunteer. If their choice of organizations is typical, how many students will volunteer in hospital or health-care services?

In which quadrant is each point located?

3. $(-2, -10)$

4. $(-1.6, 2.3)$

Find the coordinates of each point in the figure.

5. A

6. B

7. C

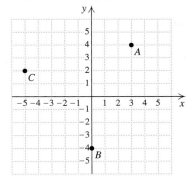

Graph.

8. $y = 2x - 1$

9. $2x - 4y = -8$

10. $y + 1 = 6$

11. $y = \frac{3}{4}x$

12. $2x - y = 3$

13. $x = -1$

Find the slope of the line containing each pair of points. If it is undefined, state this.

14. $(3, -2)$ and $(4, 3)$

15. $(-5, 6)$ and $(-1, -3)$

16. $(4, 7)$ and $(4, -8)$

17. *Running.*   Jon reached the 3-km mark of a race at 2:15 P.M. and the 6-km mark at 2:24 P.M. What is his running rate?

18. At one point Filbert Street, the steepest street in San Francisco, drops 63 ft over a horizontal distance of 200 ft. Find the road grade.

19. Find the x-intercept and the y-intercept of the line given by $5x - y = 30$.

20. Find the slope and the y-intercept of the line given by $y - 8x = 10$.

21. Write the slope–intercept equation of the line with slope $-\frac{1}{3}$ and y-intercept $(0, -11)$.

Determine without graphing whether each pair of lines is parallel, perpendicular, or neither.

22. $4y + 2 = 3x,$
$-3x + 4y = -12$

23. $y = -2x + 5,$
$2y - x = 6$

24. Write the slope–intercept equation of the line that is perpendicular to the line $2x - 5y = 8$ and that contains the point $(-3, 2)$.

25. *Aerobic exercise.*   A person's target heart rate is the number of beats per minute that brings the most aerobic benefit to his or her heart. The target heart rate for a 20-year-old is 150 beats per minute; for a 60-year-old, it is 120 beats per minute.

a) Graph the data and determine an equation for the related line. Let $a =$ age and $r =$ target heart rate, in number of beats per minute.

b) Calculate the target heart rate for a 36-year-old.

Graph.

26. $y = \frac{1}{4}x - 2$

27. $y + 4 = -\frac{1}{2}(x - 3)$

Synthesis

28. Write an equation of the line that is parallel to the graph of $2x - 5y = 6$ and has the same y-intercept as the graph of $3x + y = 9$.

29. A diagonal of a square connects the points $(-3, -1)$ and $(2, 4)$. Find the area and the perimeter of the square.

30. List the coordinates of three other points that are on the same line as $(-2, 14)$ and $(17, -5)$. Answers may vary.

Cumulative Review: Chapters 1–2

1. Evaluate $\dfrac{x}{5y}$ for $x = 70$ and $y = 2$.

2. Multiply: $6(2a - b + 3)$.

3. Factor: $8x - 4y + 4$.

4. Find the prime factorization of 54.

5. Find decimal notation: $-\frac{3}{20}$.

6. Find the absolute value: $|-37|$.

7. Find the opposite of $-\frac{1}{10}$.

8. Find the reciprocal of $-\frac{1}{10}$.

9. Find decimal notation: 36.7%.

Simplify.

10. $\frac{3}{5} - \frac{5}{12}$

11. $3.4 + (-0.8)$

12. $(-2)(-1.4)(2.6)$

13. $\frac{3}{8} \div \left(-\frac{9}{10}\right)$

14. $1 - [32 \div (4 + 2^2)]$

15. $-5 + 16 \div 2 \cdot 4$

16. $y - (3y + 7)$

17. $3(x - 1) - 2[x - (2x + 7)]$

Solve.

18. $2.7 = 5.3 + x$ [1.1]

19. $\frac{5}{3}x = -45$ [1.1]

20. $3x - 7 = 41$ [1.2]

21. $\dfrac{3}{4} = \dfrac{-n}{8}$ [1.1]

22. $14 - 5x = 2x$ [1.2]

23. $3(5 - x) = 2(3x + 4)$ [1.2]

24. $\frac{1}{4}x - \frac{2}{3} = \frac{3}{4} + \frac{1}{3}x$ [1.2]

25. $y + 5 - 3y = 5y - 9$ [1.2]

26. $x - 28 < 20 - 2x$ [1.6]

27. $2(x + 2) \geq 5(2x + 3)$ [1.6]

28. Solve $A = 2\pi rh + \pi r^2$ for h. [1.3]

29. In which quadrant is the point $(3, -1)$ located? [2.1]

30. Graph on a number line: $-1 < x \leq 2$. [1.6]

31. Use a grid 10 squares wide and 10 squares high to plot $(-150, -40)$, $(40, -7)$, and $(0, 6)$. Choose the scale carefully. [2.1]

Graph.

32. $x = 3$ [2.3]

33. $2x - 5y = 10$ [2.3]

34. $y = -2x + 1$ [2.2]

35. $y = \frac{2}{3}x$ [2.2]

36. $y = -\frac{3}{4}x + 2$ [2.6]

37. $2y - 5 = 3$ [2.3]

Find the coordinates of the x- and y-intercepts. Do not graph.

38. $2x - 7y = 21$ [2.3]

39. $y = 4x + 5$ [2.3]

40. Find the slope and the y-intercept of the line given by $3x - y = 2$. [2.6]

41. Find the slope of the line containing the points $(-4, 1)$ and $(2, -1)$. [2.5]

42. Write an equation of the line with slope $\frac{2}{7}$ and y-intercept $(0, -4)$. [2.6]

43. Write a point–slope equation of the line with slope $-\frac{3}{8}$ that contains the point $(-6, 4)$. [2.7]

44. Write the slope–intercept form of the equation in Exercise 43. [2.6]

45. Determine an equation for the following graph. [2.6], [2.7]

Solve.

46. U.S. bicycle sales rose from 15 million in 1995 to 20 million in 2005. Find the rate of change of bicycle sales. [2.4]
Sources: National Bicycle Dealers Association; U.S. Department of Transportation

47. A 150-lb person will burn 240 calories per hour when riding a bicycle at 6 mph. The same person will burn 410 calories per hour when cycling at 12 mph. [2.7]
Source: American Heart Association

   a) Graph the data and determine an equation for the related line. Let $r =$ the rate at which the person is cycling and $c =$ the number of calories burned per hour.

   b) Use the equation of part (a) to estimate the number of calories burned per hour by a 150-lb person cycling at 10 mph.

48. Americans spent an estimated $238 billion on home remodeling in 2006. This was $\frac{17}{15}$ of the amount spent on remodeling in 2005. How much was spent on remodeling in 2005? [1.5]
Source: National Association of Home Builders' Remodelers Council

49. In 2005, the mean earnings of individuals with a high school diploma was $29,448. This was about 54% of the mean earnings of those with a bachelor's degree. What were the mean earnings of individuals with a bachelor's degree in 2005? [1.4]
Source: U.S. Census Bureau

50. Recently there were 132 million Americans with either O-positive or O-negative blood. Those with O-positive blood outnumbered those with O-negative blood by 90 million. How many Americans had O-negative blood? [1.5]
Source: American Red Cross

51. Tina paid $126 for a cordless drill, including a 5% sales tax. How much did the drill itself cost? [1.4]

52. A 143-m wire is cut into three pieces. The second is 3 m longer than the first. The third is four fifths as long as the first. How long is each piece? [1.5]

53. In order to qualify for availability pay, a criminal investigator must average at least 2 hr of unscheduled duty per workday. For the first four days of one week, Alayna worked 1, 0, 3, and 2 extra hours. How many extra hours must she work on Friday in order to qualify for availability pay? [1.7]
Source: U.S. Department of Justice

Synthesis

54. Anya's salary at the end of a year is $26,780. This reflects a 4% salary increase in February and then a 3% cost-of-living adjustment in June. What was her salary at the beginning of the year? [1.4]

Solve. If no solution exists, state this.

55. $4|x| - 13 = 3$ [1.2]

56. $4(x + 2) = 9(x - 2) + 16$ [1.2]

57. $2(x + 3) + 4 = 0$ [1.2]

58. $\dfrac{2 + 5x}{4} = \dfrac{11}{28} + \dfrac{8x + 3}{7}$ [1.2]

59. $5(7 + x) = (x + 6)5$ [1.2]

60. Solve $p = \dfrac{2}{m + Q}$ for Q. [1.3]

61. The points $(-3, 0)$, $(0, 7)$, $(3, 0)$, and $(0, -7)$ are vertices of a parallelogram. Find four equations of lines that intersect to form the parallelogram. [2.6]

Polynomials and Factoring

CHRIS GJERSVIK
PRINCIPAL NETWORK ENGINEER
Upper Saddle River, New Jersey

The math skills we use in net-working–telecommunications help us in so many ways. For instance, we use math when planning the budgets for a computer network or phone system and when determining capacity of a network. We need to accurately size network circuits so they have enough bandwidth to carry phone calls, Internet access, streaming video, e-mail, and other such applications. Finally, we use math when we need to analyze network traffic and break it down into its most basic form, which uses the binary numeral system.

AN APPLICATION

The number N, in millions, of broadband cable and DSL subscribers in the United States t years after 1998 can be approximated by

$$N = 0.3t^2 + 0.6t.$$

When will there be 36 million broadband cable and DSL subscribers?

Source: Based on information from Leichtman Research Group

This problem appears as Exercise 19 in Section 3.8.

151

3.1 Introduction to Factoring

Factoring Monomials ▪ Factoring When Terms Have a Common Factor ▪ Factoring by Grouping ▪ Checking by Evaluating

Just as a number like 15 can be factored as $3 \cdot 5$, a polynomial like $x^2 + 7x$ can be factored as $x(x + 7)$. In both cases, we ask ourselves, "What was multiplied to obtain the given result?" The situation is much like a popular television game show in which an "answer" is given and participants must find the "question" to which the answer corresponds.

STUDY SKILLS

You've Got Mail

Many students overlook an excellent opportunity to get questions answered—e-mail. If your instructor makes his or her e-mail address available, consider using it to get help. Often, just the act of writing out your question brings some clarity. If you do use e-mail, allow some time for your instructor to reply.

Factoring

To *factor* a polynomial is to find an equivalent expression that is a product. An equivalent expression of this type is called a *factorization* of the polynomial.

Factoring Monomials

To factor a monomial, we find two monomials whose product is equivalent to the original monomial. For example, $20x^2$ can be factored as $2 \cdot 10x^2$, $4x \cdot 5x$, or $10x \cdot 2x$, as well as several other ways. To check, we multiply.

EXAMPLE 1

Find three factorizations of $15x^3$.

SOLUTION

a) $15x^3 = (3 \cdot 5)(x \cdot x^2)$ Thinking of how 15 and x^3 can be factored

$\quad = (3x)(5x^2)$ The factors are $3x$ and $5x^2$. *Check*: $3x \cdot 5x^2 = 15x^3$.

b) $15x^3 = (3 \cdot 5)(x^2 \cdot x)$

$\quad = (3x^2)(5x)$ The factors are $3x^2$ and $5x$. *Check*: $3x^2 \cdot 5x = 15x^3$.

c) $15x^3 = ((-5)(-3))x^3$

$\quad = (-5)(-3x^3)$ The factors are -5 and $-3x^3$.
    Check: $(-5)(-3x^3) = 15x^3$.

$(3x)(5x^2)$, $(3x^2)(5x)$, and $(-5)(-3x^3)$ are all factorizations of $15x^3$. Other factorizations exist as well.

> TRY EXERCISE 9

The word "factor" can be a verb or a noun, depending on the context in which it appears.

Factoring When Terms Have a Common Factor

To multiply a polynomial of two or more terms by a monomial, we use the distributive law: $a(b + c) = ab + ac$. To factor a polynomial with two or more terms of the form $ab + ac$, we use the distributive law with the sides of the equation switched: $ab + ac = a(b + c)$.

Multiply   *Factor*

$3(x + 2y - z)$ $3x + 6y - 3z$
$\quad = 3 \cdot x + 3 \cdot 2y - 3 \cdot z$ $\quad = 3 \cdot x + 3 \cdot 2y - 3 \cdot z$
$\quad = 3x + 6y - 3z$ $\quad = 3(x + 2y - z)$

In the factorization on the right, note that since 3 appears as a factor of $3x$, $6y$, and $-3z$, it is a *common factor* for all the terms of the trinomial $3x + 6y - 3z$.

When we factor, we are forming an equivalent expression that is a product.

EXAMPLE 2   Factor to form an equivalent expression: $10y + 15$.

SOLUTION   We write the prime factorization of both terms to determine any common factors:

The prime factorization of $10y$ is $2 \cdot 5 \cdot y$; $\left.\right\}$ 5 is a common factor.
The prime factorization of 15 is $3 \cdot 5$.

We "factor out" the common factor 5 using the distributive law:

> We can always check a factorization by multiplying.

$10y + 15 = 5 \cdot 2y + 5 \cdot 3$ Try to do this step mentally.
$\quad\quad\quad = 5(2y + 3)$.   Using the distributive law

Check: $5(2y + 3) = 5 \cdot 2y + 5 \cdot 3 = 10y + 15$.

The factorization of $10y + 15$ is $5(2y + 3)$.   TRY EXERCISE 15

We generally factor out the *largest* common factor.

EXAMPLE 3   Factor: $8a - 12$.

SOLUTION   Lining up common factors in columns can help us determine the largest common factor:

The prime factorization of $8a$ is $2 \cdot 2 \cdot 2 \cdot \quad a$;
The prime factorization of 12 is $2 \cdot 2 \cdot \quad\quad 3$.

Since both factorizations include two factors of 2, the largest common factor is $2 \cdot 2$, or 4:

$8a - 12 = 4 \cdot 2a - 4 \cdot 3$ 4 is a factor of $8a$ and of 12.
$8a - 12 = 4(2a - 3)$.   Try to go directly to this step.

Check: $4(2a - 3) = 4 \cdot 2a - 4 \cdot 3 = 8a - 12$, as expected.

The factorization of $8a - 12$ is $4(2a - 3)$.   TRY EXERCISE 17

> **CAUTION!** $2 \cdot 2 \cdot 2a - 2 \cdot 2 \cdot 3$ is a factorization of the *terms* of $8a - 12$ but not of the polynomial itself. The factorization of $8a - 12$ is $4(2a - 3)$.

A common factor may contain a variable.

EXAMPLE **4**

Factor: $24x^5 + 30x^2$.

SOLUTION

The prime factorization of $24x^5$ is $2 \cdot 2 \cdot 2 \cdot 3 \cdot \quad x \cdot x \cdot x \cdot x \cdot x$.
The prime factorization of $30x^2$ is $2 \cdot \quad 3 \cdot 5 \cdot x \cdot x$.

The largest common factor is $2 \cdot 3 \cdot x \cdot x$, or $6x^2$.

$$24x^5 + 30x^2 = 6x^2 \cdot 4x^3 + 6x^2 \cdot 5 \qquad \text{Factoring each term}$$
$$= 6x^2(4x^3 + 5) \qquad \text{Factoring out } 6x^2$$

Check: $6x^2(4x^3 + 5) = 6x^2 \cdot 4x^3 + 6x^2 \cdot 5 = 24x^5 + 30x^2$, as expected.

The factorization of $24x^5 + 30x^2$ is $6x^2(4x^3 + 5)$.

TRY EXERCISE 27

The largest common factor of a polynomial is the largest common factor of the coefficients times the largest common factor of the variable(s) in all the terms. Suppose in Example 4 that you did not recognize the *largest* common factor, and removed only part of it, as follows:

$$24x^5 + 30x^2 = 2x^2 \cdot 12x^3 + 2x^2 \cdot 15 \qquad 2x^2 \text{ is a common factor.}$$
$$= 2x^2(12x^3 + 15). \qquad 12x^3 + 15 \text{ itself contains a common factor.}$$

Note that $12x^3 + 15$ still has a common factor, 3. To find the largest common factor, continue factoring out common factors, as follows, until no more exist:

$$24x^5 + 30x^2 = 2x^2[3(4x^3 + 5)] \qquad \text{Factoring } 12x^3 + 15. \text{ Remember to rewrite the first common factor, } 2x^2.$$
$$= 6x^2(4x^3 + 5). \qquad \text{Using an associative law; } 2x^2 \cdot 3 = 6x^2$$

Since $4x^3 + 5$ cannot be factored any further, we say that we have factored *completely*. When we are directed simply to factor, it is understood that we should always factor completely.

EXAMPLE **5**

Factor: $12x^5 - 15x^4 + 27x^3$.

SOLUTION

The prime factorization of $12x^5$ is $2 \cdot 2 \cdot 3 \cdot \quad x \cdot x \cdot x \cdot x \cdot x$.
The prime factorization of $15x^4$ is $3 \cdot \quad 5 \cdot x \cdot x \cdot x \cdot x$.
The prime factorization of $27x^3$ is $3 \cdot 3 \cdot 3 \cdot \quad x \cdot x \cdot x$.

The largest common factor is $3 \cdot x \cdot x \cdot x$, or $3x^3$.

$$12x^5 - 15x^4 + 27x^3 = 3x^3 \cdot 4x^2 - 3x^3 \cdot 5x + 3x^3 \cdot 9$$
$$= 3x^3(4x^2 - 5x + 9)$$

Since $4x^2 - 5x + 9$ has no common factor, we are done, except for a check:

$$3x^3(4x^2 - 5x + 9) = 3x^3 \cdot 4x^2 - 3x^3 \cdot 5x + 3x^3 \cdot 9$$
$$= 12x^5 - 15x^4 + 27x^3,$$

as expected. The factorization of $12x^5 - 15x^4 + 27x^3$ is $3x^3(4x^2 - 5x + 9)$.

TRY EXERCISE 31

Note in Examples 4 and 5 that the *largest* common variable factor is the *smallest* power of x in the original polynomial.

With practice, we can determine the largest common factor without writing the prime factorization of each term. Then, to factor, we write the largest common factor and parentheses and then fill in the parentheses. It is customary for the leading coefficient of the polynomial inside the parentheses to be positive.

EXAMPLE 6

Factor: **(a)** $8r^3s^2 + 16rs^3$; **(b)** $-3xy + 6xz - 3x$.

SOLUTION

a) $8r^3s^2 + 16rs^3 = 8rs^2(r^2 + 2s)$ Try to go directly to this step.

The largest common factor is $8rs^2$. $\longleftarrow$ $\begin{cases} 8r^3s^2 = 2 \cdot 2 \cdot 2 \cdot \quad r \cdot r^2 \cdot s^2 \\ 16rs^3 = 2 \cdot 2 \cdot 2 \cdot 2 \cdot r \cdot \quad\quad s^2 \cdot s \end{cases}$

Check: $8rs^2(r^2 + 2s) = 8r^3s^2 + 16rs^3$.

b) $-3xy + 6xz - 3x = -3x(y - 2z + 1)$ Note that either $-3x$ or $3x$ can be the largest common factor.

We generally factor out a negative when the first coefficient is negative. The way we factor can depend on the situation in which we are working. We might also factor as follows:

$$-3xy + 6xz - 3x = 3x(-y + 2z - 1).$$

The checks are left to the student.

TRY EXERCISE 35

STUDENT NOTES

The 1 in $(y - 2z + 1)$ plays an important role in Example 6(b). If left out of the factorization, the term $-3x$ would not appear in the check.

In some texts, the largest common factor is referred to as the *greatest* common factor. We have avoided this language because, as shown in Example 6(b), the largest common factor may represent a negative value that is actually *less* than other common factors.

> **Tips for Factoring**
> 1. Factor out the largest common factor, if one exists.
> 2. The common factor multiplies a polynomial with the same number of terms as the original polynomial.
> 3. Factoring can always be checked by multiplying. Multiplication should yield the original polynomial.

Factoring by Grouping

Sometimes algebraic expressions contain a common factor with two or more terms.

EXAMPLE 7

Factor: $x^2(x + 1) + 2(x + 1)$.

SOLUTION   The binomial $x + 1$ is a factor of both $x^2(x + 1)$ and $2(x + 1)$. Thus, $x + 1$ is a common factor:

$$x^2(x + 1) + 2(x + 1) = (x + 1)x^2 + (x + 1)2$$ Using a commutative law twice. Try to do this step mentally.

$$= (x + 1)(x^2 + 2).$$ Factoring out the common factor, $x + 1$

To check, we could simply reverse the above steps.
The factorization is $(x + 1)(x^2 + 2)$.

TRY EXERCISE 37

In Example 7, the common binomial factor was clearly visible. How do we find such a factor in a polynomial like $5x^3 - x^2 + 15x - 3$? Although there is no factor, other than 1, common to all four terms, $5x^3 - x^2$ and $15x - 3$ can be grouped and factored separately:

$$5x^3 - x^2 = x^2(5x - 1) \quad \text{and} \quad 15x - 3 = 3(5x - 1).$$

Note that $5x^3 - x^2$ and $15x - 3$ share a common factor, $5x - 1$. This means that the original polynomial, $5x^3 - x^2 + 15x - 3$, can be factored:

$$5x^3 - x^2 + 15x - 3 = (5x^3 - x^2) + (15x - 3) \qquad \text{Each binomial has a common factor.}$$
$$= x^2(5x - 1) + 3(5x - 1) \qquad \text{Factoring each binomial}$$
$$= (5x - 1)(x^2 + 3). \qquad \text{Factoring out the common factor, } 5x - 1$$

Check: $(5x - 1)(x^2 + 3) = 5x \cdot x^2 + 5x \cdot 3 - 1 \cdot x^2 - 1 \cdot 3$
$$= 5x^3 - x^2 + 15x - 3.$$

If a polynomial can be split into groups of terms and the groups share a common factor, then the original polynomial can be factored. This method, known as **factoring by grouping**, can be tried on any polynomial with four or more terms.

EXAMPLE   8   Factor by grouping.

a) $2x^3 + 8x^2 + x + 4$ 　　　　　　　　　 **b)** $8x^4 + 6x - 28x^3 - 21$

SOLUTION

a) $2x^3 + 8x^2 + x + 4 = (2x^3 + 8x^2) + (x + 4)$
$$= 2x^2(x + 4) + 1(x + 4) \qquad \text{Factoring } 2x^3 + 8x^2 \text{ to find a common binomial factor. Writing the 1 helps with the next step.}$$
$$= (x + 4)(2x^2 + 1) \qquad \text{Factoring out the common factor, } x + 4. \text{ The 1 is essential in the factor } 2x^2 + 1.$$

CAUTION!   Be sure to include the term 1. The check below shows why it is essential.

Check: $(x + 4)(2x^2 + 1) = x \cdot 2x^2 + x \cdot 1 + 4 \cdot 2x^2 + 4 \cdot 1 \qquad \text{Using FOIL}$
$$= 2x^3 + x + 8x^2 + 4$$
$$= 2x^3 + 8x^2 + x + 4. \qquad \text{Using a commutative law}$$

The factorization is $(x + 4)(2x^2 + 1)$.

b) We have a choice of either

$$8x^4 + 6x - 28x^3 - 21 = (8x^4 + 6x) + (-28x^3 - 21)$$
$$= 2x(4x^3 + 3) + 7(-4x^3 - 3) \longleftarrow \text{No common factor}$$

or

$$8x^4 + 6x - 28x^3 - 21 = (8x^4 + 6x) + (-28x^3 - 21)$$
$$= 2x(4x^3 + 3) + (-7)(4x^3 + 3). \longleftarrow \text{Common factor}$$

Because of the common factor $4x^3 + 3$, we choose the latter:

$$8x^4 + 6x - 28x^3 - 21 = 2x(4x^3 + 3) + (-7)(4x^3 + 3)$$
$$= (4x^3 + 3)(2x + (-7)) \qquad \text{Try to do this step mentally.}$$
$$= (4x^3 + 3)(2x - 7). \qquad \text{The common factor } 4x^3 + 3 \text{ was factored out.}$$

Check: $(4x^3 + 3)(2x - 7) = 8x^4 - 28x^3 + 6x - 21$
$$= 8x^4 + 6x - 28x^3 - 21. \qquad \text{This is the original polynomial.}$$

The factorization is $(4x^3 + 3)(2x - 7)$.

> **TRY EXERCISE** 43

Although factoring by grouping can be useful, some polynomials, like $x^3 + x^2 + 2x - 2$, cannot be factored this way. Factoring polynomials of this type is beyond the scope of this text.

Checking by Evaluating

One way to check a factorization is to multiply. A second type of check uses the fact that equivalent expressions have the same value when evaluated for the same replacement. Thus a quick, partial check of Example 8(a) can be made by using a convenient replacement for x (say, 1) and evaluating both $2x^3 + 8x^2 + x + 4$ and $(x + 4)(2x^2 + 1)$:

$$2 \cdot 1^3 + 8 \cdot 1^2 + 1 + 4 = 2 + 8 + 1 + 4$$
$$= 15;$$

$$(1 + 4)(2 \cdot 1^2 + 1) = 5 \cdot 3$$
$$= 15.$$

Since the value of both expressions is the same, the factorization is probably correct.

Keep in mind the possibility that two expressions that are not equivalent may share the same value when evaluated at a certain value. Because of this, unless several values are used (at least one more than the degree of the polynomial, it turns out), evaluating offers only a partial check. Consult with your instructor before making extensive use of this type of check.

TECHNOLOGY CONNECTION

A partial check of a factorization can be performed using a table or a graph. To check Example 8(a), we let

$$y_1 = 2x^3 + 8x^2 + x + 4 \quad \text{and} \quad y_2 = (x + 4)(2x^2 + 1).$$

Then we set up a table in AUTO mode (see p. 12). If the factorization is correct, the values of y_1 and y_2 will be the same regardless of the table settings used.

ΔTBL = 1

X	Y1	Y2
0	4	4
1	15	15
2	54	54
3	133	133
4	264	264
5	459	459
6	730	730
X = 0		

We can also graph $y_1 = 2x^3 + 8x^2 + x + 4$ and $y_2 = (x + 4)(2x^2 + 1)$. If the graphs appear to coincide, the factorization is probably correct. The TRACE feature can be used to confirm this.

$y_1 = 2x^3 + 8x^2 + x + 4,$
$y_2 = (x + 4)(2x^2 + 1)$

Yscl = 2

Use a table or a graph to determine whether each factorization is correct.

1. $x^2 - 7x - 8 = (x - 8)(x + 1)$
2. $4x^2 - 5x - 6 = (4x + 3)(x - 2)$
3. $5x^2 + 17x - 12 = (5x + 3)(x - 4)$
4. $10x^2 + 37x + 7 = (5x - 1)(2x + 7)$
5. $12x^2 - 17x - 5 = (6x + 1)(2x - 5)$
6. $12x^2 - 17x - 5 = (4x + 1)(3x - 5)$
7. $x^2 - 4 = (x - 2)(x - 2)$
8. $x^2 - 4 = (x + 2)(x - 2)$

3.1 EXERCISE SET

For Extra Help MyMathLab Math XL PRACTICE WATCH DOWNLOAD

Concept Reinforcement *In each of Exercises 1–8, match the phrase with the most appropriate choice from the column on the right.*

1. _____ A factorization of $35a^2b$
2. _____ A factor of $35a^2b$
3. _____ A common factor of $5x + 10$ and $4x + 8$
4. _____ A factorization of $3x^4 - 9x^2$
5. _____ A factorization of $9x^4 - 3x^2$
6. _____ A common factor of $2x + 10$ and $4x + 8$
7. _____ A factor of $3a + 6a^2$
8. _____ A factorization of $3a + 6a^2$

a) $3a(1 + 2a)$
b) $x + 2$
c) $3x^2(3x^2 - 1)$
d) $1 + 2a$
e) $3x^2(x^2 - 3)$
f) $5a^2$
g) 2
h) $7a \cdot 5ab$

Find three factorizations for each monomial. Answers may vary.

9. $14x^3$
10. $22x^3$
11. $-15a^4$
12. $-8t^5$
13. $25t^5$
14. $9a^4$

Factor. Remember to use the largest common factor and to check by multiplying. Factor out a negative factor if the first coefficient is negative.

15. $8x + 24$
16. $10x + 50$
17. $6x - 30$
18. $7x - 21$
19. $2x^2 + 2x - 8$
20. $6x^2 + 3x - 15$
21. $3t^2 + t$
22. $2t^2 + t$
23. $-5y^2 - 10y$
24. $-4y^2 - 12y$
25. $x^3 + 6x^2$
26. $5x^4 - x^2$

27. $16a^4 - 24a^2$

28. $25a^5 + 10a^3$

29. $-6t^6 + 9t^4 - 4t^2$

30. $-10t^5 + 15t^4 + 9t^3$

31. $6x^8 + 12x^6 - 24x^4 + 30x^2$

32. $10x^4 - 30x^3 - 50x - 20$

33. $x^5y^5 + x^4y^3 + x^3y^3 - x^2y^2$

34. $x^9y^6 - x^7y^5 + x^4y^4 + x^3y^3$

35. $-35a^3b^4 + 10a^2b^3 - 15a^3b^2$

36. $-21r^5t^4 - 14r^4t^6 + 21r^3t^6$

Factor.

37. $n(n - 6) + 3(n - 6)$

38. $b(b + 5) + 3(b + 5)$

39. $x^2(x + 3) - 7(x + 3)$

40. $3z^2(2z + 9) + (2z + 9)$

41. $y^2(2y - 9) + (2y - 9)$

42. $x^2(x - 7) - 3(x - 7)$

Factor by grouping, if possible, and check.

43. $x^3 + 2x^2 + 5x + 10$

44. $z^3 + 3z^2 + 7z + 21$

45. $5a^3 + 15a^2 + 2a + 6$

46. $3a^3 + 2a^2 + 6a + 4$

47. $9n^3 - 6n^2 + 3n - 2$

48. $10x^3 - 25x^2 + 2x - 5$

49. $4t^3 - 20t^2 + 3t - 15$

50. $8a^3 - 2a^2 + 12a - 3$

51. $7x^3 + 5x^2 - 21x - 15$

52. $5x^3 + 4x^2 - 10x - 8$

53. $6a^3 + 7a^2 + 6a + 7$

54. $7t^3 - 5t^2 + 7t - 5$

55. $2x^3 + 12x^2 - 5x - 30$

56. $x^3 - x^2 - 2x + 5$

57. $p^3 + p^2 - 3p + 10$

58. $w^3 + 7w^2 + 4w + 28$

59. $y^3 + 8y^2 - 2y - 16$

60. $3x^3 + 18x^2 - 5x - 25$

61. $2x^3 - 8x^2 - 9x + 36$

62. $20g^3 - 4g^2 - 25g + 5$

63. In answering a factoring problem, Taylor says the largest common factor is $-5x^2$ and Madison says the largest common factor is $5x^2$. Can they both be correct? Why or why not?

64. Write a two-sentence paragraph in which the word "factor" is used at least once as a noun and once as a verb.

Skill Review

To prepare for Section 3.2, review multiplying binomials using FOIL.

Multiply.

65. $(x + 2)(x + 7)$

66. $(x - 2)(x - 7)$

67. $(x + 2)(x - 7)$

68. $(x - 2)(x + 7)$

69. $(a - 1)(a - 3)$

70. $(t + 3)(t + 5)$

71. $(t - 5)(t + 10)$

72. $(a + 4)(a - 6)$

Synthesis

73. Azrah recognizes that evaluating provides only a partial check of her factoring. Because of this, she often performs a second check with a different replacement value. Is this a good idea? Why or why not?

74. Holly factors $12x^2y - 18xy^2$ as $6xy \cdot 2x - 6xy \cdot 3y$. Is this the factorization of the polynomial? Why or why not?

Factor, if possible.

75. $4x^5 + 6x^2 + 6x^3 + 9$

76. $x^6 + x^2 + x^4 + 1$

77. $2x^4 + 2x^3 - 4x^2 - 4x$

78. $x^3 + x^2 - 2x + 2$

Aha! **79.** $5x^5 - 5x^4 + x^3 - x^2 + 3x - 3$

Aha! **80.** $ax^2 + 2ax + 3a + x^2 + 2x + 3$

81. Write a trinomial of degree 7 for which $8x^2y^3$ is the largest common factor. Answers may vary.

3.2 Factoring Trinomials of the Type $x^2 + bx + c$

When the Constant Term Is Positive ▪ When the Constant Term Is Negative ▪ Prime Polynomials

We now learn how to factor trinomials like

$$x^2 + 5x + 4 \quad \text{or} \quad x^2 + 3x - 10,$$

for which no common factor exists and the leading coefficient is 1. Recall that when factoring, we are writing an equivalent expression that is a product. For these trinomials, the factors will be binomials.

As preparation for the factoring that follows, compare the following multiplications:

$$
\begin{aligned}
&\quad\quad\quad\quad\quad\quad \text{F} \quad\ \text{O} \quad\ \text{I} \quad\quad\ \text{L} \\
(x + 2)(x + 5) &= x^2 + 5x + 2x + 2 \cdot 5 \\
&= x^2 + \quad 7x \quad + 10; \\
(x - 2)(x - 5) &= x^2 - 5x - 2x + (-2)(-5) \\
&= x^2 - \quad 7x \quad + \quad 10; \\
(x + 3)(x - 7) &= x^2 - 7x + 3x + 3(-7) \\
&= x^2 - \quad 4x \quad - \quad 21; \\
(x - 3)(x + 7) &= x^2 + 7x - 3x + (-3)7 \\
&= x^2 + \quad 4x \quad - \quad 21.
\end{aligned}
$$

Note that for all four products:

- The product of the two binomials is a trinomial.
- The coefficient of x in the trinomial is the sum of the constant terms in the binomials.
- The constant term in the trinomial is the product of the constant terms in the binomials.

These observations lead to a method for factoring certain trinomials. We first consider trinomials that have a positive constant term, just as in the first two multiplications above.

When the Constant Term Is Positive

To factor a polynomial like $x^2 + 7x + 10$, we think of FOIL in reverse. The x^2 resulted from x times x, which suggests that the first term of each binomial factor is x. Next, we look for numbers p and q such that

$$x^2 + 7x + 10 = (x + p)(x + q).$$

To get the middle term and the last term of the trinomial, we need two numbers, p and q, whose product is 10 and whose sum is 7. Those numbers are 2 and 5. Thus the factorization is

$$(x + 2)(x + 5).$$

Check: $(x + 2)(x + 5) = x^2 + 5x + 2x + 10$
$$= x^2 + 7x + 10.$$

STUDY SKILLS

Leave a Trail

Students sometimes make the mistake of viewing their supporting work as "scrap" work. Most instructors regard your reasoning as important as your final answer. Try to organize your supporting work so that your instructor (and you as well) can follow your steps.

STUDENT NOTES

One way to approach finding the numbers p and q is to think of filling in a diamond:

$p \cdot q = 10$

$p + q = 7$

Since $2 \cdot 5 = 10$ and $2 + 5 = 7$, the numbers we want are 2 and 5.

EXAMPLE 1

Factor to form an equivalent expression: $x^2 + 5x + 6$.

SOLUTION   Think of FOIL in reverse. The first term of each factor is x:

$$(x + \quad)(x + \quad).$$

To complete the factorization, we need a constant term for each binomial. The constants must have a product of 6 and a sum of 5. We list some pairs of numbers that multiply to 6 and then check the sum of each pair of factors.

Pairs of Factors of 6	Sums of Factors
1, 6	7
2, 3	5 ← The numbers we seek are 2 and 3.
−1, −6	−7
−2, −3	−5

One pair has a sum of 5.
Every pair has a product of 6.

Since

$$2 \cdot 3 = 6 \quad \text{and} \quad 2 + 3 = 5,$$

the factorization of $x^2 + 5x + 6$ is $(x + 2)(x + 3)$.

Check: $(x + 2)(x + 3) = x^2 + 3x + 2x + 6$
$$= x^2 + 5x + 6.$$

Thus, $(x + 2)(x + 3)$ is a product that is equivalent to $x^2 + 5x + 6$.

Note that since 5 and 6 are both positive, when factoring $x^2 + 5x + 6$ we need not consider negative factors of 6. Note too that changing the signs of the factors changes only the sign of the sum (see the table above).

TRY EXERCISE 7

A GEOMETRIC APPROACH TO EXAMPLE 1

The product of two binomials can be regarded as the sum of the areas of four rectangles. Thus we can regard the factoring of $x^2 + 5x + 6$ as a search for p and q so that the sum of areas A, B, C, and D is $x^2 + 5x + 6$.

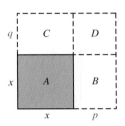

Note that area D is simply the product of p and q. In order for area D to be 6, p and q must be either 1 and 6 or 2 and 3. We illustrate both below.

When p and q are 1 and 6, the total area is $x^2 + 7x + 6$, but when p and q are 2 and 3, as shown on the right, the total area is $x^2 + 5x + 6$, as desired. Thus the factorization of $x^2 + 5x + 6$ is $(x + 2)(x + 3)$.

At the beginning of this section, we considered the multiplication $(x - 2)(x - 5)$. For this product, the resulting trinomial, $x^2 - 7x + 10$, has a positive constant term but a negative coefficient of x. This is because the *product* of two negative numbers is always positive, whereas the *sum* of two negative numbers is always negative.

To Factor $x^2 + bx + c$ When c Is Positive

When the constant term c of a trinomial is positive, look for two numbers with the same sign. Select pairs of numbers with the sign of b, the coefficient of the middle term.

$$x^2 - 7x + 10 = (x - 2)(x - 5);$$

$$x^2 + 7x + 10 = (x + 2)(x + 5)$$

EXAMPLE 2

Factor: $y^2 - 8y + 12$.

SOLUTION Since the constant term is positive and the coefficient of the middle term is negative, we look for a factorization of 12 in which both factors are negative. Their sum must be -8.

Pairs of Factors of 12	Sums of Factors
$-1, -12$	-13
$-2, \ -6$	-8 ← We need a sum of -8. The numbers we need are -2 and -6.
$-3, \ -4$	-7

The factorization of $y^2 - 8y + 12$ is $(y - 2)(y - 6)$. The check is left to the student.

TRY EXERCISE 13

STUDENT NOTES

It is important to be able to list *all* the pairs of factors of a number. See Example 1 on p. 21 for an organized approach for listing pairs of factors.

When the Constant Term Is Negative

As we saw in two of the multiplications at the start of this section, the product of two binomials can have a negative constant term:

$$(x + 3)(x - 7) = x^2 - 4x - 21$$

and

$$(x - 3)(x + 7) = x^2 + 4x - 21.$$

It is important to note that when the signs of the constants in the binomials are reversed, only the sign of the middle term of the trinomial changes.

EXAMPLE 3

Factor: $x^2 - 8x - 20$.

SOLUTION The constant term, -20, must be expressed as the product of a negative number and a positive number. Since the sum of these two numbers must be negative (specifically, -8), the negative number must have the greater absolute value.

Pairs of Factors of -20	Sums of Factors
$1, -20$	-19
$2, -10$	-8 ← The numbers we need are 2 and -10.
$4, \ -5$	-1
$5, \ -4$	1
$10, \ -2$	8
$20, \ -1$	19

Because in these three pairs, the positive number has the greater absolute value, these sums are all positive. For this problem, these pairs can be eliminated even before calculating the sum.

The numbers that we are looking for are 2 and -10.

Check: $(x + 2)(x - 10) = x^2 - 10x + 2x - 20$
$$= x^2 - 8x - 20.$$

The factorization of $x^2 - 8x - 20$ is $(x + 2)(x - 10)$.

TRY EXERCISE 21

To Factor $x^2 + bx + c$ When c Is Negative

When the constant term c of a trinomial is negative, look for a positive number and a negative number that multiply to c. Select pairs of numbers for which the number with the larger absolute value has the same sign as b, the coefficient of the middle term.

$$x^2 - 4x - 21 = (x + 3)(x - 7);$$

$$x^2 + 4x - 21 = (x - 3)(x + 7)$$

EXAMPLE 4

Factor: $t^2 - 24 + 5t$.

SOLUTION It helps to first write the trinomial in descending order: $t^2 + 5t - 24$. The factorization of the constant term, -24, must have one factor positive and one factor negative. The sum must be 5, so the positive factor must have the larger absolute value. Thus we consider only pairs of factors in which the positive factor has the larger absolute value.

Pairs of Factors of -24	Sums of Factors
$-1, 24$	23
$-2, 12$	10
$-3, \;8$	5 ← The numbers we need are -3 and 8.
$-4, \;6$	2

The factorization is $(t - 3)(t + 8)$. The check is left to the student.

TRY EXERCISE 23

Polynomials in two or more variables, such as $a^2 + 4ab - 21b^2$, are factored in a similar manner.

EXAMPLE 5

Factor: $a^2 + 4ab - 21b^2$.

SOLUTION It may help to write the trinomial in the equivalent form

$$a^2 + 4ba - 21b^2.$$

We now regard $-21b^2$ as the "constant" term and $4b$ as the "coefficient" of a. Then we try to express $-21b^2$ as a product of two factors whose sum is $4b$. Those factors are $-3b$ and $7b$.

Check: $(a - 3b)(a + 7b) = a^2 + 7ab - 3ba - 21b^2$
$$= a^2 + 4ab - 21b^2.$$

The factorization of $a^2 + 4ab - 21b^2$ is $(a - 3b)(a + 7b)$.

TRY EXERCISE 55

Prime Polynomials

EXAMPLE　6

Factor: $x^2 - x + 5$.

SOLUTION　Since 5 has very few factors, we can easily check all possibilities.

Pairs of Factors of 5	Sums of Factors
5, 1	6
−5, −1	−6

Since there are no factors whose sum is −1, the polynomial is *not* factorable into binomials.

TRY EXERCISE　37

In this text, a polynomial like $x^2 - x + 5$ that cannot be factored further is said to be **prime**. In more advanced courses, other types of numbers are considered. There, polynomials like $x^2 - x + 5$ can be factored and are not considered prime.

Often factoring requires two or more steps. Remember, when told to factor, we should *factor completely*. This means that the final factorization should contain only prime polynomials.

EXAMPLE　7

Factor: $-2x^3 + 20x^2 - 50x$.

SOLUTION　*Always* look first for a common factor. Since the leading coefficient is negative, we begin by factoring out $-2x$:

$$-2x^3 + 20x^2 - 50x = -2x(x^2 - 10x + 25).$$

Now consider $x^2 - 10x + 25$. Since the constant term is positive and the coefficient of the middle term is negative, we look for a factorization of 25 in which both factors are negative. Their sum must be -10.

STUDENT NOTES ————

Whenever a new set of parentheses is created while factoring, check the expression inside the parentheses to see if it can be factored further.

Pairs of Factors of 25	Sums of Factors	
−25, −1	−26	
−5, −5	−10 ←	The numbers we need are −5 and −5.

The factorization of $x^2 - 10x + 25$ is $(x - 5)(x - 5)$, or $(x - 5)^2$.

> **CAUTION!**　When factoring involves more than one step, be careful to write out the *entire* factorization.

Check:　$-2x(x - 5)(x - 5) = -2x[x^2 - 10x + 25]$　Multiplying binomials
$$= -2x^3 + 20x^2 - 50x.$$　Using the distributive law

The factorization of $-2x^3 + 20x^2 - 50x$ is $-2x(x - 5)(x - 5)$, or $-2x(x - 5)^2$.

TRY EXERCISE　27

Once any common factors have been factored out, the following summary can be used to factor $x^2 + bx + c$.

> **To Factor $x^2 + bx + c$**
>
> 1. Find a pair of factors that have c as their product and b as their sum.
>   a) If c is positive, both factors will have the same sign as b.
>   b) If c is negative, one factor will be positive and the other will be negative. Select the factors such that the factor with the larger absolute value has the same sign as b.
> 2. Check by multiplying.

Note that each polynomial has a unique factorization (except for the order in which the factors are written).

3.2 EXERCISE SET

For Extra Help **MyMathLab** Math XL PRACTICE WATCH DOWNLOAD

Concept Reinforcement *For Exercises 1–6, assume that a polynomial of the form $x^2 + bx + c$ can be factored as $(x + p)(x + q)$. Complete each sentence by replacing each blank with either "positive" or "negative."*

1. If b is positive and c is positive, then p will be _____ and q will be _____.

2. If b is negative and c is positive, then p will be _____ and q will be _____.

3. If p is negative and q is negative, then b must be _____ and c must be _____.

4. If p is positive and q is positive, then b must be _____ and c must be _____.

5. If b, c, and p are all negative, then q must be _____.

6. If b and c are negative and p is positive, then q must be _____.

Factor completely. Remember to look first for a common factor. Check by multiplying. If a polynomial is prime, state this.

7. $x^2 + 8x + 16$
8. $x^2 + 9x + 20$
9. $x^2 + 11x + 10$
10. $y^2 + 8y + 7$
11. $x^2 + 10x + 21$
12. $x^2 + 6x + 9$
13. $t^2 - 9t + 14$
14. $a^2 - 9a + 20$
15. $b^2 - 5b + 4$
16. $x^2 - 10x + 25$
17. $a^2 - 7a + 12$
18. $z^2 - 8z + 7$
19. $d^2 - 7d + 10$
20. $x^2 - 8x + 15$
21. $x^2 - 2x - 15$
22. $x^2 - x - 42$

23. $x^2 + 2x - 15$
24. $x^2 + x - 42$
25. $2x^2 - 14x - 36$
26. $3y^2 - 9y - 84$
27. $-x^3 + 6x^2 + 16x$
28. $-x^3 + x^2 + 42x$
29. $4y - 45 + y^2$
30. $7x - 60 + x^2$
31. $x^2 - 72 + 6x$
32. $-2x - 99 + x^2$
33. $-5b^2 - 35b + 150$
34. $-c^4 - c^3 + 56c^2$
35. $x^5 - x^4 - 2x^3$
36. $2a^2 - 4a - 70$
37. $x^2 + 5x + 10$
38. $x^2 + 11x + 18$
39. $32 + 12t + t^2$
40. $y^2 - y + 1$
41. $x^2 + 20x + 99$
42. $x^2 + 20x + 100$
43. $3x^3 - 63x^2 - 300x$
44. $2x^3 - 40x^2 + 192x$
45. $-2x^2 + 42x + 144$
56. $-4x^2 - 40x - 100$
47. $y^2 - 20y + 96$
48. $144 - 25t + t^2$
49. $-a^6 - 9a^5 + 90a^4$
50. $-a^4 - a^3 + 132a^2$
51. $t^2 + \frac{2}{3}t + \frac{1}{9}$
52. $x^2 - \frac{2}{5}x + \frac{1}{25}$
53. $11 + w^2 - 4w$
54. $6 + p^2 + 2p$
55. $p^2 - 7pq + 10q^2$
56. $a^2 - 2ab - 3b^2$
57. $m^2 + 5mn + 5n^2$
58. $x^2 - 11xy + 24y^2$
59. $s^2 - 4st - 12t^2$
60. $b^2 + 8bc - 20c^2$
61. $6a^{10} + 30a^9 - 84a^8$
62. $5a^8 - 20a^7 - 25a^6$

63. Without multiplying $(x - 17)(x - 18)$, explain why it cannot possibly be a factorization of $x^2 + 35x + 306$.

64. Shari factors $x^3 - 8x^2 + 15x$ as $(x^2 - 5x)(x - 3)$. Is she wrong? Why or why not? What advice would you offer?

Skill Review

To prepare for Section 3.3, review multiplying binomials using FOIL.

Multiply.

65. $(2x + 3)(3x + 4)$

66. $(2x + 3)(3x - 4)$

67. $(2x - 3)(3x + 4)$

68. $(2x - 3)(3x - 4)$

69. $(5x - 1)(x - 7)$

70. $(x + 6)(3x - 5)$

Synthesis

71. When searching for a factorization, why do we list pairs of numbers with the correct *product* instead of pairs of numbers with the correct *sum*?

72. When factoring $x^2 + bx + c$ with a large value of c, Riley begins by writing out the prime factorization of c. What is the advantage of doing this?

73. Find all integers b for which $a^2 + ba - 50$ can be factored.

74. Find all integers m for which $y^2 + my + 50$ can be factored.

Factor completely.

75. $y^2 - 0.2y - 0.08$

76. $x^2 + \frac{1}{2}x - \frac{3}{16}$

77. $-\frac{1}{3}a^3 + \frac{1}{3}a^2 + 2a$

78. $-a^7 + \frac{25}{7}a^5 + \frac{30}{7}a^6$

79. $x^{2m} + 11x^m + 28$

80. $-t^{2n} + 7t^n - 10$

Aha! **81.** $(a + 1)x^2 + (a + 1)3x + (a + 1)2$

82. $ax^2 - 5x^2 + 8ax - 40x - (a - 5)9$
(*Hint*: See Exercise 81.)

83. Find the volume of a cube if its surface area is $6x^2 + 36x + 54$ square meters.

Find a polynomial in factored form for the shaded area in each figure. (Use π in your answers where appropriate.)

84.

85.

86.

87.

88.

89.

90. A census taker asks a woman, "How many children do you have?"

"Three," she answers.

"What are their ages?"

She responds, "The product of their ages is 36. The sum of their ages is the house number next door."

The math-savvy census taker walks next door, reads the house number, appears puzzled, and returns to the woman, asking, "Is there something you forgot to tell me?"

"Oh yes," says the woman. "I'm sorry. The oldest child is at the park."

The census taker records the three ages, thanks the woman for her time, and leaves.

How old is each child? Explain how you reached this conclusion. (*Hint*: Consider factorizations.)
Source: Adapted from Anita Harnadek, *Classroom Quickies.* Pacific Grove, CA: Critical Thinking Press and Software

COLLABORATIVE

CORNER

Visualizing Factoring

Focus: Visualizing factoring
Time: 20–30 minutes
Group size: 3
Materials: Graph paper and scissors

The product $(x + 2)(x + 3)$ can be regarded as the area of a rectangle with width $x + 2$ and length $x + 3$. Similarly, factoring a polynomial like $x^2 + 5x + 6$ can be thought of as determining the length and the width of a rectangle that has area $x^2 + 5x + 6$. This is the approach used below.

ACTIVITY

1. **a)** To factor $x^2 + 11x + 10$ geometrically, the group needs to cut out shapes like those below to represent x^2, $11x$, and 10. This can be done by either tracing the figures below or by selecting a value for x, say 4, and using the squares on the graph paper to cut out the following:

   x^2:   Using the value selected for x, cut out a square that is x units on each side.

   $11x$:   Using the value selected for x, cut out a rectangle that is 1 unit wide and x units long. Repeat this to form 11 such strips.

   10:    Cut out two rectangles with whole-number dimensions and an area of 10. One should be 2 units by 5 units and the other 1 unit by 10 units.

   b) The group, working together, should then attempt to use one of the two rectangles with area 10, along with all of the other shapes, to piece together one large rectangle. Only one of the rectangles with area 10 will work.

   c) From the large rectangle formed in part (b), use the length and the width to determine the factorization of $x^2 + 11x + 10$. Where do the dimensions of the rectangle representing 10 appear in the factorization?

2. Repeat step (1) above, but this time use the other rectangle with area 10, and use only 7 of the 11 strips, along with the x^2-shape. Piece together the shapes to form one large rectangle. What factorization do the dimensions of this rectangle suggest?

3. Cut out rectangles with area 12 and use the above approach to factor $x^2 + 8x + 12$. What dimensions should be used for the rectangle with area 12?

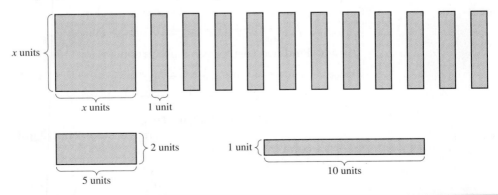

3.3 Factoring Trinomials of the Type $ax^2 + bx + c$

Factoring with FOIL ■ The Grouping Method

In Section 3.2, we learned a FOIL-based method for factoring trinomials of the type $x^2 + bx + c$. Now we learn to factor trinomials in which the leading, or x^2, coefficient is not 1. First we will use another FOIL-based method and then we will use an alternative method that involves factoring by grouping. Use the method that you prefer or the one recommended by your instructor.

Factoring with FOIL

Before factoring trinomials of the type $ax^2 + bx + c$, consider the following:

$$\begin{array}{cccc} \text{F} & \text{O} & \text{I} & \text{L} \end{array}$$
$$(2x + 5)(3x + 4) = 6x^2 + 8x + 15x + 20$$
$$= 6x^2 + \quad 23x \quad + 20.$$

To factor $6x^2 + 23x + 20$, we could reverse the multiplication and look for two binomials whose product is this trinomial. We see from the multiplication above that:

- the product of the First terms must be $6x^2$;
- the product of the Outer terms plus the product of the Inner terms must be $23x$; and
- the product of the Last terms must be 20.

How can such a factorization be found without first seeing the corresponding multiplication? Our first approach relies on trial and error and FOIL.

To Factor $ax^2 + bx + c$ Using FOIL

1. Make certain that all common factors have been removed. If any remain, factor out the largest common factor.
2. Find two First terms whose product is ax^2:

$$(\blacksquare x + \quad)(\blacksquare x + \quad) = ax^2 + bx + c.$$

3. Find two Last terms whose product is c:

$$(\ x + \blacksquare)(\ x + \blacksquare) = ax^2 + bx + c.$$

4. Check by multiplying to see if the sum of the Outer and Inner products is bx. If necessary, repeat steps 2 and 3 until the correct combination is found.

$$(\blacksquare x + \blacksquare)(\blacksquare x + \blacksquare) = ax^2 + bx + c.$$

If no correct combination exists, state that the polynomial is prime.

EXAMPLE 1   Factor: $3x^2 - 10x - 8$.

SOLUTION

1. First, check for a common factor. In this case, there is none (other than 1 or -1).

2. Find two **F**irst terms whose product is $3x^2$.
   The only possibilities for the **F**irst terms are $3x$ and x:

   $(3x + \quad)(x + \quad)$.

3. Find two **L**ast terms whose product is -8. There are four pairs of factors of -8 and each can be listed in two ways:

   $$\begin{array}{ccc} -1, & 8 & \quad 8, -1 \\ 1, & -8 & \quad -8, \ 1 \\ -2, & 4 & \quad 4, -2 \\ 2, & -4 & \quad -4, \ 2. \end{array} \quad \text{and}$$

   Important! Since the First terms are not identical, we must consider the pairs of factors in both orders.

4. Knowing that all **F**irst and **L**ast products will check, systematically inspect the **O**uter and **I**nner products resulting from steps (2) and (3). Look for the combination in which the sum of the products is the middle term, $-10x$. Our search ends as soon as the correct combination is found. If none exists, we state that the polynomial is prime.

Pair of Factors	Corresponding Trial	Product	
$-1, \ 8$	$(3x - 1)(x + 8)$	$3x^2 + 24x - x - 8$ $= 3x^2 + 23x - 8$	Wrong middle term
$1, -8$	$(3x + 1)(x - 8)$	$3x^2 - 24x + x - 8$ $= 3x^2 - 23x - 8$	Wrong middle term
$-2, \ 4$	$(3x - 2)(x + 4)$	$3x^2 + 12x - 2x - 8$ $= 3x^2 + 10x - 8$	Wrong middle term
$2, -4$	$(3x + 2)(x - 4)$	$3x^2 - 12x + 2x - 8$ $= 3x^2 - 10x - 8$	Correct middle term!
$8, -1$	$(3x + 8)(x - 1)$	$3x^2 - 3x + 8x - 8$ $= 3x^2 + 5x - 8$	Wrong middle term
$-8, \ 1$	$(3x - 8)(x + 1)$	$3x^2 + 3x - 8x - 8$ $= 3x^2 - 5x - 8$	Wrong middle term
$4, -2$	$(3x + 4)(x - 2)$	$3x^2 - 6x + 4x - 8$ $= 3x^2 - 2x - 8$	Wrong middle term
$-4, \ 2$	$(3x - 4)(x + 2)$	$3x^2 + 6x - 4x - 8$ $= 3x^2 + 2x - 8$	Wrong middle term

The correct factorization is $(3x + 2)(x - 4)$.

TRY EXERCISE 5

Two observations can be made from Example 1. First, we listed all possible trials even though we generally stop after finding the correct factorization. We did this to show that **each trial differs only in the middle term of the product.** Second, note that as in Section 3.2, **only the sign of the middle term changes when the signs in the binomials are reversed.**

EXAMPLE 2

Factor: $10x^2 + 37x + 7$.

SOLUTION

1. There is no factor (other than 1 or -1) common to all three terms.

2. Because $10x^2$ factors as $10x \cdot x$ or $5x \cdot 2x$, we have two possibilities:

$$(10x + \ )(x + \ ) \quad \text{or} \quad (5x + \ )(2x + \ ).$$

3. There are two pairs of factors of 7 and each can be listed in two ways:

$$\begin{matrix} 1, & 7 \\ -1, & -7 \end{matrix} \quad \text{and} \quad \begin{matrix} 7, & 1 \\ -7, & -1 \end{matrix}.$$

4. Look for **O**uter and **I**nner products for which the sum is the middle term. Because all coefficients in $10x^2 + 37x + 7$ are positive, we need consider only those combinations involving positive factors of 7.

Trial	*Product*	
$(10x + 1)(x + 7)$	$10x^2 + 70x + 1x + 7$ $= 10x^2 + 71x + 7$	Wrong middle term
$(10x + 7)(x + 1)$	$10x^2 + 10x + 7x + 7$ $= 10x^2 + 17x + 7$	Wrong middle term
$(5x + 7)(2x + 1)$	$10x^2 + 5x + 14x + 7$ $= 10x^2 + 19x + 7$	Wrong middle term
$(5x + 1)(2x + 7)$	$10x^2 + 35x + 2x + 7$ $= 10x^2 + 37x + 7$	Correct middle term!

The correct factorization is $(5x + 1)(2x + 7)$.

> TRY EXERCISE 9

A GEOMETRIC APPROACH TO EXAMPLE 2

The factoring of $10x^2 + 37x + 7$ can be regarded as a search for r and s so that the sum of areas A, B, C, and D is $10x^2 + 37x + 7$.

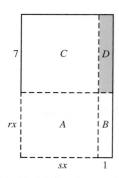

Because A must be $10x^2$, the product rs must be 10. Only when r is 2 and s is 5 will the sum of areas B and C be $37x$ (see below).

EXAMPLE 3

Factor: $24x^3 - 76x^2 + 40x$.

SOLUTION

1. First, we factor out the largest common factor, $4x$:

$$4x(6x^2 - 19x + 10).$$

2. Next, we factor $6x^2 - 19x + 10$. Since $6x^2$ can be factored as $3x \cdot 2x$ or $6x \cdot x$, we have two possibilities:

$$(3x + \ )(2x + \ ) \quad \text{or} \quad (6x + \ )(x + \ ).$$

3. There are four pairs of factors of 10 and each can be listed in two ways:

$$\begin{matrix} 1, & 10 \\ -1, & -10 \\ 2, & 5 \\ -2, & -5 \end{matrix} \quad \text{and} \quad \begin{matrix} 10, & 1 \\ -10, & -1 \\ 5, & 2 \\ -5, & -2 \end{matrix}.$$

4. The two possibilities from step (2) and the eight possibilities from step (3) give $2 \cdot 8$, or 16 possibilities for factorizations. With careful consideration,

we can eliminate some possibilities without multiplying. Since the sign of the middle term, $-19x$, is negative, but the sign of the last term, 10, is positive, the two factors of 10 must both be negative. This means only four pairings from step (3) need be considered. We first try these factors with $(3x + \quad)(2x + \quad)$, looking for **O**uter and **I**nner products for which the sum is $-19x$. If none gives the correct factorization, then we will consider $(6x + \quad)(x + \quad)$.

Trial	*Product*	
$(3x - 1)(2x - 10)$	$6x^2 - 30x - 2x + 10$	
	$= 6x^2 - 32x + 10$	Wrong middle term
$(3x - 10)(2x - 1)$	$6x^2 - 3x - 20x + 10$	
	$= 6x^2 - 23x + 10$	Wrong middle term
$(3x - 2)(2x - 5)$	$6x^2 - 15x - 4x + 10$	
	$= 6x^2 - 19x + 10$	Correct middle term!
$(3x - 5)(2x - 2)$	$6x^2 - 6x - 10x + 10$	
	$= 6x^2 - 16x + 10$	Wrong middle term

Since we have a correct factorization, we need not consider

$$(6x + \quad)(x + \quad).$$

Look again at the possibility $(3x - 5)(2x - 2)$. Without multiplying, we can reject such a possibility. To see why, note that

$$(3x - 5)(2x - 2) = (3x - 5)2(x - 1).$$

The expression $2x - 2$ has a common factor, 2. But we removed the *largest* common factor in step (1). If $2x - 2$ were one of the factors, then 2 would be *another* common factor in addition to the original, $4x$. Thus, $(2x - 2)$ cannot be part of the factorization of $6x^2 - 19x + 10$. Similar reasoning can be used to reject $(3x - 1)(2x - 10)$ as a possible factorization.

Once the largest common factor is factored out, none of the remaining factors can have a common factor.

The factorization of $6x^2 - 19x + 10$ is $(3x - 2)(2x - 5)$, but do not forget the common factor! The factorization of $24x^3 - 76x^2 + 40x$ is

$$4x(3x - 2)(2x - 5). \qquad \text{TRY EXERCISE } \blacktriangleright 15$$

STUDENT NOTES ⎯⎯⎯⎯

Keep your work organized so that you can see what you have already considered. For example, when factoring $6x^2 - 19x + 10$, we can list all possibilities and cross out those in which a common factor appears:

$~~~~\cancel{(3x - 1)(2x - 10)}$
$~~~~(3x - 10)(2x - 1)$
$~~~~(3x - 2)(2x - 5)$
$~~~~\cancel{(3x - 5)(2x - 2)}$
$~~~~(6x - 1)(x - 10)$
$~~~~\cancel{(6x - 10)(x - 1)}$
$~~~~\cancel{(6x - 2)(x - 5)}$
$~~~~(6x - 5)(x - 2)$

By being organized and not erasing, we can see that there are only four possible factorizations.

Tips for Factoring $ax^2 + bx + c$

To factor $ax^2 + bx + c\ (a > 0)$:

- Make sure that any common factor has been factored out.
- Once the largest common factor has been factored out of the original trinomial, no binomial factor can contain a common factor (other than 1 or -1).
- If c is positive, then the signs in both binomial factors must match the sign of b.
- Reversing the signs in the binomials reverses the sign of the middle term of their product.
- Organize your work so that you can keep track of which possibilities you have checked.
- Remember to include the largest common factor—if there is one—in the final factorization.
- Always check by multiplying.

EXAMPLE   4

Factor: $10x + 8 - 3x^2$.

SOLUTION   An important problem-solving strategy is to find a way to make new problems look like problems we already know how to solve. The factoring tips above apply only to trinomials of the form $ax^2 + bx + c$, with $a > 0$. This leads us to rewrite $10x + 8 - 3x^2$ in descending order:

$$10x + 8 - 3x^2 = -3x^2 + 10x + 8.$$ Using the commutative law to write descending order

Although $-3x^2 + 10x + 8$ looks similar to the trinomials we have factored, the tips above require a positive leading coefficient. This can be found by factoring out -1:

$$-3x^2 + 10x + 8 = -1(3x^2 - 10x - 8)$$ Factoring out -1 changes the signs of the coefficients.

$$= -1(3x + 2)(x - 4).$$ Using the result from Example 1

The factorization of $10x + 8 - 3x^2$ is $-1(3x + 2)(x - 4)$.   TRY EXERCISE ▶ 31

EXAMPLE   5

Factor: $6r^2 - 13rs - 28s^2$.

SOLUTION   In order for the product of the first terms to be $6r^2$ and the product of the last terms to be $-28s^2$, the binomial factors will be of the form

$$(r + s)(r + s).$$

We verify that no common factor exists and then examine the first term, $6r^2$. There are two possibilities:

$$(2r +)(3r +)   \text{ or }   (6r +)(r +).$$

The last term, $-28s^2$, has the following pairs of factors:

$$
\begin{array}{ll}
s, -28s & -28s, s \\
-s, 28s & 28s, -s \\
2s, -14s & -14s, 2s \\
-2s, 14s \quad \text{and} & 14s, -2s \\
4s, -7s & -7s, 4s \\
-4s, 7s & 7s, -4s.
\end{array}
$$

Note that listing the pairs of factors of $-28s^2$ is just like listing the pairs of factors of -28, except that each factor also contains a factor of s.

Some trials, like $(2r + 28s)(3r - s)$ and $(2r + 14s)(3r - 2s)$, cannot be correct because both $(2r + 28s)$ and $(2r + 14s)$ contain a common factor, 2. We try $(2r + 7s)(3r - 4s)$:

$$(2r + 7s)(3r - 4s) = 6r^2 - 8rs + 21rs - 28s^2$$
$$= 6r^2 + 13rs - 28s^2.$$

Our trial is incorrect, but only because of the sign of the middle term. To correctly factor $6r^2 - 13rs - 28s^2$, we simply change the signs in the binomials:

$$(2r - 7s)(3r + 4s) = 6r^2 + 8rs - 21rs - 28s^2$$
$$= 6r^2 - 13rs - 28s^2.$$

The correct factorization of $6r^2 - 13rs - 28s^2$ is $(2r - 7s)(3r + 4s)$.

TRY EXERCISE ▶ 67

The Grouping Method

Another method of factoring trinomials of the type $ax^2 + bx + c$ is known as the *grouping method*. The grouping method relies on rewriting $ax^2 + bx + c$ in the form $ax^2 + px + qx + c$ and then factoring by grouping. To develop this method, consider the following*:

$$(2x + 5)(3x + 4) = 2x \cdot 3x + 2x \cdot 4 + 5 \cdot 3x + 5 \cdot 4 \qquad \text{Using FOIL}$$
$$= 2 \cdot 3 \cdot x^2 + 2 \cdot 4x + 5 \cdot 3x + 5 \cdot 4$$
$$= 2 \cdot 3 \cdot x^2 + (2 \cdot 4 + 5 \cdot 3)x + 5 \cdot 4$$

$$\underset{a}{\big\uparrow} \qquad\qquad \underset{b}{\big\uparrow} \qquad\qquad \underset{c}{\big\uparrow}$$

$$= \quad 6x^2 \quad + \quad 23x \quad + \quad 20.$$

Note that reversing these steps shows that $6x^2 + 23x + 20$ can be rewritten as $6x^2 + 8x + 15x + 20$ and then factored by grouping. Note that the numbers that add to b (in this case, $2 \cdot 4$ and $5 \cdot 3$) also multiply to ac (in this case, $2 \cdot 3 \cdot 5 \cdot 4$).

To Factor $ax^2 + bx + c$, Using the Grouping Method

1. Factor out the largest common factor, if one exists.
2. Multiply the leading coefficient a and the constant c.
3. Find a pair of factors of ac whose sum is b.
4. Rewrite the middle term, bx, as a sum or a difference using the factors found in step (3).
5. Factor by grouping.
6. Include any common factor from step (1) and check by multiplying.

EXAMPLE 6 Factor: $3x^2 - 10x - 8$.

SOLUTION

1. First, we note that there is no common factor (other than 1 or -1).
2. We multiply the leading coefficient, 3, and the constant, -8:

$$3(-8) = -24.$$

3. We next look for a factorization of -24 in which the sum of the factors is the coefficient of the middle term, -10.

Pairs of Factors of -24	Sums of Factors
1, −24	−23
−1, 24	23
2, −12	−10 ⟵ $2 + (-12) = -10$
−2, 12	10
3, −8	−5
−3, 8	5
4, −6	−2
−4, 6	2

We normally stop listing pairs of factors once we have found the one we are after.

---

*This discussion was inspired by a lecture given by Irene Doo at Austin Community College.

4. Next, we express the middle term as a sum or a difference using the factors found in step (3):

$$-10x = 2x - 12x.$$

5. We now factor by grouping as follows:

$$3x^2 - 10x - 8 = 3x^2 + 2x - 12x - 8$$ Substituting $2x - 12x$ for $-10x$. We could also use $-12x + 2x$.

$$= x(3x + 2) - 4(3x + 2)$$ Factoring by grouping; see Section 3.1

$$= (3x + 2)(x - 4).$$ Factoring out the common factor, $3x + 2$

6. *Check:* $(3x + 2)(x - 4) = 3x^2 - 12x + 2x - 8 = 3x^2 - 10x - 8.$

The factorization of $3x^2 - 10x - 8$ is $(3x + 2)(x - 4)$.   TRY EXERCISE ▸ 51

EXAMPLE 7   Factor: $8x^3 + 22x^2 - 6x.$

SOLUTION

1. We factor out the largest common factor, $2x$:

$$8x^3 + 22x^2 - 6x = 2x(4x^2 + 11x - 3).$$

2. To factor $4x^2 + 11x - 3$ by grouping, we multiply the leading coefficient, 4, and the constant term, -3:

$$4(-3) = -12.$$

3. We next look for factors of -12 that add to 11.

Pairs of Factors of -12	Sums of Factors
1, −12	−11
−1, 12	11 ←
.	.
.	.
.	.

Since $-1 + 12 = 11$, there is no need to list other pairs of factors.

4. We then rewrite the $11x$ in $4x^2 + 11x - 3$ using

$$11x = -1x + 12x, \quad \text{or} \quad 11x = 12x - 1x.$$

5. Next, we factor by grouping:

$$4x^2 + 11x - 3 = 4x^2 - 1x + 12x - 3$$ Rewriting the middle term; $12x - 1x$ could also be used.

$$= x(4x - 1) + 3(4x - 1)$$ Factoring by grouping. Note the common factor, $4x - 1$.

$$= (4x - 1)(x + 3).$$ Factoring out the common factor

6. The factorization of $4x^2 + 11x - 3$ is $(4x - 1)(x + 3)$. But don't forget the common factor, $2x$. The factorization of the original trinomial is

$$2x(4x - 1)(x + 3).$$ TRY EXERCISE ▸ 57

3.3 EXERCISE SET

For Extra Help
MyMathLab   Math XL PRACTICE   WATCH   DOWNLOAD

Concept Reinforcement *In each of Exercises 1–4, match the polynomial with the correct factorization from the column on the right.*

1. ___ $12x^2 + 16x - 3$ **a)** $(7x - 1)(2x + 3)$

2. ___ $14x^2 + 19x - 3$ **b)** $(6x + 1)(2x - 3)$

3. ___ $14x^2 - 19x - 3$ **c)** $(6x - 1)(2x + 3)$

4. ___ $12x^2 - 16x - 3$ **d)** $(7x + 1)(2x - 3)$

Factor completely. If a polynomial is prime, state this.

5. $2x^2 + 7x - 4$ **6.** $3x^2 + x - 4$

7. $3x^2 - 17x - 6$ **8.** $5x^2 - 19x - 4$

9. $4t^2 + 12t + 5$ **10.** $6t^2 + 17t + 7$

11. $15a^2 - 14a + 3$ **12.** $10a^2 - 11a + 3$

13. $6x^2 + 17x + 12$ **14.** $6x^2 + 19x + 10$

15. $6x^2 - 10x - 4$ **16.** $5t^3 - 21t^2 + 18t$

17. $7t^3 + 15t^2 + 2t$ **18.** $15t^2 + 20t - 75$

19. $10 - 23x + 12x^2$ **20.** $-20 + 31x - 12x^2$

21. $-35x^2 - 34x - 8$ **22.** $28x^2 + 38x - 6$

23. $4 + 6t^2 - 13t$ **24.** $9 + 8t^2 - 18t$

25. $25x^2 + 40x + 16$ **26.** $49t^2 + 42t + 9$

27. $20y^2 + 59y - 3$ **28.** $25a^2 - 23a - 2$

29. $14x^2 + 73x + 45$ **30.** $35x^2 - 57x - 44$

31. $-2x^2 + 15 + x$ **32.** $2t^2 - 19 - 6t$

33. $-6x^2 - 33x - 15$ **34.** $-12x^2 - 28x + 24$

35. $10a^2 - 8a - 18$ **36.** $20y^2 - 25y + 5$

37. $12x^2 + 68x - 24$ **38.** $6x^2 + 21x + 15$

39. $4x + 1 + 3x^2$ **40.** $-9 + 18x^2 + 21x$

Factor. Use factoring by grouping even though it would seem reasonable to first combine like terms.

41. $x^2 + 3x - 2x - 6$ **42.** $x^2 + 4x - 2x - 8$

43. $8t^2 - 6t - 28t + 21$

44. $35t^2 - 40t + 21t - 24$

45. $6x^2 + 4x + 15x + 10$ **46.** $3x^2 - 2x + 3x - 2$

47. $2y^2 + 8y - y - 4$ **48.** $7n^2 + 35n - n - 5$

49. $6a^2 - 8a - 3a + 4$ **50.** $10a^2 - 4a - 5a + 2$

Factor completely. If a polynomial is prime, state this.

51. $16t^2 + 23t + 7$ **52.** $9t^2 + 14t + 5$

53. $-9x^2 - 18x - 5$ **54.** $-16x^2 - 32x - 7$

55. $10x^2 + 30x - 70$ **56.** $10a^2 + 25a - 15$

57. $18x^3 + 21x^2 - 9x$ **58.** $6x^3 - 4x^2 - 10x$

59. $89x + 64 + 25x^2$ **60.** $47 - 42y + 9y^2$

61. $168x^3 + 45x^2 + 3x$

62. $144x^5 - 168x^4 + 48x^3$

63. $-14t^4 + 19t^3 + 3t^2$

64. $-70a^4 + 68a^3 - 16a^2$

65. $132y + 32y^2 - 54$ **66.** $220y + 60y^2 - 225$

67. $2a^2 - 5ab + 2b^2$ **68.** $3p^2 - 16pq - 12q^2$

69. $8s^2 + 22st + 14t^2$ **70.** $10s^2 + 4st - 6t^2$

71. $27x^2 - 72xy + 48y^2$

72. $-30a^2 - 87ab - 30b^2$

73. $-24a^2 + 34ab - 12b^2$ **74.** $15a^2 - 5ab - 20b^2$

75. $19x^3 - 3x^2 + 14x^4$ **76.** $10x^5 - 2x^4 + 22x^3$

77. $18a^7 + 8a^6 + 9a^8$ **78.** $40a^8 + 16a^7 + 25a^9$

79. Asked to factor $2x^2 - 18x + 36$, Kay *incorrectly* answers
$$2x^2 - 18x + 36 = 2(x^2 + 9x + 18)$$
$$= 2(x + 3)(x + 6).$$
If this were a 10-point quiz question, how many points would you take off? Why?

80. Asked to factor $4x^2 + 28x + 48$, Herb *incorrectly* answers
$$4x^2 + 28x + 48 = (2x + 6)(2x + 8)$$
$$= 2(x + 3)(x + 4).$$
If this were a 10-point quiz question, how many points would you take off? Why?

Skill Review

Multiply.

81. $(x - 2)^2$ **82.** $(x + 2)^2$

83. $(x + 2)(x - 2)$ **84.** $(5t - 3)^2$

85. $(4a + 1)^2$

86. $(2n + 7)(2n - 7)$

87. $(3c - 10)^2$

88. $(1 - 5a)^2$

89. $(8n + 3)(8n - 3)$

90. $(9 - y)(9 + y)$

95. $9a^2b^3 + 25ab^2 + 16$

96. $-9t^{10} - 12t^5 - 4$

97. $16t^{10} - 8t^5 + 1$

98. $9a^2b^2 - 15ab - 2$

99. $-15x^{2m} + 26x^m - 8$

100. $-20x^{2n} - 16x^n - 3$

101. $3a^{6n} - 2a^{3n} - 1$

102. $a^{2n+1} - 2a^{n+1} + a$

103. $7(t - 3)^{2n} + 5(t - 3)^n - 2$

104. $3(a + 1)^{n+1}(a + 3)^2 - 5(a + 1)^n(a + 3)^3$

Synthesis

91. Explain how you would prove to a fellow student that a given trinomial is prime.

92. For the trinomial $ax^2 + bx + c$, suppose that a is the product of three different prime factors and c is the product of another two prime factors. How many possible factorizations (like those in Example 1) exist? Explain how you determined your answer.

Factor. If a polynomial is prime, state this.

93. $18x^2y^2 - 3xy - 10$

94. $8x^2y^3 + 10xy^2 + 2y$

CONNECTING the CONCEPTS

In Sections 3.1–3.3, we have considered factoring out a common factor, factoring by grouping, and factoring with FOIL. The following is a good strategy to follow when you encounter a mixed set of factoring problems.

1. Factor out any common factor.
2. Try factoring by grouping for polynomials with four terms.
3. Try factoring with FOIL for trinomials. If the leading coefficient of the trinomial is not 1, you may instead try factoring by grouping.

Polynomial	Number of Terms	Factorization
$12y^5 - 6y^4 + 30y^2$	3	There is a common factor: $6y^2$. $12y^5 - 6y^4 + 30y^2 = 6y^2(2y^3 - y^2 + 5)$. The trinomial in the parentheses cannot be factored further.
$t^4 - 5t^3 - 3t + 15$	4	There is no common factor. We factor by grouping. $t^4 - 5t^3 - 3t + 15 = t^3(t - 5) - 3(t - 5)$ $= (t - 5)(t^3 - 3)$
$-4x^4 + 4x^3 + 80x^2$	3	There is a common factor: $-4x^2$. $-4x^4 + 4x^3 + 80x^2 = -4x^2(x^2 - x - 20)$ The trinomial in the parentheses can be factored: $-4x^4 + 4x^3 + 80x^2 = -4x^2(x^2 - x - 20)$ $= -4x^2(x + 4)(x - 5)$.
$10n^2 - 17n + 3$	3	There is no common factor. We factor with FOIL or by grouping. $10n^2 - 17n + 3 = (2n - 3)(5n - 1)$

MIXED REVIEW

Factor completely. If a polynomial is prime, state this.

1. $6x^5 - 18x^2$
2. $x^2 + 10x + 16$
3. $2x^2 + 13x - 7$
4. $x^3 + 3x^2 + 2x + 6$
5. $5x^2 + 40x - 100$
6. $x^2 - 2x - 5$
7. $7x^2y - 21xy - 28y$
8. $15a^4 - 27a^2b^2 + 21a^2b$
9. $b^2 - 14b + 49$
10. $12x^2 - x - 1$
11. $c^3 + c^2 - 4c - 4$
12. $2x^2 + 30x - 200$
13. $t^2 + t - 10$
14. $15d^2 - 30d + 75$
15. $15p^2 + 16pq + 4q^2$
16. $-2t^3 - 10t^2 - 12t$
17. $x^2 + 4x - 77$
18. $10c^2 + 20c + 10$
19. $5 + 3x - 2x^2$
20. $2m^3n - 10m^2n - 6mn + 30n$

3.4 Factoring Perfect–Square Trinomials and Differences of Squares

Recognizing Perfect-Square Trinomials ▪ Factoring Perfect-Square Trinomials ▪
Recognizing Differences of Squares ▪ Factoring Differences of Squares ▪ Factoring Completely

Recognizing Perfect–Square Trinomials

Some trinomials are squares of binomials. For example, $x^2 + 10x + 25$ is the square of the binomial $x + 5$, because

$$(x + 5)^2 = x^2 + 2 \cdot x \cdot 5 + 5^2 = x^2 + 10x + 25.$$

A trinomial that is the square of a binomial is called a **perfect-square trinomial**.

Consider squaring binomials as a special-product rule:

$$(A + B)^2 = A^2 + 2AB + B^2;$$
$$(A - B)^2 = A^2 - 2AB + B^2.$$

Reading the right-hand sides first, we can use these equations to factor perfect-square trinomials. Note that in order for a trinomial to be the square of a binomial, it must have the following:

1. Two terms, A^2 and B^2, must be squares, such as
   $$4, \quad x^2, \quad 81m^2, \quad 16t^2.$$
2. Neither A^2 nor B^2 is being subtracted.
3. The remaining term is either $2 \cdot A \cdot B$ or $-2 \cdot A \cdot B$, where A and B are the square roots of A^2 and B^2.

EXAMPLE 1

Determine whether each of the following is a perfect-square trinomial.

a) $x^2 + 6x + 9$ **b)** $t^2 - 8t - 9$ **c)** $16x^2 + 49 - 56x$

SOLUTION

a) To see if $x^2 + 6x + 9$ is a perfect-square trinomial, note that:

STUDENT NOTES ———

If you're not already quick to recognize the squares that represent $1^2, 2^2, 3^2, \ldots, 12^2$, this would be a good time to memorize these numbers.

1. Two terms, x^2 and 9, are squares.
2. Neither x^2 nor 9 is being subtracted.
3. The remaining term, $6x$, is $2 \cdot x \cdot 3$, where x and 3 are the square roots of x^2 and 9.

Thus, $x^2 + 6x + 9$ *is* a perfect-square trinomial.

b) To see if $t^2 - 8t - 9$ is a perfect-square trinomial, note that:

1. Both t^2 and 9, are squares. But:
2. Since 9 is being subtracted, $t^2 - 8t - 9$ *is not* a perfect-square trinomial.

STUDY SKILLS ———

Fill in Your Blanks

Don't hesitate to write out any missing steps that you'd like to see included. For instance, in Example 1(c), we state (in red) that $16x^2$ is a square. To solidify your understanding, you may want to write $4x \cdot 4x = 16x^2$ in the margin of your text.

c) To see if $16x^2 + 49 - 56x$ is a perfect-square trinomial, it helps to first write it in descending order:

$$16x^2 - 56x + 49.$$

Next, note that:

1. Two terms, $16x^2$ and 49, are squares.
2. There is no minus sign before $16x^2$ or 49.
3. Twice the product of the square roots, $2 \cdot 4x \cdot 7$, is $56x$. The remaining term, $-56x$, is the opposite of this product.

Thus, $16x^2 + 49 - 56x$ *is* a perfect-square trinomial.
TRY EXERCISE 11

Factoring Perfect–Square Trinomials

Either of the factoring methods discussed in Section 3.3 can be used to factor perfect-square trinomials, but a faster method is to recognize the following patterns.

> **Factoring a Perfect-Square Trinomial**
> $$A^2 + 2AB + B^2 = (A + B)^2; \qquad A^2 - 2AB + B^2 = (A - B)^2$$

Each factorization uses the square roots of the squared terms and the sign of the remaining term. To verify these equations, you should compute $(A + B)(A + B)$ and $(A - B)(A - B)$.

EXAMPLE 2

Factor: **(a)** $x^2 + 6x + 9$; **(b)** $t^2 + 49 - 14t$; **(c)** $16x^2 - 40x + 25$.

SOLUTION

a) $x^2 + 6x + 9 = x^2 + 2 \cdot x \cdot 3 + 3^2 = (x + 3)^2$ The sign of the middle term is positive.

$$A^2 + 2 \ A \ B + B^2 = (A + B)^2$$

b) $t^2 + 49 - 14t = t^2 - 14t + 49$ Using a commutative law to write in descending order

$$= t^2 - 2 \cdot t \cdot 7 + 7^2 = (t - 7)^2$$

$$A^2 - 2 \ A \ B + B^2 = (A - B)^2$$

c) $16x^2 - 40x + 25 = (4x)^2 - 2 \cdot 4x \cdot 5 + 5^2 = (4x - 5)^2$ Recall that $(4x)^2 = 16x^2$.

$$A^2 \quad - \; 2 \quad A \quad B + B^2 = (A - B)^2$$

TRY EXERCISE 19

Polynomials in more than one variable can also be perfect-square trinomials.

EXAMPLE 3

Factor: $4p^2 - 12pq + 9q^2$.

SOLUTION   We have

$$4p^2 - 12pq + 9q^2 = (2p)^2 - 2(2p)(3q) + (3q)^2 \qquad \text{Recognizing the perfect-square trinomial}$$

$$= (2p - 3q)^2. \qquad \text{The sign of the middle term is negative.}$$

Check: $(2p - 3q)(2p - 3q) = 4p^2 - 12pq + 9q^2.$

The factorization is $(2p - 3q)^2$.

TRY EXERCISE 43

EXAMPLE 4

Factor: $-75m^3 - 60m^2 - 12m$.

SOLUTION   *Always* look first for a common factor. This time there is one. We factor out $-3m$ so that the leading coefficient of the polynomial inside the parentheses is positive:

Factor out the common factor.

$$-75m^3 - 60m^2 - 12m = -3m[25m^2 + 20m + 4]$$

$$= -3m[(5m)^2 + 2(5m)(2) + 2^2] \qquad \text{Recognizing the perfect-square trinomial. Try to do this mentally.}$$

Factor the perfect-square trinomial.

$$= -3m(5m + 2)^2.$$

Check: $-3m(5m + 2)^2 = -3m(5m + 2)(5m + 2)$

$$= -3m(25m^2 + 20m + 4)$$

$$= -75m^3 - 60m^2 - 12m.$$

The factorization is $-3m(5m + 2)^2$.

TRY EXERCISE 31

Recognizing Differences of Squares

Some binomials represent the difference of two squares. For example, the binomial $16x^2 - 9$ is a difference of two expressions, $16x^2$ and 9, that are squares. To see this, note that $16x^2 = (4x)^2$ and $9 = 3^2$.

Any expression, like $16x^2 - 9$, that can be written in the form $A^2 - B^2$ is called a **difference of squares**. Note that in order for a binomial to be a difference of squares, it must have the following.

1. There must be two expressions, both squares, such as

$$25, \quad t^2, \quad 4x^2, \quad 1, \quad x^6, \quad 49y^8, \quad 100x^2y^2.$$

2. The terms in the binomial must have different signs.

Note that in order for an expression to be a square, its coefficient must be a perfect square and the power(s) of the variable(s) must be even.

EXAMPLE 5

Determine whether each of the following is a difference of squares.

a) $9x^2 - 64$ **b)** $25 - t^3$ **c)** $-4x^{10} + 36$

SOLUTION

a) To see if $9x^2 - 64$ is a difference of squares, note that:

1. The first expression is a square: $9x^2 = (3x)^2$.
The second expression is a square: $64 = 8^2$.
2. The terms have different signs.

Thus, $9x^2 - 64$ is a difference of squares, $(3x)^2 - 8^2$.

b) To see if $25 - t^3$ is a difference of squares, note that:

1. The expression t^3 is not a square.

Thus, $25 - t^3$ is not a difference of squares.

c) To see if $-4x^{10} + 36$ is a difference of squares, note that:

1. The expressions $4x^{10}$ and 36 are squares: $4x^{10} = (2x^5)^2$ and $36 = 6^2$.
2. The terms have different signs.

Thus, $-4x^{10} + 36$ is a difference of squares, $6^2 - (2x^5)^2$. It is often useful to rewrite $-4x^{10} + 36$ in the equivalent form $36 - 4x^{10}$. **TRY EXERCISE** 51

Factoring Differences of Squares

To factor a difference of squares, we reverse a pattern.

> **Factoring a Difference of Squares**
> $A^2 - B^2 = (A + B)(A - B)$

Once we have identified the expressions that are playing the roles of A and B, the factorization can be written directly. To verify this equation, simply multiply $(A + B)(A - B)$.

EXAMPLE 6

Factor: **(a)** $x^2 - 4$; **(b)** $1 - 9p^2$; **(c)** $s^6 - 16t^{10}$; **(d)** $50x^2 - 8x^8$.

SOLUTION

a) $x^2 - 4 = x^2 - 2^2 = (x + 2)(x - 2)$
$A^2 - B^2 = (A + B)(A - B)$

b) $1 - 9p^2 = 1^2 - (3p)^2 = (1 + 3p)(1 - 3p)$
$A^2 - B^2 = (A + B)(A - B)$

c) $s^6 - 16t^{10} = (s^3)^2 - (4t^5)^2$ Using the rules for powers
$A^2 - B^2$

$= (s^3 + 4t^5)(s^3 - 4t^5)$ Try to go directly to this step.
$(A + B)(A - B)$

d) *Always* look first for a common factor. This time there is one, $2x^2$:

Factor out the common factor.

$$50x^2 - 8x^8 = 2x^2(25 - 4x^6)$$
$$= 2x^2[5^2 - (2x^3)^2] \qquad \text{Recognizing } A^2 - B^2.$$
$$\text{Try to do this mentally.}$$

Factor the difference of squares.

$$= 2x^2(5 + 2x^3)(5 - 2x^3).$$

Check: $2x^2(5 + 2x^3)(5 - 2x^3) = 2x^2(25 - 4x^6)$
$$= 50x^2 - 8x^8.$$

The factorization of $50x^2 - 8x^8$ is $2x^2(5 + 2x^3)(5 - 2x^3)$.

TRY EXERCISE 57

> **CAUTION!** Note in Example 6 that a difference of squares is *not* the square of the difference; that is,
>
> $$A^2 - B^2 \neq (A - B)^2. \qquad \text{To see this, note that}$$
> $$(A - B)^2 = A^2 - 2AB + B^2.$$

Factoring Completely

Sometimes, as in Examples 4 and 6(d), a *complete* factorization requires two or more steps. Factoring is complete when no factor can be factored further.

EXAMPLE **7**　Factor: $y^4 - 16$.

SOLUTION　We have

Factor a difference of squares.

$$y^4 - 16 = (y^2)^2 - 4^2 \qquad \text{Recognizing } A^2 - B^2$$
$$= (y^2 + 4)(y^2 - 4) \qquad \text{Note that } y^2 - 4 \text{ is not prime.}$$

Factor another difference of squares.

$$= (y^2 + 4)(y + 2)(y - 2). \qquad \text{Note that } y^2 - 4 \text{ is itself a}$$
$$\text{difference of squares.}$$

Check: $(y^2 + 4)(y + 2)(y - 2) = (y^2 + 4)(y^2 - 4)$
$$= y^4 - 16.$$

The factorization is $(y^2 + 4)(y + 2)(y - 2)$.

TRY EXERCISE 79

Note in Example 7 that the factor $y^2 + 4$ is a *sum* of squares that cannot be factored further.

> **CAUTION!** There is no general formula for factoring a sum of squares. In particular,
>
> $$A^2 + B^2 \neq (A + B)^2.$$

As you proceed through the exercises, these suggestions may prove helpful.

Tips for Factoring
1. Always look first for a common factor! If there is one, factor it out.
2. Be alert for perfect-square trinomials and for binomials that are differences of squares. Once recognized, they can be factored without trial and error.
3. Always factor completely.
4. Check by multiplying.

3.4 EXERCISE SET

For Extra Help **MyMathLab** Math XL PRACTICE WATCH DOWNLOAD

Concept Reinforcement *Identify each of the following as a perfect-square trinomial, a difference of squares, a prime polynomial, or none of these.*

1. $4x^2 + 49$
2. $x^2 - 64$
3. $t^2 - 100$
4. $x^2 - 5x + 4$
5. $9x^2 + 6x + 1$
6. $a^2 - 8a + 16$
7. $2t^2 + 10t + 6$
8. $-25x^2 - 9$
9. $16t^2 - 25$
10. $4r^2 + 20r + 25$

Determine whether each of the following is a perfect-square trinomial.

11. $x^2 + 18x + 81$
12. $x^2 - 16x + 64$
13. $x^2 - 10x - 25$
14. $x^2 - 14x - 49$
15. $x^2 - 3x + 9$
16. $x^2 + 4x + 4$
17. $9x^2 + 25 - 30x$
18. $36x^2 + 16 - 24x$

Factor completely. Remember to look first for a common factor and to check by multiplying. If a polynomial is prime, state this.

19. $x^2 + 16x + 64$
20. $x^2 + 10x + 25$
21. $x^2 - 10x + 25$
22. $x^2 - 16x + 64$
23. $5p^2 + 20p + 20$
24. $3p^2 - 12p + 12$
25. $1 - 2t + t^2$
26. $1 + t^2 + 2t$
27. $18x^2 + 12x + 2$
28. $25x^2 + 10x + 1$
29. $49 - 56y + 16y^2$
30. $75 - 60m + 12m^2$
31. $-x^5 + 18x^4 - 81x^3$
32. $-2x^2 + 40x - 200$
33. $2n^3 + 40n^2 + 200n$
34. $x^3 + 24x^2 + 144x$

35. $20x^2 + 100x + 125$
36. $27m^2 - 36m + 12$
37. $49 - 42x + 9x^2$
38. $64 - 112x + 49x^2$
39. $16x^2 + 24x + 9$
40. $2a^2 + 28a + 98$
41. $2 + 20x + 50x^2$
42. $9x^2 + 30x + 25$
43. $9p^2 + 12pq + 4q^2$
44. $x^2 - 3xy + 9y^2$
45. $a^2 - 12ab + 49b^2$
46. $25m^2 - 20mn + 4n^2$
47. $-64m^2 - 16mn - n^2$
48. $-81p^2 + 18pq - q^2$
49. $-32s^2 + 80st - 50t^2$
50. $-36a^2 - 96ab - 64b^2$

Determine whether each of the following is a difference of squares.

51. $x^2 - 100$
52. $x^2 + 49$
53. $n^4 + 1$
54. $n^4 - 81$
55. $-1 + 64t^2$
56. $-12 + 25t^2$

Factor completely. Remember to look first for a common factor. If a polynomial is prime, state this.

57. $x^2 - 25$
58. $x^2 - 36$
59. $p^2 - 9$
60. $q^2 + 1$
61. $-49 + t^2$
62. $-64 + m^2$
63. $6a^2 - 24$
64. $x^2 - 8x + 16$
65. $49x^2 - 14x + 1$
66. $3t^2 - 3$
67. $200 - 2t^2$
68. $98 - 8w^2$

69. $-80a^2 + 45$

70. $25x^2 - 4$

71. $5t^2 - 80$

72. $-4t^2 + 64$

73. $8x^2 - 162$

74. $24x^2 - 54$

75. $36x - 49x^3$

76. $16x - 81x^3$

77. $49a^4 - 20$

78. $25a^4 - 9$

79. $t^4 - 1$

80. $x^4 - 16$

81. $-3x^3 + 24x^2 - 48x$

82. $-2a^4 + 36a^3 - 162a^2$

83. $75t^3 - 27t$

84. $80s^4 - 45s^2$

85. $a^8 - 2a^7 + a^6$

86. $x^8 - 8x^7 + 16x^6$

87. $10a^2 - 10b^2$

88. $6p^2 - 6q^2$

89. $16x^4 - y^4$

90. $98x^2 - 32y^2$

91. $18t^2 - 8s^2$

92. $a^4 - 81b^4$

93. Explain in your own words how to determine whether a polynomial is a perfect-square trinomial.

94. Explain in your own words how to determine whether a polynomial is a difference of squares.

Skill Review

To prepare for Section 3.5, review the product and power rules for exponents and multiplication of polynomials.

Simplify.

95. $(2x^2y^4)^3$

96. $(-5x^2y)^3$

Multiply.

97. $(x + 1)(x + 1)(x + 1)$

98. $(x - 1)^3$

99. $(p + q)^3$

100. $(p - q)^3$

Synthesis

101. Leon concludes that since $x^2 - 9 = (x - 3)(x + 3)$, it must follow that $x^2 + 9 = (x + 3)(x - 3)$. What mistake(s) is he making?

102. Write directions that would enable someone to construct a polynomial that contains a perfect-square trinomial, a difference of squares, and a common factor.

Factor completely. If a polynomial is prime, state this.

103. $x^8 - 2^8$

104. $3x^2 - \frac{1}{3}$

105. $18x^3 - \frac{8}{25}x$

106. $0.81t - t^3$

107. $(y - 5)^4 - z^8$

108. $x^2 - \left(\frac{1}{x}\right)^2$

109. $-x^4 + 8x^2 + 9$

110. $-16x^4 + 96x^2 - 144$

Aha! **111.** $(y + 3)^2 + 2(y + 3) + 1$

112. $49(x + 1)^2 - 42(x + 1) + 9$

113. $27p^3 - 45p^2 - 75p + 125$

114. $a^{2n} - 49b^{2n}$

115. $81 - b^{4k}$

116. $9b^{2n} + 12b^n + 4$

117. Subtract $(x^2 + 1)^2$ from $x^2(x + 1)^2$.

Factor by grouping. Look for a grouping of three terms that is a perfect-square trinomial.

118. $t^2 + 4t + 4 - 25$

119. $y^2 + 6y + 9 - x^2 - 8x - 16$

Find c such that each polynomial is the square of a binomial.

120. $cy^2 + 6y + 1$

121. $cy^2 - 24y + 9$

122. Find the value of a if $x^2 + a^2x + a^2$ factors into $(x + a)^2$.

123. Show that the difference of the squares of two consecutive integers is the sum of the integers. (*Hint*: Use x for the smaller number.)

3.5 Factoring Sums or Differences of Cubes

Formulas for Factoring Sums or Differences of Cubes ■ Using the Formulas

Formulas for Factoring Sums or Differences of Cubes

We have seen that a difference of two squares can always be factored, but a *sum* of two squares is usually prime. The situation is different with cubes: The difference *or sum* of two cubes can always be factored. To see this, consider the following products:

$$(A + B)(A^2 - AB + B^2) = A(A^2 - AB + B^2) + B(A^2 - AB + B^2)$$
$$= A^3 - A^2B + AB^2 + A^2B - AB^2 + B^3$$
$$= A^3 + B^3 \quad \text{Combining like terms}$$

and

$$(A - B)(A^2 + AB + B^2) = A(A^2 + AB + B^2) - B(A^2 + AB + B^2)$$
$$= A^3 + A^2B + AB^2 - A^2B - AB^2 - B^3$$
$$= A^3 - B^3. \quad \text{Combining like terms}$$

These products allow us to factor a sum or a difference of two cubes. Observe how the location of the $+$ and $-$ signs changes.

> **Factoring a Sum or a Difference of Two Cubes**
> $A^3 + B^3 = (A + B)(A^2 - AB + B^2);$
> $A^3 - B^3 = (A - B)(A^2 + AB + B^2)$

Using the Formulas

Remembering this list of cubes may prove helpful when factoring.

N	0.2	0.1	0	1	2	3	4	5	6
N^3	0.008	0.001	0	1	8	27	64	125	216

We say that 2 is the *cube root* of 8, that 3 is the cube root of 27, and so on.

EXAMPLE 1 Write an equivalent expression by factoring: $x^3 + 27$.

SOLUTION We first observe that

$$x^3 + 27 = x^3 + 3^3. \quad \text{This is a sum of cubes.}$$

Next, in one set of parentheses, we write the first cube root, x, plus the second cube root, 3:

$$(x + 3)(\qquad).$$

To get the other factor, we think of $x + 3$ and do the following:

Square the first term: x^2.
Multiply the terms and then change the sign: $-3x$.
Square the second term: 3^2, or 9.

$$(x + 3)(x^2 - 3x + 9).$$

Check: $(x + 3)(x^2 - 3x + 9) = x^3 - 3x^2 + 9x + 3x^2 - 9x + 27$
$$= x^3 + 27. \quad \text{Combining like terms}$$

Thus, $x^3 + 27 = (x + 3)(x^2 - 3x + 9)$.

TRY EXERCISE 13

In Example 2, you will see that the pattern used to write the trinomial factor in Example 1 can be used when factoring a *difference* of two cubes as well.

EXAMPLE 2

Factor.

a) $125x^3 - y^3$

b) $m^6 + 64$

c) $128y^7 - 250x^6y$

d) $r^6 - s^6$

SOLUTION

a) We have

$$125x^3 - y^3 = (5x)^3 - y^3. \quad \text{This is a difference of cubes.}$$

In one set of parentheses, we write the cube root of the first term, $5x$, minus the cube root of the second term, y:

$(5x - y)(\quad)$. This can be regarded as $5x$ *plus* the cube root of $(-y)^3$, since $-y^3 = (-y)^3$.

To get the other factor, we think of $5x + y$ and do the following:

Square the first term: $(5x)^2$, or $25x^2$.
Multiply the terms and then change the sign: $5xy$.
Square the second term: $(-y)^2 = y^2$.

$$(5x - y)(25x^2 + 5xy + y^2).$$

Check:
$(5x - y)(25x^2 + 5xy + y^2) = 125x^3 + 25x^2y + 5xy^2 - 25x^2y - 5xy^2 - y^3$
$$= 125x^3 - y^3. \quad \text{Combining like terms}$$

Thus, $125x^3 - y^3 = (5x - y)(25x^2 + 5xy + y^2)$.

b) We have

$$m^6 + 64 = (m^2)^3 + 4^3. \quad \text{Rewriting as a sum of quantities cubed}$$

Next, we reuse the pattern used in Example 1:

$$A^3 + B^3 = (A + B)(A^2 - A \cdot B + B^2)$$
$$(m^2)^3 + 4^3 = (m^2 + 4)((m^2)^2 - m^2 \cdot 4 + 4^2)$$
$$= (m^2 + 4)(m^4 - 4m^2 + 16). \quad \text{The check is left to the student.}$$

c) We have

$$128y^7 - 250x^6y = 2y(64y^6 - 125x^6) \qquad \text{Remember: } \textit{Always} \text{ look for a common factor.}$$

$$= 2y[(4y^2)^3 - (5x^2)^3]. \qquad \text{Rewriting as a difference of quantities cubed}$$

To factor $(4y^2)^3 - (5x^2)^3$, we reuse the pattern in part (a) above:

$$A^3 \quad - \quad B^3 \quad = (A \quad - \quad B)(\quad A^2 \quad + \quad A \cdot B \quad + \quad B^2)$$

$$(4y^2)^3 - (5x^2)^3 = (4y^2 - 5x^2)((4y^2)^2 + 4y^2 \cdot 5x^2 + (5x^2)^2)$$

$$= (4y^2 - 5x^2)(16y^4 + 20x^2y^2 + 25x^4).$$

The check is left to the student. We have

$$128y^7 - 250x^6y = 2y(4y^2 - 5x^2)(16y^4 + 20x^2y^2 + 25x^4).$$

d) We have

$$r^6 - s^6 = (r^3)^2 - (s^3)^2$$

$$= (r^3 + s^3)(r^3 - s^3) \qquad \text{Factoring a difference of two } \textit{squares}$$

$$= (r + s)(r^2 - rs + s^2)(r - s)(r^2 + rs + s^2). \qquad \text{Factoring the sum and the difference of two cubes}$$

To check, read the steps in reverse order and inspect the multiplication.

TRY EXERCISES 31 and 41

In Example 2(d), suppose we first factored $r^6 - s^6$ as a difference of two cubes:

$$(r^2)^3 - (s^2)^3 = (r^2 - s^2)(r^4 + r^2s^2 + s^4)$$

$$= (r + s)(r - s)(r^4 + r^2s^2 + s^4).$$

In this case, we might have missed some factors; $r^4 + r^2s^2 + s^4$ can be factored as $(r^2 - rs + s^2)(r^2 + rs + s^2)$, but we probably would never have suspected that such a factorization exists. Given a choice, it is generally better to factor as a difference of squares before factoring as a sum or a difference of cubes.

Useful Factoring Facts

Sum of cubes: $\qquad A^3 + B^3 = (A + B)(A^2 - AB + B^2)$

Difference of cubes: $\quad A^3 - B^3 = (A - B)(A^2 + AB + B^2)$

Difference of squares: $\; A^2 - B^2 = (A + B)(A - B)$

There is no formula for factoring a sum of two squares.

3.5   EXERCISE SET

For Extra Help MyMathLab Math XL PRACTICE WATCH DOWNLOAD

Concept Reinforcement   *Classify each binomial as either a sum of cubes, a difference of cubes, a difference of squares, or none of these.*

1. $x^3 - 1$
2. $8 + t^3$
3. $9x^4 - 25$
4. $9x^2 + 25$
5. $1000t^3 + 1$
6. $x^3y^3 - 27z^3$
7. $25x^2 + 8x$
8. $100y^8 - 25x^4$
9. $s^{21} - t^{15}$
10. $14x^3 - 2x$

Factor completely.

11. $x^3 - 64$
12. $t^3 - 27$
13. $z^3 + 1$
14. $x^3 + 8$
15. $t^3 - 1000$
16. $m^3 + 125$
17. $27x^3 + 1$
18. $8a^3 + 1$
19. $64 - 125x^3$
20. $27 - 8t^3$
21. $x^3 - y^3$
22. $y^3 - z^3$
23. $a^3 + \frac{1}{8}$
24. $x^3 + \frac{1}{27}$
25. $8t^3 - 8$
26. $2y^3 - 128$
27. $54x^3 + 2$
28. $8a^3 + 1000$
29. $rs^4 + 64rs$
30. $ab^5 + 1000ab^2$
31. $5x^3 - 40z^3$
32. $2y^3 - 54z^3$
33. $y^3 - \frac{1}{1000}$
34. $x^3 - \frac{1}{8}$
35. $x^3 + 0.001$
36. $y^3 + 0.125$
37. $64x^6 - 8t^6$
38. $125c^6 - 8d^6$
39. $54y^4 - 128y$
40. $3z^5 - 3z^2$
41. $z^6 - 1$
42. $t^6 + 1$
43. $t^6 + 64y^6$
44. $p^6 - q^6$
45. $x^{12} - y^3z^{12}$
46. $a^9 + b^{12}c^{15}$

47. How could you use factoring to convince someone that $x^3 + y^3 \neq (x + y)^3$?

48. Is the following statement true or false and why? If A^3 and B^3 have a common factor, then A and B have a common factor.

Skill Review

Review graphing linear equations (Chapter 2).

49. Find the slope of the line containing the points $(-2, -5)$ and $(3, -6)$. [2.5]

50. Find the slope of the line given by $y - 3 = \frac{1}{4}x$. [2.6]

Graph.

51. $2x - 5y = 10$ [2.3]
52. $-5x = 10$ [2.3]
53. $y = \frac{2}{3}x - 1$ [2.6]
54. $y - 2 = -2(x + 4)$ [2.7]

Synthesis

55. Explain how the geometric model below can be used to verify the formula for factoring $a^3 - b^3$.

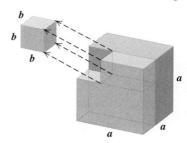

56. Explain how someone could construct a binomial that is both a difference of two cubes and a difference of two squares.

Factor.

57. $x^{6a} - y^{3b}$
58. $2x^{3a} + 16y^{3b}$

Aha! 59. $(x + 5)^3 + (x - 5)^3$
60. $\frac{1}{16}x^{3a} + \frac{1}{2}y^{6a}z^{9b}$
61. $5x^3y^6 - \frac{5}{8}$
62. $x^3 - (x + y)^3$
63. $x^{6a} - (x^{2a} + 1)^3$
64. $(x^{2a} - 1)^3 - x^{6a}$
65. $t^4 - 8t^3 - t + 8$

3.6 Factoring: A General Strategy

Choosing the Right Method

Thus far, each section in this chapter has examined one or two different methods for factoring polynomials. In practice, when the need for factoring a polynomial arises, we must decide on our own which method to use. Regardless of the polynomial with which we are faced, the guidelines listed below can always be used.

To Factor a Polynomial

A. Always look for a common factor first. If there is one, factor out the largest common factor. Be sure to include it in your final answer.

B. Then look at the number of terms.

Two terms: Try factoring as a difference of squares first: $A^2 - B^2 = (A + B)(A - B)$. Next, try factoring as a sum or a difference of cubes: $A^3 + B^3 = (A + B)(A^2 - AB + B^2)$ and $A^3 - B^3 = (A - B)(A^2 + AB + B^2)$.

Three terms: If the trinomial is a perfect-square trinomial, factor accordingly: $A^2 + 2AB + B^2 = (A + B)^2$ or $A^2 - 2AB + B^2 = (A - B)^2$. If it is not a perfect-square trinomial, try using FOIL or grouping.

Four terms: Try factoring by grouping.

C. Always *factor completely*. When a factor can itself be factored, be sure to factor it. Remember that some polynomials, like $x^2 + 9$, are prime.

D. Check by multiplying.

Choosing the Right Method

EXAMPLE 1 Factor: $5t^4 - 80$.

SOLUTION

A. We look for a common factor:

$$5t^4 - 80 = 5(t^4 - 16). \qquad \text{5 is the largest common factor.}$$

B. The factor $t^4 - 16$ is a difference of squares: $(t^2)^2 - 4^2$. We factor it, being careful to rewrite the 5 from step (A):

$$5t^4 - 80 = 5(t^2 + 4)(t^2 - 4). \qquad t^4 - 16 = (t^2 + 4)(t^2 - 4)$$

C. Since $t^2 - 4$ is a difference of squares, we continue factoring:

$$5t^4 - 80 = 5(t^2 + 4)(t^2 - 4) = 5(t^2 + 4)(t - 2)(t + 2).$$

This is a sum of squares, which cannot be factored.

D. *Check:* $5(t^2 + 4)(t - 2)(t + 2) = 5(t^2 + 4)(t^2 - 4)$
$$= 5(t^4 - 16) = 5t^4 - 80.$$

The factorization is $5(t^2 + 4)(t - 2)(t + 2)$.

TRY EXERCISE 5

EXAMPLE 2

STUDY SKILLS —————

Keep Your Focus

When you are studying with someone else, it can be very tempting to prolong conversation that has little to do with the mathematics that you need to study. If you see that this may happen, explain to your partner(s) that you enjoy the nonmathematical conversation, but would enjoy it more later—after the math work has been completed.

Factor: $2x^3 + 10x^2 + x + 5$.

SOLUTION

A. We look for a common factor. There is none.

B. Because there are four terms, we try factoring by grouping:

$$2x^3 + 10x^2 + x + 5$$
$$= (2x^3 + 10x^2) + (x + 5) \qquad \text{Separating into two binomials}$$
$$= 2x^2(x + 5) + 1(x + 5) \qquad \text{Factoring out the largest common factor from each binomial. The 1 serves as an aid.}$$
$$= (x + 5)(2x^2 + 1). \qquad \text{Factoring out the common factor, } x + 5$$

C. Nothing can be factored further, so we have factored completely.

D. *Check:* $(x + 5)(2x^2 + 1) = 2x^3 + x + 10x^2 + 5$
$$= 2x^3 + 10x^2 + x + 5.$$

The factorization is $(x + 5)(2x^2 + 1)$.

`TRY EXERCISE` 13

EXAMPLE 3

Factor: $-n^5 + 2n^4 + 35n^3$.

SOLUTION

A. We note that there is a common factor, $-n^3$:

$$-n^5 + 2n^4 + 35n^3 = -n^3(n^2 - 2n - 35).$$

B. The factor $n^2 - 2n - 35$ is not a perfect-square trinomial. We factor it using trial and error:

$$-n^5 + 2n^4 + 35n^3 = -n^3(n^2 - 2n - 35)$$
$$= -n^3(n - 7)(n + 5).$$

C. Nothing can be factored further, so we have factored completely.

D. *Check:* $-n^3(n - 7)(n + 5) = -n^3(n^2 - 2n - 35)$
$$= -n^5 + 2n^4 + 35n^3.$$

The factorization is $-n^3(n - 7)(n + 5)$.

`TRY EXERCISE` 21

EXAMPLE 4

STUDENT NOTES —————

Quickly checking the leading and constant terms of a trinomial to see if they are squares can save you time. If they aren't both squares, the trinomial can't possibly be a perfect-square trinomial.

Factor: $x^2 - 20x + 100$.

SOLUTION

A. We look first for a common factor. There is none.

B. This polynomial is a perfect-square trinomial. We factor it accordingly:

$$x^2 - 20x + 100 = x^2 - 2 \cdot x \cdot 10 + 10^2 \qquad \text{Try to do this step mentally.}$$
$$= (x - 10)^2.$$

C. Nothing can be factored further, so we have factored completely.

D. *Check:* $(x - 10)(x - 10) = x^2 - 20x + 100$.

The factorization is $(x - 10)(x - 10)$, or $(x - 10)^2$.

`TRY EXERCISE` 7

EXAMPLE 5

Factor: $6x^2y^4 - 21x^3y^5 + 3x^2y^6$.

SOLUTION

A. We first factor out the largest common factor, $3x^2y^4$:

$$6x^2y^4 - 21x^3y^5 + 3x^2y^6 = 3x^2y^4(2 - 7xy + y^2).$$

B. The constant term in $2 - 7xy + y^2$ is not a square, so we do not have a perfect-square trinomial. Note that x appears only in $-7xy$. The product of a form like $(1 - y)(2 - y)$ has no x in the middle term. Thus, $2 - 7xy + y^2$ cannot be factored.

C. Nothing can be factored further, so we have factored completely.

D. *Check:*　$3x^2y^4(2 - 7xy + y^2) = 6x^2y^4 - 21x^3y^5 + 3x^2y^6$.

The factorization is $3x^2y^4(2 - 7xy + y^2)$.

TRY EXERCISE 33

EXAMPLE 6

Factor: $x^6 - 64$.

SOLUTION

A. We look first for a common factor. There is none (other than 1 or -1).

B. There are two terms, a difference of squares: $(x^3)^2 - (8)^2$. We factor:

$$x^6 - 64 = (x^3 + 8)(x^3 - 8). \qquad \text{Note that } x^6 = (x^3)^2.$$

C. One factor is a sum of two cubes, and the other factor is a difference of two cubes. We factor both:

$$x^6 - 64 = (x + 2)(x^2 - 2x + 4)(x - 2)(x^2 + 2x + 4).$$

The factorization is complete because no factor can be factored further.

D. *Check:*　$(x + 2)(x^2 - 2x + 4)(x - 2)(x^2 + 2x + 4) = (x^3 + 8)(x^3 - 8)$
$$= x^6 - 64.$$

The factorization is $(x + 2)(x^2 - 2x + 4)(x - 2)(x^2 + 2x + 4)$.

TRY EXERCISE 31

EXAMPLE 7

Factor: $-25m^2 - 20mn - 4n^2$.

SOLUTION

A. We look first for a common factor. Since all the terms are negative, we factor out a -1:

$$-25m^2 - 20mn - 4n^2 = -1(25m^2 + 20mn + 4n^2).$$

B. There are three terms in the parentheses. Note that the first term and the last term are squares: $25m^2 = (5m)^2$ and $4n^2 = (2n)^2$. We see that twice the product of $5m$ and $2n$ is the middle term,

$$2 \cdot 5m \cdot 2n = 20mn,$$

so the trinomial is a perfect square. To factor, we write a binomial squared:

$$-25m^2 - 20mn - 4n^2 = -1(25m^2 + 20mn + 4n^2)$$
$$= -1(5m + 2n)^2.$$

C. Nothing can be factored further, so we have factored completely.

D. *Check:*　$-1(5m + 2n)^2 = -1(25m^2 + 20mn + 4n^2)$
$$= -25m^2 - 20mn - 4n^2.$$

The factorization is $-1(5m + 2n)^2$, or $-(5m + 2n)^2$.

TRY EXERCISE 59

EXAMPLE 8   Factor: $x^2y^2 + 7xy + 12$.

SOLUTION

A. We look first for a common factor. There is none.

B. Since only one term is a square, we do not have a perfect-square trinomial. We use trial and error, thinking of the product xy as a single variable:

$$(xy + \quad)(xy + \quad).$$

We factor the last term, 12. All the signs are positive, so we consider only positive factors. Possibilities are 1, 12 and 2, 6 and 3, 4. The pair 3, 4 gives a sum of 7 for the coefficient of the middle term. Thus,

$$x^2y^2 + 7xy + 12 = (xy + 3)(xy + 4).$$

C. Nothing can be factored further, so we have factored completely.

D. *Check:* $(xy + 3)(xy + 4) = x^2y^2 + 7xy + 12$.

The factorization is $(xy + 3)(xy + 4)$.   TRY EXERCISE 61

Compare the variables appearing in Example 7 with those in Example 8. Note that if the leading term contains one variable and a different variable is in the last term, as in Example 7, each binomial contains two variable terms. When two variables appear in the leading term and no variables appear in the last term, as in Example 8, each binomial contains one term that has two variables and one term that is a constant.

EXAMPLE 9   Factor: $a^4 - 16b^4$.

SOLUTION

A. We look first for a common factor. There is none.

B. There are two terms. Since $a^4 = (a^2)^2$ and $16b^4 = (4b^2)^2$, we see that we have a difference of squares. Thus,

$$a^4 - 16b^4 = (a^2 + 4b^2)(a^2 - 4b^2).$$

C. The factor $(a^2 - 4b^2)$ is itself a difference of squares. Thus,

$$a^4 - 16b^4 = (a^2 + 4b^2)(a + 2b)(a - 2b). \qquad \text{Factoring } a^2 - 4b^2$$

D. *Check:* $(a^2 + 4b^2)(a + 2b)(a - 2b) = (a^2 + 4b^2)(a^2 - 4b^2)$
$$= a^4 - 16b^4.$$

The factorization is $(a^2 + 4b^2)(a + 2b)(a - 2b)$.   TRY EXERCISE 53

3.6 EXERCISE SET

For Extra Help

🔖 ***Concept Reinforcement*** *In each of Exercises 1–4, complete the sentence.*

1. As a first step when factoring polynomials, always check for a _____.

2. When factoring a trinomial, if two terms are not squares, it cannot be a _____.

3. If a polynomial has four terms and no common factor, it may be possible to factor by _____.

4. It is always possible to check a factorization by _____.

Factor completely. If a polynomial is prime, state this.

5. $5a^2 - 125$

6. $10c^2 - 810$

7. $y^2 + 49 - 14y$

8. $a^2 + 25 + 10a$

9. $3t^2 + 16t + 21$

10. $8t^2 + 31t - 4$

11. $x^3 + 18x^2 + 81x$

12. $x^3 - 24x^2 + 144x$

13. $x^3 - 5x^2 - 25x + 125$

14. $x^3 + 3x^2 - 4x - 12$

15. $27t^3 - 3t$

16. $98t^2 - 18$

17. $9x^3 + 12x^2 - 45x$

18. $20x^3 - 4x^2 - 72x$

19. $t^2 + 25$

20. $4x^2 + 20x - 144$

21. $6y^2 + 18y - 240$

22. $4n^2 + 81$

23. $-2a^6 + 8a^5 - 8a^4$

24. $-x^5 - 14x^4 - 49x^3$

25. $5x^5 - 80x$

26. $4x^4 - 64$

27. $t^4 - 9$

28. $9 + t^8$

29. $-x^6 + 2x^5 - 7x^4$

30. $-x^5 + 4x^4 - 3x^3$

31. $x^3 - y^3$

32. $8t^3 + 1$

33. $ax^2 + ay^2$

34. $12n^2 + 24n^3$

35. $2\pi rh + 2\pi r^2$

36. $4\pi r^2 + 2\pi r$

Aha! **37.** $(a + b)5a + (a + b)3b$

38. $5c(a^3 + b) - (a^3 + b)$

39. $x^2 + x + xy + y$

40. $n^2 + 2n + np + 2p$

41. $a^2 - 2a - ay + 2y$

42. $2x^2 - 4x + xz - 2z$

43. $3x^2 + 13xy - 10y^2$

44. $-x^2 - y^2 - 2xy$

45. $8m^3n - 32m^2n^2 + 24mn$

46. $a^2 - 7a - 6$

47. $4b^2 + a^2 - 4ab$

48. $7p^4 - 7q^4$

49. $16x^2 + 24xy + 9y^2$

50. $6a^2b^3 + 12a^3b^2 - 3a^4b^2$

51. $m^2 - 5m + 8$

52. $25z^2 + 10zy + y^2$

53. $a^4b^4 - 16$

54. $a^5 - 4a^4b - 5a^3b^2$

55. $80cd^2 - 36c^2d + 4c^3$

56. $2p^2 + pq + q^2$

57. $64t^6 - 1$

58. $m^6 - 1$

59. $-12 - x^2y^2 - 8xy$

60. $m^2n^2 - 4mn - 32$

61. $5p^2q^2 + 25pq - 30$

62. $a^4b^3 + 2a^3b^2 - 15a^2b$

63. $54a^4 + 16ab^3$

64. $54x^3y - 250y^4$

65. $x^6 + x^5y - 2x^4y^2$

66. $2s^6t^2 + 10s^3t^3 + 12t^4$

67. $36a^2 - 15a + \frac{25}{16}$

68. $a^2 + 2a^2bc + a^2b^2c^2$

69. $\frac{1}{81}x^2 - \frac{8}{27}x + \frac{16}{9}$

70. $\frac{1}{4}a^2 + \frac{1}{3}ab + \frac{1}{9}b^2$

71. $1 - 16x^{12}y^{12}$

72. $b^4a - 81a^5$

73. $4a^2b^2 + 12ab + 9$

74. $9c^2 + 6cd + d^2$

75. $z^4 + 6z^3 - 6z^2 - 36z$

76. $t^5 - 2t^4 + 5t^3 - 10t^2$

77. Kelly factored $16 - 8x + x^2$ as $(x - 4)^2$, while Tony factored it as $(4 - x)^2$. Are they both correct? Why or why not?

78. Describe in your own words or draw a diagram representing a strategy for factoring polynomials.

Skill Review

To prepare for Section 3.7, review solving equations (Section 1.2).

Solve. [1.2]

79. $8x - 9 = 0$

80. $3x + 5 = 0$

81. $2x + 7 = 0$

82. $4x - 1 = 0$

83. $3 - x = 0$

84. $22 - 2x = 0$

85. $2x - 5 = 8x + 1$

86. $3(x - 1) = 9 - x$

Synthesis

87. There are third-degree polynomials in x that we are not yet able to factor, despite the fact that they are not prime. Explain how such a polynomial could be created.

88. Describe a method that could be used to find a binomial of degree 16 that can be expressed as the product of prime binomial factors.

Factor.

89. $-(x^5 + 7x^3 - 18x)$

90. $18 + a^3 - 9a - 2a^2$

91. $-x^4 + 7x^2 + 18$

92. $-3a^4 + 15a^2 - 12$

Aha! **93.** $y^2(y + 1) - 4y(y + 1) - 21(y + 1)$

94. $y^2(y - 1) - 2y(y - 1) + (y - 1)$

95. $(y + 4)^2 + 2x(y + 4) + x^2$

96. $6(x - 1)^2 + 7y(x - 1) - 3y^2$

97. $2(a + 3)^4 - (a + 3)^3(b - 2) - (a + 3)^2(b - 2)^2$

98. $5(t - 1)^5 - 6(t - 1)^4(s - 1) + (t - 1)^3(s - 1)^2$

99. $49x^4 + 14x^2 + 1 - 25x^6$

Additional Exercises

Factor.

100. $\frac{9}{16} - y^2$

101. $\frac{1}{36} a^2 - m^2$

102. $\frac{1}{9} x^2 + 6x + 81$

103. $\frac{16}{25} x^2 - \frac{4}{25} x + \frac{1}{100}$

Factor.

104. $x^4 y - 81y$

105. $13n^4 - 13$

106. $160a^2 m^4 - 10a^2$

107. $32t^4 - 162y^4$

Factor.

108. $200 - 18n^2$

109. $90 - 40x^2$

110. $100 + 90x - 90x^2$

111. $90 - 34t - 12t^2$

Factor.

112. $10x^2 - 11x - 6$

113. $24x^2 - 47x - 21$

114. $12x^2 - 17x + 6$

115. $20x^2 - 37x + 15$

116. $18m^2 + 31m + 6$

117. $20n^2 + 23n + 6$

118. $14t + 8t^2 - 15$

119. $8y - 15 + 12y^2$

120. $9 - 30y + 16y^2$

121. $15 - 38m + 24m^2$

Factor.

122. $x^3 + 5x^2 - x - 5$

123. $x^3 + 3x^2 - 16x - 48$

124. $a^3 - 2a^2 - 9a + 18$

125. $y^3 - y^2 - 25y + 25$

126. $9x^3 + 27x^2 - 4x - 12$

127. $4x^3 + 20x^2 - x - 5$

128. $2y^3 - 5y^2 - 8y + 20$

129. $3m^3 - 4m^2 - 27m + 36$

Factor.

130. $36 - 12x + x^2 - a^2$

131. $100 - 20t + t^2 - 4y^2$

132. $9 - 12y + 4y^2 - 49x^2$

133. $1 - 10m + 25m^2 - t^2$

COLLABORATIVE CORNER

Matching Factorizations*

Focus: Factoring

Time: 20 minutes

Group size: Begin with the entire class. If there is an odd number of students, the instructor should participate.

Materials: Prepared sheets of paper, pins or tape. On half of the sheets, the instructor writes a polynomial. On the remaining sheets, the instructor writes the factorization of those polynomials. The polynomials and factorizations should be similar; for example,

$$x^2 - 2x - 8, \quad (x - 2)(x - 4),$$
$$x^2 - 6x + 8, \quad (x - 1)(x - 8),$$
$$x^2 - 9x + 8, \quad (x + 2)(x - 4).$$

ACTIVITY

1. As class members enter the room, the instructor pins or tapes either a polynomial or a factorization to the back of each student. Class members are told only whether their sheet of paper contains a polynomial or a factorization.

2. After all students are wearing a sheet of paper, they should mingle with one another, attempting to match up their factorization with the appropriate polynomial or vice versa. They may ask questions of one another that relate to factoring and polynomials. Answers to the questions should be yes or no. For example, a legitimate question might be "Is my last term negative?" or "Do my factors have opposite signs?"

3. The game is over when all factorization/polynomial pairs have "found" one another.

*Thanks to Jann MacInnes of Florida Community College at Jacksonville–Kent Campus for suggesting this activity.

3.7 Solving Polynomial Equations by Factoring

The Principle of Zero Products ∎ Factoring to Solve Equations

When we factor a polynomial, we are forming an *equivalent expression*. We now use our factoring skills to *solve equations*. We already know how to solve linear equations like $x + 2 = 7$ and $2x = 9$. The equations we will learn to solve in this section contain a variable raised to a power greater than 1 and will usually have more than one solution.

Whenever two polynomials are set equal to each other, we have a *polynomial equation*. The degree of a polynomial equation is the same as the highest degree of any term in the equation. Second-degree equations like $4t^2 - 9 = 0$ and $x^2 + 6x + 5 = 0$ are called **quadratic equations**.

> ### Quadratic Equation
> A *quadratic equation* is an equation equivalent to one of the form
> $$ax^2 + bx + c = 0,$$
> where a, b, and c are constants, with $a \neq 0$.

In order to solve quadratic equations, we need to develop a new principle.

The Principle of Zero Products

Suppose we are told that the product of two numbers is 6. On the basis of this information, it is impossible to know the value of either number—the product could be $2 \cdot 3$, $6 \cdot 1$, $12 \cdot \frac{1}{2}$, and so on. However, if we are told that the product of two numbers is 0, we know that at least one of the two factors must itself be 0. For example, if $(x + 3)(x - 2) = 0$, we can conclude that either $x + 3$ is 0 or $x - 2$ is 0.

> ### The Principle of Zero Products
> An equation $AB = 0$ is true if and only if $A = 0$ or $B = 0$, or both.
> (A product is 0 if and only if at least one factor is 0.)

EXAMPLE 1

Solve: $(x + 3)(x - 2) = 0$.

SOLUTION We are looking for all values of x that will make the equation true. The equation tells us that the product of $x + 3$ and $x - 2$ is 0. In order for the product to be 0, at least one factor must be 0. Thus we look for any value of x for which $x + 3 = 0$, as well as any value of x for which $x - 2 = 0$, that is, either

$$x + 3 = 0 \quad or \quad x - 2 = 0. \qquad \text{Using the principle of zero products. There are two equations to solve.}$$

STUDY SKILLS ———

Identify the Highlights

If you haven't already tried one, consider using a highlighter as you read. By highlighting sentences or phrases that you find especially important, you will make it easier to review important material in the future. Be sure to keep your highlighter available when you study.

We solve each equation:

$$x + 3 = 0 \quad or \quad x - 2 = 0$$
$$x = -3 \quad or \quad x = 2.$$

Both -3 and 2 should be checked in the original equation.

Check: For -3:   For 2:

$$\frac{(x + 3)(x - 2) = 0}{(-3 + 3)(-3 - 2) \mid 0}$$

The factor $x + 3$ is 0 when $x = -3$. $\longrightarrow 0(-5)$

$$0 \overset{?}{=} 0 \quad \text{TRUE}$$

$$\frac{(x + 3)(x - 2) = 0}{(2 + 3)(2 - 2) \mid 0}$$

$$5(0)$$

The factor $x - 2$ is 0 when $x = 2$.

$$0 \overset{?}{=} 0 \quad \text{TRUE}$$

The solutions are -3 and 2.

TRY EXERCISE 5

When we are using the principle of zero products, the word "or" is meant to emphasize that any one of the factors could be the one that represents 0.

EXAMPLE 2   Solve: $3(5x + 1)(x - 7) = 0$.

SOLUTION   The factors in this equation are 3, $5x + 1$, and $x - 7$. Since the factor 3 is constant, the only way in which $3(5x + 1)(x - 7)$ can be 0 is for one of the other factors to be 0, that is,

$$5x + 1 = 0 \quad or \quad x - 7 = 0 \qquad \text{Using the principle of zero products}$$
$$5x = -1 \quad or \qquad x = 7 \qquad \text{Solving the two equations separately}$$
$$x = -\tfrac{1}{5} \quad or \qquad x = 7. \qquad 5x + 1 = 0 \text{ when } x = -\tfrac{1}{5}; x - 7 = 0$$
$$\text{when } x = 7$$

Check: For $-\tfrac{1}{5}$:   For 7:

$$\frac{3(5x + 1)(x - 7) = 0}{3\left(5\left(-\tfrac{1}{5}\right) + 1\right)\left(-\tfrac{1}{5} - 7\right) \mid 0}$$
$$3(-1 + 1)\left(-7\tfrac{1}{5}\right)$$
$$3(0)\left(-7\tfrac{1}{5}\right)$$
$$0 \overset{?}{=} 0 \quad \text{TRUE}$$

$$\frac{3(5x + 1)(x - 7) = 0}{3(5(7) + 1)(7 - 7) \mid 0}$$
$$3(35 + 1)0$$
$$0 \overset{?}{=} 0 \quad \text{TRUE}$$

The solutions are $-\tfrac{1}{5}$ and 7.

TRY EXERCISE 9

The constant factor 3 in Example 2 is never 0 and is not a solution of the equation. However, a variable factor such as x or t *can* equal 0, and must be considered when using the principle of zero products.

EXAMPLE 3   Solve: $7t(t - 5) = 0$.

SOLUTION   We have

$$7 \cdot t(t - 5) = 0 \qquad \text{The factors are 7, } t, \text{ and } t - 5.$$
$$t = 0 \quad or \quad t - 5 = 0 \qquad \text{Using the principle of zero products}$$
$$t = 0 \quad or \qquad t = 5. \qquad \text{Solving. Note that the constant factor, 7,}$$
$$\text{is never 0.}$$

The solutions are 0 and 5. The check is left to the student.

TRY EXERCISE 15

Factoring to Solve Equations

By factoring and using the principle of zero products, we can now solve a variety of quadratic equations.

EXAMPLE 4

Solve: $x^2 + 5x + 6 = 0$.

SOLUTION　This equation differs from those solved in Chapter 1. There are no like terms to combine, and there is a squared term. We first factor the polynomial. Then we use the principle of zero products:

$$x^2 + 5x + 6 = 0$$
$$(x + 2)(x + 3) = 0 \qquad \text{Factoring}$$
$$x + 2 = 0 \quad or \quad x + 3 = 0 \qquad \text{Using the principle of zero products}$$
$$x = -2 \quad or \qquad x = -3.$$

Check:　For -2:

$$\begin{array}{c|c} x^2 + 5x + 6 = 0 & \\ \hline (-2)^2 + 5(-2) + 6 & 0 \\ 4 - 10 + 6 & \\ -6 + 6 & \\ & 0 \stackrel{?}{=} 0 \quad \text{TRUE} \end{array}$$

For -3:

$$\begin{array}{c|c} x^2 + 5x + 6 = 0 & \\ \hline (-3)^2 + 5(-3) + 6 & 0 \\ 9 - 15 + 6 & \\ -6 + 6 & \\ & 0 \stackrel{?}{=} 0 \quad \text{TRUE} \end{array}$$

The solutions are -2 and -3.

　TRY EXERCISE　21

The principle of zero products applies even when there is a common factor.

EXAMPLE 5

Solve: $x^2 + 7x = 0$.

SOLUTION　Although there is no constant term, because of the x^2-term, the equation is still quadratic. The methods of Chapter 1 are not sufficient, so we try factoring:

$$x^2 + 7x = 0$$
$$x(x + 7) = 0 \qquad \text{Factoring out the largest common factor, } x$$
$$x = 0 \quad or \quad x + 7 = 0 \qquad \text{Using the principle of zero products}$$
$$x = 0 \quad or \qquad x = -7.$$

The solutions are 0 and -7. The check is left to the student.

　TRY EXERCISE　27

STUDENT NOTES ————

Checking for a common factor is an important step that is often overlooked. In Example 5, the equation must be factored. If we "divide both sides by x," we will not find the solution 0.

> **CAUTION!**　We *must* have 0 on one side of the equation before the principle of zero products can be used. Get all nonzero terms on one side and 0 on the other.

EXAMPLE 6

Solve: (a) $x^2 - 8x = -16$; (b) $4t^2 = 25$.

SOLUTION

a) We first add 16 to get 0 on one side:

$$x^2 - 8x = -16$$
$$x^2 - 8x + 16 = 0 \qquad \text{Adding 16 to both sides to get 0 on one side}$$

$$(x - 4)(x - 4) = 0 \qquad \text{Factoring}$$
$$x - 4 = 0 \quad or \quad x - 4 = 0 \qquad \text{Using the principle of zero products}$$
$$x = 4 \quad or \qquad x = 4.$$

There is only one solution, 4. The check is left to the student.

b) We have

$$4t^2 = 25$$
$$4t^2 - 25 = 0 \qquad \text{Subtracting 25 from both sides to get 0 on one side}$$

$$(2t - 5)(2t + 5) = 0 \qquad \text{Factoring a difference of squares}$$
$$\left.\begin{array}{lll} 2t - 5 = 0 & or & 2t + 5 = 0 \\ 2t = 5 & or & 2t = -5 \\ t = \frac{5}{2} & or & t = -\frac{5}{2}. \end{array}\right\} \quad \text{Solving the two equations separately}$$

The solutions are $\frac{5}{2}$ and $-\frac{5}{2}$. The check is left to the student.

TRY EXERCISE 41

When solving quadratic equations by factoring, remember that a factorization is not useful unless 0 is on the other side of the equation.

EXAMPLE 7

Solve: $(x + 3)(2x - 1) = 9$.

SOLUTION   Be careful with an equation like this! Since we need 0 on one side, we first multiply out the product on the left and then subtract 9 from both sides.

$$(x + 3)(2x - 1) = 9 \qquad \text{This is not a product equal to 0.}$$
$$2x^2 + 5x - 3 = 9 \qquad \text{Multiplying on the left}$$
$$2x^2 + 5x - 3 - 9 = 9 - 9 \qquad \text{Subtracting 9 from both sides to get 0 on one side}$$

$$2x^2 + 5x - 12 = 0 \qquad \text{Combining like terms}$$
$$(2x - 3)(x + 4) = 0 \qquad \text{Factoring. Now we have a product equal to 0.}$$

$$2x - 3 = 0 \quad or \quad x + 4 = 0 \qquad \text{Using the principle of zero products}$$
$$2x = 3 \quad or \qquad x = -4$$
$$x = \frac{3}{2} \quad or \qquad x = -4$$

Check: For $\frac{3}{2}$:

$$\frac{(x + 3)(2x - 1) = 9}{\left(\frac{3}{2} + 3\right)\left(2 \cdot \frac{3}{2} - 1\right) \,\Big|\, 9}$$
$$\left(\frac{9}{2}\right)(2) \,\Big|$$
$$9 \overset{?}{=} 9 \quad \text{TRUE}$$

For -4:

$$\frac{(x + 3)(2x - 1) = 9}{(-4 + 3)(2(-4)-1) \,\Big|\, 9}$$
$$(-1)(-9) \,\Big|$$
$$9 \overset{?}{=} 9 \quad \text{TRUE}$$

TRY EXERCISE 43

The solutions are $\frac{3}{2}$ and -4.

We can use the principle of zero products to solve polynomials with degree greater than 2, if they can be factored.

EXAMPLE 8 Solve: $3x^3 - 30x = 9x^2$.

SOLUTION We have

$$3x^3 - 30x = 9x^2$$

$$3x^3 - 9x^2 - 30x = 0 \qquad \text{Getting 0 on one side and writing in descending order}$$

$$3x(x^2 - 3x - 10) = 0 \qquad \text{Factoring out a common factor}$$

$$3x(x + 2)(x - 5) = 0 \qquad \text{Factoring the trinomial}$$

$$3x = 0 \quad or \quad x + 2 = 0 \quad or \quad x - 5 = 0 \qquad \text{Using the principle of zero products}$$

$$x = 0 \quad or \quad x = -2 \quad or \quad x = 5.$$

Check:

$$\begin{array}{c|c} 3x^3 - 30x & = 9x^2 \\ \hline 3 \cdot 0^3 - 30 \cdot 0 & 9 \cdot 0^2 \\ 0 - 0 & 9 \cdot 0 \\ 0 \overset{?}{=} 0 & \text{TRUE} \end{array}$$

$$\begin{array}{c|c} 3x^3 - 30x & = 9x^2 \\ \hline 3(-2)^3 - 30(-2) & 9(-2)^2 \\ 3(-8) + 60 & 9 \cdot 4 \\ -24 + 60 & 36 \\ 36 \overset{?}{=} 36 & \text{TRUE} \end{array}$$

$$\begin{array}{c|c} 3x^3 - 30x & = 9x^2 \\ \hline 3 \cdot 5^3 - 30 \cdot 5 & 9 \cdot 5^2 \\ 3 \cdot 125 - 150 & 9 \cdot 25 \\ 375 - 150 & 225 \\ 225 \overset{?}{=} 225 & \text{TRUE} \end{array}$$

The solutions are 0, −2, and 5.

TRY EXERCISE 53

ALGEBRAIC–GRAPHICAL CONNECTION

When graphing equations in Chapter 2, we found the x-intercept by replacing y with 0 and solving for x. This procedure is also used to find the x-intercepts when graphing equations of the form $y = ax^2 + bx + c$. Although the details of creating such graphs is left for Chapter 9, we consider them briefly here from the standpoint of finding x-intercepts. The graphs are shaped as shown. Note that each x-intercept represents a solution of $ax^2 + bx + c = 0$.

$$\boxed{\begin{array}{c} y = ax^2 + bx + c \\ a \neq 0 \end{array}}$$

No x-intercept

Two x-intercepts

One x-intercept

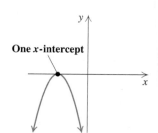

EXAMPLE 9 Find the x-intercepts for the graph of the equation shown. (The grid is intentionally not included.)

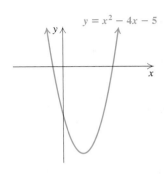

SOLUTION To find the x-intercepts, we let $y = 0$ and solve for x:

$$0 = x^2 - 4x - 5 \qquad \text{Substituting 0 for } y$$
$$0 = (x - 5)(x + 1) \qquad \text{Factoring}$$
$$x - 5 = 0 \quad or \quad x + 1 = 0 \qquad \text{Using the principle of zero products}$$
$$x = 5 \quad or \qquad x = -1. \qquad \text{Solving for } x$$

The x-intercepts are $(5, 0)$ and $(-1, 0)$.

TRY EXERCISE 61

TECHNOLOGY CONNECTION

A graphing calculator allows us to solve polynomial equations even when an equation cannot be solved by factoring. For example, to solve $x^2 - 3x - 5 = 0$, we can let $y_1 = x^2 - 3x - 5$ and $y_2 = 0$. Selecting a bold line type to the left of y_2 in the ⟨Y=⟩ window makes the line easier to see. Using the INTERSECT option of the CALC menu, we select the two graphs in which we are interested, along with a guess. The graphing calculator displays the point of intersection.

An alternative method uses only y_1 and the ZERO option of the CALC menu. This option requires you to enter an x-value to the left of each x-intercept as a LEFT BOUND. An x-value to the right of the x-intercept is then entered as a RIGHT BOUND. Finally, a GUESS value between the two bounds is entered and the x-intercept, or ZERO, is displayed.

Use a graphing calculator to find the solutions, if they exist, accurate to two decimal places.

1. $x^2 + 4x - 3 = 0$
2. $x^2 - 5x - 2 = 0$
3. $x^2 + 13.54x + 40.95 = 0$
4. $x^2 - 4.43x + 6.32 = 0$
5. $1.235x^2 - 3.409x = 0$

3.7 EXERCISE SET

For Extra Help

Concept Reinforcement *For each of Exercises 1–4, match the phrase with the most appropriate choice from the column on the right.*

1. ____ The name of equations of the type $ax^2 + bx + c = 0$, with $a \neq 0$

2. ____ The maximum number of solutions of quadratic equations

3. ____ The idea that $A \cdot B = 0$ if and only if $A = 0$ or $B = 0$

4. ____ The number that a product must equal before the principle of zero products is used

a) 2

b) 0

c) Quadratic

d) The principle of zero products

Solve using the principle of zero products.

5. $(x + 2)(x + 9) = 0$

6. $(x + 3)(x + 10) = 0$

7. $(2t - 3)(t + 6) = 0$

8. $(5t - 8)(t - 1) = 0$

9. $4(7x - 1)(10x - 3) = 0$

10. $6(4x - 3)(2x + 9) = 0$

11. $x(x - 7) = 0$

12. $x(x + 2) = 0$

13. $\left(\frac{2}{3}x - \frac{12}{11}\right)\left(\frac{7}{4}x - \frac{1}{12}\right) = 0$

14. $\left(\frac{1}{9} - 3x\right)\left(\frac{1}{5} + 2x\right) = 0$

15. $6n(3n + 8) = 0$

16. $10n(4n - 5) = 0$

17. $(20 - 0.4x)(7 - 0.1x) = 0$

18. $(1 - 0.05x)(1 - 0.3x) = 0$

19. $(3x - 2)(x + 5)(x - 1) = 0$

20. $(2x + 1)(x + 3)(x - 5) = 0$

Solve by factoring and using the principle of zero products.

21. $x^2 - 7x + 6 = 0$

22. $x^2 - 6x + 5 = 0$

23. $x^2 + 4x - 21 = 0$

24. $x^2 - 7x - 18 = 0$

25. $n^2 + 11n + 18 = 0$

26. $n^2 + 8n + 15 = 0$

27. $x^2 - 10x = 0$

28. $x^2 + 8x = 0$

29. $6t + t^2 = 0$

30. $3t - t^2 = 0$

31. $x^2 - 36 = 0$

32. $x^2 - 100 = 0$

33. $4t^2 = 49$

34. $9t^2 = 25$

35. $0 = 25 + x^2 + 10x$

36. $0 = 6x + x^2 + 9$

37. $64 + x^2 = 16x$

38. $x^2 + 1 = 2x$

39. $4t^2 = 8t$

40. $12t = 3t^2$

41. $4y^2 = 7y + 15$

42. $12y^2 - 5y = 2$

43. $(x - 7)(x + 1) = -16$

44. $(x + 2)(x - 7) = -18$

45. $15z^2 + 7 = 20z + 7$

46. $14z^2 - 3 = 21z - 3$

47. $36m^2 - 9 = 40$

48. $81x^2 - 5 = 20$

49. $(x + 3)(3x + 5) = 7$

50. $(x - 1)(5x + 4) = 2$

51. $3x^2 - 2x = 9 - 8x$

52. $x^2 - 2x = 18 + 5x$

53. $x^2(2x - 1) = 3x$

54. $x^2 = x(10 - 3x^2)$

55. $(2x - 5)(3x^2 + 29x + 56) = 0$

56. $(4x + 9)(15x^2 - 7x - 2) = 0$

57. Use this graph to solve $x^2 - 3x - 4 = 0$.

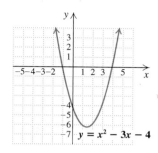

58. Use this graph to solve $x^2 + x - 6 = 0$.

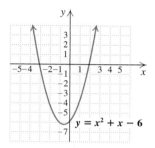

59. Use this graph to solve $-x^2 - x + 6 = 0$.

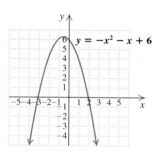

60. Use this graph to solve $-x^2 + 2x + 3 = 0$.

Find the x-intercepts for the graph of each equation. Grids are intentionally not included.

61. $y = x^2 - x - 6$

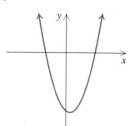

62. $y = x^2 + 3x - 4$

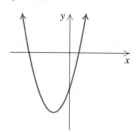

63. $y = x^2 + 2x - 8$

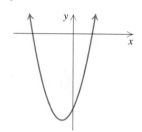

64. $y = x^2 - 2x - 15$

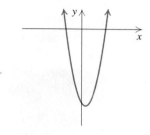

65. $y = 2x^2 + 3x - 9$

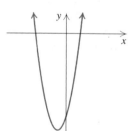

66. $y = 2x^2 + x - 10$

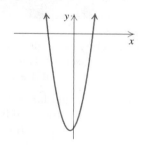

67. The equation $x^2 + 1 = 0$ has no real-number solutions. What implications does this have for the graph of $y = x^2 + 1$?

68. What is the difference between a quadratic polynomial and a quadratic equation?

Skill Review

To prepare for Section 3.8, review solving problems using the five-step strategy (Section 1.5).

Translate to an algebraic expression.

69. The square of the sum of two numbers

70. The sum of the squares of two numbers

71. The product of two consecutive integers

Solve. [1.5]

72. In 2005, shoppers spent $22.8 billion on gifts for Mother's Day and for Father's Day combined. They spent $4.8 billion more for Mother's Day than for Father's Day. How much did shoppers spend for each holiday?
Source: National Retail Federation

73. The first angle of a triangle is four times as large as the second. The measure of the third angle is 30° less than that of the second. How large are the angles?

74. A rectangular table top is twice as long as it is wide. The perimeter of the table is 192 in. What are the dimensions of the table?

Synthesis

75. What is wrong with solving $x^2 = 3x$ by dividing both sides of the equation by x?

76. When the principle of zero products is used to solve a quadratic equation, will there always be two different solutions? Why or why not?

77. Find an equation with integer coefficients that has the given numbers as solutions. For example, 3 and -2 are solutions to $x^2 - x - 6 = 0$.

a) $-4, 5$ **b)** $-1, 7$ **c)** $\frac{1}{4}, 3$
d) $\frac{1}{2}, \frac{1}{3}$ **e)** $\frac{2}{3}, \frac{3}{4}$ **f)** $-1, 2, 3$

Solve.

78. $16(x - 1) = x(x + 8)$

79. $a(9 + a) = 4(2a + 5)$

80. $(t - 5)^2 = 2(5 - t)$ **81.** $-x^2 + \frac{9}{25} = 0$

82. $a^2 = \frac{49}{100}$

Aha! **83.** $(t + 1)^2 = 9$

84. $\frac{27}{25} x^2 = \frac{1}{3}$

85. For each equation on the left, find an equivalent equation on the right.

a) $x^2 + 10x - 2 = 0$ $4x^2 + 8x + 36 = 0$
b) $(x - 6)(x + 3) = 0$ $(2x + 8)(2x - 5) = 0$
c) $5x^2 - 5 = 0$ $9x^2 - 12x + 24 = 0$
d) $(2x - 5)(x + 4) = 0$ $(x + 1)(5x - 5) = 0$
e) $x^2 + 2x + 9 = 0$ $x^2 - 3x - 18 = 0$
f) $3x^2 - 4x + 8 = 0$ $2x^2 + 20x - 4 = 0$

86. Explain how to construct an equation that has seven solutions.

87. Explain how the graph in Exercise 59 can be used to visualize the solutions of
$$-x^2 - x + 6 = 4.$$

Use a graphing calculator to find the solutions of each equation. Round solutions to the nearest hundredth.

88. $-x^2 + 0.63x + 0.22 = 0$

89. $x^2 - 9.10x + 15.77 = 0$

90. $6.4x^2 - 8.45x - 94.06 = 0$

91. $x^2 + 13.74x + 42.00 = 0$

92. $0.84x^2 - 2.30x = 0$

93. $1.23x^2 + 4.63x = 0$

94. $x^2 + 1.80x - 5.69 = 0$

Solve by factoring and using the principle of zero products.

95. $\frac{1}{50} x^2 - 2 = 0$ **96.** $2x^2 - \frac{9}{50} = 0$

97. $\frac{1}{4} x^2 = \frac{1}{10} x$ **98.** $\frac{1}{20} x^2 = \frac{2}{5} x$

99. $\frac{1}{3} x^2 + \frac{1}{12} x = 0$ **100.** $\frac{2}{15} x^2 - \frac{1}{5} x = 0$

101. $\frac{3}{2} x^2 = \frac{2}{3}$ **102.** $\frac{5}{4} x^2 = \frac{1}{5}$

Solve by factoring and using the principle of zero products.

103. $0.12x^2 - 0.32x + 0.05 = 0$

104. $0.06x^2 - 0.05x - 0.04 = 0$

105. $0.13x + 0.15 = 0.2x^2$

106. $0.16x^2 - 0.34x = 0.15$

Solve by factoring and using the principle of zero products.

107. $x^3 + 4x^2 - 9x - 36 = 0$

108. $x^3 - 5x^2 - x + 5 = 0$

109. $5x^3 - x^2 - 20x + 4 = 0$

110. $4x^3 + x^2 - 36x - 9 = 0$

CONNECTING the CONCEPTS

Recall that an *equation* is a statement that two *expressions* are equal. When we simplify expressions, combine expressions, and form equivalent expressions, each result is an expression. When we are asked to solve an equation, the result is one or more numbers. Remember to read the directions to an exercise carefully so you do not attempt to "solve" an expression.

MIXED REVIEW

For Exercises 1–6, tell whether each is an example of an expression or an equation.

1. $x^2 - 25$

2. $x^2 - 25 = 0$

3. $x^2 + 2x = 5$

4. $(x + 3)(2x - 1)$

5. $x(x + 3) - 2(2x - 7) - (x - 5)$

6. $x = 10$

7. Add the expressions:
   $(2x^3 - 5x + 1) + (x^2 - 3x - 1)$.

8. Subtract the expressions:
   $(x^2 - x - 5) - (3x^2 - x + 6)$.

9. Solve the equation: $t^2 - 100 = 0$.

10. Multiply the expressions: $(3a - 2)(2a - 5)$.

11. Factor the expression: $n^2 - 10n + 9$.

12. Solve the equation: $x^2 + 16 = 10x$.

13. Solve: $4t^2 + 20t + 25 = 0$.

14. Add: $(3x^3 - 5x + 1) + (4x^3 + 7x - 8)$.

15. Factor: $16x^2 - 81$.

16. Solve: $y^2 - 5y - 24 = 0$.

17. Subtract: $(a^2 - 2) - (5a^2 + a + 9)$.

18. Factor: $18x^4 - 24x^3 + 20x^2$.

19. Solve: $3x^2 + 5x + 2 = 0$.

20. Multiply: $4x^2(2x^3 - 5x^2 + 3)$.

3.8   Solving Applications

Applications   •   The Pythagorean Theorem

Applications

We can use the five-step problem-solving process and our new methods of solving quadratic equations to solve new types of problems.

EXAMPLE 1

Race numbers. Terry and Jody each entered a boat in the Lakeport Race. The racing numbers of their boats were consecutive numbers, the product of which was 156. Find the numbers.

SOLUTION

STUDY SKILLS

Finishing a Chapter

Reaching the end of a chapter often signals the arrival of a quiz or test. Almost always, it indicates the end of a particular area of study. Success in future work will depend on your mastery of previous topics studied. Use the chapter review and test to solidify your understanding of a chapter's material.

1. **Familiarize.** Consecutive numbers are one apart, like 49 and 50. Let $x =$ the first boat number; then $x + 1 =$ the next boat number.

2. **Translate.** We reword the problem before translating:

Rewording: The first boat number times the next boat number is 156.

Translating: $x \cdot (x + 1) = 156$

3. **Carry out.** We solve the equation as follows:

$$x(x + 1) = 156$$
$$x^2 + x = 156 \quad \text{Multiplying}$$
$$x^2 + x - 156 = 0 \quad \text{Subtracting 156 to get 0 on one side}$$
$$(x - 12)(x + 13) = 0 \quad \text{Factoring}$$
$$x - 12 = 0 \quad or \quad x + 13 = 0 \quad \text{Using the principle of zero products}$$
$$x = 12 \quad or \quad x = -13. \quad \text{Solving each equation}$$

4. **Check.** The solutions of the equation are 12 and -13. Since race numbers are not negative, -13 must be rejected. On the other hand, if x is 12, then $x + 1$ is 13 and $12 \cdot 13 = 156$. Thus the solution 12 checks.

5. **State.** The boat numbers for Terry and Jody were 12 and 13.

TRY EXERCISE 5

EXAMPLE 2

Manufacturing. Wooden Work, Ltd., builds cutting boards that are twice as long as they are wide. The most popular board that Wooden Work makes has an area of 800 cm^2. What are the dimensions of the board?

SOLUTION

1. **Familiarize.** We first make a drawing. Recall that the area of any rectangle is Length · Width. We let $x =$ the width of the board, in centimeters. The length is then $2x$, since the board is twice as long as it is wide.

2. **Translate.** We reword and translate as follows:

   Rewording: The area of the rectangle   is   800 cm^2.

   Translating: $2x \cdot x$ $=$ 800

3. **Carry out.** We solve the equation as follows:

$$2x \cdot x = 800$$
$$2x^2 = 800$$
$$2x^2 - 800 = 0 \qquad \text{Subtracting 800 to get 0 on one side of the equation}$$
$$2(x^2 - 400) = 0 \qquad \text{Factoring out a common factor of 2}$$
$$2(x - 20)(x + 20) = 0 \qquad \text{Factoring a difference of squares}$$
$$(x - 20)(x + 20) = 0 \qquad \text{Dividing both sides by 2}$$
$$x - 20 = 0 \quad or \quad x + 20 = 0 \qquad \text{Using the principle of zero products}$$
$$x = 20 \quad or \qquad x = -20. \qquad \text{Solving each equation}$$

4. **Check.** The solutions of the equation are 20 and -20. Since the width must be positive, -20 cannot be a solution. To check 20 cm, we note that if the width is 20 cm, then the length is $2 \cdot 20$ cm $= 40$ cm and the area is 20 cm $\cdot$ 40 cm $= 800$ cm^2. Thus the solution 20 checks.

5. **State.** The cutting board is 20 cm wide and 40 cm long.   **TRY EXERCISE** 9

EXAMPLE 3   *Dimensions of a leaf.*   Each leaf of one particular *Philodendron* species is approximately a triangle. A typical leaf has an area of 320 in^2. If the leaf is 12 in. longer than it is wide, find the length and the width of the leaf.

SOLUTION

1. **Familiarize.** The formula for the area of a triangle is Area $= \frac{1}{2} \cdot$ (base) $\cdot$ (height). We let $b =$ the width, in inches, of the triangle's base and $b + 12 =$ the height, in inches.

2. **Translate.** We reword and translate as follows:

   Rewording: The area of the leaf   is   320 in^2.

   Translating: $\frac{1}{2} \cdot b(b + 12)$ $=$ 320

3. **Carry out.** We solve the equation as follows:

$$\tfrac{1}{2} \cdot b \cdot (b + 12) = 320$$

$$\tfrac{1}{2}(b^2 + 12b) = 320 \qquad \text{Multiplying}$$

$$b^2 + 12b = 640 \qquad \text{Multiplying by 2 to clear fractions}$$

$$b^2 + 12b - 640 = 0 \qquad \text{Subtracting 640 to get 0 on one side}$$

$$(b + 32)(b - 20) = 0 \qquad \text{Factoring}$$

$$b + 32 = 0 \quad or \quad b - 20 = 0 \qquad \text{Using the principle of zero products}$$

$$b = -32 \quad or \qquad b = 20.$$

4. **Check.** The width must be positive, so -32 cannot be a solution. Suppose the base is 20 in. The height would be $20 + 12$, or 32 in., and the area $\tfrac{1}{2}(20)(32)$, or 320 in^2. These numbers check in the original problem.

5. **State.** The leaf is 32 in. long and 20 in. wide.

TRY EXERCISE ▶ 13

EXAMPLE 4

Medicine. For certain people suffering an extreme allergic reaction, the drug epinephrine (adrenaline) is sometimes prescribed. The number of micrograms N of epinephrine in an adult's bloodstream t minutes after 250 micrograms have been injected can be approximated by

$$-10t^2 + 100t = N.$$

How long after an injection will there be about 210 micrograms of epinephrine in the bloodstream?

Source: Based on information in Chohan, Naina, Rita M. Doyle, and Patricia Nayle (eds.), *Nursing Handbook*, 21st ed. Springhouse, PA: Springhouse Corporation, 2001

SOLUTION

1. **Familiarize.** To familiarize ourselves with this problem, we could calculate N for different choices of t. We leave this for the student. Note that there may be two solutions, one on each side of the time at which the drug's effect peaks.

2. **Translate.** To find the length of time after injection when 210 micrograms are in the bloodstream, we replace N with 210 in the formula above:

$$-10t^2 + 100t = 210. \qquad \text{Substituting 210 for } N. \text{ This is now an equation in one variable.}$$

3. **Carry out.** We solve the equation as follows:

$$-10t^2 + 100t = 210$$

$$-10t^2 + 100t - 210 = 0 \qquad \text{Subtracting 210 from both sides to get 0 on one side}$$

$$-10(t^2 - 10t + 21) = 0 \qquad \text{Factoring out the largest common factor, } -10$$

$$-10(t - 3)(t - 7) = 0 \qquad \text{Factoring}$$

$$t - 3 = 0 \quad or \quad t - 7 = 0 \qquad \text{Using the principle of zero products}$$

$$t = 3 \quad or \qquad t = 7.$$

As a visual check for Example 4, we can either let $y_1 = -10x^2 + 100x$ and $y_2 = 210$, or let $y_1 = -10x^2 + 100x - 210$ and $y_2 = 0$. In either case, the points of intersection occur at $x = 3$ and $x = 7$, as shown.

4. **Check.** Since $-10 \cdot 3^2 + 100 \cdot 3 = -90 + 300 = 210$, the number 3 checks. Since $-10 \cdot 7^2 + 100 \cdot 7 = -490 + 700 = 210$, the number 7 also checks.

5. **State.** There will be 210 micrograms of epinephrine in the bloodstream approximately 3 minutes and 7 minutes after injection.

> TRY EXERCISE 17

The Pythagorean Theorem

The following problems involve the Pythagorean theorem, which relates the lengths of the sides of a *right* triangle. A triangle is a **right triangle** if it has a 90°, or *right*, angle. The side opposite the 90° angle is called the **hypotenuse**. The other sides are called **legs**.

The Pythagorean Theorem

In any right triangle, if a and b are the lengths of the legs and c is the length of the hypotenuse, then

$$a^2 + b^2 = c^2, \quad \text{or}$$

$$(\text{Leg})^2 + (\text{Other leg})^2 = (\text{Hypotenuse})^2.$$

The equation $a^2 + b^2 = c^2$ is called the **Pythagorean equation.***

The Pythagorean theorem is named for the Greek mathematician Pythagoras (569?–500? B.C.). We can think of this relationship as adding areas.

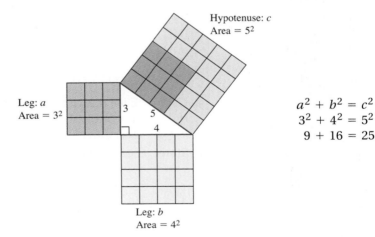

$$a^2 + b^2 = c^2$$
$$3^2 + 4^2 = 5^2$$
$$9 + 16 = 25$$

If we know the lengths of any two sides of a right triangle, we can use the Pythagorean equation to determine the length of the third side.

---

*The *converse* of the Pythagorean theorem is also true. That is, if $a^2 + b^2 = c^2$, then the triangle is a right triangle.

EXAMPLE 5   *Travel.* A zipline canopy tour in Alaska includes a cable that slopes downward from a height of 135 ft to a height of 100 ft. The trees that the cable connects are 120 ft apart. Find the minimum length of the cable.

SOLUTION

1. **Familiarize.** We first make a drawing or visualize the situation. The difference in height between the platforms is 35 ft. Note that the cable must have some extra length to allow for the rider's movement, but we will approximate its length as the hypotenuse of a right triangle, as shown.

2. **Translate.** Since a right triangle is formed, we can use the Pythagorean theorem:

   $$a^2 + b^2 = c^2$$
   $$35^2 + 120^2 = x^2. \qquad \text{Substituting}$$

3. **Carry out.** We solve the equation as follows:

$1225 + 14{,}400 = x^2$	Squaring 35 and 120
$15{,}625 = x^2$	Adding
$0 = x^2 - 15{,}625$	Subtracting 15,625 from both sides
$0 = (x + 125)(x - 125)$	Note that $15{,}625 = 125^2$. A calculator would be helpful here.
$x + 125 = 0 \quad or \quad x - 125 = 0$	Using the principle of zero products
$x = -125 \quad or \qquad x = 125.$	

4. **Check.** Since the length of the cable must be positive, -125 is not a solution. If the length is 125 ft, we have $35^2 + 120^2 = 1225 + 14{,}400 = 15{,}625$, which is 125^2. Thus the solution 125 checks.

5. **State.** The minimum length of the cable is 125 ft.   TRY EXERCISE 27

EXAMPLE **6**   *Bridge design.*   A 50-ft diagonal brace on a bridge connects a support at the center of the bridge to a side support on the bridge. The horizontal distance that it spans is 10 ft longer than the height that it reaches on the side of the bridge. Find both distances.

SOLUTION

1. **Familiarize.** We first make a drawing. The diagonal brace and the missing distances form the hypotenuse and the legs of a right triangle. We let x = the length of the vertical leg. Then $x + 10$ = the length of the horizontal leg. The hypotenuse has length 50 ft.

2. **Translate.** Since the triangle is a right triangle, we can use the Pythagorean theorem:

$$a^2 + b^2 = c^2$$
$$x^2 + (x + 10)^2 = 50^2. \qquad \text{Substituting}$$

3. **Carry out.** We solve the equation as follows:

$x^2 + (x^2 + 20x + 100) = 2500$	Squaring
$2x^2 + 20x + 100 = 2500$	Combining like terms
$2x^2 + 20x - 2400 = 0$	Subtracting 2500 to get 0 on one side
$2(x^2 + 10x - 1200) = 0$	Factoring out a common factor
$2(x + 40)(x - 30) = 0$	Factoring. A calculator would be helpful here.
$x + 40 = 0 \quad or \quad x - 30 = 0$	Using the principle of zero products
$x = -40 \quad or \quad x = 30.$	

4. **Check.** The integer -40 cannot be a length of a side because it is negative. If the length is 30 ft, $x + 10 = 40$, and $30^2 + 40^2 = 900 + 1600 = 2500$, which is 50^2. So the solution 30 checks.

5. **State.** The height that the brace reaches on the side of the bridge is 30 ft, and the distance that it reaches to the middle of the bridge is 40 ft.

TRY EXERCISE 31

Translating for Success

1. *Angle measures.* The measures of the angles of a triangle are three consecutive integers. Find the measures of the angles.

2. *Rectangle dimensions.* The area of a rectangle is 3604 ft^2. The length is 15 ft longer than the width. Find the dimensions of the rectangle.

3. *Sales tax.* Claire paid \$3604 for a used pickup truck. This included 6% for sales tax. How much did the truck cost before tax?

4. *Wire cutting.* A 180-m wire is cut into three pieces. The third piece is 2 m longer than the first. The second is two-thirds as long as the first. How long is each piece?

5. *Perimeter.* The perimeter of a rectangle is 240 ft. The length is 2 ft greater than the width. Find the length and the width.

Translate each word problem to an equation and select a correct translation from equations A–O.

A. $2x \cdot x = 288$

B. $x(x + 60) = 7021$

C. $59 = x \cdot 60$

D. $x^2 + (x + 15)^2 = 3604$

E. $x^2 + (x + 70)^2 = 130^2$

F. $0.06x = 3604$

G. $2(x + 2) + 2x = 240$

H. $\frac{1}{2}x(x - 1) = 1770$

I. $x + \frac{2}{3}x + (x + 2) = 180$

J. $0.59x = 60$

K. $x + 0.06x = 3604$

L. $2x^2 + x = 288$

M. $x(x + 15) = 3604$

N. $x^2 + 60 = 7021$

O. $x + (x + 1) + (x + 2) = 180$

Answers on page A-14

An additional, animated version of this activity appears in MyMathLab. To use MyMathLab, you need a course ID and a student access code. Contact your instructor for more information.

---

6. *Cell-phone tower.* A guy wire on a cell-phone tower is 130 ft long and is attached to the top of the tower. The height of the tower is 70 ft longer than the distance from the point on the ground where the wire is attached to the bottom of the tower. Find the height of the tower.

7. *Sales meeting attendance.* PTQ Corporation holds a sales meeting in Tucson. Of the 60 employees, 59 of them attend the meeting. What percent attend the meeting?

8. *Dimensions of a pool.* A rectangular swimming pool is twice as long as it is wide. The area of the surface is 288 ft^2. Find the dimensions of the pool.

9. *Dimensions of a triangle.* The height of a triangle is 1 cm less than the length of the base. The area of the triangle is 1770 cm^2. Find the height and the length of the base.

10. *Width of a rectangle.* The length of a rectangle is 60 ft longer than the width. Find the width if the area of the rectangle is 7021 ft^2.

3.8 EXERCISE SET

For Extra Help MyMathLab Math XL PRACTICE WATCH DOWNLOAD

Solve. Use the five-step problem-solving approach.

1. A number is 6 less than its square. Find all such numbers.

2. A number is 30 less than its square. Find all such numbers.

3. One leg of a right triangle is 2 m longer than the other leg. The length of the hypotenuse is 10 m. Find the length of each side.

4. One leg of a right triangle is 7 cm shorter than the other leg. The length of the hypotenuse is 13 cm. Find the length of each side.

5. *Parking-space numbers.* The product of two consecutive parking spaces is 132. Find the parking-space numbers.

6. *Page numbers.* The product of the page numbers on two facing pages of a book is 420. Find the page numbers.

7. The product of two consecutive even integers is 168. Find the integers.

8. The product of two consecutive odd integers is 195. Find the integers.

9. *Construction.* The front porch on Trent's new home is five times as long as it is wide. If the area of the porch is 180 ft², find the dimensions.

5w w

10. *Furnishings.* The work surface of Anita's desk is a rectangle that is twice as long as it is wide. If the area

w 2w

of the desktop is 18 ft², find the length and the width of the desk.

11. *Design.* The screen of the TI-84 Plus graphing calculator is nearly rectangular. The length of the rectangle is 2 cm more than the width. If the area of the rectangle is 24 cm², find the length and the width.

w + 2 w

12. *Area of a garden.* The length of a rectangular garden is 4 m greater than the width. The area of the garden is 96 m². Find the length and the width.

w w + 4

13. *Dimensions of a triangle.* The height of a triangle is 3 in. less than the length of the base. If the area of the triangle is 54 in², find the height and the length of the base.

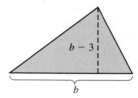

b − 3 b

14. *Dimensions of a triangle.* A triangle is 10 cm wider than it is tall. The area is 48 cm². Find the height and the base.

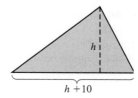

h h + 10

15. *Dimensions of a sail.* The height of the jib sail on a Lightning sailboat is 5 ft greater than the length of its "foot." If the area of the sail is 42 ft², find the length of the foot and the height of the sail.

16. *Road design.* A triangular traffic island has a base half as long as its height. Find the base and the height if the island has an area of 64 m².

17. *Medicine.* For many people suffering from constricted bronchial muscles, the drug Albuterol is prescribed. The number of micrograms A of Albuterol in a person's bloodstream t minutes after 200 micrograms have been inhaled can be approximated by

$$A = -50t^2 + 200t.$$

How long after an inhalation will there be about 150 micrograms of Albuterol in the bloodstream?
Source: Based on information in Chohan, Naina, Rita M. Doyle, and Patricia Nayle (eds.), *Nursing Handbook*, 21st ed. Springhouse, PA: Springhouse Corporation, 2001

18. *Medicine.* For adults with certain heart conditions, the drug Primacor (milrinone lactate) is prescribed. The number of milligrams M of Primacor in the bloodstream of a 132-lb patient t hours after a 3-mg dose has been injected can be approximated by

$$M = -\frac{1}{2}t^2 + \frac{5}{2}t.$$

How long after an injection will there be about 2 mg in the bloodstream?
Source: Based on information in Chohan, Naina, Rita M. Doyle, and Patricia Nayle (eds.), *Nursing Handbook*, 21st ed. Springhouse, PA: Springhouse Corporation, 2001

19. *High-speed Internet.* The number N, in millions, of broadband cable and DSL subscribers in the United States t years after 1998 can be approximated by

$$N = 0.3t^2 + 0.6t.$$

When will there be 36 million broadband cable and DSL subscribers?
Source: Based on information from Leichtman Research Group

20. *Wave height.* The height of waves in a storm depends on the speed of the wind. Assuming the wind has no obstructions for a long distance, the maximum wave height H for a wind speed x can be approximated by

$$H = 0.006x^2 + 0.6x.$$

Here H is in feet and x is in knots (nautical miles per hour). For what wind speed would the maximum wave height be 6.6 ft?
Source: Based on information from cimss.ssec.wisc.edu

Games in a league's schedule. In a sports league of x teams in which all teams play each other twice, the total number N of games played is given by

$$x^2 - x = N.$$

Use this formula for Exercises 21 and 22.

21. The Colchester Youth Soccer League plays a total of 240 games, with all teams playing each other twice. How many teams are in the league?

22. The teams in a women's softball league play each other twice, for a total of 132 games. How many teams are in the league?

Number of handshakes. The number of possible handshakes H within a group of n people is given by $H = \frac{1}{2}(n^2 - n)$. *Use this formula for Exercises 23–26.*

23. At a meeting, there are 12 people. How many handshakes are possible?

24. At a party, there are 25 people. How many handshakes are possible?

25. *High-fives.* After winning the championship, all San Antonio Spurs teammates exchanged "high-fives." Altogether there were 66 high-fives. How many players were there?

26. *Toasting.* During a toast at a party, there were 105 "clicks" of glasses. How many people took part in the toast?

27. *Construction.* The diagonal braces in a lookout tower are 15 ft long and span a horizontal distance of 12 ft. How high does each brace reach vertically?

28. *Reach of a ladder.* Twyla has a 26-ft ladder leaning against her house. If the bottom of the ladder is 10 ft from the base of the house, how high does the ladder reach?

29. *Roadway design.* Elliott Street is 24 ft wide when it ends at Main Street in Brattleboro, Vermont. A 40-ft long diagonal crosswalk allows pedestrians to cross Main Street to or from either corner of Elliott Street (see the figure). Determine the width of Main Street.

30. *Aviation.* Engine failure forced Robbin to pilot her Cessna 150 to an emergency landing. To land, Robbin's plane glided 17,000 ft over a 15,000-ft stretch of deserted highway. From what altitude did the descent begin?

31. *Archaeology.* Archaeologists have discovered that the 18th-century garden of the Charles Carroll House in Annapolis, Maryland, was a right triangle. One leg of the triangle was formed by a 400-ft long sea wall. The hypotenuse of the triangle was 200 ft longer than the other leg. What were the dimensions of the garden?
Source: www.bsos.umd.edu

32. *Guy wire.* The guy wire on a TV antenna is 1 m longer than the height of the antenna. If the guy wire is anchored 3 m from the foot of the antenna, how tall is the antenna?

33. *Architecture.* An architect has allocated a rectangular space of 264 ft^2 for a square dining room and a 10-ft wide kitchen, as shown in the figure. Find the dimensions of each room.

34. *Design.* A window panel for a sun porch consists of a 7-ft high rectangular window stacked above a square window. The windows have the same width. If the total area of the window panel is 18 ft^2, find the dimensions of each window.

Height of a rocket. *For Exercises 35–38, assume that a water rocket is launched upward with an initial velocity of 48 ft/sec. Its height h, in feet, after t seconds, is given by* $h = 48t - 16t^2$.

35. Determine the height of the rocket $\frac{1}{2}$ sec after it has been launched.

36. Determine the height of the rocket 2.5 sec after it has been launched.

37. When will the rocket be exactly 32 ft above the ground?

38. When will the rocket crash into the ground?

39. Do we now have the ability to solve *any* problem that translates to a quadratic equation? Why or why not?

40. Write a problem for a classmate to solve such that only one of two solutions of a quadratic equation can be used as an answer.

Skill Review

To prepare for Chapter 4, review addition, subtraction, multiplication, and division using fraction notation.

Simplify.

41. $-\dfrac{3}{5} \cdot \dfrac{4}{7}$

42. $-\dfrac{3}{5} \div \dfrac{4}{7}$

43. $-\dfrac{5}{6} - \dfrac{1}{6}$

44. $\dfrac{3}{4} + \left(-\dfrac{5}{2}\right)$

45. $-\dfrac{3}{8} \cdot \left(-\dfrac{10}{15}\right)$

46. $\dfrac{-\dfrac{8}{15}}{-\dfrac{2}{3}}$

47. $\dfrac{5}{24} + \dfrac{3}{28}$

48. $\dfrac{5}{6} - \left(-\dfrac{2}{9}\right)$

Synthesis

The converse of the Pythagorean theorem is also true. That is, if $a^2 + b^2 = c^2$, then the triangle is a right triangle (where a and b are the lengths of the legs and c is the length of the hypotenuse). Use this result to answer Exercises 49 and 50.

49. An archaeologist has measuring sticks of 3 ft, 4 ft, and 5 ft. Explain how she could draw a 7-ft by 9-ft rectangle on a piece of land being excavated.

50. Explain how measuring sticks of 5 cm, 12 cm, and 13 cm can be used to draw a right triangle that has two 45° angles.

51. *Sailing.* The mainsail of a Lightning sailboat is a right triangle in which the hypotenuse is called the leech. If a 24-ft tall mainsail has a leech length of 26 ft and if Dacron® sailcloth costs $1.50 per square foot, find the cost of the fabric for a new mainsail.

52. *Roofing.* A *square* of shingles covers 100 ft^2 of surface area. How many squares will be needed to re-shingle the house shown?

53. Solve for x.

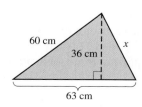

To divide a polynomial by a monomial, we note that since

$$\frac{A}{C} + \frac{B}{C} = \frac{A + B}{C},$$

it follows that

$$\frac{A + B}{C} = \frac{A}{C} + \frac{B}{C}. \qquad \text{Switching the left side and the right side of the equation}$$

This is actually how we perform divisions like $86 \div 2$. Although we might simply write

$$\frac{86}{2} = 43,$$

we are really saying

$$\frac{80 + 6}{2} = \frac{80}{2} + \frac{6}{2} = 40 + 3.$$

Similarly, to divide a polynomial by a monomial, we divide each term by the monomial:

$$\frac{80x^5 + 6x^7}{2x^3} = \frac{80x^5}{2x^3} + \frac{6x^7}{2x^3}$$

$$= \frac{80}{2}x^{5-3} + \frac{6}{2}x^{7-3} \qquad \text{Dividing coefficients and subtracting exponents}$$

$$= 40x^2 + 3x^4.$$

EXAMPLE   1   Divide $x^4 + 15x^3 - 6x^2$ by $3x$.

SOLUTION   We divide each term of $x^4 + 15x^3 - 6x^2$ by $3x$:

$$\frac{x^4 + 15x^3 - 6x^2}{3x} = \frac{x^4}{3x} + \frac{15x^3}{3x} - \frac{6x^2}{3x}$$

$$= \frac{1}{3}x^{4-1} + \frac{15}{3}x^{3-1} - \frac{6}{3}x^{2-1} \qquad \text{Dividing coefficients and subtracting exponents}$$

$$= \frac{1}{3}x^3 + 5x^2 - 2x. \qquad \text{This is the quotient.}$$

To check, we multiply our answer by $3x$, using the distributive law:

$$3x\left(\frac{1}{3}x^3 + 5x^2 - 2x\right) = 3x \cdot \frac{1}{3}x^3 + 3x \cdot 5x^2 - 3x \cdot 2x$$

$$= x^4 + 15x^3 - 6x^2.$$

This is the polynomial that was being divided, so our answer, $\frac{1}{3}x^3 + 5x^2 - 2x$, checks.

TRY EXERCISE   5

EXAMPLE **2** Divide and check: $(10a^5b^4 - 2a^3b^2 + 6a^2b) \div (-2a^2b)$.

SOLUTION   We have

$$\frac{10a^5b^4 - 2a^3b^2 + 6a^2b}{-2a^2b} = \frac{10a^5b^4}{-2a^2b} - \frac{2a^3b^2}{-2a^2b} + \frac{6a^2b}{-2a^2b}$$

We divide coefficients and subtract exponents. $= -\frac{10}{2}a^{5-2}b^{4-1} - \left(-\frac{2}{2}\right)a^{3-2}b^{2-1} + \left(-\frac{6}{2}\right)$

$$= -5a^3b^3 + ab - 3.$$

Check: $-2a^2b(-5a^3b^3 + ab - 3)$

$$= -2a^2b(-5a^3b^3) + (-2a^2b)(ab) + (-2a^2b)(-3)$$

$$= 10a^5b^4 - 2a^3b^2 + 6a^2b$$

Our answer, $-5a^3b^3 + ab - 3$, checks.

> TRY EXERCISE 7

Dividing by a Binomial

The divisors in Examples 1 and 2 have just one term. For divisors with more than one term, we use long division, much as we do in arithmetic. Polynomials are written in descending order and any missing terms in the dividend are written in, using 0 for the coefficients.

EXAMPLE **3** Divide $x^2 + 5x + 6$ by $x + 3$.

SOLUTION   We begin by dividing x^2 by x:

Divide the first term, x^2, by the first term in the divisor: $x^2/x = x$. Ignore the term 3 for the moment.

$$\begin{array}{r} x \\ x + 3 \overline{)x^2 + 5x + 6} \\ -(x^2 + 3x) \\ \hline 2x. \end{array}$$

Multiply $x + 3$ by x, using the distributive law.

Subtract both x^2 and $3x$: $x^2 + 5x - (x^2 + 3x) = 2x.$

Now we "bring down" the next term—in this case, 6. The current remainder, $2x + 6$, now becomes the focus of our division. We divide $2x$ by x.

$$\begin{array}{r} x + 2 \\ x + 3 \overline{)x^2 + 5x + 6} \\ -(x^2 + 3x) \\ \hline 2x + 6 \\ -(2x + 6) \\ \hline 0 \end{array}$$

Divide $2x$ by x: $2x/x = 2$.

Multiply 2 by the divisor, $x + 3$, using the distributive law.

Subtract $(2x + 6) - (2x + 6) = 0.$

STUDENT NOTES

Long division of polynomials offers many opportunities to make errors. Rather than have one small mistake throw off all your work, we recommend that you double-check each step of your work as you move forward.

The quotient is $x + 2$. The notation R 0 indicates a remainder of 0, although a remainder of 0 is generally not listed in an answer.

Check: To check, we multiply the quotient by the divisor and add any remainder to see if we get the dividend:

$$\underbrace{(x+3)}_{\text{Divisor}} \quad \underbrace{(x+2)}_{\text{Quotient}} + \quad \underbrace{0}_{\text{Remainder}} \quad = \quad \underbrace{x^2 + 5x + 6}_{\text{Dividend}}.$$

Our answer, $x + 2$, checks.

TRY EXERCISE 17

EXAMPLE 4

Divide: $(2x^2 + 5x - 1) \div (2x - 1)$.

SOLUTION We begin by dividing $2x^2$ by $2x$:

Divide the first term by the first term: $2x^2/(2x) = x$.

$$
\begin{array}{r}
x \\
2x - 1 \overline{)2x^2 + 5x - 1} \\
-(2x^2 - x) \\
\hline
6x
\end{array}
$$

Multiply $2x - 1$ by x.

Subtract by changing signs and adding: $(2x^2 + 5x) - (2x^2 - x) = 6x$.

> **CAUTION!** Write the parentheses around the polynomial being subtracted to remind you to subtract all its terms.

Now, we bring down the -1 and divide $6x - 1$ by $2x - 1$.

$$
\begin{array}{r}
x + 3 \\
2x - 1 \overline{)2x^2 + 5x - 1} \\
-(2x^2 - x) \\
\hline
6x - 1 \\
-(6x - 3) \\
\hline
2
\end{array}
$$

Divide $6x$ by $2x$: $6x/(2x) = 3$.

Multiply 3 by the divisor, $2x - 1$.

Subtract. Note that $-1 - (-3) = -1 + 3 = 2$.

The answer is $x + 3$ with R 2.

Another way to write $x + 3$ R 2 is as

$$\underbrace{x + 3}_{\text{Quotient}} + \dfrac{\overset{\text{Remainder}}{2}}{\underset{\text{Divisor}}{2x - 1}}.$$

(This is the way answers will be given at the back of the book.)

Check: To check, we multiply the divisor by the quotient and add the remainder:

$$(2x - 1)(x + 3) + 2 = 2x^2 + 5x - 3 + 2$$
$$= 2x^2 + 5x - 1. \quad \text{Our answer checks.}$$

TRY EXERCISE 29

Our division procedure ends when the degree of the remainder is less than that of the divisor. Check that this was indeed the case in Example 4.

EXAMPLE 5

Divide each of the following.

a) $(x^3 + 1) \div (x + 1)$

b) $(x^4 - 3x^2 + 4x - 3) \div (x^2 - 5)$

SOLUTION

a)
$$
\begin{array}{r}
x^2 - x + 1 \\
x + 1 \overline{\smash{)}x^3 + 0x^2 + 0x + 1} \\
-(x^3 + x^2) \\
\hline
-x^2 + 0x \\
-(-x^2 - x) \\
\hline
x + 1 \\
-(x + 1) \\
\hline
0
\end{array}
$$

⟵ Writing in the missing terms

⟵ Subtracting $x^3 + x^2$ from $x^3 + 0x^2$ and bringing down the $0x$

⟵ Subtracting $-x^2 - x$ from $-x^2 + 0x$ and bringing down the 1

The answer is $x^2 - x + 1$.

Check: $(x + 1)(x^2 - x + 1) = x^3 - x^2 + x + x^2 - x + 1$
$$= x^3 + 1.$$

b)
$$
\begin{array}{r}
x^2 + 2 \\
x^2 - 5 \overline{\smash{)}x^4 + 0x^3 - 3x^2 + 4x - 3} \\
-(x^4 - 5x^2) \\
\hline
2x^2 + 4x - 3 \\
-(2x^2 - 10) \\
\hline
4x + 7
\end{array}
$$

Writing in the missing term

⟵ Subtracting $x^4 - 5x^2$ from $x^4 - 3x^2$ and bringing down $4x - 3$

⟵ Subtracting $2x^2 - 10$ from $2x^2 + 4x - 3$

Since the remainder, $4x + 7$, is of lower degree than the divisor, the division process stops. The answer is

$$x^2 + 2 + \frac{4x + 7}{x^2 - 5}.$$

Check: $(x^2 - 5)(x^2 + 2) + 4x + 7 = x^4 + 2x^2 - 5x^2 - 10 + 4x + 7$
$$= x^4 - 3x^2 + 4x - 3.$$

TRY EXERCISE 35

3.9 EXERCISE SET

For Extra Help
MyMathLab | MathXL PRACTICE | WATCH | DOWNLOAD

Divide and check.

1. $\dfrac{40x^6 - 25x^3}{5}$

2. $\dfrac{16a^5 - 24a^2}{8}$

3. $\dfrac{u - 2u^2 + u^7}{u}$

4. $\dfrac{50x^5 - 7x^4 + 2x}{x}$

5. $(18t^3 - 24t^2 + 6t) \div (3t)$

6. $(20t^3 - 15t^2 + 30t) \div (5t)$

7. $(42x^5 - 36x^3 + 9x^2) \div (6x^2)$

8. $(24x^6 + 18x^4 + 8x^3) \div (4x^3)$

9. $(32t^5 + 16t^4 - 8t^3) \div (-8t^3)$

10. $(36t^6 - 27t^5 - 9t^2) \div (-9t^2)$

11. $\dfrac{8x^2 - 10x + 1}{2x}$

12. $\dfrac{9x^2 + 3x - 2}{3x}$

13. $\dfrac{5x^3y + 10x^5y^2 + 15x^2y}{5x^2y}$

14. $\dfrac{12a^3b^2 + 4a^4b^5 + 16ab^2}{4ab^2}$

15. $\dfrac{9r^2s^2 + 3r^2s - 6rs^2}{-3rs}$

16. $\dfrac{4x^4y - 8x^6y^2 + 12x^8y^6}{4x^4y}$

17. $(x^2 - 8x + 12) \div (x - 2)$

18. $(x^2 + 2x - 15) \div (x + 5)$

19. $(t^2 - 10t - 20) \div (t - 5)$

20. $(t^2 + 8t - 15) \div (t + 4)$

21. $(2x^2 + 11x - 5) \div (x + 6)$

22. $(3x^2 - 2x - 13) \div (x - 2)$

23. $\dfrac{t^3 + 27}{t + 3}$ **24.** $\dfrac{a^3 + 8}{a + 2}$

25. $\dfrac{a^2 - 21}{a - 5}$ **26.** $\dfrac{t^2 - 13}{t - 4}$

27. $(5x^2 - 16x) \div (5x - 1)$

28. $(3x^2 - 7x + 1) \div (3x - 1)$

29. $(6a^2 + 17a + 8) \div (2a + 5)$

30. $(10a^2 + 19a + 9) \div (2a + 3)$

31. $\dfrac{2t^3 - 9t^2 + 11t - 3}{2t - 3}$

32. $\dfrac{8t^3 - 22t^2 - 5t + 12}{4t + 3}$

33. $(x^3 - x^2 + x - 1) \div (x - 1)$

34. $(t^3 - t^2 + t - 1) \div (t + 1)$

35. $(t^4 + 4t^2 + 3t - 6) \div (t^2 + 5)$

36. $(t^4 - 2t^2 + 4t - 5) \div (t^2 - 3)$

37. $(6x^4 - 3x^2 + x - 4) \div (2x^2 + 1)$

38. $(4x^4 - 4x^2 - 3) \div (2x^2 - 3)$

39. How is the distributive law used when dividing a polynomial by a binomial?

40. On an assignment, Emmy Lou *incorrectly* writes

$$\frac{12x^3 - 6x}{3x} = 4x^2 - 6x.$$

What mistake do you think she is making and how might you convince her that a mistake has been made?

Skill Review

Review graphing linear equations (Chapter 2).

Graph.

41. $3x - 4y = 12$ [2.3]   **42.** $y = -\frac{2}{3}x + 4$ [2.6]

43. $3y - 2 = 7$ [2.3]   **44.** $8x = 4y$ [2.2]

45. Find the slope of the line containing the points $(3, 2)$ and $(-7, 5)$. [2.5]

46. Find the slope and the y-intercept of the line given by $2y = 8x + 7$. [2.6]

47. Find the slope–intercept form of the line with slope -5 and y-intercept $(0, -10)$. [2.6]

48. Find the slope–intercept form of the line containing the points $(6, 3)$ and $(-2, -7)$. [2.7]

Synthesis

49. Explain how to form trinomials for which division by $x - 5$ results in a remainder of 3.

50. Under what circumstances will the quotient of two binomials have more than two terms?

Divide.

51. $(10x^{9k} - 32x^{6k} + 28x^{3k}) \div (2x^{3k})$

52. $(45a^{8k} + 30a^{6k} - 60a^{4k}) \div (3a^{2k})$

53. $(6t^{3h} + 13t^{2h} - 4t^h - 15) \div (2t^h + 3)$

54. $(x^4 + a^2) \div (x + a)$

55. $(5a^3 + 8a^2 - 23a - 1) \div (5a^2 - 7a - 2)$

56. $(15y^3 - 30y + 7 - 19y^2) \div (3y^2 - 2 - 5y)$

57. Divide the sum of $4x^5 - 14x^3 - x^2 + 3$ and $2x^5 + 3x^4 + x^3 - 3x^2 + 5x$ by $3x^3 - 2x - 1$.

58. Divide $5x^7 - 3x^4 + 2x^2 - 10x + 2$ by the sum of $(x - 3)^2$ and $5x - 8$.

If the remainder is 0 when one polynomial is divided by another, the divisor is a factor of the dividend. Find the value(s) of c for which $x - 1$ is a factor of each polynomial.

59. $x^2 - 4x + c$

60. $2x^2 - 3cx - 8$

61. $c^2x^2 + 2cx + 1$

Study Summary

KEY TERMS AND CONCEPTS   **EXAMPLES**

SECTION 3.1: INTRODUCTION TO FACTORING

To **factor** a polynomial means to write it as a product. Always begin by factoring out the **largest common factor**.

Factor: $12x^4 - 30x^3$.
$$12x^4 - 30x^3 = 6x^3(2x - 5)$$

Some polynomials with four terms can be **factored by grouping**.

Factor: $3x^3 - x^2 - 6x + 2$.
$$3x^3 - x^2 - 6x + 2 = x^2(3x - 1) - 2(3x - 1)$$
$$= (3x - 1)(x^2 - 2)$$

SECTION 3.2: FACTORING TRINOMIALS OF THE TYPE $x^2 + bx + c$

Some trinomials of the type $x^2 + bx + c$ can be factored by reversing the steps of FOIL.

Factor: $x^2 - 11x + 18$.

Pairs of Factors of 18	Sums of Factors
$-1, -18$	-19
$-2, \ -9$	-11

18 is positive and -11 is negative, so both factors will be negative.

←The numbers we need are -2 and -9.

The factorization is $(x - 2)(x - 9)$.

SECTION 3.3: FACTORING TRINOMIALS OF THE TYPE $ax^2 + bx + c$

One method for factoring trinomials of the type $ax^2 + bx + c$ is a FOIL-based method.

Factor: $6x^2 - 5x - 6$.

The factors will be in the form $(3x + \ )(2x + \ )$ or $(6x + \ )(x + \ )$. We list all pairs of factors of -6, and check possible products by multiplying any possibilities that do not contain a common factor.

$$(3x - 2)(2x + 3) = 6x^2 + 5x - 6,$$
$$(3x + 2)(2x - 3) = 6x^2 - 5x - 6. \leftarrow \text{This is the correct product, so we stop here.}$$

The factorization is $(3x + 2)(2x - 3)$.

Another method for factoring trinomials of the type $ax^2 + bx + c$ involves factoring by grouping.

Factor: $6x^2 - 5x - 6$.

Multiply the leading coefficient and the constant term: $6(-6) = -36$. Look for factors of -36 that add to -5.

Pairs of Factors of -36	Sums of Factors
$1, -36$	-35
$2, -18$	-16
$3, -12$	-9
$4, \ -9$	-5

-5 is negative, so the negative factor must have the greater absolute value.

←The numbers we want are 4 and -9.

Rewrite $-5x$ as $4x - 9x$ and factor by grouping:
$$6x^2 - 5x - 6 = 6x^2 + 4x - 9x - 6$$
$$= 2x(3x + 2) - 3(3x + 2)$$
$$= (3x + 2)(2x - 3).$$

SECTION 3.4: FACTORING PERFECT-SQUARE TRINOMIALS AND DIFFERENCES OF SQUARES

Factoring a perfect-square trinomial

$$A^2 + 2AB + B^2 = (A + B)^2;$$
$$A^2 - 2AB + B^2 = (A - B)^2$$

Factor: $y^2 + 100 - 20y$.

$$A^2 - 2AB + B^2 = (A - B)^2$$
$$y^2 + 100 - 20y = y^2 - 20y + 100 = (y - 10)^2$$

Factoring a difference of squares

$$A^2 - B^2 = (A + B)(A - B)$$

Factor: $9t^2 - 1$.

$$A^2 - B^2 = (A + B)(A - B)$$
$$9t^2 - 1 = (3t + 1)(3t - 1)$$

SECTION 3.5: FACTORING SUMS OR DIFFERENCES OF CUBES

Factoring a sum or a difference of cubes

$$A^3 + B^3 = (A + B)(A^2 - AB + B^2)$$
$$A^3 - B^3 = (A - B)(A^2 + AB + B^2)$$

$$x^3 + 1000 = (x + 10)(x^2 - 10x + 100)$$
$$z^6 - 8w^3 = (z^2 - 2w)(z^4 + 2wz^2 + 4w^2)$$

SECTION 3.6: FACTORING: A GENERAL STRATEGY

To factor a polynomial:

A. Factor out the largest common factor.

B. Look at the number of terms.

Two terms: If a difference of squares, use $A^2 - B^2 = (A + B)(A - B)$.
If a sum of cubes, use
$A^3 + B^3 = (A + B)(A^2 - AB + B^2)$.
If a difference of cubes, use
$A^3 - B^3 = (A - B)(A^2 + AB + B^2)$.

Three terms: If a trinomial square, use
$A^2 + 2AB + B^2 = (A + B)^2$ or
$A^2 - 2AB + B^2 = (A - B)^2$.
Otherwise, try FOIL or grouping.

Four terms: Try factoring by grouping.

C. Factor completely.

D. Check by multiplying.

Factor: $5x^5 - 80x$.

$$5x^5 - 80x = 5x(x^4 - 16)$$ — $5x$ is the largest common factor.

$$= 5x(x^2 + 4)(x^2 - 4)$$ — $x^4 - 16$ is a difference of squares.

$$= 5x(x^2 + 4)(x + 2)(x - 2)$$ — $x^2 - 4$ is also a difference of squares.

Check: $5x(x^2 + 4)(x + 2)(x - 2) = 5x(x^2 + 4)(x^2 - 4)$
$$= 5x(x^4 - 16) = 5x^5 - 80x.$$

Factor: $-x^2y^2 - 3xy + 10$.

$$-x^2y^2 - 3xy + 10 = -(x^2y^2 + 3xy - 10)$$ — Factor out -1 to make the leading coefficient positive.

$$= -(xy + 5)(xy - 2)$$

Check: $-(xy + 5)(xy - 2) = -(x^2y^2 + 3xy - 10)$
$$= -x^2y^2 - 3xy + 10.$$

SECTION 3.7: SOLVING POLYNOMIAL EQUATIONS BY FACTORING

The Principle of Zero Products

An equation $AB = 0$ is true if and only if $A = 0$ or $B = 0$, or both.

Solve: $x^2 + 7x = 30$.

$$x^2 + 7x = 30$$
$$x^2 + 7x - 30 = 0$$ — Getting 0 on one side
$$(x + 10)(x - 3) = 0$$ — Factoring
$$x + 10 = 0 \quad or \quad x - 3 = 0$$ — Using the principle of zero products

$$x = -10 \quad or \quad x = 3$$

The solutions are -10 and 3.

SECTION 3.8: SOLVING APPLICATIONS

The Pythagorean Theorem

In any right triangle, if a and b are the lengths of the legs and c is the length of the hypotenuse, then

$a^2 + b^2 = c^2$, or

$(\text{Leg})^2 + (\text{Other leg})^2 = (\text{Hypotenuse})^2$.

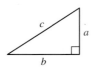

Aaron has a 25-ft ladder leaning against his house. The height that the ladder reaches on the house is 17 ft more than the distance that the bottom of the ladder is from the house. Find both distances.

$$x^2 + (x + 17)^2 = 25^2$$
$$x^2 + x^2 + 34x + 289 = 625 \qquad \text{Squaring}$$
$$2x^2 + 34x - 336 = 0$$
$$2(x + 24)(x - 7) = 0 \qquad \text{Factoring}$$
$$x + 24 = 0 \quad or \quad x - 7 = 0 \qquad \text{Using the principle of zero products}$$
$$x = -24 \quad or \qquad x = 7.$$

Since -24 cannot be a length, we check 7. When $x = 7$, $x + 17 = 24$, and $7^2 + 24^2 = 49 + 576 = 625 = 25^2$.

The ladder reaches 24 ft up the side of the house, and the bottom of the ladder is 7 ft from the house.

Review Exercises: Chapter 3

Concept Reinforcement　*Classify each statement as either true or false.*

1. The largest common variable factor is the largest power of the variable in the polynomial.　[3.1]

2. A prime polynomial has no common factor other than 1 or −1.　[3.2]

3. Every perfect-square trinomial can be expressed as a binomial squared.　[3.4]

4. Every binomial can be regarded as a difference of squares.　[3.4]

5. Every quadratic equation has two different solutions.　[3.7]

6. The principle of zero products can be applied whenever a product equals 0.　[3.7]

7. In a right triangle, the hypotenuse is always longer than either leg.　[3.8]

8. The Pythagorean theorem can be applied to any triangle that has an angle measuring at least 90°.　[3.8]

Find three factorizations of each monomial.　[3.1]

9. $20x^3$　　　　　10. $-18x^5$

Factor completely. If a polynomial is prime, state this.

11. $12x^4 - 18x^3$　[3.1]　　12. $8a^2 - 12a$　[3.1]

13. $100t^2 - 1$　[3.4]　　14. $x^2 + x - 12$　[3.2]

15. $x^2 + 14x + 49$　[3.4]　　16. $12x^3 + 12x^2 + 3x$　[3.4]

17. $6x^3 + 9x^2 + 2x + 3$　[3.1]　18. $6a^2 + a - 5$　[3.3]

19. $25t^2 + 9 - 30t$　[3.4]　　20. $48t^2 - 28t + 6$　[3.1]

21. $81a^4 - 1$　[3.4]　　22. $9x^3 + 12x^2 - 45x$　[3.3]

23. $2x^3 - 250$ [3.5]

24. $x^4 + 4x^3 - 2x - 8$ [3.1]

25. $a^2b^4 - 64$ [3.4]

26. $-8x^6 + 32x^5 - 4x^4$ [3.1]

27. $75 + 12x^2 - 60x$ [3.4]

28. $y^2 + 9$ [3.4]

29. $-t^3 + t^2 + 42t$ [3.2]

30. $4x^2 - 25$ [3.4]

31. $n^2 - 60 - 4n$ [3.2]

32. $5z^2 - 30z + 10$ [3.1]

33. $4t^2 + 13t + 10$ [3.3]

34. $2t^2 - 7t - 4$ [3.3]

35. $7x^3 + 35x^2 + 28x$ [3.2]

36. $8y^3 + 27x^6$ [3.5]

37. $20x^2 - 20x + 5$ [3.4]

38. $-6x^3 + 150x$ [3.4]

39. $15 - 8x + x^2$ [3.2]

40. $3x + x^2 + 5$ [3.2]

41. $x^2y^2 + 6xy - 16$ [3.2]

42. $12a^2 + 84ab + 147b^2$ [3.4]

43. $m^2 + 5m + mt + 5t$ [3.1]

44. $32x^4 - 128y^4z^4$ [3.4]

45. $6m^2 + 2mn + n^2 + 3mn$ [3.1], [3.3]

46. $6r^2 + rs - 15s^2$ [3.3]

Solve. [3.7]

47. $(x - 9)(x + 11) = 0$

48. $x^2 + 2x - 35 = 0$

49. $16x^2 = 9$

50. $3x^2 + 2 = 5x$

51. $2x^2 - 7x = 30$

52. $(x + 1)(x - 2) = 4$

53. $9t - 15t^2 = 0$

54. $3x^2 + 3 = 6x$

55. The square of a number is 12 more than the number. Find all such numbers. [3.8]

56. The formula $x^2 - x = N$ can be used to determine the total number of games played, N, in a league of x teams in which all teams play each other twice. Serena referees for a soccer league in which all teams play each other twice and a total of 90 games is played. How many teams are in the league? [3.8]

57. Find the x-intercepts for the graph of $y = 2x^2 - 3x - 5$. [3.7]

58. The front of a house is a triangle that is as wide as it is tall. Its area is 98 ft². Find the height and the base. [3.8]

59. Josh needs to add a diagonal brace to his LEGO® robot. The brace must span a height of 8 holes and a width of 6 holes. How long should the brace be? [3.8]

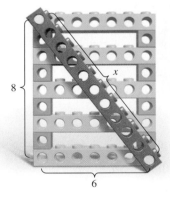

Synthesis

60. On a quiz, Celia writes the factorization of $4x^2 - 100$ as $(2x - 10)(2x + 10)$. If this were a 10-point question, how many points would you give Celia? Why? [3.4]

61. How do the equations solved in this chapter differ from those solved in previous chapters? [3.7]

Solve.

62. The pages of a book measure 15 cm by 20 cm. Margins of equal width surround the printing on each page and constitute one half of the area of the page. Find the width of the margins. [3.8]

63. The cube of a number is the same as twice the square of the number. Find the number. [3.8]

64. The length of a rectangle is two times its width. When the length is increased by 20 cm and the width is decreased by 1 cm, the area is 160 cm^2. Find the original length and width. [3.8]

65. The length of each side of a square is increased by 5 cm to form a new square. The area of the new square is $2\frac{1}{4}$ times the area of the original square. Find the area of each square. [3.8]

Solve. [3.7]

66. $(x - 2)2x^2 + x(x - 2) - (x - 2)15 = 0$

Aha! **67.** $x^2 + 25 = 0$

Test: Chapter 3

Test Prep VIDEO CD

Step-by-step test solutions are found on the video CD in the front of this book.

1. Find three factorizations of $12x^4$.

Factor completely. If a polynomial is prime, state this.

2. $x^2 - 13x + 36$

3. $x^2 + 25 - 10x$

4. $6y^2 - 8y^3 + 4y^4$

5. $x^3 + x^2 + 2x + 2$

6. $t^7 - 3t^5$

7. $a^3 + 3a^2 - 4a$

8. $28x - 48 + 10x^2$

9. $4t^2 - 25$

10. $x^2 - x - 6$

11. $-6m^3 - 9m^2 - 3m$

12. $3r^3 - 3$

13. $45r^2 + 60r + 20$

14. $3x^4 - 48$

15. $49t^2 + 36 + 84t$

16. $x^4 + 2x^3 - 3x - 6$

17. $x^2 + 3x + 6$

18. $4x^2 - 4x - 15$

19. $6t^3 + 9t^2 - 15t$

20. $3m^2 - 9mn - 30n^2$

Solve.

21. $x^2 - 6x + 5 = 0$

22. $2x^2 - 7x = 15$

23. $4t - 10t^2 = 0$

24. $25t^2 = 1$

25. $x(x - 1) = 20$

26. Find the x-intercepts for the graph of $y = 3x^2 - 5x - 8$.

27. The length of a rectangle is 6 m more than the width. The area of the rectangle is 40 m^2. Find the length and the width.

28. The number of possible handshakes H within a group of n people is given by $H = \frac{1}{2}(n^2 - n)$. At a meeting, everyone shook hands once with everyone else. If there were 45 handshakes, how many people were at the meeting?

29. A mason wants to be sure she has a right corner in a building's foundation. She marks a point 3 ft from the corner along one wall and another point 4 ft from the corner along the other wall. If the corner is a right angle, what should the distance be between the two marked points?

Synthesis

30. *Dimensions of an open box.* A rectangular piece of cardboard is twice as long as it is wide. A 4-cm square is cut out of each corner, and the sides are turned up to make a box with an open top. The volume of the box is 616 cm^3. Find the original dimensions of the cardboard.

31. Factor: $(a + 3)^2 - 2(a + 3) - 35$.

32. Solve: $20x(x + 2)(x - 1) = 5x^3 - 24x - 14x^2$.

Cumulative Review: Chapters 1-3

Simplify. Do not use negative exponents in the answer.

1. $\frac{3}{8} \div \frac{3}{4}$

2. $\frac{3}{8} \cdot \frac{3}{4}$

3. $\frac{3}{8} + \frac{3}{4}$

4. $-2 + (20 \div 4)^2 - 6 \cdot (-1)^3$

5. $(3x^2y^3)^{-2}$

6. $(t^2)^3 \cdot t^4$

7. $(3x^4 - 2x^2 + x - 7) + (5x^3 + 2x^2 - 3)$

8. $(a^2b - 2ab^2 + 3b^3) - (4a^2b - ab^2 + b^3)$

9. $\dfrac{3t^3s^{-1}}{12t^{-5}s}$

10. $\left(\dfrac{-2x^2y}{3z^4}\right)^3$

11. Evaluate $-x$ for $x = -8$.

12. Evaluate $-(-x)$ for $x = -8$.

13. Determine the leading term of the polynomial
$$4x^3 - 6x^2 - x^4 + 7.$$

14. Divide: $(8x^4 - 20x^3 + 2x^2 - 4x) \div (4x)$. [3.9]

Multiply.

15. $-4t^8(t^3 - 2t - 5)$

16. $(3x - 5)^2$

17. $(10x^5 + y)(10x^5 - y)$

18. $(x - 1)(x^2 - x - 1)$

Factor completely.

19. $c^2 - 1$ [3.4]

20. $5x + 5y + 10x^2 + 10xy$ [3.1]

21. $4r^2 - 4rt + t^2$ [3.4]

22. $6x^2 - 19x + 10$ [3.3]

23. $10y^2 + 40$ [3.1]

24. $x^2y - 3xy + 2y$ [3.2]

25. $12x^2 - 5xy - 2y^2$ [3.3]

26. $125a^3 + 64b^3$ [3.5]

Solve.

27. $\frac{1}{3} + 2x = \frac{1}{2}$ [1.2]

28. $3(t - 1) = 2 - (t + 1)$ [1.2]

29. $8y - 6(y - 2) = 3(2y + 7)$ [1.2]

30. $3x - 7 \geq 4 - 8x$ [1.6]

31. $(x - 1)(x + 3) = 0$ [3.7]

32. $x^2 + x = 12$ [3.7]

33. $3x^2 = 12$ [3.7]

34. $3x^2 = 12x$ [3.7]

35. Solve $a = bc + dc$ for c. [1.3]

36. Find the slope of the line containing the points $(6, 7)$ and $(-2, 7)$. [2.5]

37. Find the slope and the y-intercept of the line given by $2x + y = 5$. [2.6]

38. Write the slope–intercept equation for the line with slope 5 and y-intercept $\left(0, -\frac{1}{3}\right)$. [2.6]

39. Write the slope–intercept equation for the line with slope 5 that contains the point $\left(-\frac{1}{3}, 0\right)$. [2.7]

Graph.

40. $4(x + 1) = 8$ [2.3]

41. $x + y = 5$ [2.3]

42. $y = \frac{3}{2}x - 2$ [2.6]

43. $3x + 5y = 10$ [2.6]

44. Use a grid 10 squares wide and 10 squares high to plot $(5, 40)$, $(18, -60)$, and $(30, -22)$. Choose the scale carefully. [2.1]

Solve.

45. On average, men talk 97 min more per month on cell phones than do women. The sum of men's average minutes and women's average minutes is 647 min. What is the average number of minutes per month that men talk on cell phones? [1.5]
Source: *International Communications Research for Cingular Wireless*

46. The number of cell-phone subscribers increased from 680,000 in 1986 to 233,000,000 in 2006. What was the average rate of increase? [2.4]
Source: CTIA – The Wireless Association

47. In 2007, there were 1.2 billion Internet users worldwide. Of these, 5% spoke French. How many Internet users spoke French? [1.4]
Source: Internetworldstats.com

48. The number of people in the United States, in thousands, who are on a waiting list for an organ transplant can be approximated by the polynomial $2.38t + 77.38$, where t is the number of years since 2000. Estimate the number of people on a waiting list for an organ transplant in 2010.
Source: Based on information from The Organ Procurement and Transplantation Network

49. A 13-ft ladder is placed against a building in such a way that the distance from the top of the ladder to the ground is 7 ft more than the distance from the bottom of the ladder to the building. Find both distances. [3.8]

50. A rectangular table in Arlo's House of Tunes is six times as long as it is wide. If the area of the table is 24 ft^2, find the length and the width of the table. [3.8]

51. Donna's quiz grades are 8, 3, 5, and 10. What scores on the fifth quiz will make her average quiz grade at least 7? [1.7]

52. The average amount of sodium in a serving of Chef Boyardee foods dropped from 1100 mg in 2003 to 900 mg in 2007. [2.7]
Source: *The Indianapolis Star*, 11/25/07

a) Graph the data and determine an equation for the related line. Let s represent the average amount of sodium per serving and t the number of years after 2000.

b) Use the equation of part (a) to estimate the average amount of sodium in a serving of Chef Boyardee foods in 2006.

Synthesis

53. Solve $x = \dfrac{abx}{2 - b}$ for b. [1.3]

54. Write an equation of the line parallel to the x-axis and passing through $(-6, -8)$. [2.3]

55. a) Multiply: $(3y + 2 + x)(3y + 2 - x)$.
b) Factor: $9y^2 + 12y + 4 - x^2$. [3.4]

56. Solve: $6x^3 + 4x^2 = 2x$. [3.7]

Rational Expressions and Equations

FRED JENKINS
TECHNICAL SERVICES
MANAGER
Goose Creek, South Carolina

As a chemist involved in the quality control of all chemicals used and manufactured where I work, I use mathematics to calculate purities, density, refractive index, acidity, and other parameters that determine whether a material meets intended specifications. Even though many calculations are performed by instrument software, it is important for me as a chemist and manager to know how to verify results and troubleshoot with math when problems occur.

AN APPLICATION

As one alternative to gasoline-powered vehicles, flex fuel vehicles can use both regular gasoline and E85, a fuel containing 85% ethanol. Because using E85 results in a lower fuel economy, its price per gallon must be lower than the price of gasoline in order to make it an economical fuel option. A 2007 Chevrolet Tahoe gets 21 mpg on the highway using gasoline and only 15 mpg on the highway using E85. If the price of gasoline is $3.36 a gallon, what must the price of E85 be in order for the fuel cost per mile to be the same?

Source: www.caranddriver.com

This problem appears as Example 7 in Section 4.7.

Rational expressions are similar to fractions in arithmetic, in that both are ratios of two expressions. We now learn how to simplify, add, subtract, multiply, and divide rational expressions. These skills will then be used to solve the equations that arise from real-life problems like the one on the preceding page.

4.1 Rational Expressions

Simplifying Rational Expressions • Factors That Are Opposites

Just as a rational number is any number that can be written as a quotient of two integers, a **rational expression** is any expression that can be written as a quotient of two polynomials. The following are examples of rational expressions:

$$\frac{7}{3}, \quad \frac{5}{x + 6}, \quad \frac{t^2 - 5t + 6}{4t^2 - 7}.$$

Rational expressions are examples of *algebraic fractions*. They are also examples of *fraction expressions*.

Because rational expressions indicate division, we must be careful to avoid denominators that are 0. For example, in the expression

$$\frac{x + 3}{x - 7},$$

when x is replaced with 7, the denominator is 0, and the expression is undefined:

$$\frac{x + 3}{x - 7} = \frac{7 + 3}{7 - 7} = \frac{10}{0}. \leftarrow \text{Division by 0 is undefined.}$$

When x is replaced with a number other than 7—say, 6—the expression *is* defined because the denominator is not 0:

$$\frac{x + 3}{x - 7} = \frac{6 + 3}{6 - 7} = \frac{9}{-1} = -9.$$

The expression is also defined when $x = -3$:

$$\frac{x + 3}{x - 7} = \frac{-3 + 3}{-3 - 7} = \frac{0}{-10} = 0. \qquad \text{0 divided by a nonzero number is 0.}$$

Any replacement for the variable that makes the *denominator* 0 will cause an expression to be undefined.

EXAMPLE 1 Find all numbers for which the rational expression

$$\frac{x + 4}{x^2 - 3x - 10}$$

is undefined.

SOLUTION   The value of the numerator has no bearing on whether or not a rational expression is defined. To determine which numbers make the rational expression undefined, we set the *denominator* equal to 0 and solve:

$$x^2 - 3x - 10 = 0 \qquad \text{We set the denominator equal to 0.}$$
$$(x - 5)(x + 2) = 0 \qquad \text{Factoring}$$
$$x - 5 = 0 \quad or \quad x + 2 = 0 \qquad \text{Using the principle of zero products}$$
$$x = 5 \quad or \qquad x = -2. \qquad \text{Solving each equation}$$

Check:

For $x = 5$:

$$\frac{x + 4}{x^2 - 3x - 10} = \frac{5 + 4}{5^2 - 3 \cdot 5 - 10} \qquad \text{There are no restrictions on the numerator.}$$

$$= \frac{9}{25 - 15 - 10} = \frac{9}{0}. \qquad \text{This expression is undefined, as expected.}$$

For $x = -2$:

$$\frac{x + 4}{x^2 - 3x - 10} = \frac{-2 + 4}{(-2)^2 - 3(-2) - 10}$$

$$= \frac{2}{4 + 6 - 10} = \frac{2}{0}. \qquad \text{This expression is undefined, as expected.}$$

Thus, $\dfrac{x + 4}{x^2 - 3x - 10}$ is undefined for $x = 5$ and $x = -2$.   ▶ TRY EXERCISE   7

Simplifying Rational Expressions

A rational expression is said to be *simplified* when the numerator and the denominator have no factors (other than 1) in common. To simplify a rational expression, we first factor the numerator and the denominator. We then identify factors common to the numerator and the denominator, rewrite the expression as a product of two rational expressions (one of which is equal to 1), and then remove the factor equal to 1.

$$\frac{15}{40} = \frac{3 \cdot 5}{8 \cdot 5} \qquad \text{Factoring the numerator and the denominator. Note the common factor, 5.}$$

$$= \frac{3}{8} \cdot \frac{5}{5} \qquad \text{Rewriting as a product of two fractions}$$

$$= \frac{3}{8} \cdot 1 \qquad \frac{5}{5} = 1$$

$$= \frac{3}{8}. \qquad \text{Using the identity property of 1 to remove the factor 1}$$

Similar steps are followed when simplifying rational expressions: We factor and remove a factor equal to 1, using the fact that

$$\frac{ab}{cb} = \frac{a}{c} \cdot \frac{b}{b}.$$

EXAMPLE **2** Simplify: $\dfrac{8x^2}{24x}$.

SOLUTION

$$\dfrac{8x^2}{24x} = \dfrac{8 \cdot x \cdot x}{3 \cdot 8 \cdot x}$$ Factoring the numerator and the denominator. Note the common factor of $8 \cdot x$.

$$= \dfrac{x}{3} \cdot \dfrac{8x}{8x}$$ Rewriting as a product of two rational expressions

$$= \dfrac{x}{3} \cdot 1 \qquad \dfrac{8x}{8x} = 1$$

$$= \dfrac{x}{3}$$ Removing the factor 1 TRY EXERCISE 17

We say that $\dfrac{8x^2}{24x}$ *simplifies* to $\dfrac{x}{3}$.* In the work that follows, we assume that all denominators are nonzero.

EXAMPLE **3** Simplify: $\dfrac{5a + 15}{10}$.

SOLUTION

$$\dfrac{5a + 15}{10} = \dfrac{5(a + 3)}{5 \cdot 2}$$ Factoring the numerator and the denominator. Note the common factor of 5.

$$= \dfrac{5}{5} \cdot \dfrac{a + 3}{2}$$ Rewriting as a product of two rational expressions

$$= 1 \cdot \dfrac{a + 3}{2} \qquad \dfrac{5}{5} = 1$$

$$= \dfrac{a + 3}{2}$$ Removing the factor 1 TRY EXERCISE 19

The result in Example 3 can be partially checked using a replacement for a—say, $a = 2$.

Original expression: *Simplified expression:*

$$\dfrac{5a + 15}{10} = \dfrac{5 \cdot 2 + 15}{10} \qquad\qquad \dfrac{a + 3}{2} = \dfrac{2 + 3}{2}$$

$$= \dfrac{25}{10} = \dfrac{5}{2} \quad \text{The results are the same.} \qquad = \dfrac{5}{2}$$

To see why this check is not foolproof, see Exercise 65.

If we do not get the same result when evaluating both expressions, we know that a mistake has been made. For example, if $(5a + 15)/10$ is *incorrectly* simplified as $(a + 15)/2$ and we evaluate using $a = 2$, we have the following.

Original expression: *Incorrectly simplified expression:*

$$\dfrac{5a + 15}{10} = \dfrac{5 \cdot 2 + 15}{10} \qquad\qquad \dfrac{a + 15}{2} = \dfrac{2 + 15}{2}$$

$$= \dfrac{5}{2} \quad \text{The results are different.} \qquad = \dfrac{17}{2}$$

This demonstrates that a mistake has been made.

---

*In more advanced courses, we would *not* say that $8x^2/(24x)$ simplifies to $x/3$, but would instead say that $8x^2/(24x)$ simplifies to $x/3$ *with the restriction that $x \neq 0$.*

Sometimes the common factor has two or more terms.

EXAMPLE 4

Simplify.

a) $\dfrac{6x - 12}{7x - 14}$

b) $\dfrac{18t^2 + 6t}{6t^2 + 15t}$

c) $\dfrac{x^2 + 3x + 2}{x^2 - 1}$

SOLUTION

a) $\dfrac{6x - 12}{7x - 14} = \dfrac{6(x - 2)}{7(x - 2)}$ Factoring the numerator and the denominator. Note the common factor of $x - 2$.

$\phantom{\dfrac{6x - 12}{7x - 14}} = \dfrac{6}{7} \cdot \dfrac{x - 2}{x - 2}$ Rewriting as a product of two rational expressions

$\phantom{\dfrac{6x - 12}{7x - 14}} = \dfrac{6}{7} \cdot 1$ $\dfrac{x - 2}{x - 2} = 1$

$\phantom{\dfrac{6x - 12}{7x - 14}} = \dfrac{6}{7}$ Removing the factor 1

b) $\dfrac{18t^2 + 6t}{6t^2 + 15t} = \dfrac{3t \cdot 2(3t + 1)}{3t(2t + 5)}$ Factoring the numerator and the denominator. Note the common factor of $3t$.

$\phantom{\dfrac{18t^2 + 6t}{6t^2 + 15t}} = \dfrac{3t}{3t} \cdot \dfrac{2(3t + 1)}{2t + 5}$ Rewriting as a product of two rational expressions

$\phantom{\dfrac{18t^2 + 6t}{6t^2 + 15t}} = 1 \cdot \dfrac{2(3t + 1)}{2t + 5}$ $\dfrac{3t}{3t} = 1$

$\phantom{\dfrac{18t^2 + 6t}{6t^2 + 15t}} = \dfrac{2(3t + 1)}{2t + 5}$ Removing the factor 1. The numerator and the denominator have no common factor so the simplification is complete.

c) $\dfrac{x^2 + 3x + 2}{x^2 - 1} = \dfrac{(x + 1)(x + 2)}{(x + 1)(x - 1)}$ Factoring; $x + 1$ is the common factor.

$\phantom{\dfrac{x^2 + 3x + 2}{x^2 - 1}} = \dfrac{x + 1}{x + 1} \cdot \dfrac{x + 2}{x - 1}$ Rewriting as a product of two rational expressions

$\phantom{\dfrac{x^2 + 3x + 2}{x^2 - 1}} = 1 \cdot \dfrac{x + 2}{x - 1}$ $\dfrac{x + 1}{x + 1} = 1$

$\phantom{\dfrac{x^2 + 3x + 2}{x^2 - 1}} = \dfrac{x + 2}{x - 1}$ Removing the factor 1

TRY EXERCISE 23

Canceling is a shortcut that can be used—and easily *misused*—to simplify rational expressions. Canceling must be done with care and understanding. Essentially, canceling streamlines the process of removing a factor equal to 1. Example 4(c) could have been streamlined as follows:

$\dfrac{x^2 + 3x + 2}{x^2 - 1} = \dfrac{\cancel{(x + 1)}(x + 2)}{\cancel{(x + 1)}(x - 1)}$ When a factor equal to 1 is noted, it is "canceled": $\dfrac{x + 1}{x + 1} = 1$.

$\phantom{\dfrac{x^2 + 3x + 2}{x^2 - 1}} = \dfrac{x + 2}{x - 1}.$ Simplifying

---

TECHNOLOGY CONNECTION

We can use the TABLE feature as a partial check that rational expressions have been simplified correctly. To check the simplification in Example 4(c),

$$\dfrac{x^2 + 3x + 2}{x^2 - 1} = \dfrac{x + 2}{x - 1},$$

we enter $y_1 = (x^2 + 3x + 2)/(x^2 - 1)$ and $y_2 = (x + 2)/(x - 1)$ and select the mode AUTO to look at a table of values of y_1 and y_2. The values should match for all allowable replacements.

X	Y1	Y2
−4	.4	.4
−3	.25	.25
−2	0	0
−1	ERROR	−.5
0	−2	−2
1	ERROR	ERROR
2	4	4

X = −4

The ERROR messages indicate that −1 and 1 are not allowable replacements in y_1 and 1 is not an allowable replacement in y_2. For all other numbers, y_1 and y_2 are the same, so the simplification appears to be correct.

Use the TABLE feature to determine whether each of the following appears to be correct.

1. $\dfrac{8x^2}{24x} = \dfrac{x}{3}$

2. $\dfrac{5x + 15}{10} = \dfrac{x + 3}{2}$

3. $\dfrac{x + 3}{x} = 3$

4. $\dfrac{x^2 + 3x - 4}{x^2 - 16} = \dfrac{x - 1}{x + 4}$

> **CAUTION!** Canceling is often used incorrectly. The following cancellations are *incorrect*:
>
> $$\frac{\cancel{x+7}}{x+3}; \quad \frac{a^2 - \cancel{5}}{\cancel{5}}, \quad \frac{6x^2 + 5x + \cancel{1}}{4x^2 - 3x}.$$
>
> Wrong! Wrong! Wrong!
>
> None of the above cancellations removes a factor equal to 1. Factors are parts of products. For example, in $x \cdot 7$, x and 7 are factors, but in $x + 7$, x and 7 are terms, *not* factors. Only factors can be canceled.

EXAMPLE 5 Simplify: $\dfrac{3x^2 - 2x - 1}{x^2 - 3x + 2}$.

SOLUTION We factor the numerator and the denominator and look for common factors:

$$\frac{3x^2 - 2x - 1}{x^2 - 3x + 2} = \frac{(3x + 1)\cancel{(x-1)}}{(x - 2)\cancel{(x-1)}} \qquad \begin{array}{l} \text{Try to visualize this as} \\ \dfrac{3x + 1}{x - 2} \cdot \dfrac{x - 1}{x - 1}. \end{array}$$

$$= \frac{3x + 1}{x - 2}. \qquad \begin{array}{l} \text{Removing a factor equal to 1:} \\ \dfrac{x - 1}{x - 1} = 1 \end{array}$$

TRY EXERCISE 31

Factors That Are Opposites

Consider

$$\frac{x - 4}{8 - 2x}, \quad \text{or, equivalently,} \quad \frac{x - 4}{2(4 - x)}.$$

At first glance, the numerator and the denominator do not appear to have any common factors. But $x - 4$ and $4 - x$ are opposites, or additive inverses, of each other. Thus we can find a common factor by factoring out -1 in one expression.

EXAMPLE 6 Simplify $\dfrac{x - 4}{8 - 2x}$ and check by evaluating.

SOLUTION We have

$$\frac{x - 4}{8 - 2x} = \frac{x - 4}{2(4 - x)} \qquad \text{Factoring}$$

$$= \frac{x - 4}{2(-1)(x - 4)} \qquad \text{Note that } 4 - x = -x + 4 = -1(x - 4).$$

$$= \frac{x - 4}{-2(x - 4)} \qquad \begin{array}{l} \text{Had we originally factored out } -2, \text{ we} \\ \text{could have gone directly to this step.} \end{array}$$

$$= \frac{1}{-2} \cdot \frac{x - 4}{x - 4} \qquad \begin{array}{l} \text{Rewriting as a product. It is important} \\ \text{to write the 1 in the numerator.} \end{array}$$

$$= -\frac{1}{2}. \qquad \begin{array}{l} \text{Removing a factor equal to 1:} \\ (x - 4)/(x - 4) = 1 \end{array}$$

As a partial check, note that for any choice of x other than 4, the value of the rational expression is $-\frac{1}{2}$. For example, if $x = 5$, then

$$\frac{x - 4}{8 - 2x} = \frac{5 - 4}{8 - 2 \cdot 5}$$

$$= \frac{1}{-2} = -\frac{1}{2}.$$

TRY EXERCISE 47

4.1   EXERCISE SET

For Extra Help

🌙 **Concept Reinforcement**   *In each of Exercises 1–6, match the rational expression with the list of numbers in the column on the right for which the rational expression is undefined.*

1. ____ $\dfrac{x - 5}{(x - 2)(x + 3)}$

2. ____ $\dfrac{3t}{(t + 1)(t - 4)}$

3. ____ $\dfrac{a + 7}{a^2 - a - 12}$

4. ____ $\dfrac{m - 3}{m^2 - 2m - 15}$

5. ____ $\dfrac{2t + 7}{(2t - 1)(3t + 4)}$

6. ____ $\dfrac{4x - 1}{(3x - 1)(3x - 2)}$

a) $-1, 4$

b) $-3, 5$

c) $-\dfrac{4}{3}, \dfrac{1}{2}$

d) $-3, 4$

e) $-3, 2$

f) $\dfrac{1}{3}, \dfrac{2}{3}$

List all numbers for which each rational expression is undefined.

7. $\dfrac{18}{-11x}$

8. $\dfrac{13}{-5t}$

9. $\dfrac{y - 3}{y + 5}$

10. $\dfrac{a + 6}{a - 10}$

11. $\dfrac{t - 5}{3t - 15}$

12. $\dfrac{x^2 - 4}{5x + 10}$

13. $\dfrac{x^2 - 25}{x^2 - 3x - 28}$

14. $\dfrac{p^2 - 9}{p^2 - 7p + 10}$

15. $\dfrac{t^2 + t - 20}{2t^2 + 11t - 6}$

16. $\dfrac{x^2 + 2x + 1}{3x^2 - x - 14}$

Simplify by removing a factor equal to 1. Show all steps.

17. $\dfrac{50a^2b}{40ab^3}$

18. $\dfrac{-24x^4y^3}{6x^7y}$

19. $\dfrac{6t + 12}{6t - 18}$

20. $\dfrac{5n - 30}{5n + 5}$

21. $\dfrac{21t - 7}{24t - 8}$

22. $\dfrac{10n + 25}{8n + 20}$

23. $\dfrac{a^2 - 9}{a^2 + 4a + 3}$

24. $\dfrac{a^2 + 5a + 6}{a^2 - 9}$

Simplify, if possible. Then check by evaluating, as in Example 6.

25. $\dfrac{-36x^8}{54x^5}$

26. $\dfrac{45a^4}{30a^6}$

27. $\dfrac{-2y + 6}{-8y}$

28. $\dfrac{-4m^2 + 4m}{-8m^2 + 12m}$

29. $\dfrac{t^2 - 16}{t^2 - t - 20}$

30. $\dfrac{a^2 - 4}{a^2 + 5a + 6}$

31. $\dfrac{3a^2 + 9a - 12}{6a^2 - 30a + 24}$

32. $\dfrac{2t^2 - 6t + 4}{4t^2 + 12t - 16}$

33. $\dfrac{x^2 - 8x + 16}{x^2 - 16}$

34. $\dfrac{x^2 - 25}{x^2 + 10x + 25}$

35. $\dfrac{n - 2}{n^3 - 8}$

36. $\dfrac{n^6 + 27}{n^2 + 3}$

37. $\dfrac{t^2 - 1}{t + 1}$

38. $\dfrac{a^2 - 1}{a - 1}$

39. $\dfrac{y^2 + 4}{y + 2}$

40. $\dfrac{m^2 + 9}{m + 3}$

41. $\dfrac{5x^2 + 20}{10x^2 + 40}$

42. $\dfrac{6x^2 + 54}{4x^2 + 36}$

43. $\dfrac{y^2 + 6y}{2y^2 + 13y + 6}$

44. $\dfrac{t^2 + 2t}{2t^2 + t - 6}$

45. $\dfrac{4x^2 - 12x + 9}{10x^2 - 11x - 6}$

46. $\dfrac{4x^2 - 4x + 1}{6x^2 + 5x - 4}$

47. $\dfrac{10 - x}{x - 10}$

48. $\dfrac{x - 8}{8 - x}$

49. $\dfrac{7t - 14}{2 - t}$

50. $\dfrac{3 - n}{5n - 15}$

51. $\dfrac{a - b}{4b - 4a}$

52. $\dfrac{2p - 2q}{q - p}$

53. $\dfrac{3x^2 - 3y^2}{2y^2 - 2x^2}$

54. $\dfrac{7a^2 - 7b^2}{3b^2 - 3a^2}$

Aha! **55.** $\dfrac{7s^2 - 28t^2}{28t^2 - 7s^2}$

56. $\dfrac{9m^2 - 4n^2}{4n^2 - 9m^2}$

57. Explain how simplifying is related to the identity property of 1.

58. If a rational expression is undefined for $x = 5$ and $x = -3$, what is the degree of the denominator? Why?

Skill Review

To prepare for Section 4.2, review multiplication and division using fraction notation.

Simplify.

59. $-\dfrac{2}{15} \cdot \dfrac{10}{7}$

60. $\left(\dfrac{3}{4}\right)\left(\dfrac{-20}{9}\right)$

61. $\dfrac{5}{8} \div \left(-\dfrac{1}{6}\right)$

62. $\dfrac{7}{10} \div \left(-\dfrac{8}{15}\right)$

63. $\dfrac{7}{9} - \dfrac{2}{3} \cdot \dfrac{6}{7}$

64. $\dfrac{2}{3} - \left(\dfrac{3}{4}\right)^2$

Synthesis

65. Keith *incorrectly* simplifies

$$\dfrac{x^2 + x - 2}{x^2 + 3x + 2} \quad \text{as} \quad \dfrac{x - 1}{x + 2}.$$

He then checks his simplification by evaluating both expressions for $x = 1$. Use this situation to explain why evaluating is not a foolproof check.

66. How could you convince someone that $a - b$ and $b - a$ are opposites of each other?

Simplify.

67. $\dfrac{16y^4 - x^4}{(x^2 + 4y^2)(x - 2y)}$

68. $\dfrac{(x - 1)(x^4 - 1)(x^2 - 1)}{(x^2 + 1)(x - 1)^2(x^4 - 2x^2 + 1)}$

69. $\dfrac{x^5 - 2x^3 + 4x^2 - 8}{x^7 + 2x^4 - 4x^3 - 8}$

70. $\dfrac{10t^4 - 8t^3 + 15t - 12}{8 - 10t + 12t^2 - 15t^3}$

71. $\dfrac{(t^4 - 1)(t^2 - 9)(t - 9)^2}{(t^4 - 81)(t^2 + 1)(t + 1)^2}$

72. $\dfrac{(t + 2)^3(t^2 + 2t + 1)(t + 1)}{(t + 1)^3(t^2 + 4t + 4)(t + 2)}$

73. $\dfrac{(x^2 - y^2)(x^2 - 2xy + y^2)}{(x + y)^2(x^2 - 4xy - 5y^2)}$

74. $\dfrac{x^4 - y^4}{(y - x)^4}$

75. Select any number x, multiply by 2, add 5, multiply by 5, subtract 25, and divide by 10. What do you get? Explain how this procedure can be used for a number trick.

Additional Exercises

Simplify.

76. $\dfrac{x^3 - 4x^2 - 9x + 36}{x^2 - 7x + 12}$

77. $\dfrac{x^3 + 6x^2 - 4x - 24}{x^2 + 4x - 12}$

78. $\dfrac{10x^2 - 10}{5x^3 - 30x^2 - 5x + 30}$

79. $\dfrac{3x^2 - 12}{3x^3 - 6x^2 - 75x + 150}$

80. $\dfrac{x^4 - x^3 - 9x^2 + 9x}{x^3 + 4x^2 + 3x}$

81. $\dfrac{x^3 + x^2 - 16x - 16}{x^3 + 4x^2 - x - 4}$

Simplify.

82. $\dfrac{a^2 - 1}{a^3 - 1}$

83. $\dfrac{t^3 + 1}{t^2 - 1}$

84. $\dfrac{5x^3 + 5y^3}{10x^2 - 10y^2}$

85. $\dfrac{x^2y - y^3}{x^3y - y^4}$

86. $\dfrac{10x^2 - 11x - 6}{15x^2 + x - 2}$

87. $\dfrac{8x^2 - 6x - 9}{8x^2 + 18x + 9}$

88. $\dfrac{6x^4 + 23x^3 + 20x^2}{18x^3 9x^2 - 20x}$

89. $\dfrac{12x^2 - 38x + 30}{8x^2 - 14x + 3}$

90. $\dfrac{100a^2 + 50a - 24}{10a^2x + 33ax + 20x}$

91. $\dfrac{16p^2w - 34pw - 15w}{80p^2 - 60p - 350}$

4.2 Multiplication and Division

Multiplication • Division

Multiplication and division of rational expressions are similar to multiplication and division with fractions. In this section, we again assume that all denominators are nonzero.

Multiplication

Recall that to multiply fractions, we multiply numerator times numerator and denominator times denominator. Rational expressions are multiplied in a similar way.

The Product of Two Rational Expressions

To multiply rational expressions, multiply numerators and multiply denominators:

$$\frac{A}{B} \cdot \frac{C}{D} = \frac{AC}{BD}.$$

Then factor and, if possible, simplify the result.

For example,

$$\frac{3}{5} \cdot \frac{8}{11} = \frac{3 \cdot 8}{5 \cdot 11} \quad \text{and} \quad \frac{x}{3} \cdot \frac{x + 2}{y} = \frac{x(x + 2)}{3y}.$$

Fraction bars are grouping symbols, so parentheses are needed when writing some products. Because we generally simplify, we often leave products involving variables in factored form. There is no need to multiply further.

EXAMPLE **1** Multiply and, if possible, simplify.

a) $\dfrac{5a^3}{4} \cdot \dfrac{2}{5a}$

b) $(x^2 - 3x - 10) \cdot \dfrac{x + 4}{x^2 - 10x + 25}$

c) $\dfrac{10x + 20}{2x^2 - 3x + 1} \cdot \dfrac{x^2 - 1}{5x + 10}$

SOLUTION

a) $\dfrac{5a^3}{4} \cdot \dfrac{2}{5a} = \dfrac{5a^3(2)}{4(5a)}$ Forming the product of the numerators and the product of the denominators

$= \dfrac{5 \cdot a \cdot a \cdot a \cdot 2}{2 \cdot 2 \cdot 5 \cdot a}$ Factoring the numerator and the denominator

$= \dfrac{5 \cdot a \cdot a \cdot a \cdot 2}{2 \cdot 2 \cdot 5 \cdot a}$

$= \dfrac{a^2}{2}$ Removing a factor equal to 1: $\dfrac{2 \cdot 5 \cdot a}{2 \cdot 5 \cdot a} = 1$

b) $(x^2 - 3x - 10) \cdot \dfrac{x + 4}{x^2 - 10x + 25}$

$= \dfrac{x^2 - 3x - 10}{1} \cdot \dfrac{x + 4}{x^2 - 10x + 25}$ Writing $x^2 - 3x - 10$ as a rational expression

$= \dfrac{(x^2 - 3x - 10)(x + 4)}{1(x^2 - 10x + 25)}$ Multiplying the numerators and the denominators

$= \dfrac{(x - 5)(x + 2)(x + 4)}{(x - 5)(x - 5)}$ Factoring the numerator and the denominator

$= \dfrac{(x - 5)(x + 2)(x + 4)}{(x - 5)(x - 5)}$ Removing a factor equal to 1: $\dfrac{x - 5}{x - 5} = 1$

$= \dfrac{(x + 2)(x + 4)}{x - 5}$

c) $\dfrac{10x + 20}{2x^2 - 3x + 1} \cdot \dfrac{x^2 - 1}{5x + 10}$

$= \dfrac{(10x + 20)(x^2 - 1)}{(2x^2 - 3x + 1)(5x + 10)}$ Multiply.

$= \dfrac{5(2)(x + 2)(x + 1)(x - 1)}{(x - 1)(2x - 1)5(x + 2)}$ Factor. Try to go directly to this step.

$= \dfrac{5(2)(x + 2)(x + 1)(x - 1)}{(x - 1)(2x - 1)5(x + 2)}$ Simplify. $\dfrac{5(x + 2)(x - 1)}{5(x + 2)(x - 1)} = 1$

$= \dfrac{2(x + 1)}{2x - 1}$

⟩ TRY EXERCISE ⟩ 19

STUDENT NOTES

Neatness is important for work with rational expressions. Consider using the lines on your notebook paper to indicate where the fraction bars should be drawn in each example. Write the equals sign at the same height as the fraction bars.

Because our results are often used in problems that require factored form, there is no need to multiply out the numerator or the denominator.

Division

As with fractions, reciprocals of rational expressions are found by interchanging the numerator and the denominator. For example,

the reciprocal of $\frac{2}{7}$ is $\frac{7}{2}$, and the reciprocal of $\frac{3x}{x+5}$ is $\frac{x+5}{3x}$.

The Quotient of Two Rational Expressions

To divide by a rational expression, multiply by its reciprocal:

$$\frac{A}{B} \div \frac{C}{D} = \frac{A}{B} \cdot \frac{D}{C} = \frac{AD}{BC}.$$

Then factor and, if possible, simplify.

For an explanation of why we divide this way, see Exercise 55 in Section 4.5.

EXAMPLE 2   Divide: **(a)** $\frac{x}{5} \div \frac{7}{y}$; **(b)** $(x+2) \div \frac{x-1}{x+3}$.

SOLUTION

a) $\frac{x}{5} \div \frac{7}{y} = \frac{x}{5} \cdot \frac{y}{7}$ Multiplying by the reciprocal of the divisor

$\qquad = \frac{xy}{35}$ Multiplying rational expressions

b) $(x+2) \div \frac{x-1}{x+3} = \frac{x+2}{1} \cdot \frac{x+3}{x-1}$ Multiplying by the reciprocal of the divisor. Writing $x+2$ as $\frac{x+2}{1}$ can be helpful.

$\qquad = \frac{(x+2)(x+3)}{x-1}$

TRY EXERCISE 41

As usual, we should simplify when possible. Often that requires us to factor one or more polynomials, hoping to discover a common factor that appears in both the numerator and the denominator.

EXAMPLE 3   Divide and, if possible, simplify: $\frac{x+1}{x^2-1} \div \frac{x+1}{x^2-2x+1}$.

SOLUTION

$$\frac{x+1}{x^2-1} \div \frac{x+1}{x^2-2x+1} = \frac{x+1}{x^2-1} \cdot \frac{x^2-2x+1}{x+1} \qquad \text{Rewrite as multiplication.}$$

$$= \frac{(x+1)(x-1)(x-1)}{(x+1)(x-1)(x+1)} \qquad \begin{array}{l}\text{Multiply.}\\[4pt]\text{Factor.}\end{array}$$

$$= \frac{\cancel{(x+1)}\cancel{(x-1)}(x-1)}{\cancel{(x+1)}\cancel{(x-1)}(x+1)} \qquad \text{Simplify.}$$

$$= \frac{x-1}{x+1} \qquad\qquad \frac{(x+1)(x-1)}{(x+1)(x-1)} = 1$$

TRY EXERCISE 47

EXAMPLE 4

Divide and, if possible, simplify.

a) $\dfrac{a^2 + 3a + 2}{a^2 + 4} \div (5a^2 + 10a)$

b) $\dfrac{x^2 - 2x - 3}{x^2 - 4} \div \dfrac{x + 1}{x + 5}$

SOLUTION

a) $\dfrac{a^2 + 3a + 2}{a^2 + 4} \div (5a^2 + 10a)$

$= \dfrac{a^2 + 3a + 2}{a^2 + 4} \cdot \dfrac{1}{5a^2 + 10a}$ Multiplying by the reciprocal of the divisor

$= \dfrac{(a + 2)(a + 1)}{(a^2 + 4)5a(a + 2)}$ Multiplying rational expressions and factoring

$= \dfrac{(a + 2)(a + 1)}{(a^2 + 4)5a(a + 2)}$

$= \dfrac{a + 1}{(a^2 + 4)5a}$ Removing a factor equal to 1: $\dfrac{a + 2}{a + 2} = 1$

b) $\dfrac{x^2 - 2x - 3}{x^2 - 4} \div \dfrac{x + 1}{x + 5}$

$= \dfrac{x^2 - 2x - 3}{x^2 - 4} \cdot \dfrac{x + 5}{x + 1}$ Multiplying by the reciprocal of the divisor

$= \dfrac{(x - 3)(x + 1)(x + 5)}{(x - 2)(x + 2)(x + 1)}$ Multiplying rational expressions and factoring

$= \dfrac{(x - 3)(x + 1)(x + 5)}{(x - 2)(x + 2)(x + 1)}$

$= \dfrac{(x - 3)(x + 5)}{(x - 2)(x + 2)}$ Removing a factor equal to 1: $\dfrac{x + 1}{x + 1} = 1$

TRY EXERCISE 51

TECHNOLOGY CONNECTION

In performing a partial check of Example 4(b), we must be careful placing parentheses. We enter the original expression as $y_1 = ((x^2 - 2x - 3)/(x^2 - 4))/((x + 1)/(x + 5))$ and the simplified expression as $y_2 = ((x - 3)(x + 5))/((x - 2)(x + 2))$. Comparing values of y_1 and y_2, we see that the simplification is probably correct.

X	Y₁	Y₂
−5	ERROR	0
−4	−.5833	−.5833
−3	−2.4	−2.4
−2	ERROR	ERROR
−1	ERROR	5.3333
0	3.75	3.75
1	4	4
X = −5		

1. Check Example 4(a).
2. Why are there 3 ERROR messages shown for y_1 on the screen above, and only 1 for y_2?

4.2 EXERCISE SET

For Extra Help MyMathLab Math XL PRACTICE   WATCH   DOWNLOAD

Multiply. Leave each answer in factored form.

1. $\dfrac{3x}{8} \cdot \dfrac{x + 2}{5x - 1}$

2. $\dfrac{2x}{7} \cdot \dfrac{3x + 5}{x - 1}$

3. $\dfrac{a - 4}{a + 6} \cdot \dfrac{a + 2}{a + 6}$

4. $\dfrac{a + 3}{a + 6} \cdot \dfrac{a + 3}{a - 1}$

5. $\dfrac{2x + 3}{4} \cdot \dfrac{x + 1}{x - 5}$

6. $\dfrac{x + 2}{3x - 4} \cdot \dfrac{4}{5x + 6}$

7. $\dfrac{n - 4}{n^2 + 4} \cdot \dfrac{n + 4}{n^2 - 4}$

8. $\dfrac{t + 3}{t^2 - 2} \cdot \dfrac{t + 3}{t^2 - 4}$

9. $\dfrac{y + 6}{1 + y} \cdot \dfrac{y - 3}{y + 3}$

10. $\dfrac{m + 4}{m + 8} \cdot \dfrac{2 + m}{m + 5}$

Multiply and, if possible, simplify.

11. $\dfrac{8t^3}{5t} \cdot \dfrac{3}{4t}$

12. $\dfrac{18}{a^5} \cdot \dfrac{2a^2}{3a}$

13. $\dfrac{3c}{d^2} \cdot \dfrac{8d}{6c^3}$

14. $\dfrac{3x^2y}{2} \cdot \dfrac{4}{xy^3}$

15. $\dfrac{x^2 - 3x - 10}{(x - 2)^2} \cdot (x - 2)$

16. $(t + 2) \cdot \dfrac{t^2 - 5t + 6}{(t + 2)^2}$

17. $\dfrac{n^2 - 6n + 5}{n + 6} \cdot \dfrac{n - 6}{n^2 + 36}$

18. $\dfrac{a + 2}{a - 2} \cdot \dfrac{a^2 + 4}{a^2 + 5a + 4}$

19. $\dfrac{a^2 - 9}{a^2} \cdot \dfrac{7a}{a^2 + a - 12}$

20. $\dfrac{x^2 + 10x - 11}{9x} \cdot \dfrac{x^3}{x + 11}$

21. $\dfrac{4v - 8}{5v} \cdot \dfrac{15v^2}{4v^2 - 16v + 16}$

22. $\dfrac{m - 2}{3m + 9} \cdot \dfrac{m^2 + 6m + 9}{2m^2 - 8}$

23. $\dfrac{t^2 + 2t - 3}{t^2 + 4t - 5} \cdot \dfrac{t^2 - 3t - 10}{t^2 + 5t + 6}$

24. $\dfrac{x^2 + 5x + 4}{x^2 - 6x + 8} \cdot \dfrac{x^2 + 5x - 14}{x^2 + 8x + 7}$

25. $\dfrac{12y + 12}{5y + 25} \cdot \dfrac{3y^2 - 75}{8y^2 - 8}$

26. $\dfrac{9t^2 - 900}{5t^2 - 20} \cdot \dfrac{5t + 10}{3t - 30}$

Aha! **27.** $\dfrac{x^2 + 4x + 4}{(x - 1)^2} \cdot \dfrac{x^2 - 2x + 1}{(x + 2)^2}$

28. $\dfrac{x^2 + 7x + 12}{x^2 + 6x + 8} \cdot \dfrac{4 - x^2}{x^2 + x - 6}$

29. $\dfrac{t^2 - 4t + 4}{2t^2 - 7t + 6} \cdot \dfrac{2t^2 + 7t - 15}{t^2 - 10t + 25}$

30. $\dfrac{5y^2 - 4y - 1}{3y^2 + 5y - 12} \cdot \dfrac{y^2 + 6y + 9}{y^2 - 2y + 1}$

31. $(10x^2 - x - 2) \cdot \dfrac{4x^2 - 8x + 3}{10x^2 - 11x - 6}$

32. $\dfrac{2x^2 - 5x + 3}{6x^2 - 5x - 1} \cdot (6x^2 + 13x + 2)$

33. $\dfrac{c^3 + 8}{c^5 - 4c^3} \cdot \dfrac{c^6 - 4c^5 + 4c^4}{c^2 - 2c + 4}$

34. $\dfrac{t^3 - 27}{t^4 - 9t^2} \cdot \dfrac{t^5 - 6t^4 + 9t^3}{t^2 + 3t + 9}$

Find the reciprocal of each expression.

35. $\dfrac{2x}{9}$

36. $\dfrac{3 - x}{x^2 + 4}$

37. $a^4 + 3a$

38. $\dfrac{1}{a^2 - b^2}$

Divide and, if possible, simplify.

39. $\dfrac{5}{9} \div \dfrac{3}{4}$

40. $\dfrac{3}{8} \div \dfrac{4}{7}$

41. $\dfrac{x}{4} \div \dfrac{5}{x}$

42. $\dfrac{5}{x} \div \dfrac{x}{12}$

43. $\dfrac{a^5}{b^4} \div \dfrac{a^2}{b}$

44. $\dfrac{x^5}{y^2} \div \dfrac{x^2}{y}$

45. $\dfrac{t - 3}{6} \div \dfrac{t + 1}{8}$

46. $\dfrac{10}{a + 3} \div \dfrac{15}{a}$

47. $\dfrac{4y - 8}{y + 2} \div \dfrac{y - 2}{y^2 - 4}$

48. $\dfrac{x^2 - 1}{x} \div \dfrac{x + 1}{2x - 2}$

49. $\dfrac{a}{a - b} \div \dfrac{b}{b - a}$

50. $\dfrac{x - y}{6} \div \dfrac{y - x}{3}$

51. $(n^2 + 5n + 6) \div \dfrac{n^2 - 4}{n + 3}$

52. $(v^2 - 1) \div \dfrac{(v + 1)(v - 3)}{v^2 + 9}$

53. $\dfrac{-3 + 3x}{16} \div \dfrac{x - 1}{5}$

54. $\dfrac{-4 + 2x}{15} \div \dfrac{x - 2}{3}$

55. $\dfrac{x - 1}{x + 2} \div \dfrac{1 - x}{4 + x^2}$

56. $\dfrac{-12 + 4x}{12} \div \dfrac{6 - 2x}{6}$

57. $\dfrac{a + 2}{a - 1} \div \dfrac{3a + 6}{a - 5}$

58. $\dfrac{t - 3}{t + 2} \div \dfrac{4t - 12}{t + 1}$

59. $(2x - 1) \div \dfrac{2x^2 - 11x + 5}{4x^2 - 1}$

60. $(a + 7) \div \dfrac{3a^2 + 14a - 49}{a^2 + 8a + 7}$

61. $\dfrac{w^2 - 14w + 49}{2w^2 - 3w - 14} \div \dfrac{3w^2 - 20w - 7}{w^2 - 6w - 16}$

62. $\dfrac{2m^2 + 59m - 30}{m^2 - 10m + 25} \div \dfrac{2m^2 - 21m + 10}{m^2 + m - 30}$

63. $\dfrac{c^2 + 10c + 21}{c^2 - 2c - 15} \div (5c^2 + 32c - 21)$

64. $\dfrac{z^2 - 2z + 1}{z^2 - 1} \div (4z^2 - z - 3)$

65. $\dfrac{x - y}{x^2 + 2xy + y^2} \div \dfrac{x^2 - y^2}{x^2 - 5xy + 4y^2}$

66. $\dfrac{a^2 - b^2}{a^2 - 4ab + 4b^2} \div \dfrac{a^2 - 3ab + 2b^2}{a - 2b}$

67. $\dfrac{x^3 - 64}{x^3 + 64} \div \dfrac{x^2 - 16}{x^2 - 4x + 16}$

68. $\dfrac{8y^3 - 27}{64y^3 - 1} \div \dfrac{4y^2 - 9}{16y^2 + 4y + 1}$

69. $\dfrac{8a^3 + b^3}{2a^2 + 3ab + b^2} \div \dfrac{8a^2 - 4ab + 2b^2}{4a^2 + 4ab + b^2}$

70. $\dfrac{x^3 + 8y^3}{2x^2 + 5xy + 2y^2} \div \dfrac{x^3 - 2x^2y + 4xy^2}{8x^2 - 2y^2}$

71. Why is it important to insert parentheses when multiplying rational expressions such as

$$\frac{x + 2}{5x - 7} \cdot \frac{3x - 1}{x + 4}?$$

72. As a first step in dividing $\frac{x}{3}$ by $\frac{7}{x}$, Jan canceled the x's. Explain why this was incorrect, and show the correct division.

Skill Review

To prepare for Section 4.3, review addition and subtraction with fraction notation and subtraction of polynomials.

Simplify.

73. $\dfrac{3}{4} + \dfrac{5}{6}$

74. $\dfrac{7}{8} + \dfrac{5}{6}$

75. $\dfrac{2}{9} - \dfrac{1}{6}$

76. $\dfrac{3}{10} - \dfrac{7}{15}$

77. $2x^2 - x + 1 - (x^2 - x - 2)$

78. $3x^2 + x - 7 - (5x^2 + 5x - 8)$

Synthesis

79. Is the reciprocal of a product the product of the two reciprocals? Why or why not?

80. Explain why the quotient

$$\frac{x + 3}{x - 5} \div \frac{x - 7}{x + 1}$$

is undefined for $x = 5$, $x = -1$, and $x = 7$, but *is* defined for $x = -3$.

81. Find the reciprocal of $2\frac{1}{3}x$.

82. Find the reciprocal of $7.25x$.

Simplify.

83. $(x - 2a) \div \dfrac{a^2x^2 - 4a^4}{a^2x + 2a^3}$

84. $\dfrac{2a^2 - 5ab}{c - 3d} \div (4a^2 - 25b^2)$

85. $\dfrac{3x^2 - 2xy - y^2}{x^2 - y^2} \div (3x^2 + 4xy + y^2)^2$

86. $\dfrac{3a^2 - 5ab - 12b^2}{3ab + 4b^2} \div (3b^2 - ab)^2$

Aha! **87.** $\dfrac{a^2 - 3b}{a^2 + 2b} \cdot \dfrac{a^2 - 2b}{a^2 + 3b} \cdot \dfrac{a^2 + 2b}{a^2 - 3b}$

88. $\dfrac{y^2 - 4xy}{y - x} \div \dfrac{16x^2y^2 - y^4}{4x^2 - 3xy - y^2} \div \dfrac{4}{x^3y^3}$

89. $\dfrac{z^2 - 8z + 16}{z^2 + 8z + 16} \div \dfrac{(z - 4)^5}{(z + 4)^5} \div \dfrac{3z + 12}{z^2 - 16}$

90. $\dfrac{(t + 2)^3}{(t + 1)^3} \div \dfrac{t^2 + 4t + 4}{t^2 + 2t + 1} \cdot \dfrac{t + 1}{t + 2}$

91. $\dfrac{a^4 - 81b^4}{a^2c - 6abc + 9b^2c} \cdot \dfrac{a + 3b}{a^2 + 9b^2} \div \dfrac{a^2 + 6ab + 9b^2}{(a - 3b)^2}$

92. $\dfrac{3y^3 + 6y^2}{y^2 - y - 12} \div \dfrac{y^2 - y}{y^2 - 2y - 8} \cdot \dfrac{y^2 + 5y + 6}{y^2}$

93. Use a graphing calculator to check that

$$\frac{x - 1}{x^2 + 2x + 1} \div \frac{x^2 - 1}{x^2 - 5x + 4}$$

is equivalent to

$$\frac{x^2 - 5x + 4}{(x + 1)^3}.$$

Additional Exercises

Multiply or divide and, if possible, simplify.

94. $\dfrac{49x^2 - 25}{4x - 14} \times \dfrac{6x^2 - 13x - 28}{28x - 20}$

95. $\dfrac{9t^2 - 4}{18t^2 - 12t + 8} \times \dfrac{27t^3 + 8}{3t - 2}$

96. $\dfrac{8x^2 + 14xy - 15y^2}{3x^3 - x^2y} \times \dfrac{3x - y}{4xy - 3y^2}$

97. $\dfrac{2x^2 - xy}{6x^2 + 7xy + 2y^2} \times \dfrac{9x^2 - 6xy - 8y^2}{4xy + 3y^2}$

98. $\dfrac{8x^3 - 27y^3}{4x^2 + 12xy + 9y^2} \div \dfrac{4x^2 + 6xy + 9y^2}{4x^2 - 9y^2}$

99. $\dfrac{12x^2 - 31x + 20}{18x^2 + 60x + 50} \div \dfrac{36x^3 - 93x^2 + 60x}{12x^2 + 2x - 30}$

Perform the indicated operations and, if possible, simplify.

100. $\dfrac{x^2 - 4y^2}{x^2 - 16y^2} \times \dfrac{x^2 + xy - 12y^2}{x^2 - 2xy - 8y^2} \div \dfrac{x^2 - 5xy + 6y^2}{x^2 - 8xy + 16y^2}$

101. $\dfrac{4x^2 + 2xy - 2y^2}{2x^2 + 5xy + 2y^2} \times \dfrac{x^3 - 4xy^2}{x^2 - y^2} \div \dfrac{2x^2 - 5xy + 2y^2}{2x^2 - xy - y^2}$

102. $\dfrac{8n^2 - 10n + 3}{4n^2 - 4n - 3} \times \dfrac{6n^2 - 5n - 6}{6n^2 + 7n - 5} \div \dfrac{12n^2 - 17n + 6}{6n^2 + 7n - 5}$

104. $\dfrac{xy - 2x + y - 2}{xy + 4x - y - 4} \times \dfrac{xy + y + 4x + 4}{xy - y - 2x + 2}$

103. $\dfrac{2p^2 - p - 6}{16p^2 - 25} \times \dfrac{12p^2 + 13p - 35}{4p^2 + 12p + 9} \div \dfrac{12p^2 + 43p + 35}{2p^2 - p - 6}$

105. $\dfrac{ab^2 + 2b^2 + a + 2}{ab - a - 3b + 3} \times \dfrac{ab^2 - 3b^2 - a + 3}{ab + a + 2b + 2}$

106. $\dfrac{2ax^2 + 4a^2x - 8ax - 16a^2}{x^2 + 2ax + 3x + 6a} \times \dfrac{4x^2 + 4ax + 12x + 12a}{a^2x^2 + a^3x - 4a^2x - 4a^3}$

107. $\dfrac{m^2y^2 + 3my^3 - 4my^2 - 12y^3}{m^2y - 2m^3 + 3my^2 - 6m^2y} \times \dfrac{2my^2 - 4m^2y - 12my + 24m^2}{3my^2 - 18my - 12y^2 + 72y}$

108. $\dfrac{3x^2 - 12x + bx - 4b}{4x^2 - 16x - bx + 4b} \div \dfrac{3bx + b^2 + 6x + 2b}{4bx - b^2 + 8x - 2b}$

109. $\dfrac{2x^2y - xy^2 + 6x^2 - 3xy}{3y^2 - xy + 9y - 3x} \div \dfrac{2x^3 - x^2y + 8x^2 - 4xy}{3xy - x^2 + 6y - 2x}$

COLLABORATIVE CORNER

Currency Exchange

Focus: Least common multiples and proportions

Time: 20 minutes

Group size: 2

International travelers usually exchange currencies. Recently one New Zealand dollar was worth 76 U.S. cents. Use this exchange rate for the activity that follows.

ACTIVITY

1. Within each group of two students, one student should play the role of a U.S. citizen visiting New Zealand. The other student should play the role of a New Zealander visiting the United States. Use the exchange rate of one New Zealand dollar for 76 U.S. cents.

2. The "U.S." student should exchange $76 U.S. and $100 U.S. for New Zealand money. The "New Zealand" student should exchange $76 New Zealand and $100 New Zealand for U.S. money.

3. The exchanges in part (2) should indicate that coins smaller than a dollar are needed to exchange $76 New Zealand for U.S. funds, or

to exchange $100 U.S. for New Zealand money. What is the smallest amount of New Zealand dollars that can be exchanged for a whole-number amount of U.S. dollars? What is the smallest amount of U.S. dollars that can be exchanged for a whole-number amount of New Zealand dollars? (*Hint*: See part 2.)

4. Use the results from part (3) to find two other amounts of U.S. dollars that can be exchanged for a whole-number amount of New Zealand dollars. Answers may vary.

5. Find the smallest number a for which both conversions—from a New Zealand dollars to U.S. funds and from a U.S. dollars to New Zealand funds—use only whole numbers. (*Hint*: Use LCMs and the results of part 2 above.)

6. At one time in 2008, one Polish zloty was worth about 40 U.S. cents. Find the smallest number a for which both conversions—from a Polish zlotys to U.S. funds and from a U.S. dollars to Polish funds—use only whole numbers. (*Hint*: See part 5.)

4.3 Addition, Subtraction, and Least Common Denominators

Addition When Denominators Are the Same • Subtraction When Denominators Are the Same •
Least Common Multiples and Denominators

Addition When Denominators Are the Same

Recall that to add fractions having the same denominator, like $\frac{2}{7}$ and $\frac{3}{7}$, we add the numerators and keep the common denominator: $\frac{2}{7} + \frac{3}{7} = \frac{5}{7}$. The same procedure is used when rational expressions share a common denominator.

> ### The Sum of Two Rational Expressions
>
> To add when the denominators are the same, add the numerators and keep the common denominator:
>
> $$\frac{A}{B} + \frac{C}{B} = \frac{A + C}{B}.$$

In this section, we again assume that all denominators are nonzero.

EXAMPLE 1 Add. Simplify the result, if possible.

a) $\dfrac{4}{a} + \dfrac{3 + a}{a}$

b) $\dfrac{3x}{x - 5} + \dfrac{2x + 1}{x - 5}$

c) $\dfrac{2x^2 + 3x - 7}{2x + 1} + \dfrac{x^2 + x - 8}{2x + 1}$

d) $\dfrac{x - 5}{x^2 - 9} + \dfrac{2}{x^2 - 9}$

SOLUTION

a) $\dfrac{4}{a} + \dfrac{3 + a}{a} = \dfrac{7 + a}{a}$ When the denominators are alike, add the numerators and keep the common denominator.

b) $\dfrac{3x}{x - 5} + \dfrac{2x + 1}{x - 5} = \dfrac{5x + 1}{x - 5}$ The denominators are alike, so we add the numerators.

c) $\dfrac{2x^2 + 3x - 7}{2x + 1} + \dfrac{x^2 + x - 8}{2x + 1} = \dfrac{(2x^2 + 3x - 7) + (x^2 + x - 8)}{2x + 1}$

$\qquad\qquad = \dfrac{3x^2 + 4x - 15}{2x + 1}$ Combining like terms

$\qquad\qquad = \dfrac{(3x - 5)(x + 3)}{2x + 1}$ Factoring. There are no common factors, so we cannot simplify further.

d) $\dfrac{x - 5}{x^2 - 9} + \dfrac{2}{x^2 - 9} = \dfrac{x - 3}{x^2 - 9}$ Combining like terms in the numerator: $x - 5 + 2 = x - 3$

$\qquad\qquad = \dfrac{x - 3}{(x - 3)(x + 3)}$ Factoring

$\qquad\qquad = \dfrac{1 \cdot (x - 3)}{(x - 3)(x + 3)}$ Removing a factor equal to 1: $\dfrac{x - 3}{x - 3} = 1$

$\qquad\qquad = \dfrac{1}{x + 3}$

TRY EXERCISE 7

STUDY SKILLS

Visualize the Steps

If you have completed all assignments and are studying for a quiz or test, don't feel that you need to redo every assigned problem. A more productive use of your time would be to work through one problem of each type. Then read through the other problems, visualizing the steps that lead to a solution. When you are unsure of how to solve a problem, work that problem in its entirety, seeking outside help as needed.

Subtraction When Denominators Are the Same

When two fractions have the same denominator, we subtract one numerator from the other and keep the common denominator: $\frac{5}{7} - \frac{2}{7} = \frac{3}{7}$. The same procedure is used with rational expressions.

> ### The Difference of Two Rational Expressions
>
> To subtract when the denominators are the same, subtract the second numerator from the first numerator and keep the common denominator:
>
> $$\frac{A}{B} - \frac{C}{B} = \frac{A - C}{B}.$$

CAUTION! The fraction bar under a numerator is a grouping symbol, just like parentheses. Thus, when a numerator is subtracted, it is important to subtract *every* term in that numerator.

EXAMPLE 2 Subtract and, if possible, simplify: **(a)** $\dfrac{3x}{x + 2} - \dfrac{x - 5}{x + 2}$; **(b)** $\dfrac{x^2}{x - 4} - \dfrac{x + 12}{x - 4}$.

SOLUTION

a) $\dfrac{3x}{x + 2} - \dfrac{x - 5}{x + 2} = \dfrac{3x - (x - 5)}{x + 2}$ The parentheses are needed to make sure that we subtract both terms.

$= \dfrac{3x - x + 5}{x + 2}$ Removing the parentheses and changing signs (using the distributive law)

$= \dfrac{2x + 5}{x + 2}$ Combining like terms

b) $\dfrac{x^2}{x - 4} - \dfrac{x + 12}{x - 4} = \dfrac{x^2 - (x + 12)}{x - 4}$ Remember the parentheses!

$= \dfrac{x^2 - x - 12}{x - 4}$ Removing parentheses (using the distributive law)

$= \dfrac{(x - 4)(x + 3)}{x - 4}$ Factoring, in hopes of simplifying

$= \dfrac{(x - 4)(x + 3)}{x - 4}$ Removing a factor equal to 1: $\dfrac{x - 4}{x - 4} = 1$

$= x + 3$

TRY EXERCISE 21

Least Common Multiples and Denominators

Thus far, every pair of rational expressions that we have added or subtracted shared a common denominator. To add or subtract rational expressions that have different denominators, we must first find equivalent rational expressions that *do* have a common denominator.

In algebra, we find a common denominator much as we do in arithmetic. Recall that to add $\frac{1}{12}$ and $\frac{7}{30}$, we first identify the smallest number that contains both 12 and 30 as factors. Such a number, the **least common multiple (LCM)** of the denominators, is then used as the **least common denominator (LCD)**.

Let's find the LCM of 12 and 30 using a method that can also be used with polynomials. We begin by writing the prime factorizations of 12 and 30:

$$12 = 2 \cdot 2 \cdot 3;$$
$$30 = 2 \cdot 3 \cdot 5.$$

The LCM must include the factors of each number, so it must include each prime factor the greatest number of times that it appears in either of the factorizations. To find the LCM for 12 and 30, we select one factorization, say

$$2 \cdot 2 \cdot 3,$$

and note that because it lacks a factor of 5, it does not contain the entire factorization of 30. If we multiply $2 \cdot 2 \cdot 3$ by 5, every prime factor occurs just often enough to contain both 12 and 30 as factors.

$$\text{LCM} = 2 \cdot 2 \cdot 3 \cdot 5$$

12 is a factor of the LCM.

30 is a factor of the LCM.

Note that each prime factor—2, 3, and 5—is used the greatest number of times that it appears in either of the individual factorizations. The factor 2 occurs twice and the factors 3 and 5 once each.

To Find the Least Common Denominator (LCD)

1. Write the prime factorization of each denominator.
2. Select one of the factorizations and inspect it to see if it completely contains the other factorization.

   a) If it does, it represents the LCM of the denominators.
   b) If it does not, multiply that factorization by any factors of the other denominator that it lacks. The final product is the LCM of the denominators.

The LCD is the LCM of the denominators. It should contain each factor the greatest number of times that it occurs in any of the individual factorizations.

STUDENT NOTES

The terms *least common multiple* and *least common denominator* are similar enough that they may be confusing. We find the LCM of polynomials, and we find the LCD of rational expressions.

EXAMPLE 3 Find the LCD of $\dfrac{5}{36x^2}$ and $\dfrac{7}{24x}$.

SOLUTION

1. We begin by writing the prime factorizations of $36x^2$ and $24x$:

   $$36x^2 = 2 \cdot 2 \cdot 3 \cdot 3 \cdot x \cdot x;$$
   $$24x = 2 \cdot 2 \cdot 2 \cdot 3 \cdot x.$$

2. We select the factorization of $36x^2$. Except for a third factor of 2, this factorization contains the entire factorization of $24x$. Thus we multiply $36x^2$ by a third factor of 2.

   $$\text{LCM} = 2 \cdot 2 \cdot 3 \cdot 3 \cdot x \cdot x \cdot 2$$

   $36x^2$ is a factor of the LCM.

   Note that each factor appears the greatest number of times that it occurs in either of the above factorizations.

   $24x$ is a factor of the LCM.

Since $2^3 \cdot 3^2 \cdot x^2$, or $72x^2$, is the smallest multiple of both $36x^2$ and $24x$, the LCM of the denominators is $72x^2$. The LCD of the expressions is $72x^2$.

Let's add $\frac{1}{12}$ and $\frac{7}{30}$:

$$\frac{1}{12} + \frac{7}{30} = \frac{1}{2 \cdot 2 \cdot 3} + \frac{7}{2 \cdot 3 \cdot 5}.$$ The least common denominator (LCD) is $2 \cdot 2 \cdot 3 \cdot 5$.

We found above that the LCD is $2 \cdot 2 \cdot 3 \cdot 5$, or 60. To get the LCD, we see that the first denominator needs a factor of 5, and the second denominator needs another factor of 2. Therefore, we multiply $\frac{1}{12}$ by 1, using $\frac{5}{5}$, and we multiply $\frac{7}{30}$ by 1, using $\frac{2}{2}$. Since $a \cdot 1 = a$, for any number a, the values of the fractions are not changed.

$$\frac{1}{12} + \frac{7}{30} = \frac{1}{2 \cdot 2 \cdot 3} \cdot \frac{5}{5} + \frac{7}{2 \cdot 3 \cdot 5} \cdot \frac{2}{2}$$ $\frac{5}{5} = 1$ and $\frac{2}{2} = 1$

$$= \frac{5}{60} + \frac{14}{60}$$ Both denominators are now the LCD.

$$= \frac{19}{60}$$ Adding the numerators and keeping the LCD

Expressions like $\frac{5}{36x^2}$ and $\frac{7}{24x}$ are added in much the same manner. In Example 3, we found that the LCD is $2 \cdot 2 \cdot 2 \cdot 3 \cdot 3 \cdot x \cdot x$, or $72x^2$. To obtain equivalent expressions with this LCD, we multiply each expression by 1, using the missing factors of the LCD to write 1:

$$\frac{5}{36x^2} + \frac{7}{24x} = \frac{5}{2 \cdot 2 \cdot 3 \cdot 3 \cdot x \cdot x} + \frac{7}{2 \cdot 2 \cdot 2 \cdot 3 \cdot x}$$

$$= \frac{5}{2 \cdot 2 \cdot 3 \cdot 3 \cdot x \cdot x} \cdot \frac{2}{2} + \frac{7}{2 \cdot 2 \cdot 2 \cdot 3 \cdot x} \cdot \frac{3 \cdot x}{3 \cdot x}$$

The LCD requires another factor of 2.   The LCD requires additional factors of 3 and x.

$$= \frac{10}{72x^2} + \frac{21x}{72x^2}$$ Both denominators are now the LCD.

$$= \frac{21x + 10}{72x^2}.$$

You now have the "big picture" of why LCMs are needed when adding rational expressions. For the remainder of this section, we will practice finding LCMs and rewriting rational expressions so that they have the LCD as the denominator. In Section 4.4, we will return to the addition and subtraction of rational expressions.

EXAMPLE 4 For each pair of polynomials, find the least common multiple.

a) $15a$ and $35b$

b) $21x^3y^6$ and $7x^5y^2$

c) $x^2 + 5x - 6$ and $x^2 - 1$

SOLUTION

a) We write the prime factorizations and then construct the LCM, starting with the factorization of $15a$.

$$15a = 3 \cdot 5 \cdot a$$
$$35b = 5 \cdot 7 \cdot b$$

15a is a factor of the LCM.

$$\text{LCM} = 3 \cdot 5 \cdot a \cdot 7 \cdot b$$

Each factor appears the greatest number of times that it occurs in either of the above factorizations.

35b is a factor of the LCM.

The LCM is $3 \cdot 5 \cdot a \cdot 7 \cdot b$, or $105ab$.

b) $21x^3y^6 = 3 \cdot 7 \cdot x \cdot x \cdot x \cdot y \cdot y \cdot y \cdot y \cdot y \cdot y$ — Try to visualize the factors of x and y mentally.

$$7x^5y^2 = 7 \cdot x \cdot x \cdot x \cdot x \cdot x \cdot y \cdot y$$

$$\text{LCM} = 3 \cdot 7 \cdot x \cdot x \cdot x \cdot y \cdot y \cdot y \cdot y \cdot y \cdot y \cdot x \cdot x$$

We start with the prime factorization of $21x^3y^6$.

We multiply by the factors of $7x^5y^2$ that are lacking.

Note that we used the highest power of each factor in $21x^3y^6$ and $7x^5y^2$. The LCM is $21x^5y^6$.

c) $x^2 + 5x - 6 = (x - 1)(x + 6)$
$\quad x^2 - 1 = (x - 1)(x + 1)$

$$\text{LCM} = (x - 1)(x + 6)(x + 1)$$

We start with the factorization of $x^2 + 5x - 6$.

We multiply by the factor of $x^2 - 1$ that is missing.

The LCM is $(x - 1)(x + 6)(x + 1)$. There is no need to multiply this out.

TRY EXERCISE 43

The procedure above can be used to find the LCM of three or more polynomials as well. We factor each polynomial and then construct the LCM using each factor the greatest number of times that it appears in any one factorization.

EXAMPLE 5

For each group of polynomials, find the LCM.

a) $12x$, $16y$, and $8xyz$

b) $x^2 + 4$, $x + 1$, and 5

STUDENT NOTES ——————

If you prefer, the LCM for a group of three polynomials can be found by finding the LCM of two of them and then finding the LCM of that result and the remaining polynomial.

SOLUTION

a) $12x = 2 \cdot 2 \cdot 3 \cdot x$

$16y = 2 \cdot 2 \cdot 2 \cdot 2 \cdot y$

$8xyz = 2 \cdot 2 \cdot 2 \cdot x \cdot y \cdot z$

$$\text{LCM} = 2 \cdot 2 \cdot 3 \cdot x \cdot 2 \cdot 2 \cdot y \cdot z$$

We start with the factorization of $12x$.

We multiply by the factors of $16y$ that are missing.

We multiply by the factor of $8xyz$ that is missing.

The LCM is $2^4 \cdot 3 \cdot xyz$, or $48xyz$.

b) Since $x^2 + 4, x + 1$, and 5 are not factorable, the LCM is their product: $5(x^2 + 4)(x + 1)$.

TRY EXERCISE ▸ 51

To add or subtract rational expressions with different denominators, we first write equivalent expressions that have the LCD. To do this, we multiply each rational expression by a carefully constructed form of 1.

EXAMPLE   **6**

Find equivalent expressions that have the LCD:

$$\frac{x + 3}{x^2 + 5x - 6}, \quad \frac{x + 7}{x^2 - 1}.$$

SOLUTION   From Example 4(c), we know that the LCD is

$$(x + 6)(x - 1)(x + 1).$$

Since

$$x^2 + 5x - 6 = (x + 6)(x - 1),$$

the factor of the LCD that is missing from the first denominator is $x + 1$. We multiply by 1 using $(x + 1)/(x + 1)$:

$$\frac{x + 3}{x^2 + 5x - 6} = \frac{x + 3}{(x + 6)(x - 1)} \cdot \frac{x + 1}{x + 1}$$

$$= \frac{(x + 3)(x + 1)}{(x + 6)(x - 1)(x + 1)}.$$

Finding an equivalent expression that has the least common denominator

For the second expression, we have

$$x^2 - 1 = (x + 1)(x - 1).$$

The factor of the LCD that is missing is $x + 6$. We multiply by 1 using $(x + 6)/(x + 6)$:

$$\frac{x + 7}{x^2 - 1} = \frac{x + 7}{(x + 1)(x - 1)} \cdot \frac{x + 6}{x + 6}$$

$$= \frac{(x + 7)(x + 6)}{(x + 1)(x - 1)(x + 6)}.$$

Finding an equivalent expression that has the least common denominator

We leave the results in factored form. In Section 4.4, we will carry out the actual addition and subtraction of such rational expressions.

TRY EXERCISE ▸ 61

4.3 EXERCISE SET

For Extra Help MyMathLab

Concept Reinforcement *Use one or more words to complete each of the following sentences.*

1. To add two rational expressions when the denominators are the same, add _____ and keep the common _____.

2. When a numerator is being subtracted, use parentheses to make sure to subtract every _____ in that numerator.

3. The least common multiple of two denominators is usually referred to as the _____ and is abbreviated _____.

4. The least common denominator of two fractions must contain the prime _____ of both _____.

Perform the indicated operation. Simplify, if possible.

5. $\dfrac{3}{t} + \dfrac{5}{t}$

6. $\dfrac{8}{y^2} + \dfrac{2}{y^2}$

7. $\dfrac{x}{12} + \dfrac{2x + 5}{12}$

8. $\dfrac{a}{7} + \dfrac{3a - 4}{7}$

9. $\dfrac{4}{a + 3} + \dfrac{5}{a + 3}$

10. $\dfrac{5}{x + 2} + \dfrac{8}{x + 2}$

11. $\dfrac{11}{4x - 7} - \dfrac{3}{4x - 7}$

12. $\dfrac{9}{2x + 3} - \dfrac{5}{2x + 3}$

13. $\dfrac{3y + 8}{2y} - \dfrac{y + 1}{2y}$

14. $\dfrac{5 + 3t}{4t} - \dfrac{2t + 1}{4t}$

15. $\dfrac{5x + 7}{x + 3} + \dfrac{x + 11}{x + 3}$

16. $\dfrac{3x + 4}{x - 1} + \dfrac{2x - 9}{x - 1}$

17. $\dfrac{5x + 7}{x + 3} - \dfrac{x + 11}{x + 3}$

18. $\dfrac{3x + 4}{x - 1} - \dfrac{2x - 9}{x - 1}$

19. $\dfrac{a^2}{a - 4} + \dfrac{a - 20}{a - 4}$

20. $\dfrac{x^2}{x + 5} + \dfrac{7x + 10}{x + 5}$

21. $\dfrac{y^2}{y + 2} - \dfrac{5y + 14}{y + 2}$

22. $\dfrac{t^2}{t - 3} - \dfrac{8t - 15}{t - 3}$

Aha! 23. $\dfrac{t^2 - 5t}{t - 1} + \dfrac{5t - t^2}{t - 1}$

24. $\dfrac{y^2 + 6y}{y + 2} + \dfrac{2y + 12}{y + 2}$

25. $\dfrac{x - 6}{x^2 + 5x + 6} + \dfrac{9}{x^2 + 5x + 6}$

26. $\dfrac{x - 5}{x^2 - 4x + 3} + \dfrac{2}{x^2 - 4x + 3}$

27. $\dfrac{t^2 - 5t}{t^2 + 6t + 9} + \dfrac{4t - 12}{t^2 + 6t + 9}$

28. $\dfrac{y^2 - 7y}{y^2 + 8y + 16} + \dfrac{6y - 20}{y^2 + 8y + 16}$

29. $\dfrac{2y^2 + 3y}{y^2 - 7y + 12} - \dfrac{y^2 + 4y + 6}{y^2 - 7y + 12}$

30. $\dfrac{3a^2 + 7}{a^2 - 2a - 8} - \dfrac{7 + 3a^2}{a^2 - 2a - 8}$

31. $\dfrac{3 - 2x}{x^2 - 6x + 8} + \dfrac{7 - 3x}{x^2 - 6x + 8}$

32. $\dfrac{1 - 2t}{t^2 - 5t + 4} + \dfrac{4 - 3t}{t^2 - 5t + 4}$

33. $\dfrac{x - 9}{x^2 + 3x - 4} - \dfrac{2x - 5}{x^2 + 3x - 4}$

34. $\dfrac{5 - 3x}{x^2 - 2x + 1} - \dfrac{x + 1}{x^2 - 2x + 1}$

Find the LCM.

35. 15, 36

36. 18, 30

37. 8, 9

38. 12, 15

39. 6, 12, 15

40. 8, 32, 50

Find the LCM.

41. $18t^2,\ 6t^5$

42. $8x^5,\ 24x^2$

43. $15a^4b^7,\ 10a^2b^8$

44. $6a^2b^7,\ 9a^5b^2$

45. $2(y - 3),\ 6(y - 3)$

46. $4(x - 1),\ 8(x - 1)$

47. $x^2 - 2x - 15,\ x^2 - 9$

48. $t^2 - 4,\ t^2 + 7t + 10$

49. $t^3 + 4t^2 + 4t,\ t^2 - 4t$

50. $y^3 - y^2,\ y^4 - y^2$

51. $6xz^2,\ 8x^2y,\ 15y^3z$

52. $12s^3t,\ 15sv^2,\ 6t^4v$

53. $a + 1,\ (a - 1)^2,\ a^2 - 1$

54. $x - 2,\ (x + 2)^2,\ x^2 - 4$

55. $2n^2 + n - 1,\ 2n^2 + 3n - 2$

56. $m^2 - 2m - 3,\ 2m^2 + 3m + 1$

57. $6x^3 - 24x^2 + 18x,\ 4x^5 - 24x^4 + 20x^3$

58. $9x^3 - 9x^2 - 18x,\ 6x^5 - 24x^4 + 24x^3$

59. $2x^3 - 2,\ x^2 - 1$

60. $3a^3 + 24,\ a^2 - 4$

Find equivalent expressions that have the LCD.

61. $\dfrac{5}{6t^4}, \dfrac{s}{18t^2}$　　**62.** $\dfrac{7}{10y^2}, \dfrac{x}{5y^6}$

63. $\dfrac{7}{3x^4y^2}, \dfrac{4}{9xy^3}$　　**64.** $\dfrac{3}{2a^2b}, \dfrac{7}{8ab^2}$

65. $\dfrac{2x}{x^2 - 4}, \dfrac{4x}{x^2 + 5x + 6}$

66. $\dfrac{5x}{x^2 - 9}, \dfrac{2x}{x^2 + 11x + 24}$

67. Explain why the product of two numbers is not always their least common multiple.

68. If the LCM of two numbers is their product, what can you conclude about the two numbers?

Skill Review

To prepare for Section 4.4, review opposites.

Write each number in two equivalent forms.

69. $-\dfrac{5}{8}$　　**70.** $\dfrac{4}{-11}$

Write an equivalent expression without parentheses.

71. $-(x - y)$　　**72.** $-(3 - a)$

Multiply and simplify.

73. $-1(2x - 7)$　　**74.** $-1(a - b)$

Synthesis

75. If the LCM of two third-degree polynomials is a sixth-degree polynomial, what can be concluded about the two polynomials?

76. If the LCM of a binomial and a trinomial is the trinomial, what relationship exists between the two expressions?

Perform the indicated operations. Simplify, if possible.

77. $\dfrac{6x - 1}{x - 1} + \dfrac{3(2x + 5)}{x - 1} + \dfrac{3(2x - 3)}{x - 1}$

78. $\dfrac{2x + 11}{x - 3} \cdot \dfrac{3}{x + 4} + \dfrac{-1}{4 + x} \cdot \dfrac{6x + 3}{x - 3}$

79. $\dfrac{x^2}{3x^2 - 5x - 2} - \dfrac{2x}{3x + 1} \cdot \dfrac{1}{x - 2}$

80. $\dfrac{x + y}{x^2 - y^2} + \dfrac{x - y}{x^2 - y^2} - \dfrac{2x}{x^2 - y^2}$

African artistry. In Southeast Mozambique, the design of every woven handbag, or gipatsi (plural, sipatsi) is created by repeating two or more geometric patterns.

Each pattern encircles the bag, sharing the strands of fabric with any pattern above or below. The length, or period, of each pattern is the number of strands required to construct the pattern. For a gipatsi to be considered beautiful, each individual pattern must fit a whole number of times around the bag.

Source: Gerdes, Paulus, *Women, Art and Geometry in Southern Africa.* Asmara, Eritrea: Africa World Press, Inc., p. 5

81. A weaver is using two patterns to create a gipatsi. Pattern A is 10 strands long, and pattern B is 3 strands long. What is the smallest number of strands that can be used to complete the gipatsi?

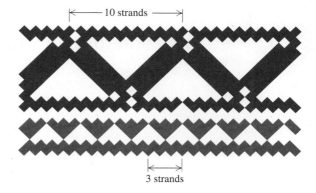

82. A weaver is using a four-strand pattern, a six-strand pattern, and an eight-strand pattern. What is the smallest number of strands that can be used to complete the gipatsi?

83. For technical reasons, the number of strands is generally a multiple of 4. Answer Exercise 79 with this additional requirement in mind.

Find the LCM.

84. 80, 96, 108

85. $4x^2 - 25,\ 6x^2 - 7x - 20,\ (9x^2 + 24x + 16)^2$

86. $9n^2 - 9$, $(5n^2 - 10n + 5)^2$, $15n - 15$

87. *Copiers.* The Brother® MFC240C copier can print 20 color pages per minute. The Lexmark X5470 copier can print 18 color pages per minute. If both machines begin printing at the same instant, how long will it be until they again begin printing a page at exactly the same time?

88. *Running.* Kim and Trey leave the starting point of a fitness loop at the same time. Kim jogs a lap in 6 min and Trey jogs one in 8 min. Assuming they continue to run at the same pace, when will they next meet at the starting place?

89. *Bus schedules.* Beginning at 5:00 A.M., a hotel shuttle bus leaves Salton Airport every 25 min, and the downtown shuttle bus leaves the airport every 35 min. What time will it be when both shuttles again leave at the same time?

90. *Appliances.* Smoke detectors last an average of 10 yr, water heaters an average of 12 yr, and refrigerators an average of 15 yr. If an apartment house is equipped with new smoke detectors, water heaters, and refrigerators in 2010, in what year will all three appliances need to be replaced at once?
Source: Demesne.info

91. Explain how evaluating can be used to perform a partial check on the result of Example 1(d):
$$\frac{x-5}{x^2-9} + \frac{2}{x^2-9} = \frac{1}{x+3}.$$

92. On p. 246, the second step in finding an LCD is to select one of the factorizations of the denominators. Does it matter which one is selected? Why or why not?

4.4	Addition and Subtraction with Unlike Denominators

Adding and Subtracting with LCDs • When Factors Are Opposites

Adding and Subtracting with LCDs

We now know how to rewrite two rational expressions in equivalent forms that use the LCD. Once rational expressions share a common denominator, they can be added or subtracted just as in Section 4.3.

> **To Add or Subtract Rational Expressions Having Different Denominators**
> 1. Find the LCD.
> 2. Multiply each rational expression by a form of 1 made up of the factors of the LCD missing from that expression's denominator.
> 3. Add or subtract the numerators, as indicated. Write the sum or the difference over the LCD.
> 4. Simplify, if possible.

EXAMPLE 1

Add: $\dfrac{5x^2}{8} + \dfrac{7x}{12}$.

SOLUTION

1. First, we find the LCD:

$$\left.\begin{array}{r} 8 = 2 \cdot 2 \cdot 2 \\ 12 = 2 \cdot 2 \cdot 3 \end{array}\right\} \quad \text{LCD} = 2 \cdot 2 \cdot 2 \cdot 3, \text{ or } 24.$$

2. The denominator 8 must be multiplied by 3 in order to obtain the LCD. The denominator 12 must be multiplied by 2 in order to obtain the LCD. Thus we multiply the first expression by $\frac{3}{3}$ and the second expression by $\frac{2}{2}$ to get the LCD:

$$\begin{aligned}
\frac{5x^2}{8} + \frac{7x}{12} &= \frac{5x^2}{2 \cdot 2 \cdot 2} + \frac{7x}{2 \cdot 2 \cdot 3} \\
&= \frac{5x^2}{2 \cdot 2 \cdot 2} \cdot \frac{3}{3} + \frac{7x}{2 \cdot 2 \cdot 3} \cdot \frac{2}{2} \qquad \text{Multiplying each expression by a form of 1 to get the LCD} \\
&= \frac{15x^2}{24} + \frac{14x}{24}.
\end{aligned}$$

3. Next, we add the numerators:

$$\frac{15x^2}{24} + \frac{14x}{24} = \frac{15x^2 + 14x}{24}.$$

4. Since $15x^2 + 14x$ and 24 have no common factor,

$$\frac{15x^2 + 14x}{24}$$

cannot be simplified any further.

▶ TRY EXERCISE ▶ 13

Subtraction is performed in much the same way.

EXAMPLE 2

Subtract: $\dfrac{7}{8x} - \dfrac{5}{12x^2}$.

SOLUTION We follow the four steps shown above. First, we find the LCD:

$$\left.\begin{array}{r} 8x = 2 \cdot 2 \cdot 2 \cdot x \\ 12x^2 = 2 \cdot 2 \cdot 3 \cdot x \cdot x \end{array}\right\} \quad \text{LCD} = 2 \cdot 2 \cdot 3 \cdot x \cdot x \cdot 2, \text{ or } 24x^2.$$

The denominator $8x$ must be multiplied by $3x$ in order to obtain the LCD. The denominator $12x^2$ must be multiplied by 2 in order to obtain the LCD. Thus we multiply by $\dfrac{3x}{3x}$ and $\dfrac{2}{2}$ to get the LCD. Then we subtract and, if possible, simplify.

$$\begin{aligned}
\frac{7}{8x} - \frac{5}{12x^2} &= \frac{7}{8x} \cdot \frac{3x}{3x} - \frac{5}{12x^2} \cdot \frac{2}{2} \\
&= \frac{21x}{24x^2} - \frac{10}{24x^2} \\
&= \frac{21x - 10}{24x^2} \qquad \text{This cannot be simplified, so we are done.}
\end{aligned}$$

CAUTION! Do not simplify *these* rational expressions or you will lose the LCD.

▶ TRY EXERCISE ▶ 5

When denominators contain polynomials with two or more terms, the same steps are used.

EXAMPLE **3** Add: $\dfrac{2a}{a^2 - 1} + \dfrac{1}{a^2 + a}$.

SOLUTION First, we find the LCD:

Find the LCD. $\left.\begin{array}{l} a^2 - 1 = (a - 1)(a + 1) \\ a^2 + a = a(a + 1). \end{array}\right\}$ $\quad$ LCD $= (a - 1)(a + 1)a$

We multiply by a form of 1 to get the LCD in each expression:

Write each expression with the LCD.

$\dfrac{2a}{a^2 - 1} + \dfrac{1}{a^2 + a} = \dfrac{2a}{(a - 1)(a + 1)} \cdot \dfrac{a}{a} + \dfrac{1}{a(a + 1)} \cdot \dfrac{a - 1}{a - 1}$ $\quad$ Multiplying by $\dfrac{a}{a}$ and $\dfrac{a - 1}{a - 1}$ to get the LCD

$\qquad = \dfrac{2a^2}{(a - 1)(a + 1)a} + \dfrac{a - 1}{a(a + 1)(a - 1)}$

Add numerators. $\qquad = \dfrac{2a^2 + a - 1}{a(a - 1)(a + 1)}$ $\quad$ Adding numerators

Simplify. $\qquad = \dfrac{(2a - 1)(a + 1)}{a(a - 1)(a + 1)}$ $\left.\vphantom{\dfrac{(2a-1)}{a}}\right]$ $\quad$ Simplifying by factoring and removing a factor equal to 1:

$\qquad = \dfrac{2a - 1}{a(a - 1)}.$ $\qquad \dfrac{a + 1}{a + 1} = 1$

TRY EXERCISE 33

EXAMPLE **4** Perform the indicated operations.

a) $\dfrac{x + 4}{x - 2} - \dfrac{x - 7}{x + 5}$ $\qquad\qquad$ b) $\dfrac{t}{t^2 + 11t + 30} + \dfrac{-5}{t^2 + 9t + 20}$

c) $\dfrac{x}{x^2 + 5x + 6} - \dfrac{2}{x^2 + 3x + 2}$

STUDENT NOTES

As you can see, adding or subtracting rational expressions can involve many steps. Therefore, it is important to double-check each step of your work as you work through each problem. Waiting to inspect your work at the end of each problem is usually a less efficient use of your time.

SOLUTION

a) First, we find the LCD. It is just the product of the denominators:

$\qquad$ LCD $= (x - 2)(x + 5).$

We multiply by a form of 1 to get the LCD in each expression. Then we subtract and try to simplify.

$\dfrac{x + 4}{x - 2} - \dfrac{x - 7}{x + 5} = \dfrac{x + 4}{x - 2} \cdot \dfrac{x + 5}{x + 5} - \dfrac{x - 7}{x + 5} \cdot \dfrac{x - 2}{x - 2}$

$\qquad = \dfrac{x^2 + 9x + 20}{(x - 2)(x + 5)} - \dfrac{x^2 - 9x + 14}{(x - 2)(x + 5)}$ $\quad$ Multiplying out numerators (but not denominators)

$\qquad = \dfrac{x^2 + 9x + 20 - (x^2 - 9x + 14)}{(x - 2)(x + 5)}$ $\quad$ When subtracting a numerator with more than one term, parentheses are important.

$\qquad = \dfrac{x^2 + 9x + 20 - x^2 + 9x - 14}{(x - 2)(x + 5)}$ $\quad$ Removing parentheses and subtracting every term

$\qquad = \dfrac{18x + 6}{(x - 2)(x + 5)}$

$\qquad = \dfrac{6(3x + 1)}{(x - 2)(x + 5)}$ $\quad$ We cannot simplify.

b) $\dfrac{t}{t^2 + 11t + 30} + \dfrac{-5}{t^2 + 9t + 20}$

$= \dfrac{t}{(t + 5)(t + 6)} + \dfrac{-5}{(t + 5)(t + 4)}$ — Factoring the denominators in order to find the LCD. The LCD is $(t + 5)(t + 6)(t + 4)$.

$= \dfrac{t}{(t + 5)(t + 6)} \cdot \dfrac{t + 4}{t + 4} + \dfrac{-5}{(t + 5)(t + 4)} \cdot \dfrac{t + 6}{t + 6}$ — Multiplying to get the LCD

$= \dfrac{t^2 + 4t}{(t + 5)(t + 6)(t + 4)} + \dfrac{-5t - 30}{(t + 5)(t + 6)(t + 4)}$ — Multiplying in each numerator

$= \dfrac{t^2 + 4t - 5t - 30}{(t + 5)(t + 6)(t + 4)}$ — Adding numerators

$= \dfrac{t^2 - t - 30}{(t + 5)(t + 6)(t + 4)}$ — Combining like terms in the numerator

$= \dfrac{(t + 5)(t - 6)}{(t + 5)(t + 6)(t + 4)}$

$= \dfrac{t - 6}{(t + 6)(t + 4)}$ — Always simplify the result, if possible, by removing a factor equal to 1; here $\dfrac{t + 5}{t + 5} = 1$.

c) $\dfrac{x}{x^2 + 5x + 6} - \dfrac{2}{x^2 + 3x + 2}$

Find the LCD. $\quad = \dfrac{x}{(x + 2)(x + 3)} - \dfrac{2}{(x + 2)(x + 1)}$ — Factoring denominators. The LCD is $(x + 2)(x + 3)(x + 1)$.

Write each expression with the LCD.

$= \dfrac{x}{(x + 2)(x + 3)} \cdot \dfrac{x + 1}{x + 1} - \dfrac{2}{(x + 2)(x + 1)} \cdot \dfrac{x + 3}{x + 3}$

$= \dfrac{x^2 + x}{(x + 2)(x + 3)(x + 1)} - \dfrac{2x + 6}{(x + 2)(x + 3)(x + 1)}$

Subtract numerators.

$= \dfrac{x^2 + x - (2x + 6)}{(x + 2)(x + 3)(x + 1)}$ — Don't forget the parentheses!

$= \dfrac{x^2 + x - 2x - 6}{(x + 2)(x + 3)(x + 1)}$ — Remember to subtract each term in $2x + 6$.

$= \dfrac{x^2 - x - 6}{(x + 2)(x + 3)(x + 1)}$ — Combining like terms in the numerator

Simplify.

$= \dfrac{(x + 2)(x - 3)}{(x + 2)(x + 3)(x + 1)}$

$= \dfrac{x - 3}{(x + 3)(x + 1)}$ — Factoring and simplifying; $\dfrac{x + 2}{x + 2} = 1$

TRY EXERCISE 45

When Factors Are Opposites

When one denominator is the opposite of the other, we can first multiply either expression by 1 using $-1/-1$.

EXAMPLE 5   Add: **(a)** $\dfrac{t}{2} + \dfrac{3}{-2}$; **(b)** $\dfrac{x}{x-5} + \dfrac{7}{5-x}$.

SOLUTION

a) $\dfrac{t}{2} + \dfrac{3}{-2} = \dfrac{t}{2} + \dfrac{3}{-2} \cdot \dfrac{-1}{-1}$ Multiplying by 1 using $\dfrac{-1}{-1}$

$\phantom{\dfrac{t}{2} + \dfrac{3}{-2}} = \dfrac{t}{2} + \dfrac{-3}{2}$ The denominators are now the same.

$\phantom{\dfrac{t}{2} + \dfrac{3}{-2}} = \dfrac{t + (-3)}{2}$

$\phantom{\dfrac{t}{2} + \dfrac{3}{-2}} = \dfrac{t - 3}{2}$

b) Recall that when an expression of the form $a - b$ is multiplied by -1, the subtraction is reversed: $-1(a - b) = -a + b = b + (-a) = b - a$. Since $x - 5$ and $5 - x$ are opposites, we can find a common denominator by multiplying one of the rational expressions by $-1/-1$. Because polynomials are usually written in descending order, we choose to reverse the subtraction in the second denominator:

$\dfrac{x}{x-5} + \dfrac{7}{5-x} = \dfrac{x}{x-5} + \dfrac{7}{5-x} \cdot \dfrac{-1}{-1}$ Multiplying by 1, where $1 = \dfrac{-1}{-1}$

$\phantom{\dfrac{x}{x-5} + \dfrac{7}{5-x}} = \dfrac{x}{x-5} + \dfrac{-7}{-5+x}$

$\phantom{\dfrac{x}{x-5} + \dfrac{7}{5-x}} = \dfrac{x}{x-5} + \dfrac{-7}{x-5}$ Note that $-5 + x = x + (-5) = x - 5$.

$\phantom{\dfrac{x}{x-5} + \dfrac{7}{5-x}} = \dfrac{x - 7}{x - 5}.$

TRY EXERCISE 53

Sometimes, after factoring to find the LCD, we find a factor in one denominator that is the opposite of a factor in the other denominator. When this happens, multiplication by $-1/-1$ can again be helpful.

EXAMPLE 6   Perform the indicated operations and simplify.

a) $\dfrac{x}{x^2 - 25} + \dfrac{3}{5 - x}$ **b)** $\dfrac{x + 9}{x^2 - 4} + \dfrac{6 - x}{4 - x^2} - \dfrac{1 + x}{x^2 - 4}$

SOLUTION

a) $\dfrac{x}{x^2 - 25} + \dfrac{3}{5 - x} = \dfrac{x}{(x-5)(x+5)} + \dfrac{3}{5-x}$ Factoring

$\phantom{\dfrac{x}{x^2-25} + \dfrac{3}{5-x}} = \dfrac{x}{(x-5)(x+5)} + \dfrac{3}{5-x} \cdot \dfrac{-1}{-1}$ Multiplication by $-1/-1$ changes $5 - x$ to $x - 5$.

$\phantom{\dfrac{x}{x^2-25} + \dfrac{3}{5-x}} = \dfrac{x}{(x-5)(x+5)} + \dfrac{-3}{x-5}$ $(5 - x)(-1) = x - 5$

$\phantom{\dfrac{x}{x^2-25} + \dfrac{3}{5-x}} = \dfrac{x}{(x-5)(x+5)} + \dfrac{-3}{(x-5)} \cdot \dfrac{x+5}{x+5}$ The LCD is $(x - 5)(x + 5)$.

$\phantom{\dfrac{x}{x^2-25} + \dfrac{3}{5-x}} = \dfrac{x}{(x-5)(x+5)} + \dfrac{-3x - 15}{(x-5)(x+5)}$

$\phantom{\dfrac{x}{x^2-25} + \dfrac{3}{5-x}} = \dfrac{-2x - 15}{(x-5)(x+5)}$

TECHNOLOGY CONNECTION

The TABLE feature can be used to check addition or subtraction of rational expressions. Below we check Example 6(a), using $y_1 = x/(x^2 - 25) + 3/(5 - x)$ and $y_2 = (-2x - 15)/((x - 5)(x + 5))$.

$\Delta TBL = 1$

X	Y₁	Y₂
1	.70833	.70833
2	.90476	.90476
3	1.3125	1.3125
4	2.5556	2.5556
5	ERROR	ERROR
6	−2.455	−2.455
7	−1.208	−1.208

$X = 1$

Because the values for y_1 and y_2 match, we have a check.

b) Since $4 - x^2$ is the opposite of $x^2 - 4$, multiplying the second rational expression by $-1/-1$ will lead to a common denominator:

$$\frac{x + 9}{x^2 - 4} + \frac{6 - x}{4 - x^2} - \frac{1 + x}{x^2 - 4} = \frac{x + 9}{x^2 - 4} + \frac{6 - x}{4 - x^2} \cdot \frac{-1}{-1} - \frac{1 + x}{x^2 - 4}$$

$$= \frac{x + 9}{x^2 - 4} + \frac{x - 6}{x^2 - 4} - \frac{1 + x}{x^2 - 4}$$

$$= \frac{x + 9 + x - 6 - 1 - x}{x^2 - 4} \quad \text{Adding and subtracting numerators}$$

$$= \frac{x + 2}{x^2 - 4}$$

$$= \frac{(x + 2) \cdot 1}{(x + 2)(x - 2)} \quad \text{Simplifying}$$

$$= \frac{1}{x - 2}.$$

TRY EXERCISE 59

4.4   **EXERCISE SET**

For Extra Help

MyMathLab   Math XL PRACTICE   WATCH   DOWNLOAD

↶ ***Concept Reinforcement***   *In Exercises 1–4, the four steps for adding rational expressions with different denominators are listed. Fill in the missing word or words for each step.*

1. To add or subtract when the denominators are different, first find the _____.

2. Multiply each rational expression by a form of 1 made up of the factors of the LCD that are _____ from that expression's _____.

3. Add or subtract the _____, as indicated. Write the sum or the difference over the _____.

4. _____, if possible.

Perform the indicated operation. Simplify, if possible.

5. $\dfrac{3}{x^2} + \dfrac{5}{x}$

6. $\dfrac{6}{x} + \dfrac{7}{x^2}$

7. $\dfrac{1}{6r} - \dfrac{3}{8r}$

8. $\dfrac{4}{9t} - \dfrac{7}{6t}$

9. $\dfrac{3}{uv^2} + \dfrac{4}{u^3v}$

10. $\dfrac{8}{cd^2} + \dfrac{1}{c^2d}$

11. $\dfrac{-2}{3xy^2} - \dfrac{6}{x^2y^3}$

12. $\dfrac{8}{9t^3} - \dfrac{5}{6t^2}$

13. $\dfrac{x + 3}{8} + \dfrac{x - 2}{6}$

14. $\dfrac{x - 4}{9} + \dfrac{x + 5}{12}$

15. $\dfrac{x - 2}{6} - \dfrac{x + 1}{3}$

16. $\dfrac{a + 2}{2} - \dfrac{a - 4}{4}$

17. $\dfrac{a + 3}{15a} + \dfrac{2a - 1}{3a^2}$

18. $\dfrac{5a + 1}{2a^2} + \dfrac{a + 2}{6a}$

19. $\dfrac{4z - 9}{3z} - \dfrac{3z - 8}{4z}$

20. $\dfrac{x - 1}{4x} - \dfrac{2x + 3}{x}$

21. $\dfrac{3c + d}{cd^2} + \dfrac{c - d}{c^2d}$

22. $\dfrac{u + v}{u^2v} + \dfrac{2u + v}{uv^2}$

23. $\dfrac{4x + 2t}{3xt^2} - \dfrac{5x - 3t}{x^2t}$

24. $\dfrac{5x + 3y}{2x^2y} - \dfrac{3x + 4y}{xy^2}$

25. $\dfrac{3}{x - 2} + \dfrac{3}{x + 2}$

26. $\dfrac{5}{x - 1} + \dfrac{5}{x + 1}$

27. $\dfrac{t}{t + 3} - \dfrac{1}{t - 1}$

28. $\dfrac{y}{y - 3} + \dfrac{12}{y + 4}$

29. $\dfrac{3}{x + 1} + \dfrac{2}{3x}$

30. $\dfrac{2}{x + 5} + \dfrac{3}{4x}$

31. $\dfrac{3}{2t^2 - 2t} - \dfrac{5}{2t - 2}$

32. $\dfrac{8}{3t^2 - 15t} - \dfrac{3}{2t - 10}$

33. $\dfrac{3a}{a^2 - 9} + \dfrac{a}{a + 3}$

34. $\dfrac{5p}{p^2 - 16} + \dfrac{p}{p - 4}$

35. $\dfrac{6}{z + 4} - \dfrac{2}{3z + 12}$

36. $\dfrac{t}{t - 3} - \dfrac{5}{4t - 12}$

37. $\dfrac{5}{q - 1} + \dfrac{2}{(q - 1)^2}$

38. $\dfrac{3}{w + 2} + \dfrac{7}{(w + 2)^2}$

39. $\dfrac{t - 3}{t^3 - 1} - \dfrac{2}{1 - t^3}$

40. $\dfrac{1 - 6m}{1 - m^3} - \dfrac{5}{m^3 - 1}$

41. $\dfrac{3a}{4a - 20} + \dfrac{9a}{6a - 30}$

42. $\dfrac{4a}{-5a - 10} + \dfrac{3a}{10a - 20}$

Aha! 43. $\dfrac{x}{x - 5} + \dfrac{x}{5 - x}$

44. $\dfrac{x + 4}{x} + \dfrac{x}{x + 4}$

45. $\dfrac{6}{a^2 + a - 2} + \dfrac{4}{a^2 - 4a + 3}$

46. $\dfrac{x}{x^2 + 2x + 1} + \dfrac{1}{x^2 + 5x + 4}$

47. $\dfrac{x}{x^2 + 9x + 20} - \dfrac{4}{x^2 + 7x + 12}$

48. $\dfrac{x}{x^2 + 5x + 6} - \dfrac{2}{x^2 + 3x + 2}$

49. $\dfrac{3z}{z^2 - 4z + 4} + \dfrac{10}{z^2 + z - 6}$

50. $\dfrac{3}{x^2 - 9} + \dfrac{2}{x^2 - x - 6}$

Aha! 51. $\dfrac{-7}{x^2 + 25x + 24} - \dfrac{0}{x^2 + 11x + 10}$

52. $\dfrac{x}{x^2 + 17x + 72} - \dfrac{1}{x^2 + 15x + 56}$

53. $\dfrac{5x}{4} - \dfrac{x - 2}{-4}$

54. $\dfrac{x}{6} - \dfrac{2x - 3}{-6}$

55. $\dfrac{y^2}{y - 3} + \dfrac{9}{3 - y}$

56. $\dfrac{t^2}{t - 2} + \dfrac{4}{2 - t}$

57. $\dfrac{c - 5}{c^2 - 64} - \dfrac{5 - c}{64 - c^2}$

58. $\dfrac{b - 4}{b^2 - 49} + \dfrac{b - 4}{49 - b^2}$

59. $\dfrac{4 - p}{25 - p^2} + \dfrac{p + 1}{p - 5}$

60. $\dfrac{y + 2}{y - 7} + \dfrac{3 - y}{49 - y^2}$

61. $\dfrac{x}{x - 4} - \dfrac{3}{16 - x^2}$

62. $\dfrac{x}{3 - x} - \dfrac{2}{x^2 - 9}$

63. $\dfrac{a}{a^2 - 1} + \dfrac{2a}{a - a^2}$

64. $\dfrac{3x + 2}{3x + 6} + \dfrac{x}{4 - x^2}$

65. $\dfrac{4x}{x^2 - y^2} - \dfrac{6}{y - x}$

66. $\dfrac{4 - a^2}{a^2 - 9} - \dfrac{a - 2}{3 - a}$

Perform the indicated operations. Simplify, if possible.

67. $\dfrac{x - 3}{2 - x} - \dfrac{x + 3}{x + 2} + \dfrac{x + 6}{4 - x^2}$

68. $\dfrac{t - 5}{1 - t} - \dfrac{t + 4}{t + 1} + \dfrac{t + 2}{t^2 - 1}$

69. $\dfrac{2x + 5}{x + 1} + \dfrac{x + 7}{x + 5} - \dfrac{5x + 17}{(x + 1)(x + 5)}$

70. $\dfrac{x + 5}{x + 3} + \dfrac{x + 7}{x + 2} - \dfrac{7x + 19}{(x + 3)(x + 2)}$

71. $\dfrac{1}{x + y} + \dfrac{1}{x - y} - \dfrac{2x}{x^2 - y^2}$

72. $\dfrac{2r}{r^2 - s^2} + \dfrac{1}{r + s} - \dfrac{1}{r - s}$

73. What is the advantage of using the *least* common denominator—rather than just *any* common denominator—when adding or subtracting rational expressions?

74. Describe a procedure that can be used to add any two rational expressions.

Skill Review

To prepare for Section 4.5, review division of fractions and rational expressions (Section 4.2).

Simplify.

75. $-\dfrac{3}{8} \div \dfrac{11}{4}$

76. $-\dfrac{7}{12} \div \left(-\dfrac{3}{4}\right)$

77. $\dfrac{\dfrac{3}{4}}{\dfrac{5}{6}}$

78. $\dfrac{\dfrac{8}{15}}{\dfrac{9}{10}}$

79. $\dfrac{2x + 6}{x - 1} \div \dfrac{3x + 9}{x - 1}$ [4.2]

80. $\dfrac{x^2 - 9}{x^2 - 4} \div \dfrac{x^2 + 6x + 9}{x^2 + 4x + 4}$ [4.2]

Synthesis

81. How could you convince someone that
$$\dfrac{1}{3 - x} \quad \text{and} \quad \dfrac{1}{x - 3}$$
are opposites of each other?

82. Are parentheses as important for adding rational expressions as they are for subtracting rational expressions? Why or why not?

Write expressions for the perimeter and the area of each rectangle.

83.

84.

Perform the indicated operations.

85. $\dfrac{x^2}{3x^2 - 5x - 2} - \dfrac{2x}{3x + 1} \cdot \dfrac{1}{x - 2}$

86. $\dfrac{2x + 11}{x - 3} \cdot \dfrac{3}{x + 4} + \dfrac{2x + 1}{4 + x} \cdot \dfrac{3}{3 - x}$

Aha! **87.** $\left(\dfrac{x}{x + 7} - \dfrac{3}{x + 2}\right)\left(\dfrac{x}{x + 7} + \dfrac{3}{x + 2}\right)$

88. $\dfrac{1}{ay - 3a + 2xy - 6x} - \dfrac{xy + ay}{a^2 - 4x^2}\left(\dfrac{1}{y - 3}\right)^2$

89. $\left(\dfrac{a}{a - b} + \dfrac{b}{a + b}\right)\left(\dfrac{1}{3a + b} + \dfrac{2a + 6b}{9a^2 - b^2}\right)$

90. $\dfrac{2x^2 + 5x - 3}{2x^2 - 9x + 9} + \dfrac{x + 1}{3 - 2x} + \dfrac{4x^2 + 8x + 3}{x - 3} \cdot \dfrac{x + 3}{9 - 4x^2}$

91. Express

$$\dfrac{a - 3b}{a - b}$$

as a sum of two rational expressions with denominators that are opposites of each other. Answers may vary.

92. Use a graphing calculator to check the answer to Exercise 29.

93. Why does the word ERROR appear in the table displayed on p. 257?

Additional Exercises

Perform the indicated operations and, if possible, simplify.

94. $\dfrac{1}{x^2 + 7x + 12} - \dfrac{2}{x^2 + 4x + 3} + \dfrac{3}{x^2 + 5x + 4}$

95. $\dfrac{4}{x^2 + x - 2} + \dfrac{2}{x^2 - 4x + 3} - \dfrac{5}{x^2 - x - 6}$

96. $\dfrac{2}{x^2 + 3x + 2} + \dfrac{4}{x^2 - 2x - 3} - \dfrac{5}{x^2 - x - 6}$

97. $\dfrac{1}{x^2 + 9x + 20} - \dfrac{7}{x^2 + x - 12} + \dfrac{8}{x^2 + 2x - 15}$

Perform the indicated operations and, if possible, simplify.

98. $\dfrac{2x - 16}{x^2 - x - 2} - \dfrac{x + 2}{x^2 - 5x + 6} - \dfrac{x + 6}{x^2 - 2x - 3}$

99. $\dfrac{2x + 8}{x^2 + 3x + 2} - \dfrac{x - 2}{x^2 + 5x + 6} - \dfrac{x + 2}{x^2 + 4x + 3}$

100. $\dfrac{4x - 7}{x^2 - 3x + 2} - \dfrac{2x + 1}{x^2 - 1} - \dfrac{2x - 1}{x^2 - x - 2}$

101. $\dfrac{3x + 11}{x^2 - x - 6} - \dfrac{2x - 3}{x^2 - 4} - \dfrac{x + 1}{x^2 - 5x + 6}$

Perform the indicated operations and, if possible, simplify.

102. $3 + \dfrac{4}{2x + 1}$

103. $2 + \dfrac{1}{5 - x}$

104. $3 - \dfrac{2}{4 - x}$

105. $4 - \dfrac{3}{3x + 2}$

CONNECTING the CONCEPTS

The process of adding and subtracting rational expressions is significantly different from multiplying and dividing them. The first thing you should take note of when combining rational expressions is the operation sign.

Operation	Need Common Denominator?	Procedure	Tips and Cautions
Addition	Yes	Write with a common denominator. Add numerators. Keep denominator.	Do not simplify after writing with the LCD. Instead, simplify after adding the numerators.
Subtraction	Yes	Write with a common denominator. Subtract numerators. Keep denominator.	Use parentheses around the numerator being subtracted. Simplify after subtracting the numerators.
Multiplication	No	Multiply numerators. Multiply denominators.	Do not carry out the multiplications. Instead, factor and try to simplify.
Division	No	Multiply by the reciprocal of the divisor.	Begin by rewriting as a multiplication using the reciprocal of the divisor.

MIXED REVIEW

Tell what operation is being performed. Then perform the operation and, if possible, simplify.

1. $\dfrac{3}{5x} + \dfrac{2}{x^2}$

2. $\dfrac{3}{5x} \cdot \dfrac{2}{x^2}$

3. $\dfrac{3}{5x} \div \dfrac{2}{x^2}$

4. $\dfrac{3}{5x} - \dfrac{2}{x^2}$

5. $\dfrac{2x - 6}{5x + 10} \cdot \dfrac{x + 2}{6x - 12}$

6. $\dfrac{2}{x + 3} \cdot \dfrac{3}{x + 4}$

7. $\dfrac{2}{x - 5} \div \dfrac{6}{x - 5}$

8. $\dfrac{x}{x + 2} - \dfrac{1}{x - 1}$

9. $\dfrac{2}{x + 3} + \dfrac{3}{x + 4}$

10. $\dfrac{5}{2x - 1} + \dfrac{10x}{1 - 2x}$

11. $\dfrac{3}{x - 4} - \dfrac{2}{4 - x}$

12. $\dfrac{(x - 2)(2x + 3)}{(x + 1)(x - 5)} \div \dfrac{(x - 2)(x + 1)}{(x - 5)(x + 3)}$

13. $\dfrac{a}{6a - 9b} - \dfrac{b}{4a - 6b}$

14. $\dfrac{x^2 - 16}{x^2 - x} \cdot \dfrac{x^2}{x^2 - 5x + 4}$

15. $\dfrac{x + 1}{x^2 - 7x + 10} + \dfrac{3}{x^2 - x - 2}$

16. $\dfrac{3u^2 - 3}{4} \div \dfrac{4u + 4}{3}$

17. $\dfrac{t + 2}{10} + \dfrac{2t + 1}{15}$

18. $(t^2 + t - 20) \cdot \dfrac{t + 5}{t - 4}$

19. $\dfrac{a^2 - 2a + 1}{a^2 - 4} \div (a^2 - 3a + 2)$

20. $\dfrac{2x - 7}{x} - \dfrac{3x - 5}{2}$

4.5 Complex Rational Expressions

Using Division to Simplify • Multiplying by the LCD

A **complex rational expression** is a rational expression that has one or more rational expressions within its numerator or denominator. Here are some examples:

$$\frac{1 + \dfrac{2}{x}}{3}, \qquad \frac{\dfrac{x+y}{7}}{\dfrac{2x}{x+1}}, \qquad \frac{\dfrac{4}{3} + \dfrac{1}{5}}{\dfrac{2}{x} - \dfrac{x}{y}}.$$

These are rational expressions within the complex rational expression.

When we simplify a complex rational expression, we rewrite it so that it is no longer complex. We will consider two methods for simplifying complex rational expressions. Each method offers certain advantages.

Using Division to Simplify (Method 1)

Our first method for simplifying complex rational expressions involves rewriting the expression as a quotient of two rational expressions.

> **To Simplify a Complex Rational Expression by Dividing**
> 1. Add or subtract, as needed, to get a single rational expression in the numerator.
> 2. Add or subtract, as needed, to get a single rational expression in the denominator.
> 3. Divide the numerator by the denominator (invert and multiply).
> 4. If possible, simplify by removing a factor equal to 1.

The key here is to express a complex rational expression as one rational expression divided by another. We can then proceed as in Section 4.2.

EXAMPLE 1 Simplify: $\dfrac{\dfrac{x}{x-3}}{\dfrac{4}{5x-15}}$.

SOLUTION Here the numerator and the denominator are already single rational expressions. This allows us to start by dividing (step 3), as in Section 4.2:

$$\frac{\dfrac{x}{x-3}}{\dfrac{4}{5x-15}} = \frac{x}{x-3} \div \frac{4}{5x-15} \qquad \text{Rewriting with a division symbol}$$

$$= \frac{x}{x-3} \cdot \frac{5x-15}{4} \qquad \text{Multiplying by the reciprocal of the divisor (inverting and multiplying)}$$

$$= \frac{x}{x-3} \cdot \frac{5(x-3)}{4} \qquad \text{Factoring and removing a factor equal to 1: } \frac{x-3}{x-3} = 1$$

$$= \frac{5x}{4}.$$

TRY EXERCISE 21

All four steps of the division method are used in Example 2(a).

EXAMPLE **2** Simplify.

a) $\dfrac{\dfrac{5}{2a} + \dfrac{1}{a}}{\dfrac{1}{4a} - \dfrac{5}{6}}$

b) $\dfrac{\dfrac{x^2}{y} - \dfrac{5}{x}}{xz}$

SOLUTION

a) $\dfrac{\dfrac{5}{2a} + \dfrac{1}{a}}{\dfrac{1}{4a} - \dfrac{5}{6}} = \dfrac{\dfrac{5}{2a} + \dfrac{1}{a} \cdot \dfrac{2}{2}}{\dfrac{1}{4a} \cdot \dfrac{3}{3} - \dfrac{5}{6} \cdot \dfrac{2a}{2a}}$ $\left.\begin{array}{l}\\ \\ \end{array}\right\}$ ← Multiplying by 1 to get the LCD, $2a$, for the numerator of the complex rational expression

$\left.\begin{array}{l}\\ \\ \end{array}\right\}$ ← Multiplying by 1 to get the LCD, $12a$, for the denominator of the complex rational expression

1. Add to get a single rational expression in the numerator.

2. Subtract to get a single rational expression in the denominator.

$= \dfrac{\dfrac{5}{2a} + \dfrac{2}{2a}}{\dfrac{3}{12a} - \dfrac{10a}{12a}} = \dfrac{\dfrac{7}{2a}}{\dfrac{3 - 10a}{12a}}$ ← Adding

← Subtracting

3. Divide the numerator by the denominator.

$= \dfrac{7}{2a} \div \dfrac{3 - 10a}{12a}$ Rewriting with a division symbol. This is often done mentally.

$= \dfrac{7}{2a} \cdot \dfrac{12a}{3 - 10a}$ Multiplying by the reciprocal of the divisor (inverting and multiplying)

4. Simplify.

$= \dfrac{7}{2a} \cdot \dfrac{2a \cdot 6}{3 - 10a}$ Removing a factor equal to 1: $\dfrac{2a}{2a} = 1$

$= \dfrac{42}{3 - 10a}$

b) $\dfrac{\dfrac{x^2}{y} - \dfrac{5}{x}}{xz} = \dfrac{\dfrac{x^2}{y} \cdot \dfrac{x}{x} - \dfrac{5}{x} \cdot \dfrac{y}{y}}{xz}$ ← Multiplying by 1 to get the LCD, xy, for the numerator of the complex rational expression

$= \dfrac{\dfrac{x^3}{xy} - \dfrac{5y}{xy}}{xz}$

$= \dfrac{\dfrac{x^3 - 5y}{xy}}{xz}$ ← Subtracting

← If you prefer, write xz as $\dfrac{xz}{1}$.

$= \dfrac{x^3 - 5y}{xy} \div (xz)$ Rewriting with a division symbol

$= \dfrac{x^3 - 5y}{xy} \cdot \dfrac{1}{xz}$ Multiplying by the reciprocal of the divisor (inverting and multiplying)

$= \dfrac{x^3 - 5y}{x^2 yz}$

TRY EXERCISE 11

Multiplying by the LCD (Method 2)

A second method for simplifying complex rational expressions relies on multiplying by a carefully chosen expression that is equal to 1. This multiplication by 1 will result in an expression that is no longer complex.

> **To Simplify a Complex Rational Expression by Multiplying by the LCD**
>
> 1. Find the LCD of *all* rational expressions within the complex rational expression.
> 2. Multiply the complex rational expression by an expression equal to 1. Write 1 as the LCD over itself (LCD/LCD).
> 3. Simplify. No fraction expressions should remain within the complex rational expression.
> 4. Factor and, if possible, simplify.

EXAMPLE   3   Simplify: $\dfrac{\frac{1}{2} + \frac{3}{4}}{\frac{5}{6} - \frac{3}{8}}$.

STUDENT NOTES ————

Pay careful attention to the difference in the ways in which Method 1 and Method 2 use an LCD. In Method 1, separate LCDs are found in the numerator and in the denominator. In Method 2, *all* rational expressions are considered in order to find one LCD.

SOLUTION

1. The LCD of $\frac{1}{2}, \frac{3}{4}, \frac{5}{6}$, and $\frac{3}{8}$ is 24.

2. We multiply by an expression equal to 1:

$$\frac{\frac{1}{2} + \frac{3}{4}}{\frac{5}{6} - \frac{3}{8}} = \frac{\frac{1}{2} + \frac{3}{4}}{\frac{5}{6} - \frac{3}{8}} \cdot \frac{24}{24}. \qquad \text{Multiplying by an expression equal to 1, using the LCD: } \frac{24}{24} = 1$$

3. Using the distributive law, we perform the multiplication:

$$\frac{\frac{1}{2} + \frac{3}{4}}{\frac{5}{6} - \frac{3}{8}} \cdot \frac{24}{24} = \frac{\left(\frac{1}{2} + \frac{3}{4}\right)24}{\left(\frac{5}{6} - \frac{3}{8}\right)24} \qquad \begin{array}{l}\leftarrow \text{Multiplying the numerator by 24}\\ \text{Don't forget the parentheses!}\\ \leftarrow \text{Multiplying the denominator by 24}\end{array}$$

$$= \frac{\frac{1}{2}(24) + \frac{3}{4}(24)}{\frac{5}{6}(24) - \frac{3}{8}(24)} \qquad \text{Using the distributive law}$$

$$= \frac{12 + 18}{20 - 9}, \quad \text{or} \quad \frac{30}{11}. \qquad \text{Simplifying}$$

4. The result, $\frac{30}{11}$, cannot be factored or simplified, so we are done.

TRY EXERCISE ▸ 5

Multiplying like this effectively clears fractions in both the top and the bottom of the complex rational expression. Compare the steps in Example 4(a) with those in Example 2(a).

EXAMPLE   **4**   Simplify.

a) $\dfrac{\dfrac{5}{2a} + \dfrac{1}{a}}{\dfrac{1}{4a} - \dfrac{5}{6}}$

b) $\dfrac{1 - \dfrac{1}{x}}{1 - \dfrac{1}{x^2}}$

SOLUTION

1. Find the LCD.

a) The denominators within the complex expression are $2a$, a, $4a$, and 6, so the LCD is $12a$. We multiply by 1 using $(12a)/(12a)$:

2. Multiply by LCD/LCD.

$$\frac{\dfrac{5}{2a} + \dfrac{1}{a}}{\dfrac{1}{4a} - \dfrac{5}{6}} = \frac{\dfrac{5}{2a} + \dfrac{1}{a}}{\dfrac{1}{4a} - \dfrac{5}{6}} \cdot \frac{12a}{12a} = \frac{\dfrac{5}{2a}(12a) + \dfrac{1}{a}(12a)}{\dfrac{1}{4a}(12a) - \dfrac{5}{6}(12a)}.$$

Using the distributive law

When we multiply by $12a$, all fractions in the numerator and the denominator of the complex rational expression are cleared:

3., 4. Simplify.

$$\frac{\dfrac{5}{2a}(12a) + \dfrac{1}{a}(12a)}{\dfrac{1}{4a}(12a) - \dfrac{5}{6}(12a)} = \frac{30 + 12}{3 - 10a} = \frac{42}{3 - 10a}.$$

All fractions have been cleared.

b) $\dfrac{1 - \dfrac{1}{x}}{1 - \dfrac{1}{x^2}} = \dfrac{1 - \dfrac{1}{x}}{1 - \dfrac{1}{x^2}} \cdot \dfrac{x^2}{x^2}$ The LCD is x^2 so we multiply by 1 using x^2/x^2.

$$= \frac{1 \cdot x^2 - \dfrac{1}{x} \cdot x^2}{1 \cdot x^2 - \dfrac{1}{x^2} \cdot x^2}$$ Using the distributive law

$$= \frac{x^2 - x}{x^2 - 1}$$ All fractions have been cleared within the complex rational expression.

$$= \frac{x(x - 1)}{(x + 1)(x - 1)}$$ Factoring and simplifying: $\dfrac{x - 1}{x - 1} = 1$

$$= \frac{x}{x + 1}$$

TRY EXERCISE 15

It is important to understand both of the methods studied in this section. Sometimes, as in Example 1, the complex rational expression is either given as— or easily written as—a quotient of two rational expressions. In these cases, Method 1 (using division) is probably the easier method to use. Other times, as in Example 4, it is not difficult to find the LCD of all denominators in the complex rational expression. When this occurs, it is usually easier to use Method 2 (multiplying by the LCD). The more practice you get using both methods, the better you will be at selecting the easier method for any given problem.

4.5 EXERCISE SET

For Extra Help — MyMathLab — MathXL PRACTICE — WATCH — DOWNLOAD

Concept Reinforcement *In each of Exercises 1–4, use the method listed to match the accompanying expression with the expression in the column on the right that arises when that method is used.*

1. $\dfrac{\dfrac{5}{x^2} + \dfrac{1}{x}}{\dfrac{7}{2} - \dfrac{3}{4x}}$;

   Multiplying by the LCD (Method 2)

2. $\dfrac{\dfrac{5}{x^2} + \dfrac{1}{x}}{\dfrac{7}{2} - \dfrac{3}{4x}}$;

   Using division to simplify (Method 1)

3. $\dfrac{\dfrac{4}{5x} - \dfrac{1}{10}}{\dfrac{8}{x^2} + \dfrac{7}{2}}$;

   Using division to simplify (Method 1)

4. $\dfrac{\dfrac{4}{5x} - \dfrac{1}{10}}{\dfrac{8}{x^2} + \dfrac{7}{2}}$;

   Multiplying by the LCD (Method 2)

a) $\dfrac{\dfrac{5+x}{x^2}}{\dfrac{14x-3}{4x}}$

b) $\dfrac{\dfrac{8-x}{10x}}{\dfrac{16+7x^2}{2x^2}}$

c) $\dfrac{\dfrac{4}{5x} \cdot 10x^2 - \dfrac{1}{10} \cdot 10x^2}{\dfrac{8}{x^2} \cdot 10x^2 + \dfrac{7}{2} \cdot 10x^2}$

d) $\dfrac{\dfrac{5}{x^2} \cdot 4x^2 + \dfrac{1}{x} \cdot 4x^2}{\dfrac{7}{2} \cdot 4x^2 - \dfrac{3}{4x} \cdot 4x^2}$

Simplify. Use either method or the method specified by your instructor.

5. $\dfrac{1 + \dfrac{1}{4}}{2 + \dfrac{3}{4}}$

6. $\dfrac{3 + \dfrac{1}{4}}{1 + \dfrac{1}{2}}$

7. $\dfrac{\dfrac{1}{2} + \dfrac{1}{3}}{\dfrac{1}{4} - \dfrac{1}{6}}$

8. $\dfrac{\dfrac{2}{5} - \dfrac{1}{10}}{\dfrac{7}{20} - \dfrac{4}{15}}$

9. $\dfrac{\dfrac{x}{4} + x}{\dfrac{4}{x} + x}$

10. $\dfrac{\dfrac{1}{c} + 2}{\dfrac{1}{c} - 5}$

11. $\dfrac{\dfrac{10}{t}}{\dfrac{2}{t^2} - \dfrac{5}{t}}$

12. $\dfrac{\dfrac{5}{x} - \dfrac{2}{x^2}}{\dfrac{2}{x^2}}$

13. $\dfrac{\dfrac{2a-5}{3a}}{\dfrac{a-7}{6a}}$

14. $\dfrac{\dfrac{a+5}{a^2}}{\dfrac{a-2}{3a}}$

15. $\dfrac{\dfrac{x}{6} - \dfrac{3}{x}}{\dfrac{1}{3} + \dfrac{1}{x}}$

16. $\dfrac{\dfrac{2}{x} + \dfrac{x}{4}}{\dfrac{3}{4} - \dfrac{2}{x}}$

17. $\dfrac{\dfrac{1}{s} - \dfrac{1}{5}}{\dfrac{s-5}{s}}$

18. $\dfrac{\dfrac{1}{9} - \dfrac{1}{n}}{\dfrac{n+9}{9}}$

19. $\dfrac{\dfrac{1}{t^2} + 1}{\dfrac{1}{t} - 1}$

20. $\dfrac{2 + \dfrac{1}{x}}{2 - \dfrac{1}{x^2}}$

21. $\dfrac{\dfrac{x^2}{x^2 - y^2}}{\dfrac{x}{x+y}}$

22. $\dfrac{\dfrac{a^2}{a-2}}{\dfrac{3a}{a^2-4}}$

23. $\dfrac{\dfrac{7}{c^2} + \dfrac{4}{c}}{\dfrac{6}{c} - \dfrac{3}{c^3}}$

24. $\dfrac{\dfrac{4}{t^3} - \dfrac{1}{t^2}}{\dfrac{3}{t} + \dfrac{5}{t^2}}$

25. $\dfrac{\dfrac{2}{7a^4} - \dfrac{1}{14a}}{\dfrac{3}{5a^2} + \dfrac{2}{15a}}$

26. $\dfrac{\dfrac{5}{4x^3} - \dfrac{3}{8x}}{\dfrac{3}{2x} + \dfrac{3}{4x^3}}$

Aha! 27. $\dfrac{\dfrac{x}{5y^3} + \dfrac{3}{10y}}{\dfrac{3}{10y} + \dfrac{x}{5y^3}}$

28. $\dfrac{\dfrac{a}{6b^3} + \dfrac{4}{9b^2}}{\dfrac{5}{6b} - \dfrac{1}{9b^3}}$

29. $\dfrac{\dfrac{3}{ab^4} + \dfrac{4}{a^3b}}{\dfrac{5}{a^3b} - \dfrac{3}{ab}}$

30. $\dfrac{\dfrac{2}{x^2y} + \dfrac{3}{xy^2}}{\dfrac{3}{xy^2} + \dfrac{2}{x^2y}}$

31. $\dfrac{t - \dfrac{9}{t}}{t + \dfrac{4}{t}}$

32. $\dfrac{s + \dfrac{2}{s}}{s - \dfrac{3}{s}}$

33. $\dfrac{\dfrac{1}{a} + \dfrac{1}{b}}{\dfrac{1}{a^3} + \dfrac{1}{b^3}}$

34. $\dfrac{x - y}{\dfrac{1}{x^3} - \dfrac{1}{y^3}}$

35. $\dfrac{3 + \dfrac{4}{ab^3}}{\dfrac{3 + a}{a^2 b}}$

36. $\dfrac{5 + \dfrac{3}{x^2 y}}{\dfrac{3 + x}{x^3 y}}$

37. $\dfrac{t + 5 + \dfrac{3}{t}}{t + 2 + \dfrac{1}{t}}$

38. $\dfrac{a + 3 + \dfrac{2}{a}}{a + 2 + \dfrac{5}{a}}$

39. $\dfrac{x - 2 - \dfrac{1}{x}}{x - 5 - \dfrac{4}{x}}$

40. $\dfrac{x - 3 - \dfrac{2}{x}}{x - 4 - \dfrac{3}{x}}$

41. Is it possible to simplify complex rational expressions without knowing how to divide rational expressions? Why or why not?

42. Why is the distributive law important when simplifying complex rational expressions?

Skill Review

To prepare for Section 4.6, review solving linear and quadratic equations (Sections 1.2 and 3.7).

Solve.

43. $3x - 5 + 2(4x - 1) = 12x - 3$ [1.2]

44. $(x - 1)7 - (x + 1)9 = 4(x + 2)$ [1.2]

45. $\dfrac{3}{4}x - \dfrac{5}{8} = \dfrac{3}{8}x + \dfrac{7}{4}$ [1.2]

46. $\dfrac{5}{9} - \dfrac{2x}{3} = \dfrac{5x}{6} + \dfrac{4}{3}$ [1.2]

47. $x^2 - 7x + 12 = 0$ [3.7]

48. $x^2 + 13x - 30 = 0$ [3.7]

Synthesis

49. Which of the two methods presented would you use to simplify Exercise 30? Why?

50. Which of the two methods presented would you use to simplify Exercise 22? Why?

In Exercises 51–54, find all x-values for which the given expression is undefined.

51. $\dfrac{\dfrac{x - 5}{x - 6}}{\dfrac{x - 7}{x - 8}}$

52. $\dfrac{\dfrac{x + 1}{x + 2}}{\dfrac{x + 3}{x + 4}}$

53. $\dfrac{\dfrac{2x + 3}{5x + 4}}{\dfrac{3}{7} - \dfrac{x^2}{21}}$

54. $\dfrac{\dfrac{3x - 5}{2x - 7}}{\dfrac{4x}{5} - \dfrac{8}{15}}$

55. Use multiplication by the LCD (Method 2) to show that

$$\frac{A}{B} \div \frac{C}{D} = \frac{A}{B} \cdot \frac{D}{C}.$$

(*Hint*: Begin by forming a complex rational expression.)

56. The formula

$$\frac{P\left(1 + \dfrac{i}{12}\right)^2}{\dfrac{\left(1 + \dfrac{i}{12}\right)^2 - 1}{\dfrac{i}{12}}},$$

where P is a loan amount and i is an interest rate, arises in certain business situations. Simplify this expression. (*Hint*: Expand the binomials.)

Simplify.

57. $\dfrac{\dfrac{x}{x + 5} + \dfrac{3}{x + 2}}{\dfrac{2}{x + 2} - \dfrac{x}{x + 5}}$

58. $\dfrac{\dfrac{5}{x + 2} - \dfrac{3}{x - 2}}{\dfrac{x}{x - 1} + \dfrac{x}{x + 1}}$

Aha! 59. $\left[\dfrac{\dfrac{x - 1}{x - 1} - 1}{\dfrac{x + 1}{x - 1} + 1}\right]^5$

60. $1 + \dfrac{1}{1 + \dfrac{1}{1 + \dfrac{1}{x}}}$

61. $\dfrac{\dfrac{z}{1 - \dfrac{z}{2 + 2z}} - 2z}{\dfrac{2z}{5z - 2} - 3}$

62. Find the simplified form for the reciprocal of

$$\frac{2}{x - 1} - \frac{1}{3x - 2}.$$

63. Under what circumstance(s) will there be no restrictions on the variable appearing in a complex rational expression?

64. Use a graphing calculator to check Example 2(a).

Additional Exercises

Simplify.

65. $\dfrac{1 - \dfrac{25}{x^2}}{1 + \dfrac{2}{x} - \dfrac{15}{x^2}}$

66. $\dfrac{9 - \dfrac{4}{x^2}}{3 - \dfrac{1}{x} - \dfrac{2}{x^2}}$

67. $\dfrac{2 - \dfrac{5}{t} - \dfrac{3}{t^2}}{2 - \dfrac{3}{t} - \dfrac{9}{t^2}}$

68. $\dfrac{3 + \dfrac{14}{t} + \dfrac{8}{t^2}}{3 + \dfrac{13}{t} + \dfrac{4}{t^2}}$

69. $\dfrac{8 + \dfrac{1}{a^3}}{2 - \dfrac{5}{a} - \dfrac{3}{a^2}}$

70. $\dfrac{27 - \dfrac{64}{a^3}}{3 - \dfrac{1}{a} - \dfrac{4}{a^2}}$

71. $\dfrac{1 - \dfrac{1}{y} + \dfrac{1}{y^2} - \dfrac{1}{y^3}}{1 - \dfrac{1}{y^4}}$

72. $\dfrac{16 - \dfrac{1}{y^4}}{8 + \dfrac{4}{y} + \dfrac{2}{y^2} + \dfrac{1}{y^3}}$

73. $\dfrac{25 - \dfrac{50}{a} - \dfrac{1}{a^2} + \dfrac{2}{a^3}}{5 - \dfrac{11}{a} + \dfrac{2}{a^2}}$

74. $\dfrac{1 + \dfrac{4}{a} + \dfrac{3}{a^2}}{1 + \dfrac{1}{a} - \dfrac{9}{a^2} - \dfrac{9}{a^3}}$

4.6 Solving Rational Equations

Solving a New Type of Equation ▪ A Visual Interpretation

Our study of rational expressions allows us to solve a type of equation that we could not have solved prior to this chapter.

Solving a New Type of Equation

A **rational**, or **fraction**, **equation** is an equation containing one or more rational expressions, often with the variable in a denominator. Here are some examples:

$$\frac{2}{3} + \frac{5}{6} = \frac{x}{9}, \qquad t + \frac{7}{t} = -5, \qquad \frac{x^2}{x-1} = \frac{1}{x-1}.$$

> **To Solve a Rational Equation**
> 1. List any restrictions that exist. Numbers that make a denominator equal 0 can never be solutions.
> 2. Clear the equation of fractions by multiplying both sides by the LCM of the denominators.
> 3. Solve the resulting equation using the addition principle, the multiplication principle, and the principle of zero products, as needed.
> 4. Check the possible solution(s) in the original equation.

When clearing an equation of fractions, we use the terminology LCM instead of LCD because we are *not* adding or subtracting rational expressions.

EXAMPLE 1

STUDY SKILLS

Does More Than One Solution Exist?

Keep in mind that many problems—in math and elsewhere—have more than one solution. When asked to solve an equation, we are expected to find any and all solutions of the equation.

Solve: $\dfrac{x}{6} - \dfrac{x}{8} = \dfrac{1}{12}$.

SOLUTION Because no variable appears in a denominator, no restrictions exist. The LCM of 6, 8, and 12 is 24, so we multiply both sides by 24:

$$24\left(\frac{x}{6} - \frac{x}{8}\right) = 24 \cdot \frac{1}{12}$$

Using the multiplication principle to multiply both sides by the LCM. Parentheses are important!

$$24 \cdot \frac{x}{6} - 24 \cdot \frac{x}{8} = 24 \cdot \frac{1}{12}$$

Using the distributive law

Be sure to multiply *each* term by the LCM.

$$\left.\begin{array}{c} \dfrac{24x}{6} - \dfrac{24x}{8} = \dfrac{24}{12} \\[2mm] 4x - 3x = 2 \end{array}\right\}$$

Simplifying. Note that all fractions have been cleared. If fractions remain, we have either made a mistake or have not used the LCM of the denominators.

$$x = 2.$$

Check:

$$\begin{array}{c|c} \dfrac{x}{6} - \dfrac{x}{8} & \dfrac{1}{12} \\[2mm] \dfrac{2}{6} - \dfrac{2}{8} & \dfrac{1}{12} \\[2mm] \dfrac{1}{3} - \dfrac{1}{4} & \\[2mm] \dfrac{4}{12} - \dfrac{3}{12} & \\[2mm] \dfrac{1}{12} \stackrel{?}{=} \dfrac{1}{12} & \text{TRUE} \end{array}$$

This checks, so the solution is 2.

TRY EXERCISE 5

Recall that the multiplication principle states that $a = b$ is equivalent to $a \cdot c = b \cdot c$, *provided c is not zero*. Because rational equations often have variables in a denominator, clearing fractions will now require us to multiply both sides by a variable expression. Since a variable expression could represent 0, *multiplying both sides of an equation by a variable expression does not always produce an equivalent equation*. Thus checking each solution in the original equation is essential.

EXAMPLE 2

Solve.

a) $\dfrac{2}{3x} + \dfrac{1}{x} = 10$

b) $x + \dfrac{6}{x} = -5$

c) $1 + \dfrac{3x}{x+2} = \dfrac{-6}{x+2}$

d) $\dfrac{3}{x-5} + \dfrac{1}{x+5} = \dfrac{2}{x^2-25}$

e) $\dfrac{x^2}{x-1} = \dfrac{1}{x-1}$

SOLUTION

List restrictions.

a) If $x = 0$, both denominators are 0. We list this restriction:

$$x \neq 0.$$

We now clear the equation of fractions and solve:

$$\frac{2}{3x} + \frac{1}{x} = 10 \qquad \text{We cannot have } x = 0. \text{ The LCM is } 3x.$$

Clear fractions.

$$3x\left(\frac{2}{3x} + \frac{1}{x}\right) = 3x \cdot 10 \qquad \begin{array}{l}\text{Using the multiplication principle to} \\ \text{multiply both sides by the LCM.} \\ \textit{Don't forget the parentheses!}\end{array}$$

$$3x \cdot \frac{2}{3x} + 3x \cdot \frac{1}{x} = 3x \cdot 10 \qquad \text{Using the distributive law}$$

$$2 + 3 = 30x \qquad \begin{array}{l}\text{Removing factors equal to 1:} \\ (3x)/(3x) = 1 \text{ and } x/x = 1. \text{ This} \\ \text{clears all fractions.}\end{array}$$

Solve.

$$5 = 30x$$

$$\frac{5}{30} = x, \quad \text{so } x = \frac{1}{6}. \qquad \begin{array}{l}\text{Dividing both sides by 30, or} \\ \text{multiplying both sides by } 1/30\end{array}$$

Since $\frac{1}{6} \neq 0$, and 0 is the only restricted value, $\frac{1}{6}$ *should* check.

Check.

Check:

$$\frac{2}{3x} + \frac{1}{x} = 10$$

$$\begin{array}{c|c} \dfrac{2}{3 \cdot \frac{1}{6}} + \dfrac{1}{\frac{1}{6}} & 10 \\[2ex] \dfrac{2}{\frac{1}{2}} + \dfrac{1}{\frac{1}{6}} & \\[2ex] 2 \cdot \frac{2}{1} + 1 \cdot \frac{6}{1} & \\[1ex] 4 + 6 & \\[1ex] 10 \overset{?}{=} 10 & \text{TRUE} \end{array}$$

The solution is $\frac{1}{6}$.

b) Again, note that if $x = 0$, the expression $6/x$ is undefined. We list the restriction:

$$x \neq 0.$$

We now clear the equation of fractions and solve:

$$x + \frac{6}{x} = -5 \qquad \text{We cannot have } x = 0. \text{ The LCM is } x.$$

$$x\left(x + \frac{6}{x}\right) = x(-5) \qquad \begin{array}{l}\text{Multiplying both sides by the LCM.} \\ \textit{Don't forget the parentheses!}\end{array}$$

$$x \cdot x + x \cdot \frac{6}{x} = -5x \qquad \text{Using the distributive law}$$

$$x^2 + 6 = -5x \qquad \begin{array}{l}\text{Removing a factor equal to 1: } x/x = 1. \\ \text{We are left with a quadratic equation.}\end{array}$$

$$x^2 + 5x + 6 = 0 \qquad \begin{array}{l}\text{Using the addition principle to add } 5x \text{ to} \\ \text{both sides}\end{array}$$

$$(x + 3)(x + 2) = 0 \qquad \text{Factoring}$$

$$x + 3 = 0 \quad \textit{or} \quad x + 2 = 0 \qquad \text{Using the principle of zero products}$$

$$x = -3 \quad \textit{or} \qquad x = -2. \qquad \begin{array}{l}\text{The only restricted value is 0, so} \\ \text{both answers should check.}\end{array}$$

Check: For -3:

$$x + \frac{6}{x} = -5$$

$$\frac{-3 + \dfrac{6}{-3} \;\Big|\; -5}{}$$

$$-3 - 2 \;\Big|$$

$$-5 \overset{?}{=} -5 \quad \text{TRUE}$$

For -2:

$$x + \frac{6}{x} = -5$$

$$\frac{-2 + \dfrac{6}{-2} \;\Big|\; -5}{}$$

$$-2 - 3 \;\Big|$$

$$-5 \overset{?}{=} -5 \quad \text{TRUE}$$

Both of these check, so there are two solutions, -3 and -2.

c) The only denominator is $x + 2$. We set this equal to 0 and solve:

$$x + 2 = 0$$
$$x = -2.$$

If $x = -2$, the rational expressions are undefined. We list the restriction:

$$x \neq -2.$$

We clear fractions and solve:

$$1 + \frac{3x}{x + 2} = \frac{-6}{x + 2}$$

We cannot have $x = -2$. The LCM is $x + 2$.

$$(x + 2)\left(1 + \frac{3x}{x + 2}\right) = (x + 2)\frac{-6}{x + 2}$$

Multiplying both sides by the LCM. *Don't forget the parentheses!*

$$(x + 2) \cdot 1 + (x + 2)\frac{3x}{x + 2} = (x + 2)\frac{-6}{x + 2}$$

Using the distributive law; removing a factor equal to 1: $(x + 2)/(x + 2) = 1$

$$x + 2 + 3x = -6$$
$$4x + 2 = -6$$
$$4x = -8$$
$$x = -2.$$

Above, we stated that $x \neq -2$.

Because of the above restriction, -2 must be rejected as a solution. The check below simply confirms this.

Check:

$$1 + \frac{3x}{x + 2} = \frac{-6}{x + 2}$$

$$\frac{1 + \dfrac{3(-2)}{-2 + 2} \;\Big|\; \dfrac{-6}{-2 + 2}}{}$$

$$1 + \frac{-6}{0} \overset{?}{=} \frac{-6}{0} \quad \text{FALSE}$$

The equation has no solution.

d) The denominators are $x - 5$, $x + 5$, and $x^2 - 25$. Setting them equal to 0 and solving, we find that the rational expressions are undefined when $x = 5$ or $x = -5$. We list the restrictions:

$$x \neq 5, \quad x \neq -5.$$

STUDENT NOTES ————

Not all checking is for finding errors in computation. For these equations, the solution process itself can introduce numbers that do not check.

We clear fractions and solve:

$$\frac{3}{x-5} + \frac{1}{x+5} = \frac{2}{x^2-25}$$

We cannot have $x = 5$ or $x = -5$. The LCM is $(x-5)(x+5)$.

$$(x-5)(x+5)\left(\frac{3}{x-5} + \frac{1}{x+5}\right) = (x-5)(x+5)\frac{2}{(x-5)(x+5)}$$

$$\frac{(x-5)(x+5)3}{x-5} + \frac{(x-5)(x+5)}{x+5} = \frac{2(x-5)(x+5)}{(x-5)(x+5)}$$

Using the distributive law

$$(x+5)3 + (x-5) = 2$$

Removing factors equal to 1:
$(x-5)/(x-5) = 1$,
$(x+5)/(x+5) = 1$,
and $\dfrac{(x-5)(x+5)}{(x-5)(x+5)} = 1$

$$3x + 15 + x - 5 = 2$$

Using the distributive law

$$4x + 10 = 2$$

$$4x = -8$$

$$x = -2.$$

$-2 \neq 5$ and $-2 \neq -5$, so -2 *should* check.

The student can check to confirm that -2 is the solution.

e) If $x = 1$, the denominators are 0. We list the restriction:

$$x \neq 1.$$

We clear fractions and solve:

$$\frac{x^2}{x-1} = \frac{1}{x-1}$$

We cannot have $x = 1$.

$$(x-1) \cdot \frac{x^2}{x-1} = (x-1) \cdot \frac{1}{x-1}$$

Multiplying both sides by $x - 1$, the LCM

$$x^2 = 1$$

Removing a factor equal to 1: $(x-1)/(x-1) = 1$

$$x^2 - 1 = 0$$

Subtracting 1 from both sides

$$(x-1)(x+1) = 0$$

Factoring

$$x - 1 = 0 \quad or \quad x + 1 = 0$$

Using the principle of zero products

$$x = 1 \quad or \quad x = -1.$$

Above, we stated that $x \neq 1$.

Because of the above restriction, 1 must be rejected as a solution. The student should check in the original equation that -1 *does* check. The solution is -1.

TRY EXERCISES 21 and 29

A Visual Interpretation

ALGEBRAIC–GRAPHICAL CONNECTION

We can obtain a visual check of the solutions of a rational equation by graphing. For example, consider the equation

$$\frac{x}{4} + \frac{x}{2} = 6.$$

We can examine the solution by graphing the equations

$$y = \frac{x}{4} + \frac{x}{2} \quad \text{and} \quad y = 6$$

using the same set of axes, as shown below.

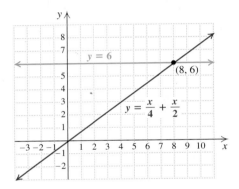

The y-values for each equation will be the same where the graphs intersect. The x-value of that point will yield that value, so it will be a solution of the equation. It appears from the graph that when $x = 8$, the value of $x/4 + x/2$ is 6. We can check by substitution:

$$\frac{x}{4} + \frac{x}{2} = \frac{8}{4} + \frac{8}{2} = 2 + 4 = 6.$$

Thus the solution is 8.

TECHNOLOGY CONNECTION

We can use a table to check possible solutions of rational equations. Consider the equation in Example 2(e),

$$\frac{x^2}{x - 1} = \frac{1}{x - 1},$$

and the possible solutions that were found, 1 and -1. To check these solutions, we enter $y_1 = x^2/(x - 1)$ and $y_2 = 1/(x - 1)$. After setting Indpnt to Ask and Depend to Auto in the TBLSET menu, we display the table and enter $x = 1$. The ERROR messages indicate that 1 is not a solution because it is not an allowable replacement for x in the equation. Next, we enter $x = -1$. Since y_1 and y_2 have the same value, we know that the equation is true when $x = -1$, and thus -1 is a solution.

X	Y₁	Y₂
1	ERROR	ERROR
−1	−.5	−.5
X =		

Use a graphing calculator to check the possible solutions of Example 1 and Example 2, parts (a)–(d).

4.6 EXERCISE SET

For Extra Help MyMathLab   PRACTICE WATCH DOWNLOAD

Concept Reinforcement *Classify each statement as either true or false.*

1. Every rational equation has at least one solution.

2. It is possible for a rational equation to have more than one solution.

3. When both sides of an equation are multiplied by a variable expression, the result is not always an equivalent equation.

4. All the equation-solving principles studied thus far may be needed when solving a rational equation.

Solve. If no solution exists, state this.

5. $\dfrac{3}{5} - \dfrac{2}{3} = \dfrac{x}{6}$

6. $\dfrac{5}{8} - \dfrac{3}{5} = \dfrac{x}{10}$

7. $\dfrac{1}{3} + \dfrac{5}{6} = \dfrac{1}{x}$

8. $\dfrac{3}{5} + \dfrac{1}{8} = \dfrac{1}{x}$

9. $\dfrac{1}{8} + \dfrac{1}{12} = \dfrac{1}{t}$

10. $\dfrac{1}{6} + \dfrac{1}{10} = \dfrac{1}{t}$

11. $y + \dfrac{4}{y} = -5$

12. $n + \dfrac{3}{n} = -4$

13. $\dfrac{x}{6} - \dfrac{6}{x} = 0$

14. $\dfrac{x}{7} - \dfrac{7}{x} = 0$

15. $\dfrac{2}{x} = \dfrac{5}{x} - \dfrac{1}{4}$

16. $\dfrac{3}{t} = \dfrac{4}{t} - \dfrac{1}{5}$

17. $\dfrac{5}{3t} + \dfrac{3}{t} = 1$

18. $\dfrac{3}{4x} + \dfrac{5}{x} = 1$

19. $\dfrac{n + 2}{n - 6} = \dfrac{1}{2}$

20. $\dfrac{a - 4}{a + 6} = \dfrac{1}{3}$

21. $x + \dfrac{12}{x} = -7$

22. $x + \dfrac{8}{x} = -9$

23. $\dfrac{3}{x - 4} = \dfrac{5}{x + 1}$

24. $\dfrac{1}{x + 3} = \dfrac{4}{x - 1}$

25. $\dfrac{a}{6} - \dfrac{a}{10} = \dfrac{1}{6}$

26. $\dfrac{t}{8} - \dfrac{t}{12} = \dfrac{1}{8}$

27. $\dfrac{x + 1}{3} - 1 = \dfrac{x - 1}{2}$

28. $\dfrac{x + 2}{5} - 1 = \dfrac{x - 2}{4}$

29. $\dfrac{y + 3}{y - 3} = \dfrac{6}{y - 3}$

30. $\dfrac{3}{a + 7} = \dfrac{a + 10}{a + 7}$

31. $\dfrac{3}{x + 4} = \dfrac{5}{x}$

32. $\dfrac{2}{x + 3} = \dfrac{7}{x}$

33. $\dfrac{n + 1}{n + 2} = \dfrac{n - 3}{n + 1}$

34. $\dfrac{n + 2}{n - 3} = \dfrac{n + 1}{n - 2}$

35. $\dfrac{5}{t - 2} + \dfrac{3t}{t - 2} = \dfrac{4}{t^2 - 4t + 4}$

36. $\dfrac{4}{t - 3} + \dfrac{2t}{t - 3} = \dfrac{12}{t^2 - 6t + 9}$

37. $\dfrac{x}{x + 5} - \dfrac{5}{x - 5} = \dfrac{14}{x^2 - 25}$

38. $\dfrac{5}{x + 1} + \dfrac{2x}{x^2 - 1} = \dfrac{1}{x + 1}$

39. $\dfrac{5}{t - 3} - \dfrac{30}{t^2 - 9} = 1$

40. $\dfrac{1}{y + 3} + \dfrac{1}{y - 3} = \dfrac{1}{y^2 - 9}$

41. $\dfrac{7}{6 - a} = \dfrac{a + 1}{a - 6}$

42. $\dfrac{t - 12}{t - 10} = \dfrac{1}{10 - t}$

Aha! 43. $\dfrac{-2}{x + 2} = \dfrac{x}{x + 2}$

44. $\dfrac{3}{2x - 6} = \dfrac{x}{2x - 6}$

45. $\dfrac{12}{x} = \dfrac{x}{3}$

46. $\dfrac{x}{2} = \dfrac{18}{x}$

47. When solving rational equations, why do we multiply each side by the LCM of the denominators?

48. Explain the difference between adding rational expressions and solving rational equations.

Skill Review

To prepare for Section 4.7, review solving applications and rates of change (Sections 1.5, 2.4, and 3.8).

49. The sum of two consecutive odd numbers is 276. Find the numbers. [1.5]

50. The length of a rectangular picture window is 3 yd greater than the width. The area of the rectangle is 10 yd². Find the perimeter. [3.8]

51. The height of a triangle is 3 cm longer than its base. If the area of the triangle is 54 cm², find the measurements of the base and the height. [3.8]

52. The product of two consecutive even integers is 48. Find the numbers. [3.8]

53. *Human physiology.* Between June 9 and June 24, Seth's beard grew 0.9 cm. Find the rate at which Seth's beard grows. [2.4]

54. *Gardening.* Between July 7 and July 12, Carla's string beans grew 1.4 in. Find the growth rate of the string beans. [2.4]

Synthesis

55. Describe a method that can be used to create rational equations that have no solution.

56. How can a graph be used to determine how many solutions an equation has?

Solve.

57. $1 + \dfrac{x-1}{x-3} = \dfrac{2}{x-3} - x$

58. $\dfrac{4}{y-2} + \dfrac{3}{y^2-4} = \dfrac{5}{y+2} + \dfrac{2y}{y^2-4}$

59. $\dfrac{12-6x}{x^2-4} = \dfrac{3x}{x+2} - \dfrac{3-2x}{2-x}$

60. $\dfrac{x}{x^2+3x-4} + \dfrac{x+1}{x^2+6x+8} = \dfrac{2x}{x^2+x-2}$

61. $7 - \dfrac{a-2}{a+3} = \dfrac{a^2-4}{a+3} + 5$

62. $\dfrac{x^2}{x^2-4} = \dfrac{x}{x+2} - \dfrac{2x}{2-x}$

63. $\dfrac{1}{x-1} + x - 5 = \dfrac{5x-4}{x-1} - 6$

64. $\dfrac{5-3a}{a^2+4a+3} - \dfrac{2a+2}{a+3} = \dfrac{3-a}{a+1}$

65. $\dfrac{\dfrac{1}{x}+1}{x} = \dfrac{\dfrac{1}{x}}{2}$

66. $\dfrac{\dfrac{1}{3}}{x} = \dfrac{1-\dfrac{1}{x}}{x}$

67. Use a graphing calculator to check your answers to Exercises 13, 21, 31, and 57.

Additional Exercises

Solve.

68. $\dfrac{x-1}{x-3} = \dfrac{2}{x-3}$

69. $\dfrac{x+5}{x+4} = \dfrac{1}{x+4}$

70. $\dfrac{6}{x^2-4} = \dfrac{x+1}{x^2-2x}$

71 $\dfrac{8}{x^2-25} = \dfrac{x-1}{x^2-5x}$

72. $\dfrac{t-1}{t^2-3t} - \dfrac{4}{t^2-9} = 0$

73. $\dfrac{10}{t^2-1} - \dfrac{t+4}{t^2-t} = 0$

74. $\dfrac{5}{3x+3} + \dfrac{1}{2x-2} = \dfrac{1}{x^2-1}$

75 $\dfrac{4}{x^2-4} + \dfrac{1}{x+2} + \dfrac{2}{3x-6} = 0$

CONNECTING the CONCEPTS

An equation contains an equals sign; an expression does not. Be careful not to confuse simplifying an expression with solving an equation. When expressions are simplified, the result is an equivalent expression. When equations are solved, the result is a solution. Compare the following.

Simplify: $\dfrac{x-1}{6x} + \dfrac{4}{9}$.

SOLUTION

$\dfrac{x-1}{6x} + \dfrac{4}{9} = \dfrac{x-1}{6x} \cdot \dfrac{3}{3} + \dfrac{4}{9} \cdot \dfrac{2x}{2x}$

> The equals signs indicate that all the expressions are equivalent.

$= \dfrac{3x-3}{18x} + \dfrac{8x}{18x}$ — Writing with the LCD, $18x$

$= \dfrac{11x-3}{18x}$ — The result is an expression equivalent to $\dfrac{x-1}{6x} + \dfrac{4}{9}$.

Solve: $\dfrac{x-1}{6x} = \dfrac{4}{9}$.

SOLUTION

$\dfrac{x-1}{6x} = \dfrac{4}{9}$

> Each line is an equivalent equation.

$18x \cdot \dfrac{x-1}{6x} = 18x \cdot \dfrac{4}{9}$ — Multiplying by the LCM, $18x$

$3 \cdot 6x \cdot \dfrac{x-1}{6x} = 2 \cdot 9 \cdot x \cdot \dfrac{4}{9}$

$3(x-1) = 2x \cdot 4$

$3x - 3 = 8x$

$-3 = 5x$

$-\dfrac{3}{5} = x$ — The result is a solution; $-\dfrac{3}{5}$ is the solution of $\dfrac{x-1}{6x} = \dfrac{4}{9}$.

MIXED REVIEW

Tell whether each of the following is an expression or an equation. Then simplify the expression or solve the equation.

1. Simplify: $\dfrac{4x^2 - 8x}{4x^2 + 4x}$.

2. Add and, if possible, simplify: $\dfrac{2}{5n} + \dfrac{3}{2n - 1}$.

3. Solve: $\dfrac{3}{y} - \dfrac{1}{4} = \dfrac{1}{y}$.

4. Simplify: $\dfrac{\dfrac{1}{z} + 1}{\dfrac{1}{z^2 - 1}}$.

5. Solve: $\dfrac{5}{x + 3} = \dfrac{3}{x + 2}$.

6. Multiply and, if possible, simplify:
$$\frac{8t + 8}{2t^2 + t - 1} \cdot \frac{t^2 - 1}{t^2 - 2t + 1}.$$

7. Subtract and, if possible, simplify:
$$\frac{2a}{a + 1} - \frac{4a}{1 - a^2}.$$

8. Solve: $\dfrac{15}{x} - \dfrac{15}{x + 2} = 2$.

9. Divide and, if possible, simplify:
$$\frac{18x^2}{25} \div \frac{12x}{5}.$$

10. Solve: $\dfrac{20}{x} = \dfrac{x}{5}$.

4.7 Applications Using Rational Equations and Proportions

Problems Involving Work • Problems Involving Motion • Problems Involving Proportions

In many areas of study, applications involving rates, proportions, or reciprocals translate to rational equations. By using the five steps for problem solving and the lessons of Section 4.6, we can now solve such problems.

Problems Involving Work

EXAMPLE 1

The roof of Finn and Paige's townhouse needs to be reshingled. Finn can do the job alone in 8 hr and Paige can do the job alone in 10 hr. How long will it take the two of them, working together, to reshingle the roof?

SOLUTION

1. **Familiarize.** This *work problem* is a type of problem we have not yet encountered. Work problems are often *incorrectly* translated to mathematical language in several ways.

   a) Add the times together: 8 hr + 10 hr = 18 hr. ← Incorrect

   This cannot be the correct approach since Finn and Paige working together should not take longer than either of them working alone.

   b) Average the times: (8 hr + 10 hr)/2 = 9 hr. ← Incorrect

   Again, this is longer than it would take Finn to do the job alone.

   c) Assume that each person does half the job. ← Incorrect

Finn would reshingle $\frac{1}{2}$ the roof in $\frac{1}{2}(8 \text{ hr})$, or 4 hr, and Paige would reshingle $\frac{1}{2}$ the roof in $\frac{1}{2}(10 \text{ hr})$, or 5 hr, so Finn would finish an hour before Paige. The problem assumes that the two are working together, so Finn will help Paige after completing his half. This tells us that the job will take between 4 and 5 hr.

Each incorrect approach started with the time it took each worker to do the job. The correct approach instead focuses on the *rate* of work, or the amount of the job that each person completes in 1 hr.

Since Finn takes 8 hr to reshingle the entire roof, in 1 hr he reshingles $\frac{1}{8}$ of the roof. Since Paige takes 10 hr to reshingle the entire roof, in 1 hr she reshingles $\frac{1}{10}$ of the roof. Thus Finn works at a rate of $\frac{1}{8}$ roof per hour, and Paige works at a rate of $\frac{1}{10}$ roof per hour.

Working together, Finn and Paige reshingle $\frac{1}{8} + \frac{1}{10}$ roof in 1 hr, so their rate, as a team, is $\frac{1}{8} + \frac{1}{10} = \frac{5}{40} + \frac{4}{40} = \frac{9}{40}$ roof per hour.

We are looking for the time required to reshingle 1 entire roof, not just a part of it. Setting up a table helps us organize the information.

Time	Fraction of the Roof Reshingled		
	By Finn	**By Paige**	**Together**
1 hr	$\frac{1}{8}$	$\frac{1}{10}$	$\frac{1}{8} + \frac{1}{10}$, or $\frac{9}{40}$
2 hr	$\frac{1}{8} \cdot 2$	$\frac{1}{10} \cdot 2$	$\left(\frac{1}{8} + \frac{1}{10}\right)2$, or $\frac{9}{40} \cdot 2$, or $\frac{9}{20}$
3 hr	$\frac{1}{8} \cdot 3$	$\frac{1}{10} \cdot 3$	$\left(\frac{1}{8} + \frac{1}{10}\right)3$, or $\frac{9}{40} \cdot 3$, or $\frac{27}{40}$
t hr	$\frac{1}{8} \cdot t$	$\frac{1}{10} \cdot t$	$\left(\frac{1}{8} + \frac{1}{10}\right)t$, or $\frac{9}{40} \cdot t$

2. **Translate.** From the table, we see that t must be some number for which

Fraction of roof done by Finn in t hr $\quad \dfrac{1}{8} \cdot t + \dfrac{1}{10} \cdot t = 1,$ $\quad$ Fraction of roof done by Paige in t hr

or

$$\frac{t}{8} + \frac{t}{10} = 1.$$

3. **Carry out.** We solve the equation:

$$\frac{t}{8} + \frac{t}{10} = 1 \qquad \text{The LCD is 40.}$$

$$40\left(\frac{t}{8} + \frac{t}{10}\right) = 40 \cdot 1 \qquad \text{Multiplying to clear fractions}$$

$$\frac{40t}{8} + \frac{40t}{10} = 40$$

$$5t + 4t = 40 \qquad \text{Simplifying}$$

$$9t = 40$$

$$t = \frac{40}{9}, \text{ or } 4\frac{4}{9}.$$

4. **Check.** In $\frac{40}{9}$ hr, Finn reshingles $\frac{1}{8} \cdot \frac{40}{9}$, or $\frac{5}{9}$, of the roof and Paige reshingles $\frac{1}{10} \cdot \frac{40}{9}$, or $\frac{4}{9}$, of the roof. Together, they reshingle $\frac{5}{9} + \frac{4}{9}$, or 1 roof. The fact that our solution is between 4 and 5 hr (see step 1 above) is also a check.

5. **State.** It will take $4\frac{4}{9}$ hr for Finn and Paige, working together, to reshingle the roof.

TRY EXERCISE 7

EXAMPLE 2

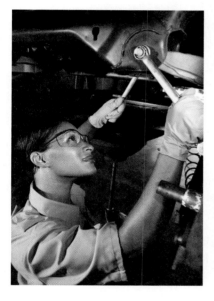

It takes Manuel 9 hr longer than Zoe to rebuild an engine. Working together, they can do the job in 20 hr. How long would it take each, working alone, to rebuild an engine?

SOLUTION

1. **Familiarize.** Unlike Example 1, this problem does not provide us with the times required by the individuals to do the job alone. Let's have $z =$ the number of hours it would take Zoe working alone and $z + 9 =$ the number of hours it would take Manuel working alone.

2. **Translate.** Using the same reasoning as in Example 1, we see that Zoe completes $\frac{1}{z}$ of the job in 1 hr and Manuel completes $\frac{1}{z+9}$ of the job in 1 hr. Thus, in 20 hr,

Zoe completes $\frac{1}{z} \cdot 20$ of the job and Manuel completes $\frac{1}{z+9} \cdot 20$ of the job.

We know that, together, Zoe and Manuel can complete the entire job in 20 hr. This gives the following:

$$\text{Fraction of job done by Zoe in 20 hr} \quad \frac{1}{z} \cdot 20 + \frac{1}{z+9} \cdot 20 = 1, \quad \text{Fraction of job done by Manuel in 20 hr}$$

or

$$\frac{20}{z} + \frac{20}{z+9} = 1.$$

3. **Carry out.** We solve the equation:

$$\frac{20}{z} + \frac{20}{z+9} = 1 \qquad \text{The LCD is } z(z+9).$$

$$z(z+9)\left(\frac{20}{z} + \frac{20}{z+9}\right) = z(z+9)1 \qquad \text{Multiplying to clear fractions}$$

$$(z+9)20 + z \cdot 20 = z(z+9) \qquad \text{Distributing and simplifying}$$

$$40z + 180 = z^2 + 9z$$

$$0 = z^2 - 31z - 180 \qquad \text{Getting 0 on one side}$$

$$0 = (z-36)(z+5) \qquad \text{Factoring}$$

$$z - 36 = 0 \quad or \quad z + 5 = 0 \qquad \text{Principle of zero products}$$

$$z = 36 \quad or \quad z = -5.$$

4. **Check.** Since negative time has no meaning in the problem, -5 is not a solution to the original problem. The number 36 checks since, if Zoe takes 36 hr alone and Manuel takes $36 + 9 = 45$ hr alone, in 20 hr they would have finished

$$\frac{20}{36} + \frac{20}{45} = \frac{5}{9} + \frac{4}{9} = 1 \text{ complete rebuild.}$$

5. **State.** It would take Zoe 36 hr to rebuild an engine alone, and Manuel 45 hr.

TRY EXERCISE 13

The equations used in Examples 1 and 2 can be generalized as follows.

The Work Principle

If

a = the time needed for A to complete the work alone,

b = the time needed for B to complete the work alone, and

t = the time needed for A and B to complete the work together,

then

$$\frac{t}{a} + \frac{t}{b} = 1.$$

The following are equivalent equations that can also be used:

$$\frac{1}{a} \cdot t + \frac{1}{b} \cdot t = 1 \quad \text{and} \quad \frac{1}{a} + \frac{1}{b} = \frac{1}{t}.$$

Problems Involving Motion

Problems dealing with distance, rate (or speed), and time are called **motion problems**. To translate them, we use either the basic motion formula, $d = rt$, or the formulas $r = d/t$ or $t = d/r$, which can be derived from $d = rt$.

EXAMPLE 3

On her road bike, Olivia bikes 15 km/h faster than Jason does on his mountain bike. In the time it takes Olivia to travel 80 km, Jason travels 50 km. Find the speed of each bicyclist.

SOLUTION

STUDENT NOTES

You need remember only the motion formula $d = rt$. Then you can divide both sides by t to get $r = d/t$, or you can divide both sides by r to get $t = d/r$.

1. **Familiarize.** Let's guess that Jason is going 10 km/h. Then the following would be true.

   Olivia's speed would be $10 + 15$, or 25 km/h.

   Jason would cover 50 km in $50/10 = 5$ hr.

   Olivia would cover 80 km in $80/25 = 3.2$ hr.

Since the times are not the same, our guess is wrong, but we can make some observations.

   If r = the rate, in kilometers per hour, of Jason's bike, then the rate of Olivia's bike = $r + 15$.

   Jason's travel time is the same as Olivia's travel time.

We make a drawing and construct a table, listing the information we know.

r km/h
50 km

$(r + 15)$ km/h
80 km

	Distance	Speed	Time
Jason's Mountain Bike	50	r	
Olivia's Road Bike	80	$r + 15$	

2. **Translate.** By looking at how we checked our guess, we see that we can fill in the **Time** column of the table using the formula *Time = Distance/Rate*, as follows.

	Distance	Speed	Time
Jason's Mountain Bike	50	r	$50/r$
Olivia's Road Bike	80	$r + 15$	$80/(r + 15)$

Since we know that the times are the same, we can write an equation:

$$\frac{50}{r} = \frac{80}{r + 15}.$$

3. **Carry out.** We solve the equation:

$$\frac{50}{r} = \frac{80}{r + 15} \qquad \text{The LCD is } r(r + 15).$$

$$r(r + 15)\frac{50}{r} = r(r + 15)\frac{80}{r + 15} \qquad \text{Multiplying to clear fractions}$$

$$50r + 750 = 80r \qquad \text{Simplifying}$$

$$750 = 30r$$

$$25 = r.$$

4. **Check.** If our answer checks, Jason's mountain bike is going 25 km/h and Olivia's road bike is going $25 + 15 = 40$ km/h.

   Traveling 80 km at 40 km/h, Olivia is riding for $\frac{80}{40} = 2$ hr. Traveling 50 km at 25 km/h, Jason is riding for $\frac{50}{25} = 2$ hr. Our answer checks since the two times are the same.

5. **State.** Olivia's speed is 40 km/h, and Jason's speed is 25 km/h.

TRY EXERCISE   19

In the next example, although distance is the same in both directions, the key to the translation lies in an additional piece of given information.

EXAMPLE   4

A Hudson River tugboat goes 10 mph in still water. It travels 24 mi upstream and 24 mi back in a total time of 5 hr. What is the speed of the current?

Sources: Based on information from the Department of the Interior, U.S. Geological Survey, and *The Tugboat Captain*, Montgomery County Community College

SOLUTION

1. **Familiarize.** Let's guess that the speed of the current is 4 mph. Then the following would be true.

   The tugboat would move $10 - 4 = 6$ mph upstream.

   The tugboat would move $10 + 4 = 14$ mph downstream.

   To travel 24 mi upstream would require $\frac{24}{6} = 4$ hr.

   To travel 24 mi downstream would require $\frac{24}{14} = 1\frac{5}{7}$ hr.

   Since the total time, $4 + 1\frac{5}{7} = 5\frac{5}{7}$ hr, is not the 5 hr mentioned in the problem, our guess is wrong, but we can make some observations.

If c = the current's rate, in miles per hour, we have the following.

The tugboat's speed upstream is $(10 - c)$ mph.

The tugboat's speed downstream is $(10 + c)$ mph.

The total travel time is 5 hr.

We make a sketch and construct a table, listing the information we know.

	Distance	Speed	Time
Upstream	24	$10 - c$	
Downstream	24	$10 + c$	

2. **Translate.** From examining our guess, we see that the time traveled can be represented using the formula *Time* = *Distance/Rate*:

	Distance	Speed	Time
Upstream	24	$10 - c$	$24/(10 - c)$
Downstream	24	$10 + c$	$24/(10 + c)$

Since the total time upstream and back is 5 hr, we use the last column of the table to form an equation:

$$\frac{24}{10 - c} + \frac{24}{10 + c} = 5.$$

3. **Carry out.** We solve the equation:

$$\frac{24}{10 - c} + \frac{24}{10 + c} = 5 \qquad \text{The LCD is } (10 - c)(10 + c).$$

$$(10 - c)(10 + c)\left[\frac{24}{10 - c} + \frac{24}{10 + c}\right] = (10 - c)(10 + c)5 \qquad \text{Multiplying to clear fractions}$$

$$24(10 + c) + 24(10 - c) = (100 - c^2)5$$

$$480 = 500 - 5c^2 \qquad \text{Simplifying}$$

$$5c^2 - 20 = 0$$

$$5(c^2 - 4) = 0$$

$$5(c - 2)(c + 2) = 0$$

$$c = 2 \quad or \quad c = -2.$$

4. **Check.** Since speed cannot be negative in this problem, -2 cannot be a solution. You should confirm that 2 checks in the original problem.

5. **State.** The speed of the current is 2 mph.

▶ TRY EXERCISE 21

Problems Involving Proportions

A **ratio** of two quantities is their quotient. For example, 37% is the ratio of 37 to 100, or $\frac{37}{100}$. A **proportion** is an equation stating that two ratios are equal.

> ### Proportion
> An equality of ratios,
> $$\frac{A}{B} = \frac{C}{D},$$
> is called a *proportion*. The numbers within a proportion are said to be *proportional* to each other.

Proportions arise in geometry when we are studying *similar triangles*. If two triangles are **similar**, then their corresponding angles have the same measure and their corresponding sides are proportional. To illustrate, if triangle ABC is similar to triangle RST, then angles A and R have the same measure, angles B and S have the same measure, angles C and T have the same measure, and

$$\frac{a}{r} = \frac{b}{s} = \frac{c}{t}.$$

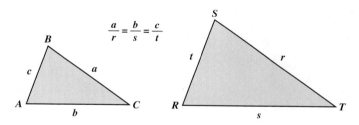

EXAMPLE 5   *Similar triangles.*   Triangles ABC and XYZ are similar. Solve for z if $x = 10$, $a = 8$, and $c = 5$.

SOLUTION   We make a drawing, write a proportion, and then solve. Note that side a is always opposite angle A, side x is always opposite angle X, and so on.

We have

$$\frac{z}{5} = \frac{10}{8} \qquad \text{The proportions } \frac{5}{z} = \frac{8}{10}, \frac{5}{8} = \frac{z}{10}, \text{ or}$$
$$\frac{8}{5} = \frac{10}{z} \text{ could also be used.}$$

$$40 \cdot \frac{z}{5} = 40 \cdot \frac{10}{8} \qquad \text{Multiplying both sides by the LCM, 40}$$

$$8z = 50 \qquad \text{Simplifying}$$

$$z = \frac{50}{8}, \text{ or } 6.25.$$

TRY EXERCISE 33

EXAMPLE 6

Architecture. A *blueprint* is a scale drawing of a building representing an architect's plans. Ellia is adding 12 ft to the length of an apartment and needs to indicate the addition on an existing blueprint. If a 10-ft long bedroom is represented by $2\frac{1}{2}$ in. on the blueprint, how much longer should Ellia make the drawing in order to represent the addition?

SOLUTION We let w represent the width, in inches, of the addition that Ellia is drawing. Because the drawing must be to scale, we have

$$\begin{array}{l}\text{Inches on drawing} \rightarrow \dfrac{w}{12} = \dfrac{2.5}{10}. \leftarrow \text{Inches on drawing} \\ \text{Feet in real life} \rightarrow \phantom{\dfrac{w}{12}} \phantom{\dfrac{2.5}{10}} \leftarrow \text{Feet in real life}\end{array}$$

To solve for w, we multiply both sides by the LCM of the denominators, 60:

$$60 \cdot \frac{w}{12} = 60 \cdot \frac{2.5}{10}$$

$$5w = 6 \cdot 2.5 \qquad \text{Simplifying}$$

$$w = \frac{15}{5}, \text{ or } 3.$$

Ellia should make the blueprint 3 in. longer.

TRY EXERCISE 37

Proportions can be used to solve a variety of applied problems.

EXAMPLE 7

Alternative fuels. As one alternative to gasoline-powered vehicles, flex fuel vehicles can use both regular gasoline and E85, a fuel containing 85% ethanol. The ethanol in E85 is derived from corn and other plants, a renewable resource, and burning E85 results in less pollution than gasoline. Because using E85 results in a lower fuel economy, its price per gallon must be lower than the price of gasoline in order to make it an economical fuel option. A 2007 Chevrolet Tahoe gets 21 mpg on the highway using gasoline and only 15 mpg on the highway using E85. If the price of gasoline is $3.36 a gallon, what must the price of E85 be in order for the fuel cost per mile to be the same?

Source: www.caranddriver.com

Alternative fuels

E85, city

87-octane gasoline, city

E85, highway

87-octane gasoline, highway

2007 Chevrolet Tahoe (miles per gallon)

Source: www.caranddriver.com

SOLUTION

1. **Familiarize.** We let $x =$ the price per gallon of E85, and organize the given information:

   Gasoline miles per gallon: 21,

   E85 miles per gallon: 15,

   Gasoline price per gallon: $3.36,

   E85 price per gallon: x.

   We need to use the given information to find the fuel cost per mile. If we divide the number of dollars per gallon by the number of miles per gallon, we can find the number of dollars per mile:

   $$\frac{\text{dollars}}{\text{gal}} \div \frac{\text{mi}}{\text{gal}} = \frac{\text{dollars}}{\cancel{\text{gal}}} \cdot \frac{\cancel{\text{gal}}}{\text{mi}} = \frac{\text{dollars}}{\text{mi}}.$$

   Thus we form ratios of the form

   $$\frac{\text{dollars per gallon}}{\text{miles per gallon}}.$$

2. **Translate.** We form a proportion in which the ratio of price per gallon and number of miles per gallon is expressed in two ways:

   $$\begin{array}{l} \text{Gasoline price} \rightarrow \\ \text{Gasoline mpg} \rightarrow \end{array} \frac{\$3.36}{21} = \frac{x}{15} \begin{array}{l} \leftarrow \text{E85 price} \\ \leftarrow \text{E85 mpg} \end{array}$$

3. **Carry out.** To solve for x, we multiply both sides of the equation by the LCM, 105:

   $$105 \cdot \frac{3.36}{21} = 105 \cdot \frac{x}{15}$$

   $$5 \cdot \cancel{21} \cdot \frac{3.36}{\cancel{21}} = 7 \cdot \cancel{15} \cdot \frac{x}{\cancel{15}} \qquad \text{Removing factors equal to 1: } 21/21 = 1 \text{ and } 15/15 = 1$$

   $$16.8 = 7x$$

   $$2.4 = x. \qquad \text{Dividing both sides by 7 and simplifying}$$

4. **Check.** If E85 costs $2.40 per gallon, the fuel cost per mile will be $2.40/15 = $0.16 per mile. The fuel cost per mile for gasoline is $3.36/21 = $0.16 per mile. The fuel costs are the same.

5. **State.** The price of E85 must be $2.40 per gallon.

TRY EXERCISE ▶ 45

EXAMPLE **8**

Wildlife population. To determine the number of brook trout in River Denys, Cape Breton, Nova Scotia, a team of volunteers and professionals caught and marked 1190 brook trout. Later, they captured 915 brook trout, of which 24 were marked. Estimate the number of brook trout in River Denys.

Source: www.gov.ns.ca

SOLUTION We let T = the brook trout population in River Denys. If we assume that the percentage of marked trout in the second group of trout captured is the same as the percentage of marked trout in the entire river, we can form a proportion in which this percentage is expressed in two ways:

Trout originally marked $\rightarrow$ $\dfrac{1190}{T}$ $=$ $\dfrac{24}{915}$. $\leftarrow$ Marked trout in second group
Entire population $\rightarrow$ $\phantom{\dfrac{1190}{T}}$ $\leftarrow$ Total trout in second group

To solve for T, we multiply by the LCM, $915T$:

$$915T \cdot \frac{1190}{T} = 915T \cdot \frac{24}{915} \qquad \text{Multiplying both sides by } 915T$$

$$915 \cdot 1190 = 24T \qquad \begin{array}{l}\text{Removing factors equal to 1:}\\ T/T = 1 \text{ and } 915/915 = 1\end{array}$$

$$\frac{915 \cdot 1190}{24} = T \text{ or } T \approx 45{,}369. \qquad \text{Dividing both sides by 24}$$

There are about 45,369 brook trout in the river.

TRY EXERCISE 57

Translating for Success

1. *Search-engine ads.* In 2006, North American advertisers spent $9.4 billion in marketing through Internet search engines such as Google®. This was a 62% increase over the amount spent in 2005. How much was spent in 2005?
Source: Search Engine Marketing Professional Organization

2. *Bicycling.* The speed of one bicyclist is 2 km/h faster than the speed of another bicyclist. The first bicyclist travels 60 km in the same amount of time that it takes the second to travel 50 km. Find the speed of each bicyclist.

3. *Filling time.* A swimming pool can be filled in 5 hr by hose A alone and in 6 hr by hose B alone. How long would it take to fill the tank if both hoses were working?

4. *Payroll.* In 2007, the total payroll for Kraftside Productions was $9.4 million. Of this amount, 62% was paid to employees working on an assembly line. How much money was paid to assembly-line workers?

Translate each word problem to an equation and select a correct translation from equations A–O.

A. $2x + 2(x + 1) = 613$

B. $x^2 + (x + 1)^2 = 613$

C. $\dfrac{60}{x + 2} = \dfrac{50}{x}$

D. $x = 62\% \cdot 9.4$

E. $\dfrac{197}{7} = \dfrac{x}{30}$

F. $x + (x + 1) = 613$

G. $\dfrac{7}{197} = \dfrac{x}{30}$

H. $x^2 + (x + 2)^2 = 612$

I. $x^2 + (x + 1)^2 = 612$

J. $\dfrac{50}{x + 2} = \dfrac{60}{x}$

K. $x + 62\% \cdot x = 9.4$

L. $\dfrac{5 + 6}{2} = t$

M. $x^2 + (x + 1)^2 = 452$

N. $\dfrac{1}{5} + \dfrac{1}{6} = \dfrac{1}{t}$

O. $x^2 + (x + 2)^2 = 452$

Answers on page A-18

An additional, animated version of this activity appears in MyMathLab. To use MyMathLab, you need a course ID and a student access code. Contact your instructor for more information.

5. *Cycling distance.* A bicyclist traveled 197 mi in 7 days. At this rate, how many miles could the cyclist travel in 30 days?

6. *Sides of a square.* If the sides of a square are increased by 2 ft, the area of the original square plus the area of the enlarged square is 452 ft². Find the length of a side of the original square.

7. *Consecutive integers.* The sum of two consecutive integers is 613. Find the integers.

8. *Sums of squares.* The sum of the squares of two consecutive odd integers is 612. Find the integers.

9. *Sums of squares.* The sum of the squares of two consecutive integers is 613. Find the integers.

10. *Rectangle dimensions.* The length of a rectangle is 1 ft longer than its width. Find the dimensions of the rectangle such that the perimeter of the rectangle is 613 ft.

4.7 EXERCISE SET

For Extra Help   PRACTICE WATCH DOWNLOAD

Concept Reinforcement   *Find each rate.*

1. If Sandy can decorate a cake in 2 hr, what is her rate?

2. If Eric can decorate a cake in 3 hr, what is his rate?

3. If Sandy can decorate a cake in 2 hr and Eric can decorate the same cake in 3 hr, what is their rate, working together?

4. If Lisa and Mark can mow a lawn together in 1 hr, what is their rate?

5. If Lisa can mow a lawn by herself in 3 hr, what is her rate?

6. If Lisa and Mark can mow a lawn together in 1 hr, and Lisa can mow the same lawn by herself in 3 hr, what is Mark's rate, working alone?

7. *Home restoration.*   Bryan can refinish the floor of an apartment in 8 hr. Caroline can refinish the floor in 6 hr. How long will it take them, working together, to refinish the floor?

8. *Custom embroidery.*   Chandra can embroider logos on a team's sweatshirts in 6 hr. Traci, a new employee, needs 9 hr to complete the same job. Working together, how long will it take them to do the job?

9. *Multifunction copiers.*   The Aficio SP C210SF can copy Mousa's dissertation in 7 min. The MX-3501N can copy the same document in 6 min. If the two machines work together, how long would they take to copy the dissertation?
   Source: Manufacturers' marketing brochures

10. *Fax machines.*   The FAXPHONE L80 can fax a year-end report in 7 min while the HP 1050 Fax Series can fax the same report in 14 min. How long would it take the two machines, working together, to fax the report? (Assume that the recipient has at least two machines for incoming faxes.)
    Source: Manufacturers' marketing brochures

11. *Pumping water.*   A $\frac{1}{2}$ HP Wayne stainless-steel sump pump can remove water from Carmen's flooded basement in 42 min. The $\frac{1}{2}$ HP Craftsman Professional sump pump can complete the same job in 35 min. How long would it take the two pumps together to pump out the basement?
    Source: Based on data from manufacturers

12. *Hotel management.*   The Honeywell Enviracaire Silent Comfort air cleaner can clean the air in an 11-ft by 17-ft conference room in 10 min. The Blueair 201 Air Purifier can clean the air in a room of the same size in 12 min. How long would it take the two machines together to clean the air in such a room?
    Source: Based on information from manufacturers' and retailers' websites

13. *Photocopiers.*   The HP Officejet H470 Mobile Printer takes twice the time required by the HP Officejet Pro K5400 color printer to photocopy brochures for the New Bretton Arts Council annual arts fair. If, working together, the two machines can complete the job in 45 min, how long would it take each machine, working alone, to copy the brochures?
    Source: www.shoppinghp.com

14. *Forest fires.*   The Erickson Air-Crane helicopter can scoop water and douse a certain forest fire four times as fast as an S-58T helicopter. Working together, the two helicopters can douse the fire in 8 hr. How long would it take each helicopter, working alone, to douse the fire?
    Sources: Based on information from www.emergency.com and www.arishelicopters.com

15. *Hotel management.*   The Austin Healthmate 400 can purify the air in a conference hall in 15 fewer minutes than it takes the Airgle 750 Air Purifier to do the same job. Together the two machines can purify the air in the conference hall in 10 min. How long would it take each machine, working alone, to purify the air in the room?
    Source: Based on information from manufacturers' and retailers' websites

16. *Photo printing.* It takes the Canon PIXMA iP6310D 15 min longer to print a set of photo proofs than it takes the HP Officejet H470b Mobile Printer. Together it would take them $\frac{180}{7}$, or $25\frac{5}{7}$ min to print the photos. How long would it take each machine, working alone, to print the photos?
Sources: www.shoppinghp.com; www.staples.com

17. *Sorting recyclables.* Together, it takes Kim and Chris 2 hr 55 min to sort recyclables. Alone, Kim would require 2 hr more than Chris. How long would it take Chris to do the job alone? (*Hint*: Convert minutes to hours or hours to minutes.)

18. *Paving.* Together, Steve and Bill require 4 hr 48 min to pave a driveway. Alone, Steve would require 4 hr more than Bill. How long would it take Bill to do the job alone? (*Hint*: Convert minutes to hours.)

19. *Train speeds.* A B & M freight train is traveling 14 km/h slower than an AMTRAK passenger train. The B & M train travels 330 km in the same time that it takes the AMTRAK train to travel 400 km. Find their speeds. Complete the following table as part of the familiarization.

Distance = Rate ⋅ Time

	Distance (in km)	Speed (in km/h)	Time (in hours)
B & M	330		
AMTRAK	400	r	$\frac{400}{r}$

20. *Speed of travel.* A loaded Roadway truck is moving 40 mph faster than a New York Railways freight train. In the time that it takes the train to travel 150 mi, the truck travels 350 mi. Find their speeds. Complete the following table as part of the familiarization.

Distance = Rate ⋅ Time

	Distance (in miles)	Speed (in miles per hour)	Time (in hours)
Truck	350	r	$\frac{350}{r}$
Train	150		

21. *Kayaking.* The speed of the current in Catamount Creek is 3 mph. Sean can kayak 4 mi upstream in the same time it takes him to kayak 10 mi downstream. What is the speed of Sean's kayak in still water?

22. *Boating.* The current in the Lazy River moves at a rate of 4 mph. Nicole's dinghy motors 6 mi upstream in the same time it takes to motor 12 mi downstream. What is the speed of the dinghy in still water?

23. *Moving sidewalks.* The moving sidewalk at O'Hare Airport in Chicago moves 1.8 ft/sec. Walking on the moving sidewalk, Roslyn travels 105 ft forward in the time it takes to travel 51 ft in the opposite direction. How fast does Roslyn walk on a nonmoving sidewalk?

24. *Moving sidewalks.* Newark Airport's moving sidewalk moves at a speed of 1.7 ft/sec. Walking on the moving sidewalk, Drew can travel 120 ft forward in the same time it takes to travel 52 ft in the opposite direction. What is Drew's walking speed on a nonmoving sidewalk?

Aha! 25. *Tractor speed.* Manley's tractor is just as fast as Caledonia's. It takes Manley 1 hr more than it takes Caledonia to drive to town. If Manley is 20 mi from town and Caledonia is 15 mi from town, how long does it take Caledonia to drive to town?

26. *Boat speed.* Tory and Emilio's motorboats travel at the same speed. Tory pilots her boat 40 km before docking. Emilio continues for another 2 hr, traveling a total of 100 km before docking. How long did it take Tory to navigate the 40 km?

27. *Boating.* LeBron's Mercruiser travels 15 km/h in still water. He motors 140 km downstream in the same time it takes to travel 35 km upstream. What is the speed of the river?

28. *Boating.* Annette's paddleboat travels 2 km/h in still water. The boat is paddled 4 km downstream in the same time it takes to go 1 km upstream. What is the speed of the river?

29. *Shipping.* A barge moves 7 km/h in still water. It travels 45 km upriver and 45 km downriver in a total time of 14 hr. What is the speed of the current?

30. *Aviation.* A Citation CV jet travels 460 mph in still air and flies 525 mi into the wind and 525 mi with the wind in a total of 2.3 hr. Find the wind speed.
Source: Blue Star Jets, Inc.

31. *Train travel.* A freight train covered 120 mi at a certain speed. Had the train been able to travel 10 mph faster, the trip would have been 2 hr shorter. How fast did the train go?

32. *Moped speed.* Cameron's moped travels 8 km/h faster than Ellia's. Cameron travels 69 km in the same time that Ellia travels 45 km. Find the speed of each person's moped.

Geometry. For each pair of similar triangles, find the value of the indicated letter.

33. b

34. a

35. f

36. r

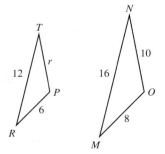

Architecture. Use the blueprint below to find the indicated length.

37. p, in inches on blueprint

38. s, in inches on blueprint

39. r, in feet on actual building

40. n, in feet on actual building

Find the indicated length.

41. l

42. h

Graphing. *Find the indicated length.*

43. *r*

44. *s*

45. *Text messaging.* Brett sent or received 384 text messages in 8 days. At this rate, how many text messages would he send or receive in 30 days?

46. *Burning calories.* The average 140-lb adult burns about 380 calories bicycling 10 mi at a moderate rate. How far should the average 140-lb adult ride in order to burn 100 calories?
Source: *ACE Fitness Matters*, Volume 1, Number 4, 1997

47. *Illegal immigration.* Between 2001 and 2006, the Border Patrol caught 12,334 people trying to cross illegally from Canada to the United States along a 295-mi stretch of the border. If this rate were the same for the entire 5525-mi border between the two countries, how many would the Border Patrol catch in those same years along the entire border?
Source: *The Wall Street Journal*, July 10, 2007

Aha! **48.** *Photography.* Aziza snapped 234 photos over a period of 14 days. At this rate, how many would she take in 42 days?

49. *Mileage.* The Honda Civic Hybrid is a gasoline–electric car that travels approximately 180 mi on 4 gal of gas. Find the amount of gas required for an 810-mi trip.
Source: www.greenhybrid.com

50. *Baking.* In a potato bread recipe, the ratio of milk to flour is $\frac{3}{13}$. If 5 cups of milk are used, how many cups of flour are used?

51. *Wing aspect ratio.* The wing aspect ratio for a bird or an airplane is the ratio of the wing span to the wing width. Generally, higher aspect ratios are more efficient during low speed flying. Herons and storks, both waders, have comparable wing aspect ratios. A grey heron has a wing span of 180 cm and a wing width of 24 cm. A white stork has a wing span of 200 cm. What is the wing width of a stork?
Source: birds.ecoport.org

Aha! **52.** *Money.* The ratio of the weight of copper to the weight of zinc in a U.S. penny is $\frac{1}{39}$. If 50 kg of zinc is being turned into pennies, how much copper is needed?
Source: United States Mint

53. *Light bulbs.* A sample of 220 compact fluorescent light bulbs contained 8 defective bulbs. How many defective bulbs would you expect in a batch of 1430 bulbs?

54. *Flash drives.* A sample of 150 flash drives contained 7 defective drives. How many defective flash drives would you expect in a batch of 2700 flash drives?

55. *Veterinary science.* The amount of water needed by a small dog depends on its weight. A moderately active 8-lb Shih Tzu needs approximately 12 oz of water per day. How much water does a moderately active 5-lb Bolognese require each day?
Source: www.smalldogsparadise.com

56. *Miles driven.* Emmanuel is allowed to drive his leased car for 45,000 mi in 4 yr without penalty. In the first $1\frac{1}{2}$ yr, Emmanuel has driven 16,000 mi. At this rate will he exceed the mileage allowed for 4 yr?

57. *Environmental science.* To determine the number of humpback whales in a pod, a marine biologist, using tail markings, identifies 27 members of the pod. Several weeks later, 40 whales from the pod are randomly sighted. Of the 40 sighted, 12 are from the 27 originally identified. Estimate the number of whales in the pod.

58. *Fox population.* To determine the number of foxes in King County, a naturalist catches, tags, and then releases 25 foxes. Later, 36 foxes are caught; 4 of them have tags. Estimate the fox population of the county.

59. *Weight on the moon.*   The ratio of the weight of an object on the moon to the weight of that object on Earth is 0.16 to 1.

   a) How much would a 12-ton rocket weigh on the moon?

   b) How much would a 180-lb astronaut weigh on the moon?

60. *Weight on Mars.*   The ratio of the weight of an object on Mars to the weight of that object on Earth is 0.4 to 1.

   a) How much would a 12-ton rocket weigh on Mars?

   b) How much would a 120-lb astronaut weigh on Mars?

61. Is it correct to assume that two workers will complete a task twice as quickly as one person working alone? Why or why not?

62. If two triangles are exactly the same shape and size, are they similar? Why or why not?

Skill Review

To prepare for Chapter 5, review graphing linear equations (Section 2.2).

Graph. [2.2]

63. $y = 2x - 6$

64. $y = -2x + 6$

65. $3x + 2y = 12$

66. $x - 3y = 6$

67. $y = -\dfrac{3}{4}x + 2$

68. $y = \dfrac{2}{5}x - 4$

Synthesis

69. Two steamrollers are paving a parking lot. Working together, will the two steamrollers take less than half as long as the slower steamroller would working alone? Why or why not?

70. Two fuel lines are filling a freighter with oil. Will the faster fuel line take more or less than twice as long to fill the freighter by itself? Why?

71. *Filling a bog.*   The Norwich cranberry bog can be filled in 9 hr and drained in 11 hr. How long will it take to fill the bog if the drainage gate is left open?

72. *Filling a tub.*   Jillian's hot tub can be filled in 10 min and drained in 8 min. How long will it take to empty a full tub if the water is left on?

73. *Escalators.*   Together, a 100-cm wide escalator and a 60-cm wide escalator can empty a 1575-person auditorium in 14 min. The wider escalator moves twice as many people as the narrower one. How many people per hour does the 60-cm wide escalator move?
Source: *McGraw-Hill Encyclopedia of Science and Technology*

74. *Aviation.*   A Coast Guard plane has enough fuel to fly for 6 hr, and its speed in still air is 240 mph. The plane departs with a 40-mph tailwind and returns to the same airport flying into the same wind. How far can the plane travel under these conditions?

75. *Boating.*   Shoreline Travel operates a 3-hr paddleboat cruise on the Missouri River. If the speed of the boat in still water is 12 mph, how far upriver can the pilot travel against a 5-mph current before it is time to turn around?

76. *Travel by car.*   Angenita drives to work at 50 mph and arrives 1 min late. She drives to work at 60 mph and arrives 5 min early. How far does Angenita live from work?

77. *Grading.*   Alma can grade a batch of placement exams in 3 hr. Kevin can grade a batch in 4 hr. If they work together to grade a batch of exams, what percentage of the exams will have been graded by Alma?

78. According to the U.S. Census Bureau, Population Division, in July 2007, there was one birth every 7 sec, one death every 13 sec, and one new international migrant every 27 sec. How many seconds does it take for a net gain of one person?

79. *Photocopying.*   The printer in an admissions office can print a 500-page document in 50 min, while the printer in the business office can print the same document in 40 min. If the two printers work together to print the document, with the faster machine starting on page 1 and the slower machine working backwards from page 500, at what page will the two machines meet to complete the job?

80. *Distances.*   The shadow from a 40-ft cliff just reaches across a water-filled quarry at the same time that a 6-ft tall diver casts a 10-ft shadow. How wide is the quarry?

81. Given that
$$\frac{A}{B} = \frac{C}{D},$$
write three other proportions using A, B, C, and D.

Average speed is defined as total distance divided by total time.

82. Ferdaws drove 200 km. For the first 100 km of the trip, she drove at a speed of 40 km/h. For the second half of the trip, she traveled at a speed of 60 km/h. What was the average speed of the entire trip? (It was *not* 50 km/h.)

83. For the first 50 mi of a 100-mi trip, Garry drove 40 mph. What speed would he have to travel for the last half of the trip so that the average speed for the entire trip would be 45 mph?

84. If two triangles are similar, are their areas and perimeters proportional? Why or why not?

85. Are the equations
$$\frac{A + B}{B} = \frac{C + D}{D} \quad \text{and} \quad \frac{A}{B} = \frac{C}{D}$$
equivalent? Why or why not?

COLLABORATIVE CORNER

Sharing the Workload

Focus: Modeling, estimation, and work problems

Time: 15–20 minutes

Group size: 3

Materials: Paper, pencils, textbooks, and a watch

Many tasks can be done by two people working together. If both people work at the same rate, each does half the task, and the project is completed in half the time. However, when the work rates differ, the faster worker performs more than half of the task.

ACTIVITY

1. The project is to write down (but not answer) Review Exercises 27–36 from Chapter 4 (p. 95) on a sheet of paper. The problems should be spaced apart and written clearly so that they can be used for studying in the future. Two of the members in each group should write down the exercises, one working slowly and one working quickly. The third group member should record the time required for each to write down all 10 exercises.

2. Using the times from step (1), calculate how long it will take the two workers, working together, to complete the task.

3. Next, have the same workers as in step (1)— working at the same speeds as in step (1)— perform the task together. To do this, one person should begin writing with Exercise 27, while the other worker begins with Exercise 36 and lists the problems counting backward. The third member is again the timekeeper and should observe when the two workers have written all the exercises. To avoid collision, each of the two writers should use a separate sheet of paper.

4. Compare the actual experimental time from part (3) with the time predicted by the model in part (2). List reasons that might account for any discrepancy.

5. Let t_1, t_2, and t_3 represent the times required for the first worker, the second worker, and the two workers together, respectively, to complete a task. Then develop a model that can be used to find t_3 when t_1 and t_2 are known.

Time Required for Worker A, Working Alone	Time Required for Worker B, Working Alone	Estimated Time for the Two Workers, Working Together	Actual Time Required for the Two Workers, Working Together

Study Summary

KEY TERMS AND CONCEPTS	EXAMPLES

SECTION 4.1: RATIONAL EXPRESSIONS

A **rational expression** can be written as a quotient of two polynomials and is undefined when the denominator is 0. We simplify rational expressions by removing a factor equal to 1.

$$\frac{x^2 - 3x - 4}{x^2 - 1} = \frac{(x + 1)(x - 4)}{(x + 1)(x - 1)}$$

Factoring the numerator and the denominator

$$= \frac{x - 4}{x - 1}$$

$$\frac{x + 1}{x + 1} = 1$$

SECTION 4.2: MULTIPLICATION AND DIVISION

The Product of Two Rational Expressions

$$\frac{A}{B} \cdot \frac{C}{D} = \frac{AC}{BD}$$

$$\frac{5v + 5}{v - 2} \cdot \frac{2v^2 - 8v + 8}{v^2 - 1}$$

$$= \frac{5(v + 1) \cdot 2(v - 2)(v - 2)}{(v - 2)(v + 1)(v - 1)}$$

Multiplying numerators, multiplying denominators, and factoring

$$= \frac{10(v - 2)}{v - 1}$$

$$\frac{(v + 1)(v - 2)}{(v + 1)(v - 2)} = 1$$

The Quotient of Two Rational Expressions

$$\frac{A}{B} \div \frac{C}{D} = \frac{A}{B} \cdot \frac{D}{C} = \frac{AD}{BC}$$

$$(x^2 - 5x - 6) \div \frac{x^2 - 1}{x + 6}$$

$$= \frac{x^2 - 5x - 6}{1} \cdot \frac{x + 6}{x^2 - 1}$$

Multiplying by the reciprocal of the divisor

$$= \frac{(x - 6)(x + 1)(x + 6)}{(x + 1)(x - 1)}$$

Multiplying numerators, multiplying denominators, and factoring

$$= \frac{(x - 6)(x + 6)}{x - 1}$$

$$\frac{x + 1}{x + 1} = 1$$

SECTION 4.3: ADDITION, SUBTRACTION, AND LEAST COMMON DENOMINATORS

The Sum of Two Rational Expressions

$$\frac{A}{B} + \frac{C}{B} = \frac{A + C}{B}$$

$$\frac{7x + 8}{x + 1} + \frac{4x + 3}{x + 1} = \frac{7x + 8 + 4x + 3}{x + 1}$$

Adding numerators and keeping the denominator

$$= \frac{11x + 11}{x + 1}$$

$$= \frac{11(x + 1)}{x + 1}$$

Factoring

$$= 11$$

$$\frac{x + 1}{x + 1} = 1$$

The Difference of Two Rational Expressions

$$\frac{A}{B} - \frac{C}{B} = \frac{A - C}{B}$$

$$\frac{7x + 8}{x + 1} - \frac{4x + 3}{x + 1} = \frac{7x + 8 - (4x + 3)}{x + 1}$$

Subtracting numerators and keeping the denominator. The parentheses are necessary.

$$= \frac{7x + 8 - 4x - 3}{x + 1}$$

Removing parentheses

$$= \frac{3x + 5}{x + 1}$$

The **least common denominator (LCD)** of rational expressions is the **least common multiple (LCM)** of the denominators. To find the LCM, write the prime factorizations of the denominators. The LCM contains each factor the greatest number of times that it occurs in any of the individual factorizations.

Find the LCM of $m^2 - 5m + 6$ and $m^2 - 4m + 4$.

$$\left. \begin{array}{l} m^2 - 5m + 6 = (m - 2)(m - 3) \\ m^2 - 4m + 4 = (m - 2)(m - 2) \end{array} \right\} \quad \text{Factoring each expression}$$

$\mathbf{LCM} = (m - 2)(m - 2)(m - 3)$ The LCM contains 2 factors of $(m - 2)$ and 1 factor of $(m - 3)$.

SECTION 4.4: ADDITION AND SUBTRACTION WITH UNLIKE DENOMINATORS

To add or subtract rational expressions with different denominators, first rewrite the expressions as equivalent expressions with a common denominator.

$$\frac{2x}{x^2 - 16} + \frac{x}{x - 4}$$

$$= \frac{2x}{(x + 4)(x - 4)} + \frac{x}{x - 4} \qquad \text{Factoring denominators:}$$
The LCD is $(x + 4)(x - 4)$.

$$= \frac{2x}{(x + 4)(x - 4)} + \frac{x}{x - 4} \cdot \frac{x + 4}{x + 4} \qquad \text{Multiplying by 1 to get the LCD in the second expression}$$

$$= \frac{2x}{(x + 4)(x - 4)} + \frac{x^2 + 4x}{(x + 4)(x - 4)}$$

$$= \frac{x^2 + 6x}{(x + 4)(x - 4)} \qquad \text{Adding numerators and keeping the denominator. This cannot be simplified.}$$

SECTION 4.5: COMPLEX RATIONAL EXPRESSIONS

Complex rational expressions contain one or more rational expressions within the numerator and/or the denominator. They can be simplified either by using division or by multiplying by a form of 1 to clear the fractions.

Using division to simplify:

$$\frac{\dfrac{1}{6} - \dfrac{1}{x}}{\dfrac{6 - x}{6}} = \frac{\dfrac{1}{6} \cdot \dfrac{x}{x} - \dfrac{1}{x} \cdot \dfrac{6}{6}}{\dfrac{6 - x}{6}} = \frac{\dfrac{x - 6}{6x}}{\dfrac{6 - x}{6}} \qquad \text{Subtracting to get a single rational expression in the numerator}$$

$$= \frac{x - 6}{6x} \div \frac{6 - x}{6} = \frac{x - 6}{6x} \cdot \frac{6}{6 - x} \qquad \text{Dividing the numerator by the denominator}$$

$$= \frac{6(x - 6)}{6x(-1)(x - 6)} = \frac{1}{-x} = -\frac{1}{x} \qquad \text{Factoring and simplifying; } \frac{6(x - 6)}{6(x - 6)} = 1$$

Multiplying by 1:

$$\frac{\dfrac{4}{x}}{\dfrac{3}{x} + \dfrac{2}{x^2}} = \frac{\dfrac{4}{x}}{\dfrac{3}{x} + \dfrac{2}{x^2}} \cdot \frac{x^2}{x^2}$$

$$= \frac{\dfrac{4}{x} \cdot \dfrac{x^2}{1}}{\left(\dfrac{3}{x} + \dfrac{2}{x^2}\right) \cdot \dfrac{x^2}{1}} \qquad \text{The LCD of all the denominators is } x^2 \text{; multiplying by } \frac{x^2}{x^2}$$

$$= \frac{\dfrac{4 \cdot x \cdot x}{x}}{\dfrac{3 \cdot x \cdot x}{x} + \dfrac{2 \cdot x^2}{x^2}} = \frac{4x}{3x + 2} \qquad \text{The fractions are cleared.}$$

SECTION 4.6: SOLVING RATIONAL EQUATIONS

To Solve a Rational Equation

1. List any restrictions.
2. Clear the equation of fractions.
3. Solve the resulting equation.
4. Check the possible solution(s) in the original equation.

Solve: $\dfrac{2}{x+1} = \dfrac{1}{x-2}$. The restrictions are $x \neq -1, x \neq 2$.

$$\frac{2}{x+1} = \frac{1}{x-2}$$

$$(x+1)(x-2) \cdot \frac{2}{x+1} = (x+1)(x-2) \cdot \frac{1}{x-2}$$

$$2(x-2) = x+1$$

$$2x-4 = x+1$$

$$x = 5$$

Check: Since $\dfrac{2}{5+1} = \dfrac{1}{5-2}$, the solution is 5.

SECTION 4.7: APPLICATIONS USING RATIONAL EQUATIONS AND PROPORTIONS

The Work Principle

If $a =$ the time needed for A to complete the work alone,

$b =$ the time needed for B to complete the work alone,

and

$t =$ the time needed for A and B to complete the work together, then:

$$\frac{t}{a} + \frac{t}{b} = 1; \quad \frac{1}{a} \cdot t + \frac{1}{b} \cdot t = 1;$$

$$\frac{1}{a} + \frac{1}{b} = \frac{1}{t}.$$

It takes Manuel 9 hr longer than Zoe to rebuild an engine. Working together, they can do the job in 20 hr. How long would it take each, working alone, to rebuild an engine?

We model the situation using the work principle, with $a = z$, $b = z + 9$, and $t = 20$:

$$\frac{20}{z} + \frac{20}{z+9} = 1 \qquad \text{Using the work principle}$$

$$z = 36. \qquad \text{Solving the equation}$$

It would take Zoe 36 hr to rebuild an engine alone, and Manuel 45 hr.

See Example 2 in Section 4.7 for a complete solution of this problem.

The Motion Formula

$$d = r \cdot t, \quad r = \frac{d}{t}, \quad \text{or} \quad t = \frac{d}{r}$$

On her road bike, Olivia bikes 15 km/h faster than Jason does on his mountain bike. In the time it takes Olivia to travel 80 km, Jason travels 50 km. Find the speed of each bicyclist.

Jason's speed: r km/h   Jason's time: $50/r$ hr
Olivia's speed: $(r+15)$ km/h   Olivia's time: $80/(r+15)$ hr

The times are equal:

$$\frac{50}{r} = \frac{80}{r+15}$$

$$r = 25 \qquad \text{Solving the equation}$$

Olivia's speed is 40 km/h, and Jason's speed is 25 km/h.

See Example 3 in Section 4.7 for a complete solution of this problem.

In geometry, proportions arise in the study of **similar triangles**.

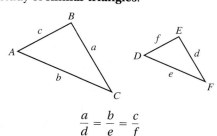

$$\frac{a}{d} = \frac{b}{e} = \frac{c}{f}$$

Triangles DEF and UVW are similar. Solve for u.

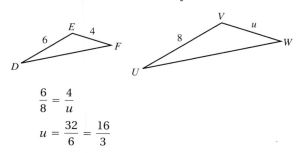

$$\frac{6}{8} = \frac{4}{u}$$

$$u = \frac{32}{6} = \frac{16}{3}$$

Review Exercises: Chapter 4

Concept Reinforcement *Classify each statement as either true or false.*

1. Every rational expression can be simplified. [4.1]

2. The expression $(t - 3)/(t^2 - 4)$ is undefined for $t = 2$. [4.1]

3. The expression $(t - 3)/(t^2 - 4)$ is undefined for $t = 3$. [4.1]

4. To multiply rational expressions, a common denominator is never required. [4.2]

5. To divide rational expressions, a common denominator is never required. [4.2]

6. To add rational expressions, a common denominator is never required. [4.3]

7. To subtract rational expressions, a common denominator is never required. [4.3]

8. The number 0 can never be a solution of a rational equation. [4.6]

List all numbers for which each expression is undefined. [4.1]

9. $\dfrac{17}{-x^2}$

10. $\dfrac{9}{2a + 10}$

11. $\dfrac{x - 5}{x^2 - 36}$

12. $\dfrac{x^2 + 3x + 2}{x^2 + x - 30}$

13. $\dfrac{-6}{(t + 2)^2}$

Simplify. [4.1]

14. $\dfrac{3x^2 - 9x}{3x^2 + 15x}$

15. $\dfrac{14x^2 - x - 3}{2x^2 - 7x + 3}$

16. $\dfrac{6y^2 - 36y + 54}{4y^2 - 36}$

17. $\dfrac{5x^2 - 20y^2}{2y - x}$

Multiply or divide and, if possible, simplify. [4.2]

18. $\dfrac{a^2 - 36}{10a} \cdot \dfrac{2a}{a + 6}$

19. $\dfrac{6y - 12}{2y^2 + 3y - 2} \cdot \dfrac{y^2 - 4}{8y - 8}$

20. $\dfrac{16 - 8t}{3} \div \dfrac{t - 2}{12t}$

21. $\dfrac{4x^4}{x^2 - 1} \div \dfrac{2x^3}{x^2 - 2x + 1}$

22. $\dfrac{x^2 + 1}{x - 2} \cdot \dfrac{2x + 1}{x + 1}$

23. $(t^2 + 3t - 4) \div \dfrac{t^2 - 1}{t + 4}$

Find the LCM. [4.3]

24. $10a^3b^8, 12a^5b$

25. $x^2 - x, x^5 - x^3, x^4$

26. $y^2 - y - 2, y^2 - 4$

Add or subtract and, if possible, simplify.

27. $\dfrac{x + 6}{x + 3} + \dfrac{9 - 4x}{x + 3}$ [4.3]

28. $\dfrac{6x - 3}{x^2 - x - 12} - \dfrac{2x - 15}{x^2 - x - 12}$ [4.3]

29. $\dfrac{3x - 1}{2x} - \dfrac{x - 3}{x}$ [4.4]

30. $\dfrac{2a + 4b}{5ab^2} - \dfrac{5a - 3b}{a^2b}$ [4.4]

31. $\dfrac{y^2}{y - 2} + \dfrac{6y - 8}{2 - y}$ [4.4]

32. $\dfrac{t}{t + 1} + \dfrac{t}{1 - t^2}$ [4.4]

33. $\dfrac{d^2}{d - 2} + \dfrac{4}{2 - d}$ [4.4]

34. $\dfrac{1}{x^2 - 25} - \dfrac{x - 5}{x^2 - 4x - 5}$ [4.4]

35. $\dfrac{3x}{x + 2} - \dfrac{x}{x - 2} + \dfrac{8}{x^2 - 4}$ [4.4]

36. $\dfrac{3}{4t} + \dfrac{3}{3t + 2}$ [4.4]

Simplify. [4.5]

37. $\dfrac{\dfrac{1}{z} + 1}{\dfrac{1}{z^2} - 1}$

38. $\dfrac{\dfrac{5}{2x^2}}{\dfrac{3}{4x} + \dfrac{4}{x^3}}$

39. $\dfrac{\dfrac{c}{d} - \dfrac{d}{c}}{\dfrac{1}{c} + \dfrac{1}{d}}$

Solve. [4.6]

40. $\dfrac{3}{x} - \dfrac{1}{4} = \dfrac{1}{2}$

41. $\dfrac{3}{x + 4} = \dfrac{1}{x - 1}$

42. $x + \dfrac{6}{x} = -7$

Solve. [4.7]

43. Jackson can sand the oak floors and stairs in a two-story home in 12 hr. Charis can do the same job in 9 hr. How long would it take if they worked together? (Assume that two sanders are available.)

44. A research company uses employees' computers to process data while the employee is not using the computer. An Intel Core 2 Quad processor can process a data file in 15 sec less time than an Intel Core 2 Duo processor. Working together, the computers can process the file in 18 sec. How long does it take each computer to process the file?

45. The distance by highway between Richmond and Waterbury is 70 km, and the distance by rail is 60 km. A car and a train leave Richmond at the same time and arrive in Waterbury at the same time, the car having traveled 15 km/h faster than the train. Find the speed of the car and the speed of the train.

46. The Black River's current is 6 mph. A boat travels 50 mi downstream in the same time that it takes to travel 30 mi upstream. What is the speed of the boat in still water?

47. To estimate the harbor seal population in Bristol Bay, scientists radio-tagged 33 seals. Several days later, they collected a sample of 40 seals, and 24 of them were tagged. Estimate the seal population of the bay.

48. Triangles ABC and XYZ are similar. Find the value of x.

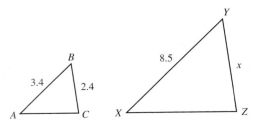

Synthesis

49. For what procedures in this chapter is the LCM of denominators used to clear fractions? [4.5], [4.6]

50. A student always uses the common denominator found by multiplying the denominators of the expressions being added. How could this approach be improved? [4.3]

Simplify.

51. $\dfrac{2a^2 + 5a - 3}{a^2} \cdot \dfrac{5a^3 + 30a^2}{2a^2 + 7a - 4} \div \dfrac{a^2 + 6a}{a^2 + 7a + 12}$ [4.2]

52. $\dfrac{12a}{(a-b)(b-c)} - \dfrac{2a}{(b-a)(c-b)}$ [4.4]

Aha! **53.** $\dfrac{5(x-y)}{(x-y)(x+2y)} - \dfrac{5(x-3y)}{(x+2y)(x-3y)}$ [4.3]

Test: Chapter 4

Step-by-step test solutions are found on the video CD in the front of this book.

List all numbers for which each expression is undefined.

1. $\dfrac{2-x}{5x}$

2. $\dfrac{5}{x+8}$

3. $\dfrac{x-7}{x^2-1}$

4. $\dfrac{x^2 + x - 30}{x^2 - 3x + 2}$

5. Simplify: $\dfrac{6x^2 + 17x + 7}{2x^2 + 7x + 3}$.

Multiply or divide and, if possible, simplify.

6. $\dfrac{t^2 - 9}{12t} \cdot \dfrac{8t^2}{t^2 - 4t + 3}$

7. $\dfrac{25y^2 - 1}{9y^2 - 6y} \div \dfrac{5y^2 + 9y - 2}{3y^2 + y - 2}$

8. $\dfrac{4a^2 + 1}{4a^2 - 1} \div \dfrac{4a^2}{4a^2 + 4a + 1}$

9. $(x^2 + 6x + 9) \cdot \dfrac{(x-3)^2}{x^2 - 9}$

10. Find the LCM:
$$y^2 - 9,\ y^2 + 10y + 21,\ y^2 + 4y - 21.$$

Add or subtract, and, if possible, simplify.

11. $\dfrac{2+x}{x^3} + \dfrac{7-4x}{x^3}$

12. $\dfrac{5-t}{t^2+1} - \dfrac{t-3}{t^2+1}$

13. $\dfrac{2x-4}{x-3} + \dfrac{x-1}{3-x}$

14. $\dfrac{2x-4}{x-3} - \dfrac{x-1}{3-x}$

15. $\dfrac{7}{t-2} + \dfrac{4}{t}$

16. $\dfrac{y}{y^2+6y+9} + \dfrac{1}{y^2+2y-3}$

17. $\dfrac{1}{x-1} + \dfrac{4}{x^2-1} - \dfrac{2}{x^2-2x+1}$

Simplify.

18. $\dfrac{9-\dfrac{1}{y^2}}{3-\dfrac{1}{y}}$

19. $\dfrac{\dfrac{x}{8}-\dfrac{8}{x}}{\dfrac{1}{8}+\dfrac{1}{x}}$

Solve.

20. $\dfrac{1}{t} + \dfrac{1}{3t} = \dfrac{1}{2}$

21. $\dfrac{15}{x} - \dfrac{15}{x-2} = -2$

22. Kopy Kwik has 2 copiers. One can copy a year-end report in 20 min. The other can copy the same document in 30 min. How long would it take both machines, working together, to copy the report?

23. The average 140-lb adult burns about 320 calories walking 4 mi at a moderate speed. How far should the average 140-lb adult walk in order to burn 100 calories?
Source: www.walking.about.com

24. Ryan drives 20 km/h faster than Alicia. In the same time that Alicia drives 225 km, Ryan drives 325 km. Find the speed of each car.

25. Pe'rez and Rema work together to mulch the flower beds around an office complex in $2\frac{6}{7}$ hr. Working alone, it would take Pe'rez 6 hr more than it would take Rema. How long would it take each of them to complete the landscaping working alone?

Synthesis

26. Simplify: $1 - \dfrac{1}{1-\dfrac{1}{1-\dfrac{1}{a}}}$.

27. The square of a number is the opposite of the number's reciprocal. Find the number.

Cumulative Review: Chapters 1–4

1. Use the commutative law of multiplication to write an expression equivalent to $a + bc$.

2. Evaluate $-x^2$ for $x = 5$.

3. Evaluate $(-x)^2$ for $x = 5$.

4. Simplify: $-3[2(x-3) - (x+5)]$.

Solve.

5. $5(x-2) = 40$ [1.2]

6. $49 = x^2$ [3.7]

7. $-18n = 30$ [1.1]

8. $4x - 3 = 9x - 11$ [1.2]

9. $4(y-5) = -2(y-2)$ [1.2]

10. $x^2 + 11x + 10 = 0$ [3.7]

11. $\dfrac{4}{9}t + \dfrac{2}{3} = \dfrac{1}{3}t - \dfrac{2}{9}$ [1.2]

12. $\dfrac{4}{x} + x = 5$ [4.6]

13. $6 - y \ge 2y + 8$ [1.6]

14. $\dfrac{2}{x-3} = \dfrac{5}{3x+1}$ [4.6]

15. $2x^2 + 7x = 4$ [3.7]

16. $4(x+7) < 5(x-3)$ [1.6]

17. $\dfrac{t^2}{t+5} = \dfrac{25}{t+5}$ [4.6]

18. $(2x+7)(x-5) = 0$ [3.7]

19. $\dfrac{2}{x^2-9} + \dfrac{5}{x-3} = \dfrac{3}{x+3}$ [4.6]

Solve each formula. [1.3]

20. $3a - b + 9 = c$, for b

21. $\frac{3}{4}(x+2y) = z$, for y

Graph. [2.2], [2.3], [2.6]

22. $y = \frac{3}{4}x + 5$

23. $x = -3$

24. $4x + 5y = 20$

25. $y = 6$

26. Find the slope of the line containing the points $(1, 5)$ and $(2, 3)$. [2.5]

27. Find the slope and the y-intercept of the line given by $2x - 4y = 1$. [2.6]

28. Write the slope–intercept equation of the line with slope $-\frac{5}{8}$ and y-intercept $(0, -4)$. [2.6]

Simplify.

29. $\dfrac{x^{-5}}{x^{-3}}$

30. $y \cdot y^{-8}$

31. $-(2a^2b^7)^2$

32. Subtract:

$$(-8y^2 - y + 2) - (y^3 - 6y^2 + y - 5).$$

Multiply.

33. $-5(3a - 2b + c)$

34. $(2x^2 - 1)(x^3 + x - 3)$

35. $(6x - 5y)^2$

36. $(3n + 2)(n - 5)$

37. $(2x^3 + 1)(2x^3 - 1)$

Factor.

38. $6x - 2x^2 - 24x^4$ [3.1]

39. $16x^2 - 81$ [3.4]

40. $10t^3 + 10$ [3.5]

41. $8x^2 + 10x + 3$ [3.3]

42. $6x^2 - 28x + 16$ [3.3]

43. $25t^2 + 40t + 16$ [3.4]

44. $x^2y^2 - xy - 20$ [3.2]

45. $x^4 + 2x^3 - 3x - 6$ [3.1]

Simplify.

46. $\dfrac{4t - 20}{t^2 - 16} \cdot \dfrac{t - 4}{t - 5}$ [4.2]

47. $\dfrac{x^2 - 1}{x^2 - x - 2} \div \dfrac{x - 1}{x - 2}$ [4.2]

48. $\dfrac{5ab}{a^2 - b^2} + \dfrac{a + b}{a - b}$ [4.4]

49. $\dfrac{x + 2}{4 - x} - \dfrac{x + 3}{x - 4}$ [4.4]

50. $\dfrac{1 + \dfrac{2}{x}}{1 - \dfrac{4}{x^2}}$ [4.5]

51. $\dfrac{3y + \dfrac{2}{y}}{y - \dfrac{3}{y^2}}$ [4.5]

Divide.

52. $\dfrac{18x^4 - 15x^3 + 6x^2 + 12x + 3}{3x^2}$

53. $(15x^4 - 12x^3 + 6x^2 + 2x + 18) \div (x + 3)$

54. For each order, HanBooks.com charges a shipping fee of $5.50 plus $1.99 per book. The shipping cost for Dae's book order was $35.35. How many books did she order? [1.5]
Source: hanbooks.com

55. In 2006, the attendance at movie theaters was 1448.5 billion. This was 425% more than the number of admissions to theme parks. How many theme park admissions were there in 2006? [1.4]
Source: MPAA, PricewaterhouseCoopers

56. A pair of 1976 two-dollar bills with consecutive serial numbers is being sold in an auction. The sum of the serial numbers is 66,679,015. What are the serial numbers of the bills? [1.5]

57. Nikki is laying out two square flower gardens in a client's lawn. Each side of one garden is 2 ft longer than each side of the smaller garden. Together, the area of the gardens is 340 ft². Find the length of a side of the smaller garden. [3.8]

58. It takes Wes 25 min to file a week's worth of receipts. Corey, a new employee, takes 75 min to do the same job. How long would it take if they worked together? [4.7]

59. A game warden catches, tags, and then releases 18 antelope. A month later, a sample of 30 antelope is caught and released and 6 of them have tags. Use this information to estimate the size of the antelope population in that area. [4.7]

60. Rachel burned 450 calories in a workout. She burned twice as many in her aerobics session as she did doing calisthenics. How many calories did she burn doing calisthenics? [1.5]

Synthesis

61. Solve: $\frac{1}{3}|n| + 8 = 56$. [1.2]

Aha! **62.** Multiply: $[4y^3 - (y^2 - 3)][4y^3 + (y^2 - 3)]$.

63. Solve: $x(x^2 + 3x - 28) - 12(x^2 + 3x - 28) = 0$. [3.7]

64. Solve: $\dfrac{2}{x - 3} \cdot \dfrac{3}{x + 3} - \dfrac{4}{x^2 - 7x + 12} = 0$. [4.6]

Functions and Graphs

MELANIE CHAMBERS
MATH TEACHER/RECIPIENT OF
THE MILKEN FAMILY
FOUNDATION'S NATIONAL
EDUCATOR AWARD
Cedar Hill, Texas

Being proficient in math not only has multiplied my career options but also opens many doors for those students who choose to sharpen their math skills. As a math instructor, I use math to calculate students' performance on assessments, disaggregate data to differentiate instruction to better meet student learning needs, and demonstrate daily how real-world problem solving often entails mathematical analysis.

AN APPLICATION

According to the National Assessment of Educational Progress (NAEP), the percentage of fourth-graders who are proficient in math has grown from 21% in 1996 to 24% in 2000 and 39% in 2007.

Estimate the percentage of fourth-graders who showed proficiency in 2004 and predict the percentage who will demonstrate proficiency in 2011.

Source: nationsreportcard.gov

This problem appears as Example 6 in Section 5.1.

In this chapter we introduce the concept of a *function*. As we will see, many functions are described using linear, polynomial, and rational expressions. Functions can also often be visualized graphically, as well as added, subtracted, multiplied, and divided. Near the end of the chapter, we solve formulas using equation-solving techniques studied earlier, and we use function notation when describing *direct* and *inverse variation*.

5.1 Introduction to Functions

Correspondences and Functions and Equations • Applications • Functions and Graphs • Function Notation

STUDY SKILLS

And Now for Something Completely Different

When a new topic, such as functions, is introduced, there are often new terms and notation to become familiar with. Listing definitions, verbalizing the vocabulary, and practicing the use of notation in exercises will all help you become comfortable with new concepts.

We now develop the idea of a *function*—one of the most important concepts in mathematics.

Correspondences and Functions

When forming ordered pairs to graph equations, we often say that the first coordinate of each ordered pair *corresponds* to the second coordinate. In much the same way, a function is a special kind of correspondence between two sets. For example,

To each person in a class	there corresponds	a date of birth.
To each bar code in a store	there corresponds	a price.
To each real number	there corresponds	the cube of that number.

In each example, the first set is called the **domain**. The second set is called the **range**. For any member of the domain, there is *exactly one* member of the range to which it corresponds. This kind of correspondence is called a **function**.

EXAMPLE 1

STUDENT NOTES

Note that not all correspondences are functions.

Determine whether each correspondence is a function.

a) Domain   Range

b) Domain   Range

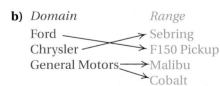

SOLUTION

a) The correspondence *is* a function because each member of the domain corresponds to *exactly one* member of the range.

b) The correspondence *is not* a function because a member of the domain (General Motors) corresponds to more than one member of the range.

TRY EXERCISE ▶ 9

> **Function**
>
> A *function* is a correspondence between a first set, called the *domain*, and a second set, called the *range*, such that each member of the domain corresponds to *exactly one* member of the range.

EXAMPLE 2

Determine whether each correspondence is a function.

Domain	*Correspondence*	*Range*
a) People in a doctor's waiting room	Each person's weight	A set of positive numbers
b) $\{-2, 0, 1, 2\}$	Each number's square	$\{0, 1, 4\}$
c) Authors of best-selling books	The titles of books written by each author	A set of book titles

SOLUTION

a) The correspondence *is* a function, because each person has *only one* weight.

b) The correspondence *is* a function, because every number has *only one* square.

c) The correspondence *is not* a function, because some authors have written *more than one* book.

TRY EXERCISE 17

Although the correspondence in Example 2(c) is not a function, it is a *relation*.

> **Relation**
>
> A *relation* is a correspondence between a first set, called the *domain*, and a second set, called the *range*, such that each member of the domain corresponds to *at least one* member of the range.

Functions and Graphs

The functions in Examples 1(a) and 2(b) can be expressed as sets of ordered pairs. Example 1(a) can be written $\{(-3, 5), (1, 2), (4, 2)\}$ and Example 2(b) can be written $\{(-2, 4), (0, 0), (1, 1), (2, 4)\}$. We can graph these functions as follows.

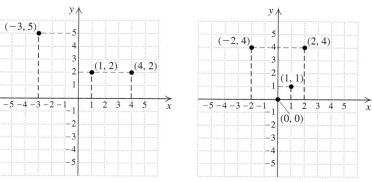

The function $\{(-3, 5), (1, 2), (4, 2)\}$
Domain is $\{-3, 1, 4\}$
Range is $\{5, 2\}$

The function $\{(-2, 4), (0, 0), (1, 1), (2, 4)\}$
Domain is $\{-2, 0, 1, 2\}$
Range is $\{4, 0, 1\}$

We can find the domain and the range of a function directly from its graph. The domain is read from the horizontal axis and the range is read from the vertical axis. Note in the graphs above that if we move along the red dashed lines from the points to the horizontal axis, we find the members, or elements, of the domain. Similarly, if we move along the blue dashed lines from the points to the vertical axis, we find the elements of the range.

Functions are generally named using lowercase or uppercase letters. The function in the following example is named f.

EXAMPLE 3   For the function f represented below, determine each of the following.

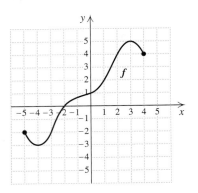

a) The member of the range that is paired with 2

b) The member of the domain that is paired with -3

SOLUTION

a) To determine what member of the range is paired with 2, first note that we are considering 2 in the domain. Thus we locate 2 on the horizontal axis. Next, we find the point directly above 2 on the graph of f. From that point, we can look to the vertical axis to find the corresponding y-coordinate, 4. Thus, 4 is the member of the range that is paired with 2.

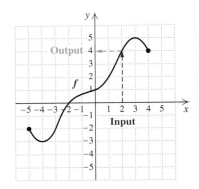

b) To determine what member of the domain is paired with -3, we note that we are considering -3 in the range. Thus we locate -3 on the vertical axis. From there we look at the graph of f to find any points for which -3 is the second coordinate. One such point exists, $(-4, -3)$. We observe that -4 is the only element of the domain paired with -3.

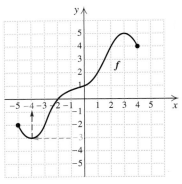

A closed dot on a graph, such as in Example 3, indicates that the point is part of the function. An open dot indicates that the point is *not* part of the function. (See Exercises 33 and 34 on p. 452.)

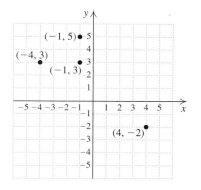

Recall that a function is a correspondence in which each member of the domain corresponds to *exactly* one member of the range. Thus the correspondence

$$\{(-1, 3), (4, -2), (-4, 3), (-1, 5)\}$$

is not a function because the member -1 of the domain corresponds to the members 3 and 5 of the range. Note on the graph at left that the point $(-1, 5)$ is directly above the point $(-1, 3)$.

Any time two points, such as $(-1, 3)$ and $(-1, 5)$, lie on the same vertical line, the graph containing those points cannot represent a function. This observation is the basis of the *vertical-line test*.

> ## The Vertical-Line Test
> If it is possible for a vertical line to cross a graph more than once, then the graph is not the graph of a function.

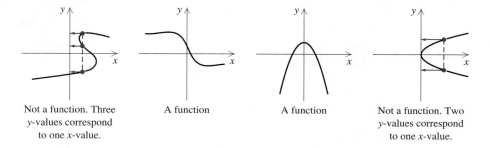

Not a function. Three *y*-values correspond to one *x*-value.

A function

A function

Not a function. Two *y*-values correspond to one *x*-value.

Function Notation and Equations

To understand function notation, it helps to imagine a "function machine." Think of putting a member of the domain (an *input*) into the machine. The machine is programmed to produce the appropriate member of the range (the *output*).

The function pictured has been named f. Here x represents an input, and $f(x)$ represents the corresponding output. In function notation, "$f(x)$" is read "f of x," or "f at x," or "the value of f at x." In Example 3(a), we showed that $f(2) = 4$, read "f of 2 equals 4."

> **CAUTION!** $f(x)$ *does not* mean f *times* x.

Most functions are described by equations. For example, $f(x) = 2x + 3$ describes the function that takes an input x, multiplies it by 2, and then adds 3.

$$f(x) \;=\; \underset{\text{Double}}{2x} \;\; \underset{\text{Add 3}}{+ 3}$$
Input

To calculate the output $f(4)$, we take the input 4, double it, and add 3 to get 11. That is, we substitute 4 into the formula for $f(x)$:

$$f(4) = 2 \cdot 4 + 3$$
$$= 11.$$

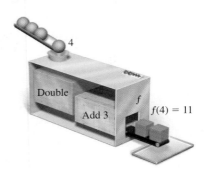

Sometimes, in place of $f(x) = 2x + 3$, we write $y = 2x + 3$, where it is understood that the value of y, the *dependent variable*, depends on our choice of x, the *independent variable*. To understand why $f(x)$ notation is so useful, consider two equivalent statements:

a) If $f(x) = 2x + 3$, then $f(4) = 11$.

b) If $y = 2x + 3$, then the value of y is 11 when x is 4.

The notation used in part (a) is far more concise and emphasizes that x is the independent variable.

EXAMPLE **4** Find each indicated function value.

a) $f(5)$, for $f(x) = 3x + 2$ **b)** $g(-2)$, for $g(r) = 5r^2 + 3r$

c) $h(4)$, for $h(x) = 11$ **d)** $F(a) + 1$, for $F(x) = 2x - 7$

e) $F(a + 1)$, for $F(x) = 2x - 7$

SOLUTION Finding function values is much like evaluating an algebraic expression.

a) $f(5) = 3(5) + 2 = 17$

b) $g(-2) = 5(-2)^2 + 3(-2)$
$$= 5 \cdot 4 - 6 = 14$$

c) For the function given by $h(x) = 11$, all inputs share the same output, 11. Therefore, $h(4) = 11$. The function h is an example of a *constant function*.

d) $F(a) + 1 = 2(a) - 7 + 1$ The input is a; $F(a) = 2a - 7$
$$= 2a - 6$$

e) $F(a + 1) = 2(a + 1) - 7$ The input is $a + 1$.
$$= 2a + 2 - 7 = 2a - 5$$

TRY EXERCISE 41

STUDENT NOTES

In Example 4(e), it is important to note that the parentheses on the left are for function notation, whereas those on the right indicate multiplication.

Note that whether we write $f(x) = 3x + 2$, or $f(t) = 3t + 2$, or $f(\square) = 3\square + 2$, we still have $f(5) = 17$. The variable in the parentheses (the independent variable) is the variable used in the algebraic expression. The letter chosen for the independent variable is not as important as the algebraic manipulations to which it is subjected.

Applications

Function notation is often used in formulas. For example, to emphasize that the area A of a circle is a function of its radius r, instead of

$$A = \pi r^2,$$

we can write

$$A(r) = \pi r^2.$$

EXAMPLE 5

A typical adult dosage of an antihistamine is 24 mg. Young's rule for determining the dosage size $c(a)$ for a typical child of age a is

$$c(a) = \frac{24a}{a + 12}.^*$$

What should the dosage be for a typical 8-yr-old child?

SOLUTION   We find $c(8)$:

$$c(8) = \frac{24(8)}{8 + 12} = \frac{192}{20} = 9.6.$$

The dosage for a typical 8-yr-old child is 9.6 mg.

TRY EXERCISE 47

When a function is given as a graph, we can use the graph to estimate an unknown function value using known values.

EXAMPLE 6

Elementary school math proficiency.   According to the National Assessment of Educational Progress (NAEP), the percentage of fourth-graders who are proficient in math has grown from 21% in 1996 to 24% in 2000 and 39% in 2007. Estimate the percentage of fourth-graders who showed proficiency in 2004 and predict the percentage who will demonstrate proficiency in 2011.

Source: nationsreportcard.gov

SOLUTION

1., 2. Familiarize., Translate.   The given information enables us to plot and connect three points. We let the horizontal axis represent the year and the vertical axis the percentage of fourth-graders demonstrating mathematical proficiency. We label the function itself P.

---

*Source: Olsen, June Looby, Leon J. Ablon, and Anthony Patrick Giangrasso, *Medical Dosage Calculations*, 6th ed.

3. Carry out. To estimate the percentage of fourth-graders showing mathematical proficiency in 2004, we locate the point directly above the year 2004. We then estimate its second coordinate by moving horizontally from that point to the y-axis. Although our result is not exact, we see that $P(2004) \approx 33$.

To predict the percentage of fourth-graders showing proficiency in 2011, we extend the graph and extrapolate. It appears that $P(2011) \approx 48$.

4. Check. A precise check requires consulting an outside information source. Since 33% is between 24% and 39% and 48% is greater than 39%, our estimates seem plausible.

5. State. In 2004, about 33% of all fourth-graders showed proficiency in math. By 2011, that figure is predicted to grow to 48%.

TRY EXERCISE 59

5.1 EXERCISE SET

For Extra Help MyMathLab | MathXL PRACTICE | WATCH | DOWNLOAD

↪ **Concept Reinforcement** *Complete each of the following sentences.*

1. A function is a special kind of _____ between two sets.

2. In any function, each member of the domain is paired with _____ one member of the range.

3. For any function, the set of all inputs, or first values, is called the _____.

4. For any function, the set of all outputs, or second values, is called the _____.

5. When a function is graphed, members of the domain are located on the _____ axis.

6. When a function is graphed, members of the range are located on the _____ axis.

7. The notation $f(3)$ is read _____.

8. The _____-line test can be used to determine whether or not a graph represents a function.

Determine whether each correspondence is a function.

9.

10.

11. *Girl's age*   *Average daily*
    (in months)   *weight gain (in grams)*

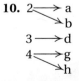

Source: *American Family Physician*, December 1993, p. 1435

12.

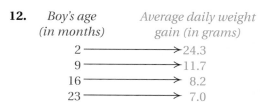

Boy's age (in months) | Average daily weight gain (in grams)
2 → 24.3
9 → 11.7
16 → 8.2
23 → 7.0

Source: *American Family Physician*, December 1993, p. 1435

13.

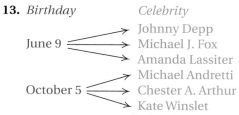

Birthday | Celebrity
June 9 → Johnny Depp, Michael J. Fox, Amanda Lassiter
October 5 → Michael Andretti, Chester A. Arthur, Kate Winslet

Source: www.leannesbirthdays.com

14.

Celebrity | Birthday
Tom Brady, P. D. James, Martha Stewart → August 3
Kim Basinger, Sinéad O'Connor, James Galway → December 8

Source: www.leannesbirthdays.com

15.

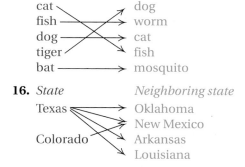

Predator | Prey
cat → fish
fish → worm
dog → cat
tiger → dog
bat → mosquito

16.

State | Neighboring state
Texas → Oklahoma, New Mexico, Arkansas, Louisiana
Colorado → Oklahoma, New Mexico, Arkansas, Louisiana

Determine whether each of the following is a function. Identify any relations that are not functions.

Domain	Correspondence	Range
17. A pile of USB flash drives	The storage capacity of each flash drive	A set of storage capacities
18. The members of a rock band	An instrument the person can play	A set of instruments
19. The players on a team	The uniform number of each player	A set of numbers
20. A set of triangles	The area of each triangle	A set of numbers

*For each graph of a function, determine **(a)** $f(1)$ and **(b)** any x-values for which $f(x) = 2$.*

21.

22.

23.

24.

25.

26.

27.

28.

29.

30.

31.

32.

33.

34.

Determine whether each of the following is the graph of a function.

35.

36.

37.

38.

39.

40.

Find the function values.

41. $g(x) = 2x + 5$

   a) $g(0)$ **b)** $g(-4)$ **c)** $g(-7)$
   d) $g(8)$ **e)** $g(a + 2)$ **f)** $g(a) + 2$

42. $h(x) = 5x - 1$

   a) $h(4)$ **b)** $h(8)$ **c)** $h(-3)$
   d) $h(-4)$ **e)** $h(a - 1)$ **f)** $h(a) + 3$

43. $f(n) = 5n^2 + 4n$

   a) $f(0)$ **b)** $f(-1)$ **c)** $f(3)$
   d) $f(t)$ **e)** $f(2a)$ **f)** $f(3) - 9$

44. $g(n) = 3n^2 - 2n$

   a) $g(0)$ **b)** $g(-1)$ **c)** $g(3)$
   d) $g(t)$ **e)** $g(2a)$ **f)** $g(3) - 4$

45. $f(x) = \dfrac{x - 3}{2x - 5}$

   a) $f(0)$ **b)** $f(4)$ **c)** $f(-1)$
   d) $f(3)$ **e)** $f(x + 2)$ **f)** $f(a + h)$

46. $r(x) = \dfrac{3x - 4}{2x + 5}$

   a) $r(0)$ **b)** $r(2)$ **c)** $r\left(\frac{4}{3}\right)$
   d) $r(-1)$ **e)** $r(x + 3)$ **f)** $r(a + h)$

The function A described by $A(s) = s^2 \dfrac{\sqrt{3}}{4}$ *gives the area of an equilateral triangle with side s.*

47. Find the area when a side measures 4 cm.

48. Find the area when a side measures 6 in.

The function V described by $V(r) = 4\pi r^2$ *gives the surface area of a sphere with radius r.*

49. Find the surface area when the radius is 3 in.

50. Find the surface area when the radius is 5 cm.

Archaeology. *The function H described by*
$$H(x) = 2.75x + 71.48$$
can be used to predict the height, in centimeters, of a woman whose humerus (the bone from the elbow to the shoulder) is x cm long. Predict the height of a woman whose humerus is the length given.

51. 34 cm   **52.** 31 cm

Chemistry. *The function F described by*

$$F(C) = \frac{9}{5}C + 32$$

gives the Fahrenheit temperature corresponding to the Celsius temperature C.

53. Find the Fahrenheit temperature equivalent to $-5°$ Celsius.

54. Find the Fahrenheit temperature equivalent to $10°$ Celsius.

Heart attacks and cholesterol. *For Exercises 55 and 56, use the following graph, which shows the annual heart attack rate per 10,000 men as a function of blood cholesterol level.**

Blood cholesterol (in milligrams per deciliter)

55. Approximate the annual heart attack rate for those men whose blood cholesterol level is 225 mg/dl. That is, find $H(225)$.

56. Approximate the annual heart attack rate for those men whose blood cholesterol level is 275 mg/dl. That is, find $H(275)$.

Films. *For Exercises 57 and 58, use the following graph, which shows the number of movies released in the United States.*

Source: Nash Information Services

Movies Released in the United States

Year

*Copyright 1989, CSPI. Adapted from *Nutrition Action Health-letter* (1875 Connecticut Avenue, N.W., Suite 300, Washington, DC 20009-5728. $24 for 10 issues).

57. Approximate the number of movies released in 2000. That is, find $F(2000)$.

58. Approximate the number of movies released in 2007. That is, find $F(2007)$.

Energy-saving lightbulbs. *An energy bill signed into law in 2007 requires the United States to phase out standard incandescent lightbulbs. A more efficient replacement is the compact fluorescent (CFL) bulb. The table below lists incandescent wattage and the CFL wattage required to create the same amount of light.*

Source: U.S. Department of Energy

Input, Incandescent wattage	Output, Wattage of CFL equivalent
25	5
60	15
100	25

59. Use the data in the figure above to draw a graph. Estimate the wattage of a CFL bulb that creates light equivalent to a 75-watt incandescent bulb. Then predict the wattage of a CFL bulb that creates light equivalent to a 120-watt incandescent bulb.

60. Use the graph from Exercise 59 to estimate the wattage of a CFL bulb that creates light equivalent to a 40-watt incandescent bulb. Then predict the wattage of a CFL bulb that creates light equivalent to a 150-watt incandescent bulb.

Blood alcohol level. *The following table can be used to predict the number of drinks required for a person of a specified weight to be considered legally intoxicated (blood alcohol level of 0.08 or above). One 12-oz glass of beer, a 5-oz glass of wine, or a cocktail containing 1 oz of a distilled liquor all count as one drink. Assume that all drinks are consumed within one hour.*

12 oz = 5 oz = 1 oz

Input, Body Weight (in pounds)	Output, Number of Drinks
100	2.5
160	4
180	4.5
200	5

61. Use the data in the table above to draw a graph and to estimate the number of drinks that a 140-lb person would have to drink to be considered intoxicated. Then predict the number of drinks it would take for a 230-lb person to be considered intoxicated.

62. Use the graph from Exercise 61 to estimate the number of drinks that a 120-lb person would have to drink to be considered intoxicated. Then predict the number of drinks it would take for a 250-lb person to be considered intoxicated.

63. *Retailing.* Mountain View Gifts is experiencing constant growth. They recorded a total of $250,000 in sales in 2003 and $285,000 in 2008. Use a graph that displays the store's total sales as a function of time to estimate sales for 2004 and for 2011.

64. Use the graph in Exercise 63 to estimate sales for 2006 and for 2012.

Researchers at Yale University have suggested that the following graphs* may represent three different aspects of love.

Passion Intimacy Commitment

65. In what unit would you measure time if the horizontal length of each graph were ten units? Why?

66. Do you agree with the researchers that these graphs should be shaped as they are? Why or why not?

*From "A Triangular Theory of Love," by R. J. Sternberg, 1986, *Psychological Review*, **93**(2), 119–135. Copyright 1986 by the American Psychological Association, Inc. Reprinted by permission.

Skill Review

Review solving equations (Sections 1.2, 3.7, and 4.6).

Solve.

67. $2(x - 5) - 3 = 4 - (x - 1)$ [1.2]

68. $x^2 = 36$ [3.7]

69. $\frac{1}{x} = -2$ [4.6]

70. $\frac{1}{x} = x$ [4.6]

71. $(x - 2)(x + 3) = 6$ [3.7]

72. $\frac{1}{3}x + 2 = \frac{5}{4} + 3x$ [1.2]

73. $\frac{x + 1}{x} = 8$ [4.6]

74. $(x - 2)^2 = 36$ [3.7]

Synthesis

75. Jaylan is asked to write a function relating the number of fish in an aquarium to the amount of food needed for the fish. Which quantity should he choose as the independent variable? Why?

76. Explain in your own words why every function is a relation, but not every relation is a function.

For Exercises 77 and 78, let $f(x) = 3x^2 - 1$ and $g(x) = 2x + 5$.

77. Find $f(g(-4))$ and $g(f(-4))$.

78. Find $f(g(-1))$ and $g(f(-1))$.

79. If f represents the function in Exercise 15, find $f(f(f(f(\text{tiger}))))$.

Pregnancy. *For Exercises 80–83, use the following graph of a woman's "stress test." This graph shows the size of a pregnant woman's contractions as a function of time.*

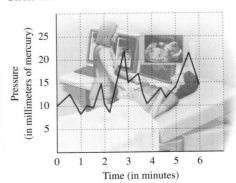

Stress test

80. How large is the largest contraction that occurred during the test?

81. At what time during the test did the largest contraction occur?

82. On the basis of the information provided, how large a contraction would you expect 60 seconds after the end of the test? Why?

83. What is the frequency of the largest contraction?

84. Suppose that a function g is such that $g(-1) = -7$ and $g(3) = 8$. Find a formula for g if $g(x)$ is of the form $g(x) = mx + b$, where m and b are constants.

85. The *greatest integer function* $f(x) = [x]$ is defined as follows: $[x]$ is the greatest integer that is less than or equal to x. For example, if $x = 3.74$, then $[x] = 3$; and if $x = -0.98$, then $[x] = -1$. Graph the greatest integer function for $-5 \le x \le 5$. (The notation $f(x) = \text{INT}(x)$ is used in many graphing calculators and computer programs.)

86. *Energy expenditure.*   On the basis of the information given below, what burns more energy: walking $4\frac{1}{2}$ mph for two hours or bicycling 14 mph for one hour?

Approximate Energy Expenditure by a 150-Pound Person in Various Activities

Activity	Calories per Hour
Walking, $2\frac{1}{2}$ mph	210
Bicycling, $5\frac{1}{2}$ mph	210
Walking, $3\frac{3}{4}$ mph	300
Bicycling, 13 mph	660

Source: Based on material prepared by Robert E. Johnson, M.D., Ph.D., and colleagues, University of Illinois.

5.2   Domain and Range

Determining the Domain and the Range   •   Restrictions on Domain   •   Functions Defined Piecewise

In Section 5.1, we saw that a function is a correspondence from a set called the *domain* to a set called the *range*. In this section, we look more closely at the concepts of domain and range.

Determining the Domain and the Range

When a function is given as a set of ordered pairs, the domain is the set of all first coordinates and the range is the set of all second coordinates.

EXAMPLE 1   Find the domain and the range for the function f given by

$$f = \{(2, 0), (-1, 5), (8, 0), (-3, 2)\}.$$

SOLUTION   The first coordinates are $2, -1, 8$, and -3. The second coordinates are $0, 5$, and 2. Thus we have

Domain of $f = \{2, -1, 8, -3\}$ and
Range of $f = \{0, 5, 2\}$.

▶ TRY EXERCISE   7

We can also determine the domain and the range of a function from its graph.

EXAMPLE 2 Find the domain and the range of the function f below.

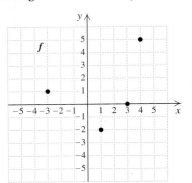

SOLUTION   Here f can be written $\{(-3, 1), (1, -2), (3, 0), (4, 5)\}$. The domain is the set of all first coordinates, $\{-3, 1, 3, 4\}$, and the range is the set of all second coordinates, $\{1, -2, 0, 5\}$.

TRY EXERCISE 11

In Example 2, we could also have found the domain and the range directly, without first writing f, by observing the x- and y-values used in the graph.

EXAMPLE 3 Find the domain and the range of the function f shown here.

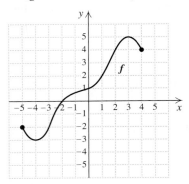

SOLUTION   The domain of the function is the set of all x-values that are used in the points on the curve. Because there are no breaks in the graph of f, these extend continuously from -5 to 4 and can be viewed as the curve's shadow, or *projection*, on the x-axis. Thus the domain is $\{x \mid -5 \leq x \leq 4\}$, or $[-5, 4]$, shown below left.

The range of the function is the set of all y-values that are used in the points on the curve. These extend continuously from -3 to 5, and can be viewed as the curve's projection on the y-axis. Thus the range is $\{y \mid -3 \leq y \leq 5\}$, or $[-3, 5]$, shown below right.

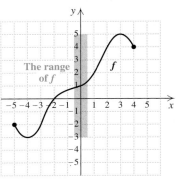

TRY EXERCISE 15

In Example 3, the *endpoints* $(-5, -2)$ and $(4, 4)$ emphasize that the function is not defined for values of x less than -5 or greater than 4.

The graphs of some functions have no endpoints. Thus a function may have a domain and/or a range that extends without bound toward positive infinity or negative infinity.

EXAMPLE 4

For the function g represented below, determine **(a)** the domain of g and **(b)** the range of g.

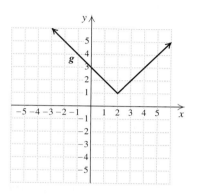

SOLUTION

a) The domain of g is the set of all x-values that are used in the points on the curve. The arrows on the ends of the graph indicate that it extends both left and right without end. Thus the shadow, or projection, of the graph on the x-axis is the entire x-axis. (See the graph on the left below.) The domain is $\{x \mid x \text{ is a real number}\}$, or $(-\infty, \infty)$.

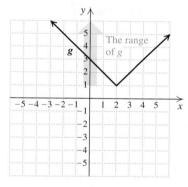

b) The range of g is the set of all y-values that are used in the points on the curve. The arrows on the ends of the graph indicate that it extends up without end. Thus the projection of the graph on the y-axis is the portion of the y-axis greater than or equal to 1. (See the graph on the right above.) The range is $\{y \mid y \geq 1\}$, or $[1, \infty)$.

TRY EXERCISE 25

The set of all real numbers is often abbreviated R. Thus, in Example 4, we could write

Domain of g = R.

EXAMPLE 5

Find the domain and the range of the function f shown here.

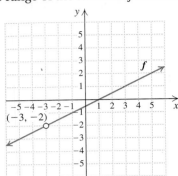

SOLUTION The domain of f is the set of all x-values that are used in points on the curve. The open dot in the graph at $(-3, -2)$ indicates that there is no y-value that corresponds to $x = -3$; that is, the function is not defined for $x = -3$. Thus, -3 is not in the domain of the function, and

Domain of $f = \{x \mid x \text{ is a real number } and \ x \neq -3\}$.

There is no function value at $(-3, -2)$, so -2 is not in the range of the function. Thus we have

Range of $f = \{y \mid y \text{ is a real number } and \ y \neq -2\}$. **TRY EXERCISE** 27

When a function is described by an equation, we assume that the domain is the set of all real numbers for which function values can be calculated. If an x-value is not in the domain of a function, the graph of the function will not include any point above or below that x-value.

EXAMPLE 6

For each equation, determine the domain of f.

a) $f(x) = |x|$
b) $f(x) = \dfrac{7}{2x - 6}$
c) $f(t) = \dfrac{t + 1}{t^2 - 4}$

SOLUTION

a) We ask ourselves, "Is there any number x for which we cannot compute $|x|$?" Since we can find the absolute value of *any* number, the answer is no. Thus the domain of f is $\mathbb{R}$, the set of all real numbers.

b) Is there any number x for which $\dfrac{7}{2x - 6}$ cannot be computed? Since $\dfrac{7}{2x - 6}$ cannot be computed when $2x - 6$ is 0, the answer is yes. To determine what x-value causes the denominator to be 0, we solve an equation:

$2x - 6 = 0$ Setting the denominator equal to 0

$2x = 6$ Adding 6 to both sides

$x = 3.$ Dividing both sides by 2

Thus, 3 is *not* in the domain of f, whereas all other real numbers are. The domain of f is $\{x \mid x \text{ is a real number } and \ x \neq 3\}$.

c) The expression $\dfrac{t + 1}{t^2 - 4}$ is undefined when $t^2 - 4 = 0$:

$t^2 - 4 = 0$ Setting the denominator equal to 0

$(t + 2)(t - 2) = 0$ Factoring

$t + 2 = 0$ *or* $t - 2 = 0$ Using the principle of zero products

$t = -2$ *or* $t = 2.$ Solving; these are the values for which $(t + 1)/(t^2 - 4)$ is undefined.

TECHNOLOGY CONNECTION

To visualize Example 6(a), note that the graph of $y_1 = |x|$ (which is entered $y_1 = \text{abs}(x)$, using the NUM option of the MATH menu) appears without interruption for any piece of the x-axis that we examine.

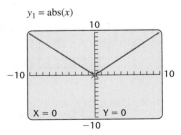

$y_1 = \text{abs}(x)$

In contrast, the graph of $y_2 = \dfrac{7}{2x - 6}$ in Example 6(b) has a break at $x = 3$.

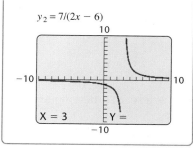

$y_2 = 7/(2x - 6)$

Thus we have

Domain of f = $\{t | t$ is a real number and $t \neq -2$ and $t \neq 2\}$.

Note that when the numerator, $t + 1$, is zero, the function value is 0 and *is* defined.

TRY EXERCISE 31

Restrictions on Domain

If a function is used as a model for an application, the problem situation may require restrictions on the domain; for example, length and time are generally nonnegative, and a person's age does not increase indefinitely.

EXAMPLE 7

Prize tee shirts. During intermission at sporting events, it has become common for team mascots to use a powerful slingshot to launch tightly rolled tee shirts into the stands. The height $h(t)$, in feet, of an airborne tee shirt t seconds after being launched can be approximated by

$$h(t) = -15t^2 + 70t + 25.$$

What is the domain of the function?

SOLUTION   The expression $-15t^2 + 70t + 25$ can be evaluated for any number t, so any restrictions on the domain will come from the problem situation.

First, we note that t cannot be negative, since it represents time from launch, so we have $t \geq 0$. If we make a drawing, we also note that the function will not be defined for values of t that make the height negative.

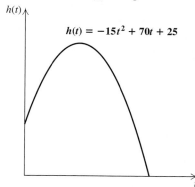

$h(t) = -15t^2 + 70t + 25$

Thus an upper limit for t will be the positive value of t for which $h(t) = 0$. Solving, we obtain

$$h(t) = 0$$
$$-15t^2 + 70t + 25 = 0 \qquad \text{Substituting}$$
$$\left.\begin{array}{l} -5(3t^2 - 14t - 5) = 0 \\ -5(3t + 1)(t - 5) = 0 \end{array}\right\} \qquad \text{Factoring}$$
$$3t + 1 = 0 \quad or \quad t - 5 = 0 \qquad \text{Using the principle of zero products}$$
$$\left.\begin{array}{l} 3t = -1 \quad or \quad t = 5 \\ t = -\dfrac{1}{3} \quad or \quad t = 5. \end{array}\right\} \qquad \text{Solving for } t$$

We already know that $-\frac{1}{3}$ is not in the domain of the function because of the restriction $t \geq 0$ above.

The tee shirt will hit the ground after 5 sec, so we have $t \leq 5$. Putting the two restrictions together, we have $t \geq 0$ and $t \leq 5$, so the

Domain of h = $\{t | t$ is a real number and $0 \leq t \leq 5\}$, or $[0, 5]$.

TRY EXERCISE 45

If the domain of a function is not specifically listed, it can be determined from a table, a graph, an equation, or an application.

Domain of a Function

The domain of a function $f(x)$ is the set of all inputs x.

- If the correspondence is listed in a table or as a set of ordered pairs, the domain is the set of all first coordinates.
- If the function is described by a graph, the domain is the set of all x-coordinates of the points on the graph.
- If the function is described by an equation, the domain is the set of all numbers for which the value can be calculated.
- If the function is used in an application, the domain is the set of all numbers that make sense in the problem.

Functions Defined Piecewise

Piecewise-defined functions are described by different equations for various parts of their domains. For example, the function $f(x) = |x|$ is described by

$$f(x) = \begin{cases} x, & \text{if } x \geq 0, \\ -x, & \text{if } x < 0. \end{cases}$$

To evaluate a piecewise-defined function for an input a, we first determine what part of the domain a belongs to. Then we use the formula corresponding to that part of the domain.

EXAMPLE 8   Find each function value for the function f given by

$$f(x) = |x| = \begin{cases} x, & \text{if } x \geq 0, \\ -x, & \text{if } x < 0. \end{cases}$$

a) $f(4)$ **b)** $f(-10)$

SOLUTION

a) Since $4 \geq 0$, we use the equation $f(x) = x$. Thus, $f(4) = 4$.

b) Since $-10 < 0$, we use the equation $f(x) = -x$. Thus, $f(-10) = -(-10) = 10$.

TRY EXERCISE 53

EXAMPLE 9   Find each function value for the function g given by

$$g(x) = \begin{cases} x + 2, & \text{if } x \leq -2, \\ x^2, & \text{if } -2 < x \leq 5, \\ 3x, & \text{if } x > 5. \end{cases}$$

a) $g(-2)$ **b)** $g(3)$ **c)** $g(10)$

SOLUTION

a) Since $-2 \leq -2$, we use the first equation, $g(x) = x + 2$:

$$g(-2) = -2 + 2 = 0.$$

b) Since $-2 < 3 \leq 5$, we use the second equation, $g(x) = x^2$:

$$g(3) = 3^2 = 9.$$

c) Since $10 > 5$, we use the last equation, $g(x) = 3x$:

$$g(10) = 3 \cdot 10 = 30.$$

TRY EXERCISE 55

5.2 EXERCISE SET

For Extra Help
MyMathLab
Math XL PRACTICE
WATCH
DOWNLOAD

Concept Reinforcement *For Exercises 1–6, use the function f given by*

$$f(x) = \begin{cases} x - 5, & \text{if } x < -6, \\ 2x^2, & \text{if } -6 \le x < -1, \\ |x|, & \text{if } -1 \le x < 10, \\ 3x + 1, & \text{if } x \ge 10. \end{cases}$$

Write the letter of the equation that should be used to find each function value. Letters may be used more than once or not at all.

1. _____ $f(0)$ **a)** $f(x) = x - 5$

2. _____ $f(15)$ **b)** $f(x) = 2x^2$

3. _____ $f(10)$ **c)** $f(x) = |x|$

4. _____ $f(-6)$ **d)** $f(x) = 3x + 1$

5. _____ $f(-1)$

6. _____ $f(-3)$

Find the domain and the range for each function given.

7. $f = \{(2, 8), (9, 3), (-2, 10), (-4, 4)\}$

8. $g = \{(1, 2), (2, 3), (3, 4), (4, 5)\}$

9. $g = \{(0, 0), (4, -2), (-5, 0), (-1, -2)\}$

10. $f = \{(3, 7), (2, 7), (1, 7), (0, 7)\}$

For each graph of a function f, determine the domain and the range of f.

11.

12.

13.

14.

15.

16.

17.

18.

19.

20.

21.

22.

23.

24.

25.

26.

27.

28.

29.

30.
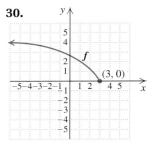

Find the domain of f.

31. $f(x) = \dfrac{5}{x - 3}$

32. $f(x) = \dfrac{7}{6 - x}$

33. $f(x) = \dfrac{x}{2x - 1}$

34. $f(x) = \dfrac{2x}{4x + 3}$

35. $f(x) = 2x + 1$

36. $f(x) = x^2 + 3$

37. $f(x) = |5 - x|$

38. $f(x) = |3x - 4|$

39. $f(x) = \dfrac{5}{x^2 - 9}$

40. $f(x) = \dfrac{x}{x^2 - 2x + 1}$

41. $f(x) = x^2 - 9$

42. $f(x) = x^2 - 2x + 1$

43. $f(x) = \dfrac{2x - 7}{x^2 + 8x + 7}$

44. $f(x) = \dfrac{x + 5}{2x^2 - x - 3}$

45. *Records in the 400-m run.* The record R for the 400-m run t years after 1930 is given by

$$R(t) = 46.8 - 0.075t.$$

What is the domain of the function?

46. *Records in the 1500-m run.* The record R for the 1500-m run t years after 1930 is given by

$$R(t) = 3.85 - 0.0075t.$$

What is the domain of the function?

47. *Consumer demand.* The amount A of coffee that consumers are willing to buy at price p is given by

$$A(p) = -2.5p + 26.5.$$

What is the domain of the function?

48. *Seller's supply.* The amount A of coffee that suppliers are willing to supply at price p is given by

$$A(p) = 2p - 11.$$

What is the domain of the function?

49. *Pressure at sea depth.* The pressure P, in atmospheres, at a depth d feet beneath the surface of the ocean is given by

$$P(d) = 0.03d + 1.$$

What is the domain of the function?

50. *Perimeter.* The perimeter P of an equilateral triangle with sides of length s is given by

$$P(s) = 3s.$$

What is the domain of the function?

51. *Fireworks displays.* The height h, in feet, of a "weeping willow" fireworks display, t seconds after having been launched from an 80-ft high rooftop, is given by

$$h(t) = -16t^2 + 64t + 80.$$

What is the domain of the function?

52. *Safety flares.* The height h, in feet, of a safety flare, t seconds after having been launched from a height of 224 ft, is given by

$$h(t) = -16t^2 + 80t + 224.$$

What is the domain of the function?

Find the indicated function values for each function.

53. $f(x) = \begin{cases} x, & \text{if } x < 0, \\ 2x + 1, & \text{if } x \geq 0 \end{cases}$

   a) $f(-5)$ **b)** $f(0)$ **c)** $f(10)$

54. $g(x) = \begin{cases} x - 5, & \text{if } x \leq 5, \\ 3x, & \text{if } x > 5 \end{cases}$

   a) $g(0)$ **b)** $g(5)$ **c)** $g(6)$

55. $G(x) = \begin{cases} x - 5, & \text{if } x < -1, \\ x, & \text{if } -1 \leq x \leq 2, \\ x + 2, & \text{if } x > 2 \end{cases}$

   a) $G(0)$ **b)** $G(2)$ **c)** $G(5)$

56. $F(x) = \begin{cases} 2x, & \text{if } x \leq 0, \\ x, & \text{if } 0 < x \leq 3, \\ -5x, & \text{if } x > 3 \end{cases}$

   a) $F(-1)$ **b)** $F(3)$ **c)** $F(10)$

57. $f(x) = \begin{cases} x^2 - 10, & \text{if } x < -10, \\ x^2, & \text{if } -10 \le x \le 10, \\ x^2 + 10, & \text{if } x > 10 \end{cases}$

a) $f(-10)$ **b)** $f(10)$ **c)** $f(11)$

58. $f(x) = \begin{cases} 2x^2 - 3, & \text{if } x < 2, \\ x^2, & \text{if } 2 \le x \le 4, \\ 5x - 7, & \text{if } x > 4 \end{cases}$

a) $f(0)$ **b)** $f(3)$ **c)** $f(6)$

59. Explain why the domain of the function given by $f(x) = \dfrac{x+3}{2}$ is $\mathbb{R}$, but the domain of the function given by $g(x) = \dfrac{2}{x+3}$ is not $\mathbb{R}$.

60. Chloe asserts that for a function described by a set of ordered pairs, the range of the function will always have the same number of elements as there are ordered pairs. Is she correct? Why or why not?

Skill Review

To prepare for Section 5.3, review graphs of linear equations (Section 2.6).

Graph. [2.6]

61. $y = 2x - 3$ **62.** $y = x + 5$

Find the slope and the y-intercept of each line. [2.6]

63. $y = \dfrac{2}{3}x - 4$ **64.** $y = -\dfrac{1}{4}x + 6$

65. $y = \dfrac{4}{3}x$ **66.** $y = -5x$

Synthesis

67. Ramiro states that $f(x) = \dfrac{x^2}{x}$ and $g(x) = x$ represent the same function. Is he correct? Why or why not?

68. Explain why the domain of a function can be viewed as the projection of its graph on the x-axis.

Sketch the graph of a function for which the domain and range are as given. Graphs may vary.

69. Domain: $\mathbb{R}$; range: $\mathbb{R}$

70. Domain: $\{3, 1, 4\}$; range: $\{0, 5\}$

71. Domain: $\{x \mid 1 \le x \le 5\}$; range: $\{y \mid 0 \le y \le 2\}$

72. Domain: $\{x \mid x \text{ is a real number } and \ x \ne 1\}$; range: $\{y \mid y \text{ is a real number } and \ y \ne -2\}$

For each graph of a function f, determine the domain and the range of f.

73.

74.

75.

76.

Graph each function on a graphing calculator and estimate its domain and range from the graph.

77. $f(x) = |x - 3|$ **78.** $f(x) = |x| - 3$

79. $f(x) = \dfrac{3}{x - 2}$ **80.** $f(x) = \dfrac{-1}{x + 3}$

81. Use a graphing calculator to estimate the range of the function in Exercise 51.

82. Use a graphing calculator to estimate the range of the function in Exercise 52.

83.–88. *For Exercises 83–88, graph the functions given in each of Exercises 53–58, respectively.*

89. A graphing calculator will interpret an expression like $x \ge 1$ as true or false, depending on the value of x. If the expression is true, the graphing calculator assigns a value of 1 to the expression. If the expression is false, the graphing calculator assigns a value of 0. To graph a piecewise-defined function using a graphing calculator, multiply each part of the definition by its domain, using the TEST menu to enter the inequality symbol. Thus the function in Exercise 53 is entered as $y_1 = x(x < 0) + (2x + 1)(x \ge 0)$. Use a graphing calculator in DOT mode to check your answers to Exercises 83–88.

5.3 Graphs of Functions

Linear Functions • Nonlinear Functions

A function can be classified both by the type of equation that is used and by the type of graph it represents. In this section, we will graph a variety of functions that are described by different equations.

Linear Functions

In Chapter 2, we graphed *linear equations*. Here we review such graphs and determine which types of linear graphs represent functions.

Any linear equation can be written in *standard form* $Ax + By = C$. If $B \neq 0$, the equation can also be written in *slope–intercept form*. The *point–slope form* is often used to write equations.

> **Equations of Lines**
>
> | Standard form: | $Ax + By = C$ |
> | Slope–intercept form: | $y = mx + b$ |
> | Point–slope form: | $y - y_1 = m(x - x_1)$ |

Two points determine a line. If we know that an equation is linear, we can graph the equation by plotting two points that are on the line and drawing the line that goes through those points.

When an equation is written in slope–intercept form $y = mx + b$, the slope of the line is m and the y-intercept is $(0, b)$. Knowing the y-intercept gives us one point on the line, and we can use the slope to determine another point.

EXAMPLE **1**

Graph: $4y = -3x + 8$.

SOLUTION To graph $4y = -3x + 8$, we first rewrite it in slope–intercept form:

$$4y = -3x + 8$$
$$y = \tfrac{1}{4}(-3x + 8) \qquad \text{Multiplying both sides by } \tfrac{1}{4}$$
$$y = -\tfrac{3}{4}x + 2. \qquad \text{Using the distributive law}$$

The slope is $-\frac{3}{4}$ and the y-intercept is $(0, 2)$. We plot $(0, 2)$ and think of the slope as either $\frac{-3}{4}$ or $\frac{3}{-4}$. Using the form $\frac{-3}{4}$, we start at $(0, 2)$ and move *down* 3 units (since the numerator is *negative*) and *to the right* 4 units (since the denominator is *positive*). We plot the new point, $(4, -1)$.

Alternatively, we can think of the slope as $\frac{3}{-4}$. Starting at $(0, 2)$, we move *up* 3 units (since the numerator is *positive*) and *to the left* 4 units (since the denominator is *negative*). This leads to another point on the graph, $(-4, 5)$. Using the points found, we draw and label the graph at left.

TRY EXERCISE 7

The graphs of equations of the form $y = b$ are horizontal lines with a slope of 0, and the graphs of equations of the form $x = a$ are vertical lines. The slope of a vertical line is undefined.

We can use the vertical-line test to determine which types of linear graphs represent functions. Consider the following graphs.

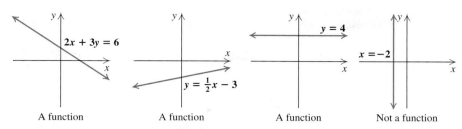

| A function | A function | A function | Not a function |

Any vertical line that passes through the graphs of $2x + 3y = 6$, $y = \frac{1}{2}x - 3$, and $y = 4$ will cross the graph only once. However, the vertical line through the point $(-2, 0)$ will cross the graph of $x = -2$ at *every* point. In general, *any* straight line that is not vertical is the graph of a function. A **linear function** is a function described by any linear equation whose graph is not vertical. A horizontal line represents a **constant function**.

Linear Function

A function described by an equation of the form $f(x) = mx + b$ is a *linear function*. Its graph is a straight line with slope m and y-intercept $(0, b)$.

When $m = 0$, the function described by $f(x) = b$ is called a *constant function*. Its graph is a horizontal line through $(0, b)$.

EXAMPLE 2   Graph: $f(x) = 3x + 2$.

SOLUTION   The notations

$$f(x) = 3x + 2 \quad \text{and} \quad y = 3x + 2$$

are often used interchangeably. The function notation emphasizes that the second coordinate in each ordered pair is determined by the first coordinate of that pair.

We graph $f(x) = 3x + 2$ in the same way that we would graph $y = 3x + 2$. The vertical axis can be labeled y or $f(x)$. We could use a table of values or, since this is a linear function, use the slope and the y-intercept to graph the function.

Since $f(x) = 3x + 2$ is in the form $f(x) = mx + b$, we can tell from the equation that the slope is 3, or $\frac{3}{1}$, and the y-intercept is $(0, 2)$. We plot $(0, 2)$ and go *up* 3 units and *to the right* 1 unit to determine another point on the line, $(1, 5)$. After we have sketched the line, a third point can be calculated as a check.

TRY EXERCISE 19

EXAMPLE 3   Graph: $f(x) = -3$.

SOLUTION   This is a constant function. For every input x, the output is -3. The graph is a horizontal line.

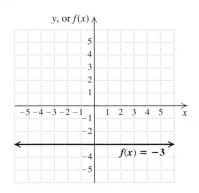

TRY EXERCISE 23

Linear functions are common in today's world.

EXAMPLE 4

Cell-phone costs. In 2008, an Apple iPhone cost $400. AT&T offered a plan including 450 daytime minutes a month for $60 per month. Formulate a mathematical model for the cost. Then use the model to estimate the number of months required for the total cost to reach $700.

Source: www.apple.com

SOLUTION

1. **Familiarize.** For this plan, a monthly fee is charged after an initial purchase has been made. After 1 month of service, the total cost will be $400 + $60 = $460. After 2 months, the total cost will be $400 + $60 \cdot 2 = $520. We can write a general model if we let $C(t)$ represent the total cost, in dollars, for t months of service.

2. **Translate.** We reword and translate as follows:

Rewording: The total cost　is　the cost of the phone　plus　$60 per month.

Translating: $C(t)$　$=$　400　$+$　$60 \cdot t$

where $t \geq 0$ (since there cannot be a negative number of months).

3. **Carry out.** To determine the time required for the total cost to reach $700, we substitute 700 for $C(t)$ and solve for t:

$$C(t) = 400 + 60t$$
$$700 = 400 + 60t \qquad \text{Substituting}$$
$$300 = 60t \qquad \text{Subtracting 400 from both sides}$$
$$5 = t. \qquad \text{Dividing both sides by 60}$$

4. **Check.** We evaluate:

$$C(5) = 60 \cdot 5 + 400 = 300 + 400 = 700.$$

5. **State.** It takes 5 months for the total cost to reach $700.　**TRY EXERCISE** 25

Since $f(x) = mx + b$ can be evaluated for any choice of x, the domain of all linear functions is $\mathbb{R}$, the set of all real numbers.

The second coordinate of every ordered pair in a constant function $f(x) = b$ is the number b. The range of a constant function thus consists of one number, b. For a nonconstant linear function, the graph extends indefinitely both up and down, so the range is the set of all real numbers, or $\mathbb{R}$.

> ## Domain and Range of a Linear Function
> The domain of any linear function $f(x) = mx + b$ is
> $$\{x \mid x \text{ is a real number}\}, \text{ or } \mathbb{R}.$$
> The range of any linear function $f(x) = mx + b$, $m \neq 0$, is
> $$\{y \mid y \text{ is a real number}\}, \text{ or } \mathbb{R}.$$
> The range of any constant function $f(x) = b$ is $\{b\}$.

EXAMPLE 5

Determine the domain and the range of each of the following functions.

a) f, where $f(x) = 2x - 10$ 　　　　**b)** g, where $g(x) = 4$

SOLUTION

a) Since $f(x) = 2x - 10$ describes a linear function, but not a constant function,

Domain of $f = \mathbb{R}$ and
Range of $f = \mathbb{R}$.

b) The function described by $g(x) = 4$ is a constant function. Thus,

Domain of $g = \mathbb{R}$ and
Range of $g = \{4\}$.

 TRY EXERCISE 41

The graphs of nonlinear functions can get quite complex. We will now define several types of nonlinear functions and discuss some of their characteristics. The detailed study of their graphs appears later in this text or in other courses.

Nonlinear Functions

A function for which the graph is not a straight line is a **nonlinear function**. Some important types of nonlinear functions are listed below.

Type of function	*Example*
Absolute-value function	$f(x) = |x|$
Polynomial function	$p(x) = x^3 - 4x^2 + 1$
Quadratic function	$q(x) = x^2 + 5x + 2$
Rational function	$r(x) = \dfrac{x + 1}{x - 2}$

Note that linear and quadratic functions are special kinds of polynomial functions.

EXAMPLE 6 State whether each equation describes a linear function, an absolute-value function, a general polynomial function, a quadratic function, or a rational function.

a) $f(x) = x^2 - 9$

b) $g(x) = \dfrac{3}{x}$

c) $h(x) = \dfrac{1}{4}x - 16$

d) $v(x) = 4x^4 - 13$

SOLUTION

a) Since f is described by a polynomial equation of degree 2, f is a *quadratic function*.

b) Since g is described by a rational equation, g is a *rational function*.

c) The function h is described by a linear equation, so h is a *linear function*. Note that although $\frac{1}{4}$ is a fraction, there are no variables in a denominator.

d) Since v is described by a polynomial equation, v is a *polynomial function*.

Since the graphs of nonlinear functions are not straight lines, we usually need to calculate more than two or three points to determine the shape of the graph.

EXAMPLE 7 Graph the function given by $f(x) = |x|$, and determine the domain and the range of f.

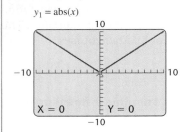
SOLUTION   We calculate function values for several choices of x and list the results in a table.

$$f(0) = |0| = 0,$$
$$f(1) = |1| = 1,$$
$$f(2) = |2| = 2,$$
$$f(-1) = |-1| = 1,$$
$$f(-2) = |-2| = 2$$

x	$f(x) = |x|$	$(x, f(x))$
0	0	$(0, 0)$
1	1	$(1, 1)$
2	2	$(2, 2)$
-1	1	$(-1, 1)$
-2	2	$(-2, 2)$

When we plot these points, we observe a pattern. The value of the function is 0 when x is 0. Function values increase both as x increases from 0 and as x decreases from 0. The graph of f is V-shaped, with the "point" of the V at the origin.

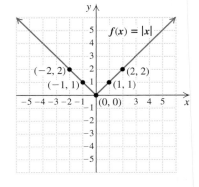

Because we can find the absolute value of any real number, we have

Domain of $f = \mathbb{R}$, or $(-\infty, \infty)$.

Because the absolute value of a number is never negative, we have

Range of $f = \{y \mid y \geq 0\}$, or $[0, \infty)$.

TRY EXERCISE 65

Graphs of *polynomial functions* generally become more complex as the degree of the polynomial increases. In Chapter 9, we will study in greater detail the graphs of *quadratic functions*, or functions of the form

$$q(x) = ax^2 + bx + c, a \neq 0.$$

Since a polynomial can be evaluated for any real number, the domain of a polynomial is the set of all real numbers.

A *rational function* contains a variable in a denominator; thus its domain may be restricted. Division by zero is undefined, so any values of the variable that make a denominator 0 are not in the domain of the function.

EXAMPLE 8

Determine the domain of f.

a) $f(x) = x^3 + 5x^2 - 4x + 1$ 　　　　**b)** $f(x) = \dfrac{x^2 - 4}{x + 2}$

SOLUTION

a) $f(x) = x^3 + 5x^2 - 4x + 1$ describes a polynomial function. The domain of any polynomial function is $\mathbb{R}$, so the domain of f is $\mathbb{R}$.

b) $f(x) = \dfrac{x^2 - 4}{x + 2}$ describes a rational function. Note that $f(x)$ is undefined for $x + 2 = 0$, or, equivalently, for $x = -2$. Thus the domain of $f = \{x \mid x$ is a real number and $x \neq -2\}$.

TRY EXERCISE 43

Visualizing for Success

A

B

C

D

E

Match each equation or function with its graph.

1. $f(x) = x$

2. $f(x) = |x|$

3. $f(x) = x^2$

4. $f(x) = 3$

5. $x = 3$

6. $f(x) = x + 3$

7. $f(x) = x - 3$

8. $f(x) = 2x$

9. $f(x) = -2x$

10. $f(x) = \dfrac{1}{x}$

Answers on page A-22

An alternate, animated version of this activity appears in MyMathLab. To use MyMathLab, you need a course ID and a student access code. Contact your instructor for more information.

F

G

H

I

J

5.3 EXERCISE SET

For Extra Help **MyMathLab** Math XL PRACTICE WATCH DOWNLOAD

↪ *Concept Reinforcement* *Answer true or false.*

1. The vertical-line test states that a graph is not that of a function if it contains a vertical line.

2. The graph of a constant function is a horizontal line.

3. The domain of a constant function consists of a single element.

4. The domain of a linear function is the set of all real numbers.

5. Linear functions are typically written in slope–intercept form.

6. Rational functions may have some restrictions on their domains.

Graph.

7. $y = 2x - 1$

8. $y = \frac{1}{3}x + 2$

9. $y = -\frac{2}{3}x + 3$

10. $y = -4x - 2$

11. $3y = 6 - 4x$

12. $5y = 2x - 15$

13. $x - y = 4$

14. $x + y = 3$

15. $y = -2$

16. $y = 3$

17. $x = 4$

18. $x = -1$

19. $f(x) = x + 3$

20. $f(x) = 2 - x$

21. $f(x) = \frac{3}{4}x + 1$

22. $f(x) = 3x + 2$

23. $g(x) = 4$

24. $g(x) = -5$

25. *Truck rentals.* Titanium Trucks charges $30 for a one-day truck rental, plus $0.75 per mile. Formulate a linear function to model the cost $C(d)$ of a one-day rental driven d miles, and determine the number of miles driven if the total cost is $75.

26. *Taxis.* A taxi ride in New York City costs $2.50 plus $2.00 per mile.* Formulate a linear function to model the cost $C(d)$ of a d-mile taxi ride, and determine the length of a ride that cost $23.50.

27. *Hair growth.* Lauren had her hair cut to a length of 5 inches in order to donate the hair to Locks of Love. Her hair then grew at a rate of $\frac{1}{2}$ inch per month. Formulate a linear function to model the length $L(t)$

*Rates are higher between 4 P.M. and 8 P.M. (*Source:* Based on data from New York City Taxi and Limousine Commission, 2007)

of Lauren's hair t months after she had the haircut, and determine when her hair will be 15 inches long.

28. *Landscaping.* On Saturday, Shelby Lawncare cut the lawn at Great Harrington Community College to a height of 2 in. Since then, the grass has grown at a rate of $\frac{1}{8}$ in. per day. Formulate a linear function to model the length $L(t)$ of the lawn t days after having been cut, and determine when the grass will be $3\frac{1}{2}$ in. high.

29. *Organic cotton.* In 2006, 5960 acres in the U.S. were planted with organic cotton. This number is increasing by 849 acres each year. Formulate a linear function to model the number of acres of organic cotton $A(t)$ that is planted t years after 2006, and determine when 10,205 acres of organic cotton will be planted.
Source: Based on data from the Organic Trade Association

30. *Catering.* Chrissie's Catering charges a setup fee of $75 plus $25 a person for catering a party. Formulate a linear function to model the cost $C(x)$ for a party for x people, and determine the number of people at a party if the cost was $775.

In Exercises 31–40, assume that a constant rate of change exists for each model formed.

31. *Automobile production.* As demand has grown, worldwide production of small cars rose from 14.5 million in 2002 to 19 million in 2007. Let $a(t)$ represent the number of small cars produced t years after 2000.
Source: *The Wall Street Journal*, 10/22/07

a) Find a linear function that fits the data.

b) Use the function from part (a) to predict the number of small cars produced in 2013.

c) In what year will 25 million small cars be produced?

32. *Convention attendees.* In recent years, Las Vegas has become a popular location for conventions. The number of convention attendees in Las Vegas rose from 4.6 million in 2002 to 6.1 million in 2006. Let $v(t)$ represent the number of convention attendees in Las Vegas t years after 2000.
Source: Las Vegas Convention and Visitors Authority

   a) Find a linear function that fits the data.
   b) Use the function from part (a) to predict the number of convention attendees in Las Vegas in 2011.
   c) In what year will there be 8 million convention attendees in Las Vegas?

33. *Life expectancy of females in the United States.* In 1994, the life expectancy of females was 79.0 yr. In 2004, it was 80.4 yr. Let $E(t)$ represent life expectancy and t the number of years since 1990.
Source: *Statistical Abstract of the United States*, 2007

   a) Find a linear function that fits the data.
Aha! b) Use the function of part (a) to predict the life expectancy of females in 2012.

34. *Life expectancy of males in the United States.* In 1994, the life expectancy of males was 72.4 yr. In 2004, it was 75.2 yr. Let $E(t)$ represent life expectancy and t the number of years since 1990.
Source: *Statistical Abstract of the United States*, 2007

   a) Find a linear function that fits the data.
   b) Use the function of part (a) to predict the life expectancy of males in 2012.

35. *PAC contributions.* In 2002, Political Action Committees (PACs) contributed $282 million to federal candidates. In 2006, the figure rose to $372.1 million. Let $A(t)$ represent the amount of PAC contributions, in millions, and t the number of years since 2000.
Source: Federal Election Commission

PAC contributions to federal candidates

2002 — $282 million
2006 — $372.1 million

   a) Find a linear function that fits the data.
   b) Use the function of part (a) to predict the amount of PAC contributions in 2010.

36. *Recycling.* In 2000, Americans recycled 52.7 million tons of solid waste. In 2005, the figure grew to 58.4 million tons. Let $N(t)$ represent the number of tons recycled, in millions, and t the number of years since 2000.
Sources: U.S. EPA; Franklin Associates, Ltd.

   a) Find a linear function that fits the data.
   b) Use the function of part (a) to predict the amount recycled in 2012.

37. *Online banking.* In 2000, about 16 million Americans conducted at least some of their banking online. By 2005, that number had risen to about 63 million. Let $N(t)$ represent the number of Americans using online banking, in millions, t years after 2000.

   a) Find a linear function that fits the data.
Aha! b) Use the function of part (a) to predict the number of Americans who will use online banking in 2010.
   c) In what year will 157 million Americans use online banking?

38. *Records in the 100-meter run.* In 1999, the record for the 100-m run was 9.79 sec. In 2007, it was 9.77 sec. Let $R(t)$ represent the record in the 100-m run and t the number of years since 1999.
Sources: International Association of Athletics Federation; *Guinness World Records*

   a) Find a linear function that fits the data.
   b) Use the function of part (a) to predict the record in 2015 and in 2030.
   c) When will the record be 9.6 sec?

39. *National Park land.* In 1994, the National Park system consisted of about 74.9 million acres. By 2005, the figure had grown to 79 million acres. Let $A(t)$ represent the amount of land in the National Park system, in millions of acres, t years after 1990.
Source: *Statistical Abstract of the United States*, 2007

a) Find a linear function that fits the data.
b) Use the function of part (a) to predict the amount of land in the National Park system in 2010.

40. *Pressure at sea depth.* The pressure 100 ft beneath the ocean's surface is approximately 4 atm (atmospheres), whereas at a depth of 200 ft, the pressure is about 7 atm.

a) Find a linear function that expresses pressure as a function of depth.
b) Use the function of part (a) to determine the pressure at a depth of 690 ft.

Classify each function as a linear function, an absolute-value function, a quadratic function, another polynomial function, or a rational function, and determine the domain of the function.

41. $f(x) = \dfrac{1}{3}x - 7$

42. $g(x) = \dfrac{x}{x + 1}$

43. $p(x) = x^2 + x + 1$

44. $t(x) = |x - 7|$

45. $f(t) = \dfrac{12}{3t + 4}$

46. $g(n) = 15 - 10n$

47. $f(x) = 0.02x^4 - 0.1x + 1.7$

48. $f(a) = 2|a + 3|$

49. $f(x) = \dfrac{x}{2x - 5}$

50. $g(x) = \dfrac{2x}{3x - 4}$

51. $f(n) = \dfrac{4n - 7}{n^2 + 3n + 2}$

52. $h(x) = \dfrac{x - 5}{2x^2 - 2}$

53. $f(n) = 200 - 0.1n$

54. $g(t) = \dfrac{t^2 - 3t + 7}{8}$

Given the graph of each function, determine the range of f.

55.

56.

57.

58.

59.

60.

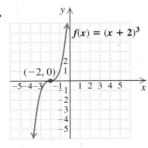

Graph each function and determine its domain and range.

61. $f(x) = x + 3$

62. $f(x) = 2x - 1$

63. $f(x) = -1$

64. $g(x) = 2$

65. $f(x) = |x| + 1$

66. $g(x) = |x - 3|$

67. $g(x) = x^2$

68. $f(x) = x^2 + 2$

69. Bob believes that the domain and range of all polynomial functions is $\mathbb{R}$. How could you convince him that he is mistaken?

70. Explain why the range of a constant function consists of only one number.

Skill Review

To prepare for Section 5.4, review polynomial operations.

Perform the indicated operations.

71. $(x^2 + 2x + 7) + (3x^2 - 8)$

72. $(3x^3 - x^2 + x) - (x^3 + 2x - 7)$

73. $(2x + 1)(x - 7)$

74. $(x - 3)(x + 4)$

75. $(x^3 + x^2 - 4x + 7) - (3x^2 - x + 2)$

76. $(2x^2 + x - 3) + (x^3 + 7)$

Synthesis

77. In 2004, Political Action Committees contributed $310.5 million to federal candidates. Does this information make your answer to Exercise 35(b) seem too low or too high? Why?

78. On the basis of your answers to Exercises 33 and 34, would you predict that at some point in the future the life expectancy of males will exceed that of females? Why or why not?

Given that $f(x) = mx + b$, classify each of the following as true or false.

79. $f(c + d) = f(c) + f(d)$

80. $f(cd) = f(c)f(d)$

81. $f(kx) = kf(x)$

82. $f(c - d) = f(c) - f(d)$

For Exercises 83–86, assume that a linear equation models each situation.

83. *Temperature conversion.* Water freezes at 32° Fahrenheit and at 0° Celsius. Water boils at 212°F and at 100°C. What Celsius temperature corresponds to a room temperature of 70°F?

84. *Depreciation of a computer.* After 6 mos of use, the value of Don's computer had dropped to $900. After 8 mos, the value had gone down to $750. How much did the computer cost originally?

85. *Cell-phone charges.* The total cost of Tam's cell phone was $410 after 5 mos of service and $690 after 9 mos. What costs had Tam already incurred when her service just began? Assume that Tam's monthly charge is constant.

86. *Operating expenses.* The total cost for operating Ming's Wings was $7500 after 4 mos and $9250 after 7 mos. Predict the total cost after 10 mos.

87. For a linear function g, $g(3) = -5$ and $g(7) = -1$.

   a) Find an equation for g.

   b) Find $g(-2)$.

   c) Find a such that $g(a) = 75$.

88. When several data points are available and they appear to be nearly collinear, a procedure known as *linear regression* can be used to find an equation for the line that most closely fits the data.

   a) Use a graphing calculator with a LINEAR REGRESSION option and the table that follows to find a linear function that predicts the wattage of a CFL (compact fluorescent) lightbulb as a function of the wattage of a standard incandescent bulb of equivalent brightness. Round coefficients to the nearest thousandth.

Energy Conservation

Incandescent Wattage	CFL Equivalent
25 W	5 W
50 W	9 W
60 W	15 W
100 W	25 W
120 W	28 W

Source: U.S. Department of Energy

   b) Use the function from part (a) to estimate the CFL wattage that is equivalent to a 75-watt incandescent bulb. Then compare your answer with the corresponding answer to Exercise 59 in Section 5.1. Which answer seems more reliable? Why?

CONNECTING the CONCEPTS

A function is a correspondence. This correspondence can be listed as a set of ordered pairs or described by an equation. The correspondence is between two sets, the domain and the range, and each member of the domain corresponds to exactly one member of the range.

For the function f: $\{(2, 3), (0, -4), (-8, 7)\}$:

The domain is $\{-8, 0, 2\}$.

The range is $\{-4, 3, 7\}$.

The input 2 corresponds to the output 3.

$f(2) = 3$

For the function given by $f(x) = x^2$:

The domain is $\mathbb{R}$.

The range is $[0, \infty)$.

The input -3 corresponds to the output 9.

$f(-3) = 9$

The independent variable is x.

MIXED REVIEW

Let $f = \{(3, 6), (4, 8), (-1, -2), (0, 0)\}$.

1. Find the domain of f.

2. Find the range of f.

3. Find $f(-1)$.

4. Graph f.

Let $g(x) = x - 1$ *and* $h(x) = \dfrac{2}{x}$.

5. Find the domain of g.

6. Find the domain of h.

7. Find $h(10)$.

8. Find $g(1) + h(1)$.

9. Find $(g \cdot h)(-2)$.

10. Find the domain of h/g.

11. Determine whether g is a linear function, a quadratic function, or a rational function.

12. Determine whether h is a linear function, a quadratic function, or a rational function.

13. Graph g and determine its range.

Use the following graph of F for Exercises 14–17.

14. Determine from the graph whether F is a function.

15. Find $F(2)$.

16. Find the domain of F.

17. Find the range of F.

$$\text{Let } G(x) = \begin{cases} 1 - x, & \text{if } x < 1, \\ 10, & \text{if } x = 1, \\ x + 1, & \text{if } x > 1. \end{cases}$$

18. Find $G(3)$.

19. Find $G(1)$.

20. Find $G(-12)$.

5.4 The Algebra of Functions

The Sum, Difference, Product, or Quotient of Two Functions ● Domains and Graphs

We now examine four ways in which functions can be combined.

The Sum, Difference, Product, or Quotient of Two Functions

Suppose that a is in the domain of two functions, f and g. The input a is paired with $f(a)$ by f and with $g(a)$ by g. The outputs can then be added to get $f(a) + g(a)$.

EXAMPLE 1

Let $f(x) = x + 4$ and $g(x) = x^2 + 1$. Find $f(2) + g(2)$.

SOLUTION We visualize two function machines. Because 2 is in the domain of each function, we can compute $f(2)$ and $g(2)$.

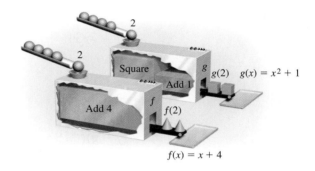

Since

$$f(2) = 2 + 4 = 6 \quad \text{and} \quad g(2) = 2^2 + 1 = 5,$$

we have

$$f(2) + g(2) = 6 + 5 = 11.$$

TRY EXERCISE 7

In Example 1, suppose that we were to write $f(x) + g(x)$ as $(x + 4) + (x^2 + 1)$, or $f(x) + g(x) = x^2 + x + 5$. This could then be regarded as a "new" function. The notation $(f + g)(x)$ is generally used to denote a function formed in this manner. Similar notations exist for subtraction, multiplication, and division of functions.

> **The Algebra of Functions**
>
> If f and g are functions and x is in the domain of both functions, then:
> 1. $(f + g)(x) = f(x) + g(x)$;
> 2. $(f - g)(x) = f(x) - g(x)$;
> 3. $(f \cdot g)(x) = f(x) \cdot g(x)$;
> 4. $(f/g)(x) = f(x)/g(x)$, provided $g(x) \neq 0$.

EXAMPLE 2

For $f(x) = x^2 - x$ and $g(x) = x + 2$, find the following.

a) $(f + g)(4)$

b) $(f - g)(x)$ and $(f - g)(-1)$

c) $(f/g)(x)$ and $(f/g)(-4)$

d) $(f \cdot g)(4)$

SOLUTION

a) Since $f(4) = 4^2 - 4 = 12$ and $g(4) = 4 + 2 = 6$, we have

$$(f + g)(4) = f(4) + g(4)$$
$$= 12 + 6 \qquad \text{Substituting}$$
$$= 18.$$

Alternatively, we could first find $(f + g)(x)$:

$$(f + g)(x) = f(x) + g(x)$$
$$= x^2 - x + x + 2$$
$$= x^2 + 2. \qquad \text{Combining like terms}$$

Thus,

$$(f + g)(4) = 4^2 + 2 = 18. \qquad \text{Our results match.}$$

b) We have

$$(f - g)(x) = f(x) - g(x)$$
$$= x^2 - x - (x + 2) \qquad \text{Substituting}$$
$$= x^2 - 2x - 2. \qquad \text{Removing parentheses and combining like terms}$$

Thus,

$$(f - g)(-1) = (-1)^2 - 2(-1) - 2 \qquad \text{Using } (f - g)(x) \text{ is faster than using } f(x) - g(x).$$
$$= 1. \qquad \text{Simplifying}$$

c) We have

$$(f/g)(x) = f(x)/g(x)$$
$$= \frac{x^2 - x}{x + 2}. \qquad \text{We assume that } x \neq -2.$$

Thus,

$$(f/g)(-4) = \frac{(-4)^2 - (-4)}{-4 + 2} \qquad \text{Substituting}$$
$$= \frac{20}{-2} = -10.$$

d) Using our work in part (a), we have

$$(f \cdot g)(4) = f(4) \cdot g(4)$$
$$= 12 \cdot 6$$
$$= 72.$$

Alternatively, we could first find $(f \cdot g)(x)$:

$$
\begin{aligned}
(f \cdot g)(x) &= f(x) \cdot g(x) \\
&= (x^2 - x)(x + 2) \\
&= x^3 + x^2 - 2x. \qquad \text{Multiplying and combining like terms.}
\end{aligned}
$$

Then

$$
\begin{aligned}
(f \cdot g)(4) &= 4^3 + 4^2 - 2 \cdot 4 \\
&= 64 + 16 - 8 \\
&= 72.
\end{aligned}
$$

TRY EXERCISE 17

Domains and Graphs

Although applications involving products and quotients of functions rarely appear in newspapers, situations involving sums or differences of functions often do appear in print. For example, the following graphs are similar to those published by the California Department of Education to promote breakfast programs in which students eat a balanced meal of fruit or juice, toast or cereal, and 2% or whole milk. The combination of carbohydrate, protein, and fat gives a sustained release of energy, delaying the onset of hunger for several hours.

When the three graphs are superimposed, and the calorie expenditures added, it becomes clear that a balanced meal results in a steady, sustained supply of energy.

For any point $(t, N(t))$, we have

$$N(t) = (C + P + F)(t) = C(t) + P(t) + F(t).$$

To find $(f + g)(a)$, $(f - g)(a)$, $(f \cdot g)(a)$, or $(f/g)(a)$, we must know that $f(a)$ and $g(a)$ exist. This means a must be in the domain of both f and g.

EXAMPLE 3 Let

$$f(x) = \frac{5}{x} \quad \text{and} \quad g(x) = \frac{2x - 6}{x + 1}.$$

Find the domain of $f + g$, the domain of $f - g$, and the domain of $f \cdot g$.

SOLUTION Note that because division by 0 is undefined, we have

Domain of $f = \{x \mid x$ is a real number *and* $x \neq 0\}$

and

Domain of $g = \{x \mid x$ is a real number *and* $x \neq -1\}$.

In order to find $f(a) + g(a)$, $f(a) - g(a)$, or $f(a) \cdot g(a)$, we must know that a is in *both* of the above domains. Thus,

Domain of $f + g =$ Domain of $f - g =$ Domain of $f \cdot g$

$\qquad = \{x \mid x$ is a real number *and* $x \neq 0$ *and* $x \neq -1\}$.

TRY EXERCISE 43

Suppose that for $f(x) = x^2 - x$ and $g(x) = x + 2$, we want to find $(f/g)(-2)$. Finding $f(-2)$ and $g(-2)$ poses no problem:

$$f(-2) = 6 \quad \text{and} \quad g(-2) = 0;$$

but then

$$(f/g)(-2) = f(-2)/g(-2)$$
$$= 6/0. \quad \text{Division by 0 is undefined.}$$

Thus, although -2 is in the domain of both f and g, it is not in the domain of f/g.

We can also see this by writing $(f/g)(x)$:

$$(f/g)(x) = \frac{f(x)}{g(x)} = \frac{x^2 - x}{x + 2}.$$

Since $x + 2 = 0$ when $x = -2$, the domain of f/g must exclude -2.

Determining the Domain

The domain of $f + g$, $f - g$, or $f \cdot g$ is the set of all values common to the domains of f and g.

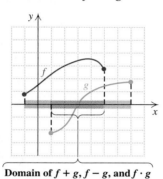

Domain of $f + g$, $f - g$, and $f \cdot g$

The domain of f/g is the set of all values common to the domains of f and g, excluding any values for which $g(x)$ is 0.

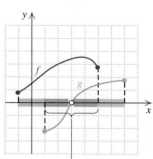

Domain of f/g

EXAMPLE 4   Given $f(x) = 1/x$ and $g(x) = 2x - 7$, find the domains of $f + g$, $f - g$, $f \cdot g$, and f/g.

SOLUTION   We first find the domain of f and the domain of g:

The domain of f is $\{x \mid x$ is a real number *and* $x \neq 0\}$.

The domain of g is $\mathbb{R}$.

The domains of $f + g$, $f - g$, and $f \cdot g$ are the set of all elements common to the domains of f and g. This consists of all real numbers except 0.

The domain of $f + g =$ the domain of $f - g =$ the domain of $f \cdot g$
$$= \{x \mid x \text{ is a real number } and \; x \neq 0\}.$$

Because we cannot divide by 0, the domain of f/g must also exclude any values of x for which $g(x)$ is 0. We determine those values by solving $g(x) = 0$:

$$g(x) = 0$$
$$2x - 7 = 0 \quad \text{Replacing } g(x) \text{ with } 2x - 7$$
$$2x = 7$$
$$x = \tfrac{7}{2}.$$

The domain of f/g is the domain of the sum, difference, and product of f and g, found above, excluding $\tfrac{7}{2}$.

The domain of $f/g = \left\{x \mid x \text{ is a real number } and \; x \neq 0 \; and \; x \neq \tfrac{7}{2}\right\}$.

> TRY EXERCISE 55

STUDENT NOTES ———————

The concern over a denominator being 0 arises throughout this course. Try to develop the habit of checking for any possible input values that would create a denominator of 0 whenever you work with functions.

TECHNOLOGY CONNECTION

A partial check of Example 4 can be performed by setting up a table so the TBLSTART is 0 and the increment of change (ΔTbl) is 0.7. (Other choices, like 0.1, will also work.) Next, we let $y_1 = 1/x$ and $y_2 = 2x - 7$. Using Y-VARS to write $y_3 = y_1 + y_2$ and $y_4 = y_1/y_2$, we can create the table of values shown here. Note that when x is 3.5, a value for y_3 can be found, but y_4 is undefined. If we "de-select" y_1 and y_2 as we enter them, the columns for y_3 and y_4 appear without scrolling through the table.

X	Y3	Y4
0	ERROR	ERROR
.7	−4.171	−.2551
1.4	−3.486	−.1701
2.1	−2.324	−.1701
2.8	−1.043	−.2551
3.5	.28571	ERROR
4.2	1.6381	.17007

X = 0

Use a similar approach to partially check Example 3.

Division by 0 is not the only condition that can force restrictions on the domain of a function. In Chapter 8, we will examine functions similar to that given by $f(x) = \sqrt{x}$, for which the concern is taking the square root of a negative number.

5.4 EXERCISE SET

Concept Reinforcement *Make each of the following sentences true by selecting the correct word for each blank.*

1. If f and g are functions, then $(f + g)(x)$ is the _____ of the functions.
   sum/difference

2. One way to compute $(f - g)(2)$ is to _____ $g(2)$ from $f(2)$.
   erase/subtract

3. One way to compute $(f - g)(2)$ is to simplify $f(x) - g(x)$ and then _____ the result
   evaluate/substitute
   for $x = 2$.

4. The domain of $f + g$, $f - g$, and $f \cdot g$ is the set of all values common to the _____ of f and g.
   domains/ranges

5. The domain of f/g is the set of all values common to the domains of f and g, _____ any
   including/excluding
   values for which $g(x)$ is 0.

6. The height of $(f + g)(a)$ on a graph is the _____ of the heights of $f(a)$ and $g(a)$.
   product/sum

Let $f(x) = -2x + 3$ and $g(x) = x^2 - 5$. Find each of the following.

7. $f(3) + g(3)$

8. $f(4) + g(4)$

9. $f(1) - g(1)$

10. $f(2) - g(2)$

11. $f(-2) \cdot g(-2)$

12. $f(-1) \cdot g(-1)$

13. $f(-4)/g(-4)$

14. $f(3)/g(3)$

15. $g(1) - f(1)$

16. $g(-3)/f(-3)$

17. $(f + g)(x)$

18. $(g - f)(x)$

Let $F(x) = x^2 - 2$ and $G(x) = 5 - x$. Find each of the following.

19. $(F + G)(x)$

20. $(F + G)(a)$

21. $(F - G)(3)$

22. $(F - G)(2)$

23. $(F \cdot G)(a)$

24. $(G \cdot F)(x)$

25. $(F/G)(x)$

26. $(G - F)(x)$

27. $(G/F)(-2)$

28. $(F/G)(-1)$

29. $(F + F)(1)$

30. $(G \cdot G)(6)$

The following graph shows the number of births in the United States, in millions, from 1970–2004. Here $C(t)$ represents the number of Caesarean section births, $B(t)$ the number of non-Caesarean section births, and $N(t)$ the total number of births in year t.

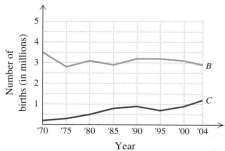

Source: National Center for Health Statistics

31. Use estimates of $C(2004)$ and $B(2004)$ to estimate $N(2004)$.

32. Use estimates of $C(1985)$ and $B(1985)$ to estimate $N(1985)$.

In 2004, a study comparing high doses of the cholesterol-lowering drugs Lipitor and Pravachol indicated that patients taking Lipitor were significantly less likely to have heart attacks or require angioplasty or surgery.

In the graph below, $L(t)$ is the percentage of patients on Lipitor (80 mg) and $P(t)$ is the percentage of patients on Pravachol (40 mg) who suffered heart problems or death t years after beginning to take the medication.
Source: *New York Times*, March 9, 2004

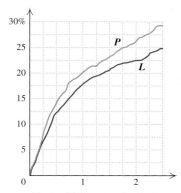

Source: New England Journal of Medicine

33. Use estimates of $P(2)$ and $L(2)$ to estimate $(P - L)(2)$.

34. Use estimates of $P(1)$ and $L(1)$ to estimate $(P - L)(1)$.

Often function addition is represented by stacking the individual functions directly on top of each other. The graph below indicates how U.S. municipal solid waste has been managed. The braces indicate the values of the individual functions.

Source: Environmental Protection Agency

35. Estimate $(p + r)('05)$. What does it represent?

36. Estimate $(p + r + b)('05)$. What does it represent?

37. Estimate $F('96)$. What does it represent?

38. Estimate $F('06)$. What does it represent?

39. Estimate $(F - p)('04)$. What does it represent?

40. Estimate $(F - l)('03)$. What does it represent?

For each pair of functions f and g, determine the domain of the sum, difference, and product of the two functions.

41. $f(x) = x^2$,
$g(x) = 7x - 4$

42. $f(x) = 5x - 1$,
$g(x) = 2x^2$

43. $f(x) = \dfrac{1}{x + 5}$,
$g(x) = 4x^3$

44. $f(x) = 3x^2$,
$g(x) = \dfrac{1}{x - 9}$

45. $f(x) = \dfrac{2}{x}$,
$g(x) = x^2 - 4$

46. $f(x) = x^3 + 1$,
$g(x) = \dfrac{5}{x}$

47. $f(x) = x + \dfrac{2}{x - 1}$,
$g(x) = 3x^3$

48. $f(x) = 9 - x^2$,
$g(x) = \dfrac{3}{x + 6} + 2x$

49. $f(x) = \dfrac{3}{2x + 9}$,

   $g(x) = \dfrac{5}{1 - x}$

50. $f(x) = \dfrac{5}{3 - x}$,

   $g(x) = \dfrac{1}{4x - 1}$

For each pair of functions f and g, determine the domain of f/g.

51. $f(x) = x^4$,
   $g(x) = x - 3$

52. $f(x) = 2x^3$,
   $g(x) = 5 - x$

53. $f(x) = 3x - 2$,
   $g(x) = 2x + 8$

54. $f(x) = 5 + x$,
   $g(x) = 6 - 2x$

55. $f(x) = \dfrac{3}{x - 4}$,
   $g(x) = 5 - x$

56. $f(x) = \dfrac{1}{2 - x}$,
   $g(x) = 7 + x$

57. $f(x) = \dfrac{2x}{x + 1}$,
   $g(x) = 2x + 5$

58. $f(x) = \dfrac{7x}{x - 2}$,
   $g(x) = 3x + 7$

For Exercises 59–66, consider the functions F and G as shown.

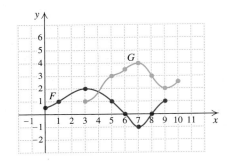

59. Determine $(F + G)(5)$ and $(F + G)(7)$.

60. Determine $(F \cdot G)(6)$ and $(F \cdot G)(9)$.

61. Determine $(G - F)(7)$ and $(G - F)(3)$.

62. Determine $(F/G)(3)$ and $(F/G)(7)$.

63. Find the domains of F, G, $F + G$, and F/G.

64. Find the domains of $F - G$, $F \cdot G$, and G/F.

65. Graph $F + G$.

66. Graph $G - F$.

In the following graph, S(t) represents the number of gallons of carbonated soft drinks consumed by the average American in year t, M(t) the number of gallons of milk, J(t) the number of gallons of fruit juice, and W(t) the number of gallons of bottled water.

Beverage consumption

Source: Economic Research Service, U. S. Department of Agriculture

67. Between what years did the average American drink more soft drinks than juice, bottled water, and milk combined? Explain how you determined this.

68. Examine the graphs before Exercises 31 and 32. Did the total number of births increase or decrease from 1970 to 2004? Did the percent of births by Caesarean section increase or decrease from 1970 to 2004? Explain how you determined your answers.

Skill Review

To prepare for Section 5.5, review solving a formula for a variable (Section 1.3).

Solve. [1.3]

69. $ac = b$, for c

70. $x - wz = y$, for w

71. $pq - rq = st$, for q

72. $ab = d - cb$, for b

73. $ab - cd = 3b + d$, for b

74. $ab - cd = 3b + d$, for d

Synthesis

75. Examine the graphs following Example 2 and explain how they might be modified to represent the absorption of 200 mg of Advil® taken four times a day.

76. If $f(x) = c$, where c is some positive constant, describe how the graphs of $y = g(x)$ and $y = (f + g)(x)$ will differ.

77. Find the domain of F/G, if

   $$F(x) = \dfrac{1}{x - 4} \quad \text{and} \quad G(x) = \dfrac{x^2 - 4}{x - 3}.$$

78. Find the domain of f/g, if

   $$f(x) = \dfrac{3x}{2x + 5} \quad \text{and} \quad g(x) = \dfrac{x^4 - 1}{3x + 9}.$$

79. Sketch the graph of two functions f and g such that the domain of f/g is

$$\{x \mid -2 \le x \le 3 \; and \; x \ne 1\}.$$

80. Find the domains of $f + g, f - g, f \cdot g,$ and f/g, if
$f = \{(-2, 1), (-1, 2), (0, 3), (1, 4), (2, 5)\}$
and
$g = \{(-4, 4), (-3, 3), (-2, 4), (-1, 0), (0, 5), (1, 6)\}.$

81. Find the domain of m/n, if

$$m(x) = 3x \quad for \; -1 < x < 5$$

and

$$n(x) = 2x - 3.$$

82. For f and g as defined in Exercise 80, find
$(f + g)(-2), (f \cdot g)(0),$ and $(f/g)(1).$

83. Write equations for two functions f and g such that the domain of $f + g$ is

$$\{x \mid x \text{ is a real number } and \; x \ne -2 \; and \; x \ne 5\}.$$

84. Let $y_1 = 2.5x + 1.5$, $y_2 = x - 3$, and $y_3 = y_1/y_2$. Depending on whether the CONNECTED or DOT mode is used, the graph of y_3 appears as follows. Use algebra to determine which graph more accurately represents y_3.

CONNECTED MODE

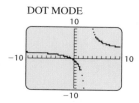
DOT MODE

85. Using the window $[-5, 5, -1, 9]$, graph $y_1 = 5$, $y_2 = x + 2$, and $y_3 = \sqrt{x}$. Then predict what shape the graphs of $y_1 + y_2$, $y_1 + y_3$, and $y_2 + y_3$ will take. Use a graphing calculator to check each prediction.

86. Use the TABLE feature on a graphing calculator to check your answers to Exercises 45, 47, 55, and 57. (See the Technology Connection on p. 336.)

COLLABORATIVE CORNER

Time On Your Hands

Focus: The algebra of functions
Time: 10–15 minutes
Group size: 2–3

The graph and the data at right chart the average retirement age $R(x)$ and life expectancy $E(x)$ of U.S. citizens in year x.

ACTIVITY

1. Working as a team, perform the appropriate calculations and then graph $E - R$.

2. What does $(E - R)(x)$ represent? In what fields of study or business might the function $E - R$ prove useful?

3. Should E and R really be calculated separately for men and women? Why or why not?

4. What advice would you give to someone considering early retirement?

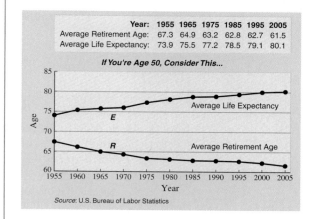

Year:	1955	1965	1975	1985	1995	2005
Average Retirement Age:	67.3	64.9	63.2	62.8	62.7	61.5
Average Life Expectancy:	73.9	75.5	77.2	78.5	79.1	80.1

If You're Age 50, Consider This...

Source: U.S. Bureau of Labor Statistics

5.5 Formulas, Applications, and Variation

Formulas ▪ Direct Variation ▪ Inverse Variation ▪ Joint Variation and Combined Variation

Formulas

Formulas occur frequently as mathematical models. Many formulas contain rational expressions, and to solve such formulas for a specified letter, we proceed as when solving rational equations.

EXAMPLE 1

Electronics. The formula

$$\frac{1}{R} = \frac{1}{r_1} + \frac{1}{r_2}$$

is used by electricians to determine the resistance R of two resistors r_1 and r_2 connected in parallel.* Solve for r_1.

SOLUTION We use the same approach as in Section 4.6:

$$Rr_1r_2 \cdot \frac{1}{R} = Rr_1r_2 \cdot \left(\frac{1}{r_1} + \frac{1}{r_2}\right) \quad \text{Multiplying both sides by the LCD to clear fractions}$$

$$Rr_1r_2 \cdot \frac{1}{R} = Rr_1r_2 \cdot \frac{1}{r_1} + Rr_1r_2 \cdot \frac{1}{r_2} \quad \text{Multiplying to remove parentheses}$$

$$r_1r_2 = Rr_2 + Rr_1. \quad \text{Simplifying by removing factors equal to 1: } \frac{R}{R} = 1; \frac{r_1}{r_1} = 1; \frac{r_2}{r_2} = 1$$

At this point it is tempting to multiply by $1/r_2$ to get r_1 alone on the left, *but note that there is an r_1 on the right.* We must get all the terms involving r_1 on the *same side* of the equation.

$$r_1r_2 - Rr_1 = Rr_2 \quad \text{Subtracting } Rr_1 \text{ from both sides}$$

$$r_1(r_2 - R) = Rr_2 \quad \text{Factoring out } r_1 \text{ in order to combine like terms}$$

$$r_1 = \frac{Rr_2}{r_2 - R} \quad \text{Dividing both sides by } r_2 - R \text{ to get } r_1 \text{ alone}$$

This formula can be used to calculate r_1 whenever R and r_2 are known.

TRY EXERCISE ▸ 17

EXAMPLE 2

Astronomy. The formula

$$\frac{V^2}{R^2} = \frac{2g}{R + h}$$

is used to find a satellite's *escape velocity V*, where R is a planet's radius, h is the satellite's height above the planet, and g is the planet's gravitational constant. Solve for h.

---

*Recall that the subscripts 1 and 2 merely indicate that r_1 and r_2 are different variables representing similar quantities.

SOLUTION We first multiply by the LCD, $R^2(R + h)$, to clear fractions:

$$\frac{V^2}{R^2} = \frac{2g}{R + h}$$

$$R^2(R + h)\frac{V^2}{R^2} = R^2(R + h)\frac{2g}{R + h} \quad \text{Multiplying to clear fractions}$$

$$\frac{R^2(R + h)V^2}{R^2} = \frac{R^2(R + h)2g}{R + h}$$

$$(R + h)V^2 = R^2 \cdot 2g. \quad \text{Removing factors equal to 1:}$$
$$\frac{R^2}{R^2} = 1 \text{ and } \frac{R + h}{R + h} = 1$$

Remember: We are solving for h. Although we *could* distribute V^2, since h appears only within the factor $R + h$, it is easier to divide both sides by V^2:

$$\frac{(R + h)V^2}{V^2} = \frac{2R^2g}{V^2} \quad \text{Dividing both sides by } V^2$$

$$R + h = \frac{2R^2g}{V^2} \quad \text{Removing a factor equal to 1: } \frac{V^2}{V^2} = 1$$

$$h = \frac{2R^2g}{V^2} - R. \quad \text{Subtracting } R \text{ from both sides}$$

The last equation can be used to determine the height of a satellite above a planet when the planet's radius and gravitational constant, along with the satellite's escape velocity, are known.

TRY EXERCISE 29

EXAMPLE 3

Acoustics (the Doppler Effect). The formula

$$f = \frac{sg}{s + v}$$

is used to determine the frequency f of a sound that is moving at velocity v toward a listener who hears the sound as frequency g. Here s is the speed of sound in a particular medium. Solve for s.

STUDENT NOTES —————

The steps used to solve equations are precisely the same steps used to solve formulas. If you feel "rusty" in this regard, study the earlier section in which this type of equation first appeared. Then make sure that you can consistently solve those equations before returning to the work with formulas.

SOLUTION We first clear fractions by multiplying by the LCD, $s + v$:

$$f \cdot (s + v) = \frac{sg}{s + v}(s + v)$$

$$fs + fv = sg. \quad \text{The variable for which we are solving, } s, \text{ appears on both sides, forcing us to distribute on the left side.}$$

Next, we must get all terms containing s on one side:

$$fv = sg - fs \qquad \text{Subtracting } fs \text{ from both sides}$$

$$fv = s(g - f) \qquad \text{Factoring out } s. \text{ This is like combining like terms.}$$

$$\frac{fv}{g - f} = s. \qquad \text{Dividing both sides by } g - f$$

Since s is isolated on one side, we have solved for s. This last equation can be used to determine the speed of sound whenever f, v, and g are known.

TRY EXERCISE ▶ 19

To Solve a Rational Equation for a Specified Variable

1. Multiply both sides by the LCD to clear fractions, if necessary.
2. Multiply to remove parentheses, if necessary.
3. Get all terms with the specified variable alone on one side.
4. Factor out the specified variable if it is in more than one term.
5. Multiply or divide on both sides to isolate the specified variable.

Variation

To extend our study of formulas and functions, we now examine three real-world situations: direct variation, inverse variation, and combined variation.

DIRECT VARIATION

A computer technician earns \$22 per hour. In 1 hr, \$22 is earned. In 2 hr, \$44 is earned. In 3 hr, \$66 is earned, and so on. This gives rise to a set of ordered pairs:

$$(1, 22), (2, 44), (3, 66), (4, 88), \quad \text{and so on.}$$

Note that the ratio of earnings E to time t is $\frac{22}{1}$ in every case.

If a situation is modeled by pairs for which the ratio is constant, we say there is **direct variation**. Here earnings *vary directly* as the time:

We have $\dfrac{E}{t} = 22$, so $E = 22t$ or, using function notation, $E(t) = 22t$.

Direct Variation

When a situation is modeled by a linear function of the form $f(x) = kx$, or $y = kx$, where k is a nonzero constant, we say that there is *direct variation*, that *y varies directly* as x, or that *y is proportional to* x. The number k is called the *variation constant*, or *constant of proportionality*.

Note that for $k > 0$, any equation of the form $y = kx$ indicates that as x increases, y increases as well.

EXAMPLE 4 Find the variation constant and an equation of variation if y varies directly as x, and $y = 32$ when $x = 2$.

SOLUTION We know that $(2, 32)$ is a solution of $y = kx$. Therefore,

$$32 = k \cdot 2 \qquad \text{Substituting}$$

$$\frac{32}{2} = k, \quad \text{or} \quad k = 16. \qquad \text{Solving for } k$$

The variation constant is 16. The equation of variation is $y = 16x$. The notation $y(x) = 16x$ or $f(x) = 16x$ is also used.

TRY EXERCISE 43

EXAMPLE 5 *Ocean waves.* The speed v of a train of ocean waves varies directly as the swell period t, or time between successive waves. Waves with a swell period of 12 sec are traveling 21 mph. How fast are waves traveling that have a swell period of 20 sec?

Source: www.rodntube.com

SOLUTION

1. **Familiarize.** Because of the phrase "v . . . varies directly as . . . t," we express the speed of the wave v, in miles per hour, as a function of the swell period t, in seconds. Thus, $v(t) = kt$, where k is the variation constant. Because we are using ratios, we can use the units "seconds" and "miles per hour" without converting sec to hr or hr to sec. Knowing that waves with a swell period of 12 sec are traveling 21 mph, we have $v(12) = 21$.

2. **Translate.** We find the variation constant using the data and then use it to write the equation of variation:

$$v(t) = kt$$
$$v(12) = k \cdot 12 \qquad \text{Replacing } t \text{ with } 12$$
$$21 = k \cdot 12 \qquad \text{Replacing } v(12) \text{ with } 21$$
$$\frac{21}{12} = k \qquad \text{Solving for } k$$
$$1.75 = k. \qquad \text{This is the variation constant.}$$

The equation of variation is $v(t) = 1.75t$. This is the translation.

3. **Carry out.** To find the speed of waves with a swell period of 20 sec, we compute $v(20)$:

$$v(t) = 1.75t$$
$$v(20) = 1.75(20) \qquad \text{Substituting 20 for } t$$
$$= 35.$$

4. **Check.** To check, we could reexamine all our calculations. Note that our answer seems reasonable since the ratios 21/12 and 35/20 are both 1.75.

5. **State.** Waves with a swell period of 20 sec are traveling 35 mph.

TRY EXERCISE 55

INVERSE VARIATION

Suppose a bus travels 20 mi. At 20 mph, the trip takes 1 hr. At 40 mph, it takes $\frac{1}{2}$ hr. At 60 mph, it takes $\frac{1}{3}$ hr, and so on. This gives pairs of numbers, all having the same product:

$$(20, 1), \left(40, \tfrac{1}{2}\right), \left(60, \tfrac{1}{3}\right), \left(80, \tfrac{1}{4}\right), \quad \text{and so on.}$$

Note that the product of each pair is 20. When a situation is modeled by pairs for which the product is constant, we say that there is **inverse variation**. Since $r \cdot t = 20$, we have

$$t = \frac{20}{r} \quad \text{or, using function notation,} \quad t(r) = \frac{20}{r}.$$

Inverse Variation

When a situation is modeled by a rational function of the form $f(x) = k/x$, or $y = k/x$, where k is a nonzero constant, we say that there is *inverse variation*, that y *varies inversely as* x, or that y *is inversely proportional to* x. The number k is called the *variation constant*, or *constant of proportionality*.

Note that for $k > 0$, any equation of the form $y = k/x$ indicates that as x increases, y decreases.

EXAMPLE 6 Find the variation constant and an equation of variation if y varies inversely as x, and $y = 32$ when $x = 0.2$.

SOLUTION We know that $(0.2, 32)$ is a solution of

$$y = \frac{k}{x}.$$

Therefore,

$$32 = \frac{k}{0.2} \quad \text{Substituting}$$
$$(0.2)32 = k$$
$$6.4 = k. \quad \text{Solving for } k$$

The variation constant is 6.4. The equation of variation is

$$y = \frac{6.4}{x}.$$

 TRY EXERCISE 49

There are many real-life quantities that vary inversely.

EXAMPLE 7 *Movie downloads.* The time t that it takes to download a movie file varies inversely as the transfer speed s of the Internet connection. A typical full-length movie file will transfer in 48 min at a transfer speed of 256 KB/s (kilobytes per second). How long will it take to transfer the same movie file at a transfer speed of 32 KB/s?

Source: www.xsvidmovies.com

SOLUTION

1. **Familiarize.** Because of the phrase ". . . varies inversely as the transfer speed," we express the download time t, in minutes, as a function of the transfer speed s, in kilobytes per second. Thus, $t(s) = k/s$.

2. **Translate.** We use the given information to solve for k. We will then use that result to write the equation of variation.

$$t(s) = \frac{k}{s}$$

$$t(256) = \frac{k}{256} \qquad \text{Replacing } s \text{ with } 256$$

$$48 = \frac{k}{256} \qquad \text{Replacing } t(256) \text{ with } 48$$

$$12{,}288 = k.$$

The equation of variation is $t(s) = 12{,}288/s$. This is the translation.

3. **Carry out.** To find the download time at a transfer speed of 32 KB/s, we calculate $t(32)$:

$$t(32) = \frac{12{,}288}{32} = 384.$$

4. **Check.** Note that, as expected, as the transfer speed goes *down*, the download time goes *up*. Also, the products $48 \cdot 256$ and $32 \cdot 384$ are both 12,288.

5. **State.** At a transfer speed of 32 KB/s, it will take 384 min, or 6 hr 24 min, to download the movie file.

> TRY EXERCISE 57

JOINT VARIATION AND COMBINED VARIATION

When a variable varies directly with more than one other variable, we say that there is *joint variation*. For example, in the formula for the volume of a right circular cylinder, $V = \pi r^2 h$, we say that V varies *jointly* as h and the square of r.

> ### Joint Variation
> y varies *jointly* as x and z if, for some nonzero constant k, $y = kxz$.

EXAMPLE 8   Find an equation of variation if y varies jointly as x and z, and $y = 30$ when $x = 2$ and $z = 3$.

SOLUTION   We have

$$y = kxz,$$

so

$$30 = k \cdot 2 \cdot 3$$
$$k = 5. \qquad \text{The variation constant is 5.}$$

The equation of variation is $y = 5xz$.

> TRY EXERCISE 73

Joint variation is one form of *combined variation*. In general, when a variable varies directly and/or inversely, at the same time, with more than one other variable, there is **combined variation**. Examples 8 and 9 are both examples of combined variation.

EXAMPLE 9 Find an equation of variation if y varies jointly as x and z and inversely as the square of w, and $y = 105$ when $x = 3$, $z = 20$, and $w = 2$.

SOLUTION The equation of variation is of the form

$$y = k \cdot \frac{xz}{w^2},$$

so, substituting, we have

$$105 = k \cdot \frac{3 \cdot 20}{2^2}$$
$$105 = k \cdot 15$$
$$k = 7.$$

Thus,

$$y = 7 \cdot \frac{xz}{w^2}.$$

TRY EXERCISE 75

5.5 EXERCISE SET

For Extra Help   PRACTICE WATCH DOWNLOAD

Concept Reinforcement *Match each statement with the correct term that completes it from the list on the right.*

1. To clear fractions, we can multiply both sides of an equation by the _____.

2. With direct variation, pairs of numbers have a constant _____.

3. With inverse variation, pairs of numbers have a constant _____.

4. If $y = k/x$, then y varies _____ as x.

5. If $y = kx$, then y varies _____ as x.

6. If $y = kxz$, then y varies _____ as x and z.

a) Directly

b) Inversely

c) Jointly

d) LCD

e) Product

f) Ratio

Determine whether each situation represents direct variation or inverse variation.

7. Two painters can scrape a house in 9 hr, whereas three painters can scrape the house in 6 hr.

8. Andres planted 5 bulbs in 20 min and 7 bulbs in 28 min.

9. Salma swam 2 laps in 7 min and 6 laps in 21 min.

10. It took 2 band members 80 min to set up for a show; with 4 members working, it took 40 min.

11. It took 3 hr for 4 volunteers to wrap the campus' collection of Toys for Tots, but only 1.5 hr with 8 volunteers working.

12. Ayana's air conditioner cooled off 1000 ft^3 in 10 min and 3000 ft^3 in 30 min.

Solve each formula for the specified variable.

13. $f = \dfrac{L}{d}$; d

14. $\dfrac{W_1}{W_2} = \dfrac{d_1}{d_2}$; W_1

15. $s = \dfrac{(v_1 + v_2)t}{2}$; v_1

16. $s = \dfrac{(v_1 + v_2)t}{2}$; t

17. $\dfrac{t}{a} + \dfrac{t}{b} = 1$; b

18. $\dfrac{1}{R} = \dfrac{1}{r_1} + \dfrac{1}{r_2}$; R

19. $R = \dfrac{gs}{g + s}$; g

20. $K = \dfrac{rt}{r - t}$; t

21. $I = \dfrac{nE}{R + nr}$; n

22. $I = \dfrac{nE}{R + nr}$; r

23. $\dfrac{1}{p} + \dfrac{1}{q} = \dfrac{1}{f}$; q

24. $\dfrac{1}{p} + \dfrac{1}{q} = \dfrac{1}{f}$; p

25. $S = \dfrac{H}{m(t_1 - t_2)}$; t_1

26. $S = \dfrac{H}{m(t_1 - t_2)}$; H

27. $\dfrac{E}{e} = \dfrac{R + r}{r}$; r

28. $\dfrac{E}{e} = \dfrac{R + r}{R}$; R

29. $S = \dfrac{a}{1 - r}$; r

30. $S = \dfrac{a - ar^n}{1 - r}$; a

Aha! **31.** $c = \dfrac{f}{(a + b)c}$; $a + b$

32. $d = \dfrac{g}{d(c + f)}$; $c + f$

33. *Interest.* The formula

$$P = \frac{A}{1 + r}$$

is used to determine what principal P should be invested for one year at $(100 \cdot r)\%$ simple interest in order to have A dollars after a year. Solve for r.

34. *Taxable interest.* The formula

$$I_t = \frac{I_f}{1 - T}$$

gives the *taxable interest rate* I_t equivalent to the *tax-free interest rate* I_f for a person in the $(100 \cdot T)\%$ tax bracket. Solve for T.

35. *Average speed.* The formula

$$v = \frac{d_2 - d_1}{t_2 - t_1}$$

gives an object's average speed v when that object has traveled d_1 miles in t_1 hours and d_2 miles in t_2 hours. Solve for t_1.

36. *Average acceleration.* The formula

$$a = \frac{v_2 - v_1}{t_2 - t_1}$$

gives a vehicle's *average acceleration* when its velocity changes from v_1 at time t_1 to v_2 at time t_2. Solve for t_2.

37. *Work rate.* The formula

$$\frac{1}{t} = \frac{1}{a} + \frac{1}{b}$$

gives the total time t required for two workers to complete a job, if the workers' individual times are a and b. Solve for t.

38. *Planetary orbits.* The formula

$$\frac{x^2}{a^2} + \frac{y^2}{b^2} = 1$$

can be used to plot a planet's elliptical orbit of width $2a$ and length $2b$.
Solve for b^2.

39. *Semester average.* The formula

$$A = \frac{2Tt + Qq}{2T + Q}$$

gives a student's average A after T tests and Q quizzes, where each test counts as 2 quizzes, t is the test average, and q is the quiz average. Solve for Q.

40. *Astronomy.* The formula

$$L = \frac{dR}{D - d},$$

where D is the diameter of the sun, d is the diameter of the earth, R is the earth's distance from the sun, and L is some fixed distance, is used in calculating when lunar eclipses occur. Solve for D.

41. *Body-fat percentage.* The YMCA calculates men's body-fat percentage p using the formula

$$p = \frac{-98.42 + 4.15c - 0.082w}{w},$$

where c is the waist measurement, in inches, and w is the weight, in pounds. Solve for w.
Source: YMCA guide to Physical Fitness Assessment

42. *Preferred viewing distance.* Researchers model the distance D from which an observer prefers to watch television in "picture heights"—that is, multiples of the height of the viewing screen. The preferred viewing distance is given by

$$D = \frac{3.55H + 0.9}{H},$$

where D is in picture heights and H is in meters. Solve for H.
Source: www.tid.es, Telefonica Investigación y Desarrollo, S.A. Unipersonal

Find the variation constant and an equation of variation if y varies directly as x and the following conditions apply.

43. $y = 30$ when $x = 5$

44. $y = 80$ when $x = 16$

45. $y = 3.4$ when $x = 2$

46. $y = 2$ when $x = 5$

47. $y = 2$ when $x = \frac{1}{5}$

48. $y = 0.9$ when $x = 0.5$

Find the variation constant and an equation of variation in which y varies inversely as x, and the following conditions exist.

49. $y = 5$ when $x = 20$

50. $y = 40$ when $x = 8$

51. $y = 11$ when $x = 4$

52. $y = 9$ when $x = 10$

53. $y = 27$ when $x = \frac{1}{3}$

54. $y = 81$ when $x = \frac{1}{9}$

55. *Hooke's law.* Hooke's law states that the distance d that a spring is stretched by a hanging object varies directly as the mass m of the object. If the distance is 20 cm when the mass is 3 kg, what is the distance when the mass is 5 kg?

56. *Ohm's law.* The electric current I, in amperes, in a circuit varies directly as the voltage V. When 15 volts are applied, the current is 5 amperes. What is the current when 18 volts are applied?

57. *Work rate.* The time T required to do a job varies inversely as the number of people P working. It takes 5 hr for 7 volunteers to pick up rubbish from 1 mi of roadway. How long would it take 10 volunteers to complete the job?

58. *Pumping rate.* The time t required to empty a tank varies inversely as the rate r of pumping. If a Briggs and Stratton pump can empty a tank in 45 min at the rate of 600 kL/min, how long will it take the pump to empty the tank at 1000 kL/min?

59. *Water from melting snow.* The number of centimeters W of water produced from melting snow varies directly as the number of centimeters S of snow. Meteorologists know that under certain conditions, 150 cm of snow will melt to 16.8 cm of water. The average annual snowfall in Alta, Utah, is 500 in. Assuming the above conditions, how much water will replace the 500 in. of snow?

60. *Gardening.* The number of calories burned by a gardener is directly proportional to the time spent gardening. It takes 30 min to burn 180 calories. How long would it take to burn 240 calories when gardening?
Source: www.healthstatus.com

Aha! **61.** *Mass of water in a human.* The number of kilograms W of water in a human body varies directly as the mass of the body. A 96-kg person contains 64 kg of water. How many kilograms of water are in a 48-kg person?

62. *Weight on Mars.* The weight M of an object on Mars varies directly as its weight E on Earth. A person who weighs 95 lb on Earth weighs 38 lb on Mars. How much would a 100-lb person weigh on Mars?

63. *String length and frequency.* The frequency of a string is inversely proportional to its length. A violin string that is 33 cm long vibrates with a frequency of 260 Hz. What is the frequency when the string is shortened to 30 cm?

64. *Wavelength and frequency.* The wavelength W of a radio wave varies inversely as its frequency F. A wave with a frequency of 1200 kilohertz has a length of 300 meters. What is the length of a wave with a frequency of 800 kilohertz?

65. *Ultraviolet index.* At an ultraviolet, or UV, rating of 4, those people who are less sensitive to the sun will burn in 75 min. Given that the number of minutes it takes to burn, t, varies inversely with the UV rating, u, how long will it take less sensitive people to burn when the UV rating is 14?
Source: *The Electronic Textbook of Dermatology* at www.telemedicine.org

66. *Current and resistance.* The current I in an electrical conductor varies inversely as the resistance R of the conductor. If the current is $\frac{1}{2}$ ampere when the resistance is 240 ohms, what is the current when the resistance is 540 ohms?

67. *Air pollution.* The average U.S. household of 2.6 people released 0.94 ton of carbon monoxide into the environment in a recent year. How many tons were released nationally? Use 305,000,000 as the U.S. population.
Sources: Based on data from the U.S. Environmental Protection Agency and the U.S. Census Bureau

68. *Relative aperture.* The relative aperture, or f-stop, of a 23.5-mm lens is directly proportional to the focal length F of the lens. If a lens with a 150-mm focal length has an f-stop of 6.3, find the f-stop of a 23.5-mm lens with a focal length of 80 mm.

Find an equation of variation in which:

69. y varies directly as the square of x, and $y = 50$ when $x = 10$.

70. y varies directly as the square of x, and $y = 0.15$ when $x = 0.1$.

71. y varies inversely as the square of x, and $y = 50$ when $x = 10$.

72. y varies inversely as the square of x, and $y = 0.15$ when $x = 0.1$.

73. y varies jointly as x and z, and $y = 105$ when $x = 14$ and $z = 5$.

74. y varies jointly as x and z, and $y = \frac{3}{2}$ when $x = 2$ and $z = 10$.

75. y varies jointly as w and the square of x and inversely as z, and $y = 49$ when $w = 3$, $x = 7$, and $z = 12$.

76. y varies directly as x and inversely as w and the square of z, and $y = 4.5$ when $x = 15$, $w = 5$, and $z = 2$.

77. *Stopping distance of a car.* The stopping distance d of a car after the brakes have been applied varies directly as the square of the speed r. Once the brakes are applied, a car traveling 60 mph can stop in 138 ft. What stopping distance corresponds to a speed of 40 mph?
Source: Based on data from Edmunds.com

78. *Reverberation time.* A sound's reverberation time T is the time it takes for the sound level to decrease by 60 dB (decibels) after the sound has been turned off. Reverberation time varies directly as the volume V of a room and inversely as the sound absorption A of the room. A given sound has a reverberation time of 1.5 sec in a room with a volume of 90 m^3 and a sound absorption of 9.6. What is the reverberation time of the same sound in a room with a volume of 84 m^3 and a sound absorption of 10.5?
Source: www.isover.co.uk

79. *Volume of a gas.* The volume V of a given mass of a gas varies directly as the temperature T and inversely as the pressure P. If $V = 231 \text{ cm}^3$ when $T = 300°\text{K}$ (Kelvin) and $P = 20 \text{ lb/cm}^2$, what is the volume when $T = 320°\text{K}$ and $P = 16 \text{ lb/cm}^2$?

80. *Intensity of a signal.* The intensity I of a television signal varies inversely as the square of the distance d from the transmitter. If the intensity is 25 W/m^2 at a distance of 2 km, what is the intensity 6.25 km from the transmitter?

81. *Atmospheric drag.* Wind resistance, or atmospheric drag, tends to slow down moving objects. Atmospheric drag W varies jointly as an object's surface area A and velocity v. If a car traveling at a speed of 40 mph with a surface area of 37.8 ft^2 experiences a drag of 222 N (Newtons), how fast must a car with 51 ft^2 of surface area travel in order to experience a drag force of 430 N?

82. *Drag force.* The drag force F on a boat varies jointly as the wetted surface area A and the square of the velocity of the boat. If a boat traveling 6.5 mph experiences a drag force of 86 N when the wetted surface area is 41.2 ft^2, find the wetted surface area of a boat traveling 8.2 mph with a drag force of 94 N.

83. If y varies directly as x, does doubling x cause y to be doubled as well? Why or why not?

84. Which exercise did you find easier to work: Exercise 15 or Exercise 19? Why?

Skill Review

To prepare for Chapter 6, review solving an equation for y and translating phrases to algebraic expressions (Section 1.3).

Solve. [1.3]

85. $x - 6y = 3$, for y

86. $3x - 8y = 5$, for y

87. $5x + 2y = -3$, for y

88. $x + 8y = 4$, for y

Translate each of the following. Do not solve.

89. Five more than twice a number is 49.

90. Three less than half of some number is 57.

91. The sum of two consecutive integers is 145.

92. The difference between a number and its opposite is 20.

Synthesis

93. Suppose that the number of customer complaints is inversely proportional to the number of employees hired. Will a firm reduce the number of complaints more by expanding from 5 to 10 employees, or from 20 to 25? Explain. Consider using a graph to help justify your answer.

94. Why do you think subscripts are used in Exercises 15 and 25 but not in Exercises 27 and 28?

95. *Escape velocity.* A satellite's escape velocity is 6.5 mi/sec, the radius of the earth is 3960 mi, and the earth's gravitational constant is 32.2 ft/sec^2. How far is the satellite from the surface of the earth? (See Example 2.)

96. The *harmonic mean* of two numbers a and b is a number M such that the reciprocal of M is the average of the reciprocals of a and b. Find a formula for the harmonic mean.

97. *Health-care.* Young's rule for determining the size of a particular child's medicine dosage c is

$$c = \frac{a}{a + 12} \cdot d,$$

where a is the child's age and d is the typical adult dosage. If a child's age is doubled, the dosage increases. Find the ratio of the larger dosage to the smaller dosage. By what percent does the dosage increase?
Source: Olsen, June Looby, Leon J. Ablon, and Anthony Patrick Giangrasso, *Medical Dosage Calculations*, 6th ed.

98. Solve for x:

$$x^2\left(1 - \frac{2pq}{x}\right) = \frac{2p^2q^3 - pq^2x}{-q}.$$

99. *Average acceleration.* The formula

$$a = \frac{\dfrac{d_4 - d_3}{t_4 - t_3} - \dfrac{d_2 - d_1}{t_2 - t_1}}{t_4 - t_2}$$

can be used to approximate average acceleration, where the d's are distances and the t's are the corresponding times. Solve for t_1.

100. If y varies inversely as the cube of x and x is multiplied by 0.5, what is the effect on y?

101. *Intensity of light.* The intensity I of light from a bulb varies directly as the wattage of the bulb and inversely as the square of the distance d from the bulb. If the wattage of a light source and its distance from reading matter are both doubled, how does the intensity change?

102. Describe in words the variation represented by $W = \dfrac{km_1 M_1}{d^2}$. Assume k is a constant.

103. *Tension of a musical string.* The tension T on a string in a musical instrument varies jointly as the string's mass per unit length m, the square of its length l, and the square of its fundamental frequency f. A 2-m long string of mass 5 gm/m with a fundamental frequency of 80 has a tension of 100 N (Newtons). How long should the same string be if its tension is going to be changed to 72 N?

104. *Volume and cost.* A peanut butter jar in the shape of a right circular cylinder is 4 in. high and 3 in. in diameter and sells for $1.20. If we assume that cost is proportional to volume, how much should a jar 6 in. high and 6 in. in diameter cost?

105. *Golf distance finder.* A device used in golf to estimate the distance d to a hole measures the size s that the 7-ft pin *appears* to be in a viewfinder. The viewfinder uses the principle, diagrammed here, that s gets bigger when d gets smaller. If $s = 0.56$ in. when $d = 50$ yd, find an equation of variation that expresses d as a function of s. What is d when $s = 0.40$ in.?

HOW IT WORKS:
Just sight the flagstick through the viewfinder... fit flag between top dashed line and the solid line below... ...read the distance, 50 – 220 yards.

50 70 90 110 130 150 170 190 210
RANGE YARDS

Nothing to focus.

Gives you exact distance that your ball lies from the flagstick.

Choose proper club on every approach shot.

Figure new pin placement instantly.

Train your naked eye for formal and tournament play.

Eliminate the need to remember every stake, tree, and bush on the course.

Additional Exercises

Solve each formula for the specified variable.

106. $ax + 8 = bx - 1$, for x

107. $cx + 10 = bx + 12$, for x

108. $ay - 11 = 13 - dy$, for y

109. $cy - 1 = 18 - dy$, for y

110. $am - h = cm + k$, for m

111. $bn + c = an + d$, for n

112. $ab - cx = dx + b$, for x

113. $uv - dx = bx - v$, for x

Solve for y.

114. $\dfrac{x}{2} + \dfrac{y}{8} = 1$

115. $\dfrac{x}{3} - \dfrac{y}{6} = 1$

116. $\dfrac{x}{5} - \dfrac{y}{6} = 2$

117. $\dfrac{x}{10} + \dfrac{y}{4} = -1$

118. $\dfrac{x}{-5} + \dfrac{y}{3} = 1$

119. $\dfrac{x}{-2} + \dfrac{y}{-4} = 1$

120. $\dfrac{x}{-10} + \dfrac{y}{3} = 8$

121. $\dfrac{x}{4} + \dfrac{y}{-5} = 10$

Find an equation of variation in which . . .

122. y varies directly as the square of x and inversely as w and z, and $y = 12$ when $w = 2$, $x = 12$, and $z = 18$

123. y varies jointly as x and z and inversely as the square of w, and $y = 24$ when $w = 5$, $x = 10$, and $z = 15$

124. y varies jointly as the x and the cube of w and inversely as z, and $y = \frac{24}{5}$ when $w = 2$, $x = 9$, and $z = 5$

125. y varies directly as x and inversely as z and the cube of w, and $y = \frac{1}{60}$ when $w = 2$, $x = 8$, and $z = 6$

126. y varies jointly as w, z, and p and inversely as the square of x, and $y = 2205$ when $p = 6$, $w = 14$, $x = 0.2$, and $z = 0.5$

127. y varies jointly as p and the square of z and inversely as w and x, and $y = 0.016$ when $p = 6$, $w = 0.2$, $x = 30$, and $z = 0.1$

128. Using the Mosteller formula, the body surface area B of a person varies jointly as the square root of the weight w and the square root of the height h. If $B = 1.95$ m^2 when $w = 81$ kg and $h = 169$ cm, what is the body surface area when $w = 64$ kg and $h = 144$ cm?

129. The weight W of a fish varies jointly as the length l of the fish and the square of the girth g of the fish. If $W = 4.32$ lb when $l = 24$ in. and $g = 12$ in., what is the weight of a fish when $l = 18$ in. and $g = 10$ in.?

130. The centripetal force F acting on an object being spun in a circle varies directly as the square of the linear velocity v and inversely as the radius r of the circle. If $F = 1250$ N when $v = 10$ m/s and $r = 8$ m, what is the centripetal force when $v = 12$ m/s and $r = 2.5$ m?

131. The volume V of a pyramid with a square base varies jointly as the height h of the pyramid and the square of the length b of a side of the base. If $V = 100$ cm^3 when $h = 12$ cm and $b = 5$ cm, what is the volume of a pyramid with a square base when $h = 16$ cm and $b = 9$ cm.

132. If y varies directly as x and $y = 15$ when $x = 5$, find y when $x = 3$.

133. If y varies directly as x and $y = 30$ when $x = 2$, find y when $x = 10$.

134. If y varies directly as x and $y = 6$ when $x = \frac{1}{2}$, find y when $x = 9$.

135. If y varies directly as x and $y = 0.2$ when $x = 0.5$, find y when $x = 1.2$.

136. If y varies inversely as x and $y = 12$ when $x = 3$, find y when $x = 9$.

137. If y varies inversely as x and $y = 100$ when $x = 2$, find y when $x = 25$.

138. If y varies inversely as x and $y = 0.4$ when $x = 1.5$, find y when $x = 3$.

139. If y varies inversely as x and $y = \frac{1}{2}$ when $x = \frac{1}{3}$, find y when $x = 2$.

140. If y varies directly as the square of x and $y = 8$ when $x = 4$, find y when $x = 10$.

141. If y varies directly as the square of x and $y = 5$ when $x = 0.1$, find y when $x = 2$.

142. If y varies inversely as the square of x and $y = \frac{1}{5}$ when $x = 10$, find y when $x = 4$.

143. If y varies inversely as the square of x and $y = 3$ when $x = 5$, find y when $x = 10$.

144. If y varies jointly as x and z, and $y = 2$ when $x = 10$ and $z = 5$, find y when $x = 4$ and $z = 6$.

145. If y varies jointly as x and z, and $y = 120$ when $x = 5$ and $z = 6$, find x when $y = 40$ and $z = 2$.

146. If y varies jointly as x and the square of z, and $y = 40$ when $x = 2$ and $z = 10$, find x when $y = 750$ and $z = 5$.

147. If y varies jointly as x and the square of z, and $y = 0.5$ when $x = 8$ and $z = 0.1$, find y when $x = 100$ and $z = 2$.

148. If y varies inversely as the cube of x and $y = 40$ when $x = 2$, find y when $x = 5$.

149. If y varies inversely as the cube of x and $y = 15$ when $x = 0.2$, find x when $y = 1.875$.

150. If y varies directly as x and inversely as the square of z, and $y = 18$ when $x = 2$ and $z = 3$, find x when $y = 12$ and $z = \frac{1}{2}$.

151. If y varies directly as x and inversely as the square of z, and $y = 0.9$ when $x = 12$ and $z = 0.5$, find y when $x = 16$ and $z = 2$.

Study Summary

KEY TERMS AND CONCEPTS	EXAMPLES

SECTION 5.1: INTRODUCTION TO FUNCTIONS

A **function** is a correspondence between a first set, called the **domain**, and a second set, called the **range**, such that each member of the domain corresponds to *exactly one* member of the range.

The correspondence f: $\{(-1, \frac{1}{2}), (0, 1), (1, 2), (2, 4), (3, 8)\}$ is a function.

The domain of $f = \{-1, 0, 1, 2, 3\}$.

The range of $f = \{\frac{1}{2}, 1, 2, 4, 8\}$.

$f(-1) = \frac{1}{2}$

The input -1 corresponds to the output $\frac{1}{2}$.

The Vertical-Line Test

If it is possible for a vertical line to cross a graph more than once, then the graph is not the graph of a function.

 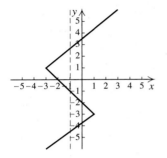

This *is* the graph of a function. This *is not* the graph of a function.

SECTION 5.2: DOMAIN AND RANGE

The domain of a function is the set of all x-coordinates of the points on the graph.

The range of a function is the set of all y-coordinates of the points on the graph.

Consider the function given by
$f(x) = |x| - 3$.

The domain of the function is $\mathbb{R}$.
The range of the function
is $\{y | y \geq -3\}$, or $[-3, \infty)$.

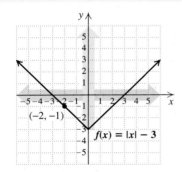

Unless otherwise stated, the domain of a function is the set of all numbers for which function values can be calculated.

Consider the function given by $f(x) = \dfrac{x + 2}{x - 7}$.

Function values cannot be calculated when the denominator is 0.
Since $x - 7 = 0$ when $x = 7$, the domain of f is

$\{x | x$ is a real number *and* $x = 7\}$.

SECTION 5.3: GRAPHS OF FUNCTIONS

Linear Function

$$f(x) = mx + b$$

Constant Function

$$f(x) = b$$

Graph: $f(x) = \frac{1}{2}x - 3$.

We plot the y-intercept, $(0, -3)$.
From there, we count off a slope of $\frac{1}{2}$: We go up 1 unit and to the right 2 units to the point $(2, -2)$.
We then draw the graph.

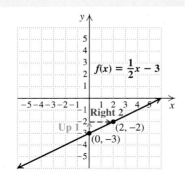

Graphs of nonlinear functions are not straight lines.

x	$f(x) = x^2 - 3$	$(x, f(x))$
0	-3	$(0, -3)$
-1	-2	$(-1, -2)$
1	-2	$(1, -2)$
-2	1	$(-2, 1)$
2	1	$(2, 1)$

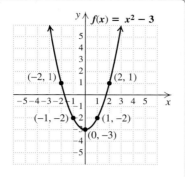

f is a quadratic function.

Domain of $f = \mathbb{R}$, or $(-\infty, \infty)$.

Range of $f = \{y | y \geq -3\}$, or $[-3, \infty)$.

SECTION 5.4: THE ALGEBRA OF FUNCTIONS

For $f(x) = x^2 + 3x$ and $g(x) = x - 5$:

$(f + g)(x) = f(x) + g(x)$

$$(f + g)(x) = f(x) + g(x)$$
$$= x^2 + 3x + x - 5 = x^2 + 4x - 5;$$

$(f - g)(x) = f(x) - g(x)$

$$(f - g)(x) = f(x) - g(x)$$
$$= x^2 + 3x - (x - 5) = x^2 + 2x + 5;$$

$(f \cdot g)(x) = f(x) \cdot g(x)$

$$(f \cdot g)(x) = f(x) \cdot g(x)$$
$$= (x^2 + 3x)(x - 5) = x^3 - 2x^2 - 15x;$$

$(f/g)(x) = f(x)/g(x)$, provided $g(x) \neq 0$

$$(f/g)(x) = f(x)/g(x), \text{ provided } g(x) \neq 0$$
$$= \frac{x^2 + 3x}{x - 5}, \text{ provided } x \neq 5. \qquad g(5) = 0$$

SECTION 5.5: FORMULAS, APPLICATIONS, AND VARIATION

Direct Variation

$$y = kx$$

If y varies directly as x and $y = 45$ when $x = 0.15$, find the equation of variation.

$$y = kx$$
$$45 = k(0.15)$$
$$300 = k$$

The equation of variation is $y = 300x$.

Inverse Variation

$$y = \frac{k}{x}$$

If y varies inversely as x and $y = 45$ when $x = 0.15$, find the equation of variation.

$$y = \frac{k}{x}$$
$$45 = \frac{k}{0.15}$$
$$6.75 = k$$

The equation of variation is $y = \dfrac{6.75}{x}$.

Joint Variation $y = kxz$	*If y varies jointly as x and z and y* $= 40$ *when x* $= 5$ *and z* $= 4$, *find the equation of variation.*
	$$y = kxz$$ $$40 = k \cdot 5 \cdot 4$$ $$2 = k$$ The equation of variation is $y = 2xz$.

Review Exercises: Chapter 5

Concept Reinforcement *Classify each of the following as either true or false.*

1. Every function is a relation. [5.1]

2. When we are discussing functions, the notation $f(3)$ does not mean $f \cdot 3$. [5.1]

3. If a graph includes both $(9, 5)$ and $(7, 5)$, it cannot represent a function. [5.1]

4. The domain and the range of a function can be the same set of numbers. [5.2]

5. The horizontal-line test is a quick way to determine whether a graph represents a function. [5.1]

6. In a piecewise-defined function, the function values are determined using more than one rule. [5.2]

7. $(f + g)(x) = f(x) + g(x)$ is not an example of the distributive law when f and g are functions. [5.4]

8. In order for $(f/g)(a)$ to exist, we must have $g(a) \neq 0$. [5.4]

9. If x varies inversely as y, then there exists some constant k for which $x = k/y$. [5.5]

10. If 2 people can decorate for a party in 5 hr, and 10 people can decorate for the same party in 4 hr, the situation represents inverse variation. [5.5]

11. For the following graph of f, determine **(a)** $f(2)$; **(b)** the domain of f; **(c)** any x-values for which $f(x) = 2$; and **(d)** the range of f. [5.1], [5.2]

12. Find $g(-3)$ for $g(x) = \dfrac{x}{x + 1}$. [5.1]

13. Find $f(2a)$ for $f(x) = x^2 + 2x - 3$. [5.1]

14. The function $A(t) = 0.233t + 5.87$ can be used to estimate the median age of cars in the United States t years after 1990. (In this context, a median age of 3 yr means that half the cars are more than 3 yr old and half are less.) Predict the median age of cars in 2010; that is, find $A(20)$. [5.1]

Source: The Polk Co.

15. The following table shows the U.S. minimum hourly wage. Use the data in the table to draw a graph and to estimate the U.S. minimum hourly wage in 2012. [5.1]

Input, Year	Output, U.S. Minimum Hourly Wage
1997	$5.15
2007	5.85
2008	6.55
2009	7.25

For each of the graphs in Exercises 16–19, **(a)** *determine whether the graph represents a function and* **(b)** *if so, determine the domain and the range of the function.* [5.1], [5.2]

16.

17.

18.

19.

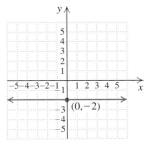

Find the domain of each function.

20. $f(x) = 3x^2 - 7$ [5.2]

21. $g(x) = \dfrac{x^2}{x - 1}$ [5.2]

22. $f(t) = \dfrac{1}{t^2 + 5t + 4}$ [5.2]

23. If a service agreement is cancelled, the amount that Vale Appliances will refund on the agreement is given by the function

$$r(t) = 900 - 15t,$$

where t is the number of weeks since the date of purchase. What is the domain of the function? [5.2]

24. For the function given by

$$f(x) = \begin{cases} 2 - x, & \text{if } x \le -2, \\ x^2, & \text{if } -2 < x \le 5, \\ x + 10, & \text{if } x > 5, \end{cases}$$

find **(a)** $f(-3)$; **(b)** $f(-2)$; **(c)** $f(4)$; and **(d)** $f(25)$. [5.2]

25. It costs $90 plus $30 a month to join the Family Fitness Center. Formulate a linear function to model the cost $C(t)$ for t months of membership, and determine the time required for the cost to reach $300. [5.3]

26. *Records in the 200-meter run.* In 1983, the record for the 200-m run was 19.75 sec. In 2007, it was 19.32 sec. Let $R(t)$ represent the record in the 200-m run and t the number of years since 1980. [5.3]

Source: International Association of Athletics Federation

a) Find a linear function that fits the data.

b) Use the function of part (a) to predict the record in 2013 and in 2020.

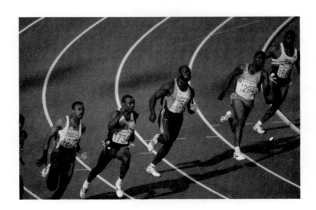

Classify each function as a linear function, an absolute-value function, a quadratic function, another polynomial function, or a rational function. [5.3]

27. $f(x) = |3x - 7|$

28. $g(x) = 4x^5 - 8x^3 + 7$

29. $p(x) = x^2 + x - 10$

30. $h(n) = 4n - 17$

31. $s(t) = \dfrac{t + 1}{t + 2}$

Graph each function and determine its domain and range. [5.3]

32. $f(x) = 3$

33. $f(x) = 2x + 1$

34. $g(x) = |x + 1|$

Let $g(x) = 3x - 6$ and $h(x) = x^2 + 1$. Find the following.

35. $(g \cdot h)(4)$ [5.4]

36. $(g - h)(-2)$ [5.4]

37. $(g/h)(-1)$ [5.4]

38. The domains of $g + h$ and $g \cdot h$ [5.4]

39. The domain of h/g [5.4]

Solve. [5.5]

40. $I = \dfrac{2V}{R + 2r}$, for r

41. $S = \dfrac{H}{m(t_1 - t_2)}$, for m

42. $\dfrac{1}{ac} = \dfrac{2}{ab} - \dfrac{3}{bc}$, for c

43. $T = \dfrac{A}{v(t_2 - t_1)}$, for t_1

44. Find an equation of variation in which y varies directly as x, and $y = 30$ when $x = 4$. [5.5]

45. Find an equation of variation in which y varies inversely as x, and $y = 3$ when $x = \frac{1}{4}$. [5.5]

46. Find an equation of variation in which y varies jointly as x and the square of w and inversely as z, and $y = 150$ when $x = 6$, $w = 10$, and $z = 2$. [5.5]

Solve. [5.5]

47. For those people with highly sensitive skin, an ultraviolet, or UV, rating of 6 will cause sunburn after 10 min. Given that the number of minutes it takes to burn t varies inversely as the UV rating u, how long will it take a highly sensitive person to burn on a day with a UV rating of 4?
Source: *The Electronic Textbook of Dermatology* found at www.telemedicine.org

48. The amount of waste generated by a family varies directly as the number of people in the family. The average U.S. family has 3.2 people and generates 14.4 lb of waste daily. How many pounds of waste would be generated daily by a family of 5?
Sources: Based on data from the U.S. Census Bureau and the U.S. Statistical Abstract 2007

49. *Electrical safety.* The amount of time t needed for an electrical shock to stop a 150-lb person's heart varies inversely as the square of the current flowing through the body. It is known that a 0.089-amp current is deadly to a 150-lb person after 3.4 sec. How long would it take a 0.096-amp current to be deadly?
Source: Safety Consulting Services

Synthesis

50. If two functions have the same domain and range, are the functions identical? Why or why not? [5.2]

51. Jenna believes that 0 is never in the domain of a rational function. Is she correct? Why or why not? [5.2]

52. Treasure Tea charges $7.99 for each package of loose tea. Shipping charges are $2.95 per package plus $20 per order for overnight delivery. Find a linear function for determining the cost of one order of x packages of tea, including shipping and overnight delivery. [5.3]

53. Determine the domain and the range of the function graphed below. [5.2]

Test: Chapter 5

1. For the following graph of f, determine (a) $f(-2)$; (b) the domain of f; (c) any x-value for which $f(x) = \frac{1}{2}$; and (d) the range of f.

2. There were 41.9 million international visitors to the United States in 2002 and 51.0 million visitors in 2006. Draw a graph and estimate the number of international visitors in 2005.
   Sources: U.S. Department of Commerce, ITA, Office of Travel and Tourism Industries; Global Insight, Inc.

For each of the following graphs, (a) determine whether the graph represents a function and (b) if so, determine the domain and the range of the function.

3.

4.

(2, 1)

5.

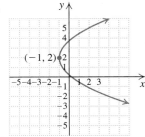

(−1, 2)

6. The distance d, in miles, that Kerry is from Chicago is given by the function $d(t) = 240 - 60t$, where t is the number of hours since he left Indianapolis. What is the domain of the function?

7. For the function given by
$$f(x) = \begin{cases} x^2, & \text{if } x < 0, \\ 3x - 5, & \text{if } 0 \le x \le 2, \\ x + 7, & \text{if } x > 2, \end{cases}$$
find (a) $f(0)$; (b) $f(3)$.

8. Porter paid $180 for his phone. His monthly service fee is $55. Formulate a linear function to model the cost $C(t)$ for t months of service, and determine the amount of time required for the total cost to reach $840.

9. If you rent a truck for one day and drive it 250 mi, the cost is $100. If you rent it for one day and drive it 300 mi, the cost is $115. Let $C(m)$ represent the cost, in dollars, of driving m miles.
   a) Find a linear function that fits the data.
   b) Use the function to determine how much it will cost to rent the truck for one day and drive it 500 mi.

Classify each function as a linear function, a quadratic function, another polynomial function, an absolute-value function, or a rational function. Then find the domain of each function.

10. $f(x) = \dfrac{1}{4}x + 7$

11. $g(x) = \dfrac{3}{x^2 - 16}$

12. $p(x) = 4x^2 + 7$

Graph each function and determine its domain and range.

13. $f(x) = \dfrac{1}{3}x - 2$ 14. $g(x) = x^2 - 1$

15. $h(x) = -\dfrac{1}{2}$

Find the following, given that $g(x) = \dfrac{1}{x}$ and $h(x) = 2x + 1$.

16. $g(-1)$ 17. $h(5a)$

18. $(g + h)(x)$

19. The domain of g

20. The domain of $g + h$

21. The domain of g/h

22. Solve $R = \dfrac{gs}{g+s}$ for s.

23. Find an equation of variation in which y varies directly as x, and $y = 10$ when $x = 20$.

24. The number of workers n needed to clean a stadium after a game varies inversely as the amount of time t allowed for the cleanup. If it takes 25 workers to clean the stadium when there are 6 hr allowed for the job, how many workers are needed if the stadium must be cleaned in 5 hr?

25. The surface area of a balloon varies directly as the square of its radius. The area is 325 in² when the radius is 5 in. What is the area when the radius is 7 in.?

Synthesis

26. The function $f(t) = 5 + 15t$ can be used to determine a bicycle racer's location, in miles from the starting line, measured t hours after passing the 5-mi mark.

  a) How far from the start will the racer be 1 hr and 40 min after passing the 5-mi mark?

  b) Assuming a constant rate, how fast is the racer traveling?

27. Given that $f(x) = 5x^2 + 1$ and $g(x) = 4x - 3$, find an expression for $h(x)$ so that the domain of $f/g/h$ is $\{x \mid x \text{ is a real number } and \ x \neq \frac{3}{4} \text{ and } x \neq \frac{2}{7}\}$.
Answers may vary.

Cumulative Review: Chapters 1–5

1. Evaluate
$$\frac{2x - y^2}{x + y}$$
for $x = 3$ and $y = -4$.

2. Convert to scientific notation: 391,000,000.

3. Determine the slope and the y-intercept for the line given by $7x - 4y = 12$. [2.6]

4. Find an equation for the line that passes through the points $(-1, 7)$ and $(4, -3)$. [2.7]

5. If
$$f(x) = \frac{x - 3}{x^2 - 11x + 30},$$
find **(a)** $f(3)$ and **(b)** the domain of f. [5.1], [5.2]

Graph on a plane.

6. $5x = y$ [2.2]

7. $8y + 2x = 16$ [2.3]

8. $f(x) = -4$ [5.2]

9. $y = \frac{1}{3}x - 2$ [2.6]

Perform the indicated operations and simplify.

10. $(8x^3y^2)(-3xy^2)$

11. $(5x^2 - 2x + 1)(3x^2 + x - 2)$

12. $(3x^2 + y)^2$

13. $(2x^2 - 9)(2x^2 + 9)$

14. $(-5m^3n^2 - 3mn^3) + (-4m^2n^2 + 4m^3n^2) - (2mn^3 - 3m^2n^2)$

15. $\dfrac{y^2 - 36}{2y + 8} \cdot \dfrac{y + 4}{y + 6}$ [4.2]

16. $\dfrac{x^4 - 1}{x^2 - x - 2} \div \dfrac{x^2 + 1}{x - 2}$ [4.2]

17. $\dfrac{5ab}{a^2 - b^2} + \dfrac{a + b}{a - b}$ [4.4]

18. $\dfrac{2}{m + 1} + \dfrac{3}{m - 5} - \dfrac{m^2 - 1}{m^2 - 4m - 5}$ [4.4]

19. $y - \dfrac{2}{3y}$ [4.4]

20. Simplify: $\dfrac{\dfrac{1}{x} - \dfrac{1}{y}}{x + y}$. [4.5]

Factor.

21. $4x^3 + 400x$ [3.1]

22. $x^2 + 8x - 84$ [3.2]

23. $16y^2 - 25$ [3.4]

24. $64x^3 + 8$ [3.5]

25. $t^2 - 16t + 64$ [3.4]

26. $x^6 - x^2$ [3.4]

27. $\frac{1}{8}b^3 - c^3$ [3.5]

28. $3t^2 + 17t - 28$ [3.3]

29. $x^5 - x^3y + x^2y - y^2$ [3.1]

Solve.

30. $8x = 1 + 16x^2$ [3.7]

31. $288 = 2y^2$ [3.7]

32. $\frac{1}{3}x - \frac{1}{5} \geq \frac{1}{5}x - \frac{1}{3}$ [1.6]

33. $5(x - 2) - (x - 3) = 7x - 2(5 - x)$ [1.2]

34. $\dfrac{6}{x - 5} = \dfrac{2}{2x}$ [4.6]

35. $\dfrac{3x}{x - 2} - \dfrac{6}{x + 2} = \dfrac{24}{x^2 - 4}$ [4.6]

36. $P = \dfrac{4a}{a + b}$, for a [5.5]

37. Find the slope of the line containing $(2, 5)$ and $(1, 10)$. [2.5]

38. Find the slope of the line given by $f(x) = 8x + 3$. [5.3]

39. Find the slope of the line given by $y + 6 = -4$. [2.5]

40. Find an equation of the line containing $(5, -2)$ and perpendicular to the line given by $x - y = 5$. [2.7]

Find the following, given that $f(x) = x + 5$ and $g(x) = x^2 - 1$.

41. $g(-10)$ [5.1]

42. $(g/f)(x)$ [5.4]

43. Find the domain of f if $f(x) = \dfrac{x}{x + 6}$. [5.2]

44. Determine the domain and the range of the function f represented below. [5.2]

45. *Broadway revenue.* Gross revenue from Broadway shows has grown from $20 million in 1986–1987 to $939 million in 2006–2007. Let $r(t)$ represent gross revenue, in millions of dollars, from Broadway shows t seasons after the 1986–1987 season. [5.3]
Source: The League of American Theatres and Producers

a) Find a linear function that fits the data.

b) Use the function from part (a) to predict the gross revenue from Broadway shows in 2009–2010.

c) In what season will the gross revenue from Broadway shows reach $1.4 billion?

46. *Broadway performances.* In January 2006, *The Phantom of the Opera* became the longest-running Broadway show with 7486 performances. By January 2008, the show had played 8302 times. Calculate the rate at which the number of performances was rising. [2.4]

47. *Quilting.* A rectangular quilted wall hanging is 4 in. longer than it is wide. The area of the quilt is 320 in^2. Find the perimeter of the quilt. [3.8]

48. *Hotel management.* The IQAir HealthPro Plus air purifier can clean the air in a 20-ft by 25-ft meeting room in 5 fewer minutes than it takes the Austin Healthmate HM400 to do the same job. Together the two machines can purify the air in the room in 6 min. How long would it take each machine, working alone, to purify the air in the room? [4.7]
Source: Manufacturers' and retailers' websites

49. *Driving delays.* According to the National Surface Transportation Policy and Revenue Study Commission, the best-case scenario for driving delays due to road work in 2055 will be 250% of the delays in 2005. If the commission predicts 30 billion hr of driving delays in 2055, how many hours of driving delays were there in 2005? [1.5]

50. *Driving time.* The time t that it takes for Johann to drive to work varies inversely as his speed. On a day when Johann averages 45 mph, it takes him 20 min to drive to work. How long will it take him to drive to work when he averages only 40 mph? [5.5]

51. *Disaster relief.* Six months after Hurricane Katrina struck the Gulf Coast in 2005, $2.18 billion of relief money had been distributed to disaster victims. This was $\frac{2}{3}$ of the amount raised by charity for disaster relief. How much money was still to be distributed? [1.5]
Source: www.washingtonpost.com

Synthesis

52. Multiply: $(x - 4)^3$.

53. Find all roots for $f(x) = x^4 - 34x^2 + 225$. [3.6], [5.3]

Solve.

54. $\dfrac{18}{x - 9} + \dfrac{10}{x + 5} = \dfrac{28x}{x^2 - 4x - 45}$ [4.6]

55. $16x^3 = x$ [3.7]

56. *Photo books.* An Everyday Photo Book costs $12 for the first 20 pages plus $0.75 for each additional page. Formulate a piecewise-defined function to model the cost $C(x)$ for a book with x pages. [5.2]
Source: snapfish.com

Systems of Linear Equations and Problem Solving

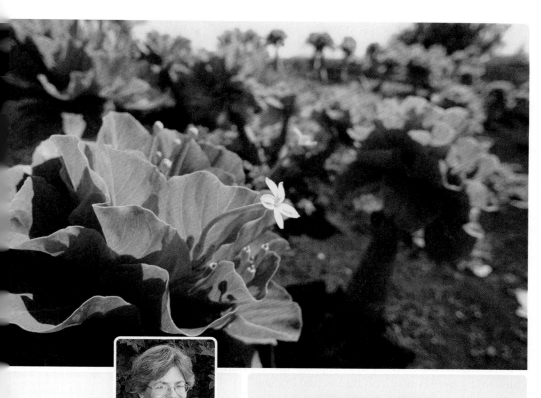

JUDITH L. BRONSTEIN
NATURALIST/ECOLOGIST
Tucson, Arizona

As an ecologist, I often use equations both to estimate numbers of organisms and to make predictions about how those numbers will change under different conditions. In this way, math helps us to answer questions like these: How quickly is the human population growing, and will food production be able to keep up? How many polar bears are left in the wild, how will their numbers be affected as the climate continues to change, and what approaches should be most successful for preserving them?

AN APPLICATION

The number of plant species listed as threatened or endangered has more than tripled in the past 20 years. In 2008, there were 746 species of plants in the United States that were considered threatened or endangered. The number of species considered threatened was 4 less than one-fourth of the number considered endangered. How many U.S. plant species were considered endangered and how many were considered threatened in 2008?

Source: U.S. Fish and Wildlife Service

This problem appears as Example 1 in Section 6.1 and as Example 1 in Section 6.3.

6.1
Systems of Equations in Two Variables

6.2
Solving by Substitution or Elimination

CONNECTING THE CONCEPTS

6.3
Solving Applications: Systems of Two Equations

6.4
Systems of Equations in Three Variables

6.5
Solving Applications: Systems of Three Equations

6.6
Elimination Using Matrices

6.7
Determinants and Cramer's Rule

6.8
Business and Economics Applications

STUDY SUMMARY
REVIEW EXERCISES
CHAPTER TEST
CUMULATIVE REVIEW

363

The most difficult part of problem solving is almost always translating the problem situation to mathematical language. In this chapter, we study *systems of equations* and how to solve them using graphing, substitution, elimination, and matrices. Systems of equations often provide the easiest way to model real-world situations in fields such as psychology, sociology, business, education, engineering, and science.

6.1 Systems of Equations in Two Variables

Translating • Identifying Solutions • Solving Systems Graphically

Translating

Problems involving two unknown quantities are often translated most easily using two equations in two unknowns. Together these equations form a **system of equations**. We look for a solution to the problem by attempting to find a pair of numbers for which *both* equations are true.

EXAMPLE 1

Endangered species. The number of plant species listed as threatened (likely to become endangered) or endangered (in danger of becoming extinct) has more than tripled in the past 20 years. In 2008, there were 746 species of plants in the United States that were considered threatened or endangered. The number of species considered threatened was 4 less than one-fourth of the number considered endangered. How many U.S. plant species were considered endangered and how many were considered threatened in 2008?

Source: U.S. Fish and Wildlife Service

SOLUTION

1. **Familiarize.** Often statements of problems contain information that has no bearing on the question asked. In this case, the fact that the number of threatened or endangered species has tripled in the past 20 years does not help us solve the problem. Instead, we focus on the number of endangered species and the number of threatened species in 2008. We let t represent the number of threatened plant species and d represent the number of endangered plant species in 2008.

2. **Translate.** There are two statements to translate. First, we look at the total number of endangered or threatened species of plants:

Rewording: The number of threatened species plus the number of endangered species was 746.

Translating: $t + d = 746$

The second statement compares the two amounts, d and t:

Rewording: The number of threatened species was 4 less than one-fourth of the number of endangered species.

Translating: $t = \dfrac{1}{4}d - 4$

We have now translated the problem to a pair, or **system**, **of equations**:

$$t + d = 746,$$
$$t = \frac{1}{4}d - 4.$$

We complete the solution of this problem in Section 6.3.

TRY EXERCISE 41

System of Equations

A *system of equations* is a set of two or more equations, in two or more variables, for which a common solution is sought.

Problems like Example 1 *can* be solved using one variable; however, as problems become complicated, you will find that using more than one variable (and more than one equation) is often the preferable approach.

EXAMPLE 2

Jewelry design. A jewelry designer purchased 80 beads for a total of $39 (excluding tax) to make a necklace. Some of the beads were sterling silver beads that cost 40¢ each and the rest were gemstone beads that cost 65¢ each. How many of each type did the designer buy?

SOLUTION

1. **Familiarize.** To familiarize ourselves with this problem, let's guess that the designer bought 20 beads at 40¢ each and 60 beads at 65¢ each. The total cost would then be

   $$20 \cdot 40¢ + 60 \cdot 65¢ = 800¢ + 3900¢, \quad \text{or} \quad 4700¢.$$

   Since 4700¢ = $47 and $47 ≠ $39, our guess is incorrect. Rather than guess again, let's see how algebra can be used to translate the problem.

2. **Translate.** We let s = the number of silver beads and g = the number of gemstone beads. Since the cost of each bead is given in cents and the total cost is in dollars, we must choose one of the units to use throughout the problem. We choose to work in cents, so the total cost is 3900¢. The information can be organized in a table, which will help with the translating.

Type of Bead	Silver	Gemstone	Total	
Number Bought	s	g	80	→ $s + g = 80$
Price	40¢	65¢		
Amount	40s¢	65g¢	3900¢	→ $40s + 65g = 3900$

The first row of the table and the first sentence of the problem indicate that a total of 80 beads were bought:

$$s + g = 80.$$

Since each silver bead cost 40¢ and s beads were bought, $40s$ represents the amount paid, in cents, for the silver beads. Similarly, $65g$ represents the amount paid, in cents, for the gemstone beads. This leads to a second equation:

$$40s + 65g = 3900.$$

We now have the following system of equations as the translation:

$$s + g = 80,$$
$$40s + 65g = 3900.$$

We will complete the solution of this problem in Section 6.3.

TRY EXERCISE ▶ 49

Identifying Solutions

A *solution* of a system of two equations in two variables is an ordered pair of numbers that makes *both* equations true.

EXAMPLE   3   Determine whether $(-4, 7)$ is a solution of the system

$$x + y = 3,$$
$$5x - y = -27.$$

SOLUTION   As discussed in Chapter 2, unless stated otherwise, we use alphabetical order of the variables. Thus we replace x with -4 and y with 7:

CAUTION! Be sure to check the ordered pair in *both* equations.

$$\begin{array}{c|c} x + y = 3 \\ \hline -4 + 7 & 3 \\ 3 \stackrel{?}{=} 3 & \text{TRUE} \end{array}$$

$$\begin{array}{c|c} 5x - y = -27 \\ \hline 5(-4) - 7 & -27 \\ -20 - 7 & \\ -27 \stackrel{?}{=} -27 & \text{TRUE} \end{array}$$

The pair $(-4, 7)$ makes both equations true, so it is a solution of the system. We can also describe the solution by writing $x = -4$ and $y = 7$. Set notation can also be used to list the solution set $\{(-4, 7)\}$.

TRY EXERCISE ▶ 9

Solving Systems Graphically

Recall that the graph of an equation is a drawing that represents its solution set. If we graph the equations in Example 3, we find that $(-4, 7)$ is the only point common to both lines. Thus one way to solve a system of two equations is to graph both equations and identify any points of intersection. **The coordinates of each point of intersection represent a solution of that system.**

$$x + y = 3,$$
$$5x - y = -27$$

The point of intersection of the graphs is $(-4, 7)$.

The solution of the system is $(-4, 7)$.

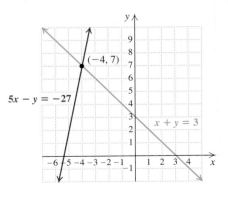

Most pairs of lines have exactly one point in common. We will soon see, however, that this is not always the case.

EXAMPLE   4   Solve each system graphically.

a) $y - x = 1,$
$\quad y + x = 3$

b) $y = -3x + 5,$
$\quad y = -3x - 2$

c) $\quad 3y - 2x = 6,$
$\quad -12y + 8x = -24$

SOLUTION

a) We graph each equation using any method studied in Chapter 2. All ordered pairs from line L_1 are solutions of the first equation. All ordered pairs from line L_2 are solutions of the second equation. The point of intersection has coordinates that make *both* equations true. Apparently, $(1, 2)$ is the solution. Graphs are not always accurate, so solving by graphing may yield approximate answers. Our check below shows that $(1, 2)$ is indeed the solution.

Graph both equations.

Look for any points in common.

$$y - x = 1,$$
$$y + x = 3$$

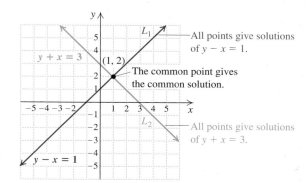

Check.

Check:

$$\begin{array}{c|c} y - x = 1 \\ \hline 2 - 1 & 1 \\ 1 \overset{?}{=} 1 & \text{TRUE} \end{array}$$

$$\begin{array}{c|c} y + x = 3 \\ \hline 2 + 1 & 3 \\ 3 \overset{?}{=} 3 & \text{TRUE} \end{array}$$

b) We graph the equations. The lines have the same slope, -3, and different y-intercepts, so they are parallel. There is no point at which they cross, so the system has no solution.

$$y = -3x + 5,$$
$$y = -3x - 2$$

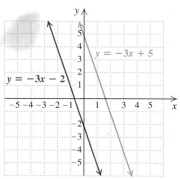

STUDENT NOTES ——————

Although the system in Example 4(c) is true for an infinite number of ordered pairs, those pairs must be of a certain form. Only pairs that are solutions of $3y - 2x = 6$ or $-12y + 8x = -24$ are solutions of the system. It is incorrect to think that *all* ordered pairs are solutions.

c) We graph the equations and find that the same line is drawn twice. Thus any solution of one equation is a solution of the other. Each equation has an infinite number of solutions, so the system itself has an infinite number of solutions. We check one solution, $(0, 2)$, which is the y-intercept of each equation.

$$3y - 2x = 6,$$
$$-12y + 8x = -24$$

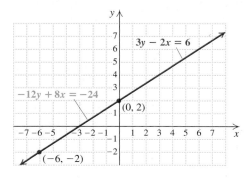

Check:

$$\frac{3y - 2x = 6}{\begin{array}{c|c} 3(2) - 2(0) & 6 \\ 6 - 0 & \\ 6 \stackrel{?}{=} 6 & \text{TRUE} \end{array}}$$

$$\frac{-12y + 8x = -24}{\begin{array}{c|c} -12(2) + 8(0) & -24 \\ -24 + 0 & \\ -24 \stackrel{?}{=} -24 & \text{TRUE} \end{array}}$$

You can check that $(-6, -2)$ is another solution of both equations. In fact, any pair that is a solution of one equation is a solution of the other equation as well. Thus the solution set is

$$\{(x, y) \mid 3y - 2x = 6\}$$

or, in words, "the set of all pairs (x, y) for which $3y - 2x = 6$." Since the two equations are equivalent, we could have written instead $\{(x, y) \mid -12y + 8x = -24\}$.

TRY EXERCISE 17

When we graph a system of two linear equations in two variables, one of the following three outcomes will occur.

1. The lines have one point in common, and that point is the only solution of the system (see Example 4a). Any system that has *at least one solution* is said to be **consistent**.

2. The lines are parallel, with no point in common, and the system has *no solution* (see Example 4b). This type of system is called **inconsistent**.

3. The lines coincide, sharing the same graph. Because every solution of one equation is a solution of the other, the system has an infinite number of solutions (see Example 4c). Since it has at least one solution, this type of system is also consistent.

TECHNOLOGY CONNECTION

On most graphing calculators, an INTERSECT option allows us to find the coordinates of the intersection directly.

To illustrate, consider the following system:

$$3.45x + 4.21y = 8.39,$$
$$7.12x - 5.43y = 6.18.$$

After solving for y in each equation, we obtain the graph below. Using INTERSECT, we see that, to the nearest hundredth, the coordinates of the intersection are $(1.47, 0.79)$.

$y_1 = (8.39 - 3.45x)/4.21,$
$y_2 = (6.18 - 7.12x)/(-5.43)$

Use a graphing calculator to solve each of the following systems. Round all x- and y-coordinates to the nearest hundredth.

1. $y = -5.43x + 10.89,$
   $y = 6.29x - 7.04$
2. $y = 123.52x + 89.32,$
   $y = -89.22x + 33.76$
3. $2.18x + 7.81y = 13.78,$
   $5.79x - 3.45y = 8.94$
4. $-9.25x - 12.94y = -3.88,$
   $21.83x + 16.33y = 13.69$

When one equation in a system can be obtained by multiplying both sides of another equation by a constant, the two equations are said to be **dependent**. Thus the equations in Example 4(c) are dependent, but those in Examples 4(a) and 4(b) are **independent**. For systems of three or more equations, the definitions of dependent and independent will be slightly modified.

ALGEBRAIC–GRAPHICAL CONNECTION

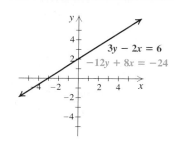

Graphs intersect at one point.

The system

$$y - x = 1,$$
$$y + x = 3$$

is *consistent* and has one solution.

Since neither equation is a multiple of the other, the equations are *independent*.

Graphs are parallel.

The system

$$y = -3x - 2,$$
$$y = -3x + 5$$

is *inconsistent* because there is no solution.

Since neither equation is a multiple of the other, the equations are *independent*.

Equations have the same graph.

The system

$$3y - 2x = 6,$$
$$-12y + 8x = -24$$

is *consistent* and has an infinite number of solutions.

Since one equation is a multiple of the other, the equations are *dependent*.

Graphing is helpful when solving systems because it allows us to "see" the solution. It can also be used on systems of nonlinear equations, and in many applications, it provides a satisfactory answer. However, graphing often lacks precision, especially when fraction or decimal solutions are involved. In Section 6.2, we will develop two algebraic methods of solving systems. Both methods produce exact answers.

Visualizing for Success

A

B

C

D

E

F

G

H

I

J

Match each equation or system of equations with its graph.

1. $x + y = 2,$
   $x - y = 2$

2. $y = \frac{1}{3}x - 5$

3. $4x - 2y = -8$

4. $2x + y = 1,$
   $x + 2y = 1$

5. $8y + 32 = 0$

6. $f(x) = -x + 4$

7. $\frac{2}{3}x + y = 4$

8. $x = 4,$
   $y = 3$

9. $y = \frac{1}{2}x + 3,$
   $2y - x = 6$

10. $y = -x + 5,$
    $y = 3 - x$

Answers on page A-27

An additional, animated version of this activity appears in MyMathLab. To use MyMathLab, you need a course ID and a student access code. Contact your instructor for more information.

6.1 EXERCISE SET

For Extra Help

⤸ **Concept Reinforcement** *Classify each statement as either true or false.*

1. Every system of equations has at least one solution.

2. It is possible for a system of equations to have an infinite number of solutions.

3. Every point of intersection of the graphs of the equations in a system corresponds to a solution of the system.

4. The graphs of the equations in a system of two equations may coincide.

5. The graphs of the equations in a system of two equations could be parallel lines.

6. Any system of equations that has at most one solution is said to be consistent.

7. Any system of equations that has more than one solution is said to be inconsistent.

8. The equations $x + y = 5$ and $2(x + y) = 2(5)$ are dependent.

Determine whether the ordered pair is a solution of the given system of equations. Remember to use alphabetical order of variables.

9. $(2, 3)$; $2x - y = 1$,
$\qquad 5x - 3y = 1$

10. $(4, 0)$; $2x + 7y = 8$,
$\qquad x - 9y = 4$

11. $(-5, 1)$; $x + 5y = 0$,
$\qquad y = 2x + 9$

12. $(-1, -2)$; $x + 3y = -7$,
$\qquad 3x - 2y = 12$

13. $(0, -5)$; $x - y = 5$,
$\qquad y = 3x - 5$

14. $(5, 2)$; $a + b = 7$,
$\qquad 2a - 8 = b$

Aha! 15. $(3, -1)$; $3x - 4y = 13$,
$\qquad 6x - 8y = 26$

16. $(4, -2)$; $-3x - 2y = -8$,
$\qquad 8 = 3x + 2y$

Solve each system graphically. Be sure to check your solution. If a system has an infinite number of solutions, use set-builder notation to write the solution set. If a system has no solution, state this.

17. $x - y = 1$,
$\qquad x + y = 5$

18. $x + y = 6$,
$\qquad x - y = 4$

19. $3x + y = 5$,
$\qquad x - 2y = 4$

20. $2x - y = 4$,
$\qquad 5x - y = 13$

21. $2y = 3x + 5$,
$\qquad x = y - 3$

22. $4x - y = 9$,
$\qquad x - 3y = 16$

23. $x = y - 1$,
$\qquad 2x = 3y$

24. $a = 1 + b$,
$\qquad b = 5 - 2a$

25. $y = -1$,
$\qquad x = 3$

26. $y = 2$,
$\qquad x = -4$

27. $t + 2s = -1$,
$\qquad s = t + 10$

28. $b + 2a = 2$,
$\qquad a = -3 - b$

29. $2b + a = 11$,
$\qquad a - b = 5$

30. $y = -\frac{1}{3}x - 1$,
$\qquad 4x - 3y = 18$

31. $y = -\frac{1}{4}x + 1$,
$\qquad 2y = x - 4$

32. $6x - 2y = 2$,
$\qquad 9x - 3y = 1$

33. $y - x = 5$,
$\qquad 2x - 2y = 10$

34. $y = x + 2$,
$\qquad 3y - 2x = 4$

35. $y = 3 - x$,
$\qquad 2x + 2y = 6$

36. $2x - 3y = 6$,
$\qquad 3y - 2x = -6$

37. For the systems in the odd-numbered exercises 17–35, which are consistent?

38. For the systems in the even-numbered exercises 18–36, which are consistent?

39. For the systems in the odd-numbered exercises 17–35, which contain dependent equations?

40. For the systems in the even-numbered exercises 18–36, which contain dependent equations?

Translate each problem situation to a system of equations. Do not attempt to solve, but save for later use.

41. The sum of two numbers is 10. The first number is $\frac{2}{3}$ of the second number. What are the numbers?

42. The sum of two numbers is 30. The first number is twice the second number. What are the numbers?

43. *e-mail usage.* In 2007, the average e-mail user sent 578 personal and business e-mails each week. The number of business e-mails was 30 more than the number of personal e-mails. How many of each type were sent each week?
Source: *JupiterResearch*

44. *Nontoxic furniture polish.* A nontoxic wood furniture polish can be made by mixing mineral (or olive) oil with vinegar. To make a 16-oz batch for a squirt bottle, Jazmun uses an amount of mineral oil that is 4 oz more than twice the amount of vinegar. How much of each ingredient is required?
Sources: Based on information from Chittenden Solid Waste District and *Clean House, Clean Planet* by Karen Logan

45. *Geometry.* Two angles are supplementary.* One angle is 3° less than twice the other. Find the measures of the angles.

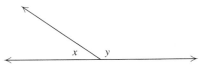

Supplementary angles

46. *Geometry.* Two angles are complementary.† The sum of the measures of the first angle and half the second angle is 64°. Find the measures of the angles.

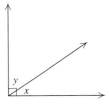

Complementary angles

47. *Basketball scoring.* Wilt Chamberlain once scored 100 points, setting a record for points scored in an NBA game. Chamberlain took only two-point shots and (one-point) foul shots and made a total of 64 shots. How many shots of each type did he make?

48. *Basketball scoring.* The Fenton College Cougars made 40 field goals in a recent basketball game, some 2-pointers and the rest 3-pointers. Altogether the 40 baskets counted for 89 points. How many of each type of field goal was made?

---

*The sum of the measures of two supplementary angles is 180°.
†The sum of the measures of two complementary angles is 90°.

49. *Retail sales.* Simply Souvenirs sold 45 hats and tee shirts. The hats sold for $14.50 each and the tee shirts for $19.50 each. In all, $697.50 was taken in for the souvenirs. How many of each type of souvenir were sold?

50. *Retail sales.* Cool Treats sold 60 ice cream cones. Single-dip cones sold for $2.50 each and double-dip cones for $4.15 each. In all, $179.70 was taken in for the cones. How many of each size cone were sold?

51. *Sales of pharmaceuticals.* In 2008, the Diabetic Express charged $83.29 for a 10-mL vial of Humalog insulin and $76.76 for a 10-mL vial of Lantus insulin. If a total of $3981.66 was collected for 50 vials of insulin, how many vials of each type were sold?

52. *Fundraising.* The Buck Creek Fire Department served 250 dinners. A child's plate cost $5.50 and an adult's plate cost $9.00. A total of $1935 was collected. How many of each type of plate was served?

53. *Lacrosse.* The perimeter of an NCAA men's lacrosse field is 340 yd. The length is 50 yd longer than the width. Find the dimensions.

$P = 340$ yd

54. *Tennis.* The perimeter of a standard tennis court used for doubles is 228 ft. The width is 42 ft less than the length. Find the dimensions.

55. Write a problem for a classmate to solve that requires writing a system of two equations. Devise the problem so that the solution is "The Fever made 6 three-point baskets and 31 two-point baskets."

56. Write a problem for a classmate to solve that can be translated into a system of two equations. Devise the problem so that the solution is "In 2009, Diana took five 3-credit classes and two 4-credit classes."

Skill Review

To prepare for Section 6.2, review solving equations and formulas (Sections 1.2 and 1.3).

Solve. [1.2]

57. $3x + 2(5x - 1) = 6$

58. $4(3y + 2) - 7y = 3$

59. $9y = 5 - (y + 6)$

60. $2x - (x - 7) = 18$

Solve. [1.3]

61. $3x - y = 4$, for y

62. $5y - 2x = 7$, for x

Synthesis

Advertising media. For Exercises 63 and 64, consider the following graph showing the U.S. market share for various advertising media.

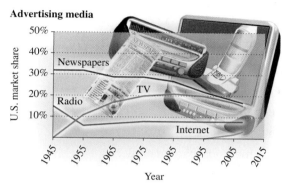

Source: The Wall Street Journal, 12/30/07

63. In what year did no one medium have a higher advertising market share than the others? Explain.

64. Will the Internet advertising market share ever exceed that of radio? TV? newspapers? If so, when? Explain your answers.

65. For each of the following conditions, write a system of equations.

  a) $(5, 1)$ is a solution.
  b) There is no solution.
  c) There is an infinite number of solutions.

66. A system of linear equations has $(1, -1)$ and $(-2, 3)$ as solutions. Determine:

  a) a third point that is a solution, and
  b) how many solutions there are.

67. The solution of the following system is $(4, -5)$. Find A and B.

$$Ax - 6y = 13,$$
$$x - By = -8.$$

Translate to a system of equations. Do not solve.

68. *Ages.* Tyler is twice as old as his son. Ten years ago, Tyler was three times as old as his son. How old are they now?

69. *Work experience.* Dell and Juanita are mathematics professors at a state university. Together, they have 46 years of service. Two years ago, Dell had taught 2.5 times as many years as Juanita. How long has each taught at the university?

70. *Design.* A piece of posterboard has a perimeter of 156 in. If you cut 6 in. off the width, the length becomes four times the width. What are the dimensions of the original piece of posterboard?

$P = 156$ in.

71. *Nontoxic scouring powder.* A nontoxic scouring powder is made up of 4 parts baking soda and 1 part vinegar. How much of each ingredient is needed for a 16-oz mixture?

72. Solve Exercise 41 graphically.

73. Solve Exercise 44 graphically.

Solve graphically.

74. $y = |x|,$
$3y - x = 8$

75. $x - y = 0,$
$y = x^2$

In Exercises 76–79, use a graphing calculator to solve each system of linear equations for x and y. Round all coordinates to the nearest hundredth.

76. $y = 8.23x + 2.11,$
$y = -9.11x - 4.66$

77. $y = -3.44x - 7.72,$
$y = 4.19x - 8.22$

78. $14.12x + 7.32y = 2.98,$
$21.88x - 6.45y = -7.22$

79. $5.22x - 8.21y = -10.21,$
$-12.67x + 10.34y = 12.84$

6.2 Solving by Substitution or Elimination

The Substitution Method • The Elimination Method

The Substitution Method

Algebraic (nongraphical) methods for solving systems are often superior to graphing, especially when fractions are involved. One algebraic method, the *substitution method*, relies on having a variable isolated.

EXAMPLE **1** Solve the system

$$x + y = 4, \quad (1) \qquad \text{For easy reference, we have}$$
$$x = y + 1. \quad (2) \qquad \text{numbered the equations.}$$

STUDY SKILLS ⸻

Learn from Your Mistakes

Immediately after each quiz or test, write out a step-by-step solution to any questions you missed. Visit your professor during office hours or consult a tutor for help with problems that still give you trouble. Misconceptions tend to resurface if not corrected as soon as possible.

SOLUTION   Equation (2) says that x and $y + 1$ name the same number. Thus we can substitute $y + 1$ for x in equation (1):

$$x + y = 4 \qquad \text{Equation (1)}$$
$$(y + 1) + y = 4. \qquad \text{Substituting } y + 1 \text{ for } x$$

We solve this last equation, using methods learned earlier:

$$(y + 1) + y = 4$$
$$2y + 1 = 4 \qquad \text{Removing parentheses and combining like terms}$$
$$2y = 3 \qquad \text{Subtracting 1 from both sides}$$
$$y = \tfrac{3}{2}. \qquad \text{Dividing both sides by 2}$$

We now return to the original pair of equations and substitute $\frac{3}{2}$ for y in either equation so that we can solve for x. For this problem, calculations are slightly easier if we use equation (2):

$$x = y + 1 \qquad \text{Equation (2)}$$
$$= \tfrac{3}{2} + 1 \qquad \text{Substituting } \tfrac{3}{2} \text{ for } y$$
$$= \tfrac{3}{2} + \tfrac{2}{2} = \tfrac{5}{2}.$$

We obtain the ordered pair $\left(\frac{5}{2}, \frac{3}{2}\right)$. A check ensures that it is a solution.

Check:
$$\frac{x + y = 4}{\begin{array}{c|c} \frac{5}{2} + \frac{3}{2} & 4 \\ \frac{8}{2} & \\ 4 \stackrel{?}{=} 4 & \text{TRUE} \end{array}} \qquad \frac{x = y + 1}{\begin{array}{c|c} \frac{5}{2} & \frac{3}{2} + 1 \\ & \frac{3}{2} + \frac{2}{2} \\ \frac{5}{2} \stackrel{?}{=} \frac{5}{2} & \text{TRUE} \end{array}}$$

Since $\left(\frac{5}{2}, \frac{3}{2}\right)$ checks, it is the solution.

TRY EXERCISE 7

The exact solution to Example 1 is difficult to find graphically because it involves fractions. The graph shown serves as a partial check and provides a visualization of the problem.

If neither equation in a system has a variable alone on one side, we first isolate a variable in one equation and then substitute.

EXAMPLE **2** Solve the system

$$2x + y = 6, \quad (1)$$
$$3x + 4y = 4. \quad (2)$$

SOLUTION   First, we select an equation and solve for one variable. We can isolate y by subtracting $2x$ from both sides of equation (1):

$$2x + y = 6 \qquad (1)$$
$$y = 6 - 2x. \qquad (3) \qquad \text{Subtracting } 2x \text{ from both sides}$$

Next, we proceed as in Example 1, by substituting:

$$3x + 4(6 - 2x) = 4 \qquad \text{Substituting } 6 - 2x \text{ for } y \text{ in equation (2).}$$
$$\text{Use parentheses!}$$
$$3x + 24 - 8x = 4 \qquad \text{Distributing to remove parentheses}$$
$$3x - 8x = 4 - 24 \qquad \text{Subtracting 24 from both sides}$$
$$-5x = -20$$
$$x = 4. \qquad \text{Dividing both sides by } -5$$

Next, we substitute 4 for x in either equation (1), (2), or (3). It is easiest to use equation (3) because it has already been solved for y:

$$y = 6 - 2x$$
$$= 6 - 2(4)$$
$$= 6 - 8 = -2.$$

A visualization of Example 2

The pair $(4, -2)$ appears to be the solution. We check in equations (1) and (2).

Check:

$2x + y = 6$		$3x + 4y = 4$	
$2(4) + (-2)$	6	$3(4) + 4(-2)$	4
$8 - 2$		$12 - 8$	
$6 \overset{?}{=} 6$	TRUE	$4 \overset{?}{=} 4$	TRUE

Since $(4, -2)$ checks, it is the solution.

TRY EXERCISE ▶ 11

Some systems have no solution, as we saw graphically in Section 6.1. How do we recognize such systems if we are solving by an algebraic method?

EXAMPLE 3

Solve the system

$$y = -3x + 5, \qquad (1)$$
$$y = -3x - 2. \qquad (2)$$

SOLUTION   We solved this system graphically in Example 4(b) of Section 6.1, and found that the lines are parallel and the system has no solution. Let's now try to solve the system by substitution. Proceeding as in Example 1, we substitute $-3x - 2$ for y in the first equation:

$$-3x - 2 = -3x + 5 \qquad \text{Substituting } -3x - 2 \text{ for } y \text{ in equation (1)}$$
$$-2 = 5. \qquad \text{Adding } 3x \text{ to both sides; } -2 = 5 \text{ is a contradiction. The equation is always false.}$$

A visualization of Example 3

Since there is no solution of $-2 = 5$, there is no solution of the system. We state that there is no solution.

TRY EXERCISE ▶ 21

When solving a system algebraically yields a contradiction, the system has no solution.

As we will see in Example 7, when solving a system of two equations algebraically yields an identity, the system has an infinite number of solutions.

The Elimination Method

The *elimination method* for solving systems of equations makes use of the *addition principle*: If $a = b$, then $a + c = b + c$. Consider the following system:

$$2x - 3y = 0,$$
$$-4x + 3y = -1.$$

Note that the $-3y$ in one equation and the $3y$ in the other are opposites. If we add all terms on the left side of the equations, the sum of $-3y$ and $3y$ is 0, so in effect, the variable y is "eliminated."

EXAMPLE   4

Solve the system

$$2x - 3y = 0, \qquad (1)$$
$$-4x + 3y = -1. \qquad (2)$$

SOLUTION   Note that according to equation (2), $-4x + 3y$ and -1 are the same number. Thus we can use the addition principle to work vertically and add $-4x + 3y$ to the left side of equation (1) and -1 to the right side:

$$
\begin{array}{ll}
2x - 3y = 0 & (1) \\
\underline{-4x + 3y = -1} & (2) \\
-2x + 0y = -1. & \text{Adding}
\end{array}
$$

This eliminates the variable y, and leaves an equation with just one variable, x, for which we solve:

$$-2x = -1$$
$$x = \tfrac{1}{2}.$$

Next, we substitute $\tfrac{1}{2}$ for x in equation (1) and solve for y:

$$2 \cdot \tfrac{1}{2} - 3y = 0 \qquad \text{Substituting. We also could have used equation (2).}$$
$$1 - 3y = 0$$
$$-3y = -1, \text{ so } y = \tfrac{1}{3}.$$

Check:

$$
\begin{array}{c|c}
2x - 3y = 0 & \\
\hline
2\left(\tfrac{1}{2}\right) - 3\left(\tfrac{1}{3}\right) & 0 \\
1 - 1 & \\
0 \stackrel{?}{=} 0 & \text{TRUE}
\end{array}
\qquad
\begin{array}{c|c}
-4x + 3y = -1 & \\
\hline
-4\left(\tfrac{1}{2}\right) + 3\left(\tfrac{1}{3}\right) & -1 \\
-2 + 1 & \\
-1 \stackrel{?}{=} -1 & \text{TRUE}
\end{array}
$$

A visualization of Example 4

Since $\left(\tfrac{1}{2}, \tfrac{1}{3}\right)$ checks, it is the solution. See also the graph at left.

TRY EXERCISE 23

To eliminate a variable, we must sometimes multiply before adding.

EXAMPLE   5

Solve the system

$$5x + 4y = 22, \qquad (1)$$
$$-3x + 8y = 18. \qquad (2)$$

STUDENT NOTES

It is wise to double-check each step of your work as you go, rather than checking all steps at the end of a problem. Finding and correcting an error as it occurs saves you time in the long run. One common error is to forget to multiply *both* sides of the equation when you use the multiplication principle.

SOLUTION   If we add the left sides of the two equations, we will not eliminate a variable. However, if the $4y$ in equation (1) were changed to $-8y$, we would. To accomplish this change, we multiply both sides of equation (1) by -2:

$$
\begin{array}{ll}
-10x - 8y = -44 & \text{Multiplying both sides of equation (1) by } -2 \\
\underline{-3x + 8y = 18} & \\
-13x + 0 = -26 & \text{Adding} \\
x = 2. & \text{Solving for } x
\end{array}
$$

Then

$$
\begin{array}{ll}
-3 \cdot 2 + 8y = 18 & \text{Substituting 2 for } x \text{ in equation (2)} \\
-6 + 8y = 18 & \\
\left.\begin{array}{l} 8y = 24 \\ y = 3. \end{array}\right\} & \text{Solving for } y
\end{array}
$$

We obtain $(2, 3)$, or $x = 2$, $y = 3$. We leave it to the student to confirm that this checks and is the solution.

TRY EXERCISE ▶ 29

Sometimes we must multiply twice in order to make two terms become opposites.

EXAMPLE 6   Solve the system

$$
\begin{array}{ll}
2x + 3y = 17, & (1) \\
5x + 7y = 29. & (2)
\end{array}
$$

SOLUTION   We multiply so that the x-terms will be eliminated when we add.

Eliminate x.

Solve for y.

$$
\begin{array}{lll}
2x + 3y = 17, & \xrightarrow{\text{Multiplying both sides by 5}} & 10x + 15y = 85 \\
5x + 7y = 29 & \xrightarrow{\text{Multiplying both sides by }-2} & \underline{-10x - 14y = -58} \\
& & 0 + y = 27 \quad \text{Adding} \\
& & y = 27
\end{array}
$$

Next, we substitute to find x:

$$
\begin{array}{ll}
2x + 3 \cdot 27 = 17 & \text{Substituting 27 for } y \text{ in equation (1)} \\
2x + 81 = 17 & \\
\left.\begin{array}{l} 2x = -64 \\ x = -32. \end{array}\right\} & \text{Solving for } x
\end{array}
$$

Solve for x.

Check.

Check:

$$
\begin{array}{c|c}
\underline{2x + 3y = 17} & \\
2(-32) + 3(27) & 17 \\
-64 + 81 & \\
17 \overset{?}{=} 17 & \text{TRUE}
\end{array}
\qquad
\begin{array}{c|c}
\underline{5x + 7y = 29} & \\
5(-32) + 7(27) & 29 \\
-160 + 189 & \\
29 \overset{?}{=} 29 & \text{TRUE}
\end{array}
$$

We obtain $(-32, 27)$, or $x = -32$, $y = 27$, as the solution.

TRY EXERCISE ▶ 31

EXAMPLE 7

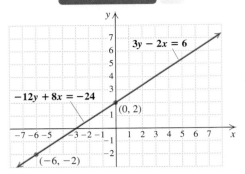

A visualization of Example 7

Solve the system

$$3y - 2x = 6, \qquad (1)$$
$$-12y + 8x = -24. \qquad (2)$$

SOLUTION   We graphed this system in Example 4(c) of Section 6.1, and found that the lines coincide and the system has an infinite number of solutions. Suppose we were to solve this system using the elimination method:

$$12y - 8x = 24 \qquad \text{Multiplying both sides of equation (1) by 4}$$
$$\underline{-12y + 8x = -24}$$
$$0 = 0. \qquad \text{We obtain an identity; } 0 = 0 \text{ is always true.}$$

Note that both variables have been eliminated and what remains is an identity—that is, an equation that is always true. Any pair that is a solution of equation (1) is also a solution of equation (2). The equations are dependent and the solution set is infinite:

$$\{(x, y) \mid 3y - 2x = 6\}, \text{ or equivalently, } \{(x, y) \mid -12y + 8x = -24\}.$$

TRY EXERCISE 47

Example 3 and Example 7 illustrate how to tell algebraically whether a system of two equations is inconsistent or whether the equations are dependent.

Rules for Special Cases

When solving a system of two linear equations in two variables:

1. If we obtain an identity such as $0 = 0$, then the system has an infinite number of solutions. The equations are dependent and, since a solution exists, the system is consistent.*
2. If we obtain a contradiction such as $0 = 7$, then the system has no solution. The system is inconsistent.

Should decimals or fractions appear, it often helps to *clear* before solving.

EXAMPLE 8   Solve the system

$$0.2x + 0.3y = 1.7,$$
$$\tfrac{1}{7}x + \tfrac{1}{5}y = \tfrac{29}{35}.$$

SOLUTION   We have

$$0.2x + 0.3y = 1.7, \longrightarrow \text{Multiplying both sides by } 10 \longrightarrow 2x + 3y = 17$$
$$\tfrac{1}{7}x + \tfrac{1}{5}y = \tfrac{29}{35} \longrightarrow \text{Multiplying both sides by } 35 \longrightarrow 5x + 7y = 29.$$

We multiplied both sides of the first equation by 10 to clear the decimals. Multiplication by 35, the least common denominator, clears the fractions in the second equation. The problem now happens to be identical to Example 6. The solution is $(-32, 27)$, or $x = -32$, $y = 27$.

TRY EXERCISE 35

The steps for each algebraic method for solving systems of two equations are given below. Note that in both methods, we find the value of one variable and then substitute to find the corresponding value of the other variable.

---

*Consistent systems and dependent equations are discussed in greater detail in Section 6.4.

To Solve a System Using Substitution

1. Isolate a variable in one of the equations (unless one is already isolated).
2. Substitute for that variable in the other equation, using parentheses.
3. Solve for the remaining variable.
4. Substitute the value of the second variable in any of the equations, and solve for the first variable.
5. Form an ordered pair and check in the original equations.

To Solve a System Using Elimination

1. Write both equations in standard form.
2. Multiply both sides of one or both equations by a constant, if necessary, so that the coefficients of one of the variables are opposites.
3. Add the left sides and the right sides of the resulting equations. One variable should be eliminated in the sum.
4. Solve for the remaining variable.
5. Substitute the value of the second variable in any of the equations, and solve for the first variable.
6. Form an ordered pair and check in the original equations.

6.2   EXERCISE SET

For Extra Help   *MyMathLab*   PRACTICE   WATCH   DOWNLOAD

↪ *Concept Reinforcement In each of Exercises 1–6, match the system listed with the choice from the column on the right that would be a subsequent step in solving the system.*

1. _____ $3x - 4y = 6,$
   $5x + 4y = 1$

2. _____ $2x - y = 8,$
   $y = 5x + 3$

3. _____ $x - 2y = 3,$
   $5x + 3y = 4$

4. _____ $8x + 6y = -15,$
   $5x - 3y = 8$

5. _____ $y = 4x - 7,$
   $6x + 3y = 19$

6. _____ $y = 4x - 1,$
   $y = -\frac{2}{3}x - 1$

a) $-5x + 10y = -15,$
   $5x + 3y = 4$

b) The lines intersect at $(0, -1)$.

c) $6x + 3(4x - 7) = 19$

d) $8x = 7$

e) $2x - (5x + 3) = 8$

f) $8x + 6y = -15,$
   $10x - 6y = 16$

For Exercises 7–54, if a system has an infinite number of solutions, use set-builder notation to write the solution set. If a system has no solution, state this.

Solve using the substitution method.

7. $y = 3 - 2x,$
   $3x + y = 5$

8. $3y + x = 4,$
   $x = 2y - 1$

9. $3x + 5y = 3,$
   $x = 8 - 4y$

10. $9x - 2y = 3,$
    $3x - 6 = y$

11. $3s - 4t = 14,$
    $5s + t = 8$

12. $m - 2n = 16,$
    $4m + n = 1$

13. $4x - 2y = 6,$
    $2x - 3 = y$

14. $t = 4 - 2s,$
    $t + 2s = 6$

15. $-5s + t = 11,$
    $4s + 12t = 4$

16. $5x + 6y = 14,$
    $-3y + x = 7$

17. $2x + 2y = 2,$
    $3x - y = 1$

18. $4p - 2q = 16,$
    $5p + 7q = 1$

19. $2a + 6b = 4,$
    $3a - b = 6$

20. $3x - 4y = 5,$
    $2x - y = 1$

21. $2x - 3 = y,$
    $y - 2x = 1$

22. $a - 2b = 3,$
    $3a = 6b + 9$

Solve using the elimination method.

23. $x + 3y = 7,$
    $-x + 4y = 7$

24. $2x + y = 6,$
    $x - y = 3$

25. $x - 2y = 11,$
    $3x + 2y = 17$

26. $5x - 3y = 8,$
    $-5x + y = 4$

27. $9x + 3y = -3,$
    $2x - 3y = -8$

28. $6x - 3y = 18,$
    $6x + 3y = -12$

29. $5x + 3y = 19,$
$x - 6y = 11$

30. $3x + 2y = 3,$
$9x - 8y = -2$

31. $5r - 3s = 24,$
$3r + 5s = 28$

32. $5x - 7y = -16,$
$2x + 8y = 26$

33. $6s + 9t = 12,$
$4s + 6t = 5$

34. $10a + 6b = 8,$
$5a + 3b = 2$

35. $\frac{1}{2}x - \frac{1}{6}y = 10,$
$\frac{2}{5}x + \frac{1}{2}y = 8$

36. $\frac{1}{3}x + \frac{1}{5}y = 7,$
$\frac{1}{6}x - \frac{2}{5}y = -4$

37. $\frac{x}{2} + \frac{y}{3} = \frac{7}{6},$
$\frac{2x}{3} + \frac{3y}{4} = \frac{5}{4}$

38. $\frac{2x}{3} + \frac{3y}{4} = \frac{11}{12},$
$\frac{x}{3} + \frac{7y}{18} = \frac{1}{2}$

Aha! **39.** $12x - 6y = -15,$
$-4x + 2y = 5$

40. $8s + 12t = 16,$
$6s + 9t = 12$

41. $0.3x + 0.2y = 0.3,$
$0.5x + 0.4y = 0.4$

42. $0.3x + 0.2y = 5,$
$0.5x + 0.4y = 11$

Solve using any appropriate method.

43. $a - 2b = 16,$
$b + 3 = 3a$

44. $5x - 9y = 7,$
$7y - 3x = -5$

45. $10x + y = 306,$
$10y + x = 90$

46. $3(a - b) = 15,$
$4a = b + 1$

47. $6x - 3y = 3,$
$4x - 2y = 2$

48. $x + 2y = 8,$
$x = 4 - 2y$

49. $3s - 7t = 5,$
$7t - 3s = 8$

50. $2s - 13t = 120,$
$-14s + 91t = -840$

51. $0.05x + 0.25y = 22,$
$0.15x + 0.05y = 24$

52. $2.1x - 0.9y = 15,$
$-1.4x + 0.6y = 10$

53. $13a - 7b = 9,$
$2a - 8b = 6$

54. $3a - 12b = 9,$
$4a - 5b = 3$

55. Describe a procedure that can be used to write an inconsistent system of equations.

56. Describe a procedure that can be used to write a system that has an infinite number of solutions.

Skill Review

To prepare for Section 6.3, review solving problems using the five-step problem-solving strategy (Section 1.5).

Solve. [1.5]

57. *Energy consumption.* With average use, a toaster oven and a convection oven together consume 15 kilowatt hours (kWh) of electricity each month. A convection oven uses four times as much electricity as a toaster oven. How much does each use per month?
Source: Lee County Electric Cooperative

58. *Test scores.* Ellia needs to average 80 on her tests in order to earn a B in her math class. Her average after 4 tests is 77.5. What score is needed on the fifth test in order to raise the average to 80?

59. *Real estate.* After her house had been on the market for 6 months, Gina reduced the price to $94,500. This was $\frac{9}{10}$ of the original asking price. How much did Gina originally ask for her house?

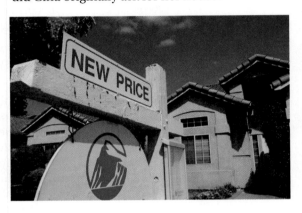

60. *Car rentals.* National Car Rental rents minivans to a university for $69 a day plus 30¢ per mile. An English professor rented a minivan for 2 days to take a group of students to a seminar. The bill was $225. How far did the professor drive the van?
Source: www.nationalcar.com

61. *Carpentry.* Anazi cuts a 96-in. piece of wood trim into three pieces. The second piece is twice as long as the first. The third piece is one-tenth as long as the second. How long is each piece?

62. *Telephone calls.* Terri's voice over the Internet (VoIP) phone service charges $0.36 for the first minute of each call and $0.06 for each additional $\frac{1}{2}$ minute. One month she was charged $28.20 for 35 calls. How many minutes did she use?

Synthesis

63. Some systems are more easily solved by substitution and some are more easily solved by elimination. What guidelines could be used to help someone determine which method to use?

64. Explain how it is possible to solve Exercise 39 mentally.

65. If $(1, 2)$ and $(-3, 4)$ are two solutions of $f(x) = mx + b$, find m and b.

66. If $(0, -3)$ and $\left(-\frac{3}{2}, 6\right)$ are two solutions of $px - qy = -1$, find p and q.

67. Determine a and b for which $(-4, -3)$ is a solution of the system

$$ax + by = -26,$$
$$bx - ay = 7.$$

68. Solve for x and y in terms of a and b:

$$5x + 2y = a,$$
$$x - y = b.$$

Solve.

69. $\dfrac{x + y}{2} - \dfrac{x - y}{5} = 1,$

$\dfrac{x - y}{2} + \dfrac{x + y}{6} = -2$

70. $3.5x - 2.1y = 106.2,$
$4.1x + 16.7y = -106.28$

Each of the following is a system of nonlinear equations. However, each is reducible to linear, since an appropriate substitution (say, u for $1/x$ and v for $1/y$) yields a linear system. Make such a substitution, solve for the new variables, and then solve for the original variables.

71. $\dfrac{2}{x} + \dfrac{1}{y} = 0,$

$\dfrac{5}{x} + \dfrac{2}{y} = -5$

72. $\dfrac{1}{x} - \dfrac{3}{y} = 2,$

$\dfrac{6}{x} + \dfrac{5}{y} = -34$

73. A student solving the system

$$17x + 19y = 102,$$
$$136x + 152y = 826$$

graphs both equations on a graphing calculator and gets the following screen. The student then (incorrectly) concludes that the equations are dependent and the solution set is infinite. How can algebra be used to convince the student that a mistake has been made?

Additional Exercises

Solve.

74. $y = \frac{4}{3}x + 2,$

$x = \frac{3}{5}y$

75. $y = \frac{5}{4}x - 2,$

$x = \frac{2}{3}y$

76. $x + \frac{4}{3}y = 0,$

$\frac{5}{6}x + \frac{2}{3}y = 4$

77. $x + \frac{3}{2}y = 0,$

$\frac{2}{3}x + \frac{3}{2}y = 5$

78. $y = \frac{5}{2}x + 1,$

$y = \frac{3}{4}x - 6$

79. $y = \frac{2}{3}x + 1,$

$y = \frac{7}{6}x - 2$

Solve.

80. $2x + 5y = 14,$
$3x + 4y = 7$

81. $3p + 5w = 5,$
$5p - 2w = 29$

82. $7m - 10p = 44,$
$2m - 3p = 14$

83. $8w - 3y = 6,$
$5w - 2y = 3$

84. $3a - 10b = 7,$
$5a + 4b = 53$

85. $10x + 2y = -16,$
$8x + 3y = -17$

Solve.

86. $\dfrac{x}{3} + \dfrac{y}{4} = \dfrac{1}{2},$

$\dfrac{3x}{5} + \dfrac{3y}{10} = \dfrac{12}{5}$

87. $\dfrac{5x}{6} + \dfrac{2y}{3} = \dfrac{1}{2},$

$\dfrac{x}{6} + \dfrac{5y}{12} = \dfrac{2}{3}$

88. $\dfrac{2w}{5} - \dfrac{p}{6} = \dfrac{2}{3},$

$\dfrac{2w}{9} - \dfrac{p}{12} = \dfrac{4}{9}$

89. $\dfrac{a}{9} - \dfrac{b}{4} = \dfrac{2}{3},$

$\dfrac{2a}{15} + \dfrac{b}{20} = -\dfrac{3}{5}$

CONNECTING the CONCEPTS

We now have three different methods for solving systems of equations. Each method has certain strengths and weaknesses, as outlined below.

Method	Strengths	Weaknesses
Graphical	Solutions are displayed graphically. Can be used with any system that can be graphed.	For some systems, only approximate solutions can be found graphically. The graph drawn may not be large enough to show the solution.
Substitution	Yields exact solutions. Easy to use when a variable has a coefficient of 1.	Introduces extensive computations with fractions when solving more complicated systems. Solutions are not displayed graphically.
Elimination	Yields exact solutions. Easy to use when fractions or decimals appear in the system. The preferred method for systems of 3 or more equations in 3 or more variables (see Section 6.4).	Solutions are not displayed graphically.

When selecting a method to use, consider the strengths and weaknesses listed above. If possible, begin solving the system mentally to help discover the method that seems best suited for that particular system.

MIXED REVIEW

Solve using the best method.

1. $x = y,$
$x + y = 2$

2. $x + y = 10,$
$x - y = 8$

3. $y = \frac{1}{2}x + 1,$
$y = 2x - 5$

4. $y = 2x - 3,$
$x + y = 12$

5. $x = 5,$
$y = 10$

6. $3x + 5y = 8,$
$3x - 5y = 4$

7. $2x - y = 1,$
$2y - 4x = 3$

8. $x = 2 - y,$
$3x + 3y = 6$

9. $x + 2y = 3,$
$3x = 4 - y$

10. $9x + 8y = 0,$
$11x - 7y = 0$

11. $10x + 20y = 40,$
$x - y = 7$

12. $y = \frac{5}{3}x + 7,$
$y = \frac{5}{3}x - 8$

13. $2x - 5y = 1,$
$3x + 2y = 11$

14. $\frac{x}{2} + \frac{y}{3} = \frac{2}{3},$
$\frac{x}{5} + \frac{5y}{2} = \frac{1}{4}$

15. $1.1x - 0.3y = 0.8,$
$2.3x + 0.3y = 2.6$

16. $y = -3,$
$x = 11$

17. $x - 2y = 5,$
$3x - 15 = 6y$

18. $12x - 19y = 13,$
$8x + 19y = 7$

19. $0.2x + 0.7y = 1.2,$
$0.3x - 0.1y = 2.7$

20. $\frac{1}{4}x = \frac{1}{3}y,$
$\frac{1}{2}x - \frac{1}{15}y = 2$

6.3 Solving Applications: Systems of Two Equations

Total-Value and Mixture Problems • Motion Problems

You are in a much better position to solve problems now that you know how systems of equations can be used. Using systems often makes the translating step easier.

EXAMPLE 1

Patch of Brighamia Insignis with flower

Endangered species. The number of plant species listed as threatened (likely to become endangered) or endangered (in danger of becoming extinct) has more than tripled in the past 20 years. In 2008, there were 746 species of plants in the United States that were considered threatened or endangered. The number considered threatened was 4 less than one-fourth of the number considered endangered. How many U.S. plant species were considered endangered and how many were considered threatened in 2008?

Source: U.S. Fish and Wildlife Service

SOLUTION   The *Familiarize* and *Translate* steps were completed in Example 1 of Section 6.1. The resulting system of equations is

$$t + d = 746,$$
$$t = \tfrac{1}{4}d - 4,$$

where d is the number of endangered plant species and t is the number of threatened plant species in the United States in 2008.

3. **Carry out.** We solve the system of equations. Since one equation already has a variable isolated, let's use the substitution method:

$$t + d = 746$$
$$\tfrac{1}{4}d - 4 + d = 746 \qquad \text{Substituting } \tfrac{1}{4}d - 4 \text{ for } t$$
$$\tfrac{5}{4}d - 4 = 746 \qquad \text{Combining like terms}$$
$$\tfrac{5}{4}d = 750 \qquad \text{Adding 4 to both sides}$$
$$d = \tfrac{4}{5} \cdot 750 \qquad \text{Multiplying both sides by } \tfrac{4}{5}: \tfrac{4}{5} \cdot \tfrac{5}{4} = 1$$
$$d = 600. \qquad \text{Simplifying}$$

Next, using either of the original equations, we substitute and solve for t:

$$t = \tfrac{1}{4} \cdot 600 - 4 = 150 - 4 = 146.$$

4. **Check.** The sum of 600 and 146 is 746, so the total number of species is correct. Since 4 less than one-fourth of 600 is $150 - 4$, or 146, the numbers check.

5. **State.** In 2008, there were 600 endangered plant species and 146 threatened plant species in the United States.

TRY EXERCISE 45

STUDENT NOTES

It is very important that you clearly label precisely what each variable represents. Not only will this assist you in writing equations, but it will help you to identify and state solutions.

Total-Value and Mixture Problems

EXAMPLE 2

Jewelry design. In order to make a necklace, a jewelry designer purchased 80 beads for a total of $39 (excluding tax). Some of the beads were sterling silver beads that cost 40¢ each and the rest were gemstone beads that cost 65¢ each. How many of each type did the designer buy?

SOLUTION   The *Familiarize* and *Translate* steps were completed in Example 2 of Section 6.1.

3. **Carry out.** We are to solve the system of equations

$$s + g = 80, \quad (1)$$
$$40s + 65g = 3900, \quad (2) \quad \text{Working in cents rather than dollars}$$

where s is the number of silver beads bought and g is the number of gemstone beads bought. Because both equations are in the form $Ax + By = C$, let's use the elimination method to solve the system. We can eliminate s by multiplying both sides of equation (1) by -40 and adding them to the corresponding sides of equation (2):

$$
\begin{array}{rl}
-40s - 40g = -3200 & \text{Multiplying both sides of equation (1) by } -40 \\
\underline{40s + 65g = 3900} & \\
25g = 700 & \text{Adding} \\
g = 28. & \text{Solving for } g
\end{array}
$$

To find s, we substitute 28 for g in equation (1) and then solve for s:

$$
\begin{array}{rl}
s + g = 80 & \text{Equation (1)} \\
s + 28 = 80 & \text{Substituting 28 for } g \\
s = 52. & \text{Solving for } s
\end{array}
$$

We obtain $(28, 52)$, or $g = 28$ and $s = 52$.

4. **Check.** We check in the original problem. Recall that g is the number of gemstone beads and s the number of silver beads.

$$
\begin{array}{ll}
\textit{Number of beads}: & g + s = 28 + 52 = 80 \\
\textit{Cost of gemstone beads}: & 65g = 65 \times 28 = 1820¢ \\
\textit{Cost of silver beads}: & 40s = 40 \times 52 = \underline{2080¢} \\
& \text{Total} = 3900¢
\end{array}
$$

The numbers check.

5. **State.** The designer bought 28 gemstone beads and 52 silver beads.

> **TRY EXERCISE** 15

Example 2 involved two types of items (silver beads and gemstone beads), the quantity of each type bought, and the total value of the items. We refer to this type of problem as a *total-value problem*.

EXAMPLE 3

Blending teas. Tea Pots n Treasures sells loose Oolong tea for $2.15 an ounce. Donna mixed Oolong tea with shaved almonds that sell for $0.95 an ounce to create the Market Street Oolong blend that sells for $1.85 an ounce. One week, she made 300 oz of Market Street Oolong. How much tea and how much shaved almonds did Donna use?

SOLUTION

1. **Familiarize.** This problem is similar to Example 2. Rather than silver beads and gemstone beads, we have ounces of tea and ounces of almonds. Instead of a different price for each type of bead, we have a different price per ounce for each ingredient. Finally, rather than knowing the total cost of the beads, we know the weight and the price per ounce of the mixture. Thus we can find the total value of the blend by multiplying 300 ounces times $1.85 per ounce. We let l = the number of ounces of Oolong tea and a = the number of ounces of shaved almonds.

2. **Translate.** Since a 300-oz batch was made, we must have

$$l + a = 300.$$

To find a second equation, note that the total value of the 300-oz blend must match the combined value of the separate ingredients:

Rewording: The value of the Oolong tea plus the value of the almonds is the value of the Market Street blend.

Translating: $l \cdot \$2.15 + a \cdot \$0.95 = 300 \cdot \$1.85$

These equations can also be obtained from a table.

	Oolong Tea	Almonds	Market Street Blend	
Number of Ounces	l	a	300	→ $l + a = 300$
Price per Ounce	$2.15	$0.95	$1.85	
Value of Tea	$2.15l	$0.95a	$300 \cdot \$1.85$, or $555	→ $2.15l + 0.95a = 555$

Clearing decimals in the second equation, we have $215l + 95a = 55,500$. We have translated to a system of equations:

$$l + \quad a = 300, \quad (1)$$
$$215l + 95a = 55,500. \quad (2)$$

3. **Carry out.** We can solve using substitution. When equation (1) is solved for l, we have $l = 300 - a$. Substituting $300 - a$ for l in equation (2), we find a:

$$215(300 - a) + 95a = 55,500 \quad \text{Substituting}$$
$$64,500 - 215a + 95a = 55,500 \quad \text{Using the distributive law}$$
$$-120a = -9000 \quad \text{Combining like terms; subtracting } 64,500 \text{ from both sides}$$
$$a = 75. \quad \text{Dividing both sides by } -120$$

We have $a = 75$ and, from equation (1) above, $l + a = 300$. Thus, $l = 225$.

4. **Check.** Combining 225 oz of Oolong tea and 75 oz of almonds will give a 300-oz blend. The value of 225 oz of Oolong is 225($2.15), or $483.75. The value of 75 oz of almonds is 75($0.95), or $71.25. Thus the combined value of the blend is $483.75 + $71.25, or $555. A 300-oz blend priced at $1.85 an ounce would also be worth $555, so our answer checks.

5. **State.** The Market Street blend was made by combining 225 oz of Oolong tea and 75 oz of almonds.

TRY EXERCISE 23

EXAMPLE 4

Student loans. Rani's student loans totaled $9600. Part was a PLUS loan made at 8.5% interest and the rest was a Stafford loan made at 6.8% interest. After one year, Rani's loans accumulated $729.30 in interest. What was the original amount of each loan?

SOLUTION

1. **Familiarize.** We begin with a guess. If $3000 was borrowed at 8.5% and $6600 was borrowed at 6.8%, the two loans would total $9600. The interest would then be 0.085($3000), or $255, and 0.068($6600), or $448.80, for a total of only $703.80 in interest. Our guess was wrong, but checking the guess familiarized us with the problem. More than $3000 was borrowed at the higher rate.

2. **Translate.** We let p = the amount of the PLUS loan and s = the amount of the Stafford loan. Next, we organize a table in which the entries in each column come from the formula for simple interest:

$$Principal \cdot Rate \cdot Time = Interest.$$

	PLUS Loan	Stafford Loan	Total
Principal	p	s	$9600	$\longrightarrow p + s = 9600$
Rate of Interest	8.5%	6.8%	
Time	1 yr	1 yr	
Interest	$0.085p$	$0.068s$	$729.30	$\longrightarrow 0.085p + 0.068s = 729.30$

The total amount borrowed is found in the first row of the table:

$$p + s = 9600.$$

A second equation, representing the accumulated interest, can be found in the last row:

$$0.085p + 0.068s = 729.30, \quad \text{or} \quad 85p + 68s = 729{,}300. \qquad \text{Clearing decimals}$$

3. **Carry out.** The system can be solved by elimination:

$$\begin{array}{lll}
p + s = 9600, & \longrightarrow \text{Multiplying both} \longrightarrow & -85p - 85s = -816{,}000 \\
85p + 68s = 729{,}300. & \quad\text{sides by } -85 & \underline{85p + 68s = 729{,}300} \\
& & -17s = -86{,}700
\end{array}$$

$$p + s = 9600 \longleftarrow \qquad s = 5100$$
$$p + 5100 = 9600$$
$$p = 4500.$$

We find that $p = 4500$ and $s = 5100$.

4. **Check.** The total amount borrowed is $4500 + $5100, or $9600. The interest on $4500 at 8.5% for 1 yr is 0.085($4500), or $382.50. The interest on $5100 at 6.8% for 1 yr is 0.068($5100), or $346.80. The total amount of interest is $382.50 + $346.80, or $729.30, so the numbers check.

5. **State.** The PLUS loan was for $4500 and the Stafford loan was for $5100.

TRY EXERCISE 29

Before proceeding to Example 5, briefly scan Examples 2–4 for similarities. Note that in each case, one of the equations in the system is a simple sum while the other equation represents a sum of products. Example 5 continues this pattern with what is commonly called a *mixture problem*.

> **Problem-Solving Tip**
>
> When solving a problem, see if it is patterned or modeled after a problem that you have already solved.

EXAMPLE 5

Mixing fertilizers.   Nature's Green Gardening, Inc., carries two brands of fertilizer containing nitrogen and water. "Gentle Grow" is 3% nitrogen and "Sun Saver" is 8% nitrogen. Nature's Green needs to combine the two types of solutions into a 90-L mixture that is 6% nitrogen. How much of each brand should be used?

SOLUTION

1. **Familiarize.** We make a drawing and note that we must consider not only the size of the mixture, but also its strength. Let's make a guess to gain familiarity with the problem.

Suppose that 40 L of Gentle Grow and 50 L of Sun Saver are mixed. The resulting mixture will be the right size, 90 L, but will it be the right strength? To find out, note that 40 L of Gentle Grow would contribute $0.03(40) = 1.2$ L of nitrogen to the mixture while 50 L of Sun Saver would contribute $0.08(50) = 4$ L of nitrogen to the mixture. The total amount of nitrogen in the mixture would then be $1.2 + 4$, or 5.2 L. But we want 6% of 90, or 5.4 L, to be nitrogen. Our guess of 40 L and 50 L is close but incorrect. Checking our guess has familiarized us with the problem.

2. **Translate.** Let $g =$ the number of liters of Gentle Grow and $s =$ the number of liters of Sun Saver. The information can be organized in a table.

	Gentle Grow	Sun Saver	Mixture	
Number of Liters	g	s	90	→ $g + s = 90$
Percent of Nitrogen	3%	8%	6%	
Amount of Nitrogen	$0.03g$	$0.08s$	0.06×90, or 5.4 liters	→ $0.03g + 0.08s = 5.4$

If we add g and s in the first row, we get one equation. It represents the total amount of mixture: $g + s = 90$.

If we add the amounts of nitrogen listed in the third row, we get a second equation. This equation represents the amount of nitrogen in the mixture: $0.03g + 0.08s = 5.4$.

After clearing decimals, we have translated the problem to the system

$$g + \ s = 90, \qquad (1)$$
$$3g + 8s = 540. \qquad (2)$$

3. **Carry out.** We use the elimination method to solve the system:

$$-3g - 3s = -270 \qquad \text{Multiplying both sides of equation (1) by } -3$$
$$\underline{3g + 8s = \ \ \ 540}$$
$$5s = \ \ \ 270 \qquad \text{Adding}$$
$$s = 54; \qquad \text{Solving for } s$$
$$g + 54 = 90 \qquad \text{Substituting into equation (1)}$$
$$g = 36. \qquad \text{Solving for } g$$

4. **Check.** Remember, g is the number of liters of Gentle Grow and s is the number of liters of Sun Saver.

Total amount of mixture: $\qquad\qquad g + s = 36 + 54 = 90$

Total amount of nitrogen: $\qquad 3\% \text{ of } 36 + 8\% \text{ of } 54 = 1.08 + 4.32 = 5.4$

Percentage of nitrogen in mixture: $\dfrac{\text{Total amount of nitrogen}}{\text{Total amount of mixture}} = \dfrac{5.4}{90} = 6\%$

The numbers check in the original problem.

5. **State.** Nature's Green Gardening should mix 36 L of Gentle Grow with 54 L of Sun Saver.

TRY EXERCISE 25

Motion Problems

When a problem deals with distance, speed (rate), and time, recall the following.

Distance, Rate, and Time Equations

If r represents rate, t represents time, and d represents distance, then:

$$d = rt, \qquad r = \frac{d}{t}, \quad \text{and} \quad t = \frac{d}{r}.$$

Be sure to remember at least one of these equations. The others can be obtained by multiplying or dividing on both sides as needed.

EXAMPLE 6

Train travel. A Vermont Railways freight train, loaded with logs, leaves Boston, heading to Washington, D.C., at a speed of 60 km/h. Two hours later, an Amtrak® Metroliner leaves Boston, bound for Washington, D.C., on a parallel track at 90 km/h. At what point will the Metroliner catch up to the freight train?

SOLUTION

1. **Familiarize.** Let's make a guess and check to see if it is correct. Suppose the trains meet after traveling 180 km. We can then calculate the time for each train.

	Distance	Rate	Time
Freight Train	180 km	60 km/h	$\frac{180}{60} = 3$ hr
Metroliner	180 km	90 km/h	$\frac{180}{90} = 2$ hr

We see that the distance cannot be 180 km, since the difference in travel times for the trains is *not* 2 hr. Although our guess is wrong, we can use a similar chart to organize the information in this problem.

The distance at which the trains meet is unknown, but we do know that the trains will have traveled the same distance when they meet. We let d = this distance.

The time that the trains are running is also unknown, but we do know that the freight train has a 2-hr head start. Thus if we let t = the number of hours that the freight train is running before they meet, then $t - 2$ is the number of hours that the Metroliner runs before catching up to the freight train.

60 km/h
d kilometers
t hours

90 km/h
d kilometers
$t - 2$ hours

Trains meet here

2. **Translate.** We can organize the information in a chart. Each row is determined by the formula *Distance = Rate · Time*.

	Distance	Rate	Time	
Freight Train	d	60	t	$\rightarrow d = 60t$
Metroliner	d	90	$t - 2$	$\rightarrow d = 90(t - 2)$

Using *Distance = Rate · Time* twice, we get two equations:

$$d = 60t, \qquad (1)$$
$$d = 90(t - 2). \qquad (2)$$

3. **Carry out.** We solve the system using substitution:

$$60t = 90(t - 2) \qquad \text{Substituting } 60t \text{ for } d \text{ in equation (2)}$$
$$60t = 90t - 180$$
$$-30t = -180$$
$$t = 6.$$

The time for the freight train is 6 hr, which means that the time for the Metroliner is 6 − 2, or 4 hr. Remember that it is distance, not time, that the problem asked for. Thus for $t = 6$, we have $d = 60 \cdot 6 = 360$ km.

4. **Check.** At 60 km/h, the freight train will travel $60 \cdot 6$, or 360 km, in 6 hr. At 90 km/h, the Metroliner will travel $90 \cdot (6 − 2) = 360$ km in 4 hr. The numbers check.

5. **State.** The freight train will catch up to the Metroliner at a point 360 km from Boston.

TRY EXERCISE 37

EXAMPLE 7

Jet travel. A Boeing 747-400 jet flies 4 hr west with a 60-mph tailwind. Returning *against* the wind takes 5 hr. Find the speed of the jet with no wind.

SOLUTION

1. **Familiarize.** We imagine the situation and make a drawing. Note that the wind *speeds up* the jet on the outbound flight but *slows down* the jet on the return flight.

With tailwind,
$r + 60$

60-mph wind,
4 hours
d miles

d miles

Into headwind
$r − 60$

60-mph wind,
5 hours
d miles

Let's make a guess of the jet's speed if there were no wind. Note that the distances traveled each way must be the same.

Speed with no wind: 400 mph

Speed with the wind: 400 + 60 = 460 mph

Speed against the wind: 400 − 60 = 340 mph

Distance with the wind: 460 · 4 = 1840 mi

Distance against the wind: 340 · 5 = 1700 mi

Since the distances are not the same, our guess of 400 mph is incorrect.

We let r = the speed, in miles per hour, of the jet in still air. Then $r + 60$ = the jet's speed with the wind and $r - 60$ = the jet's speed against the wind. We also let d = the distance traveled, in miles.

2. **Translate.** The information can be organized in a chart. The distances traveled are the same, so we use *Distance* = *Rate* (or *Speed*) · *Time*. Each row of the chart gives an equation.

	Distance	Rate	Time	
With Wind	d	$r + 60$	4	→ $d = (r + 60)4$
Against Wind	d	$r - 60$	5	→ $d = (r - 60)5$

The two equations constitute a system:

$$d = (r + 60)4, \qquad (1)$$
$$d = (r - 60)5. \qquad (2)$$

3. **Carry out.** We solve the system using substitution:

$(r - 60)5 = (r + 60)4$ Substituting $(r - 60)5$ for d in equation (1)

$5r - 300 = 4r + 240$ Using the distributive law

$r = 540.$ Solving for r

4. **Check.** When $r = 540$, the speed with the wind is $540 + 60 = 600$ mph, and the speed against the wind is $540 - 60 = 480$ mph. The distance with the wind, $600 \cdot 4 = 2400$ mi, matches the distance into the wind, $480 \cdot 5 = 2400$ mi, so we have a check.

5. **State.** The speed of the jet with no wind is 540 mph.   ▶ TRY EXERCISE ▶ 39

Tips for Solving Motion Problems

1. Draw a diagram using an arrow or arrows to represent distance and the direction of each object in motion.
2. Organize the information in a chart.
3. Look for times, distances, or rates that are the same. These often can lead to an equation.
4. Translating to a system of equations allows for the use of two variables.
5. Always make sure that you have answered the question asked.

6.3 EXERCISE SET

For Extra Help

1.–14. For Exercises 1–14, solve Exercises 41–54 from pp. 394–395.

15. *Recycled paper.* Staples® recently charged $3.79 per ream (package of 500 sheets) of regular paper and $5.49 per ream of paper made of recycled fibers. Last semester, Valley College spent $582.44 for 116 reams of paper. How many of each type were purchased?

16. *Photocopying.* Quick Copy recently charged 49¢ per page for color copies and 7¢ per page for black-and-white copies. If Shirlee's bill for 90 copies was $11.34, how many copies of each type were made?

17. *Lighting.* Lowe's Home Improvement recently sold 13-watt Feit Electric Ecobulbs® for $5 each and 18-watt Ecobulbs® for $6 each. If River County Hospital purchased 200 such bulbs for a total of $1140, how many of each type did they purchase?

18. *Office supplies.* Staples® recently charged $17.99 per box of Pilot Precise® rollerball pens and $7.49 per box for Bic® Matic Grip mechanical pencils. If Kelling Community College purchased 120 such boxes for a total of $1234.80, how many boxes of each type did they purchase?

19. *Sales.* Recently, officedepot.com sold a black HP C7115A Laser Jet print cartridge for $64.99 and a color Apple computer M3908GA ink cartridge for $58.99. During a promotion offering free shipping, a total of 450 of these cartridges was purchased for a total of $27,625.50. How many of each type were purchased?

20. *Sales.* Office Max® recently advertised a three-subject notebook for $2.49 and a five-subject notebook for $3.79. At the start of a recent spring semester, a combination of 50 of these notebooks was sold for a total of $166.10. How many of each type were sold?

Aha! **21.** *Blending coffees.* The Roasted Bean charges $13.00 per pound for Fair Trade Organic Mexican coffee and $11.00 per pound for Fair Trade Organic Peruvian coffee. How much of each type should be used to make a 28-lb blend that sells for $12.00 per pound?

22. *Mixed nuts.* Oh Nuts! sells pistachio kernels for $6.50 per pound and almonds for $8.00 per pound. How much of each type should be used to make a 50-lb mixture that sells for $7.40 per pound?

23. *Event planning.* As part of the refreshments for Yvette's 25th birthday party, Kim plans to provide a bowl of M&M candies. She wants to mix custom-printed M&Ms costing 60¢ per ounce with bulk M&Ms costing 25¢ per ounce to create 20 lb of a mixture costing 32¢ per ounce. How much of each type of M&M should she use?
Source: www.mymms.com

24. *Blending spices.* Spice of Life sells ground sumac for $1.35 an ounce and ground thyme for $1.85 an ounce. Aman wants to make a 20-oz Zahtar seasoning blend using the two spices that sells for $1.65 an ounce. How much of each spice should Aman use?

25. *Catering.* Cati's Catering is planning an office reception. The office administrator has requested a candy mixture that is 25% chocolate. Cati has available mixtures that are either 50% chocolate or 10% chocolate. How much of each type should be mixed to get a 20-lb mixture that is 25% chocolate?

26. *Ink remover.* Etch Clean Graphics uses one cleanser that is 25% acid and a second that is 50% acid. How many liters of each should be mixed to get 30 L of a solution that is 40% acid?

27. *Blending granola.* Deep Thought Granola is 25% nuts and dried fruit. Oat Dream Granola is 10% nuts and dried fruit. How much of Deep Thought and how much of Oat Dream should be mixed to form a 20-lb batch of granola that is 19% nuts and dried fruit?

28. *Livestock feed.* Soybean meal is 16% protein and corn meal is 9% protein. How many pounds of each should be mixed to get a 350-lb mixture that is 12% protein?

29. *Student loans.* Stacey's two student loans totaled $12,000. One of her loans was at 6.5% simple interest and the other at 7.2%. After one year, Stacey owed $811.50 in interest. What was the amount of each loan?

30. *Investments.* A self-employed contractor nearing retirement made two investments totaling $15,000. In one year, these investments yielded $1023 in simple interest. Part of the money was invested at 6% and the rest at 7.5%. How much was invested at each rate?

31. *Investments.* When Kari began her new job, she was given a signing bonus of $10,000. She invested part of the bonus at 4% and the rest of it at 5.5%. In one year, these investments yielded $496 in simple interest. How much was invested at each rate?

32. *Loans.* To start her new business, Jessica borrowed a total of $9000 from two sources. One of her loans was at 7.5% simple interest and the other at 8.4%. After one year, Jessica owed $683.10 in interest. What was the amount of each loan?

33. *Loans.* Scott borrowed twice as much at 6% simple interest than he did at 8% simple interest. After one year, he owed $315 in interest. What was the amount of each loan?

34. *Investments.* Kyle invested half as much at 7.5% simple interest than he did at 5% simple interest. In one year, these investments yielded $56 in interest. How much was invested at each rate?

35. *Investments.* Maya wants to make two investments totaling $8400, one at 3% simple interest and the other at 4.5%. She would like to make as much in interest as possible, but in order to remain eligible for financial aid, she cannot make more than $300 in interest. How much should she invest at each rate?

36. *Investments.* Lisa wants to make two investments totaling $12,000, one at 2.4% simple interest and the other at 5.65%. She would like to make as much in interest as possible, but for tax purposes, she does not want to make more than $600 in interest. How much should she invest at each rate?

37. *Loans.* Thomas borrowed $2500 from City Bank and $1300 from Farm Bank. The interest rate at City Bank was 2% greater than the interest rate at Farm Bank. After one year, Thomas owed $97.50 in simple interest. What were the interest rates?

38. *Investments.* Elena invested $550 in an account at First Bank and $750 in an account at Second Bank. The interest rate at First Bank was 1% less than the interest rate at Second Bank. In one year, these investments yielded a total of $43.25 in simple interest. What were the interest rates?

39. *Loans.* Quincy borrowed $1200 at one interest rate and $8500 at a second interest rate that was half as high as the first rate. After one year, Quincy owed $370.60 in simple interest. What were the interest rates?

40. *Loans.* Todd borrowed $4800 at one interest rate and $3000 at a second interest rate that was twice as high as the first rate. After one year, Todd owed $270 in simple interest. What were the interest rates?

41. *Loans.* Kerry borrowed $16,000 less at 8% simple interest than he did at 7.2%. After one year, he owed $1836 in interest. How much did he borrow at each rate?

42. *Investments.* Sara invested $3000 more at 4.35% than she did at 2.8%. In one year, these investments yielded a total of $309.25 in simple interest. How much did she invest at each rate?

43. *Investments.* Megan invested a total of $6000 in two accounts. One account paid 5% simple interest and the other 6%. In one year, the total value of these investments was $6342. How much did she invest at each rate?

44. *Investments.* Patrick invested a total of $7000 in two accounts. One account paid 3% simple interest and the other 8%. In one year, the total value of these investments was $7390. How much did he invest at each rate?

45. *Automotive maintenance.* "Steady State" antifreeze is 18% alcohol and "Even Flow" is 10% alcohol. How many liters of each should be mixed to get 20 L of a mixture that is 15% alcohol?

46. *Chemistry.* E-Chem Testing has a solution that is 80% base and another that is 30% base. A technician needs 150 L of a solution that is 62% base. The 150 L will be prepared by mixing the two solutions on hand. How much of each should be used?

47. *Octane ratings.* The octane rating of a gasoline is a measure of the amount of isooctane in the gas. Manufacturers recommend using 93-octane gasoline on retuned motors. How much 87-octane gas and 95-octane gas should Yousef mix in order to make 10 gal of 93-octane gas for his retuned Ford F-150?
Source: Champlain Electric and Petroleum Equipment

48. *Octane ratings.* The octane rating of a gasoline is a measure of the amount of isooctane in the gas. Subaru recommends 91-octane gasoline for the 2008 Legacy 3.0 R. How much 87-octane gas and 93-octane gas should Kelsey mix in order to make 12 gal of 91-octane gas for her Legacy?
Sources: Champlain Electric and Petroleum Equipment: Dean Team Ballwin

49. *Food science.* The following bar graph shows the milk fat percentages in three dairy products. How many pounds each of whole milk and cream should be mixed to form 200 lb of milk for cream cheese?

Milk fat

50. *Food science.* How much lowfat milk (1% fat) and how much whole milk (4% fat) should be mixed to make 5 gal of reduced fat milk (2% fat)?

51. *Train travel.* A train leaves Danville Union and travels north at a speed of 75 km/h. Two hours later, an express train leaves on a parallel track and travels north at 125 km/h. How far from the station will they meet?

52. *Car travel.* Two cars leave Salt Lake City, traveling in opposite directions. One car travels at a speed of 80 km/h and the other at 96 km/h. In how many hours will they be 528 km apart?

53. *Canoeing.* Kahla paddled for 4 hr with a 6-km/h current to reach a campsite. The return trip against the same current took 10 hr. Find the speed of Kahla's canoe in still water.

54. *Boating.* Cody's motorboat took 3 hr to make a trip downstream with a 6-mph current. The return trip against the same current took 5 hr. Find the speed of the boat in still water.

55. *Point of no return.* A plane flying the 3458-mi trip from New York City to London has a 50-mph tailwind. The flight's *point of no return* is the point at which the flight time required to return to New York is the same as the time required to continue to London. If the speed of the plane in still air is 360 mph, how far is New York from the point of no return?

56. *Point of no return.* A plane is flying the 2553-mi trip from Los Angeles to Honolulu into a 60-mph headwind. If the speed of the plane in still air is 310 mph, how far from Los Angeles is the plane's point of no return? (See Exercise 41.)

57. *Architecture.* The rectangular ground floor of the John Hancock building has a perimeter of 860 ft. The length is 100 ft more than the width. Find the length and the width.

$x + 100$

x

58. *Real estate.* The perimeter of a rectangular ocean-front lot is 190 m. The width is one-fourth of the length. Find the dimensions.

59. In 2007, Nintendo Co. sold three times as many Wii game machines in Japan as Sony Corp. sold PlayStation 3 consoles. Together, they sold 4.84 million game machines in Japan. How many of each were sold?
Source: Bloomberg.com

60. *Hockey rankings.* Hockey teams receive 2 points for a win and 1 point for a tie. The Wildcats once won a championship with 60 points. They won 9 more games than they tied. How many wins and how many ties did the Wildcats have?

61. *Video rentals.* At one time, Netflix offered an unlimited 1 DVD at-a-time rental plan for $8.99 per month and a rental plan with a limit of 2 DVDs per month for $4.99. During one week, 250 new subscribers paid $1975.50 for these plans. How many of each type of plan were purchased?

62. *Radio airplay.* Roscoe must play 12 commercials during his 1-hr radio show. Each commercial is either 30 sec or 60 sec long. If the total commercial time during that hour is 10 min, how many commercials of each type does Roscoe play?

63. *Making change.* Monica makes a $9.25 purchase at the bookstore with a $20 bill. The store has no bills and gives her the change in quarters and fifty-cent pieces. There are 30 coins in all. How many of each kind are there?

64. *Teller work.* Sabina goes to a bank and gets change for a $50 bill consisting of all $5 bills and $1 bills. There are 22 bills in all. How many of each kind are there?

65. In what ways are Examples 3 and 4 similar? In what sense are their systems of equations similar?

66. Write at least three study tips of your own for someone beginning this exercise set.

Skill Review

To prepare for Section 6.4, review evaluating expressions with three variables.

Evaluate.

67. $2x - 3y - z$, for $x = 5$, $y = 2$, and $z = 3$

68. $4x + y - 6z$, for $x = \frac{1}{2}$, $y = \frac{1}{2}$, and $z = \frac{1}{3}$

69. $x + y + 2z$, for $x = 1$, $y = -4$, and $z = -5$

70. $3a - b + 2c$, for $a = 1$, $b = -6$, and $c = 4$

71. $a - 2b - 3c$, for $a = -2$, $b = 3$, and $c = -5$

72. $2a - 5b - c$, for $a = \frac{1}{4}$, $b = -\frac{1}{4}$, and $c = -\frac{3}{2}$

Synthesis

73. Suppose that in Example 3 you are asked only for the amount of almonds needed for the Market Street blend. Would the method of solving the problem change? Why or why not?

74. Write a problem similar to Example 2 for a classmate to solve. Design the problem so that the solution is "The bakery sold 24 loaves of bread and 18 packages of sandwich rolls."

75. *Recycled paper.* Unable to purchase 60 reams of paper that contains 20% post-consumer fiber, the Naylor School bought paper that was either 0% post-consumer fiber or 30% post-consumer fiber. How many reams of each should be purchased in order to use the same amount of post-consumer fiber as if the 20% post-consumer fiber paper were available?

76. *Automotive maintenance.* The radiator in Natalie's car contains 6.3 L of antifreeze and water. This mixture is 30% antifreeze. How much of this mixture should she drain and replace with pure antifreeze so that there will be a mixture of 50% antifreeze?

77. *Metal alloys.* In order for a metal to be labeled "sterling silver," the silver alloy must contain at least 92.5% pure silver. Nicole has 32 oz of coin silver, which is 90% pure silver. How much pure silver must she add to the coin silver in order to have a sterling-silver alloy?
Source: *The Jewelry Repair Manual*, R. Allen Hardy, Courier Dover Publications, 1996, p. 271.

78. *Exercise.* Elyse jogs and walks to school each day. She averages 4 km/h walking and 8 km/h jogging. From home to school is 6 km and Elyse makes the trip in 1 hr. How far does she jog in a trip?

79. *Book sales.* *American Economic History* can be purchased as a three-volume set for $88 or each volume can be purchased separately for $39. An economics class spent $1641 for 51 volumes. How many three-volume sets were ordered?
Source: National History Day, www.nhd.org

80. The tens digit of a two-digit positive integer is 2 more than three times the units digit. If the digits are interchanged, the new number is 13 less than half the given number. Find the given integer. (*Hint*: Let $x =$ the tens-place digit and $y =$ the units-place digit; then $10x + y$ is the number.)

81. *Wood stains.* Williams' Custom Flooring has 0.5 gal of stain that is 20% brown and 80% neutral. A customer orders 1.5 gal of a stain that is 60% brown and 40% neutral. How much pure brown stain and how much neutral stain should be added to the original 0.5 gal in order to make up the order?*

82. *Train travel.* A train leaves Union Station for Central Station, 216 km away, at 9 A.M. One hour later, a train leaves Central Station for Union Station. They meet at noon. If the second train had started at 9 A.M. and the first train at 10:30 A.M., they would still have met at noon. Find the speed of each train.

83. *Fuel economy.* Grady's station wagon gets 18 miles per gallon (mpg) in city driving and 24 mpg in highway driving. The car is driven 465 mi on 23 gal of gasoline. How many miles were driven in the city and how many were driven on the highway?

84. *Biochemistry.* Industrial biochemists routinely use a machine to mix a buffer of 10% acetone by adding 100% acetone to water. One day, instead of adding 5 L of acetone to create a vat of buffer, a machine added 10 L. How much additional water was needed to bring the concentration down to 10%?

85. See Exercise 67 above. Let $x =$ the amount of pure brown stain added to the original 0.5 gal. Find a function $P(x)$ that can be used to determine the percentage of brown stain in the 1.5-gal mixture. On a graphing calculator, draw the graph of P and use INTERSECT to confirm the answer to Exercise 67.

86. *Gender.* Phil and Phyllis are twins. Phyllis has twice as many brothers as she has sisters. Phil has the same number of brothers as sisters. How many girls and how many boys are in the family?

---

*This problem was suggested by Professor Chris Burditt of Yountville, California.

COLLABORATIVE CORNER

How Many Two's? How Many Three's?

Focus: Systems of linear equations

Time: 20 minutes

Group size: 3

The box score at right, from the 2008 NBA All-Star game, contains information on how many field goals (worth either 2 or 3 points) and free throws (worth 1 point) each player attempted and made. For example, the line "Allen 10-14 3-5 28" means that the East's Ray Allen made 10 field goals out of 14 attempts and 3 free throws out of 5 attempts, for a total of 28 points.

ACTIVITY

1. Work as a group to develop a system of two equations in two unknowns that can be used to determine how many 2-pointers and how many 3-pointers were made by the West.

2. Each group member should solve the system from part (1) in a different way: one person algebraically, one person by making a table and methodically checking all combinations of 2- and 3-pointers, and one person by

guesswork. Compare answers when this has been completed.

3. Determine, as a group, how many 2- and 3-pointers the East made.

East (134)
James 12–22 1–1 27, Bosh 7–15 0–2 14, Howard 7–7 2–3 16,
Wade 7–12 0–2 14, Kidd 1–2 0–0 2, Hamilton 4–9 0–0 9,
Wallace 1–5 0–0 3, Billups 3–10 0–1 6, Jamison 1–3 0–0 2,
Pierce 5–9 0–0 10, Johnson 1–2 0–0 3, Allen 10–14 3–5 28
Totals 59–110 6–14 134

West (128)
Anthony 8–17 2–3 18, Duncan 2–7 0–0 4, Ming 2–5 2–2 6,
Bryant 0–0 0–0 0, Iverson 3–7 1–2 7, Nash 4–8 0–0 8,
Stoudemire 8–11 1–3 18, Nowitzki 5–14 2–2 13, Paul 7–14 0–0 16,
West 3–6 0–0 6, Roy 8–10 0–0 18, Boozer 7–15 0–2 14
Totals 57–114 8–14 128

East   34 40 32 28 — 134
West   28 37 28 35 — 128

6.4   Systems of Equations in Three Variables

Identifying Solutions   •   Solving Systems in Three Variables   •   Dependency, Inconsistency, and Geometric Considerations

Some problems translate directly to two equations. Others more naturally call for a translation to three or more equations. In this section, we learn how to solve systems of three linear equations. Later, we will use such systems in problem-solving situations.

Identifying Solutions

A **linear equation in three variables** is an equation equivalent to one in the form $Ax + By + Cz = D$, where A, B, C, and D are real numbers. We refer to the form $Ax + By + Cz = D$ as *standard form* for a linear equation in three variables.

A solution of a system of three equations in three variables is an ordered triple (x, y, z) that makes *all three* equations true. The numbers in an ordered triple correspond to the variables in alphabetical order unless otherwise indicated.

EXAMPLE 1 Determine whether $\left(\frac{3}{2}, -4, 3\right)$ is a solution of the system

$$4x - 2y - 3z = 5,$$
$$-8x - y + z = -5,$$
$$2x + y + 2z = 5.$$

SOLUTION We substitute $\left(\frac{3}{2}, -4, 3\right)$ into the three equations, using alphabetical order:

$$\frac{4x - 2y - 3z = 5}{4 \cdot \frac{3}{2} - 2(-4) - 3 \cdot 3 \;\bigg|\; 5}$$
$$6 + 8 - 9 \;\bigg|$$
$$5 \overset{?}{=} 5 \quad \text{TRUE}$$

$$\frac{-8x - y + z = -5}{-8 \cdot \frac{3}{2} - (-4) + 3 \;\bigg|\; -5}$$
$$-12 + 4 + 3 \;\bigg|$$
$$-5 \overset{?}{=} -5 \quad \text{TRUE}$$

$$\frac{2x + y + 2z = 5}{2 \cdot \frac{3}{2} + (-4) + 2 \cdot 3 \;\bigg|\; 5}$$
$$3 - 4 + 6 \;\bigg|$$
$$5 \overset{?}{=} 5 \quad \text{TRUE}$$

The triple makes all three equations true, so it is a solution.

TRY EXERCISE 7

Solving Systems in Three Variables

The graph of a linear equation in three variables is a plane. Because a three-dimensional coordinate system is required, solving systems in three variables graphically is difficult. The substitution method *can* be used but becomes cumbersome unless one or more of the equations has only two variables. Fortunately, the elimination method works well for a system of three equations in three variables. We first eliminate one variable to form a system of two equations in two variables. Once that simpler system has been solved, we substitute into one of the three original equations and solve for the third variable.

EXAMPLE 2 Solve the following system of equations:

$$x + y + z = 4, \quad (1)$$
$$x - 2y - z = 1, \quad (2)$$
$$2x - y - 2z = -1. \quad (3)$$

SOLUTION We select *any* two of the three equations and work to get an equation in two variables. Let's add equations (1) and (2):

$$\begin{array}{rl} x + y + z = 4 & (1) \\ x - 2y - z = 1 & (2) \\ \hline 2x - y = 5. & (4) \quad \text{Adding to eliminate } z \end{array}$$

Next, we select a different pair of equations and eliminate the *same variable* that we did above. Let's use equations (1) and (3) to again eliminate z. Be careful! A common error is to eliminate a different variable in this step.

> *CAUTION!* Be sure to eliminate the same variable in both pairs of equations.

$$\begin{array}{l} x + y + z = 4, \\ 2x - y - 2z = -1 \end{array} \xrightarrow[\text{of equation (1) by 2}]{\text{Multiplying both sides}} \begin{array}{rl} 2x + 2y + 2z = 8 \\ 2x - y - 2z = -1 \\ \hline 4x + y = 7 & (5) \end{array}$$

STUDY SKILLS ————

Know Yourself

Not everyone learns in the same way. Use a learning center on campus, a book, or the Internet to find out what your learning style is. Then study in a way that fits your learning style best.

Now we solve the resulting system of equations (4) and (5). That solution will give us two of the numbers in the solution of the original system.

$$2x - y = 5 \quad (4)$$
$$4x + y = 7 \quad (5)$$
$$6x \quad\quad = 12 \quad \text{Adding}$$
$$x = 2$$

Note that we now have two equations in two variables. Had we not eliminated the *same* variable in both of the above steps, this would not be the case.

We can use either equation (4) or (5) to find y. We choose equation (5):

$$4x + y = 7 \quad (5)$$
$$4 \cdot 2 + y = 7 \quad \text{Substituting 2 for } x \text{ in equation (5)}$$
$$8 + y = 7$$
$$y = -1.$$

We now have $x = 2$ and $y = -1$. To find the value for z, we use any of the original three equations and substitute to find the third number, z. Let's use equation (1) and substitute our two numbers in it:

$$x + y + z = 4 \quad (1)$$
$$2 + (-1) + z = 4 \quad \text{Substituting 2 for } x \text{ and } -1 \text{ for } y$$
$$1 + z = 4$$
$$z = 3.$$

We have obtained the triple $(2, -1, 3)$. It should check in *all three* equations:

$$\frac{x + y + z = 4}{2 + (-1) + 3 \mid 4}$$
$$4 \overset{?}{=} 4 \quad \text{TRUE}$$

$$\frac{x - 2y - z = 1}{2 - 2(-1) - 3 \mid 1}$$
$$1 \overset{?}{=} 1 \quad \text{TRUE}$$

$$\frac{2x - y - 2z = -1}{2 \cdot 2 - (-1) - 2 \cdot 3 \mid -1}$$
$$-1 \overset{?}{=} -1 \quad \text{TRUE}$$

The solution is $(2, -1, 3)$.

TRY EXERCISE 9

> **Solving Systems of Three Linear Equations**
>
> To use the elimination method to solve systems of three linear equations:
>
> 1. Write all equations in the standard form $Ax + By + Cz = D$.
> 2. Clear any decimals or fractions.
> 3. Choose a variable to eliminate. Then select two of the three equations and work to get one equation in which the selected variable is eliminated.
> 4. Next, use a different pair of equations and eliminate the same variable that you did in step (3).
> 5. Solve the system of equations that resulted from steps (3) and (4).
> 6. Substitute the solution from step (5) into one of the original three equations and solve for the third variable. Then check.

EXAMPLE 3 Solve the system

$$4x - 2y - 3z = 5, \quad (1)$$
$$-8x - y + z = -5, \quad (2)$$
$$2x + y + 2z = 5. \quad (3)$$

SOLUTION

Write in standard form.

1., 2. The equations are already in standard form with no fractions or decimals.

3. Next, select a variable to eliminate. We decide on y because the y-terms are opposites of each other in equations (2) and (3). We add:

Eliminate a variable. (We choose y.)

$$\begin{array}{rl} -8x - y + z = -5 & (2) \\ 2x + y + 2z = 5 & (3) \\ \hline -6x + 3z = 0. & (4) \qquad \text{Adding} \end{array}$$

4. We use another pair of equations to create a second equation in x and z. That is, we eliminate the same variable, y, as in step (3). We use equations (1) and (3):

Eliminate the same variable using a different pair of equations.

$$\begin{array}{l} 4x - 2y - 3z = 5, \\ 2x + y + 2z = 5 \end{array} \xrightarrow[\text{of equation (3) by 2}]{\text{Multiplying both sides}} \begin{array}{r} 4x - 2y - 3z = 5 \\ 4x + 2y + 4z = 10 \\ \hline 8x + z = 15. \quad (5) \end{array}$$

5. Now we solve the resulting system of equations (4) and (5). That allows us to find two parts of the ordered triple.

Solve the system of two equations in two variables.

$$\begin{array}{l} -6x + 3z = 0, \\ 8x + z = 15 \end{array} \xrightarrow[\text{of equation (5) by } -3]{\text{Multiplying both sides}} \begin{array}{r} -6x + 3z = 0 \\ -24x - 3z = -45 \\ \hline -30x = -45 \\ x = \frac{-45}{-30} = \frac{3}{2} \end{array}$$

We use equation (5) to find z:

$$\begin{aligned} 8x + z &= 15 \\ 8 \cdot \tfrac{3}{2} + z &= 15 \qquad \text{Substituting } \tfrac{3}{2} \text{ for } x \\ 12 + z &= 15 \\ z &= 3. \end{aligned}$$

6. Finally, we use any of the original equations and substitute to find the third number, y. We choose equation (3):

Solve for the remaining variable.

$$\begin{aligned} 2x + y + 2z &= 5 \qquad (3) \\ 2 \cdot \tfrac{3}{2} + y + 2 \cdot 3 &= 5 \qquad \text{Substituting } \tfrac{3}{2} \text{ for } x \text{ and } 3 \text{ for } z \\ 3 + y + 6 &= 5 \\ y + 9 &= 5 \\ y &= -4. \end{aligned}$$

Check.

The solution is $\left(\tfrac{3}{2}, -4, 3\right)$. The check was performed as Example 1.

> **TRY EXERCISE** 23

Sometimes, certain variables are missing at the outset.

EXAMPLE 4

Solve the system

$$\begin{array}{rl} x + y + z = 180, & (1) \\ x - z = -70, & (2) \\ 2y - z = 0. & (3) \end{array}$$

SOLUTION

1., 2. The equations appear in standard form with no fractions or decimals.

3., 4. Note that there is no y in equation (2). Thus, at the outset, we already have y eliminated from one equation. We need another equation with y eliminated, so we work with equations (1) and (3):

$$x + y + z = 180, \quad \xrightarrow{\substack{\text{Multiplying both sides} \\ \text{of equation (1) by } -2}} \quad \begin{array}{r} -2x - 2y - 2z = -360 \\ 2y - z = 0 \\ \hline -2x - 3z = -360. \end{array} \quad (4)$$

5., 6. Now we solve the resulting system of equations (2) and (4):

$$\begin{array}{r} x - z = -70, \\ -2x - 3z = -360 \end{array} \quad \xrightarrow{\substack{\text{Multiplying both sides} \\ \text{of equation (2) by } 2}} \quad \begin{array}{r} 2x - 2z = -140 \\ -2x - 3z = -360 \\ \hline -5z = -500 \\ z = 100. \end{array}$$

Continuing as in Examples 2 and 3, we get the solution $(30, 50, 100)$. The check is left to the student.

TRY EXERCISE 27

Dependency, Inconsistency, and Geometric Considerations

Each equation in Examples 2, 3, and 4 has a graph that is a plane in three dimensions. The solutions are points common to the planes of each system. Since three planes can have an infinite number of points in common or no points at all in common, we need to generalize the concept of *consistency*.

Planes intersect at one point. System is *consistent* and has one solution.

Planes intersect along a common line. System is *consistent* and has an infinite number of solutions.

Three parallel planes. System is *inconsistent;* it has no solution.

Planes intersect two at a time, with no point common to all three. System is *inconsistent;* it has no solution.

Consistency

A system of equations that has at least one solution is said to be **consistent**.

A system of equations that has no solution is said to be **inconsistent**.

EXAMPLE 5 Solve:

$$\begin{array}{rcl} y + 3z &=& 4, \quad (1) \\ -x - y + 2z &=& 0, \quad (2) \\ x + 2y + z &=& 1. \quad (3) \end{array}$$

SOLUTION The variable x is missing in equation (1). By adding equations (2) and (3), we can find a second equation in which x is missing:

$$\begin{array}{r} -x - y + 2z = 0 \quad (2) \\ x + 2y + z = 1 \quad (3) \\ \hline y + 3z = 1. \quad (4) \quad \text{Adding} \end{array}$$

Equations (1) and (4) form a system in y and z. We solve as before:

$$y + 3z = 4, \quad \xrightarrow{\text{Multiplying both sides of equation (1) by } -1} \quad \begin{array}{r} -y - 3z = -4 \\ y + 3z = 1 \end{array}$$

$$\text{This is a contradiction.} \xrightarrow{} 0 = -3. \qquad \text{Adding}$$

Since we end up with a *false* equation, or contradiction, we state that the system has no solution. It is *inconsistent*.   **TRY EXERCISE** 15

The notion of *dependency* from Section 6.1 can also be extended.

EXAMPLE 6   Solve:

$$\begin{array}{rcl} 2x + y + z &=& 3, \quad (1) \\ x - 2y - z &=& 1, \quad (2) \\ 3x + 4y + 3z &=& 5. \quad (3) \end{array}$$

SOLUTION   Our plan is to first use equations (1) and (2) to eliminate z. Then we will select another pair of equations and again eliminate z:

$$\begin{array}{r} 2x + y + z = 3 \\ x - 2y - z = 1 \\ \hline 3x - y = 4. \quad (4) \end{array}$$

Next, we use equations (2) and (3) to eliminate z again:

$$\begin{array}{l} x - 2y - z = 1, \\ 3x + 4y + 3z = 5 \end{array} \quad \xrightarrow{\text{Multiplying both sides of equation (2) by 3}} \quad \begin{array}{r} 3x - 6y - 3z = 3 \\ 3x + 4y + 3z = 5 \\ \hline 6x - 2y = 8. \quad (5) \end{array}$$

We now try to solve the resulting system of equations (4) and (5):

$$\begin{array}{l} 3x - y = 4, \\ 6x - 2y = 8 \end{array} \quad \xrightarrow{\text{Multiplying both sides of equation (4) by } -2} \quad \begin{array}{r} -6x + 2y = -8 \\ 6x - 2y = 8 \\ \hline 0 = 0. \quad (6) \end{array}$$

Equation (6), which is an identity, indicates that equations (1), (2), and (3) are *dependent*. This means that the original system of three equations is equivalent to a system of two equations. One way to see this is to observe that two times equation (1), minus equation (2), is equation (3). Thus removing equation (3) from the system does not affect the solution of the system.* In writing an answer to this problem, we simply state that "the equations are dependent."   **TRY EXERCISE** 21

Recall that when dependent equations appeared in Section 6.1, the solution sets were always infinite in size and were written in set-builder notation. There, all systems of dependent equations were *consistent*. This is not always the case for

---

*A set of equations is dependent if at least one equation can be expressed as a sum of multiples of other equations in that set.

systems of three or more equations. The following figures illustrate some possibilities geometrically.

The planes intersect along a common line. The equations are *dependent* and the system is *consistent*. There is an infinite number of solutions.

The planes coincide. The equations are *dependent* and the system is *consistent*. There is an infinite number of solutions.

Two planes coincide. The third plane is parallel. The equations are *dependent* and the system is *inconsistent*. There is no solution.

6.4 EXERCISE SET

For Extra Help

Concept Reinforcement *Classify each statement as either true or false.*

1. $3x + 5y + 4z = 7$ is a linear equation in three variables.

2. Every system of three equations in three unknowns has at least one solution.

3. It is not difficult to solve a system of three equations in three unknowns by graphing.

4. If, when we are solving a system of three equations, a false equation results from adding a multiple of one equation to another, the system is inconsistent.

5. If, when we are solving a system of three equations, an identity results from adding a multiple of one equation to another, the equations are dependent.

6. Whenever a system of three equations contains dependent equations, there is an infinite number of solutions.

7. Determine whether $(2, -1, -2)$ is a solution of the system
$$x + y - 2z = 5,$$
$$2x - y - z = 7,$$
$$-x - 2y - 3z = 6.$$

8. Determine whether $(-1, -3, 2)$ is a solution of the system
$$x - y + z = 4,$$
$$x - 2y - z = 3,$$
$$3x + 2y - z = 1.$$

Solve each system. If a system's equations are dependent or if there is no solution, state this.

9. $x - y - z = 0,$
   $2x - 3y + 2z = 7,$
   $-x + 2y + z = 1$

10. $x + y - z = 0,$
    $2x - y + z = 3,$
    $-x + 5y - 3z = 2$

11. $x - y - z = 1,$
    $2x + y + 2z = 4,$
    $x + y + 3z = 5$

12. $x + y - 3z = 4,$
    $2x + 3y + z = 6,$
    $2x - y + z = -14$

13. $3x + 4y - 3z = 4,$
    $5x - y + 2z = 3,$
    $x + 2y - z = -2$

14. $2x - 3y + z = 5,$
    $x + 3y + 8z = 22,$
    $3x - y + 2z = 12$

15. $x + y + z = 0,$
    $2x + 3y + 2z = -3,$
    $-x - 2y - z = 1$

16. $3a - 2b + 7c = 13,$
    $a + 8b - 6c = -47,$
    $7a - 9b - 9c = -3$

17. $2x - 3y - z = -9,$
    $2x + 5y + z = 1,$
    $x - y + z = 3$

18. $4x + y + z = 17,$
    $x - 3y + 2z = -8,$
    $5x - 2y + 3z = 5$

Aha! 19. $a + b + c = 5,$
    $2a + 3b - c = 2,$
    $2a + 3b - 2c = 4$

20. $u - v + 6w = 8,$
    $3u - v + 6w = 14,$
    $-u - 2v - 3w = 7$

21. $-2x + 8y + 2z = 4,$
    $x + 6y + 3z = 4,$
    $3x - 2y + z = 0$

22. $x - y + z = 4,$
    $5x + 2y - 3z = 2,$
    $4x + 3y - 4z = -2$

23. $2u - 4v - w = 8,$
    $3u + 2v + w = 6,$
    $5u - 2v + 3w = 2$

24. $4p + q + r = 3,$
    $2p - q + r = 6,$
    $2p + 2q - r = -9$

25. $r + \frac{3}{2}s + 6t = 2,$
$2r - 3s + 3t = 0.5,$
$r + s + t = 1$

26. $5x + 3y + \frac{1}{2}z = \frac{7}{2},$
$0.5x - 0.9y - 0.2z = 0.3,$
$3x - 2.4y + 0.4z = -1$

27. $4a + 9b = 8,$
$8a + 6c = -1,$
$6b + 6c = -1$

28. $3p + 2r = 11,$
$q - 7r = 4,$
$p - 6q = 1$

29. $x + y + z = 57,$
$-2x + y = 3,$
$x - z = 6$

30. $x + y + z = 105,$
$10y - z = 11,$
$2x - 3y = 7$

31. $a - 3c = 6,$
$b + 2c = 2,$
$7a - 3b - 5c = 14$

32. $2a - 3b = 2,$
$7a + 4c = \frac{3}{4},$
$2c - 3b = 1$

Aha! 33. $x + y + z = 83,$
$y = 2x + 3,$
$z = 40 + x$

34. $l + m = 7,$
$3m + 2n = 9,$
$4l + n = 5$

35. $x + z = 0,$
$x + y + 2z = 3,$
$y + z = 2$

36. $x + y = 0,$
$x + z = 1,$
$2x + y + z = 2$

37. $x + y + z = 1,$
$-x + 2y + z = 2,$
$2x - y = -1$

38. $y + z = 1,$
$x + y + z = 1,$
$x + 2y + 2z = 2$

39. Rondel always begins solving systems of three equations in three variables by using the first two equations to eliminate x. Is this a good approach? Why or why not?

40. Describe a method for writing an inconsistent system of three equations in three variables.

Skill Review

To prepare for Section 6.5, review translating sentences to equations.

Translate each sentence to an equation.

41. One number is half another.

42. The difference of two numbers is twice the first number.

43. The sum of three consecutive numbers is 100.

44. The sum of three numbers is 100.

45. The product of two numbers is five times a third number.

46. The product of two numbers is twice their sum.

Synthesis

47. Is it possible for a system of three linear equations to have exactly two ordered triples in its solution set? Why or why not?

48. Describe a procedure that could be used to solve a system of four equations in four variables.

Solve.

49. $\frac{x + 2}{3} - \frac{y + 4}{2} + \frac{z + 1}{6} = 0,$
$\frac{x - 4}{3} + \frac{y + 1}{4} - \frac{z - 2}{2} = -1,$
$\frac{x + 1}{2} + \frac{y}{2} + \frac{z - 1}{4} = \frac{3}{4}$

50. $w + x - y + z = 0,$
$w - 2x - 2y - z = -5,$
$w - 3x - y + z = 4,$
$2w - x - y + 3z = 7$

51. $w + x + y + z = 2,$
$w + 2x + 2y + 4z = 1,$
$w - x + y + z = 6,$
$w - 3x - y + z = 2$

For Exercises 52 and 53, let u represent 1/x, v represent 1/y, and w represent 1/z. Solve for u, v, and w, and then solve for x, y, and z.

52. $\frac{2}{x} + \frac{2}{y} - \frac{3}{z} = 3,$
$\frac{1}{x} - \frac{2}{y} - \frac{3}{z} = 9,$
$\frac{7}{x} - \frac{2}{y} + \frac{9}{z} = -39$

53. $\frac{2}{x} - \frac{1}{y} - \frac{3}{z} = -1,$
$\frac{2}{x} - \frac{1}{y} + \frac{1}{z} = -9,$
$\frac{1}{x} + \frac{2}{y} - \frac{4}{z} = 17$

Determine k so that each system is dependent.

54. $x - 3y + 2z = 1,$
$2x + y - z = 3,$
$9x - 6y + 3z = k$

55. $5x - 6y + kz = -5,$
$x + 3y - 2z = 2,$
$2x - y + 4z = -1$

In each case, three solutions of an equation in x, y, and z are given. Find the equation.

56. $Ax + By + Cz = 12;$
$\left(1, \frac{3}{4}, 3\right), \left(\frac{4}{3}, 1, 2\right),$ and $(2, 1, 1)$

57. $z = b - mx - ny;$
$(1, 1, 2), (3, 2, -6),$ and $\left(\frac{3}{2}, 1, 1\right)$

58. Write an inconsistent system of equations that contains dependent equations.

59. Kadi and Ahmed both correctly solve the system
$x + 2y - z = 1,$
$-x - 2y + z = 3,$
$2x + 4y - 2z = 2.$

Kadi states "the equations are dependent" while Ahmed states "there is no solution." How did each person reach the conclusion?

COLLABORATIVE CORNER

Finding the Preferred Approach

Focus: Systems of three linear equations
Time: 10–15 minutes
Group size: 3

Consider the six steps outlined on p. 399 along with the following system:

$$2x + 4y = 3 - 5z,$$
$$0.3x = 0.2y + 0.7z + 1.4,$$
$$0.04x + 0.03y = 0.07 + 0.04z.$$

ACTIVITY

1. Working independently, each group member should solve the system above. One person should begin by eliminating x, one should first eliminate y, and one should first eliminate z. Write neatly so that others can follow your steps.

2. Once all group members have solved the system, compare your answers. If the answers do not check, exchange notebooks and check each other's work. If a mistake is detected, allow the person who made the mistake to make the repair.

3. Decide as a group which of the three approaches above (if any) ranks as easiest and which (if any) ranks as most difficult. Then compare your rankings with the other groups in the class.

6.5 Solving Applications: Systems of Three Equations

Applications of Three Equations in Three Unknowns

Solving systems of three or more equations is important in many applications. Such systems arise in the natural and social sciences, business, and engineering. To begin, let's first look at a purely numerical application.

EXAMPLE 1

The sum of three numbers is 4. The first number minus twice the second, minus the third is 1. Twice the first number minus the second, minus twice the third is -1. Find the numbers.

SOLUTION

1. **Familiarize.** There are three statements involving the same three numbers. Let's label these numbers x, y, and z.

2. **Translate.** We can translate directly as follows.

The sum of the three numbers is 4.
$$x + y + z = 4$$

The first number minus twice the second minus the third is 1.
$$x - 2y - z = 1$$

Twice the first number minus the second minus twice the third is -1.
$$2x - y - 2z = -1$$

We now have a system of three equations:

$$x + y + z = 4,$$
$$x - 2y - z = 1,$$
$$2x - y - 2z = -1.$$

3. **Carry out.** We need to solve the system of equations. Note that we found the solution, $(2, -1, 3)$, in Example 2 of Section 6.4.

4. **Check.** The first statement of the problem says that the sum of the three numbers is 4. That checks, because $2 + (-1) + 3 = 4$. The second statement says that the first number minus twice the second, minus the third is 1: $2 - 2(-1) - 3 = 1$. That checks. The check of the third statement is left to the student.

5. **State.** The three numbers are 2, -1, and 3.

▶ TRY EXERCISE ▶ 1

EXAMPLE **2**

Architecture. In a triangular cross section of a roof, the largest angle is 70° greater than the smallest angle. The largest angle is twice as large as the remaining angle. Find the measure of each angle.

SOLUTION

1. **Familiarize.** The first thing we do is make a drawing, or a sketch.

Since we don't know the size of any angle, we use x, y, and z to represent the three measures, from smallest to largest. Recall that the measures of the angles in any triangle add up to 180°.

2. **Translate.** This geometric fact about triangles gives us one equation:

$$x + y + z = 180.$$

Two of the statements can be translated almost directly.

The largest angle is 70° greater than the smallest angle.
$$z = x + 70$$

The largest angle is twice as large as the remaining angle.
$$z = 2y$$

We now have a system of three equations:

$$\begin{aligned} x + y + z &= 180, \\ x + 70 &= z, \quad \text{or} \\ 2y &= z; \end{aligned} \qquad \begin{aligned} x + y + z &= 180, \\ x - z &= -70, \\ 2y - z &= 0. \end{aligned} \qquad \text{Rewriting in standard form}$$

3. **Carry out.** The system was solved in Example 4 of Section 6.4. The solution is (30, 50, 100).

4. **Check.** The sum of the numbers is 180, so that checks. The measure of the largest angle, 100°, is 70° greater than the measure of the smallest angle, 30°, so that checks. The measure of the largest angle is also twice the measure of the remaining angle, 50°. Thus we have a check.

5. **State.** The angles in the triangle measure 30°, 50°, and 100°.

> TRY EXERCISE 5

EXAMPLE 3

Downloads. Kaya frequently downloads music, TV shows, and iPod games. In January, she downloaded 5 songs, 10 TV shows, and 3 games for a total of $40. In February, she spent a total of $135 for 25 songs, 25 TV shows, and 12 games. In March, she spent a total of $56 for 15 songs, 8 TV shows, and 5 games. Assuming each song is the same price, each TV show is the same price, and each iPod game is the same price, how much does each cost?

Source: www.iTunes.com

SOLUTION

1. **Familiarize.** We let s = the cost, in dollars, per song, t = the cost, in dollars, per TV show, and g = the cost, in dollars, per game. Then in January, Kaya spent $5 \cdot s$ for songs, $10 \cdot t$ for TV shows, and $3 \cdot g$ for iPod games. The sum of these amounts was $40. Each month's downloads will translate to an equation.

2. **Translate.** We can organize the information in a table.

	Cost of Songs	Cost of TV Shows	Cost of iPod Games	Total Cost	
January	$5s$	$10t$	$3g$	40	$\longrightarrow 5s + 10t + 3g = 40$
February	$25s$	$25t$	$12g$	135	$\longrightarrow 25s + 25t + 12g = 135$
March	$15s$	$8t$	$5g$	56	$\longrightarrow 15s + 8t + 5g = 56$

We now have a system of three equations:

$$5s + 10t + 3g = 40, \quad (1)$$
$$25s + 25t + 12g = 135, \quad (2)$$
$$15s + 8t + 5g = 56. \quad (3)$$

3. **Carry out.** We begin by using equations (1) and (2) to eliminate s.

$$\begin{array}{l} 5s + 10t + 3g = 40, \\ 25s + 25t + 12g = 135 \end{array} \xrightarrow[\text{of equation (1) by } -5]{\text{Multiplying both sides}} \begin{array}{r} -25s - 50t - 15g = -200 \\ 25s + 25t + 12g = 135 \\ \hline -25t - 3g = -65 \quad (4) \end{array}$$

We then use equations (1) and (3) to again eliminate s.

$$\begin{array}{l} 5s + 10t + 3g = 40, \\ 15s + 8t + 5g = 56 \end{array} \xrightarrow[\text{of equation (1) by } -3]{\text{Multiplying both sides}} \begin{array}{r} -15s - 30t - 9g = -120 \\ 15s + 8t + 5g = 56 \\ \hline -22t - 4g = -64 \quad (5) \end{array}$$

Now we solve the resulting system of equations (4) and (5).

$$-25t - 3g = -65 \quad \xrightarrow[\text{of equation (4) by} -4]{\text{Multiplying both sides}} \quad 100t + 12g = 260$$

$$-22t - 4g = -64 \quad \xrightarrow[\text{of equation (5) by } 3]{\text{Multiplying both sides}} \quad \underline{-66t - 12g = -192}$$

$$34t = 68$$
$$t = 2$$

To find g, we use equation (4):

$$-25t - 3g = -65$$
$$-25 \cdot 2 - 3g = -65 \qquad \text{Substituting 2 for } t$$
$$-50 - 3g = -65$$
$$-3g = -15$$
$$g = 5.$$

Finally, we use equation (1) to find s:

$$5s + 10t + 3g = 40$$
$$5s + 10 \cdot 2 + 3 \cdot 5 = 40 \qquad \text{Substituting 2 for } t \text{ and 5 for } g$$
$$5s + 20 + 15 = 40$$
$$5s + 35 = 40$$
$$5s = 5$$
$$s = 1.$$

4. **Check.** If a song costs $1, a TV show costs $2, and an iPod game costs $5, then the total cost for each month's downloads is as follows:

January: $\quad 5 \cdot \$1 + 10 \cdot \$2 + 3 \cdot \$5 = \$5 + \$20 + \$15 = \$40;$

February: $\quad 25 \cdot \$1 + 25 \cdot \$2 + 12 \cdot \$5 = \$25 + \$50 + \$60 = \$135;$

March: $\quad 15 \cdot \$1 + 8 \cdot \$2 + 5 \cdot \$5 = \$15 + \$16 + \$25 = \$56.$

This checks with the information given in the problem.

5. **State.** A song costs $1, a TV show costs $2, and an iPod game costs $5.

> TRY EXERCISE 19

6.5 **EXERCISE SET**

For Extra Help
MyMathLab
 Math XL PRACTICE
 WATCH
 DOWNLOAD

Solve.

1. The sum of three numbers is 85. The second is 7 more than the first. The third is 2 more than four times the second. Find the numbers.

2. The sum of three numbers is 5. The first number minus the second plus the third is 1. The first minus the third is 3 more than the second. Find the numbers.

3. The sum of three numbers is 26. Twice the first minus the second is 2 less than the third. The third is the second minus three times the first. Find the numbers.

4. The sum of three numbers is 105. The third is 11 less than ten times the second. Twice the first is 7 more than three times the second. Find the numbers.

5. *Geometry.* In triangle ABC, the measure of angle B is three times that of angle A. The measure of angle C is 20° more than that of angle A. Find the angle measures.

6. *Geometry.* In triangle ABC, the measure of angle B is twice the measure of angle A. The measure of angle C is 80° more than that of angle A. Find the angle measures.

7. *Scholastic Aptitude Test.* Many high-school students take the Scholastic Aptitude Test (SAT). Beginning in March 2005, students taking the SAT received three scores: a critical reading score, a mathematics score, and a writing score. The average total score of 2007 high-school seniors who took the SAT was 1511. The average mathematics score exceeded the reading score by 13 points and the average writing score was 8 points less than the reading score. What was the average score for each category?
Source: College Entrance Examination Board

8. *Advertising.* In 2006, U.S. companies spent a total of $123.4 billion on newspaper, television, and magazine ads. The total amount spent on television ads was $7.4 billion more than the amount spent on newspaper and magazine ads together. The amount spent on magazine ads was $2 billion more than the amount spent on newspaper ads. How much was spent on each form of advertising?
Source: TNS Media Intelligence

9. *Nutrition.* Most nutritionists now agree that a healthy adult diet includes 25–35 g of fiber each day. A breakfast of 2 bran muffins, 1 banana, and a 1-cup serving of Wheaties® contains 9 g of fiber; a breakfast of 1 bran muffin, 2 bananas, and a 1-cup serving of Wheaties® contains 10.5 g of fiber; and a breakfast of 2 bran muffins and a 1-cup serving of Wheaties® contains 6 g of fiber. How much fiber is in each of these foods?
Sources: usda.gov and InteliHealth.com

10. *Nutrition.* Refer to Exercise 9. A breakfast consisting of 2 pancakes and a 1-cup serving of strawberries contains 4.5 g of fiber, whereas a breakfast of 2 pancakes and a 1-cup serving of Cheerios® contains 4 g of fiber. When a meal consists of 1 pancake, a 1-cup serving of Cheerios®, and a 1-cup serving of strawberries, it contains 7 g of fiber. How much fiber is in each of these foods?
Source: InteliHealth.com

Aha! 11. *Automobile pricing.* The basic model of a 2008 Jeep Grand Cherokee Rocky Mountain (2WD) with a tow package costs $30,815. When equipped with a tow package and a rear backup camera, the vehicle's price rose to $31,565. The cost of the basic model with a rear camera was $31,360. Find the basic price, the cost of a tow package, and the cost of a rear camera.
Source: www.jeep.com

12. *Telemarketing.* Sven, Tina, and Laurie can process 740 telephone orders per day. Sven and Tina together can process 470 orders, while Tina and Laurie together can process 520 orders per day. How many orders can each person process alone?

13. *Coffee prices.* Reba works at a Starbucks® coffee shop where a 12-oz cup of coffee costs $1.65, a 16-oz cup costs $1.85, and a 20-oz cup costs $1.95. During one busy period, Reba served 55 cups of coffee, emptying six 144-oz "brewers" while collecting a total of $99.65. How many cups of each size did Reba fill?

| 12 oz | 16 oz | 20 oz |
| $1.65 | $1.85 | $1.95 |

14. *Restaurant management.* Chick-fil-A® recently sold small lemonades for $1.29, medium lemonades for $1.49, and large lemonades for $1.85. During a lunch-time rush, Chris sold 40 lemonades for a total of $59.40. The number of small and large drinks, combined, was 10 fewer than the number of medium drinks. How many drinks of each size were sold?

15. *Small-business loans.* Chelsea took out three loans for a total of $120,000 to start an organic orchard. Her bank loan was at an interest rate of 8%, the small-business loan was at an interest rate of 5%, and the mortgage on her house was at an interest rate of 4%. The total simple interest due on the loans in one year was $5750. The annual simple interest on the mortgage was $1600 more than the interest on the bank loan. How much did she borrow from each source?

16. *Investments.* A business class divided an imaginary investment of $80,000 among three mutual funds. The first fund grew by 10%, the second by 6%, and the third by 15%. Total earnings were $8850. The earnings from the first fund were $750 more than the earnings from the third. How much was invested in each fund?

17. *Gold alloys.* Gold used to make jewelry is often a blend of gold, silver, and copper. The relative amounts of the metals determine the color of the alloy. Red gold is 75% gold, 5% silver, and 20% copper. Yellow gold is 75% gold, 12.5% silver, and 12.5% copper. White gold is 37.5% gold and 62.5% silver. If 100 g of red gold costs $2265.40, 100 g of yellow gold costs $2287.75, and 100 g of white gold costs $1312.50, how much do gold, silver, and copper cost?
Source: World Gold Council

18. *Blending teas.* Verity has recently created three custom tea blends. A 5-oz package of Southern Sandalwood sells for $13.15 and contains 2 oz of Keemun tea, 2 oz of Assam tea, and 1 oz of a berry blend. A 4-oz package of Golden Sunshine sells for $12.50 and contains 3 oz of Assam tea and 1 oz of the berry blend. A 6-oz package of Mountain Morning sells for $12.50 and contains 2 oz of the berry blend, 3 oz of Keemun tea, and 1 oz of Assam tea. What is the price per ounce of Keemun tea, Assam tea, and the berry blend?

19. *Nutrition.* A dietician in a hospital prepares meals under the guidance of a physician. Suppose that for a particular patient a physician prescribes a meal to have 800 calories, 55 g of protein, and 220 mg of vitamin C. The dietician prepares a meal of roast beef, baked potatoes, and broccoli according to the data in the following table.

Serving Size	Calories	Protein (in grams)	Vitamin C (in milligrams)
Roast Beef, 3 oz	300	20	0
Baked Potato, 1	100	5	20
Broccoli, 156 g	50	5	100

How many servings of each food are needed in order to satisfy the doctor's orders?

20. *Nutrition.* Repeat Exercise 19 but replace the broccoli with asparagus, for which a 180-g serving contains 50 calories, 5 g of protein, and 44 mg of vitamin C. Which meal would you prefer eating?

21. Students in a Listening Responses class bought 40 tickets for a piano concert. The number of tickets purchased for seats in either the first mezzanine or the main floor was the same as the number purchased for seats in the second mezzanine. First mezzanine seats cost $52, main floor seats cost $38, and second mezzanine seats cost $28. The total cost of the tickets was $1432. How many of each type of ticket were purchased?

22. *Basketball scoring.* The New York Knicks recently scored a total of 92 points on a combination of 2-point field goals, 3-point field goals, and 1-point foul shots. Altogether, the Knicks made 50 baskets and 19 more 2-pointers than foul shots. How many shots of each kind were made?

23. *World population growth.* The world population is projected to be 9.4 billion in 2050. At that time, there is expected to be approximately 3.5 billion more people in Asia than in Africa. The population for the rest of the world will be approximately 0.3 billion less than two-fifths the population of Asia. Find the projected populations of Asia, Africa, and the rest of the world in 2050.
Source: U.S. Census Bureau

24. *History.* Find the year in which the first U.S. transcontinental railroad was completed. The following are some facts about the number. The sum of the digits in the year is 24. The ones digit is 1 more than the hundreds digit. Both the tens and the ones digits are multiples of 3.

25. Problems like Exercises 13 and 14 could be classified as total-value problems. How do these problems differ from the total-value problems of Section 6.3?

26. Write a problem for a classmate to solve. Design the problem so that it translates to a system of three equations in three variables.

Skill Review

To prepare for Section 6.6, review simplifying expressions.

Simplify.

27. $-2(2x - 3y)$

28. $-(x - 6y)$

29. $-6(x - 2y) + (6x - 5y)$

30. $3(2a + 4b) + (5a - 12b)$

31. $-(2a - b - 6c)$

32. $-10(5a + 3b - c)$

33. $-2(3x - y + z) + 3(-2x + y - 2z)$

34. $(8x - 10y + 7z) + 5(3x + 2y - 4z)$

Synthesis

35. Consider Exercise 22. Suppose there were no foul shots made. Would there still be a solution? Why or why not?

36. Consider Exercise 13. Suppose Reba collected $50. Could the problem still be solved? Why or why not?

37. *Health insurance.* In 2008, UNICARE® health insurance for a 35-year-old and his or her spouse cost $174/month. That rate increased to $221/month if a child were included and $263/month if two children were included. The rate dropped to $134/month for just the applicant and one child. Find the separate costs for insuring the applicant, the spouse, the first child, and the second child.
Source: UNICARE Life and Health Insurance Company® through www.ehealth.com

38. Find a three-digit positive integer such that the sum of all three digits is 14, the tens digit is 2 more than the ones digit, and if the digits are reversed, the number is unchanged.

39. *Ages.* Tammy's age is the sum of the ages of Carmen and Dennis. Carmen's age is 2 more than the sum of the ages of Dennis and Mark. Dennis's age is four times Mark's age. The sum of all four ages is 42. How old is Tammy?

40. *Ticket revenue.* A magic show's audience of 100 people consists of adults, students, and children. The ticket prices are $10 for adults, $3 for students, and 50¢ for children. The total amount of money taken in is $100. How many adults, students, and children are in attendance? Does there seem to be some information missing? Do some more careful reasoning.

41. *Sharing raffle tickets.* Hal gives Tom as many raffle tickets as Tom first had and Gary as many as Gary first had. In like manner, Tom then gives Hal and Gary as many tickets as each then has. Similarly, Gary gives Hal and Tom as many tickets as each then has. If each finally has 40 tickets, with how many tickets does Tom begin?

42. Find the sum of the angle measures at the tips of the star in this figure.

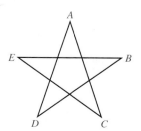

6.6 Elimination Using Matrices

Matrices and Systems • Row-Equivalent Operations

In solving systems of equations, we perform computations with the constants. If we agree to keep all like terms in the same column, we can simplify writing a system by omitting the variables. For example, the system

$$3x + 4y = 5, \qquad \text{simplifies to} \qquad \begin{matrix} 3 & 4 & 5 \\ 1 & -2 & 1 \end{matrix}$$
$$x - 2y = 1$$

if we do not write the variables, the operation of addition, and the equals signs.

Matrices and Systems

In the example above, we have written a rectangular array of numbers. Such an array is called a **matrix** (plural, **matrices**). We ordinarily write brackets around matrices. The following are matrices:

$$\begin{bmatrix} -3 & 1 \\ 0 & 5 \end{bmatrix}, \quad \begin{bmatrix} 2 & 0 & -1 & 3 \\ -5 & 2 & 7 & -1 \\ 4 & 5 & 3 & 0 \end{bmatrix}, \quad \begin{bmatrix} 2 & 3 \\ 7 & 15 \\ -2 & 23 \\ 4 & 1 \end{bmatrix}$$

The individual numbers are called *elements* or *entries*.

The **rows** of a matrix are horizontal, and the **columns** are vertical.

$$\begin{bmatrix} 5 & -2 & 2 \\ 1 & 0 & 1 \\ 0 & 1 & 2 \end{bmatrix} \begin{matrix} \longrightarrow \text{row 1} \\ \longrightarrow \text{row 2} \\ \longrightarrow \text{row 3} \end{matrix}$$

column 1 column 2 column 3

Let's see how matrices can be used to solve a system.

EXAMPLE 1 Solve the system

$$5x - 4y = -1,$$
$$-2x + 3y = 2.$$

As an aid for understanding, we list the corresponding system in the margin.

$$5x - 4y = -1,$$
$$-2x + 3y = 2$$

SOLUTION We write a matrix using only coefficients and constants, listing x-coefficients in the first column and y-coefficients in the second. A dashed line separates the coefficients from the constants:

$$\begin{bmatrix} 5 & -4 & | & -1 \\ -2 & 3 & | & 2 \end{bmatrix}.$$ Consult the notes in the margin for further information.

Our goal is to transform

$$\begin{bmatrix} 5 & -4 & | & -1 \\ -2 & 3 & | & 2 \end{bmatrix} \quad \text{into the form} \quad \begin{bmatrix} a & b & | & c \\ 0 & d & | & e \end{bmatrix}.$$

We can then reinsert the variables x and y, form equations, and complete the solution.

Our calculations are similar to those that we would do if we wrote the entire equations. The first step is to multiply and/or interchange the rows so that each number in the first column below the first number is a multiple of that number. Here that means multiplying Row 2 by 5. This corresponds to multiplying both sides of the second equation by 5.

$$5x - 4y = -1,$$
$$-10x + 15y = 10$$

$$\begin{bmatrix} 5 & -4 & \vdots & -1 \\ -10 & 15 & \vdots & 10 \end{bmatrix}$$

New Row 2 = 5(Row 2 from the step above)
$$= 5(-2 \quad 3 \ \vdots \ 2) = (-10 \quad 15 \ \vdots \ 10)$$

Next, we multiply the first row by 2, add this to Row 2, and write that result as the "new" Row 2. This corresponds to multiplying the first equation by 2 and adding the result to the second equation in order to eliminate a variable. Write out these computations as necessary.

$$5x - 4y = -1,$$
$$7y = 8$$

$$\begin{bmatrix} 5 & -4 & \vdots & -1 \\ 0 & 7 & \vdots & 8 \end{bmatrix}$$

2(Row 1) $= 2(5 \quad -4 \ \vdots \ -1) = (10 \ -8 \ \vdots \ -2)$
New Row 2 $= (10 \ -8 \ \vdots \ -2) + (-10 \quad 15 \ \vdots \ 10)$
$= (0 \quad 7 \ \vdots \ 8)$

If we now reinsert the variables, we have

$$5x - 4y = -1, \qquad (1) \qquad \text{From Row 1}$$
$$7y = 8. \qquad (2) \qquad \text{From Row 2}$$

Solving equation (2) for y gives us

$$7y = 8 \qquad (2)$$
$$y = \tfrac{8}{7}.$$

Next, we substitute $\tfrac{8}{7}$ for y in equation (1):

$$5x - 4y = -1 \qquad (1)$$
$$5x - 4 \cdot \tfrac{8}{7} = -1 \qquad \text{Substituting } \tfrac{8}{7} \text{ for } y \text{ in equation (1)}$$
$$x = \tfrac{5}{7}. \qquad \text{Solving for } x$$

The solution is $\left(\tfrac{5}{7}, \tfrac{8}{7}\right)$. The check is left to the student. **TRY EXERCISE** 7

EXAMPLE 2 Solve the system

$$2x - y + 4z = -3,$$
$$x \qquad - 4z = 5,$$
$$6x - y + 2z = 10.$$

SOLUTION We first write a matrix, using only the constants. Where there are missing terms, we must write 0's:

$$2x - y + 4z = -3,$$
$$x \qquad - 4z = 5,$$
$$6x - y + 2z = 10$$

$$\begin{bmatrix} 2 & -1 & 4 & \vdots & -3 \\ 1 & 0 & -4 & \vdots & 5 \\ 6 & -1 & 2 & \vdots & 10 \end{bmatrix}.$$

Our goal is to transform the matrix to one of the form

$$ax + by + cz = d,$$
$$ey + fz = g,$$
$$hz = i$$

$$\begin{bmatrix} a & b & c & \vdots & d \\ 0 & e & f & \vdots & g \\ 0 & 0 & h & \vdots & i \end{bmatrix}. \qquad \text{This matrix is in row-echelon form.}$$

A matrix of this form can be rewritten as a system of equations that is equivalent to the original system, and from which a solution can be easily found.

The first step is to multiply and/or interchange the rows so that each number in the first column is a multiple of the first number in the first row. In this case, we begin by interchanging Rows 1 and 2:

$$x \quad - 4z = 5,$$
$$2x - y + 4z = -3,$$
$$6x - y + 2z = 10$$

$$\begin{bmatrix} 1 & 0 & -4 & \vdots & 5 \\ 2 & -1 & 4 & \vdots & -3 \\ 6 & -1 & 2 & \vdots & 10 \end{bmatrix}.$$ This corresponds to interchanging the first two equations.

Next, we multiply the first row by -2, add it to the second row, and replace Row 2 with the result:

$$x \quad - \quad 4z = 5,$$
$$-y + 12z = -13,$$
$$6x - y + \quad 2z = 10$$

$$\begin{bmatrix} 1 & 0 & -4 & \vdots & 5 \\ 0 & -1 & 12 & \vdots & -13 \\ 6 & -1 & 2 & \vdots & 10 \end{bmatrix}.$$ $-2(1 \quad 0 \quad -4 \quad \vdots \quad 5) = (-2 \quad 0 \quad 8 \quad \vdots \quad -10)$ and $(-2 \quad 0 \quad 8 \quad \vdots \quad -10) + (2 \quad -1 \quad 4 \quad \vdots \quad -3) = (0 \quad -1 \quad 12 \quad \vdots \quad -13)$

Now we multiply the first row by -6, add it to the third row, and replace Row 3 with the result:

$$x \quad - \quad 4z = 5,$$
$$-y + 12z = -13,$$
$$-y + 26z = -20$$

$$\begin{bmatrix} 1 & 0 & -4 & \vdots & 5 \\ 0 & -1 & 12 & \vdots & -13 \\ 0 & -1 & 26 & \vdots & -20 \end{bmatrix}.$$ $-6(1 \quad 0 \quad -4 \quad \vdots \quad 5) = (-6 \quad 0 \quad 24 \quad \vdots \quad -30)$ and $(-6 \quad 0 \quad 24 \quad \vdots \quad -30) + (6 \quad -1 \quad 2 \quad \vdots \quad 10) = (0 \quad -1 \quad 26 \quad \vdots \quad -20)$

Next, we multiply Row 2 by -1, add it to the third row, and replace Row 3 with the result:

$$x \quad - \quad 4z = 5,$$
$$-y + 12z = -13,$$
$$14z = -7$$

$$\begin{bmatrix} 1 & 0 & -4 & \vdots & 5 \\ 0 & -1 & 12 & \vdots & -13 \\ 0 & 0 & 14 & \vdots & -7 \end{bmatrix}.$$ $-1(0 \quad -1 \quad 12 \quad \vdots \quad -13) = (0 \quad 1 \quad -12 \quad \vdots \quad 13)$ and $(0 \quad 1 \quad -12 \quad \vdots \quad 13) + (0 \quad -1 \quad 26 \quad \vdots \quad -20) = (0 \quad 0 \quad 14 \quad \vdots \quad -7)$

Reinserting the variables gives us

$$x \quad -4z \quad = \quad 5,$$
$$-y + 12z \quad = -13,$$
$$14z \quad = \quad -7.$$

We now solve this last equation for z and get $z = -\frac{1}{2}$. Next, we substitute $-\frac{1}{2}$ for z in the preceding equation and solve for y: $-y + 12\left(-\frac{1}{2}\right) = -13$, so $y = 7$. Since there is no y-term in the first equation of this last system, we need only substitute $-\frac{1}{2}$ for z to solve for x: $x - 4\left(-\frac{1}{2}\right) = 5$, so $x = 3$. The solution is $\left(3, 7, -\frac{1}{2}\right)$. The check is left to the student.

> TRY EXERCISE ▶ 13

The operations used in the preceding example correspond to those used to produce equivalent systems of equations, that is, systems of equations that have the same solution. We call the matrices **row-equivalent** and the operations that produce them **row-equivalent operations.**

Row–Equivalent Operations

Row-Equivalent Operations

Each of the following row-equivalent operations produces a row-equivalent matrix:

a) Interchanging any two rows.
b) Multiplying all elements of a row by a nonzero constant.
c) Replacing a row with the sum of that row and a multiple of another row.

STUDENT NOTES ——————

Note that row-equivalent matrices are not *equal*. It is the solutions of the corresponding systems that are the same.

The best overall method for solving systems of equations is by row-equivalent matrices; even computers are programmed to use them. Matrices are part of a branch of mathematics known as linear algebra. They are also studied in many courses in finite mathematics.

TECHNOLOGY CONNECTION

Row-equivalent operations can be performed on a graphing calculator. For example, to interchange the first and second rows of the matrix, as in step (1) of Example 2 above, we enter the matrix as matrix **A** and select "rowSwap" from the MATRIX MATH menu. Some graphing calculators will not automatically store the matrix produced using a row-equivalent operation, so when several operations are to be performed in succession, it is helpful to store the result of each operation as it is produced. In the window at right, we see both the matrix produced by the rowSwap operation and the indication that this matrix is stored, using **STO▸**, as matrix **B**.

```
rowSwap([A],1,2)→[B]
[[1  0 −4  5]
 [2 −1  4 −3]
 [6 −1  2 10]]
```

1. Use a graphing calculator to proceed through all the steps in Example 2.

6.6 EXERCISE SET

For Extra Help **MyMathLab** Math XP PRACTICE WATCH DOWNLOAD

 Concept Reinforcement *Complete each of the following statements.*

1. A(n) _____ is a rectangular array of numbers.

2. The rows of a matrix are _____ and the _____ are vertical.

3. Each number in a matrix is called a(n) _____ or element.

4. The plural of the word matrix is _____.

5. As part of solving a system using matrices, we can interchange any two _____.

6. Before we reinsert the variables, the leftmost column in the matrix has zeros in all rows except the _____ one.

Solve using matrices.

7. $x + 2y = 11,$
$3x - y = 5$

8. $x + 3y = 16,$
$6x + y = 11$

9. $3x + y = -1,$
$6x + 5y = 13$

10. $2x - y = 6,$
$8x + 2y = 0$

11. $6x - 2y = 4,$
$7x + y = 13$

12. $3x + 4y = 7,$
$-5x + 2y = 10$

13. $3x + 2y + 2z = 3,$
$x + 2y - z = 5,$
$2x - 4y + z = 0$

14. $4x - y - 3z = 19,$
$8x + y - z = 11,$
$2x + y + 2z = -7$

15. $p - 2q - 3r = 3,$
$2p - q - 2r = 4,$
$4p + 5q + 6r = 4$

16. $x + 2y - 3z = 9,$
$2x - y + 2z = -8,$
$3x - y - 4z = 3$

17. $3p + 2r = 11,$
$q - 7r = 4,$
$p - 6q = 1$

18. $4a + 9b = 8,$
$8a + 6c = -1,$
$6b + 6c = -1$

19. $2x + 2y - 2z - 2w = -10,$
$w + y + z + x = -5,$
$x - y + 4z + 3w = -2,$
$w - 2y + 2z + 3x = -6$

20. $-w - 3y + z + 2x = -8,$
$\quad x + y - z - w = -4,$
$\quad w + y + z + x = 22,$
$\quad x - y - z - w = -14$

Solve using matrices.

21. *Coin value.* A collection of 42 coins consists of dimes and nickels. The total value is $3.00. How many dimes and how many nickels are there?

22. *Coin value.* A collection of 43 coins consists of dimes and quarters. The total value is $7.60. How many dimes and how many quarters are there?

23. *Snack mix.* Bree sells a dried-fruit mixture for $5.80 per pound and Hawaiian macadamia nuts for $14.75 per pound. She wants to blend the two to get a 15-lb mixture that she will sell for $9.38 per pound. How much of each should she use?

24. *Mixing paint.* Higher quality paint typically contains more solids. Alex has available paint that contains 45% solids and paint that contains 25% solids. How much of each should he use to create 20 gal of paint that contains 39% solids?

25. *Investments.* Elena receives $212 per year in simple interest from three investments totaling $2500. Part is invested at 7%, part at 8%, and part at 9%. There is $1100 more invested at 9% than at 8%. Find the amount invested at each rate.

26. *Investments.* Miguel receives $306 per year in simple interest from three investments totaling $3200. Part is invested at 8%, part at 9%, and part at 10%. There is $1900 more invested at 10% than at 9%. Find the amount invested at each rate.

27. Explain how you can recognize dependent equations when solving with matrices.

28. Explain how you can recognize an inconsistent system when solving with matrices.

Skill Review

To prepare for Section 6.7, review order of operations.

Simplify.

29. $3(-1) - (-4)(5)$

30. $7(-5) - 2(-8)$

31. $-2(5 \cdot 3 - 4 \cdot 6) - 3(2 \cdot 7 - 15) + 4(3 \cdot 8 - 5 \cdot 4)$

32. $6(2 \cdot 7 - 3(-4)) - 4(3(-8) - 10) + 5(4 \cdot 3 - (-2)7)$

Synthesis

33. If the matrices

$$\begin{bmatrix} a_1 & b_1 & c_1 \\ d_1 & e_1 & f_1 \end{bmatrix} \quad \text{and} \quad \begin{bmatrix} a_2 & b_2 & c_2 \\ d_2 & e_2 & f_2 \end{bmatrix}$$

share the same solution, does it follow that the corresponding entries are all equal to each other ($a_1 = a_2$, $b_1 = b_2$, etc.)? Why or why not?

34. Explain how the row-equivalent operations make use of the addition, multiplication, and distributive properties.

35. The sum of the digits in a four-digit number is 10. Twice the sum of the thousands digit and the tens digit is 1 less than the sum of the other two digits. The tens digit is twice the thousands digit. The ones digit equals the sum of the thousands digit and the hundreds digit. Find the four-digit number.

36. Solve for x and y:
$$ax + by = c,$$
$$dx + ey = f.$$

6.7 Determinants and Cramer's Rule

Determinants of 2×2 Matrices • Cramer's Rule: 2×2 Systems • Cramer's Rule: 3×3 Systems

Determinants of 2×2 Matrices

When a matrix has m rows and n columns, it is called an "m by n" matrix. Thus its *dimensions* are denoted by $m \times n$. If a matrix has the same number of rows and columns, it is called a **square matrix**. Associated with every square matrix is a number called its **determinant**, defined as follows for 2×2 matrices.

2 × 2 Determinants

The determinant of a two-by-two matrix $\begin{bmatrix} a & c \\ b & d \end{bmatrix}$ is denoted $\begin{vmatrix} a & c \\ b & d \end{vmatrix}$ and is defined as follows:

$$\begin{vmatrix} a & c \\ b & d \end{vmatrix} = ad - bc.$$

EXAMPLE 1

Evaluate: $\begin{vmatrix} 2 & -5 \\ 6 & 7 \end{vmatrix}$.

SOLUTION   We multiply and subtract as follows:

$$\begin{vmatrix} 2 & -5 \\ 6 & 7 \end{vmatrix} = 2 \cdot 7 - 6 \cdot (-5) = 14 + 30 = 44.$$

TRY EXERCISE 7

STUDY SKILLS

Find the Highlights

If you do not already own one, consider purchasing a highlighter to use as you read this text and work on the exercises. Often the best time to highlight an important sentence or step in an example is after you have read through the section the first time.

Cramer's Rule: 2 × 2 Systems

One of the many uses for determinants is in solving systems of linear equations in which the number of variables is the same as the number of equations and the constants are not all 0. Let's consider a system of two equations:

$$a_1x + b_1y = c_1,$$
$$a_2x + b_2y = c_2.$$

If we use the elimination method, a series of steps can show that

$$x = \frac{c_1b_2 - c_2b_1}{a_1b_2 - a_2b_1} \quad \text{and} \quad y = \frac{a_1c_2 - a_2c_1}{a_1b_2 - a_2b_1}.$$

These fractions can be rewritten using determinants.

Cramer's Rule: 2 × 2 Systems

The solution of the system

$$a_1x + b_1y = c_1,$$
$$a_2x + b_2y = c_2,$$

if it is unique, is given by

$$x = \frac{\begin{vmatrix} c_1 & b_1 \\ c_2 & b_2 \end{vmatrix}}{\begin{vmatrix} a_1 & b_1 \\ a_2 & b_2 \end{vmatrix}}, \qquad y = \frac{\begin{vmatrix} a_1 & c_1 \\ a_2 & c_2 \end{vmatrix}}{\begin{vmatrix} a_1 & b_1 \\ a_2 & b_2 \end{vmatrix}}.$$

These formulas apply only if the denominator is not 0. If the denominator *is* 0, then one of two things happens:

1. If the denominator is 0 and the numerators are also 0, then the equations in the system are dependent.
2. If the denominator is 0 and at least one numerator is not 0, then the system is inconsistent.

To use Cramer's rule, we find the determinants and compute x and y as shown above. Note that the denominators are identical and the coefficients of x and y appear in the same position as in the original equations. In the numerator of x, the constants c_1 and c_2 replace a_1 and a_2. In the numerator of y, the constants c_1 and c_2 replace b_1 and b_2.

EXAMPLE **2** Solve using Cramer's rule:

$$2x + 5y = 7,$$
$$5x - 2y = -3.$$

SOLUTION We have

$$x = \frac{\begin{vmatrix} 7 & 5 \\ -3 & -2 \end{vmatrix}}{\begin{vmatrix} 2 & 5 \\ 5 & -2 \end{vmatrix}}$$

←── The constants $\begin{smallmatrix}7\\-3\end{smallmatrix}$ form the first column.

←── The columns are the coefficients of the variables.

$$= \frac{7(-2) - (-3)5}{2(-2) - 5 \cdot 5} = \frac{1}{-29} = -\frac{1}{29}$$

and

$$y = \frac{\begin{vmatrix} 2 & 7 \\ 5 & -3 \end{vmatrix}}{\begin{vmatrix} 2 & 5 \\ 5 & -2 \end{vmatrix}}$$

←── The constants $\begin{smallmatrix}7\\-3\end{smallmatrix}$ form the second column.

←── The denominator is the same as in the expression for x.

$$= \frac{2(-3) - 5 \cdot 7}{-29} = \frac{-41}{-29} = \frac{41}{29}.$$

The solution is $\left(-\frac{1}{29}, \frac{41}{29}\right)$. The check is left to the student. **TRY EXERCISE** 17

Cramer's Rule: 3 × 3 Systems

Cramer's rule can be extended for systems of three linear equations. However, before doing so, we must define what a 3 × 3 determinant is.

> ### 3 × 3 Determinants
> The determinant of a three-by-three matrix can be defined as follows:
>
> Subtract. Add.
>
> $$\begin{vmatrix} a_1 & b_1 & c_1 \\ a_2 & b_2 & c_2 \\ a_3 & b_3 & c_3 \end{vmatrix} = a_1 \begin{vmatrix} b_2 & c_2 \\ b_3 & c_3 \end{vmatrix} - a_2 \begin{vmatrix} b_1 & c_1 \\ b_3 & c_3 \end{vmatrix} + a_3 \begin{vmatrix} b_1 & c_1 \\ b_2 & c_2 \end{vmatrix}$$

STUDENT NOTES ─────────

Cramer's rule and the evaluation of determinants rely on patterns. Recognizing and remembering the patterns will help you understand and use the definitions.

Note that the a's come from the first column. Note too that the 2 × 2 determinants above can be obtained by crossing out the row and the column in which the a occurs.

For a_1:

$$\begin{vmatrix} \cancel{a_1} & \cancel{b_1} & \cancel{c_1} \\ a_2 & b_2 & c_2 \\ a_3 & b_3 & c_3 \end{vmatrix}$$

For a_2:

$$\begin{vmatrix} a_1 & b_1 & c_1 \\ \cancel{a_2} & \cancel{b_2} & \cancel{c_2} \\ a_3 & b_3 & c_3 \end{vmatrix}$$

For a_3:

$$\begin{vmatrix} a_1 & b_1 & c_1 \\ a_2 & b_2 & c_2 \\ \cancel{a_3} & \cancel{b_3} & \cancel{c_3} \end{vmatrix}$$

EXAMPLE 3 Evaluate:

$$\begin{vmatrix} -1 & 0 & 1 \\ -5 & 1 & -1 \\ 4 & 8 & 1 \end{vmatrix}.$$

TECHNOLOGY CONNECTION

Determinants can be evaluated on most graphing calculators using **2ND** **MATRIX**. After entering a matrix, we select the determinant operation from the MATRIX MATH menu and enter the name of the matrix. The graphing calculator will return the value of the determinant of the matrix. For example, if

$$\mathbf{A} = \begin{bmatrix} 1 & 6 & -1 \\ -3 & -5 & 3 \\ 0 & 4 & 2 \end{bmatrix},$$

we have

| det ([A]) |
| 26 |

1. Confirm the calculations in Example 4.

SOLUTION We have

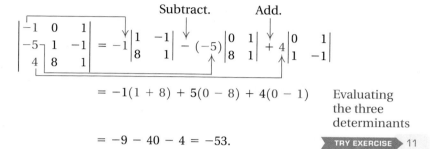

$$= -1(1 + 8) + 5(0 - 8) + 4(0 - 1) \qquad \text{Evaluating the three determinants}$$

$$= -9 - 40 - 4 = -53.$$

TRY EXERCISE 11

Cramer's Rule: 3 × 3 Systems

The solution of the system

$$a_1 x + b_1 y + c_1 z = d_1,$$
$$a_2 x + b_2 y + c_2 z = d_2,$$
$$a_3 x + b_3 y + c_3 z = d_3$$

can be found using the following determinants:

$$D = \begin{vmatrix} a_1 & b_1 & c_1 \\ a_2 & b_2 & c_2 \\ a_3 & b_3 & c_3 \end{vmatrix}, \qquad D_x = \begin{vmatrix} d_1 & b_1 & c_1 \\ d_2 & b_2 & c_2 \\ d_3 & b_3 & c_3 \end{vmatrix},$$

D contains only coefficients.
In D_x the d's replace the a's.

$$D_y = \begin{vmatrix} a_1 & d_1 & c_1 \\ a_2 & d_2 & c_2 \\ a_3 & d_3 & c_3 \end{vmatrix}, \qquad D_z = \begin{vmatrix} a_1 & b_1 & d_1 \\ a_2 & b_2 & d_2 \\ a_3 & b_3 & d_3 \end{vmatrix}.$$

In D_y, the d's replace the b's.
In D_z, the d's replace the c's.

If a unique solution exists, it is given by

$$x = \frac{D_x}{D}, \qquad y = \frac{D_y}{D}, \qquad z = \frac{D_z}{D}.$$

EXAMPLE 4 Solve using Cramer's rule:

$$x - 3y + 7z = 13,$$
$$x + y + z = 1,$$
$$x - 2y + 3z = 4.$$

SOLUTION We compute D, D_x, D_y, and D_z:

$$D = \begin{vmatrix} 1 & -3 & 7 \\ 1 & 1 & 1 \\ 1 & -2 & 3 \end{vmatrix} = -10; \qquad D_x = \begin{vmatrix} 13 & -3 & 7 \\ 1 & 1 & 1 \\ 4 & -2 & 3 \end{vmatrix} = 20;$$

$$D_y = \begin{vmatrix} 1 & 13 & 7 \\ 1 & 1 & 1 \\ 1 & 4 & 3 \end{vmatrix} = -6; \qquad D_z = \begin{vmatrix} 1 & -3 & 13 \\ 1 & 1 & 1 \\ 1 & -2 & 4 \end{vmatrix} = -24.$$

Then

$$x = \frac{D_x}{D} = \frac{20}{-10} = -2;$$

$$y = \frac{D_y}{D} = \frac{-6}{-10} = \frac{3}{5};$$

$$z = \frac{D_z}{D} = \frac{-24}{-10} = \frac{12}{5}.$$

The solution is $\left(-2, \frac{3}{5}, \frac{12}{5}\right)$. The check is left to the student. **TRY EXERCISE** 21

In Example 4, we need not have evaluated D_z. Once x and y were found, we could have substituted them into one of the equations to find z.

To use Cramer's rule, we divide by D, provided $D \neq 0$. If $D = 0$ and at least one of the other determinants is not 0, then the system is inconsistent. If *all* the determinants are 0, then the equations in the system are dependent.

6.7 EXERCISE SET

For Extra Help

👉 *Concept Reinforcement* *Classify each statement as either true or false.*

1. A square matrix has the same number of rows and columns.

2. A 3×4 matrix has 3 rows and 4 columns.

3. A determinant is a number.

4. Cramer's rule exists only for 2×2 systems.

5. Whenever Cramer's rule yields a denominator that is 0, the system has no solution.

6. Whenever Cramer's rule yields a numerator that is 0, the equations are dependent.

Evaluate.

7. $\begin{vmatrix} 3 & 5 \\ 4 & 8 \end{vmatrix}$

8. $\begin{vmatrix} 3 & 2 \\ 2 & -3 \end{vmatrix}$

9. $\begin{vmatrix} 10 & 8 \\ -5 & -9 \end{vmatrix}$

10. $\begin{vmatrix} 3 & 2 \\ -7 & 11 \end{vmatrix}$

11. $\begin{vmatrix} 1 & 4 & 0 \\ 0 & -1 & 2 \\ 3 & -2 & 1 \end{vmatrix}$

12. $\begin{vmatrix} 2 & 4 & -2 \\ 1 & 0 & 2 \\ 0 & 1 & 3 \end{vmatrix}$

13. $\begin{vmatrix} -1 & -2 & -3 \\ 3 & 4 & 2 \\ 0 & 1 & 2 \end{vmatrix}$

14. $\begin{vmatrix} 5 & 2 & 2 \\ 0 & 1 & -1 \\ 3 & 3 & 1 \end{vmatrix}$

15. $\begin{vmatrix} -4 & -2 & 3 \\ -3 & 1 & 2 \\ 3 & 4 & -2 \end{vmatrix}$

16. $\begin{vmatrix} 2 & -1 & 1 \\ 1 & 2 & -1 \\ 3 & 4 & -3 \end{vmatrix}$

Solve using Cramer's rule.

17. $5x + 8y = 1,$
$3x + 7y = 5$

18. $3x - 4y = 6,$
$5x + 9y = 10$

19. $5x - 4y = -3,$
$7x + 2y = 6$

20. $-2x + 4y = 3,$
$3x - 7y = 1$

21. $3x - y + 2z = 1,$
$x - y + 2z = 3,$
$-2x + 3y + z = 1$

22. $3x + 2y - z = 4,$
$3x - 2y + z = 5,$
$4x - 5y - z = -1$

23. $2x - 3y + 5z = 27,$
$x + 2y - z = -4,$
$5x - y + 4z = 27$

24. $x - y + 2z = -3,$
$x + 2y + 3z = 4,$
$2x + y + z = -3$

25. $r - 2s + 3t = 6,$
$2r - s - t = -3,$
$r + s + t = 6$

26. $a - 3c = 6,$
$b + 2c = 2,$
$7a - 3b - 5c = 14$

27. Describe at least one of the patterns that you see in Cramer's rule.

28. Which version of Cramer's rule do you find more useful: the version for 2×2 systems or the version for 3×3 systems? Why?

Skill Review

To prepare for Section 6.8, review functions (Sections 5.1 and 5.4).

Find each of the following, given $f(x) = 80x + 2500$ and $g(x) = 150x$.

29. $f(90)$ [5.1]

30. $(g - f)(x)$ [5.4]

31. $(g - f)(10)$ [5.4]

32. $(g - f)(100)$ [5.4]

33. All values of x for which $f(x) = g(x)$ [5.1]

34. All values of x for which $(g - f)(x) = 0$ [5.4]

Synthesis

35. Cramer's rule states that if $a_1x + b_1y = c_1$ and $a_2x + b_2y = c_2$ are dependent, then
$$\begin{vmatrix} a_1 & b_1 \\ a_2 & b_2 \end{vmatrix} = 0.$$
Explain why this will always happen.

36. Under what conditions can a 3×3 system of linear equations be consistent but unable to be solved using Cramer's rule?

Solve.

37. $\begin{vmatrix} y & -2 \\ 4 & 3 \end{vmatrix} = 44$

38. $\begin{vmatrix} 2 & x & -1 \\ -1 & 3 & 2 \\ -2 & 1 & 1 \end{vmatrix} = -12$

39. $\begin{vmatrix} m+1 & -2 \\ m-2 & 1 \end{vmatrix} = 27$

40. Show that an equation of the line through (x_1, y_1) and (x_2, y_2) can be written
$$\begin{vmatrix} x & y & 1 \\ x_1 & y_1 & 1 \\ x_2 & y_2 & 1 \end{vmatrix} = 0.$$

6.8 Business and Economics Applications

Break-Even Analysis • Supply and Demand

Break-Even Analysis

The money that a business spends to manufacture a product is its *cost*. The **total cost** of production can be thought of as a function C, where $C(x)$ is the cost of producing x units. When the company sells the product, it takes in money. This is *revenue* and can be thought of as a function R, where $R(x)$ is the **total revenue** from the sale of x units. **Total profit** is the money taken in less the money spent, or total revenue minus total cost. Total profit from the production and sale of x units is a function P given by

Profit = Revenue − Cost, or $P(x) = R(x) - C(x)$.

If $R(x)$ is greater than $C(x)$, there is a gain and $P(x)$ is positive. If $C(x)$ is greater than $R(x)$, there is a loss and $P(x)$ is negative. When $R(x) = C(x)$, the company breaks even.

There are two kinds of costs. First, there are costs like rent, insurance, machinery, and so on. These costs, which must be paid regardless of how many items are produced, are called *fixed costs*. Second, costs for labor, materials, marketing, and so on are called *variable costs*, because they vary according to the amount being produced. The sum of the fixed cost and the variable cost gives the **total cost**.

> **CAUTION!** Do not confuse "cost" with "price." When we discuss the *cost* of an item, we are referring to what it costs to produce the item. The *price* of an item is what a consumer pays to purchase the item and is used when calculating revenue.

EXAMPLE 1

Manufacturing chairs. Renewable Designs is planning to make a new chair. Fixed costs will be $90,000, and it will cost $25 to produce each chair (variable costs). Each chair sells for $48.

a) Find the total cost $C(x)$ of producing x chairs.

b) Find the total revenue $R(x)$ from the sale of x chairs.

c) Find the total profit $P(x)$ from the production and sale of x chairs.

d) What profit will the company realize from the production and sale of 3000 chairs? of 8000 chairs?

e) Graph the total-cost, total-revenue, and total-profit functions using the same set of axes. Determine the break-even point.

SOLUTION

a) Total cost, in dollars, is given by

$$C(x) = \text{(Fixed costs) plus (Variable costs)},$$
$$\text{or} \quad C(x) = \quad 90{,}000 \quad + \quad 25x$$

where x is the number of chairs produced.

b) Total revenue, in dollars, is given by

$$R(x) = 48x. \qquad \text{\$48 times the number of chairs sold.}$$
We assume that every chair produced is sold.

c) Total profit, in dollars, is given by

$$P(x) = R(x) - C(x) \qquad \text{Profit is revenue minus cost.}$$
$$= 48x - (90{,}000 + 25x)$$
$$= 23x - 90{,}000.$$

d) Profits will be

$$P(3000) = 23 \cdot 3000 - 90{,}000 = -\$21{,}000$$

when 3000 chairs are produced and sold, and

$$P(8000) = 23 \cdot 8000 - 90,000 = \$94,000$$

when 8000 chairs are produced and sold. Thus the company loses money if only 3000 chairs are sold, but makes money if 8000 are sold.

e) The graphs of each of the three functions are shown below:

$C(x) = 90,000 + 25x,$ This represents the cost function.

$R(x) = 48x,$ This represents the revenue function.

$P(x) = 23x - 90,000.$ This represents the profit function.

$C(x)$, $R(x)$, and $P(x)$ are all in dollars.

The revenue function has a graph that goes through the origin and has a slope of 48. The cost function has an intercept on the $-axis of 90,000 and has a slope of 25. The profit function has an intercept on the $-axis of $-90,000$ and has a slope of 23. It is shown by the red and black dashed line. The red portion of the dashed line shows a "negative" profit, which is a loss. (That is what is known as "being in the red.") The black portion of the dashed line shows a "positive" profit, or gain. (That is what is known as "being in the black.")

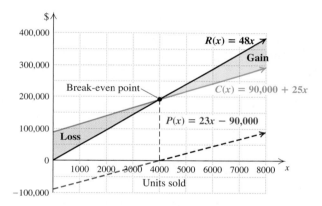

Gains occur where revenue exceeds cost. Losses occur where revenue is less than cost. The **break-even point** occurs where the graphs of R and C cross. Thus to find the break-even point, we solve a system:

$R(x) = 48x,$

$C(x) = 90,000 + 25x.$

Since both revenue and cost are in *dollars* and they are equal at the break-even point, the system can be rewritten as

$d = 48x,$ (1)

$d = 90,000 + 25x$ (2)

and solved using substitution:

$48x = 90,000 + 25x$ Substituting $48x$ for d in equation (2)

$23x = 90,000$

$x \approx 3913.04.$

The firm will break even if it produces and sells about 3913 chairs (3913 will yield a tiny loss and 3914 a tiny gain), and takes in a total of $R(3913) = 48 \cdot 3913 = \$187,824$ in revenue. Note that the x-coordinate of the break-even point can also be found by solving $P(x) = 0$. The break-even point is (3913 chairs, \$187,824).

TRY EXERCISE 9

Supply and Demand

As the price of coffee varies, so too does the amount sold. The table and graph below show that *consumers will demand less as the price goes up.*

Demand Function, D

Price, p, per Kilogram	Quantity, $D(p)$ (in millions of kilograms)
$ 8.00	25
9.00	20
10.00	15
11.00	10
12.00	5

As the price of coffee varies, the amount made available varies as well. The table and graph below show that *sellers will supply more as the price goes up.*

Supply Function, S

Price, p, per Kilogram	Quantity, $S(p)$ (in millions of kilograms)
$ 9.00	5
9.50	10
10.00	15
10.50	20
11.00	25

Let's look at the above graphs together. We see that as price increases, demand decreases. As price increases, supply increases. The point of intersection is called the **equilibrium point**. At that price, the amount that the seller will supply is the same amount that the consumer will buy. The situation is similar to a buyer and a seller negotiating the price of an item. The equilibrium point is the price and quantity that they finally agree on.

Any ordered pair of coordinates from the graph is (price, quantity), because the horizontal axis is the price axis and the vertical axis is the quantity axis. If D is a demand function and S is a supply function, then the equilibrium point is where demand equals supply:

$$D(p) = S(p).$$

EXAMPLE **2**   Find the equilibrium point for the demand and supply functions given:

$$D(p) = 1000 - 60p, \quad (1)$$
$$S(p) = 200 + 4p. \quad (2)$$

SOLUTION   Since both demand and supply are *quantities* and they are equal at the equilibrium point, we rewrite the system as

$$q = 1000 - 60p, \quad (1)$$
$$q = 200 + 4p. \quad (2)$$

We substitute $200 + 4p$ for q in equation (1) and solve:

$$200 + 4p = 1000 - 60p \qquad \text{Substituting } 200 + 4p \text{ for } q \text{ in equation (1)}$$
$$200 + 64p = 1000 \qquad \text{Adding } 60p \text{ to both sides}$$
$$64p = 800 \qquad \text{Adding } -200 \text{ to both sides}$$
$$p = \tfrac{800}{64} = 12.5.$$

Thus the equilibrium price is \$12.50 per unit.

To find the equilibrium quantity, we substitute \$12.50 into either $D(p)$ or $S(p)$. We use $S(p)$:

$$S(12.5) = 200 + 4(12.5) = 200 + 50 = 250.$$

Therefore, the equilibrium quantity is 250 units, and the equilibrium point is (\$12.50, 250).

TRY EXERCISE 19

6.8   EXERCISE SET

For Extra Help
MyMathLab
PRACTICE   WATCH   DOWNLOAD

Concept Reinforcement   *In each of Exercises 1–8, match the word or phrase with the most appropriate choice from the column on the right.*

1. _____ Total cost

2. _____ Fixed costs

3. _____ Variable costs

4. _____ Total revenue

5. _____ Total profit

6. _____ Price

7. _____ Break-even point

8. _____ Equilibrium point

a) The amount of money that a company takes in

b) The sum of fixed costs and variable costs

c) The point at which total revenue equals total cost

d) What consumers pay per item

e) The difference between total revenue and total cost

f) What companies spend whether or not a product is produced

g) The point at which supply equals demand

h) The costs that vary according to the number of items produced

For each of the following pairs of total-cost and total-revenue functions, find **(a)** *the total-profit function and* **(b)** *the break-even point.*

9. $C(x) = 35x + 200{,}000,$
   $R(x) = 55x$

10. $C(x) = 20x + 500{,}000,$
    $R(x) = 70x$

11. $C(x) = 15x + 3100,$
    $R(x) = 40x$

12. $C(x) = 30x + 49{,}500,$
    $R(x) = 85x$

13. $C(x) = 40x + 22{,}500,$
    $R(x) = 85x$

14. $C(x) = 20x + 10,000,$
$R(x) = 100x$

15. $C(x) = 24x + 50,000,$
$R(x) = 40x$

16. $C(x) = 40x + 8010,$
$R(x) = 58x$

Aha! **17.** $C(x) = 75x + 100,000,$
$R(x) = 125x$

18. $C(x) = 20x + 120,000,$
$R(x) = 50x$

Find the equilibrium point for each of the following pairs of demand and supply functions.

19. $D(p) = 2000 - 15p,$
$S(p) = 740 + 6p$

20. $D(p) = 1000 - 8p,$
$S(p) = 350 + 5p$

21. $D(p) = 760 - 13p,$
$S(p) = 430 + 2p$

22. $D(p) = 800 - 43p,$
$S(p) = 210 + 16p$

23. $D(p) = 7500 - 25p,$
$S(p) = 6000 + 5p$

24. $D(p) = 8800 - 30p,$
$S(p) = 7000 + 15p$

25. $D(p) = 1600 - 53p,$
$S(p) = 320 + 75p$

26. $D(p) = 5500 - 40p,$
$S(p) = 1000 + 85p$

Solve.

27. *Manufacturing MP3 players.* SoundGen, Inc., is planning to manufacture a new type of MP3 player/cell phone. The fixed costs for production are $45,000. The variable costs for producing each unit are estimated to be $40. The revenue from each unit is to be $130. Find the following.

a) The total cost $C(x)$ of producing x MP3/cell phones

b) The total revenue $R(x)$ from the sale of x MP3/cell phones

c) The total profit $P(x)$ from the production and sale of x MP3/cell phones

d) The profit or loss from the production and sale of 3000 MP3/cell phones; of 400 MP3/cell phones

e) The break-even point

28. *Computer manufacturing.* Current Electronics is planning to introduce a new laptop computer. The fixed costs for production are $125,300. The variable costs for producing each computer are $450. The revenue from each computer is $800. Find the following.

a) The total cost $C(x)$ of producing x computers

b) The total revenue $R(x)$ from the sale of x computers

c) The total profit $P(x)$ from the production and sale of x computers

d) The profit or loss from the production and sale of 100 computers; of 400 computers

e) The break-even point

29. *Pet safety.* Ava designed and is now producing a pet car seat. The fixed costs for setting up production are $10,000. The variable costs for producing each seat are $30. The revenue from each seat is to be $80. Find the following.

a) The total cost $C(x)$ of producing x seats

b) The total revenue $R(x)$ from the sale of x seats

c) The total profit $P(x)$ from the production and sale of x seats

d) The profit or loss from the production and sale of 2000 seats; of 50 seats

e) The break-even point

30. *Manufacturing caps.* Martina's Custom Printing is planning on adding painter's caps to its product line. For the first year, the fixed costs for setting up production are $16,404. The variable costs for producing a dozen caps are $6.00. The revenue on each dozen caps will be $18.00. Find the following.

a) The total cost $C(x)$ of producing x dozen caps

b) The total revenue $R(x)$ from the sale of x dozen caps

c) The total profit $P(x)$ from the production and sale of x dozen caps

d) The profit or loss from the production and sale of 3000 dozen caps; of 1000 dozen caps

e) The break-even point

31. In Example 1, the slope of the line representing Revenue is the sum of the slopes of the other two lines. This is not a coincidence. Explain why.

32. Variable costs and fixed costs are often compared to the slope and the y-intercept, respectively, of an equation for a line. Explain why you feel this analogy is or is not valid.

Skill Review

To prepare for Chapter 7, review solving equations using the addition and multiplication principles (Section 1.2).

Solve. [1.2]

33. $4x - 3 = 21$

34. $5 - x = 7$

35. $3x - 5 = 12x + 6$

36. $x - 4 = 9x - 10$

37. $3 - (x + 2) = 7$

38. $1 - 3(2x + 1) = 3 - 5x$

Synthesis

39. Rosie claims that since her fixed costs are $3000, she need sell only 10 custom birdbaths at $300 each in order to break even. Does this sound plausible? Why or why not?

40. In this section, we examined supply and demand functions for coffee. Does it seem realistic to you for the graph of D to have a constant slope? Why or why not?

41. *Yo-yo production.* Bing Boing Hobbies is willing to produce 100 yo-yo's at $2.00 each and 500 yo-yo's at $8.00 each. Research indicates that the public will buy 500 yo-yo's at $1.00 each and 100 yo-yo's at $9.00 each. Find the equilibrium point.

42. *Loudspeaker production.* Sonority Speakers, Inc., has fixed costs of $15,400 and variable costs of $100 for each pair of speakers produced. If the speakers sell for $250 per pair, how many pairs of speakers must be produced (and sold) in order to have enough profit to cover the fixed costs of two additional facilities? Assume that all fixed costs are identical.

Use a graphing calculator to solve.

43. *Dog food production.* Puppy Love, Inc., will soon begin producing a new line of puppy food. The marketing department predicts that the demand function will be $D(p) = -14.97p + 987.35$ and the supply function will be $S(p) = 98.55p - 5.13$.

a) To the nearest cent, what price per unit should be charged in order to have equilibrium between supply and demand?

b) The production of the puppy food involves $87,985 in fixed costs and $5.15 per unit in variable costs. If the price per unit is the value you found in part (a), how many units must be sold in order to break even?

44. *Computer production.* Brushstroke Computers, Inc., is planning a new line of computers, each of which will sell for $970. The fixed costs in setting up production are $1,235,580 and the variable costs for each computer are $697.

a) What is the break-even point?

b) The marketing department at Brushstroke is not sure that $970 is the best price. Their demand function for the new computers is given by $D(p) = -304.5p + 374,580$ and their supply function is given by $S(p) = 788.7p - 576,504$. To the nearest dollar, what price p would result in equilibrium between supply and demand?

c) If the computers are sold for the equilibrium price found in part (b), what is the break-even point?

Study Summary

KEY TERMS AND CONCEPTS   **EXAMPLES**

SECTION 6.1: SYSTEMS OF EQUATIONS IN TWO VARIABLES

A **system of equations** is a set of two or more equations, in two or more variables. A solution of a system of equations must make all the equations true.

A system is **consistent** if it has at least one solution. Otherwise it is **inconsistent**.

The equations in a system are **dependent** if one of them can be written as a multiple and/or a sum of the other equation(s). Otherwise, they are **independent**.

Systems of two equations in two unknowns can be solved graphically.

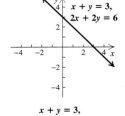

$x + y = 3,$
$y = x - 1$

The graphs intersect at $(2, 1)$.
The solution is $(2, 1)$.
The system is consistent.
The equations are independent.

$x + y = 3,$
$x + y = 1$

The graphs do not intersect.
There is no solution.
The system is inconsistent.
The equations are independent.

$x + y = 3,$
$2x + 2y = 6$

The graphs are the same.
The solution set is
$\{(x, y) \,|\, x + y = 3\}$.
The system is consistent.
The equations are dependent.

SECTION 6.2: SOLVING BY SUBSTITUTION OR ELIMINATION

Systems of equations can be solved using substitution.

Solve:

$2x + 3y = 8,$
$x = y + 1.$

Substitute and solve for y:

$2(y + 1) + 3y = 8$
$2y + 2 + 3y = 8$
$y = \frac{6}{5}.$

The solution is $\left(\frac{11}{5}, \frac{6}{5}\right)$.

Substitute and solve for x:

$x = y + 1$
$x = \frac{6}{5} + 1$
$x = \frac{11}{5}.$

Systems of equations can be solved using elimination.

Solve:

$4x - 2y = 6,$
$3x + y = 7.$

The solution is $(2, 1)$.

Eliminate y and solve for x:

$$4x - 2y = 6$$
$$\underline{6x + 2y = 14}$$
$$10x \quad\;\; = 20$$
$$x = 2.$$

Substitute and solve for y:

$3x + y = 7$
$3 \cdot 2 + y = 7$
$y = 1.$

SECTION 6.3: SOLVING APPLICATIONS: SYSTEMS OF TWO EQUATIONS

Total-value, mixture, and **motion problems** often translate directly to systems of equations.

Total Value

A jewelry designer purchased 80 beads for a total of $39 to make a necklace. Some of the beads were sterling silver beads that cost 40¢ each and the rest were gemstone beads that cost 65¢ each. How many of each type were bought? (See Example 2 on pp. 383–384 for a solution.)

Mixture

Nature's Green Gardening, Inc., carries two brands of fertilizer containing nitrogen and water. "Gentle Grow" is 3% nitrogen and "Sun Saver" is 8% nitrogen. Nature's Green needs to combine the two types of solutions into a 90-L mixture that is 6% nitrogen. How much of each brand should be used? (See Example 5 on pp. 387–388 for a solution.)

Motion

A Boeing 747-400 jet flies 4 hr west with a 60-mph tailwind. Returning against the wind takes 5 hr. Find the speed of the jet with no wind. (See Example 7 on pp. 390–391 for a solution.)

SECTION 6.4: SYSTEMS OF EQUATIONS IN THREE VARIABLES

Systems of three equations in three variables are usually easiest to solve using elimination.

Solve:

$$x + y - z = 3, \quad (1)$$
$$-x + y + 2z = -5, \quad (2)$$
$$2x - y - 3z = 9 \quad (3)$$

Eliminate x using two equations:

$$\begin{aligned} x + y - z &= 3 \quad (1) \\ -x + y + 2z &= -5 \quad (2) \\ \hline 2y + z &= -2. \end{aligned}$$

Eliminate x again using two different equations:

$$\begin{aligned} -2x - 2y + 2z &= -6 \quad (1) \\ 2x - y - 3z &= 9 \quad (3) \\ \hline -3y - z &= 3. \end{aligned}$$

Solve the system of two equations for y and z:

$$\begin{aligned} 2y + z &= -2 \\ -3y - z &= 3 \\ \hline -y &= 1 \\ y &= -1 \end{aligned}$$

$$2(-1) + z = -2$$
$$z = 0.$$

Substitute and solve for x:

$$x + y - z = 3$$
$$x + (-1) - 0 = 3$$
$$x = 4.$$

The solution is $(4, -1, 0)$.

SECTION 6.5: SOLVING APPLICATIONS: SYSTEMS OF THREE EQUATIONS

Many problems with three unknowns can be solved after translating to a system of three equations.

In a triangular cross section of a roof, the largest angle is 70° greater than the smallest angle. The largest angle is twice as large as the remaining angle. Find the measure of each angle. (See Example 2 on pp. 406–407 for a solution.)

SECTION 6.6: ELIMINATION USING MATRICES

A **matrix** (plural, **matrices**) is a rectangular array of numbers. The individual numbers are called **entries** or **elements**.

$$\begin{bmatrix} 1 & 3 & -4 \\ -2 & 5 & 11 \end{bmatrix} \begin{matrix} \longrightarrow \text{row 1} \\ \longrightarrow \text{row 2} \end{matrix}$$

column 1 column 2 column 3

The *dimensions* of this matrix are 2×3, read "two by three."

By using **row-equivalent** operations, we can solve systems of equations using matrices.

Solve: $\quad x + 4y = 1,$
$$\qquad 2x - y = 3.$$

Write as a matrix in row-echelon form:

$$\begin{bmatrix} 1 & 4 & | & 1 \\ 2 & -1 & | & 3 \end{bmatrix} \longrightarrow \begin{bmatrix} 1 & 4 & | & 1 \\ 0 & -9 & | & 1 \end{bmatrix}.$$

Rewrite as equations and solve:

$$\begin{aligned} -9y &= 1 \\ y &= -\tfrac{1}{9} \end{aligned} \longrightarrow \begin{aligned} x + 4\left(-\tfrac{1}{9}\right) &= 1 \\ x &= \tfrac{13}{9}. \end{aligned}$$

The solution is $\left(\tfrac{13}{9}, -\tfrac{1}{9}\right)$.

SECTION 6.7: DETERMINANTS AND CRAMER'S RULE

A **determinant** is a number associated with a square matrix.

Determinant of a 2 × 2 Matrix

$$\begin{vmatrix} a & c \\ b & d \end{vmatrix} = ad - bc$$

$$\begin{vmatrix} 2 & 3 \\ -1 & 5 \end{vmatrix} = 2 \cdot 5 - (-1)(3) = 13$$

Determinant of a 3 × 3 Matrix

$$\begin{vmatrix} a_1 & b_1 & c_1 \\ a_2 & b_2 & c_2 \\ a_3 & b_3 & c_3 \end{vmatrix} =$$

$$a_1 \begin{vmatrix} b_2 & c_2 \\ b_3 & c_3 \end{vmatrix} - a_2 \begin{vmatrix} b_1 & c_1 \\ b_3 & c_3 \end{vmatrix} + a_3 \begin{vmatrix} b_1 & c_1 \\ b_2 & c_2 \end{vmatrix}$$

$$\begin{vmatrix} 2 & 3 & 2 \\ 0 & 1 & 0 \\ -1 & 5 & -4 \end{vmatrix} = 2 \begin{vmatrix} 1 & 0 \\ 5 & -4 \end{vmatrix} - 0 \begin{vmatrix} 3 & 2 \\ 5 & -4 \end{vmatrix} + (-1) \begin{vmatrix} 3 & 2 \\ 1 & 0 \end{vmatrix}$$

$$= 2(-4 - 0) - 0 - 1(0 - 2)$$

$$= -8 + 2 = -6$$

We can use matrices and **Cramer's rule** to solve systems of equations.

Cramer's rule for 2 × 2 matrices is given on p. 416.

Cramer's rule for 3 × 3 matrices is given on p. 418.

Solve:

$$x - 3y = 7,$$
$$2x + 5y = 4.$$

$$x = \dfrac{\begin{vmatrix} 7 & -3 \\ 4 & 5 \end{vmatrix}}{\begin{vmatrix} 1 & -3 \\ 2 & 5 \end{vmatrix}}; \qquad y = \dfrac{\begin{vmatrix} 1 & 7 \\ 2 & 4 \end{vmatrix}}{\begin{vmatrix} 1 & -3 \\ 2 & 5 \end{vmatrix}}$$

$$x = \tfrac{47}{11} \qquad y = \tfrac{-10}{11}$$

The solution is $\left(\tfrac{47}{11}, -\tfrac{10}{11} \right)$.

SECTION 6.8: BUSINESS AND ECONOMICS APPLICATIONS

The **break-even point** occurs where the **revenue** equals the **cost**, or where **profit** is 0.

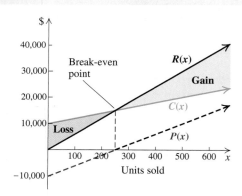

An **equilibrium point** occurs where the **supply** equals the **demand**.

Review Exercises: Chapter 6

Concept Reinforcement *Complete each of the following sentences.*

1. The system

$$5x + 3y = 7,$$
$$y = 2x + 1$$

is most easily solved using the _____ method. [6.2]

2. The system

$$-2x + 3y = 8,$$
$$2x + 2y = 7$$

is most easily solved using the _____ method. [6.2]

3. Of the methods used to solve systems of equations, the _____ method may yield only approximate solutions. [6.1], [6.2]

4. When one equation in a system is a multiple of another equation in that system, the equations are said to be _____. [6.1]

5. A system for which there is no solution is said to be _____. [6.1]

6. When we are using an algebraic method to solve a system of equations, obtaining a _____ tells us that the system is inconsistent. [6.2]

7. When we are graphing to solve a system of two equations, if there is no solution, the lines will be _____. [6.1]

8. When a matrix has the same number of rows and columns, it is said to be _____. [6.7]

9. Cramer's rule is a formula in which the numerator and the denominator of each fraction is a(n) _____. [6.7]

10. At the break-even point, the value of the profit function is _____. [6.8]

For Exercises 11–19, if a system has an infinite number of solutions, use set-builder notation to write the solution set. If a system has no solution, state this.

Solve graphically. [6.1]

11. $y = x - 3,$
    $y = \frac{1}{4}x$

12. $2x - 3y = 12,$
    $4x + y = 10$

Solve using the substitution method. [6.2]

13. $5x - 2y = 4,$
    $x = y - 2$

14. $y = x + 2,$
    $y - x = 8$

15. $x - 3y = -2,$
    $7y - 4x = 6$

Solve using the elimination method. [6.2]

16. $2x + 5y = 8,$
    $6x - 5y = 10$

17. $4x - 7y = 18,$
    $9x + 14y = 40$

18. $3x - 5y = 9,$
    $5x - 3y = -1$

19. $1.5x - 3 = -2y,$
    $3x + 4y = 6$

Solve. [6.3]

20. Ana bought two melons and one pineapple for $8.96. If she had purchased one melon and two pineapples, she would have spent $1.49 more. What is the price of a melon? of a pineapple?

21. A freight train leaves Houston at midnight traveling north at a speed of 44 mph. One hour later, a passenger train, going 55 mph, travels north from Houston on a parallel track. How many hours will the passenger train travel before it overtakes the freight train?

22. D'Andre wants 14 L of fruit punch that is 10% juice. At the store, he finds only punch that is 15% juice or punch that is 8% juice. How much of each should he purchase?

Solve. If a system's equations are dependent or if there is no solution, state this. [6.4]

23. $x + 4y + 3z = 2,$
    $2x + y + z = 10,$
    $-x + y + 2z = 8$

24. $4x + 2y - 6z = 34,$
    $2x + y + 3z = 3,$
    $6x + 3y - 3z = 37$

25. $2x - 5y - 2z = -4,$
    $7x + 2y - 5z = -6,$
    $-2x + 3y + 2z = 4$

26. $3x + y = 2,$
    $x + 3y + z = 0,$
    $x + z = 2$

Solve.

27. In triangle ABC, the measure of angle A is four times the measure of angle C, and the measure of angle B is 45° more than the measure of angle C. What are the measures of the angles of the triangle? [6.5]

28. A nontoxic floor wax can be made from lemon juice and food-grade linseed oil. The amount of oil should be twice the amount of lemon juice. How much of each ingredient is needed to make 32 oz of floor wax? (The mix should be spread with a rag and buffed when dry.) [6.3]

29. The sum of the average number of times a man, a woman, and a one-year-old child cry each month is 56.7. A woman cries 3.9 more times than a man. The average number of times a one-year-old cries per month is 43.3 more than the average number of times combined that a man and a woman cry. What is the average number of times per month that each cries? [6.5]

Solve using matrices. Show your work. [6.6]

30. $3x + 4y = -13,$
$5x + 6y = 8$

31. $3x - y + z = -1,$
$2x + 3y + z = 4,$
$5x + 4y + 2z = 5$

Evaluate. [6.7]

32. $\begin{vmatrix} -2 & -5 \\ 3 & 10 \end{vmatrix}$

33. $\begin{vmatrix} 2 & 3 & 0 \\ 1 & 4 & -2 \\ 2 & -1 & 5 \end{vmatrix}$

Solve using Cramer's rule. Show your work. [6.7]

34. $2x + 3y = 6,$
$x - 4y = 14$

35. $2x + y + z = -2,$
$2x - y + 3z = 6,$
$3x - 5y + 4z = 7$

36. Find the equilibrium point for the demand and supply functions
$$S(p) = 60 + 7p$$
and
$$D(p) = 120 - 13p. \quad [6.8]$$

37. Danae is beginning to produce organic honey. For the first year, the fixed costs for setting up production are $54,000. The variable costs for producing each pint of honey are $4.75. The revenue from each pint of honey is $9.25. Find the following. [6.8]

a) The total cost $C(x)$ of producing x pints of honey

b) The total revenue $R(x)$ from the sale of x pints of honey

c) The total profit $P(x)$ from the production and sale of x pints of honey

d) The profit or loss from the production and sale of 5000 pints of honey; of 15,000 pints of honey

e) The break-even point

Synthesis

38. How would you go about solving a problem that involves four variables? [6.5]

39. Explain how a system of equations can be both dependent and inconsistent. [6.4]

40. Danae is leaving a job that pays $36,000 a year to make honey (see Exercise 37). How many pints of honey must she produce and sell in order to make as much money as she earned at her previous job? [6.8]

41. Recently, Staples® charged $5.99 for a 2-count pack of Bic® Round Stic Grip mechanical pencils and $7.49 for a 12-count pack of Bic® Matic Grip mechanical pencils. Wiese Accounting purchased 138 of these two types of mechanical pencils for a total of $157.26. How many packs of each did they buy? [6.3]

42. Solve graphically:
$$y = x + 2,$$
$$y = x^2 + 2. \quad [6.1]$$

43. The graph of $f(x) = ax^2 + bx + c$ contains the points $(-2, 3)$, $(1, 1)$, and $(0, 3)$. Find a, b, and c and give a formula for the function. [6.5]

Test: Chapter 6

Step-by-step test solutions are found on the video CD in the front of this book.

For Exercises 1–6, if a system has an infinite number of solutions, use set-builder notation to write the solution set. If a system has no solution, state this.

1. Solve graphically:
$$2x + y = 8,$$
$$y - x = 2.$$

Solve using the substitution method.

2. $x + 3y = -8,$
$4x - 3y = 23$

3. $2x - 4y = -6,$
$x = 2y - 3$

Solve using the elimination method.

4. $3x - y = 7,$
$x + y = 1$

5. $4y + 2x = 18,$
$3x + 6y = 26$

6. $4x - 6y = 3,$
$6x - 4y = -3$

7. The perimeter of a standard basketball court is 288 ft. The length is 44 ft longer than the width. Find the dimensions.

$P = 288$ ft

8. Pepperidge Farm® Goldfish is a snack food for which 40% of its calories come from fat. Rold Gold® Pretzels receive 9% of their calories from fat. How many grams of each would be needed to make 620 g of a snack mix for which 15% of the calories are from fat?

9. A truck leaves Gaston at noon traveling 55 mph. An hour later, a car leaves Gaston following the same route as the truck but traveling 65 mph. In how many hours will the car catch up to the truck?

Solve. If a system's equations are dependent or if there is no solution, state this.

10. $-3x + y - 2z = 8$,
$-x + 2y - z = 5$,
$2x + y + z = -3$

11. $6x + 2y - 4z = 15$,
$-3x - 4y + 2z = -6$,
$4x - 6y + 3z = 8$

12. $2x + 2y = 0$,
$4x + 4z = 4$,
$2x + y + z = 2$

13. $3x + 3z = 0$,
$2x + 2y = 2$,
$3y + 3z = 3$

Solve using matrices.

14. $4x + y = 12$,
$3x + 2y = 2$

15. $x + 3y - 3z = 12$,
$3x - y + 4z = 0$,
$-x + 2y - z = 1$

Evaluate.

16. $\begin{vmatrix} 4 & -2 \\ 3 & -5 \end{vmatrix}$

17. $\begin{vmatrix} 3 & 4 & 2 \\ -2 & -5 & 4 \\ 0 & 5 & -3 \end{vmatrix}$

18. Solve using Cramer's rule:
$3x + 4y = -1$,
$5x - 2y = 4$.

19. An electrician, a carpenter, and a plumber are hired to work on a house. The electrician earns $30 per hour, the carpenter $28.50 per hour, and the plumber $34 per hour. The first day on the job, they worked a total of 21.5 hr and earned a total of $673.00. If the plumber worked 2 more hours than the carpenter did, how many hours did each work?

20. Find the equilibrium point for the demand and supply functions
$$D(p) = 79 - 8p \quad \text{and} \quad S(p) = 37 + 6p,$$
where p is the price, in dollars, $D(p)$ is the number of units demanded, and $S(p)$ is the number of units supplied.

21. Kick Back, Inc., is producing a new hammock. For the first year, the fixed costs for setting up production are $44,000. The variable costs for producing each hammock are $25. The revenue from each hammock is $80. Find the following.

a) The total cost $C(x)$ of producing x hammocks
b) The total revenue $R(x)$ from the sale of x hammocks
c) The total profit $P(x)$ from the production and sale of x hammocks
d) The profit or loss from the production and sale of 300 hammocks; of 900 hammocks
e) The break-even point

Synthesis

22. The graph of the function $f(x) = mx + b$ contains the points $(-1, 3)$ and $(-2, -4)$. Find m and b.

23. Some of the world's best and most expensive coffee is Hawaii's Kona coffee. In order for coffee to be labeled "Kona Blend," it must contain at least 30% Kona beans. Bean Town Roasters has 40 lb of Mexican coffee. How much Kona coffee must they add if they wish to market it as Kona Blend?

Cumulative Review: Chapters 1–6

1. Evaluate $9t \div 6t^3$ for $t = -2$.

2. Find the opposite of $-\frac{1}{10}$.

3. Find the reciprocal of $-\frac{1}{10}$.

4. Remove parentheses and simplify:
$$3x^2 - 2(-5x^2 + y) + y.$$

Simplify. Do not leave negative exponents in your answers.

5. $40 - 8^2 \div 4 \cdot 4$

6. $\dfrac{|-2 \cdot 5 - 3 \cdot 4|}{5^2 - 2 \cdot 7}$

7. $x^4 \cdot x^{-6} \cdot x^{13}$

8. $(6x^2y^3)^2(-2x^0y^4)^{-3}$

9. $\dfrac{-10a^7b^{-11}}{25a^{-4}b^{22}}$

10. $\left(\dfrac{3x^4y^{-2}}{4x^{-5}}\right)^4$

11. $(5.5 \times 10^{-3})(3.4 \times 10^8)$

12. $\dfrac{2.42 \times 10^5}{6.05 \times 10^{-2}}$

Solve.

13. $2x + 1 = 5(2 - x)$ [1.2]

14. $x^2 + 5x + 6 = 0$ [3.7]

15. $t + \dfrac{6}{t} = 5$ [4.6]

16. $\frac{1}{2}t + \frac{1}{6} = \frac{1}{3} - t$ [1.2]

17. $2y + 9 \le 5y + 11$ [1.6]

18. $n^2 = 100$ [3.7]

19. $3x + y = 5,$
$y = x + 1$ [6.2]

20. $\dfrac{4}{x - 1} = \dfrac{3}{x + 2}$ [4.6]

21. $6x^2 = x + 2$ [3.7]

22. $x + y = 10,$
$x - y = 4$ [6.2]

23. $x + y + z = -5,$
$2x + 3y - 2z = 8,$
$x - y + 4z = -21$ [6.4]

24. $2x + 5y - 3z = -11,$
$-5x + 3y - 2z = -7,$
$3x - 2y + 5z = 12$ [6.4]

Solve each formula. [1.3]

25. $t = \frac{1}{3}pq$, for p

26. $A = \dfrac{r + s}{2}$, for s

Add and, if possible, simplify.

27. $(8a^2 - 6a - 7) + (3a^3 + 6a - 7)$

28. $\dfrac{m + n}{2m + n} + \dfrac{n}{m - n}$ [4.4]

Subtract.

29. $(8a^2 - 6a - 7) - (3a^3 + 6a - 7)$

30. $\dfrac{x + 5}{x - 2} - \dfrac{x - 1}{2 - x}$ [4.4]

Multiply.

31. $(5a^2 + b)(5a^2 - b)$

32. $-3x^2(5x^3 - 6x^2 - 2x + 1)$

33. $(2n + 5)^2$

34. $(8t^2 + 5)(t^3 + 4)$

35. $\dfrac{x^2 - 2x + 1}{x^2 - 4} \cdot \dfrac{x^2 + 4x + 4}{x^2 - 3x + 2}$ [4.2]

Divide.

36. $(2x^2 - 5x - 3) \div (x - 3)$

37. $\dfrac{x^2 - x}{4x^2 + 8x} \div \dfrac{x^2 - 1}{2x}$ [4.2]

Factor completely.

38. $x^3 + x^2 + 2x + 2$ [3.1]

39. $m^4 - 1$ [3.4]

40. $2x^3 + 18x^2 + 40x$ [3.2]

41. $x^4 - 6x^2 + 9$ [3.4]

42. $4x^2 - 2x - 10$ [3.1]

43. $10x^2 - 29x + 10$ [3.3]

Graph.

44. $2x + y = 6$ [2.3]

45. $f(x) = -2x + 8$ [5.3]

46. $2x = 10$ [2.3]

47. $x = 2y$ [2.2]

48. Find the x-intercept and the y-intercept of the line given by $10x - 15y = 60$. [2.3]

49. Write the slope–intercept equation for the line with slope -2 and y-intercept $\left(0, \frac{4}{7}\right)$. [2.6]

50. Find an equation in slope–intercept form of the line containing the points $(-6, 3)$ and $(4, 2)$. [2.7]

51. Determine whether the lines given by the following equations are parallel, perpendicular, or neither:
$$2x = 4y + 7,$$
$$x - 2y = 5. \quad [2.6]$$

52. Find an equation of the line containing the point $(2, 1)$ and perpendicular to the line $x - 2y = 5$. [2.7]

53. For the graph of f shown, determine the domain, the range, $f(-3)$, and any value of x for which $f(x) = 5$. [5.2]

54. Determine the domain of the function given by

$$f(x) = \frac{7}{x + 10}. \quad [5.2]$$

Given $g(x) = 4x - 3$ and $h(x) = -2x^2 + 1$, find the following function values.

55. $h(4)$ [5.1]

56. $-g(0)$ [5.1]

57. $(g - h)(a)$ [5.4]

58. Evaluate: $\begin{vmatrix} 2 & -3 \\ 4 & 1 \end{vmatrix}$. [6.7]

Solve.

59. A library was mistakenly charged sales tax on an order of children's books. The invoice, including 5% sales tax, was for $1323. How much should the library have been charged? [1.4]

60. A snowmobile is traveling 40 mph faster than a dog sled. In the same time that the dog sled travels 24 mi, the snowmobile travels 104 mi. Find the speeds of the sled and the snowmobile. [4.7]

61. Each nurse practitioner at the Midway Clinic is required to see an average of at least 40 patients per day. During the first 4 workdays of one week, Michael saw 50, 35, 42, and 38 patients. How many patients must he see on the fifth day in order to meet his requirements? [1.7]

62. Tia and Avery live next door to each other on Meachin Street. Their house numbers are consecutive odd numbers, and the product of their house numbers is 143. Find the house numbers. [3.8]

63. Long-distance calls made using the "Ruby" prepaid calling card cost 1.4¢ per minute plus a maintenance fee of 99¢ per week. The "Sapphire" plan has a maintenance fee of only 69¢ per week, but calls cost 1.7¢ per minute. For what number of minutes per week will the two cards cost the same? [6.3]
Source: www.enjoyprepaid.com

64. The second angle of a triangle is twice as large as the first. The third angle is 15° less than the sum of the first two angles. Find the measure of each angle. [1.5]

65. A newspaper uses self-employed copywriters to write its advertising copy. If they use 12 copywriters, each person works 35 hr per week. How many hours per week would each person work if the newspaper uses 10 copywriters? [5.5]

Synthesis

66. Solve $t = px - qx$ for x. [1.3]

67. Write the slope–intercept equation of the line that contains the point $(-2, 3)$ and is parallel to the line $2x - y = 7$. [2.7]

68. Simplify: $\dfrac{t^2 - 9}{2t + 1} \div \dfrac{t^2 - 4t + 3}{6t^2 + 3t} \cdot \dfrac{2t^3 - t^2 + t}{4t + 12}$. [4.2]

69. Given that $f(x) = mx + b$ and that $f(5) = -3$ when $f(-4) = 2$, find m and b. [5.1], [6.3]

70. The maximum length of a postcard that can be mailed with one postcard stamp is $\frac{7}{4}$ in. longer than the maximum width. The maximum area is $\frac{51}{2}$ in². Find the maximum length and width of a postcard. [3.8]
Source: USPS

Inequalities and Problem Solving

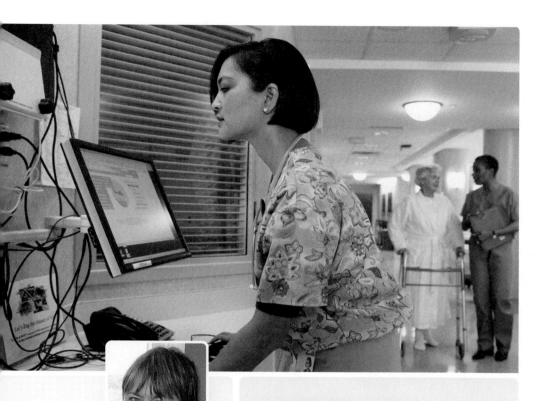

ANNE SAMUELS
REGISTERED NURSE/
NURSE MANAGEMENT
Springfield, Massachusetts

As a nurse, I use math every day to calculate dosages of medication. If an order prescribes a dosage of 2.5 mg/kg twice a day, I need to know the patient's weight, change that weight from pounds to kilograms, and then calculate the dosage. As a nurse manager, I use math to determine the number of nurses needed to care for patients and to work out a budget for salaries and equipment.

AN APPLICATION

The number of registered nurses $R(t)$ employed in the United States, in millions, t years after 2000, can be approximated by

$$R(t) = 0.05t + 2.2.$$

Determine (using an inequality) those years for which more than 3 million registered nurses will be employed in the United States.

Source: Based on data from the U.S. Department of Health and Human Services and the Bureau of Labor Statistics

This problem appears as Example 5 in Section 7.1.

Inequalities are mathematical sentences containing symbols such as < (is less than). In this chapter, we use the principles for solving inequalities developed in Chapter 1 to solve compound inequalities. We also combine our knowledge of inequalities and systems of equations to solve systems of inequalities.

7.1 Inequalities and Domain

Solving Inequalities Graphically • Domain • Problem Solving

Solving Inequalities Graphically

Recall that an **inequality** is any sentence containing $<, >, \leq, \geq,$ or $\neq$ —for example,

$$-2 < a, \qquad x > 4, \qquad x + 3 \leq 6, \qquad 6 - 7y \geq 10y - 4, \quad \text{and} \quad 5x \neq 10.$$

Any replacement for the variable that makes an inequality true is called a **solution**. The set of all solutions is called the **solution set**. When all solutions of an inequality are found, we say that we have **solved** the inequality.

We can use two principles, developed in Chapter 1, to solve inequalities.

The Addition Principle for Inequalities

For any real numbers a, b, and c:

$$a < b \text{ is equivalent to } a + c < b + c;$$
$$a > b \text{ is equivalent to } a + c > b + c.$$

Similar statements hold for $\leq$ and $\geq$.

The Multiplication Principle for Inequalities

For any real numbers a and b, and for any *positive* number c,

$$a < b \text{ is equivalent to } ac < bc;$$
$$a > b \text{ is equivalent to } ac > bc.$$

For any real numbers a and b, and for any *negative* number c,

$$a < b \text{ is equivalent to } ac > bc;$$
$$a > b \text{ is equivalent to } ac < bc.$$

Similar statements hold for $\leq$ and $\geq$.

EXAMPLE 1

Solve: $2x + 4 < -x + 1$.

SOLUTION

$$2x + 4 < -x + 1$$
$$2x + 4 - 4 < -x + 1 - 4 \quad \text{Subtracting 4 from both sides}$$
$$2x < -x - 3$$
$$2x + x < -x - 3 + x \quad \text{Adding } x \text{ to both sides}$$
$$3x < -3$$
$$\frac{3x}{3} < \frac{-3}{3} \quad \text{Dividing both sides by 3. The } < \text{ symbol stays the same since 3 is positive.}$$
$$x < -1$$

The solution set is $\{x \,|\, x < -1\}$, or $(-\infty, -1)$.

TRY EXERCISE 19

We now look at a graphical method for solving inequalities.

To solve the inequality in Example 1, $2x + 4 < -x + 1$, we let $f(x) = 2x + 4$ and $g(x) = -x + 1$. Consider the graphs of the functions $f(x) = 2x + 4$ and $g(x) = -x + 1$.

Graphs of $f(x)$ and $g(x)$

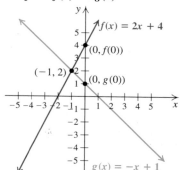

The graphs intersect at the point $(-1, 2)$. Thus, when $x = -1$, $f(x) = g(x)$. At all x-values except -1, either $f(x) > g(x)$ or $f(x) < g(x)$. Note from the graphs that $f(x) > g(x)$ when the graph of f lies above the graph of g. Also, $f(x) < g(x)$ when the graph of f lies below the graph of g.

Compare $f(0)$ and $g(0)$. Note from the graphs that $f(0)$ lies above $g(0)$. In fact, for all values of x greater than -1, $f(x) > g(x)$. For all values of x less than -1, $f(x) < g(x)$. In this way, the point of intersection of the graphs marks the endpoint of the solution set of an inequality.

Note that using the graphs of $f(x)$ and $g(x)$ to solve an inequality is not the same as graphing the solutions of the inequality.

For $f(x) = 2x + 4$ and $g(x) = -x + 1$, compare the following.

Equation/Inequality	Solution Set	Graph of Solution Set
$f(x) = g(x)$	$\{-1\}$	
$f(x) < g(x)$	$(-\infty, -1)$	
$f(x) > g(x)$	$(-1, \infty)$	

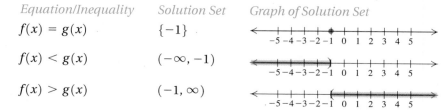

EXAMPLE **2**

TECHNOLOGY CONNECTION

On most calculators,
$4x - 1 \geq 5x - 2$ can be solved
by graphing
$y_1 = 4x - 1 \geq 5x - 2$
($\geq$ is often found by pressing
2ND **MATH**). The solution set is
then displayed as an interval
(shown by a horizontal line
1 unit above the x-axis).

A check can also be made
by graphing $y_1 = 4x - 1$ and
$y_2 = 5x - 2$ and identifying
those x-values for which
$y_1 \geq y_2$.

The INTERSECT option helps
us find that $y_1 = y_2$ when
$x = 1$. Note that $y_1 \geq y_2$ for
x-values in the interval $(-\infty, 1]$.

Solve graphically: $-3x + 1 \geq x - 7$.

SOLUTION We let $f(x) = -3x + 1$ and $g(x) = x - 7$, and graph both functions. The solution set will consist of the interval for which the graph of f lies on or above the graph of g.

To find the point of intersection, we solve the system of equations

$$y = -3x + 1,$$
$$y = x - 7.$$

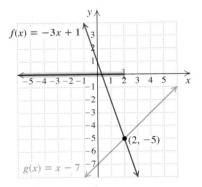

Using substitution, we have

$$-3x + 1 = x - 7$$
$$-4x = -8$$
$$x = 2.$$

Then $y = -3(2) + 1 = -5$.

Thus the point of intersection is

$$(2, -5).$$

The graph of f lies *on* the graph of g when $x = 2$. It lies *above* the graph of g when $x < 2$. Thus the solution of $-3x + 1 \geq x - 7$ is

$$\{x \mid x \leq 2\}, \quad \text{or} \quad (-\infty, 2].$$

This set is indicated by the purple shading on the x-axis. **TRY EXERCISE** 33

Domain

Although radical notation is not discussed in detail until Chapter 8, we know that only nonnegative numbers have square roots that are real numbers. Thus finding the domain of a radical function often involves solving an inequality.

EXAMPLE **3**

Find the domain of f if $f(x) = \sqrt{7 - x}$.

SOLUTION In order for $\sqrt{7 - x}$ to exist as a real number, $7 - x$ must be nonnegative. Thus we solve $7 - x \geq 0$:

$$7 - x \geq 0 \qquad 7 - x \text{ must be nonnegative.}$$
$$-x \geq -7 \qquad \text{Subtracting 7 from both sides}$$
$$\text{The symbol must be reversed.}$$
$$x \leq 7. \qquad \text{Multiplying both sides by } -1$$

When $x \leq 7$, the expression $7 - x$ is nonnegative. Thus the domain of f is $\{x \mid x \leq 7\}$, or $(-\infty, 7]$. **TRY EXERCISE** 43

EXAMPLE 4

Find the domain of g if $g(x) = \sqrt{\frac{1}{2}x - 10}$.

SOLUTION In order for $\sqrt{\frac{1}{2}x - 10}$ to exist as a real number, $\frac{1}{2}x - 10$ must be nonnegative. Thus we solve $\frac{1}{2}x - 10 \geq 0$:

$$\frac{1}{2}x - 10 \geq 0 \qquad \frac{1}{2}x - 10 \text{ must be nonnegative.}$$

$$\frac{1}{2}x \geq 10 \qquad \text{Adding 10 to both sides}$$

$$x \geq 20. \qquad \text{Multiplying both sides by 2.}$$
$$\qquad\qquad\text{The symbol } \geq \text{ remains the same.}$$

Thus the domain of g is $\{x \mid x \geq 20\}$, or $[20, \infty)$.

TRY EXERCISE 49

Problem Solving

Many problem-solving situations translate to inequalities.

EXAMPLE 5

Registered nurses. The number of registered nurses $R(t)$ employed in the United States, in millions, t years after 2000 can be approximated by

$$R(t) = 0.05t + 2.2.$$

Determine (using an inequality) those years for which more than 3 million registered nurses will be employed in the United States.

Source: Based on data from the U.S. Department of Health and Human Services and the Bureau of Labor Statistics

SOLUTION

1. **Familiarize.** We already have a formula. The number 0.05 tells us that employment of registered nurses is growing at a rate of 0.05 million (or 50,000) per year. The number 2.2 tells us that in 2000, there were approximately 2.2 million registered nurses employed in the United States.

2. **Translate.** We are asked to find the years for which *more than* 3 million registered nurses will be employed in the United States. Thus we have

$$R(t) > 3$$
$$0.05t + 2.2 > 3. \qquad \text{Substituting } 0.05t + 2.2 \text{ for } R(t)$$

3. **Carry out.** We solve the inequality:

$$0.05t + 2.2 > 3$$
$$0.05t > 0.8 \qquad \text{Subtracting 2.2 from both sides}$$
$$t > 16. \qquad \text{Dividing both sides by 0.05}$$

Note that this corresponds to years after 2016.

4. **Check.** We can partially check our answer by finding $R(t)$ for a value of t greater than 16. For example,

$$R(20) = 0.05 \cdot 20 + 2.2 = 3.2, \text{ and } 3.2 > 3.$$

5. **State.** More than 3 million registered nurses will be employed in the United States for years after 2016.

TRY EXERCISE 57

EXAMPLE 6   *Job offers.*   After graduation, Rose had two job offers in sales:

Uptown Fashions: A salary of $600 per month, plus a commission of 4% of sales;

Ergo Designs: A salary of $800 per month, plus a commission of 6% of sales in excess of $10,000.

If sales always exceed $10,000, for what amount of sales would Uptown Fashions provide higher pay?

SOLUTION

1. **Familiarize.** Listing the given information in a table will be helpful.

Uptown Fashions Monthly Income	Ergo Designs Monthly Income
$600 salary 4% of sales *Total*: $600 + 4% of sales	$800 salary 6% of sales over $10,000 *Total*: $800 + 6% of sales over $10,000

Next, suppose that Rose sold a certain amount—say, $12,000—in one month. Which offer would be better? Working for Uptown, she would earn $600 plus 4% of $12,000, or $600 + 0.04(12,000) = \$1080$. Since with Ergo Designs commissions are paid only on sales in excess of $10,000, Rose would earn $800 plus 6% of ($12,000 − $10,000), or $800 + 0.06(2000) = \$920$.

For monthly sales of $12,000, Uptown pays better. Similar calculations will show that for sales of $30,000 a month, Ergo pays better. To determine *all* values for which Uptown pays more money, we must solve an inequality that is based on the calculations above.

2. **Translate.** We let S = the amount of monthly sales, in dollars, and will assume $S > 10,000$ so that both plans will pay a commission. Examining the calculations in the *Familiarize* step, we see that monthly income from Uptown is $600 + 0.04S$ and from Ergo is $800 + 0.06(S − 10,000)$. We want to find all values of S for which

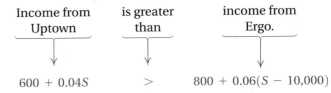

$$600 + 0.04S \quad > \quad 800 + 0.06(S - 10,000)$$

3. **Carry out.** We solve the inequality:

$$600 + 0.04S > 800 + 0.06(S - 10,000)$$
$$600 + 0.04S > 800 + 0.06S - 600 \quad \text{Using the distributive law}$$
$$600 + 0.04S > 200 + 0.06S \quad \text{Combining like terms}$$
$$400 > 0.02S \quad \text{Subtracting 200 and } 0.04S \text{ from both sides}$$
$$20,000 > S, \text{ or } S < 20,000. \quad \text{Dividing both sides by 0.02}$$

4. **Check.** The above steps indicate that income from Uptown Fashions is higher than income from Ergo Designs for sales less than $20,000. In the *Familiarize* step, we saw that for sales of $12,000, Uptown pays more. Since $12,000 < 20,000$, this is a partial check.

5. **State.** When monthly sales are less than $20,000, Uptown Fashions provides the higher pay.

TRY EXERCISE 59

7.1 EXERCISE SET

For Extra Help

↪ **Concept Reinforcement** *Classify each of the following as equivalent inequalities, equivalent equations, equivalent expressions, or not equivalent.*

1. $5x + 7 = 6 - 3x$, $8x + 7 = 6$

2. $2(4x + 1)$, $8x + 2$

3. $x - 7 > -2$, $x > 5$

4. $t + 3 < 1$, $t < 2$

5. $-4t \le 12$, $t \le -3$

6. $\frac{3}{5}a + \frac{1}{5} = 2$, $3a + 1 = 10$

7. $6a + 9$, $3(2a + 3)$

8. $-4x \ge -8$, $x \ge 2$

9. $-\frac{1}{2}x < 7$, $x > 14$

10. $-\frac{1}{3}t \le -5$, $t \ge 15$

Solve algebraically.

11. $3x + 1 < 7$

12. $2x - 5 \ge 9$

13. $3 - x \ge 12$

14. $8 - x < 15$

15. $\dfrac{2x + 7}{5} < -9$

16. $\dfrac{5y + 13}{4} > -2$

17. $\dfrac{3t - 7}{-4} \le 5$

18. $\dfrac{2t - 9}{-3} \ge 7$

19. $3 - 8y \ge 9 - 4y$

20. $4m + 7 \ge 9m - 3$

21. $5(t - 3) + 4t < 2(7 + 2t)$

22. $2(4 + 2x) > 2x + 3(2 - 5x)$

23. $5[3m - (m + 4)] > -2(m - 4)$

24. $8x - 3(3x + 2) - 5 \ge 3(x + 4) - 2x$

Solve each inequality using the given graph.

25. $f(x) \ge g(x)$

26. $f(x) < g(x)$

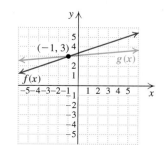

27. $f(x) < g(x)$

28. $f(x) \ge g(x)$

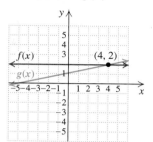

Solve graphically.

29. $x - 3 < 4$

30. $x + 4 \ge 6$

31. $2x - 3 \ge 1$

32. $3x + 1 < 1$

33. $x + 3 > 2x - 5$

34. $3x - 5 \le 3 - x$

35. $\frac{1}{2}x - 2 \le 1 - x$

36. $x + 5 > \frac{1}{3}x - 1$

37. Let $f(x) = 7 - 3x$ and $g(x) = 2x - 3$. Find all values of x for which $f(x) \le g(x)$.

38. Let $f(x) = 8x - 9$ and $g(x) = 3x - 11$. Find all values of x for which $f(x) \le g(x)$.

39. Let $y_1 = 2x - 7$ and $y_2 = 5x - 9$. Find all values of x for which $y_1 < y_2$.

40. Let $y_1 = 2x + 1$ and $y_2 = -\frac{1}{2}x + 6$. Find all values of x for which $y_1 < y_2$.

Find the domain of each function.

41. $f(x) = \sqrt{x - 10}$

42. $f(x) = \sqrt{x + 2}$

43. $f(x) = \sqrt{3 - x}$

44. $f(x) = \sqrt{11 - x}$

45. $f(x) = \sqrt{2x + 7}$

46. $f(x) = \sqrt{8 - 5x}$

47. $f(x) = \sqrt{8 - 2x}$

48. $f(x) = \sqrt{2x - 10}$

49. $f(x) = \sqrt{\frac{1}{3}x + 5}$

50. $f(x) = \sqrt{2x + \frac{1}{2}}$

51. $f(x) = \sqrt{\frac{x - 5}{4}}$

52. $f(x) = \sqrt{\frac{x + 7}{12}}$

Solve.

53. *Photography.* Eli will photograph a wedding for a flat fee of $900 or for an hourly rate of $120. For what lengths of time would the hourly rate be less expensive?

54. *Truck rentals.* Jenn can rent a moving truck for either $99 with unlimited mileage or $49 plus 80¢ per mile. For what mileages would the unlimited mileage plan save money?

55. *Exam scores.* There are 80 questions on a college entrance examination. Two points are awarded for each correct answer, and one half point is deducted for each incorrect answer. How many questions does Tami need to answer correctly in order to score at least 100 on the test? Assume that Tami answers every question.

56. *Insurance claims.* After a serious automobile accident, most insurance companies will replace the damaged car with a new one if repair costs exceed 80% of the NADA, or "blue-book," value of the car. Lorenzo's car recently sustained $9200 worth of damage but was not replaced. What was the blue-book value of his car?

57. *Crude-oil production.* The yearly U.S. production of crude oil $C(t)$, in millions of barrels, t years after 2000 can be approximated by

$$C(t) = -40.5t + 2159.$$

Determine (using an inequality) those years for which domestic production will drop below 1750 million barrels.

Source: U.S. Energy Information Administration

58. *HDTVs.* The percentage of U.S. households $p(t)$ with an HDTV t years after 2005 can be approximated by

$$p(t) = 8t + 12.5.$$

Determine (using an inequality) those years for which more than half of all U.S. households will have an HDTV.

Source: Based on data from Consumer Electronics Association

59. *Wages.* Toni can be paid in one of two ways:

Plan A: A salary of $400 per month, plus a commission of 8% of gross sales;

Plan B: A salary of $610 per month, plus a commission of 5% of gross sales.

For what amount of gross sales should Toni select plan A?

60. *Wages.* Eric can be paid for his masonry work in one of two ways:

Plan A: $300 plus $9.00 per hour;

Plan B: Straight $12.50 per hour.

Suppose that the job takes n hours. For what values of n is plan B better for Eric?

61. *Insurance benefits.* Under the "Green Badge" medical insurance plan, Carlee would pay the first $2000 of her medical bills and 30% of all remaining bills. Under the "Blue Seal" plan, Carlee would pay the first $2500 of bills, but only 20% of the rest. For what amount of medical bills will the "Blue Seal" plan save Carlee money? (Assume that her bills will exceed $2500.)

62. *Checking accounts.*   North Bank charges $10 per month for a student checking account. The first 8 checks are free, and each additional check costs $0.75. South Bank offers a student checking account with no monthly charge. The first 8 checks are free, and each additional check costs $3. For what numbers of checks is the South Bank plan more expensive? (Assume that the student will always write more than 8 checks.)

63. *Body fat percentage.*   The function given by

$$F(d) = (4.95/d - 4.50) \times 100$$

can be used to estimate the body fat percentage $F(d)$ of a person with an average body density d, in kilograms per liter.

a) A man is considered obese if his body fat percentage is at least 25%. Find the body densities of an obese man.

b) A woman is considered obese if her body fat percentage is at least 32%. Find the body densities of an obese woman.

64. *Temperature conversion.*   The function

$$C(F) = \tfrac{5}{9}(F - 32)$$

can be used to find the Celsius temperature $C(F)$ that corresponds to $F°$ Fahrenheit.

a) Gold is solid at Celsius temperatures less than 1063°C. Find the Fahrenheit temperatures for which gold is solid.

b) Silver is solid at Celsius temperatures less than 960.8°C. Find the Fahrenheit temperatures for which silver is solid.

65. *Manufacturing.*   Bright Ideas is planning to make a new kind of lamp. Fixed costs will be $90,000, and variable costs will be $25 for the production of each lamp. The total-cost function for x lamps is

$$C(x) = 90,000 + 25x.$$

The company makes $48 in revenue for each lamp sold. The total-revenue function for x lamps is

$$R(x) = 48x.$$

(See Section 6.8.)

a) When $R(x) < C(x)$, the company loses money. Find the values of x for which the company loses money.

b) When $R(x) > C(x)$, the company makes a profit. Find the values of x for which the company makes a profit.

66. *Publishing.*   The demand and supply functions for a locally produced poetry book are approximated by

$$D(p) = 2000 - 60p \quad \text{and}$$
$$S(p) = 460 + 94p,$$

where p is the price, in dollars (see Section 6.8).

a) Find those values of p for which demand exceeds supply.

b) Find those values of p for which demand is less than supply.

67. How is the solution of $x + 3 = 8$ related to the solution sets of

$$x + 3 > 8 \quad \text{and} \quad x + 3 < 8?$$

68. Can a negative number be in the domain of a radical function? Why or why not?

Skill Review

To prepare for Section 5.2, review finding domains of rational functions (Section 5.2).

Find the domain of f. [5.2]

69. $f(x) = \dfrac{5}{x}$

70. $f(x) = \dfrac{3}{x - 6}$

71. $f(x) = \dfrac{x - 2}{2x + 1}$

72. $f(x) = \dfrac{x + 3}{5x - 7}$

73. $f(x) = \dfrac{x + 10}{8}$

74. $f(x) = \dfrac{3}{x} + 5$

Synthesis

75. The percentage of the U.S. population that owns an HDTV cannot exceed 100%. How does this affect the answer to Exercise 58?

76. Explain how the addition principle can be used to avoid ever needing to multiply or divide both sides of an inequality by a negative number.

Solve for x and y. Assume that a, b, c, d, and m are positive constants.

77. $3ax + 2x \geq 5ax - 4$; assume $a > 1$

78. $6by - 4y \leq 7by + 10$

79. $a(by - 2) \geq b(2y + 5)$; assume $a > 2$

80. $c(6x - 4) < d(3 + 2x)$; assume $3c > d$

81. $c(2 - 5x) + dx > m(4 + 2x)$;
assume $5c + 2m < d$

82. $a(3 - 4x) + cx < d(5x + 2)$;
assume $c > 4a + 5d$

Determine whether each statement is true or false. If false, give an example that shows this.

83. For any real numbers a, b, c, and d, if $a < b$ and $c < d$, then $a - c < b - d$.

84. For all real numbers x and y, if $x < y$, then $x^2 < y^2$.

85. Are the inequalities
$$x < 3 \quad \text{and} \quad x + \frac{1}{x} < 3 + \frac{1}{x}$$
equivalent? Why or why not?

86. Are the inequalities
$$x < 3 \quad \text{and} \quad 0 \cdot x < 0 \cdot 3$$
equivalent? Why or why not?

Solve. Then graph.

87. $x + 5 \leq 5 + x$

88. $x + 8 < 3 + x$

89. $x^2 > 0$

90. $y_1 < y_2$

91. $y_1 \geq y_2$

92. The graphs of $f(x) = 2x + 1$, $g(x) = -\frac{1}{2}x + 3$, and $h(x) = x - 1$ are as shown below. Solve each inequality, referring only to the figure.

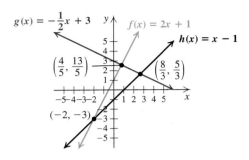

a) $2x + 1 \leq x - 1$
b) $x - 1 > -\frac{1}{2}x + 3$
c) $-\frac{1}{2}x + 3 < 2x + 1$

93. Assume that the graphs of $y_1 = -\frac{1}{2}x + 5$, $y_2 = x - 1$, and $y_3 = 2x - 3$ are as shown below. Solve each inequality, referring only to the figure.

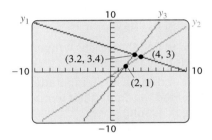

a) $-\frac{1}{2}x + 5 > x - 1$
b) $x - 1 \leq 2x - 3$
c) $2x - 3 \geq -\frac{1}{2}x + 5$

94. Using an approach similar to that in the Technology Connection on p. 440, use a graphing calculator to check your answers to Exercises 11, 37, and 40.

95. Use a graphing calculator to confirm the domains of the functions in Exercises 41, 43, and 47.

COLLABORATIVE **CORNER**

Saving on Shipping Costs

Focus: Inequalities and problem solving

Time: 20–30 minutes

Group size: 2–3

For overnight delivery packages weighing up to 10 lb sent by Express Mail, the United States Postal Service charges (as of May 2008) $19.00 for up to one pound delivered to Zone 3 and, on average, $2.12 for each pound or part of a pound after the first. UPS Next Day Air charges $22.05 for a one-pound delivery to Zone 3 and each additional pound or part of a pound costs $1.45.*

ACTIVITY

1. One group member should determine the function p, where $p(x)$ represents the

cost, in dollars, of mailing x pounds using Express Mail.

2. One member should determine the function r, where $r(x)$ represents the cost, in dollars, of shipping x pounds using UPS Next Day Air.

3. A third member should graph p and r on the same set of axes.

4. Finally, working together, use the graph to determine those weights for which Express Mail is less expensive than UPS Next Day Air shipping. Express your answer in both set-builder notation and interval notation.

*This activity is based on an article by Michael Contino in *Mathematics Teacher*, May 1995.

7.2 Intersections, Unions, and Compound Inequalities

Intersections of Sets and Conjunctions of Sentences ▪ Unions of Sets and Disjunctions of Sentences ▪ Interval Notation and Domains

Two inequalities joined by the word "and" or the word "or" are called **compound inequalities**. Thus, "$x < -3 \ or \ x > 0$" and "$x < 5 \ and \ x > 3$" are two examples of compound inequalities. To discuss how to solve compound inequalities, we must first study ways in which sets can be combined.

Intersections of Sets and Conjunctions of Sentences

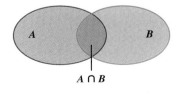

The **intersection** of two sets A and B is the set of all elements that are common to both A and B. We denote the intersection of sets A and B as

$$A \cap B.$$

The intersection of two sets is represented by the purple region shown in the figure at left. For example, if $A = \{$all students who are taking a math class$\}$ and $B = \{$all students who are taking a history class$\}$, then $A \cap B = \{$all students who are taking a math class *and* a history class$\}$.

EXAMPLE **1** Find the intersection: $\{1, 2, 3, 4, 5\} \cap \{-2, -1, 0, 1, 2, 3\}$.

SOLUTION The numbers 1, 2, and 3 are common to both sets, so the intersection is $\{1, 2, 3\}$. **TRY EXERCISE** 11

When two or more sentences are joined by the word *and* to make a compound sentence, the new sentence is called a **conjunction** of the sentences. The following is a conjunction of inequalities:

$$-2 < x \quad and \quad x < 1.$$

A number is a solution of a conjunction if it is a solution of *both* of the separate parts. For example, -1 is a solution because it is a solution of $-2 < x$ as well as $x < 1$; that is, -1 is *both* greater than -2 *and* less than 1.

The solution set of a conjunction is the intersection of the solution sets of the individual sentences.

EXAMPLE **2** Graph and write interval notation for the conjunction

$$-2 < x \quad and \quad x < 1.$$

SOLUTION We first graph $-2 < x$, then $x < 1$, and finally the conjunction $-2 < x$ and $x < 1$.

$\{x \mid -2 < x\}$ (number line from -7 to 7, open at -2 shaded right) $(-2, \infty)$

$\{x \mid x < 1\}$ (number line from -7 to 7, open at 1 shaded left) $(-\infty, 1)$

$\{x \mid -2 < x\} \cap \{x \mid x < 1\}$
$= \{x \mid -2 < x \text{ and } x < 1\}$ (number line from -7 to 7, shaded between -2 and 1) $(-2, 1)$

Because there are numbers that are both greater than -2 and less than 1, the solution set of the conjunction $-2 < x$ and $x < 1$ is the interval $(-2, 1)$. In set-builder notation, this is written $\{x \mid -2 < x < 1\}$, the set of all numbers that are *simultaneously* greater than -2 *and* less than 1. **TRY EXERCISE** 33

For $a < b$,

$$a < x \quad and \quad x < b \quad \text{can be abbreviated} \quad a < x < b;$$

and, equivalently,

$$b > x \quad and \quad x > a \quad \text{can be abbreviated} \quad b > x > a.$$

> ## Mathematical Use of the Word "and"
> The word "and" corresponds to "intersection" and to the symbol "$\cap$". Any solution of a conjunction must make each part of the conjunction true.

EXAMPLE **3** Solve and graph: $-1 \le 2x + 5 < 13$.

SOLUTION This inequality is an abbreviation for the conjunction

$$-1 \le 2x + 5 \quad and \quad 2x + 5 < 13.$$

The word *and* corresponds to set *intersection*. To solve the conjunction, we solve each of the two inequalities separately and then find the intersection of the solution sets:

$$-1 \leq 2x + 5 \quad and \quad 2x + 5 < 13$$
$$-6 \leq 2x \qquad and \qquad 2x < 8 \qquad \text{Subtracting 5 from both sides of each inequality}$$
$$-3 \leq x \qquad and \qquad x < 4. \qquad \text{Dividing both sides of each inequality by 2}$$

The solution of the conjunction is the intersection of the two separate solution sets.

$\{x \mid -3 \leq x\}$ $[-3, \infty)$

$\{x \mid x < 4\}$ $(-\infty, 4)$

$\{x \mid -3 \leq x\} \cap \{x \mid x < 4\}$ $= \{x \mid -3 \leq x < 4\}$ $[-3, 4)$

We can abbreviate the answer as $-3 \leq x < 4$. The solution set is $\{x \mid -3 \leq x < 4\}$, or, in interval notation, $[-3, 4)$.

TRY EXERCISE 45

The steps in Example 3 are often combined as follows:

$$-1 \leq 2x + 5 < 13$$
$$-1 - 5 \leq 2x + 5 - 5 < 13 - 5 \qquad \text{Subtracting 5 from all three regions}$$
$$-6 \leq 2x < 8$$
$$-3 \leq x < 4. \qquad \text{Dividing by 2 in all three regions}$$

Such an approach saves some writing and will prove useful in Section 7.3.

CAUTION!   The abbreviated form of a conjunction, like $-3 \leq x < 4$, can be written only if both inequality symbols point in the same direction. It is *not acceptable* to write a sentence like $-1 > x < 5$ since doing so does not indicate if *both* $-1 > x$ and $x < 5$ must be true or if it is enough for one of the separate inequalities to be true.

EXAMPLE 4

Solve and graph: $2x - 5 \geq -3 \; and \; 5x + 2 \geq 17$.

SOLUTION   We first solve each inequality, retaining the word *and*:

$$2x - 5 \geq -3 \quad and \quad 5x + 2 \geq 17$$
$$2x \geq 2 \qquad and \qquad 5x \geq 15$$
$$x \geq 1 \qquad and \qquad x \geq 3.$$

Keep the word "and."

Next, we find the intersection of the two separate solution sets.

$\{x \mid x \geq 1\}$ $[1, \infty)$

$\{x \mid x \geq 3\}$ $[3, \infty)$

$\{x \mid x \geq 1\} \cap \{x \mid x \geq 3\}$ $= \{x \mid x \geq 3\}$ $[3, \infty)$

The numbers common to both sets are those greater than or equal to 3. Thus the solution set is $\{x\,|\,x \geq 3\}$, or, in interval notation, $[3, \infty)$. You should check that any number in $[3, \infty)$ satisfies the conjunction whereas numbers outside $[3, \infty)$ do not.

> TRY EXERCISE 67

Sometimes there is no way to solve both parts of a conjunction at once.

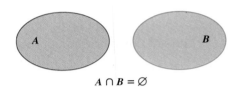

When $A \cap B = \varnothing$, A and B are said to be *disjoint*.

$A \cap B = \varnothing$

EXAMPLE 5

Solve and graph: $2x - 3 > 1 \;and\; 3x - 1 < 2$.

SOLUTION We solve each inequality separately:

$$2x - 3 > 1 \quad and \quad 3x - 1 < 2$$
$$2x > 4 \quad and \quad 3x < 3$$
$$x > 2 \quad and \quad x < 1.$$

The solution set is the intersection of the individual inequalities.

$\{x\,|\,x > 2\}$ — number line from -7 to 7, $(2, \infty)$

$\{x\,|\,x < 1\}$ — number line from -7 to 7, $(-\infty, 1)$

$\{x\,|\,x > 2\} \cap \{x\,|\,x < 1\}$
$= \{x\,|\,x > 2 \;and\; x < 1\} = \varnothing$ — number line from -7 to 7, $\varnothing$

Since no number is both greater than 2 and less than 1, the solution set is the empty set, $\varnothing$.

> TRY EXERCISE 69

Unions of Sets and Disjunctions of Sentences

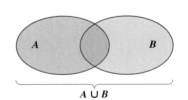

$A \cup B$

The **union** of two sets A and B is the collection of elements belonging to A and/or B. We denote the union of A and B by

$$A \cup B.$$

The union of two sets is often pictured as shown at left. For example, if $A = \{$all students who are taking a math class$\}$ and $B = \{$all students who are taking a history class$\}$, then $A \cup B = \{$all students who are taking a math class *or* a history class$\}$. Note that this set includes students who are taking a math class *and* a history class.

EXAMPLE 6

Find the union: $\{2, 3, 4\} \cup \{3, 5, 7\}$.

SOLUTION The numbers in either or both sets are 2, 3, 4, 5, and 7, so the union is $\{2, 3, 4, 5, 7\}$.

> TRY EXERCISE 13

STUDENT NOTES ——————

Remember that the union or the intersection of two sets is itself a set and should be written with set braces.

When two or more sentences are joined by the word *or* to make a compound sentence, the new sentence is called a **disjunction** of the sentences. Here is an example:

$$x < -3 \quad or \quad x > 3.$$

A number is a solution of a disjunction if it is a solution of at least one of the separate parts. For example, -5 is a solution of this disjunction since -5 is a solution of $x < -3$.

The solution set of a disjunction is the union of the solution sets of the individual sentences.

EXAMPLE 7

Graph and write interval notation for the disjunction

$$x < -3 \quad or \quad x > 3.$$

SOLUTION   We first graph $x < -3$, then $x > 3$, and finally the disjunction $x < -3 \; or \; x > 3$.

$\{x \mid x < -3\}$ $(-\infty, -3)$

$\{x \mid x > 3\}$ $(3, \infty)$

$\{x \mid x < -3\} \cup \{x \mid x > 3\}$
$= \{x \mid x < -3 \; or \; x > 3\}$ $(-\infty, -3) \cup (3, \infty)$

The solution set of $x < -3 \; or \; x > 3$ is $\{x \mid x < -3 \; or \; x > 3\}$, or, in interval notation, $(-\infty, -3) \cup (3, \infty)$. There is no simpler way to write the solution.

TRY EXERCISE 27

> ### Mathematical Use of the Word "or"
>
> The word "or" corresponds to "union" and to the symbol "$\cup$". For a number to be a solution of a disjunction, it must be in *at least one* of the solution sets of the individual sentences.

EXAMPLE 8

Solve and graph: $7 + 2x < -1 \; or \; 13 - 5x \leq 3$.

SOLUTION   We solve each inequality separately, retaining the word *or*:

$$7 + 2x < -1 \quad or \quad 13 - 5x \leq 3$$
$$2x < -8 \quad or \quad -5x \leq -10$$

Dividing by a negative and reversing the symbol

$$x < -4 \quad or \quad x \geq 2.$$

To find the solution set of the disjunction, we consider the individual graphs. We graph $x < -4$ and then $x \geq 2$. Then we take the union of the graphs.

$\{x \mid x < -4\}$ $(-\infty, -4)$

$\{x \mid x \geq 2\}$ $[2, \infty)$

$\{x \mid x < -4\} \cup \{x \mid x \geq 2\}$
$= \{x \mid x < -4 \; or \; x \geq 2\}$ $(-\infty, -4) \cup [2, \infty)$

The solution set is $\{x \mid x < -4 \; or \; x \geq 2\}$, or $(-\infty, -4) \cup [2, \infty)$.

TRY EXERCISE 63

> ***CAUTION!*** A compound inequality like
>
> $$x < -4 \quad or \quad x \ge 2,$$
>
> as in Example 8, *cannot* be expressed as $2 \le x < -4$ because to do so would be to say that x is *simultaneously* less than -4 and greater than or equal to 2. No number is both less than -4 *and* greater than 2, but many are less than -4 *or* greater than 2.

EXAMPLE **9**

Solve: $-2x - 5 < -2 \ or \ x - 3 < -10.$

SOLUTION We solve the individual inequalities, retaining the word *or*:

$$-2x - 5 < -2 \quad or \quad x - 3 < -10$$
$$-2x < 3 \quad or \quad x < -7$$

Dividing by a negative and reversing the symbol ———————— Keep the word "or."

$$x > -\tfrac{3}{2} \quad or \quad x < -7.$$

The solution set is $\left\{ x \mid x < -7 \ or \ x > -\tfrac{3}{2} \right\}$, or $(-\infty, -7) \cup \left(-\tfrac{3}{2}, \infty \right)$.

TRY EXERCISE 65

EXAMPLE **10**

Solve: $3x - 11 < 4 \ or \ 4x + 9 \ge 1.$

SOLUTION We solve the individual inequalities separately, retaining the word *or*:

$$3x - 11 < 4 \quad or \quad 4x + 9 \ge 1$$
$$3x < 15 \quad or \quad 4x \ge -8$$
$$x < 5 \quad or \quad x \ge -2.$$

———————— Keep the word "or."

To find the solution set, we first look at the individual graphs.

$\{x \mid x < 5\}$ $(-\infty, 5)$

$\{x \mid x \ge -2\}$ $[-2, \infty)$

$\{x \mid x < 5\} \cup \{x \mid x \ge -2\}$
$= \{x \mid x < 5 \ or \ x \ge -2\}$ $(-\infty, \infty) = \mathbb{R}$

Since *all* numbers are less than 5 or greater than or equal to -2, the two sets fill the entire number line. Thus the solution set is $\mathbb{R}$, the set of all real numbers.

TRY EXERCISE 51

Interval Notation and Domains

In Section 5.2, we saw that if $g(x) = \dfrac{5x - 2}{x - 3}$, then the number 3 is not in the domain of g. We can represent the domain of g using set-builder notation or interval notation.

EXAMPLE 11   Use interval notation to write the domain of g if $g(x) = \dfrac{5x - 2}{x - 3}$.

SOLUTION   The expression $\dfrac{5x - 2}{x - 3}$ is not defined when the denominator is 0. We set $x - 3$ equal to 0 and solve:

$$x - 3 = 0$$
$$x = 3. \qquad \text{The number 3 is } not \text{ in the domain.}$$

We have the domain of $g = \{x \mid x \text{ is a real number } and \ x \neq 3\}$. If we graph this set, we see that the domain can be written as a union of two intervals.

$$(-\infty, 3) \cup (3, \infty)$$

Thus the domain of $g = (-\infty, 3) \cup (3, \infty)$.

TRY EXERCISE ▶ 73

7.2   EXERCISE SET

For Extra Help   MyMathLab   MathXL PRACTICE   WATCH   DOWNLOAD

Concept Reinforcement   *In each of Exercises 1–10, match the set with the most appropriate choice from the column on the right.*

1. ____ $\{x \mid x < -2 \text{ or } x > 2\}$

2. ____ $\{x \mid x < -2 \text{ and } x > 2\}$

3. ____ $\{x \mid x > -2\} \cap \{x \mid x < 2\}$

4. ____ $\{x \mid x \leq -2\} \cup \{x \mid x \geq 2\}$

5. ____ $\{x \mid x \leq -2\} \cup \{x \mid x \leq 2\}$

6. ____ $\{x \mid x \leq -2\} \cap \{x \mid x \leq 2\}$

7. ____ $\{x \mid x \geq -2\} \cap \{x \mid x \geq 2\}$

8. ____ $\{x \mid x \geq -2\} \cup \{x \mid x \geq 2\}$

9. ____ $\{x \mid x \leq 2\} \text{ and } \{x \mid x \geq -2\}$

10. ____ $\{x \mid x \leq 2\} \text{ or } \{x \mid x \geq -2\}$

i) $\mathbb{R}$

j) $\varnothing$

Find each indicated intersection or union.

11. $\{2, 4, 16\} \cap \{4, 16, 256\}$

12. $\{1, 2, 4\} \cup \{4, 6, 8\}$

13. $\{0, 5, 10, 15\} \cup \{5, 15, 20\}$

14. $\{2, 5, 9, 13\} \cap \{5, 8, 10\}$

15. $\{a, b, c, d, e, f\} \cap \{b, d, f\}$

16. $\{u, v, w\} \cup \{u, w\}$

17. $\{x, y, z\} \cup \{u, v, x, y, z\}$

18. $\{m, n, o, p\} \cap \{m, o, p\}$

19. $\{3, 6, 9, 12\} \cap \{5, 10, 15\}$

20. $\{1, 5, 9\} \cup \{4, 6, 8\}$

21. $\{1, 3, 5\} \cup \varnothing$

22. $\{1, 3, 5\} \cap \varnothing$

Graph and write interval notation for each compound inequality.

23. $1 < x < 3$

24. $0 \le y \le 5$

25. $-6 \le y \le 0$

26. $-8 < x \le -2$

27. $x \le -1 \, or \, x > 4$

28. $x < -5 \, or \, x > 1$

29. $x \le -2 \, or \, x > 1$

30. $x \le -5 \, or \, x > 2$

31. $-4 \le -x < 2$

32. $x > -7 \, and \, x < -2$

33. $x > -2 \, and \, x < 4$

34. $3 > -x \ge -1$

35. $5 > a \, or \, a > 7$

36. $t \ge 2 \, or -3 > t$

37. $x \ge 5 \, or -x \ge 4$

38. $-x < 3 \, or \, x < -6$

39. $7 > y \, and \, y \ge -3$

40. $6 > -x \ge 0$

41. $-x < 7 \, and -x \ge 0$

42. $x \ge -3 \, and \, x < 3$

Aha! **43.** $t < 2 \, or \, t < 5$

44. $t > 4 \, or \, t > -1$

Solve and graph each solution set.

45. $-3 \le x + 2 < 9$

46. $-1 < x - 3 < 5$

47. $0 < t - 4 \, and \, t - 1 \le 7$

48. $-6 \le t + 1 \, and \, t + 8 < 2$

49. $-7 \le 2a - 3 \, and \, 3a + 1 < 7$

50. $-4 \le 3n + 5 \, and \, 2n - 3 \le 7$

Aha! **51.** $x + 3 \le -1 \, or \, x + 3 > -2$

52. $x + 5 < -3 \, or \, x + 5 \ge 4$

53. $-10 \le 3x - 1 \le 5$

54. $-18 \le 4x + 2 \le 30$

55. $5 > \dfrac{x - 3}{4} > 1$

56. $3 \ge \dfrac{x - 1}{2} \ge -4$

57. $-2 \le \dfrac{x + 2}{-5} \le 6$

58. $-10 \le \dfrac{x + 6}{-3} \le -8$

59. $2 \le f(x) \le 8$, where $f(x) = 3x - 1$

60. $7 \ge g(x) \ge -2$, where $g(x) = 3x - 5$

61. $-21 \le f(x) < 0$, where $f(x) = -2x - 7$

62. $4 > g(t) \ge 2$, where $g(t) = -3t - 8$

63. $f(t) < 3 \, or \, f(t) > 8$, where $f(t) = 5t + 3$

64. $g(x) \le -2 \, or \, g(x) \ge 10$, where $g(x) = 3x - 5$

65. $6 > 2a - 1 \, or -4 \le -3a + 2$

66. $3a - 7 > -10 \, or \, 5a + 2 \le 22$

67. $a + 3 < -2 \, and \, 3a - 4 < 8$

68. $1 - a < -2 \, and \, 2a + 1 > 9$

69. $3x + 2 < 2 \, and \, 3 - x < 1$

70. $2x - 1 > 5 \, and \, 2 - 3x > 11$

71. $2t - 7 \le 5 \, or \, 5 - 2t > 3$

72. $5 - 3a \le 8 \, or \, 2a + 1 > 7$

For $f(x)$ as given, use interval notation to write the domain of f.

73. $f(x) = \dfrac{9}{x + 6}$

74. $f(x) = \dfrac{2}{x - 5}$

75. $f(x) = \dfrac{1}{x}$

76. $f(x) = -\dfrac{6}{x}$

77. $f(x) = \dfrac{x + 3}{2x - 8}$

78. $f(x) = \dfrac{x - 1}{3x + 6}$

79. Why can the conjunction $2 < x \, and \, x < 5$ be rewritten as $2 < x < 5$, but the disjunction $2 < x \, or \, x < 5$ cannot be rewritten as $2 < x < 5$?

80. Can the solution set of a disjunction be empty? Why or why not?

Skill Review

To prepare for Section 7.3, review graphing and solving equations by graphing (Sections 5.3 and 6.1).

Graph. [5.3]

81. $g(x) = 2x$

82. $f(x) = 4$

83. $g(x) = -3$

84. $f(x) = |x|$

Solve by graphing. [6.1]

85. $x + 4 = 3$

86. $x - 1 = -5$

Synthesis

87. What can you conclude about a, b, c, and d, if $[a, b] \cup [c, d] = [a, d]$? Why?

88. What can you conclude about a, b, c, and d, if $[a, b] \cap [c, d] = [a, b]$? Why?

89. Use the accompanying graph of $f(x) = 2x - 5$ to solve $-7 < 2x - 5 < 7$.

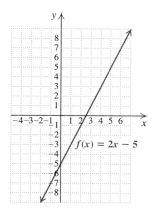

90. Use the accompanying graph of $g(x) = 4 - x$ to solve $4 - x < -2$ or $4 - x > 7$.

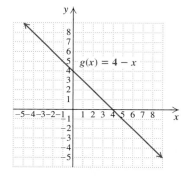

91. *Counseling.* The function given by
$$s(t) = 500t + 16,500$$
can be used to estimate the number of student visits to Cornell University's counseling center t years after 2000. For what years is the number of student visits between 18,000 and 21,000?
Source: Based on data from Cornell University

92. *Pressure at sea depth.* The function given by
$$P(d) = 1 + \frac{d}{33}$$
gives the pressure, in atmospheres (atm), at a depth of d feet in the sea. For what depths d is the pressure at least 1 atm and at most 7 atm?

93. *Converting dress sizes.* The function given by
$$f(x) = 2(x + 10)$$
can be used to convert dress sizes x in the United States to dress sizes $f(x)$ in Italy. For what dress sizes in the United States will dress sizes in Italy be between 32 and 46?

94. *Solid-waste generation.* The function given by
$$w(t) = 0.0125t + 4.525$$
can be used to estimate the number of pounds of solid waste, $w(t)$, produced daily, on average, by each person in the United States, t years after 2000. For what years will waste production range from 4.6 to 4.8 lb per person per day?

95. *Body fat percentage.* The function given by
$$F(d) = (4.95/d - 4.50) \times 100$$
can be used to estimate the body fat percentage $F(d)$ of a person with an average body density d, in kilograms per liter. A woman's body fat percentage is considered acceptable if $25 \le F(d) \le 31$. What body densities are considered acceptable for a woman?

96. *Temperatures of liquids.* The formula
$$C = \tfrac{5}{9}(F - 32)$$
can be used to convert Fahrenheit temperatures F to Celsius temperatures C.

a) Gold is liquid for Celsius temperatures C such that $1063° \le C < 2660°$. Find a comparable inequality for Fahrenheit temperatures.

b) Silver is liquid for Celsius temperatures C such that $960.8° \le C < 2180°$. Find a comparable inequality for Fahrenheit temperatures.

97. *Minimizing tolls.* A \$6.00 toll is charged to cross the bridge to Sanibel Island from mainland Florida. A six-month reduced-fare pass costs \$50 and reduces the toll to \$2.00. A six-month unlimited-trip pass costs \$300 and allows for free crossings. How many crossings in six months does it take for the reduced-fare pass to be the more economical choice?
Source: www.leewayinfo.com

Solve and graph.

98. $4a - 2 \le a + 1 \le 3a + 4$

99. $4m - 8 > 6m + 5$ or $5m - 8 < -2$

100. $x - 10 < 5x + 6 \leq x + 10$

101. $3x < 4 - 5x < 5 + 3x$

Determine whether each sentence is true or false for all real numbers a, b, and c.

102. If $-b < -a$, then $a < b$.

103. If $a \leq c$ and $c \leq b$, then $b > a$.

104. If $a < c$ and $b < c$, then $a < b$.

105. If $-a < c$ and $-c > b$, then $a > b$.

For $f(x)$ as given, use interval notation to write the domain of f.

106. $f(x) = \dfrac{\sqrt{5 + 2x}}{x - 1}$ **107.** $f(x) = \dfrac{\sqrt{3 - 4x}}{x + 7}$

108. For $f(x) = \sqrt{x - 5}$ and $g(x) = \sqrt{9 - x}$, use interval notation to write the domain of $f + g$.

109. Let $y_1 = -1$, $y_2 = 2x + 5$, and $y_3 = 13$. Then use the graphs of y_1, y_2, and y_3 to check the solution to Example 3.

110. Let $y_1 = -2x - 5$, $y_2 = -2$, $y_3 = x - 3$, and $y_4 = -10$. Then use the graphs of y_1, y_2, y_3, and y_4 to check the solution to Example 9.

111. Use a graphing calculator to check your answers to Exercises 45–48 and Exercises 63–66.

112. On many graphing calculators, the TEST key provides access to inequality symbols, while the LOGIC option of that same key accesses the conjunction *and* and the disjunction *or*. Thus, if $y_1 = x > -2$ and $y_2 = x < 4$, Exercise 33 can be checked by forming the expression $y_3 = y_1$ *and* y_2. The interval(s) in the solution set appears as a horizontal line 1 unit above the x-axis. (Be careful to "deselect" y_1 and y_2 so that only y_3 is drawn.) Use the TEST key to check Exercises 35, 39, 41, and 43.

COLLABORATIVE CORNER

Reduce, Reuse, and Recycle

Focus: Compound inequalities

Time: 15–20 minutes

Group size: 2

In the United States, the amount of solid waste (rubbish) being recovered is slowly catching up to the amount being generated. In 2002, each person generated, on average, 4.55 lb of solid waste every day, of which 1.34 lb was recovered. In 2006, each person generated, on average, 4.60 lb of solid waste, of which 1.50 lb was recovered.

Source: U.S. Environmental Protection Agency

ACTIVITY

Assume that the amount of solid waste being generated and the amount being recovered are both increasing linearly. One group member should find a linear function w for which $w(t)$ represents the number of pounds of waste generated per person per day t years after 2000. The other group member should find a linear function r for which $r(t)$ represents the number of pounds recovered per person per day t years after 2000. Finally, working together, the group should determine those years for which the amount recovered will be more than $\frac{1}{3}$ of but less than $\frac{1}{2}$ of the amount generated.

7.3 Absolute–Value Equations and Inequalities

Equations with Absolute Value • Inequalities with Absolute Value

Equations with Absolute Value

Absolute Value

The absolute value of x, denoted $|x|$, is defined as

$$|x| = \begin{cases} x, & \text{if } x \geq 0, \\ -x, & \text{if } x < 0. \end{cases}$$

(When x is nonnegative, the absolute value of x is x. When x is negative, the absolute value of x is the opposite of x.)

To better understand this definition, suppose x is -5. Then $|x| = |-5| = 5$, and 5 is the opposite of -5. This shows that when x represents a negative number, the absolute value of x is the opposite of x (which is positive).

Since distance is always nonnegative, we can think of a number's absolute value as its distance from zero on the number line.

EXAMPLE 1

Find the solution set: **(a)** $|x| = 4$; **(b)** $|x| = 0$; **(c)** $|x| = -7$.

SOLUTION

a) We interpret $|x| = 4$ to mean that the number x is 4 units from zero on the number line. There are two such numbers, 4 and -4. Thus the solution set is $\{-4, 4\}$.

b) We interpret $|x| = 0$ to mean that x is 0 units from zero on the number line. The only number that satisfies this is 0 itself. Thus the solution set is $\{0\}$.

c) Since distance is always nonnegative, it doesn't make sense to talk about a number that is -7 units from zero. Remember: The absolute value of a number is nonnegative. Thus, $|x| = -7$ has no solution; the solution set is $\varnothing$.

TRY EXERCISE 15

Example 1 leads us to the following principle for solving equations.

The Absolute-Value Principle for Equations

For any positive number p and any algebraic expression X:

a) The solutions of $|X| = p$ are those numbers that satisfy

$$X = -p \quad or \quad X = p.$$

b) The equation $|X| = 0$ is equivalent to the equation $X = 0$.

c) The equation $|X| = -p$ has no solution.

EXAMPLE 2

Find the solution set: **(a)** $|2x + 5| = 13$; **(b)** $|4 - 7x| = -8$.

SOLUTION

a) We use the absolute-value principle, knowing that $2x + 5$ must be either 13 or -13:

$$|X| = p$$
$$|2x + 5| = 13 \qquad \text{Substituting}$$
$$2x + 5 = -13 \quad or \quad 2x + 5 = 13$$
$$2x = -18 \quad or \quad 2x = 8$$
$$x = -9 \quad or \quad x = 4.$$

Check: For -9:

$$|2x + 5| = 13$$
$$\frac{|2(-9) + 5|}{} \quad 13$$
$$|-18 + 5|$$
$$|-13|$$
$$13 \overset{?}{=} 13 \quad \text{TRUE}$$

For 4:

$$|2x + 5| = 13$$
$$\frac{|2 \cdot 4 + 5|}{} \quad 13$$
$$|8 + 5|$$
$$|13|$$
$$13 \overset{?}{=} 13 \quad \text{TRUE}$$

The number $2x + 5$ is 13 units from zero if x is replaced with -9 or 4. The solution set is $\{-9, 4\}$.

b) The absolute-value principle reminds us that absolute value is always nonnegative. The equation $|4 - 7x| = -8$ has no solution. The solution set is $\varnothing$.

> TRY EXERCISE 21

To use the absolute-value principle, we must be sure that the absolute-value expression is alone on one side of the equation.

EXAMPLE 3

Given that $f(x) = 2|x + 3| + 1$, find all x for which $f(x) = 15$.

SOLUTION Since we are looking for $f(x) = 15$, we substitute:

$$f(x) = 15$$
$$2|x + 3| + 1 = 15 \qquad \text{Replacing } f(x) \text{ with } 2|x + 3| + 1$$
$$2|x + 3| = 14 \qquad \text{Subtracting 1 from both sides}$$
$$|x + 3| = 7 \qquad \text{Dividing both sides by 2}$$
$$x + 3 = -7 \quad or \quad x + 3 = 7 \qquad \text{Using the absolute-value principle for equations}$$
$$x = -10 \quad or \quad x = 4.$$

The student should check that $f(-10) = f(4) = 15$. The solution set is $\{-10, 4\}$.

> TRY EXERCISE 43

EXAMPLE 4

Solve: $|x - 2| = 3$.

SOLUTION Because this equation is of the form $|a - b| = c$, it can be solved in two different ways.

> **CAUTION!** There are two solutions of $|x - 2| = 3$. Simply solving $x - 2 = 3$ will yield only one of those solutions.

Method 1. We interpret $|x - 2| = 3$ as stating that the number $x - 2$ is 3 units from zero. Using the absolute-value principle, we replace X with $x - 2$ and p with 3:

$$|X| = p$$
$$|x - 2| = 3$$
$$x - 2 = -3 \quad or \quad x - 2 = 3 \qquad \text{Using the absolute-value principle}$$
$$x = -1 \quad or \qquad x = 5.$$

Method 2. This approach is helpful in calculus. The expressions $|a - b|$ and $|b - a|$ can be used to represent the *distance between a and b* on the number line. For example, the distance between 7 and 8 is given by $|8 - 7|$ or $|7 - 8|$. From this viewpoint, the equation $|x - 2| = 3$ states that the distance between x and 2 is 3 units. We draw a number line and locate all numbers that are 3 units from 2.

The solutions of $|x - 2| = 3$ are -1 and 5.

Check: The check consists of observing that both methods give the same solutions. The solution set is $\{-1, 5\}$.

TRY EXERCISE ▶ 25

Sometimes an equation has two absolute-value expressions. Consider $|a| = |b|$. This means that a and b are the same distance from zero.

If a and b are the same distance from zero, then either they are the same number or they are opposites.

EXAMPLE 5

Solve: $|2x - 3| = |x + 5|$.

SOLUTION The given equation tells us that $2x - 3$ and $x + 5$ are the same distance from zero. This means that they are either the same number or opposites:

This assumes the two numbers are the same. | | This assumes the two numbers are opposites.

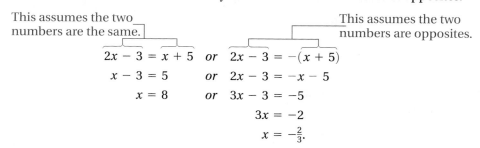

$$2x - 3 = x + 5 \quad or \quad 2x - 3 = -(x + 5)$$
$$x - 3 = 5 \quad or \quad 2x - 3 = -x - 5$$
$$x = 8 \quad or \quad 3x - 3 = -5$$
$$3x = -2$$
$$x = -\tfrac{2}{3}.$$

The check is left to the student. The solutions are 8 and $-\frac{2}{3}$ and the solution set is $\left\{-\frac{2}{3}, 8\right\}$.

TRY EXERCISE ▶ 47

Inequalities with Absolute Value

Our methods for solving equations with absolute value can be adapted for solving inequalities. Inequalities of this sort arise regularly in more advanced courses.

EXAMPLE 6

Solve $|x| < 4$. Then graph.

SOLUTION The solutions of $|x| < 4$ are all numbers whose *distance from zero is less than* 4. By substituting or by looking at the number line, we can see that numbers like $-3, -2, -1, -\frac{1}{2}, -\frac{1}{4}, 0, \frac{1}{4}, \frac{1}{2}, 1, 2$, and 3 are all solutions. In fact, the solutions are all the numbers between -4 and 4. The solution set is $\{x \mid -4 < x < 4\}$, or, in interval notation, $(-4, 4)$. The graph is as follows:

$$|x| < 4$$

TRY EXERCISE 57

EXAMPLE **7**

Solve $|x| \geq 4$. Then graph.

SOLUTION   The solutions of $|x| \geq 4$ are all numbers that are at least 4 units from zero—in other words, those numbers x for which $x \leq -4$ *or* $4 \leq x$. The solution set is $\{x \mid x \leq -4 \ or \ x \geq 4\}$. In interval notation, the solution set is $(-\infty, -4] \cup [4, \infty)$. We can check mentally with numbers like $-4.1, -5, 4.1$, and 5. The graph is as follows:

$$|x| \geq 4$$

TRY EXERCISE 59

Examples 1, 6, and 7 illustrate three types of problems in which absolute-value symbols appear. The general principle for solving such problems follows.

STUDENT NOTES

Simply ignoring the absolute-value symbol and solving the resulting equation or inequality will lead to only *part* of a solution.

$|X| = p$ corresponds to two equations.

$|X| < p$ corresponds to a conjunction.

$|X| > p$ corresponds to a disjunction.

Principles for Solving Absolute-Value Problems

For any positive number p and any expression X:

a) The solutions of $|X| = p$ are those numbers that satisfy

$$X = -p \quad or \quad X = p.$$

b) The solutions of $|X| < p$ are those numbers that satisfy

$$-p < X < p.$$

c) The solutions of $|X| > p$ are those numbers that satisfy

$$X < -p \quad or \quad p < X.$$

The above principles are true for any positive number p.

If p is negative, any value of X will satisfy the inequality $|X| > p$ because absolute value is never negative. Thus, $|2x - 7| > -3$ is true for any real number x, and the solution set is $\mathbb{R}$.

If p is not positive, the inequality $|X| < p$ has no solution. Thus, $|2x - 7| < -3$ has no solution, and the solution set is $\varnothing$.

EXAMPLE 8

Solve $|3x - 2| < 4$. Then graph.

SOLUTION   The number $3x - 2$ must be less than 4 units from zero. This is of the form $|X| < p$, so part (b) of the principles listed above applies:

$$|X| < p \qquad \text{This corresponds to } -p < X < p.$$
$$|3x - 2| < 4 \qquad \text{Replacing } X \text{ with } 3x - 2 \text{ and } p \text{ with } 4$$
$$-4 < 3x - 2 < 4 \qquad \text{The number } 3x - 2 \text{ must be within 4 units of zero.}$$
$$-2 < \quad 3x \quad < 6 \qquad \text{Adding 2}$$
$$-\tfrac{2}{3} < \quad x \quad < 2. \qquad \text{Multiplying by } \tfrac{1}{3}$$

The solution set is $\left\{x \mid -\tfrac{2}{3} < x < 2\right\}$. In interval notation, the solution is $\left(-\tfrac{2}{3}, 2\right)$. The graph is as follows:

$|3x-2| < 4$

TRY EXERCISE 61

EXAMPLE 9

Given that $f(x) = |4x + 2|$, find all x for which $f(x) \geq 6$.

SOLUTION   We have

$$f(x) \geq 6,$$
$$\text{or} \qquad |4x + 2| \geq 6. \qquad \text{Substituting}$$

To solve, we use part (c) of the principles listed above. In this case, X is $4x + 2$ and p is 6:

$$|X| \geq p \qquad \text{This corresponds to } X < -p \text{ or } p < X.$$
$$|4x + 2| \geq 6 \qquad \text{Replacing } X \text{ with } 4x + 2 \text{ and } p \text{ with } 6$$
$$4x + 2 \leq -6 \quad or \quad 6 \leq 4x + 2 \qquad \text{The number } 4x + 2 \text{ must be at least 6 units from zero.}$$
$$4x \leq -8 \quad or \quad 4 \leq 4x \qquad \text{Adding } -2$$
$$x \leq -2 \quad or \quad 1 \leq x. \qquad \text{Multiplying by } \tfrac{1}{4}$$

The solution set is $\{x \mid x \leq -2 \text{ or } x \geq 1\}$. In interval notation, the solution is $(-\infty, -2] \cup [1, \infty)$. The graph is as follows:

$|4x+2| \geq 6$

TRY EXERCISE 87

ALGEBRAIC–GRAPHICAL CONNECTION

We can visualize Examples 1(a), 6, and 7 by graphing $f(x) = |x|$ and $g(x) = 4$.

Solve: $|x| = 4$.

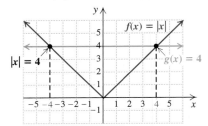

The graphs intersect at $(-4, 4)$ and $(4, 4)$.

$|x| = 4$ when $x = -4$ or $x = 4$.

The solution set of $|x| = 4$ is $\{-4, 4\}$.

Solve: $|x| < 4$.

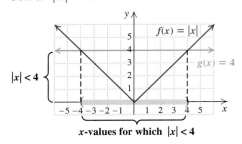

x-values for which $|x| < 4$

The graphs intersect at $(-4, 4)$ and $(4, 4)$.

$|x| < 4$ when $-4 < x < 4$.

The solution set of $|x| < 4$ is $(-4, 4)$.

Solve: $|x| \geq 4$.

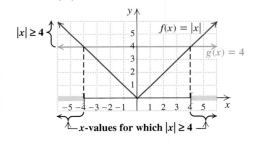

x-values for which $|x| \geq 4$

The graphs intersect at $(-4, 4)$ and $(4, 4)$.

$|x| \geq 4$ when $x \leq -4$ or $x \geq 4$.

The solution set of $|x| \geq 4$ is $(-\infty, -4] \cup [4, \infty)$.

TECHNOLOGY CONNECTION

To enter an absolute-value function on a graphing calculator, we press **MATH** and use the abs(option in the NUM menu. To solve $|4x + 2| = 6$, we graph $y_1 = \text{abs}(4x + 2)$ and $y_2 = 6$.

$y_1 = \text{abs}(4x + 2), \quad y_2 = 6$

Using the INTERSECT option of the CALC menu, we find that the graphs intersect at $(-2, 6)$ and $(1, 6)$. The x-coordinates -2 and 1 are the solutions. To solve $|4x + 2| \geq 6$, note where the graph of y_1 is *on or above* the line $y = 6$. The corresponding x-values are the solutions of the inequality.

1. How can the same graph be used to solve $|4x + 2| < 6$?
2. Solve Example 8.
3. Use a graphing calculator to show that $|4x + 2| = -6$ has no solution.

7.3 EXERCISE SET

For Extra Help   PRACTICE   WATCH   DOWNLOAD

⤻ **Concept Reinforcement** *Classify each statement as either true or false.*

1. $|x|$ is never negative.

2. $|x|$ is always positive.

3. If x is negative, then $|x| = -x$.

4. The number a is $|a|$ units from 0.

5. The distance between a and b can be expressed as $|a - b|$.

6. There are two solutions of $|3x - 8| = 17$.

7. There is no solution of $|4x + 9| > -5$.

8. All real numbers are solutions of $|2x - 7| < -3$.

Match each equation or inequality with an equivalent statement from the column on the right. Letters may be used more than once or not at all.

9. $|x - 3| = 5$
10. $|x - 3| < 5$
11. $|x - 3| > 5$
12. $|x - 3| < -5$
13. $|x - 3| = -5$
14. $|x - 3| > -5$

a) The solution set is $\varnothing$.
b) The solution set is $\mathbb{R}$.
c) $x - 3 > 5$
d) $x - 3 < -5$ or $x - 3 > 5$
e) $x - 3 = 5$
f) $x - 3 < 5$
g) $x - 3 = -5$ or $x - 3 = 5$
h) $-5 < x - 3 < 5$

Solve.

15. $|x| = 10$
16. $|x| = 5$
Aha! 17. $|x| = -1$
18. $|x| = -8$
19. $|p| = 0$
20. $|y| = 7.3$
21. $|2x - 3| = 4$
22. $|5x + 2| = 7$
23. $|3x + 5| = -8$
24. $|7x - 2| = -9$
25. $|x - 2| = 6$
26. $|x - 3| = 11$
27. $|x - 7| = 1$
28. $|x - 4| = 5$
29. $|t| + 1.1 = 6.6$
30. $|m| + 3 = 3$
31. $|5x| - 3 = 37$
32. $|2y| - 5 = 13$
33. $7|q| + 2 = 9$
34. $5|z| + 2 = 17$

35. $\left|\dfrac{2x - 1}{3}\right| = 4$
36. $\left|\dfrac{4 - 5x}{6}\right| = 3$
37. $|5 - m| + 9 = 16$
38. $|t - 7| + 1 = 4$
39. $5 - 2|3x - 4| = -5$
40. $3|2x - 5| - 7 = -1$
41. Let $f(x) = |2x + 6|$. Find all x for which $f(x) = 8$.
42. Let $f(x) = |2x - 4|$. Find all x for which $f(x) = 10$.
43. Let $f(x) = |x| - 3$. Find all x for which $f(x) = 5.7$.
44. Let $f(x) = |x| + 7$. Find all x for which $f(x) = 18$.
45. Let $f(x) = \left|\dfrac{1 - 2x}{5}\right|$. Find all x for which $f(x) = 2$.
46. Let $f(x) = \left|\dfrac{3x + 4}{3}\right|$. Find all x for which $f(x) = 1$.

Solve.

47. $|x - 7| = |2x + 1|$
48. $|3x + 2| = |x - 6|$
49. $|x + 4| = |x - 3|$
50. $|x - 9| = |x + 6|$
51. $|3a - 1| = |2a + 4|$
52. $|5t + 7| = |4t + 3|$
Aha! 53. $|n - 3| = |3 - n|$
54. $|y - 2| = |2 - y|$
55. $|7 - 4a| = |4a + 5|$
56. $|6 - 5t| = |5t + 8|$

Solve and graph.

57. $|a| \leq 3$
58. $|x| < 5$
59. $|t| > 0$
60. $|t| \geq 1$
61. $|x - 1| < 4$
62. $|x - 1| < 3$
63. $|n + 2| \leq 6$
64. $|a + 4| \leq 0$
65. $|x - 3| + 2 > 7$
66. $|x - 4| + 5 > 10$
Aha! 67. $|2y - 9| > -5$
68. $|3y - 4| > -8$
69. $|3a + 4| + 2 \geq 8$
70. $|2a + 5| + 1 \geq 9$
71. $|y - 3| < 12$
72. $|p - 2| < 3$

73. $9 - |x + 4| \leq 5$

74. $12 - |x - 5| \leq 9$

75. $6 + |3 - 2x| > 10$

76. $|7 - 2y| < -8$

Aha! **77.** $|5 - 4x| < -6$

78. $7 + |4a - 5| \leq 26$

79. $\left|\dfrac{1 + 3x}{5}\right| > \dfrac{7}{8}$

80. $\left|\dfrac{2 - 5x}{4}\right| \geq \dfrac{2}{3}$

81. $|m + 3| + 8 \leq 14$

82. $|t - 7| + 3 \geq 4$

83. $25 - 2|a + 3| > 19$

84. $30 - 4|a + 2| > 12$

85. Let $f(x) = |2x - 3|$. Find all x for which $f(x) \leq 4$.

86. Let $f(x) = |5x + 2|$. Find all x for which $f(x) \leq 3$.

87. Let $f(x) = 5 + |3x - 4|$. Find all x for which $f(x) \geq 16$.

88. Let $f(x) = |2 - 9x|$. Find all x for which $f(x) \geq 25$.

89. Let $f(x) = 7 + |2x - 1|$. Find all x for which $f(x) < 16$.

90. Let $f(x) = 5 + |3x + 2|$. Find all x for which $f(x) < 19$.

91. Explain in your own words why -7 is not a solution of $|x| < 5$.

92. Explain in your own words why $[6, \infty)$ is only part of the solution of $|x| \geq 6$.

Skill Review

To prepare for Section 7.4, review graphing equations and solving systems of equations (Sections 2.3, 2.6, and 6.2).

Graph.

93. $3x - y = 6$ [2.3]

94. $y = \frac{1}{2}x - 1$ [2.6]

95. $x = -2$ [2.3]

96. $y = 4$ [2.3]

Solve using substitution or elimination. [6.2]

97. $x - 3y = 8,$ $\quad 2x + 3y = 4$

98. $x - 2y = 3,$ $\quad x = y + 4$

99. $y = 1 - 5x,$ $\quad 2x - y = 4$

100. $3x - 2y = 4,$ $\quad 5x - 3y = 5$

Synthesis

101. Describe a procedure that could be used to solve any equation of the form $g(x) < c$ graphically.

102. Explain why the inequality $|x + 5| \geq 2$ can be interpreted as "the number x is at least 2 units from -5."

103. From the definition of absolute value, $|x| = x$ only when $x \geq 0$. Solve $|3t - 5| = 3t - 5$ using this same reasoning.

Solve.

104. $|3x - 5| = x$

105. $|x + 2| > x$

106. $2 \leq |x - 1| \leq 5$

107. $|5t - 3| = 2t + 4$

108. $t - 2 \leq |t - 3|$

Find an equivalent inequality with absolute value.

109. $-3 < x < 3$

110. $-5 \leq y \leq 5$

111. $x \leq -6 \text{ or } 6 \leq x$

112. $x < -4 \text{ or } 4 < x$

113. $x < -8 \text{ or } 2 < x$

114. $-5 < x < 1$

115. x is less than 2 units from 7.

116. x is less than 1 unit from 5.

Write an absolute-value inequality for which the interval shown is the solution.

117. ![number line from -7 to 7, shaded from -1 to right]

118. ![number line from -5 to 9, shaded from -4 to 8]

119. ![number line from -7 to 7, shaded from -7 to -1]

120. ![number line from 0 to 14, shaded from 2 to 12]

121. *Bungee jumping.* A bungee jumper is bouncing up and down so that her distance d above a river satisfies the inequality $|d - 60 \text{ ft}| \leq 10 \text{ ft}$ (see the figure below). If the bridge from which she jumped is 150 ft above the river, how far is the bungee jumper from the bridge at any given time?

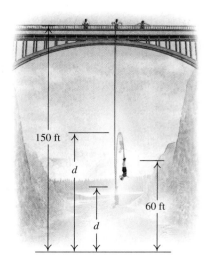

122. *Water level.*   Depending on how dry or wet the weather has been, water in a well will rise and fall. The distance d, in feet, that a well's water level is below the ground satisfies the inequality $|d - 15| \leq 2.5$ (see the figure below).

a) Solve for d.

b) How tall a column of water is in the well at any given time?

123. Use this graph of $f(x) = |2x - 6|$ to solve $|2x - 6| \leq 4$.

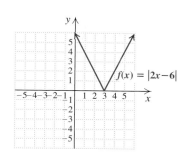

124. Is it possible for an equation in x of the form $|ax + b| = c$ to have exactly one solution? Why or why not?

125. Isabel is using the following graph to solve $|x - 3| < 4$. How can you tell that a mistake has been made in entering $y = \text{abs}(x - 3)$?

CONNECTING the CONCEPTS

We have learned to solve a variety of equations and inequalities. As we continue our study of algebra, we will learn to solve additional types of equations and inequalities, some of which will require new principles for solving. Following is a list of the principles we have used so far to solve equations and inequalities. Unless otherwise stated, a, b, and c can represent any real number.

The Addition and Multiplication Principles for Equations

$a = b$ is equivalent to $a + c = b + c$.

$a = b$ is equivalent to $ac = bc$, provided $c \neq 0$.

The Addition Principle for Inequalities

$a < b$ is equivalent to $a + c < b + c$.

$a > b$ is equivalent to $a + c > b + c$.

The Multiplication Principle for Inequalities

For any *positive* number c,

$a < b$ is equivalent to $ac < bc$;

$a > b$ is equivalent to $ac > bc$.

For any *negative* number c,

$a < b$ is equivalent to $ac > bc$;

$a > b$ is equivalent to $ac < bc$.

The Absolute-Value Principles for Equations and Inequalities

For any positive number p and any algebraic expression X:

The solutions of $|X| = p$ are those numbers that satisfy

$$X = -p \text{ or } X = p.$$

The solutions of $|X| < p$ are those numbers that satisfy

$$-p < X < p.$$

The solutions of $|X| > p$ are those numbers that satisfy

$$X < -p \text{ or } p < X.$$

MIXED REVIEW

Solve.

1. $2x + 3 = 7$

2. $3x - 1 > 8$

3. $3(t - 5) = 4 - (t + 1)$

4. $|2x + 1| = 7$

5. $-x \leq 6$

6. $5|t| < 20$

7. $2(3n + 6) - n = 4 - 3(n + 1)$

8. $3(2a + 9) = 5(3a - 7) - 6a$

9. $2 + |3x| = 10$

10. $|x - 3| \leq 10$

11. $\frac{1}{2}x - 7 = \frac{3}{4} + \frac{1}{4}x$

12. $|t| < 0$

13. $|2x + 5| + 1 \geq 13$

14. $2(x - 3) - x = 5x + 7 - 4x$

15. $|m + 6| - 8 < 10$

16. $\left|\dfrac{x + 2}{5}\right| = 8$

17. $4 - |7 - t| \leq 1$

18. $0.3x + 0.7 = 0.5x$

19. $8 - 5|a + 6| > 3$

20. $|5x + 7| + 9 \geq 4$

7.4 Inequalities in Two Variables

Graphs of Linear Inequalities • Systems of Linear Inequalities

In Section 1.6, we graphed inequalities in one variable on a number line. Now we graph inequalities in two variables on a plane.

Graphs of Linear Inequalities

When the equals sign in a linear equation is replaced with an inequality sign, a **linear inequality** is formed. Solutions of linear inequalities are ordered pairs.

EXAMPLE 1 Determine whether $(-3, 2)$ and $(6, -7)$ are solutions of $5x - 4y > 13$.

SOLUTION Below, on the left, we replace x with -3 and y with 2. On the right, we replace x with 6 and y with -7.

$$\frac{5x - 4y > 13}{\begin{array}{c|c} 5(-3) - 4 \cdot 2 & 13 \\ -15 - 8 & \\ -23 \overset{?}{>} 13 & \text{FALSE} \end{array}}$$

$$\frac{5x - 4y > 13}{\begin{array}{c|c} 5(6) - 4(-7) & 13 \\ 30 + 28 & \\ 58 \overset{?}{>} 13 & \text{TRUE} \end{array}}$$

Since $-23 > 13$ is false, $(-3, 2)$ *is not* a solution.

Since $58 > 13$ is true, $(6, -7)$ *is* a solution.

TRY EXERCISE 7

STUDENT NOTES

Pay careful attention to the inequality symbol when determining whether an ordered pair is a solution of an inequality. Writing the symbol at the end of the check, as in Example 1, will help you compare the numbers correctly.

The graph of a linear equation is a straight line. The graph of a linear inequality is a **half-plane**, with a **boundary** that is a straight line. To find the equation of the boundary, we replace the inequality sign with an equals sign.

EXAMPLE 2

Graph: $y \le x$.

SOLUTION We first graph the equation of the boundary, $y = x$. Every solution of $y = x$ is an ordered pair, like $(3, 3)$, in which both coordinates are the same. The graph of $y = x$ is shown on the left below. Since the inequality symbol is $\le$, the line is drawn solid and is part of the graph of $y \le x$.

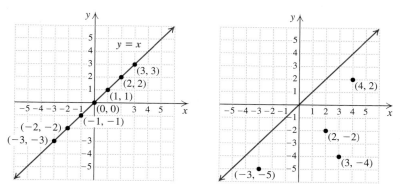

Note that in the graph on the right each ordered pair on the half-plane below $y = x$ contains a y-coordinate that is less than the x-coordinate. All these pairs represent solutions of $y \le x$. We check one pair, $(4, 2)$, as follows:

$$\frac{y \le x}{2 \overset{?}{\le} 4} \quad \text{TRUE}$$

It turns out that *any* point on the same side of $y = x$ as $(4, 2)$ is also a solution. Thus, if one point in a half-plane is a solution, then *all* points in that half-plane are solutions.

We finish drawing the solution set by shading the half-plane below $y = x$. The complete solution set consists of the shaded half-plane as well as the boundary line itself.

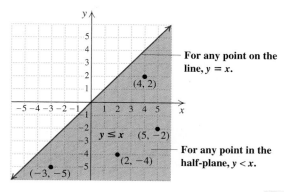

TRY EXERCISE 11

From Example 2, we see that for any inequality of the form $y \le f(x)$ or $y < f(x)$, we shade *below* the graph of $y = f(x)$.

EXAMPLE **3**

Graph: $8x + 3y > 24$.

SOLUTION First, we sketch the graph of $8x + 3y = 24$. Since the inequality sign is $>$, points on this line do not represent solutions of the inequality, and the line is drawn dashed. Points representing solutions of $8x + 3y > 24$ are in either the half-plane above the line or the half-plane below the line. To determine which, we select a point that is not on the line and check whether it is a solution of $8x + 3y > 24$. Let's use $(1, 1)$ as this *test point*:

$$\frac{8x + 3y > 24}{\begin{array}{c|c} 8(1) + 3(1) & 24 \\ 8 + 3 & \\ 11 \overset{?}{>} 24 & \text{FALSE} \end{array}}$$

Since $11 > 24$ is *false*, $(1, 1)$ is not a solution. Thus no point in the half-plane containing $(1, 1)$ is a solution. The points in the other half-plane *are* solutions, so we shade that half-plane and obtain the graph shown below.

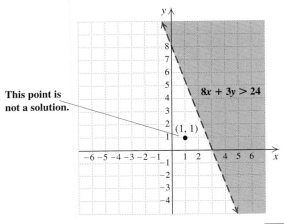

This point is not a solution.

$8x + 3y > 24$

$(1, 1)$

TRY EXERCISE 19

Steps for Graphing Linear Inequalities

1. Replace the inequality sign with an equals sign and graph this line as the boundary. If the inequality symbol is $<$ or $>$, draw the line dashed. If the symbol is $\leq$ or $\geq$, draw the line solid.
2. The graph of the inequality consists of a half-plane on one side of the line and, if the line is solid, the line as well.

   a) If the inequality is of the form $y < mx + b$ or $y \leq mx + b$, shade *below* the line.
   If the inequality is of the form $y > mx + b$ or $y \geq mx + b$, shade *above* the line.
   b) If y is not isolated, either solve for y and graph as in part (a) or simply graph the boundary and use a test point not on the line (as in Example 3). If the test point *is* a solution, shade the half-plane containing the point. If it is not a solution, shade the other half-plane.

EXAMPLE 4

Graph: $6x - 2y < 12$.

SOLUTION   We could graph $6x - 2y = 12$ and use a test point, as in Example 3. Instead, let's solve $6x - 2y < 12$ for y:

$$6x - 2y < 12$$
$$-2y < -6x + 12 \qquad \text{Adding } -6x \text{ to both sides}$$
$$y > 3x - 6. \qquad \text{Dividing both sides by } -2 \text{ and reversing the } < \text{ symbol}$$

The graph consists of the half plane above the dashed boundary line $y = 3x - 6$ (see the graph below).

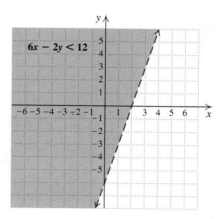

TRY EXERCISE ▸ 21

EXAMPLE 5

Graph $x > -3$ on a plane.

SOLUTION   There is only one variable in this inequality. If we graph the inequality on a line, its graph is as follows:

However, we can also write this inequality as $x + 0y > -3$ and graph it on a plane. We can use the same technique as in the examples above. First, we graph the boundary $x = -3$ in the plane, using a dashed line. Then we test some point, say, $(2, 5)$:

$$\frac{x + 0y > -3}{2 + 0 \cdot 5 \mid -3}$$
$$2 \overset{?}{>} -3 \quad \text{TRUE}$$

Since $(2, 5)$ is a solution, all points in the half-plane containing $(2, 5)$ are solutions. We shade that half-plane. Another approach is to simply note that the solutions of $x > -3$ are all pairs with first coordinates greater than -3.

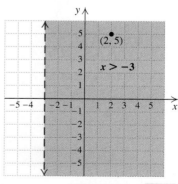

TRY EXERCISE ▸ 25

TECHNOLOGY CONNECTION

On most graphing calculators, an inequality like $y < \frac{6}{5}x + 3.49$ can be drawn by entering $(6/5)x + 3.49$ as y_1, moving the cursor to the GraphStyle icon just to the left of y_1, pressing **ENTER** until ◣ appears, and then pressing **GRAPH**.

Many calculators have an INEQUALZ program that is accessed using the **APPS** key. Running this program allows us to write inequalities at the **Y=** screen by pressing **ALPHA** and then one of the five keys just below the screen.

Although the graphs should be identical regardless of the method used, when we are using INEQUALZ, the boundary line appears dashed when $<$ or $>$ is selected.

$$y_1 < (6/5)x + 3.49, \text{ or}$$
$$◣\, y_1 = (6/5)x + 3.49$$

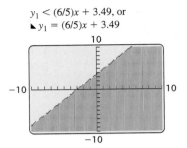

Graph each of the following. Solve for y first if necessary.

1. $y > x + 3.5$ **2.** $7y \le 2x + 5$

3. $8x - 2y < 11$ **4.** $11x + 13y + 4 \ge 0$

EXAMPLE   **6**   Graph $y \le 4$ on a plane.

SOLUTION   The inequality is of the form $y \le mx + b$ (with $m = 0$), so we shade below the solid horizontal line representing $y = 4$.

This inequality can also be graphed by drawing $y = 4$ and testing a point above or below the line. The student should check that this results in a graph identical to the one at right.

TRY EXERCISE   27

Systems of Linear Inequalities

To graph a system of equations, we graph the individual equations and then find the intersection of the graphs. We do the same thing for a system of inequalities: We graph each inequality and find the intersection of the graphs.

EXAMPLE   **7**   Graph the system

$$x + y \le 4,$$
$$x - y < 4.$$

SOLUTION   To graph $x + y \leq 4$, we graph $x + y = 4$ using a solid line. Since the test point $(0, 0)$ *is* a solution and $(0, 0)$ is below the line, we shade the half-plane below the graph red. The arrows near the ends of the line are another way of indicating the half-plane containing solutions.

Next, we graph $x - y < 4$. We graph $x - y = 4$ using a dashed line and consider $(0, 0)$ as a test point. Again, $(0, 0)$ is a solution, so we shade that side of the line blue. The solution set of the system is the region that is shaded purple (both red and blue) and part of the line $x + y = 4$.

Graph the first inequality.

Graph the second inequality.

Shade the intersection.

TRY EXERCISE 45

EXAMPLE 8

STUDENT NOTES ———

If you don't use differently colored pencils or pens to shade different regions, consider using a pencil to make slashes that tilt in different directions in each region. You may also find it useful to attach arrows to the lines, as in the graphs shown.

Graph: $-2 < x \leq 3$.

SOLUTION   This is a system of inequalities:

$$-2 < x,$$
$$x \leq 3.$$

We graph the equation $-2 = x$, and see that the graph of the first inequality is the half-plane to the right of the boundary $-2 = x$. It is shaded red.

We graph the second inequality, starting with the boundary line $x = 3$. The inequality's graph is the line and the half-plane to its left. It is shaded blue.

The solution set of the system is the region that is the intersection of the individual graphs. Since it is shaded both blue and red, it appears to be purple. All points in this region have x-coordinates that are greater than -2 but do not exceed 3.

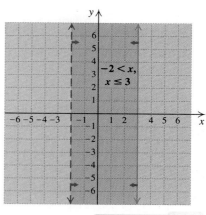

TRY EXERCISE 31

A system of inequalities may have a graph that consists of a polygon and its interior. In Section 7.5, we will have use for the corners, or *vertices* (singular, *vertex*), of such a graph.

EXAMPLE 9 Graph the system of inequalities. Find the coordinates of any vertices formed.

$$6x - 2y \leq 12, \quad (1)$$
$$y - 3 \leq 0, \quad (2)$$
$$x + y \geq 0 \quad (3)$$

SOLUTION We graph the boundaries

$$6x - 2y = 12,$$
$$y - 3 = 0,$$
and $$x + y = 0$$

using solid lines. The regions for each inequality are indicated by the arrows near the ends of the lines. We note where the regions overlap and shade the region of solutions purple.

To find the vertices, we solve three different systems of two equations. The system of boundary equations from inequalities (1) and (2) is

$$6x - 2y = 12,$$
$$y - 3 = 0.$$

The student can use graphing, substitution, or elimination to solve these systems.

Solving, we obtain the vertex $(3, 3)$.

The system of boundary equations from inequalities (1) and (3) is

$$6x - 2y = 12,$$
$$x + y = 0.$$

Solving, we obtain the vertex $\left(\frac{3}{2}, -\frac{3}{2}\right)$.

The system of boundary equations from inequalities (2) and (3) is

$$y - 3 = 0,$$
$$x + y = 0.$$

Solving, we obtain the vertex $(-3, 3)$.

TRY EXERCISE 49

TECHNOLOGY CONNECTION

Systems of inequalities can be graphed by solving for y and then graphing each inequality as in the Technology Connection on p. 470. To graph systems directly using the INEQUALZ application, enter the correct inequalities, press GRAPH, and then press ALPHA and Shades (F1 or F2). At the SHADES menu, select Ineq Intersection to see the final graph. To find the vertices, or points of intersection, select PoI-Trace from the graph menu.

$$y_1 \geq 3x - 6, \quad y_2 \leq 3, \quad y_3 \geq -x$$

1. Use a graphing calculator to check the solution of Example 7.

Visualizing for Success

A

B

C

D

E

Match each equation, inequality, or system of equations or inequalities with its graph.

1. $x - y = 3,$
   $2x + y = 1$

2. $3x - y \leq 5$

3. $x > -3$

4. $y = \dfrac{1}{3}x - 4$

5. $y > \dfrac{1}{3}x - 4,$
   $y \leq x$

6. $x = y$

7. $y = 2x - 1,$
   $y = 2x - 3$

8. $2x - 5y = 10$

9. $x + y \leq 3,$
   $2y \leq x + 1$

10. $y = \dfrac{3}{2}$

Answers on page A-30

An additional, animated version of this activity appears in MyMathLab. To use MyMathLab, you need a course ID and a student access code. Contact your instructor for more information.

F

G

H

I

J

7.4 EXERCISE SET

For Extra Help

Concept Reinforcement *In each of Exercises 1–6, match the phrase with the most appropriate choice from the column on the right.*

1. _____ A solution of a linear inequality

2. _____ The graph of a linear inequality

3. _____ The graph of a system of linear inequalities

4. _____ Often a convenient test point

5. _____ The name for the corners of a graph of a system of linear inequalities

6. _____ A dashed line

a) $(0, 0)$

b) Vertices

c) A half-plane

d) The intersection of two or more half-planes

e) An ordered pair that satisfies the inequality

f) Indicates the line is not part of the solution

Determine whether each ordered pair is a solution of the given inequality.

7. $(-2, 3)$; $2x - y > -4$

8. $(1, -6)$; $3x + y \geq -3$

9. $(5, 8)$; $3y - 5x \leq 0$

10. $(6, 20)$; $5y - 8x < 40$

Graph on a plane.

11. $y \geq \frac{1}{2}x$

12. $y \leq 3x$

13. $y > x - 3$

14. $y < x + 3$

15. $y \leq x + 2$

16. $y \geq x - 5$

17. $x - y \leq 4$

18. $x + y < 4$

19. $2x + 3y < 6$

20. $3x + 4y \leq 12$

21. $2y - x \leq 4$

22. $2y - 3x > 6$

23. $2x - 2y \geq 8 + 2y$

24. $3x - 2 \leq 5x + y$

25. $x > -2$

26. $x \geq 3$

27. $y \leq 6$

28. $y < -1$

29. $-2 < y < 7$

30. $-4 < y < -1$

31. $-5 \leq x < 4$

32. $-2 < y \leq 1$

33. $0 \leq y \leq 3$

34. $0 \leq x \leq 6$

Graph each system.

35. $y > x,$
    $y < -x + 3$

36. $y < x,$
    $y > -x + 1$

37. $y \leq x,,$
    $y \leq 2x - 5$

38. $y \geq x,$
    $y \leq -x + 4$

39. $y \leq -3,$
    $x \geq -1$

40. $y \geq -3,$
    $x \geq 1$

41. $x > -4,$
    $y < -2x + 3$

42. $x < 3,$
    $y > -3x + 2$

43. $y \leq 5,$
    $y \geq -x + 4$

44. $y \geq -2,$
    $y \geq x + 3$

45. $x + y \leq 6,$
    $x - y \leq 4$

46. $x + y < 1,$
    $x - y < 2$

47. $y + 3x > 0,$
    $y + 3x < 2$

48. $y - 2x \geq 1,$
    $y - 2x \leq 3$

Graph each system of inequalities. Find the coordinates of any vertices formed.

49. $y \leq 2x - 3,$
    $y \geq -2x + 1,$
    $x \leq 5$

50. $2y - x \leq 2,$
    $y - 3x \geq -4,$
    $y \geq -1$

51. $x + 2y \leq 12,$
    $2x + y \leq 12,$
    $x \geq 0,$
    $y \geq 0$

52. $x - y \leq 2,$
    $x + 2y \geq 8,$
    $y \leq 4$

53. $8x + 5y \leq 40,$
    $x + 2y \leq 8,$
    $x \geq 0,$
    $y \geq 0$

54. $4y - 3x \geq -12,$
    $4y + 3x \geq -36,$
    $y \leq 0,$
    $x \leq 0$

55. $y - x \geq 2,$
    $y - x \leq 4,$
    $2 \leq x \leq 5$

56. $3x + 4y \geq 12,$
    $5x + 6y \leq 30,$
    $1 \leq x \leq 3$

57. Explain in your own words why the boundary line is drawn dashed for the symbols $<$ and $>$ and why it is drawn solid for the symbols $\leq$ and $\geq$.

58. When graphing linear inequalities, Ron makes a habit of always shading above the line when the symbol $\geq$ is used. Is this wise? Why or why not?

Skill Review

To prepare for Section 7.5, review solving applications using the five-step problem-solving strategy (Sections 1.5 and 6.3).

Solve.

59. *Interest rate.* What rate of interest is required in order for a principal of \$1560 to earn \$25.35 in half a year? [1.5]

60. *Interest.* Luke invested \$5000 in two accounts. He put \$2200 in an account paying 4% simple interest and the rest in an account paying 5% simple interest. How much interest did he earn in one year from both accounts? [1.5]

61. *Investments.* Gina invested \$10,000 in two accounts, one paying 3% simple interest and one paying 5% simple interest. After one year, she had earned \$428 from both accounts. How much did she invest in each? [6.3]

62. *Catering.* Janice provided 20 lb of fresh vegetables for a reception. Carrots were \$1.50 per pound and broccoli was \$2.50 per pound. If she spent \$38, how much of each vegetable did she buy? [6.3]

63. *Admissions.* There were 170 tickets sold for a high school basketball game. Tickets were \$1 each for students and \$3 each for adults. The total amount of money collected was \$386. How many of each type of ticket were sold? [6.3]

64. *Agriculture.* Josh planted 400 acres in corn and soybeans. He planted 80 more acres in corn than he did in soybeans. How many acres of each did he plant? [6.3]

Synthesis

65. Explain how a system of linear inequalities could have a solution set containing exactly one pair.

66. In Example 7 on pp. 470–471, is the point $(4, 0)$ part of the solution set? Why or why not?

Graph.

67. $x + y > 8,$
$\quad x + y \leq -2$

68. $x + y \geq 1,$
$\quad -x + y \geq 2,$
$\qquad x \geq -2,$
$\qquad y \geq 2,$
$\qquad y \leq 4,$
$\qquad x \leq 2$

69. $\quad x - 2y \leq 0,$
$\quad -2x + y \leq 2,$
$\qquad\quad x \leq 2,$
$\qquad\quad y \leq 2,$
$\quad x + y \leq 4$

70. Write four systems of four inequalities that describe a 2-unit by 2-unit square that has $(0, 0)$ as one of the vertices.

71. *Luggage size.* Unless an additional fee is paid, most major airlines will not check any luggage for which the sum of the item's length, width, and height exceeds 62 in. The U.S. Postal Service will ship a package only if the sum of the package's length and girth (distance around its midsection) does not exceed 130 in. Video Promotions is ordering several 30-in. long cases that will be both mailed and checked as luggage. Using w and h for width and height (in inches), respectively, write and graph an inequality that represents all acceptable combinations of width and height.

Sources: U.S. Postal Service; www.case2go.com

72. *Hockey wins and losses.* The Skating Stars believe they need at least 60 points for the season in order to make the playoffs. A win is worth 2 points and a tie is worth 1 point. Graph a system of inequalities that describes the situation. (*Hint*: Let w = the number of wins and t = the number of ties.)

73. *Graduate-school admissions.* Students entering the Master of Science program in Computer Science and Engineering at University of Texas Arlington must meet minimum score requirements on the Graduate Records Examination (GRE). The GRE Quantitative score must be at least 700 and the GRE Verbal score must be at least 400. The sum of the GRE Quantitative and Verbal scores must be at least 1150. Both scores have a maximum of 800. Using q for the quantitative score and v for the verbal score, write and graph a system of inequalities that represents all combinations that meet the requirements for entrance into the program.
Source: University of Texas Arlington

74. *Widths of a basketball floor.* Sizes of basketball floors vary due to building sizes and other constraints such as cost. The length L is to be at most 94 ft and the width W is to be at most 50 ft. Graph a system of inequalities that describes the possible dimensions of a basketball floor.

75. *Elevators.* Many elevators have a capacity of 1 metric ton (1000 kg). Suppose that c children, each weighing 35 kg, and a adults, each 75 kg, are on an elevator. Graph a system of inequalities that indicates when the elevator is overloaded.

76. *Age of marriage.* The following rule of thumb for determining an appropriate difference in age between a bride and a groom appears in many Internet blogs: *The younger spouse's age should be at least seven more than half the age of the older spouse.* Let b = the age of the bride, in years, and g = the age of the groom, in years. Write and graph a system of inequalities that represents all combinations of ages that follow this rule of thumb. Should a minimum or maximum age for marriage exist? How would the graph of the system of inequalities change with such a requirement?

77. *Waterfalls.* In order for a waterfall to be classified as a classical waterfall, its height must be less than twice its crest width, and its crest width cannot exceed one-and-a-half times its height. The tallest waterfall in the world is about 3200 ft high. Let h represent a waterfall's height, in feet, and w the crest width, in feet. Write and graph a system of inequalities that represents all possible combinations of heights and crest widths of classical waterfalls.

78. Use a graphing calculator to check your answers to Exercises 35–48. Then use INTERSECT to determine any point(s) of intersection.

79. Use a graphing calculator to graph each inequality.
   a) $3x + 6y > 2$
   b) $x - 5y \le 10$
   c) $13x - 25y + 10 \le 0$
   d) $2x + 5y > 0$

CONNECTING the CONCEPTS

We have now solved a variety of equations, inequalities, systems of equations, and systems of inequalities. Below is a list of the different types of problems we have solved, illustrations of each type, and descriptions of the solutions. Note that a solution set may be empty.

Type	Example	Solution	Graph
Linear equations in one variable	$2x - 8 = 3(x + 5)$	A number	number line with point at -23
Linear inequalities in one variable	$-3x + 5 > 2$	A set of numbers; an interval	number line interval
Linear equations in two variables	$2x + y = 7$	A set of ordered pairs; a line	graph of $2x + y = 7$
Linear inequalities in two variables	$x + y \geq 4$	A set of ordered pairs; a half-plane	graph of $x + y \geq 4$
System of equations in two variables	$x + y = 3,$ $5x - y = -27$	An ordered pair or a set of ordered pairs	graph through $(-4, 7)$
System of inequalities in two variables	$6x - 2y \leq 12,$ $y - 3 \leq 0,$ $x + y \geq 0$	A set of ordered pairs; a region of a plane	graph with region, vertices $(-3, 3)$, $(3, 3)$, $\left(\frac{3}{2}, -\frac{3}{2}\right)$

MIXED REVIEW

Graph each solution on a number line.

1. $x + 2 = 7$

2. $x + 2 > 7$

3. $x + 2 \leq 7$

4. $3(x - 7) - 2 = 5 - (2 - x)$

5. $6 - 2x \geq 8$

6. $7 > 5 - x$

Graph on a plane.

7. $x + y = 2$

8. $x + y < 2$

9. $x + y \geq 2$

10. $y = 3x - 3$

11. $x = 4$

12. $2x - 5y = -10$

13. $x + y = 1,$
    $x - y = 1$

14. $y \geq 1 - x,$
    $y \leq x - 3,$
    $y \leq 2$

15. $2x + y < 6$

16. $x > 6y - 6$

17. $4x = 3y$

18. $y = 2x - 3,$
    $y = -\frac{1}{2}x + 1$

19. $x - y \leq 3,$
    $y \geq 2x,$
    $2y - x \leq 2$

20. $3y = 8$

7.5 Applications Using Linear Programming

Objective Functions and Constraints • Linear Programming

There are many real-world situations in which we need to find a greatest value (a maximum) or a least value (a minimum). For example, most businesses like to know how to make the *most* profit with the *least* expense possible. Some such problems can be solved using systems of inequalities.

Objective Functions and Constraints

Often a quantity we wish to maximize depends on two or more other quantities. For example, a gardener's profits P might depend on the number of shrubs s and the number of trees t that are planted. If the gardener makes a $10 profit from each shrub and an $18 profit from each tree, the total profit, in dollars, is given by the **objective function**

$$P = 10s + 18t.$$

Thus the gardener might be tempted to simply plant lots of trees since they yield the greater profit. This would be a good idea were it not for the fact that the number of trees and shrubs planted—and thus the total profit—is subject to the demands, or **constraints**, of the situation. For example, to improve drainage, the gardener might be required to plant at least 3 shrubs. Thus the objective function would be subject to the *constraint*

$$s \geq 3.$$

Because of limited space, the gardener might also be required to plant no more than 10 plants. This would subject the objective function to a *second* constraint:

$$s + t \leq 10.$$

Finally, the gardener might be told to spend no more than $700 on the plants. If the shrubs cost $40 each and the trees cost $100 each, the objective function is subject to a *third* constraint:

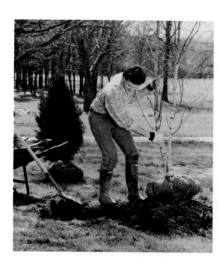

The cost of the shrubs   plus   the cost of the trees   cannot exceed $700.

$$40s \quad + \quad 100t \quad \leq \quad 700$$

In short, the gardener wishes to maximize the objective function

$$P = 10s + 18t,$$

subject to the constraints

$$s \geq 3,$$
$$s + t \leq 10,$$
$$40s + 100t \leq 700,$$
$$\left. \begin{array}{l} s \geq 0, \\ t \geq 0. \end{array} \right\} \quad \text{Because the number of trees and shrubs cannot be negative}$$

These constraints form a system of linear inequalities that can be graphed.

Linear Programming

The gardener's problem is "How many shrubs and trees should be planted, subject to the constraints listed, in order to maximize profit?" To solve such a problem, we use a result from a branch of mathematics known as **linear programming**.

The Corner Principle

Suppose an objective function $F = ax + by + c$ depends on x and y (with a, b, and c constant). Suppose also that F is subject to constraints on x and y, which form a system of linear inequalities. If F has a minimum or a maximum value, then it can be found as follows:

1. Graph the system of inequalities and find the vertices.
2. Find the value of the objective function at each vertex. The greatest and the least of those values are the maximum and the minimum of the function, respectively.
3. The ordered pair at which the maximum or minimum occurs indicates the choice of (x, y) for which that maximum or minimum occurs.

This result was proven during World War II, when linear programming was developed to help allocate troops and supplies bound for Europe.

EXAMPLE 1   Solve the gardener's problem discussed above.

SOLUTION   We are asked to maximize $P = 10s + 18t$, subject to the constraints

$$s \geq 3,$$
$$s + t \leq 10,$$
$$40s + 100t \leq 700,$$
$$s \geq 0,$$
$$t \geq 0.$$

We graph the system, using the techniques of Section 7.4. The portion of the graph that is shaded represents all pairs that satisfy the constraints. It is sometimes called the *feasible region*.

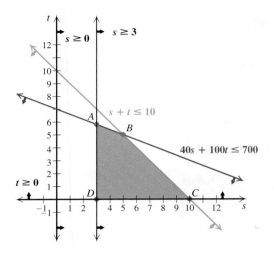

According to the corner principle, P is maximized at one of the vertices of the shaded region. To determine the coordinates of the vertices, we solve the following systems:

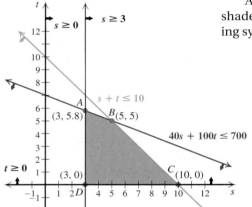

$A:$ $\left.\begin{array}{r} 40s + 100t = 700, \\ s = 3; \end{array}\right\}$ The student can verify that the solution of this system is $(3, 5.8)$. The coordinates of point A are $(3, 5.8)$.

$B:$ $\left.\begin{array}{r} s + t = 10, \\ 40s + 100t = 700; \end{array}\right\}$ The student can verify that the solution of this system is $(5, 5)$. The coordinates of point B are $(5, 5)$.

$C:$ $\left.\begin{array}{r} s + t = 10, \\ t = 0; \end{array}\right\}$ The solution of this system is $(10, 0)$. The coordinates of point C are $(10, 0)$.

$D:$ $\left.\begin{array}{r} t = 0, \\ s = 3. \end{array}\right\}$ The solution of this system is $(3, 0)$. The coordinates of point D are $(3, 0)$.

We now find the value of P at each vertex.

Vertex (s, t)	Profit $P = 10s + 18t$	
$A\ (3, 5.8)$	$10(3) + 18(5.8) = 134.4$	
$B\ (5, 5)$	$10(5) + 18(5) = 140$	← Maximum
$C\ (10, 0)$	$10(10) + 18(0) = 100$	
$D\ (3, 0)$	$10(3) + 18(0) = 30$	← Minimum

The greatest value of P occurs at $(5, 5)$. Thus profit is maximized at $140 if the gardener plants 5 shrubs and 5 trees. Incidentally, we have also shown that profit is minimized at $30 if 3 shrubs and 0 trees are planted.

TRY EXERCISE 13

EXAMPLE **2** *Grading.* For his history grade, Cy can write book summaries for 70 points each or research papers for 80 points each. He estimates that each book summary will take 9 hr and each research paper will take 15 hr and that he will have at most 120 hr to spend. He may turn in a total of no more than 12 summaries or papers. How many of each should he write in order to receive the highest score?

SOLUTION

1. **Familiarize.** Since we are looking for the number of book summaries and the number of research papers, we let b = the number of book summaries and r = the number of research papers. Cy is limited by the number of hours he can spend and by the number of summaries and papers he can turn in. These two limits are the constraints.

2. **Translate.** We organize the information in a table.

Type	Number of Points for Each	Time Required for Each	Number Written	Total Time for Each Type	Total Points for Each Type
Book summary	70	9 hr	b	$9b$	$70b$
Research paper	80	15 hr	r	$15r$	$80r$
Total			$b + r \leq 12$	$9b + 15r \leq 120$	

Because no more than 12 may be turned in

Because the time cannot exceed 120 hr

We wish to maximize the total score.

STUDENT NOTES

It is very important that you clearly label what each variable represents. It is also important to clearly label what the function is that is being maximized or minimized and how that function is evaluated.

Let T represent the total score. We see from the table that

$$T = 70b + 80r.$$

We wish to maximize T subject to the number and time constraints:

$$b + r \leq 12,$$
$$9b + 15r \leq 120,$$
$$b \geq 0,\}$$
$$r \geq 0.\}$$

We include this because the number of summaries and papers cannot be negative.

3. **Carry out.** We graph the system and evaluate T at each vertex. The graph is as follows:

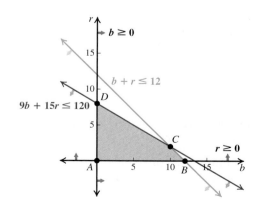

We find the coordinates of each vertex by solving a system of two linear equations. The coordinates of point A are obviously $(0, 0)$. To find the coordinates of point C, we solve the system

$$b + r = 12, \quad (1)$$
$$9b + 15r = 120. \quad (2)$$

We multiply both sides of equation (1) by -9 and add:

$$\begin{array}{r} -9b - 9r = -108 \\ 9b + 15r = 120 \\ \hline 6r = 12 \\ r = 2. \end{array}$$

Vertex (b, r)	Score $T = 70b + 80r$
A $(0, 0)$	0
B $(12, 0)$	840
C $(10, 2)$	860
D $(0, 8)$	640

Substituting, we find that $b = 10$. Thus the coordinates of C are $(10, 2)$. Point B is the intersection of $b + r = 12$ and $r = 0$, so B is $(12, 0)$. Point D is the intersection of $9b + 15r = 120$ and $b = 0$, so D is $(0, 8)$. Computing the score for each ordered pair, we obtain the table at left.

The greatest score in the table is 860, obtained when Cy writes 10 book summaries and 2 research papers.

4. **Check.** We can check that $T \leq 860$ for any other pair in the shaded region. This is left to the student.

5. **State.** In order to maximize his score, Cy should write 10 book summaries and 2 research papers.

TRY EXERCISE 19

7.5 EXERCISE SET

For Extra Help **MyMathLab** | *Math* XL PRACTICE | WATCH | DOWNLOAD

Concept Reinforcement *Complete each of the following sentences.*

1. In linear programming, the quantity we wish to maximize or minimize is given by the _____ function.

2. In linear programming, the demands arising from the given situation are known as _____.

3. To solve a linear programming problem, we make use of the _____ principle.

4. The shaded portion of a graph that represents all points that satisfy a problem's constraints is known as the _____ region.

5. In linear programming, the corners of the shaded portion of the graph are referred to as _____.

6. If it exists, the maximum value of an objective function occurs at a _____ of the feasible region.

Find the maximum and the minimum values of each objective function and the values of x and y at which they occur.

7. $F = 2x + 14y$,
   subject to
   $5x + 3y \leq 34$,
   $3x + 5y \leq 30$,
   $x \geq 0$,
   $y \geq 0$

8. $G = 7x + 8y$,
   subject to
   $3x + 2y \leq 12$,
   $2y - x \leq 4$,
   $x \geq 0$,
   $y \geq 0$

9. $P = 8x - y + 20$,
   subject to
   $6x + 8y \leq 48$,
   $0 \leq y \leq 4$,
   $0 \leq x \leq 7$

10. $Q = 24x - 3y + 52$,
    subject to
    $5x + 4y \leq 20$,
    $0 \leq y \leq 4$,
    $0 \leq x \leq 3$

11. $F = 2y - 3x$,
    subject to
    $y \leq 2x + 1$,
    $y \geq -2x + 3$,
    $x \leq 3$

12. $G = 5x + 2y + 4$,
    subject to
    $y \leq 2x + 1$,
    $y \geq -x + 3$,
    $x \leq 5$

13. *Lunch-time profits.* Art sells gumbo and sandwiches. To stay in business, Art must sell at least 10 orders of gumbo and 30 sandwiches each day. Because of limited space, no more than 40 orders of gumbo or 70 sandwiches can be made. The total number of orders cannot exceed 90. If profit is $1.65 per gumbo order and $1.05 per sandwich, how many of each item should Art sell in order to maximize profit?

14. *Gas mileage.* Caroline owns a car and a moped. She has at most 12 gal of gasoline to be used between the car and the moped. The car's tank holds at most 18 gal and the moped's 3 gal. The mileage for the car is 20 mpg and for the moped is 100 mpg. How many gallons of gasoline should each vehicle use if Caroline wants to travel as far as possible? What is the maximum number of miles?

15. *Photo albums.* Photo Perfect prints pages of photographs for albums. A page containing 4 photos costs $3 and a page containing 6 photos costs $5. Ann can spend no more than $90 for photo pages of her recent vacation, and can use no more than 20 pages in her album. What combination of 4-photo pages and 6-photo pages will maximize the number of photos she can display? What is the maximum number of photos that she can display?

16. *Milling.* Picture Rocks Lumber can convert logs into either lumber or plywood. In a given week, the mill can turn out 400 units of production, of which 100 units of lumber and 150 units of plywood are required by regular customers. The profit on a unit of lumber is $20 and on a unit of plywood is $30. How many units of each type should the mill produce in order to maximize profit?

Aha! **17.** *Investing.* Rosa is planning to invest up to $40,000 in corporate or municipal bonds, or both. She must invest from $6000 to $22,000 in corporate bonds, and she refuses to invest more than $30,000 in municipal bonds. The interest on corporate bonds is 8% and on municipal bonds is $7\frac{1}{2}\%$. This is simple interest for one year. How much should Rosa invest in each type of bond in order to earn the most interest? What is the maximum interest?

18. *Investing.* Jamaal is planning to invest up to $22,000 in City Bank or the Southwick Credit Union, or both. He wants to invest at least $2000 but no more than $14,000 in City Bank. Because of insurance limitations, he will invest no more than $15,000 in the Southwick Credit Union. The interest in City Bank is 6% and in the credit union is $6\frac{1}{2}\%$. This is simple interest for one year. How much should Jamaal invest in each bank in order to earn the most interest? What is the maximum interest?

19. *Test scores.* Corinna is taking a test in which short-answer questions are worth 10 points each and essay questions are worth 15 points each. She estimates that it will take 3 min to answer each short-answer question and 6 min to answer each essay question. The total time allowed is 60 min, and no more than 16 questions can be answered. Assuming that all her answers are correct, how many questions of each type should Corinna answer to get the best score?

20. *Test scores.* Edy is about to take a test that contains short-answer questions worth 4 points each and word problems worth 7 points each. Edy must do at least 5 short-answer questions, but time restricts doing more than 10. She must do at least 3 word problems, but time restricts doing more than 10. Edy can do no more than 18 questions in total. How many of each type of question must Edy do in order to maximize her score? What is this maximum score?

21. *Grape growing.* Auggie's vineyard consists of 240 acres upon which he wishes to plant Merlot and Cabernet grapes. Profit per acre of Merlot is $400 and profit per acre of Cabernet is $300. Furthermore, the total number of hours of labor available during the harvest season is 3200. Each acre of Merlot requires 20 hr of labor and each acre of Cabernet requires 10 hr of labor. Determine how the land should be divided between Merlot and Cabernet in order to maximize profit.

22. *Coffee blending.* The Coffee Peddler has 1440 lb of Sumatran coffee and 700 lb of Kona coffee. A batch of Hawaiian Blend requires 8 lb of Kona and 12 lb of Sumatran, and yields a profit of $90. A batch of Classic Blend requires 4 lb of Kona and 16 lb of Sumatran, and yields a $55 profit. How many batches of each kind should be made in order to maximize profit? What is the maximum profit? (*Hint*: Organize the information in a table.)

23. *Nutrition.* Becca is supposed to have at least 15 mg but no more than 45 mg of iron each day. She should also have at least 1500 mg but no more than 2500 mg of calcium per day. One serving of goat cheese contains 1 mg of iron, 500 mg of calcium, and 264 calories. One serving of hazelnuts contains 5 mg of iron, 100 mg of calcium, and 628 calories. How many servings of goat cheese and how many servings of hazelnuts should Becca eat in order to meet the daily requirements of iron and calcium but minimize the total number of calories?

24. *Textile production.* It takes Cosmic Stitching 2 hr of cutting and 4 hr of sewing to make a knit suit. To make a worsted suit, it takes 4 hr of cutting and 2 hr of sewing. At most 20 hr per day are available for cutting and at most 16 hr per day are available for sewing. The profit on a knit suit is $68 and on a worsted suit is $62. How many of each kind of suit should be made in order to maximize profit?

25. Before a student begins work in this section, what three sections of the text would you suggest he or she study? Why?

26. What does the use of the word "constraint" in this section have in common with the use of the word in everyday speech?

Skill Review

Review function notation and domains of functions (Sections 5.1 and 5.2).

27. If $f(x) = 4x - 7$, find $f(a) + h$. [5.1]

28. If $f(x) = 4x - 7$, find $f(a + h)$. [5.1]

Find the domain of f.

29. $f(x) = \dfrac{x - 5}{2x + 1}$ [5.2], [7.2]

30. $f(x) = \dfrac{3x}{x^2 + 1}$ [5.2]

31. $f(x) = \sqrt{2x + 8}$ [7.1]

32. $f(x) = \dfrac{3x}{x^2 - 1}$ [5.2], [7.2]

Synthesis

33. Explain how Exercises 17 and 18 can be answered by logical reasoning without linear programming.

34. Write a linear programming problem for a classmate to solve. Devise the problem so that profit must be maximized subject to at least two (nontrivial) constraints.

35. *Airplane production.* Alpha Tours has two types of airplanes, the T3 and the S5, and contracts requiring accommodations for a minimum of 2000 first-class, 1500 tourist-class, and 2400 economy-class passengers. The T3 costs $30 per mile to operate and can accommodate 40 first-class, 40 tourist-class, and 120 economy-class passengers, whereas the S5 costs $25 per mile to operate and can accommodate 80 first-class, 30 tourist-class, and 40 economy-class passengers. How many of each type of airplane should be used in order to minimize the operating cost?

36. *Airplane production.* A new airplane, the T4, is now available, having an operating cost of $37.50 per mile and accommodating 40 first-class, 40 tourist-class, and 80 economy-class passengers. If the T3 of Exercise 35 were replaced with the T4, how many S5's and how many T4's would be needed in order to minimize the operating cost?

37. *Furniture production.* P. J. Edward Furniture Design produces chairs and sofas. The chairs require 20 ft of wood, 1 lb of foam rubber, and 2 sq yd of fabric. The sofas require 100 ft of wood, 50 lb of foam rubber, and 20 sq yd of fabric. The company has 1900 ft of wood, 500 lb of foam rubber, and 240 sq yd of fabric. The chairs can be sold for $80 each and the sofas for $1200 each. How many of each should be produced in order to maximize income?

Study Summary

KEY TERMS AND CONCEPTS

EXAMPLES

SECTION 7.1: INEQUALITIES AND DOMAIN

Inequalities can be solved graphically by determining the x-values for which one graph lies above or below another.

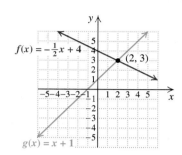

From the graph above, we can read the solution sets of the following inequalities.

Inequality	Solution Set
$f(x) < g(x)$	$\{x \mid x > 2\}$, or $(2, \infty)$
$f(x) \leq g(x)$	$\{x \mid x \geq 2\}$, or $[2, \infty)$
$f(x) > g(x)$	$\{x \mid x < 2\}$, or $(-\infty, 2)$
$f(x) \geq g(x)$	$\{x \mid x \leq 2\}$, or $(-\infty, 2]$

Only nonnegative numbers have square roots that are real numbers.

Find the domain of f if $f(x) = \sqrt{2x - 3}$.

$2x - 3 \geq 0$ $2x - 3$ must be nonnegative

$2x \geq 3$ Adding 3 to both sides

$x \geq \dfrac{3}{2}$ Dividing both sides by 2

The domain of f is $\left\{x \mid x \geq \frac{3}{2}\right\}$, or $\left[\frac{3}{2}, \infty\right)$.

SECTION 7.2: INTERSECTIONS, UNIONS, AND COMPOUND INEQUALITIES

A **conjunction** consists of two or more sentences joined by the word *and*. The solution set of the conjunction is the **intersection** of the solution sets of the individual sentences.

$$-4 \leq x - 1 \leq 5$$

$-4 \leq x - 1$ *and* $x - 1 \leq 5$

$-3 \leq x$ *and* $x \leq 6$

The solution set is $\{x \mid -3 \leq x \leq 6\}$, or $[-3, 6]$.

A **disjunction** consists of two or more sentences joined by the word *or*. The solution set of the disjunction is the **union** of the solution sets of the individual sentences.

$$2x + 9 < 1 \quad or \quad 5x - 2 \geq 3$$
$$2x < -8 \quad or \quad 5x \geq 5$$
$$x < -4 \quad or \quad x \geq 1$$

The solution set is $\{x \mid x < -4 \ or \ x \geq 1\}$, or $(-\infty, -4) \cup [1, \infty)$.

SECTION 7.3: ABSOLUTE-VALUE EQUATIONS AND INEQUALITIES

The Absolute-Value Principles for Equations and Inequalities

For any positive number p and any algebraic expression X:

a) The solutions of $|X| = p$ are those numbers that satisfy
$$X = -p \quad or \quad X = p.$$

b) The solutions of $|X| < p$ are those numbers that satisfy
$$-p < X < p.$$

c) The solutions of $|X| > p$ are those numbers that satisfy
$$X < -p \quad or \quad p < X.$$

If $|X| = 0$, then $X = 0$. If p is negative, then $|X| = p$ and $|X| < p$ have no solution, and any value of X will satisfy $|X| > p$.

$$|x + 3| = 4$$
$$x + 3 = 4 \quad or \quad x + 3 = -4 \qquad \text{Using part (a)}$$
$$x = 1 \quad or \qquad x = -7$$

The solution set is $\{-7, 1\}$.

$$|x + 3| < 4$$
$$-4 < x + 3 < 4 \qquad \text{Using part (b)}$$
$$-7 < x < 1$$

The solution set is $\{x \mid -7 < x < 1\}$, or $(-7, 1)$.

$$|x + 3| \geq 4$$
$$x + 3 \leq -4 \quad or \quad 4 \leq x + 3 \qquad \text{Using part (c)}$$
$$x \leq -7 \quad or \quad 1 \leq x$$

The solution set is $\{x \mid x \leq -7 \ or \ x \geq 1\}$, or $(-\infty, -7] \cup [1, \infty)$.

SECTION 7.4: INEQUALITIES IN TWO VARIABLES

To graph a linear inequality:

1. Graph the **boundary line**. Draw a dashed line if the inequality symbol is $<$ or $>$, and draw a solid line if the inequality symbol is $\leq$ or $\geq$.

2. Determine which side of the boundary line contains the solution set, and shade that **half-plane**.

Graph: $x + y < -1$.

1. Graph $x + y = -1$ using a dashed line.

2. Choose a test point not on the line: $(0, 0)$.

$$\frac{x + y < -1}{0 + 0 \ | \ -1}$$
$$0 \overset{?}{<} -1 \quad \text{FALSE}$$

Since $0 < -1$ is false, shade the half-plane that does *not* contain $(0, 0)$.

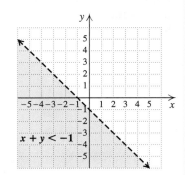

SECTION 7.5: APPLICATIONS USING LINEAR PROGRAMMING

The Corner Principle

The maximum or minimum value of an **objective function** over a *feasible region* is the maximum or minimum value of the function at a **vertex** of that region.

Maximize $F = x + 2y$ subject to

$$x + y \leq 5,$$
$$x \geq 0,$$
$$y \geq 1.$$

1. Graph the feasible region.
2. Find the value of F at the vertices.

Vertex	$F = x + 2y$
$(0, 1)$	2
$(0, 5)$	10
$(4, 1)$	6

⟵ The maximum value of F is 10.

Review Exercises: Chapter 7

↪ *Concept Reinforcement* *Classify each statement as either true or false.*

1. If x cannot exceed 10, then $x \leq 10$. [7.1]

2. It is always true that if $a > b$, then $ac > bc$. [7.1]

3. The solution of $|3x - 5| \leq 8$ is a closed interval. [7.3]

4. The inequality $2 < 5x + 1 < 9$ is equivalent to $2 < 5x + 1$ *or* $5x + 1 < 9$. [7.2]

5. The solution set of a disjunction is the union of two solution sets. [7.2]

6. The equation $|x| = r$ has no solution when r is negative. [7.3]

7. $|f(x)| > 3$ is equivalent to $f(x) < -3$ *or* $f(x) > 3$. [7.3]

8. A test point is used to determine whether the line in a linear inequality is drawn solid or dashed. [7.4]

9. The graph of a system of linear inequalities is always a half-plane. [7.4]

10. The corner principle states that every objective function has a maximum or minimum value. [7.5]

Solve algebraically. [7.1]

11. $-6x - 5 < 4$

12. $-\dfrac{1}{2}x - \dfrac{1}{4} > \dfrac{1}{2} - \dfrac{1}{4}x$

13. $0.3y - 7 < 2.6y + 15$

14. $-2(x - 5) \geq 6(x + 7) - 12$

Solve graphically. [7.1]

15. $x - 2 < 3$

16. $4 - 3x > 1$

17. $x - 1 \leq 2x + 3$

18. $\dfrac{1}{2}x \geq \dfrac{1}{3}x + 1$

19. Let $f(x) = 3x + 2$ and $g(x) = 10 - x$. Find all values of x for which $f(x) \leq g(x)$. [7.1]

Solve. [7.1]

20. Mariah has two offers for a summer job. She can work in a sandwich shop for $8.40 an hour, or she can do carpentry work for $16 an hour. In order to do the carpentry work, she must spend $950 for tools. For how many hours must Mariah work in order for carpentry to be more profitable than the sandwich shop?

21. Clay is going to invest $9000, part at 3% and the rest at 3.5%. What is the most he can invest at 3% and still be guaranteed $300 in interest each year?

22. Find the intersection:
$$\{a, b, c, d\} \cap \{a, c, e, f, g\}. \quad [7.2]$$

23. Find the union:
$$\{a, b, c, d\} \cup \{a, c, e, f, g\}. \quad [7.2]$$

Graph and write interval notation. [7.2]

24. $x \le 2$ *and* $x > -3$

25. $x \le 3$ *or* $x > -5$

Solve and graph each solution set. [7.2]

26. $-3 < x + 5 \le 5$

27. $-15 < -4x - 5 < 0$

28. $3x < -9$ *or* $-5x < -5$

29. $2x + 5 < -17$ *or* $-4x + 10 \le 34$

30. $2x + 7 \le -5$ *or* $x + 7 \ge 15$

31. $f(x) < -5$ *or* $f(x) > 5$, where $f(x) = 3 - 5x$

For $f(x)$ as given, use interval notation to write the domain of f.

32. $f(x) = \dfrac{2x}{x + 3}$ [7.2]

33. $f(x) = \sqrt{5x - 10}$ [7.1]

34. $f(x) = \sqrt{1 - 4x}$ [7.1]

Solve. [7.3]

35. $|x| = 11$

36. $|t| \ge 21$

37. $|x - 8| = 3$

38. $|4a + 3| < 11$

39. $|3x - 4| \ge 15$

40. $|2x + 5| = |x - 9|$

41. $|5n + 6| = -11$

42. $\left|\dfrac{x + 4}{6}\right| \le 2$

43. $2|x - 5| - 7 > 3$

44. $19 - 3|x + 1| \ge 4$

45. Let $f(x) = |8x - 3|$. Find all x for which $f(x) < 0$. [7.3]

46. Graph $x - 2y \ge 6$ on a plane. [7.4]

Graph each system of inequalities. Find the coordinates of any vertices formed. [7.4]

47. $x + 3y > -1,$
$x + 3y < 4$

48. $x - 3y \le 3,$
$x + 3y \ge 9,$
$y \le 6$

49. Find the maximum and the minimum values of
$$F = 3x + y + 4$$
subject to
$$y \le 2x + 1,$$
$$x \le 7,$$
$$y \ge 3. \qquad [7.5]$$

50. Custom Computers has two manufacturing plants. The Oregon plant cannot produce more than 60 computers per week, while the Ohio plant cannot produce more than 120 computers per week. The Electronics Outpost sells at least 160 Custom computers each week. It costs $40 to ship a computer to The Electronics Outpost from the Oregon plant and $25 to ship from the Ohio plant. How many computers should be shipped from each plant in order to minimize cost? [7.5]

Synthesis

51. Explain in your own words why $|X| = p$ has two solutions when p is positive and no solution when p is negative. [7.3]

52. Explain why the graph of the solution of a system of linear inequalities is the intersection, not the union, of the individual graphs. [7.4]

53. Solve: $|2x + 5| \le |x + 3|$. [7.3]

54. Classify as true or false: If $x < 3$, then $x^2 < 9$. If false, give an example showing why. [7.1]

55. Super Lock manufactures brass doorknobs with a 2.5-in. diameter and a ± 0.003-in. manufacturing tolerance, or allowable variation in diameter. Write the tolerance as an inequality with absolute value. [7.3]

Test: Chapter 7

Step-by-step test solutions are found on the video CD in the front of this book.

Solve algebraically.

1. $-4y - 3 \geq 5$

2. $3(7 - x) < 2x + 5$

3. $-2(3x - 1) - 5 \geq 6x - 4(3 - x)$

Solve graphically.

4. $3 - x < 2$

5. $2x - 3 \geq x + 1$

6. Let $f(x) = -5x - 1$ and $g(x) = -9x + 3$. Find all values of x for which $f(x) > g(x)$.

7. Dani can rent a van for either $80 with unlimited mileage or $45 with 100 free miles and an extra charge of 40¢ for each mile over 100. For what numbers of miles traveled would the unlimited mileage plan save Dani money?

8. A refrigeration repair company charges $80 for the first half-hour of work and $60 for each additional hour. Blue Mountain Camp has budgeted $200 to repair its walk-in cooler. For what lengths of a service call will the budget not be exceeded?

9. Find the intersection:
   $\{a, e, i, o, u\} \cap \{a, b, c, d, e\}$.

10. Find the union:
   $\{a, e, i, o, u\} \cup \{a, b, c, d, e\}$.

For $f(x)$ as given, use interval notation to write the domain of f.

11. $f(x) = \sqrt{6 - 3x}$

12. $f(x) = \dfrac{x}{x - 7}$

Solve and graph each solution set.

13. $-5 < 4x + 1 \leq 3$

14. $3x - 2 < 7 \text{ or } x - 2 > 4$

15. $-3x > 12 \text{ or } 4x \geq -10$

16. $1 \leq 3 - 2x \leq 9$

17. $|n| = 15$

18. $|a| > 5$

19. $|3x - 1| < 7$

20. $|-5t - 3| \geq 10$

21. $|2 - 5x| = -12$

22. $g(x) < -3 \text{ or } g(x) > 3$, where $g(x) = 4 - 2x$

23. Let $f(x) = |2x - 1|$ and $g(x) = |2x + 7|$. Find all values of x for which $f(x) = g(x)$.

24. Graph $y \leq 2x + 1$ on a plane.

Graph the system of inequalities. Find the coordinates of any vertices formed.

25. $x + y \geq 3,$
    $x - y \geq 5$

26. $2y - x \geq -7,$
    $2y + 3x \leq 15,$
    $y \leq 0,$
    $x \leq 0$

27. Find the maximum and the minimum values of
    $$F = 5x + 3y$$
    subject to
    $$x + y \leq 15,$$
    $$1 \leq x \leq 6,$$
    $$0 \leq y \leq 12.$$

28. Swift Cuts makes $12 on each manicure and $18 on each haircut. A manicure takes 30 min and a haircut takes 50 min, and there are 5 stylists who each work 6 hr a day. If the salon can schedule 50 appointments a day, how many should be manicures and how many haircuts in order to maximize profit? What is the maximum profit?

Synthesis

Solve. Write the solution set using interval notation.

29. $|2x - 5| \leq 7 \text{ and } |x - 2| \geq 2$

30. $7x < 8 - 3x < 6 + 7x$

31. Write an absolute-value inequality for which the interval shown is the solution.

Cumulative Review: Chapters 1–7

Simplify. Do not leave negative exponents in your answers.

1. $3 + 24 \div 2^2 \cdot 3 - (6 - 7)$

2. $3c - [8 - 2(1 - c)]$

3. -10^{-2}

4. $(3xy^{-4})(-2x^3y)$

5. $\left(\dfrac{18a^2b^{-1}}{12a^{-1}b}\right)^2$

6. $\dfrac{2x - 10}{x^3 - 125}$ [4.1]

Perform the indicated operations.

7. $(x - 5)(x + 5)$

8. $(3n - 2)(5n + 7)$

9. $\dfrac{1}{x + 5} - \dfrac{1}{x - 5}$ [4.4]

10. $\dfrac{x^2 - 3x}{2x^2 - x - 3} \div \dfrac{x^3}{x^2 - 2x - 3}$ [4.2]

Factor.

11. $25x^2 - 50x + 25$ [3.4]

12. $8mn + 14n - 12m - 21$ [3.1]

13. $8t^2 + 800$ [3.1]

Solve.

14. $3(x - 2) = 14 - x$ [1.2]

15. $x - 2 < 6 \text{ or } 2x + 1 > 5$ [7.2]

16. $x^2 - 2x - 3 = 5$ [3.7]

17. $\dfrac{3}{x + 1} = \dfrac{x}{4}$ [4.6]

18. $y = \frac{1}{2}x - 7,$
$2x - 4y = 3$ [6.2]

19. $x + 3y = 8,$
$2x - 3y = 7$ [6.2]

20. $|2x - 1| = 8$ [7.3]

21. $9(x - 3) - 4x < 2 - (3 - x)$ [1.6], [7.1]

22. $|4t| > 12$ [7.3]

23. $|3x - 2| \le 8$ [7.3]

Graph on a plane.

24. $y = \frac{2}{3}x - 4$ [2.6]

25. $x = -3$ [2.3]

26. $3x - y = 3$ [2.3]

27. $x + y \ge -2$ [7.4]

28. $f(x) = -x + 1$ [5.3]

29. $x - 2y > 4,$
$x + 2y \ge -2$ [7.4]

30. Find the slope and the y-intercept of the line given by $4x - 9y = 18$. [2.6]

31. Write a slope–intercept equation for the line with slope -7 and containing the point $(-3, -4)$. [2.7]

32. Find an equation of the line with y-intercept $(0, 4)$ and perpendicular to the line given by $3x + 2y = 1$. [2.6]

33. For the graph of f shown, determine the domain and the range of f. [5.2]

34. Determine the domain of the function given by $f(x) = \dfrac{3}{2x + 5}$. [5.2], [7.2]

35. Find $g(-2)$ if $g(x) = 3x^2 - 5x$. [5.1]

36. Find $(f - g)(x)$ if $f(x) = x^2 + 3x$ and $g(x) = 9 - 3x$. [5.4]

37. Graph the solution set of $-3 \le f(x) \le 2$, where $f(x) = 1 - x$. [7.2]

38. Find the domain of h/g if $h(x) = \dfrac{1}{x}$ and $g(x) = 3x - 1$. [5.4]

39. Solve for t: $at - dt = c$. [1.3]

40. The Baqueira, a resort in Spain, uses 549 snow cannons to make snow for its 4344 acres of ski runs. How many snow cannons should a resort containing 1448 acres of runs use in order to make a comparable amount of snow? [4.7]
Sources: www.bluebookski.com

41. *Water usage.* In dry climates, it takes about 11,600 gal of water to produce a pound of beef and a pound of wheat. The pound of beef requires 7000 more gallons of water than the pound of wheat. How much water does it take to produce each? [6.3]
Source: *The Wall Street Journal,* 1/28/08

42. *Book sales.* U.S. sales of books and maps were $34.6 billion in 2001 and $41.4 billion in 2004. Let $b(t)$ represent U.S. book sales t years after 2001. [5.3]
Source: *Bureau of Economic Analysis*

  a) Find a linear function that fits the data.
  b) Use the function from part (a) to predict U.S. book sales in 2010.
  c) In what year will U.S. book sales be $50 billion?

43. *Fundraising.* Michelle is planning a fundraising dinner for Happy Hollow Children's Camp. The banquet facility charges a rental fee of $1500, but will waive the rental fee if more than $6000 is spent for catering. Michelle knows that 150 people will attend the dinner. [7.1]

  a) How much should each dinner cost in order for the rental fee to be waived?
  b) For what costs per person will the total cost (including the rental fee) exceed $6000?

44. *Perimeter of a rectangle.* The perimeter of a rectangle is 32 cm. If five times the width equals three times the length, what are the dimensions of the rectangle? [6.3]

45. *Utility bills.* One month Lori and Tony spent $920 for electricity, rent, and cell phone. The electric bill was $\frac{1}{4}$ of the rent, and the phone bill was $40 less than the electric bill. How much was the rent? [6.5]

46. *Banking.* Banks charge a fee to a customer whose checking account does not contain enough money to pay for a debit-card purchase or a written check. These insufficient-funds fees totaled $35 billion in the United States in a recent year. This was 70% of the total fee income of banks. What was the total fee income of banks in that year? [1.5]

47. *Catering.* Dan charges $35 per person for a vegetarian meal and $40 per person for a steak dinner. For one event, he served 28 dinners for a total cost of $1060. How many dinners were vegetarian and how many were steak? [6.3]

Synthesis

48. If $(2, 6)$ and $(-1, 5)$ are two solutions of $f(x) = mx + b$, find m and b. [6.2]

49. Find k such that the line containing $(-2, k)$ and $(3, 8)$ is parallel to the line containing $(1, 6)$ and $(4, -2)$. [2.6]

50. Use interval notation to write the domain of the function given by

$$f(x) = \frac{\sqrt{x + 4}}{x}. \quad [7.2]$$

51. Simplify: $\dfrac{2^{a-1} \cdot 2^{4a}}{2^{3(-2a+5)}}$.

Exponents and Radicals

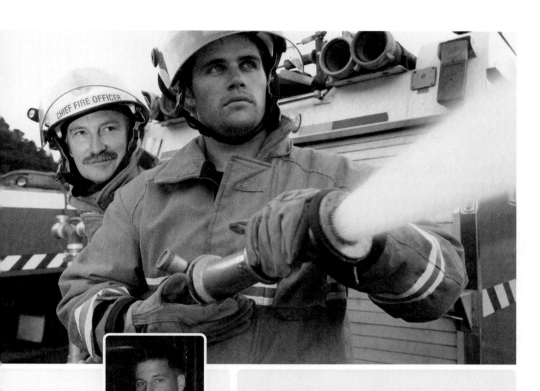

MICHAEL MANOLAKIS
FIREFIGHTER
Boston, Massachusetts

Firefighters use math every day. Hosing down a fire may seem simple, but there are considerations to take into account when getting water from its source to the end of the hose where the "pipeman" is attacking the fire. For example, the safest force or psi (pounds per square inch) needed at the tip of a hose is determined by its size. The safest force needed at the tip of a $1\frac{3}{4}$-in. line is 120 psi. To achieve this pressure, we must consider the distance and height of the hose line from the source of water. These two factors are necessary to accurately calculate and deliver the appropriate psi at the tip.

AN APPLICATION

The velocity of water flow, in feet per second, from a nozzle is given by

$$v(p) = 12.1\sqrt{p},$$

where p is the nozzle pressure, in pounds per square inch. Find the nozzle pressure if the water flow is 100 feet per second.

Source: Houston Fire Department Continuing Education

This problem appears as Exercise 65 in Section 8.6.

In this chapter, we learn about square roots, cube roots, fourth roots, and so on. These roots can be expressed in radical notation and appear in both radical expressions and radical equations. Exponents that are fractions are also studied and will ease some of our work with radicals. The chapter closes with an introduction to the complex-number system.

8.1　Radical Expressions and Functions

Square Roots and Square-Root Functions　•　Expressions of the Form $\sqrt{a^2}$　•　Cube Roots　•　Odd and Even nth Roots

STUDY SKILLS

Advance Planning Pays Off

The best way to prepare for a final exam is to do so over a period of at least two weeks. First review each chapter, studying the words, formulas, problems, properties, and procedures in the Study Summaries and Review Exercises. Then retake your quizzes and tests. If you miss any questions, spend extra time reviewing the corresponding topics. Watch the videos on DVD that accompany the text or use the accompanying tutorial resources. Also consider participating in a study group or attending a tutoring or review session.

In this section, we consider roots, such as square roots and cube roots. We look at the symbolism that is used and ways in which symbols can be manipulated to get equivalent expressions. All of this will be important in problem solving.

Square Roots and Square-Root Functions

When a number is multiplied by itself, we say that the number is squared. Often we need to know what number was squared in order to produce some value a. If such a number can be found, we call that number a *square root* of a.

> **Square Root**
> The number c is a *square root* of a if $c^2 = a$.

For example,

　9 has -3 and 3 as square roots because $(-3)^2 = 9$ and $3^2 = 9$.

　25 has -5 and 5 as square roots because $(-5)^2 = 25$ and $5^2 = 25$.

　-4 does not have a real-number square root because there is no real number c for which $c^2 = -4$.

Note that every positive number has two square roots, whereas 0 has only itself as a square root. Negative numbers do not have real-number square roots, although later in this chapter we introduce the *complex-number* system in which such square roots do exist.

EXAMPLE　1　Find the two square roots of 36.

SOLUTION　The square roots are 6 and -6, because $6^2 = 36$ and $(-6)^2 = 36$.

▶ TRY EXERCISE　9

STUDENT NOTES

It is important to remember the difference between *the* square root of 9 and *a* square root of 9. *A* square root of 9 means either 3 or -3, whereas *the* square root of 9, denoted $\sqrt{9}$, means the principal square root of 9, or 3.

Whenever we refer to *the* square root of a number, we mean the nonnegative square root of that number. This is often referred to as the *principal square root* of the number.

> **Principal Square Root**
> The *principal square root* of a nonnegative number is its nonnegative square root. The symbol $\sqrt{}$ is called a *radical sign* and is used to indicate the principal square root of the number over which it appears.

EXAMPLE 2

Simplify each of the following.

a) $\sqrt{25}$ **b)** $\sqrt{\dfrac{25}{64}}$ **c)** $-\sqrt{64}$ **d)** $\sqrt{0.0049}$

SOLUTION

a) $\sqrt{25} = 5$ — $\sqrt{}$ indicates the principal square root. Note that $\sqrt{25} \neq -5$.

b) $\sqrt{\dfrac{25}{64}} = \dfrac{5}{8}$ — Since $\left(\dfrac{5}{8}\right)^2 = \dfrac{25}{64}$

c) $-\sqrt{64} = -8$ — Since $\sqrt{64} = 8, -\sqrt{64} = -8.$

d) $\sqrt{0.0049} = 0.07$ — $(0.07)(0.07) = 0.0049.$ Note too that

$$\sqrt{0.0049} = \sqrt{\dfrac{49}{10,000}} = \dfrac{7}{100}.$$

 TRY EXERCISE 19

TECHNOLOGY CONNECTION

To approximate $\sqrt{5}$, most calculators require you to press either ⑤ √ or √ ⑤ ENTER. Most calculators that require √ to be pressed first display a left parenthesis with the radical sign on the viewing screen. You should enter a right parenthesis to indicate the end of the radicand. Some calculators will assume a right parenthesis at the end of an expression if none is entered.

In addition to being read as "the principal square root of a," $\sqrt{a}$ is also read as "the square root of a," "root a," or "radical a." Any expression in which a radical sign appears is called a *radical expression*. The following are radical expressions:

$$\sqrt{5}, \quad \sqrt{a}, \quad -\sqrt{3x}, \quad \sqrt{\dfrac{y^2 + 7}{y}}, \quad \sqrt{x} + 8.$$

The expression under the radical sign is called the **radicand**. In the expressions above, the radicands are 5, a, $3x$, $(y^2 + 7)/y$, and x, respectively.

Values for square roots found on calculators are, for the most part, approximations. For example, a calculator will show a number like

2.23606798

for $\sqrt{5}$. The exact value of $\sqrt{5}$ is not given by any repeating or terminating decimal. In general, for any whole number a that is not a perfect square, $\sqrt{a}$ is a nonterminating, nonrepeating decimal or an *irrational number*.

The square-root function, given by

$$f(x) = \sqrt{x},$$

has $[0, \infty)$ as its domain and $[0, \infty)$ as its range. We can draw its graph by selecting convenient values for x and calculating the corresponding outputs. Once these ordered pairs have been graphed, a smooth curve can be drawn.

$$f(x) = \sqrt{x}$$

x	$\sqrt{x}$	$(x, f(x))$
0	0	$(0, 0)$
1	1	$(1, 1)$
4	2	$(4, 2)$
9	3	$(9, 3)$

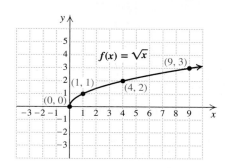

EXAMPLE 3

For each function, find the indicated function value.

a) $f(x) = \sqrt{3x - 2}$; $f(1)$ **b)** $g(z) = -\sqrt{6z + 4}$; $g(3)$

SOLUTION

a) $f(1) = \sqrt{3 \cdot 1 - 2}$ — Substituting

$\quad = \sqrt{1} = 1$ — Simplifying

b) $g(3) = -\sqrt{6 \cdot 3 + 4}$ Substituting

$= -\sqrt{22}$ Simplifying. This answer is exact.

≈ -4.69041576 Using a calculator to write an approximation

> **TRY EXERCISE** 35

Expressions of the Form $\sqrt{a^2}$

As the next example shows, $\sqrt{a^2}$ does not always simplify to a.

EXAMPLE 4   Evaluate $\sqrt{a^2}$ for the following values: **(a)** 5; **(b)** 0; **(c)** −5.

SOLUTION

a) $\sqrt{5^2} = \sqrt{25} = 5$ — Same

b) $\sqrt{0^2} = \sqrt{0} = 0$ — Same

c) $\sqrt{(-5)^2} = \sqrt{25} = 5$ — Opposites   Note that $\sqrt{(-5)^2} \neq -5$.

You may have noticed that evaluating $\sqrt{a^2}$ is just like evaluating $|a|$.

> **Simplifying $\sqrt{a^2}$**
>
> For any real number a,
> $$\sqrt{a^2} = |a|.$$
> (The principal square root of a^2 is the absolute value of a.)

When a radicand is the square of a variable expression, like $(x + 5)^2$ or $36t^2$, absolute-value signs are needed when simplifying. We use absolute-value signs unless we know that the expression being squared is nonnegative. This ensures that our result is never negative.

EXAMPLE 5   Simplify each expression. Assume that the variable can represent any real number.

a) $\sqrt{(x + 1)^2}$ **b)** $\sqrt{x^2 - 8x + 16}$

c) $\sqrt{a^8}$ **d)** $\sqrt{t^6}$

SOLUTION

a) $\sqrt{(x + 1)^2} = |x + 1|$ Since $x + 1$ can be negative (for example, if $x = -3$), absolute-value notation is required.

b) $\sqrt{x^2 - 8x + 16} = \sqrt{(x - 4)^2} = |x - 4|$ Since $x - 4$ can be negative, absolute-value notation is required.

c) Note that $(a^4)^2 = a^8$ and that a^4 is never negative. Thus,

$$\sqrt{a^8} = a^4.$$ Absolute-value notation is unnecessary here.

TECHNOLOGY CONNECTION

To see the necessity of absolute-value signs, let y_1 represent the left side and y_2 the right side of each of the following equations. Then use a graph or table to determine whether these equations are true.

1. $\sqrt{x^2} \overset{?}{=} x$
2. $\sqrt{x^2} \overset{?}{=} |x|$
3. $x \overset{?}{=} |x|$

d) Note that $(t^3)^2 = t^6$. Thus,

$$\sqrt{t^6} = |t^3|.$$ Since t^3 can be negative, absolute-value notation is required.

TRY EXERCISE 43

If we assume that the expression being squared is nonnegative, then absolute-value notation is not necessary.

EXAMPLE 6   Simplify each expression. Assume that no radicands were formed by squaring negative quantities.

a) $\sqrt{y^2}$ 　　　　　**b)** $\sqrt{a^{10}}$ 　　　　　**c)** $\sqrt{9x^2 - 6x + 1}$

SOLUTION

a) $\sqrt{y^2} = y$ We assume that y is nonnegative, so no absolute-value notation is necessary. When y is negative, $\sqrt{y^2} \neq y$.

b) $\sqrt{a^{10}} = a^5$ Assuming that a^5 is nonnegative. Note that $(a^5)^2 = a^{10}$.

c) $\sqrt{9x^2 - 6x + 1} = \sqrt{(3x - 1)^2} = 3x - 1$ Assuming that $3x - 1$ is nonnegative

TRY EXERCISE 69

Cube Roots

We often need to know what number cubed produces a certain value. When such a number is found, we say that we have found a *cube root*. For example,

2 is the cube root of 8 because $2^3 = 2 \cdot 2 \cdot 2 = 8$;

-4 is the cube root of -64 because $(-4)^3 = (-4)(-4)(-4) = -64$.

> **Cube Root**
>
> The number c is the *cube root* of a if $c^3 = a$. In symbols, we write $\sqrt[3]{a}$ to denote the cube root of a.

Each real number has only one real-number cube root. The cube-root function, given by

$$f(x) = \sqrt[3]{x},$$

has $\mathbb{R}$ as its domain and $\mathbb{R}$ as its range. To draw its graph, we select convenient values for x and calculate the corresponding outputs. Once these ordered pairs have been graphed, a smooth curve is drawn. Note that the cube root of a positive number is positive, and the cube root of a negative number is negative.

$$f(x) = \sqrt[3]{x}$$

x	$\sqrt[3]{x}$	$(x, f(x))$
0	0	$(0, 0)$
1	1	$(1, 1)$
8	2	$(8, 2)$
-1	-1	$(-1, -1)$
-8	-2	$(-8, -2)$

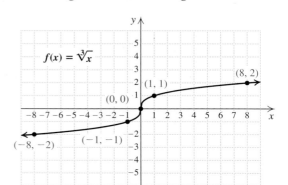

EXAMPLE 7 For each function, find the indicated function value.

a) $f(y) = \sqrt[3]{y}$; $f(125)$

b) $g(x) = \sqrt[3]{x-1}$; $g(-26)$

SOLUTION

a) $f(125) = \sqrt[3]{125} = 5$ Since $5 \cdot 5 \cdot 5 = 125$

b) $g(-26) = \sqrt[3]{-26-1}$
$= \sqrt[3]{-27}$
$= -3$ Since $(-3)(-3)(-3) = -27$

TRY EXERCISE 89

EXAMPLE 8 Simplify: $\sqrt[3]{-8y^3}$.

SOLUTION

$$\sqrt[3]{-8y^3} = -2y \quad \text{Since } (-2y)(-2y)(-2y) = -8y^3$$

TRY EXERCISE 83

Odd and Even nth Roots

The 4th root of a number a is the number c for which $c^4 = a$. There are also 5th roots, 6th roots, and so on. We write $\sqrt[n]{a}$ for the principal nth root. The number n is called the *index* (plural, *indices*). When the index is 2, we do not write it.

When the index n is odd, we are taking an *odd root*. Note that every number has exactly one real root when n is odd. Odd roots of positive numbers are positive and odd roots of negative numbers are negative. Absolute-value signs are not used when finding odd roots.

EXAMPLE 9 Simplify each expression.

a) $\sqrt[5]{32}$ **b)** $\sqrt[5]{-32}$ **c)** $-\sqrt[5]{32}$

d) $-\sqrt[5]{-32}$ **e)** $\sqrt[7]{x^7}$ **f)** $\sqrt[9]{(t-1)^9}$

SOLUTION

a) $\sqrt[5]{32} = 2$ Since $2^5 = 32$

b) $\sqrt[5]{-32} = -2$ Since $(-2)^5 = -32$

c) $-\sqrt[5]{32} = -2$ Taking the opposite of $\sqrt[5]{32}$

d) $-\sqrt[5]{-32} = -(-2) = 2$ Taking the opposite of $\sqrt[5]{-32}$

e) $\sqrt[7]{x^7} = x$ No absolute-value signs are needed.

f) $\sqrt[9]{(t-1)^9} = t-1$

TRY EXERCISE 81

When the index n is even, we are taking an *even root*. Every positive real number has two real nth roots when n is even—one positive and one negative. For example, the fourth roots of 16 are -2 and 2. Negative numbers do not have real nth roots when n is even.

When n is even, the notation $\sqrt[n]{a}$ indicates the nonnegative nth root. Thus, when we simplify even nth roots, absolute-value signs are often required.

Compare the following.

Odd Root	Even Root
$\sqrt[3]{8} = 2$	$\sqrt[4]{16} = 2$
$\sqrt[3]{-8} = -2$	$\sqrt[4]{-16}$ is not a real number.
$\sqrt[3]{x^3} = x$	$\sqrt[4]{x^4} = |x|$

EXAMPLE 10 Simplify each expression, if possible. Assume that variables can represent any real number.

a) $\sqrt[4]{81}$ **b)** $-\sqrt[4]{81}$ **c)** $\sqrt[4]{-81}$

d) $\sqrt[4]{81x^4}$ **e)** $\sqrt[6]{(y + 7)^6}$

SOLUTION

a) $\sqrt[4]{81} = 3$ Since $3^4 = 81$

b) $-\sqrt[4]{81} = -3$ Taking the opposite of $\sqrt[4]{81}$

c) $\sqrt[4]{-81}$ cannot be simplified. $\sqrt[4]{-81}$ is not a real number.

d) $\sqrt[4]{81x^4} = |3x|$, or $3|x|$ Use absolute-value notation since x could represent a negative number.

e) $\sqrt[6]{(y + 7)^6} = |y + 7|$ Use absolute-value notation since $y + 7$ is negative for $y < -7$.

TRY EXERCISE 59

We summarize as follows.

Simplifying nth Roots

n	a	$\sqrt[n]{a}$	$\sqrt[n]{a^n}$
Even	Positive	Positive	$|a|$
	Negative	Not a real number	
Odd	Positive	Positive	a
	Negative	Negative	

EXAMPLE 11 Determine the domain of g if $g(x) = \sqrt[6]{7 - 3x}$.

SOLUTION Since the index is even, the radicand, $7 - 3x$, must be nonnegative. We solve the inequality:

$$7 - 3x \geq 0$$ We cannot find the 6th root of a negative number.

$$-3x \geq -7$$

$$x \leq \tfrac{7}{3}.$$ Multiplying both sides by $-\tfrac{1}{3}$ and reversing the inequality

Thus,

$$\text{Domain of } g = \left\{ x \mid x \leq \tfrac{7}{3} \right\}$$
$$= \left(-\infty, \tfrac{7}{3} \right].$$

TRY EXERCISE 95

TECHNOLOGY CONNECTION

To enter cube or higher roots on a graphing calculator, select options 4 or 5 of the **MATH** menu. The characters $6\sqrt[x]{}$ indicate the sixth root.

1. Use a TABLE or GRAPH and TRACE to check the solution of Example 11.

Visualizing for Success

A

B

C

D

E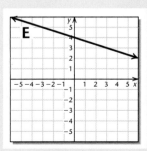

Match each function with its graph.

1. $f(x) = 2x - 5$

2. $f(x) = x^2 - 1$

3. $f(x) = \sqrt{x}$

4. $f(x) = x - 2$

5. $f(x) = -\frac{1}{3}x$

6. $f(x) = 2x$

7. $f(x) = 4 - x$

8. $f(x) = |2x - 5|$

9. $f(x) = -2$

10. $f(x) = -\frac{1}{3}x + 4$

Answers on page A-36

An additional, animated version of this activity appears in MyMathLab. To use MyMathLab, you need a course ID and a student access code. Consult your instructor for more information.

F

G

H

I

J

8.1   EXERCISE SET

For Extra Help
MyMathLab   PRACTICE   WATCH   DOWNLOAD

Concept Reinforcement   *Select the appropriate word to complete each of the following.*

1. Every positive number has _____ square root(s).   one/two

2. The principal square root is never _____.   negative/positive

3. For any _____ number a, we have negative/positive
   $\sqrt{a^2} = a$.

4. For any _____ number a, we have negative/positive
   $\sqrt{a^2} = -a$.

5. If a is a whole number that is not a perfect square, then $\sqrt{a}$ is a(n) _____ number.   irrational/rational

6. The domain of the function f given by $f(x) = \sqrt[3]{x}$ is all _____ numbers.   whole/real/positive

7. If $\sqrt[4]{x}$ is a real number, then x must be _____.   negative/positive/nonnegative

8. If $\sqrt[3]{x}$ is negative, then x must be _____.   negative/positive

For each number, find all of its square roots.

9. 64

10. 81

11. 100

12. 121

13. 400

14. 2500

15. 625

16. 225

Simplify.

17. $\sqrt{49}$

18. $\sqrt{144}$

19. $-\sqrt{16}$

20. $-\sqrt{100}$

21. $\sqrt{\dfrac{36}{49}}$

22. $\sqrt{\dfrac{4}{9}}$

23. $-\sqrt{169}$

24. $-\sqrt{196}$

25. $-\sqrt{\dfrac{16}{81}}$

26. $-\sqrt{\dfrac{81}{144}}$

27. $\sqrt{0.04}$

28. $\sqrt{0.36}$

29. $\sqrt{0.0081}$

30. $\sqrt{0.0016}$

Identify the radicand and the index for each expression.

31. $5\sqrt{p^2 + 4}$

32. $-7\sqrt{y^2 - 8}$

33. $x^2 y^3 \sqrt[5]{\dfrac{x}{y + 4}}$

34. $\dfrac{a^2}{b} \sqrt[6]{a(a + 4)}$

For each function, find the specified function value, if it exists.

35. $f(t) = \sqrt{5t - 10}$; $f(3), f(2), f(1), f(-1)$

36. $g(x) = \sqrt{x^2 - 25}$; $g(-6), g(3), g(6), g(13)$

37. $t(x) = -\sqrt{2x^2 - 1}$; $t(5), t(0), t(-1), t\left(-\frac{1}{2}\right)$

38. $p(z) = \sqrt{2z - 20}$; $p(4), p(10), p(12), p(0)$

39. $f(t) = \sqrt{t^2 + 1}$; $f(0), f(-1), f(-10)$

40. $g(x) = -\sqrt{(x + 1)^2}$; $g(-3), g(4), g(-5)$

Simplify. Remember to use absolute-value notation when necessary. If a root cannot be simplified, state this.

41. $\sqrt{100x^2}$

42. $\sqrt{16t^2}$

43. $\sqrt{(8 - t)^2}$

44. $\sqrt{(a + 3)^2}$

45. $\sqrt{y^2 + 16y + 64}$

46. $\sqrt{x^2 - 4x + 4}$

47. $\sqrt{4x^2 + 28x + 49}$

48. $\sqrt{9x^2 - 30x + 25}$

49. $-\sqrt[4]{256}$

50. $-\sqrt[4]{625}$

51. $\sqrt[3]{-1}$

52. $-\sqrt[3]{-1000}$

53. $-\sqrt[5]{-\dfrac{32}{243}}$

54. $\sqrt[5]{-\dfrac{1}{32}}$

55. $\sqrt[6]{x^6}$

56. $\sqrt[8]{y^8}$

57. $\sqrt[9]{t^9}$

58. $\sqrt[5]{a^5}$

59. $\sqrt[4]{(6a)^4}$

60. $\sqrt[4]{(7b)^4}$

61. $\sqrt[10]{(-6)^{10}}$

62. $\sqrt[12]{(-10)^{12}}$

63. $\sqrt[414]{(a + b)^{414}}$

64. $\sqrt[1976]{(2a + b)^{1976}}$

65. $\sqrt{a^{22}}$

66. $\sqrt{x^{10}}$

67. $\sqrt{-25}$

68. $\sqrt{-16}$

Simplify. Assume that no radicands were formed by raising negative quantities to even powers.

69. $\sqrt{16x^2}$

70. $\sqrt{25t^2}$

71. $-\sqrt{(3t)^2}$

72. $-\sqrt{(7c)^2}$

73. $\sqrt{(-5b)^2}$

74. $\sqrt{(-10a)^2}$

75. $\sqrt{a^2 + 2a + 1}$

76. $\sqrt{9 - 6y + y^2}$

77. $\sqrt[3]{27}$

78. $-\sqrt[3]{64}$

79. $\sqrt[4]{16x^4}$

80. $\sqrt[4]{81x^4}$

81. $\sqrt[5]{(x-1)^5}$

82. $-\sqrt[5]{(7y)^5}$

83. $-\sqrt[3]{-125y^3}$

84. $\sqrt[3]{-64x^3}$

85. $\sqrt{t^{18}}$

86. $\sqrt{a^{14}}$

87. $\sqrt{(x-2)^8}$

88. $\sqrt{(x+3)^{10}}$

For each function, find the specified function value, if it exists.

89. $f(x) = \sqrt[3]{x+1};\ f(7), f(26), f(-9), f(-65)$

90. $g(x) = -\sqrt[3]{2x-1};\ g(0), g(-62), g(-13), g(63)$

91. $g(t) = \sqrt[4]{t-3};\ g(19), g(-13), g(1), g(84)$

92. $f(t) = \sqrt[4]{t+1};\ f(0), f(15), f(-82), f(80)$

Determine the domain of each function described.

93. $f(x) = \sqrt{x-6}$

94. $g(x) = \sqrt{x+8}$

95. $g(t) = \sqrt[4]{t+8}$

96. $f(x) = \sqrt[4]{x-9}$

97. $g(x) = \sqrt[4]{10-2x}$

98. $g(t) = \sqrt[3]{2t-6}$

99. $f(t) = \sqrt[5]{2t+7}$

100. $f(t) = \sqrt[6]{4+3t}$

101. $h(z) = -\sqrt[6]{5z+2}$

102. $d(x) = -\sqrt[4]{5-7x}$

Aha! **103.** $f(t) = 7 + \sqrt[8]{t^8}$

104. $g(t) = 9 + \sqrt[6]{t^6}$

105. Explain how to write the negative square root of a number using radical notation.

106. Does the square root of a number's absolute value always exist? Why or why not?

Skill Review

To prepare for Section 8.2, review exponents.

Simplify. Do not use negative exponents in your answer.

107. $(a^2b)(a^4b)$

108. $(3xy^8)(5x^2y)$

109. $(5x^2y^{-3})^3$

110. $(2a^{-1}b^2c)^{-3}$

111. $\left(\dfrac{10x^{-1}y^5}{5x^2y^{-1}}\right)^{-1}$

112. $\left(\dfrac{8x^3y^{-2}}{2xz^4}\right)^{-2}$

Synthesis

113. Under what conditions does the nth root of x^3 exist? Explain your reasoning.

114. Under what conditions does the nth root of x^2 exist? Explain your reasoning.

115. *Biology.*   The number of species S of plants in Guyana in an area of A hectares can be estimated using the formula

$$S = 88.63\sqrt[4]{A}.$$

The Kaieteur National Park in Guyana has an area of 63,000 hectares. How many species of plants are in the park?

Source: Hans ter Steege, "A Perspective on Guyana and its Plant Richness," as found on www.bio.uu.nl

116. *Spaces in a parking lot.*   A parking lot has attendants to park the cars. The number N of stalls needed for waiting cars before attendants can get to them is given by the formula $N = 2.5\sqrt{A}$, where A is the number of arrivals in peak hours. Find the number of spaces needed for the given number of arrivals in peak hours: **(a)** 25; **(b)** 36; **(c)** 49; **(d)** 64.

Determine the domain of each function described. Then draw the graph of each function.

117. $f(x) = \sqrt{x} + 5$

118. $g(x) = \sqrt{x+5}$

119. $g(x) = \sqrt{x} - 2$

120. $f(x) = \sqrt{x-2}$

121. Find the domain of f if

$$f(x) = \frac{\sqrt{x+3}}{\sqrt[4]{2-x}}.$$

122. Find the domain of g if

$$g(x) = \frac{\sqrt[4]{5-x}}{\sqrt[6]{x+4}}.$$

123. Find the domain of F if $F(x) = \dfrac{x}{\sqrt{x^2-5x-6}}.$

124. Use a graphing calculator to check your answers to Exercises 41, 45, and 59. On some graphing calculators, a MATH key is needed to enter higher roots.

125. Use a graphing calculator to check your answers to Exercises 117 and 118. (See Exercise 124.)

8.2 Rational Numbers as Exponents

Rational Exponents ■ Negative Rational Exponents ■ Laws of Exponents ■ Simplifying Radical Expressions

We have already considered natural-number exponents and integer exponents. We now expand the study of exponents further to include all rational numbers. This will give meaning to expressions like $7^{1/3}$ and $(2x)^{-4/5}$. Such notation will help us simplify certain radical expressions.

Rational Exponents

When defining rational exponents, we want the rules for exponents to hold for rational exponents just as they do for integer exponents. In particular, we still want to add exponents when multiplying.

If $a^{1/2} \cdot a^{1/2} = a^{1/2+1/2} = a^1$, then $a^{1/2}$ should mean $\sqrt{a}$.

If $a^{1/3} \cdot a^{1/3} \cdot a^{1/3} = a^{1/3+1/3+1/3} = a^1$, then $a^{1/3}$ should mean $\sqrt[3]{a}$.

$$a^{1/n} = \sqrt[n]{a}$$

$a^{1/n}$ means $\sqrt[n]{a}$. When a is nonnegative, n can be any natural number greater than 1. When a is negative, n can be any odd natural number greater than 1.

Thus, $a^{1/5} = \sqrt[5]{a}$ and $a^{1/10} = \sqrt[10]{a}$. Note that the denominator of the exponent becomes the index and the base becomes the radicand.

EXAMPLE 1 Write an equivalent expression using radical notation and, if possible, simplify.

a) $16^{1/2}$ **b)** $(-8)^{1/3}$ **c)** $(abc)^{1/5}$ **d)** $(25x^{16})^{1/2}$

SOLUTION

a) $16^{1/2} = \sqrt{16} = 4$

b) $(-8)^{1/3} = \sqrt[3]{-8} = -2$ The denominator of the exponent becomes the index. The base becomes the radicand. Recall that for square roots, the index 2 is understood without being written.

c) $(abc)^{1/5} = \sqrt[5]{abc}$

d) $(25x^{16})^{1/2} = 25^{1/2}x^8 = \sqrt{25} \cdot x^8 = 5x^8$

TRY EXERCISE 11

EXAMPLE 2 Write an equivalent expression using exponential notation.

a) $\sqrt[5]{9ab}$ **b)** $\sqrt[7]{\dfrac{x^3y}{4}}$ **c)** $\sqrt{5x}$

SOLUTION Parentheses are required to indicate the base.

a) $\sqrt[5]{9ab} = (9ab)^{1/5}$

b) $\sqrt[7]{\dfrac{x^3y}{4}} = \left(\dfrac{x^3y}{4}\right)^{1/7}$ The index becomes the denominator of the exponent. The radicand becomes the base.

c) $\sqrt{5x} = (5x)^{1/2}$ The index 2 is understood without being written. We assume $x \geq 0$.

TRY EXERCISE 31

How shall we define $a^{2/3}$? If the property for multiplying exponents is to hold, we must have $a^{2/3} = (a^{1/3})^2$ and $a^{2/3} = (a^2)^{1/3}$. This would suggest that $a^{2/3} = \left(\sqrt[3]{a}\right)^2$ and $a^{2/3} = \sqrt[3]{a^2}$. We make our definition accordingly.

> **Positive Rational Exponents**
>
> For any natural numbers m and n ($n \neq 1$) and any real number a for which $\sqrt[n]{a}$ exists,
>
> $$a^{m/n} \quad \text{means} \quad \left(\sqrt[n]{a}\right)^m, \quad \text{or} \quad \sqrt[n]{a^m}.$$

EXAMPLE **3** Write an equivalent expression using radical notation and simplify.

a) $27^{2/3}$ **b)** $25^{3/2}$

SOLUTION

a) $27^{2/3}$ means $\left(\sqrt[3]{27}\right)^2$ or, equivalently, $\sqrt[3]{27^2}$. Let's see which is easier to simplify:

$$\left(\sqrt[3]{27}\right)^2 = 3^2 \qquad \sqrt[3]{27^2} = \sqrt[3]{729}$$
$$= 9; \qquad\qquad\qquad = 9.$$

The simplification on the left is probably easier for most people.

b) $25^{3/2}$ means $\left(\sqrt{25}\right)^3$ or, equivalently, $\sqrt{25^3}$ (the index 2 is normally omitted). Since $\sqrt{25}$ is more commonly known than $\sqrt{25^3}$, we use that form:

$$25^{3/2} = \left(\sqrt{25}\right)^3 = 5^3 = 125.$$

▶ TRY EXERCISE ▶ 23

EXAMPLE **4** Write an equivalent expression using exponential notation.

a) $\sqrt[3]{9^4}$ **b)** $\left(\sqrt[4]{7xy}\right)^5$

SOLUTION

a) $\sqrt[3]{9^4} = 9^{4/3}$ }   The index becomes the denominator of the
b) $\left(\sqrt[4]{7xy}\right)^5 = (7xy)^{5/4}$ fraction that is the exponent.   ▶ TRY EXERCISE ▶ 37

Negative Rational Exponents

Recall that $x^{-2} = 1/x^2$. Negative rational exponents behave similarly.

> **Negative Rational Exponents**
>
> For any rational number m/n and any nonzero real number a for which $a^{m/n}$ exists,
>
> $$a^{-m/n} \quad \text{means} \quad \frac{1}{a^{m/n}}.$$

> *CAUTION!* A negative exponent does not indicate that the expression in which it appears is negative: $a^{-1} \neq -a$.

STUDENT NOTES

It is important to remember both meanings of $a^{m/n}$. When the root of the base a is known, $\left(\sqrt[n]{a}\right)^m$ is generally easier to work with. When it is not known, $\sqrt[n]{a^m}$ is often more convenient.

TECHNOLOGY CONNECTION

To approximate $7^{2/3}$, we enter 7 ⌢ $(2/3)$.

1. Why are the parentheses needed above?
2. Compare the graphs of $y_1 = x^{1/2}$, $y_2 = x$, and $y_3 = x^{3/2}$ and determine those x-values for which $y_1 > y_3$.

EXAMPLE 5 Write an equivalent expression with positive exponents and, if possible, simplify.

a) $9^{-1/2}$　　　　　　b) $(5xy)^{-4/5}$　　　　　　c) $64^{-2/3}$

d) $4x^{-2/3}y^{1/5}$　　　　e) $\left(\dfrac{3r}{7s}\right)^{-5/2}$

SOLUTION

a) $9^{-1/2} = \dfrac{1}{9^{1/2}}$　　$9^{-1/2}$ is the reciprocal of $9^{1/2}$.

　　Since $9^{1/2} = \sqrt{9} = 3$, the answer simplifies to $\dfrac{1}{3}$.

b) $(5xy)^{-4/5} = \dfrac{1}{(5xy)^{4/5}}$　　$(5xy)^{-4/5}$ is the reciprocal of $(5xy)^{4/5}$.

c) $64^{-2/3} = \dfrac{1}{64^{2/3}}$　　$64^{-2/3}$ is the reciprocal of $64^{2/3}$.

　　Since $64^{2/3} = \left(\sqrt[3]{64}\right)^2 = 4^2 = 16$, the answer simplifies to $\dfrac{1}{16}$.

d) $4x^{-2/3}y^{1/5} = 4 \cdot \dfrac{1}{x^{2/3}} \cdot y^{1/5} = \dfrac{4y^{1/5}}{x^{2/3}}$

e) Earlier, we found that $(a/b)^{-n} = (b/a)^n$. This property holds for *any* negative exponent:

$$\left(\frac{3r}{7s}\right)^{-5/2} = \left(\frac{7s}{3r}\right)^{5/2}.$$　　Writing the reciprocal of the base and changing the sign of the exponent

TRY EXERCISE 53

Laws of Exponents

The same laws hold for rational exponents as for integer exponents.

Laws of Exponents

For any real numbers a and b and any rational exponents m and n for which a^m, a^n, and b^m are defined:

1. $a^m \cdot a^n = a^{m+n}$　When multiplying, add exponents if the bases are the same.

2. $\dfrac{a^m}{a^n} = a^{m-n}$　When dividing, subtract exponents if the bases are the same. (Assume $a \neq 0$.)

3. $(a^m)^n = a^{m \cdot n}$　To raise a power to a power, multiply the exponents.

4. $(ab)^m = a^m b^m$　To raise a product to a power, raise each factor to the power and multiply.

EXAMPLE 6 Use the laws of exponents to simplify.

a) $3^{1/5} \cdot 3^{3/5}$　　　　　　　　b) $\dfrac{a^{1/4}}{a^{1/2}}$

c) $(7.2^{2/3})^{3/4}$　　　　　　　　　d) $(a^{-1/3}b^{2/5})^{1/2}$

SOLUTION

a) $3^{1/5} \cdot 3^{3/5} = 3^{1/5+3/5} = 3^{4/5}$ Adding exponents

b) $\dfrac{a^{1/4}}{a^{1/2}} = a^{1/4-1/2} = a^{1/4-2/4}$ Subtracting exponents after finding a common denominator

$$= a^{-1/4}, \text{ or } \dfrac{1}{a^{1/4}} \qquad a^{-1/4} \text{ is the reciprocal of } a^{1/4}.$$

c) $(7.2^{2/3})^{3/4} = 7.2^{(2/3)(3/4)} = 7.2^{6/12}$ Multiplying exponents

$$= 7.2^{1/2} \qquad \text{Using arithmetic to simplify the exponent}$$

d) $(a^{-1/3}b^{2/5})^{1/2} = a^{(-1/3)(1/2)} \cdot b^{(2/5)(1/2)}$ Raising a product to a power and multiplying exponents

$$= a^{-1/6}b^{1/5}, \text{ or } \dfrac{b^{1/5}}{a^{1/6}}$$

TRY EXERCISE 69

Simplifying Radical Expressions

Many radical expressions contain radicands or factors of radicands that are powers. When these powers and the index share a common factor, rational exponents can be used to simplify the expression.

> ### To Simplify Radical Expressions
> 1. Convert radical expressions to exponential expressions.
> 2. Use arithmetic and the laws of exponents to simplify.
> 3. Convert back to radical notation as needed.

EXAMPLE 7   Use rational exponents to simplify. Do not use exponents that are fractions in the final answer.

a) $\sqrt[6]{(5x)^3}$
b) $\sqrt[5]{t^{20}}$
c) $\left(\sqrt[3]{ab^2c}\right)^{12}$
d) $\sqrt{\sqrt[3]{x}}$

SOLUTION

a) $\sqrt[6]{(5x)^3} = (5x)^{3/6}$ Converting to exponential notation

$$= (5x)^{1/2} \qquad \text{Simplifying the exponent}$$
$$= \sqrt{5x} \qquad \text{Returning to radical notation}$$

b) $\sqrt[5]{t^{20}} = t^{20/5}$ Converting to exponential notation

$$= t^4 \qquad \text{Simplifying the exponent}$$

c) $\left(\sqrt[3]{ab^2c}\right)^{12} = (ab^2c)^{12/3}$ Converting to exponential notation

$$= (ab^2c)^4 \qquad \text{Simplifying the exponent}$$
$$= a^4b^8c^4 \qquad \text{Using the laws of exponents}$$

d) $\sqrt{\sqrt[3]{x}} = \sqrt{x^{1/3}}$ Converting the radicand to exponential notation

$$= (x^{1/3})^{1/2} \qquad \text{Try to go directly to this step.}$$
$$= x^{1/6} \qquad \text{Using the laws of exponents}$$
$$= \sqrt[6]{x} \qquad \text{Returning to radical notation}$$

TRY EXERCISE 87

TECHNOLOGY CONNECTION

One way to check Example 7(a) is to let $y_1 = (5x)^{3/6}$ and $y_2 = \sqrt{5x}$. Then use GRAPH or TABLE to see if $y_1 = y_2$. An alternative is to let $y_3 = y_2 - y_1$ and see if $y_3 = 0$. Check Example 7(a) using one of these two methods.

1. Why are rational exponents especially useful when working on a graphing calculator?

8.2 EXERCISE SET

For Extra Help   MyMathLab   Math XL PRACTICE   WATCH   DOWNLOAD

🐍 **Concept Reinforcement** *In each of Exercises 1–8, match the expression with the equivalent expression from the column on the right.*

1. ____ $x^{2/5}$ a) $x^{3/5}$
2. ____ $x^{5/2}$ b) $\left(\sqrt[5]{x}\right)^4$
3. ____ $x^{-5/2}$ c) $\sqrt{x^5}$
4. ____ $x^{-2/5}$ d) $x^{1/2}$
5. ____ $x^{1/5} \cdot x^{2/5}$
6. ____ $(x^{1/5})^{5/2}$ e) $\dfrac{1}{\left(\sqrt{x}\right)^5}$
7. ____ $\sqrt[5]{x^4}$ f) $\sqrt[4]{x^5}$
8. ____ $\left(\sqrt[4]{x}\right)^5$ g) $\sqrt[5]{x^2}$

   h) $\dfrac{1}{\left(\sqrt[5]{x}\right)^2}$

Note: Assume for all exercises that all variables are nonnegative and that all denominators are nonzero.

Write an equivalent expression using radical notation and, if possible, simplify.

9. $y^{1/3}$ 10. $t^{1/4}$
11. $36^{1/2}$ 12. $125^{1/3}$
13. $32^{1/5}$ 14. $81^{1/4}$
15. $64^{1/2}$ 16. $100^{1/2}$
17. $(xyz)^{1/2}$ 18. $(ab)^{1/4}$
19. $(a^2b^2)^{1/5}$ 20. $(x^3y^3)^{1/4}$
21. $t^{5/6}$ 22. $a^{3/2}$
23. $16^{3/4}$ 24. $4^{7/2}$
25. $125^{4/3}$ 26. $9^{5/2}$
27. $(81x)^{3/4}$ 28. $(125a)^{2/3}$
29. $(25x^4)^{3/2}$ 30. $(9y^6)^{3/2}$

Write an equivalent expression using exponential notation.

31. $\sqrt[3]{18}$ 32. $\sqrt[4]{10}$
33. $\sqrt{30}$ 34. $\sqrt{22}$
35. $\sqrt{x^7}$ 36. $\sqrt{a^3}$
37. $\sqrt[5]{m^2}$ 38. $\sqrt[5]{n^4}$
39. $\sqrt[4]{pq}$ 40. $\sqrt[3]{cd}$

41. $\sqrt[5]{xy^2z}$ 42. $\sqrt[7]{x^3y^2z^2}$
43. $\left(\sqrt{3mn}\right)^3$ 44. $\left(\sqrt[3]{7xy}\right)^4$
45. $\left(\sqrt[7]{8x^2y}\right)^5$ 46. $\left(\sqrt[6]{2a^5b}\right)^7$

47. $\dfrac{2x}{\sqrt[3]{z^2}}$ 48. $\dfrac{3a}{\sqrt[5]{c^2}}$

Write an equivalent expression with positive exponents and, if possible, simplify.

49. $a^{-1/4}$ 50. $m^{-1/3}$
51. $(2rs)^{-3/4}$ 52. $(5xy)^{-5/6}$
53. $\left(\dfrac{1}{16}\right)^{-3/4}$ 54. $\left(\dfrac{1}{8}\right)^{-2/3}$
55. $\dfrac{8c}{a^{-3/5}}$ 56. $\dfrac{3b}{a^{-5/7}}$
57. $2a^{3/4}b^{-1/2}c^{2/3}$ 58. $5x^{-2/3}y^{4/5}z$
59. $3^{-5/2}a^3b^{-7/3}$ 60. $2^{-1/3}x^4y^{-2/7}$
61. $\left(\dfrac{2ab}{3c}\right)^{-5/6}$ 62. $\left(\dfrac{7x}{8yz}\right)^{-3/5}$
63. $\dfrac{6a}{\sqrt[4]{b}}$ 64. $\dfrac{5y}{\sqrt[3]{z}}$

Use the laws of exponents to simplify. Do not use negative exponents in any answers.

65. $11^{1/2} \cdot 11^{1/3}$ 66. $5^{1/4} \cdot 5^{1/8}$
67. $\dfrac{3^{5/8}}{3^{-1/8}}$ 68. $\dfrac{8^{7/11}}{8^{-2/11}}$
69. $\dfrac{4.3^{-1/5}}{4.3^{-7/10}}$ 70. $\dfrac{2.7^{-11/12}}{2.7^{-1/6}}$
71. $(10^{3/5})^{2/5}$ 72. $(5^{5/4})^{3/7}$
73. $a^{2/3} \cdot a^{5/4}$ 74. $x^{3/4} \cdot x^{1/3}$

Aha! 75. $(64^{3/4})^{4/3}$ 76. $(27^{-2/3})^{3/2}$
77. $(m^{2/3}n^{-1/4})^{1/2}$ 78. $(x^{-1/3}y^{2/5})^{1/4}$

Use rational exponents to simplify. Do not use fraction exponents in the final answer.

79. $\sqrt[9]{x^3}$ 80. $\sqrt[12]{a^3}$
81. $\sqrt[3]{y^{15}}$ 82. $\sqrt[4]{y^{40}}$
83. $\sqrt[12]{a^6}$ 84. $\sqrt[30]{x^5}$
85. $\left(\sqrt[7]{xy}\right)^{14}$ 86. $\left(\sqrt[3]{ab}\right)^{15}$

87. $\sqrt[4]{(7a)^2}$

88. $\sqrt[8]{(3x)^2}$

89. $\left(\sqrt[8]{2x}\right)^6$

90. $\left(\sqrt[10]{3a}\right)^5$

91. $\sqrt{\sqrt[5]{m}}$

92. $\sqrt[6]{\sqrt{n}}$

93. $\sqrt[4]{(xy)^{12}}$

94. $\sqrt{(ab)^6}$

95. $\left(\sqrt[5]{a^2b^4}\right)^{15}$

96. $\left(\sqrt[3]{x^2y^5}\right)^{12}$

97. $\sqrt[3]{\sqrt[4]{xy}}$

98. $\sqrt[5]{\sqrt[3]{2a}}$

99. If $f(x) = (x + 5)^{1/2}(x + 7)^{-1/2}$, find the domain of f. Explain how you found your answer.

100. Let $f(x) = 5x^{-1/3}$. Under what condition will we have $f(x) > 0$? Why?

Skill Review

To prepare for Section 8.3, review multiplying and factoring polynomials (Section 3.4).

Multiply.

101. $(x + 5)(x - 5)$

102. $(x - 2)(x^2 + 2x + 4)$

Factor. [3.4]

103. $4x^2 + 20x + 25$

104. $9a^2 - 24a + 16$

105. $5t^2 - 10t + 5$

106. $3n^2 + 12n + 12$

Synthesis

107. Explain why $\sqrt[3]{x^6} = x^2$ for any value of x, whereas $\sqrt[2]{x^6} = x^3$ only when $x \geq 0$.

108. If $g(x) = x^{3/n}$, in what way does the domain of g depend on whether n is odd or even?

Use rational exponents to simplify.

109. $\sqrt{x\sqrt[3]{x^2}}$

110. $\sqrt[4]{\sqrt[3]{8x^3y^6}}$

111. $\sqrt[14]{c^2 - 2cd + d^2}$

*Music.   The function given by $f(x) = k2^{x/12}$ can be used to determine the frequency, in cycles per second, of a musical note that is x half-steps above a note with frequency k.**

112. The frequency of concert A for a trumpet is 440 cycles per second. Find the frequency of the A that is two octaves (24 half-steps) above concert A (few trumpeters can reach this note.)

---

*This application was inspired by information provided by Dr. Homer B. Tilton of Pima Community College East.

113. Show that the G that is 7 half-steps (a "perfect fifth") above middle C (262 cycles per second) has a frequency that is about 1.5 times that of middle C.

114. Show that the C sharp that is 4 half-steps (a "major third") above concert A (see Exercise 112) has a frequency that is about 25% greater than that of concert A.

115. *Road pavement messages.*   In a psychological study, it was determined that the proper length L of the letters of a word printed on pavement is given by

$$L = \frac{0.000169d^{2.27}}{h},$$

where d is the distance of a car from the lettering and h is the height of the eye above the surface of the road. All units are in meters. This formula says that from a vantage point h meters above the surface of the road, if a driver is to be able to recognize a message d meters away, that message will be the most recognizable if the length of the letters is L. Find L to the nearest tenth of a meter, given d and h.

a) $h = 1\,\text{m}, d = 60\,\text{m}$
b) $h = 0.9906\,\text{m}, d = 75\,\text{m}$
c) $h = 2.4\,\text{m}, d = 80\,\text{m}$
d) $h = 1.1\,\text{m}, d = 100\,\text{m}$

116. *Baseball.*   The statistician Bill James has found that a baseball team's winning percentage P can be approximated by

$$P = \frac{r^{1.83}}{r^{1.83} + \sigma^{1.83}},$$

where r is the total number of runs scored by that team and σ (sigma) is the total number of runs scored by their opponents. During a recent season, the San Francisco Giants scored 799 runs and their opponents scored 749 runs. Use James's formula to predict the Giants' winning percentage (the team actually won 55.6% of their games).

Source: M. Bittinger, *One Man's Journey Through Mathematics.* Boston: Addison-Wesley, 2004

117. *Forestry.*   The total wood volume T, in cubic feet, in a California black oak can be estimated using the formula

$$T = 0.936\, d^{1.97} h^{0.85},$$

where d is the diameter of the tree at breast height and h is the total height of the tree. How much wood is in a California black oak that is 3 ft in diameter at breast height and 80 ft high?

Source: Norman H. Pillsbury and Michael L. Kirkley, 1984. Equations for total, wood, and saw-log volume for thirteen California hardwoods, USDA Forest Service PNW Research Note No. 414: 52 p.

118. *Physics.*   The equation $m = m_0(1 - v^2 c^{-2})^{-1/2}$, developed by Albert Einstein, is used to determine the mass m of an object that is moving v meters per second and has mass m_0 before the motion begins. The constant c is the speed of light, approximately 3×10^8 m/sec. Suppose that a particle with mass 8 mg is accelerated to a speed of $\frac{9}{5} \times 10^8$ m/sec. Without using a calculator, find the new mass of the particle.

119. Using a graphing calculator, select **MODE** SIMUL and the FORMAT EXPROFF. Then graph

$$y_1 = x^{1/2}, \qquad y_2 = 3x^{2/5},$$
$$y_3 = x^{4/7}, \quad \text{and} \quad y_4 = \tfrac{1}{5}x^{3/4}.$$

Looking only at coordinates, match each graph with its equation.

COLLABORATIVE CORNER

Are Equivalent Fractions Equivalent Exponents?

Focus: Functions and rational exponents

Time: 10–20 minutes

Group size: 3

Materials: Graph paper

In arithmetic, we have seen that $\frac{1}{3}, \frac{1}{6} \cdot 2$, and $2 \cdot \frac{1}{6}$ all represent the same number. Interestingly,

$$f(x) = x^{1/3},$$
$$g(x) = (x^{1/6})^2, \quad \text{and}$$
$$h(x) = (x^2)^{1/6}$$

represent three *different* functions.

ACTIVITY

1. Selecting a variety of values for x and using the definition of positive rational exponents, one group member should graph f, a second group member should graph g, and a third group member should graph h. Be sure to check whether negative x-values are in the domain of the function.

2. Compare the three graphs and check each other's work. How and why do the graphs differ?

3. Decide as a group which graph, if any, would best represent the graph of $k(x) = x^{2/6}$. Then be prepared to explain your reasoning to the entire class. (*Hint:* Study the definition of $a^{m/n}$ on p. 504 carefully.)

8.3   Multiplying Radical Expressions

Multiplying Radical Expressions   ▪   Simplifying by Factoring   ▪   Multiplying and Simplifying

STUDY SKILLS —————

Interested in Something Extra?

Students interested in extra-credit projects are often pleasantly surprised to find that their instructor will not only provide a possible project for them to pursue, but might even tailor that project to the student's interests. Remember that if you do an extra-credit project, you must still complete the regular course work.

Multiplying Radical Expressions

Note that $\sqrt{4}\sqrt{25} = 2 \cdot 5 = 10$. Also $\sqrt{4 \cdot 25} = \sqrt{100} = 10$. Likewise,

$$\sqrt[3]{27}\,\sqrt[3]{8} = 3 \cdot 2 = 6 \quad \text{and} \quad \sqrt[3]{27 \cdot 8} = \sqrt[3]{216} = 6.$$

These examples suggest the following.

> **The Product Rule for Radicals**
>
> For any real numbers $\sqrt[n]{a}$ and $\sqrt[n]{b}$,
> $$\sqrt[n]{a} \cdot \sqrt[n]{b} = \sqrt[n]{a \cdot b}.$$
>
> (The product of two nth roots is the nth root of the product of the two radicands.)

Rational exponents can be used to derive this rule:

$$\sqrt[n]{a} \cdot \sqrt[n]{b} = a^{1/n} \cdot b^{1/n} = (a \cdot b)^{1/n} = \sqrt[n]{a \cdot b}.$$

EXAMPLE 1   Multiply.

a) $\sqrt{2} \cdot \sqrt{7}$

b) $\sqrt{x+3}\,\sqrt{x-3}$

c) $\sqrt[3]{4} \cdot \sqrt[3]{5}$

d) $\sqrt[4]{\dfrac{y}{5}} \cdot \sqrt[4]{\dfrac{7}{x}}$

SOLUTION

a) When no index is written, roots are understood to be square roots with an unwritten index of two. We apply the product rule:

$$\sqrt{2} \cdot \sqrt{7} = \sqrt{2 \cdot 7}$$
$$= \sqrt{14}.$$

b) $\sqrt{x+3}\sqrt{x-3} = \sqrt{(x+3)(x-3)}$ The product of two square roots is
$$= \sqrt{x^2 - 9}$$ the square root of the product.

> ***CAUTION!*** $\sqrt{x^2 - 9} \neq \sqrt{x^2} - \sqrt{9}$.

c) Both $\sqrt[3]{4}$ and $\sqrt[3]{5}$ have indices of three, so to multiply we can use the product rule:

$$\sqrt[3]{4} \cdot \sqrt[3]{5} = \sqrt[3]{4 \cdot 5} = \sqrt[3]{20}.$$

d) $\sqrt[4]{\dfrac{y}{5}} \cdot \sqrt[4]{\dfrac{7}{x}} = \sqrt[4]{\dfrac{y}{5} \cdot \dfrac{7}{x}} = \sqrt[4]{\dfrac{7y}{5x}}$ In Section 8.4, we discuss other ways to write answers like this.

> **TRY EXERCISE** 7

TECHNOLOGY CONNECTION

To check Example 1(b), let $y_1 = \sqrt{x + 3}\sqrt{x - 3}$ and $y_2 = \sqrt{x^2 - 9}$ and compare:

$y_1 = \sqrt{(x + 3)}\sqrt{(x - 3)}$

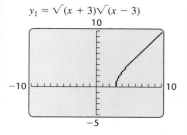

$y_2 = \sqrt{(x^2 - 9)}$

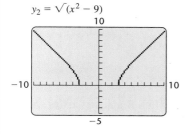

Because $y_1 = y_2$ for all x-values that can be used in *both* y_1 and y_2, Example 1(b) *is* correct.

1. Why do the graphs above differ in appearance? (*Hint*: What are the domains of the two related functions?)

CAUTION! The product rule for radicals applies only when radicals have the same index:

$$\sqrt[n]{a} \cdot \sqrt[m]{b} \neq \sqrt[nm]{a \cdot b}.$$

Simplifying by Factoring

The number p is a *perfect square* if there exists a rational number q for which $q^2 = p$. We say that p is a *perfect cube* if $q^3 = p$ for some rational number q. In general, p is a *perfect nth power* if $q^n = p$ for some rational number q. Thus, 16 and $\frac{1}{10,000}$ are both perfect 4th powers since $2^4 = 16$ and $\left(\frac{1}{10}\right)^4 = \frac{1}{10,000}$.

The product rule allows us to simplify $\sqrt[n]{ab}$ whenever ab contains a factor that is a perfect nth power.

> ### Using the Product Rule to Simplify
> $$\sqrt[n]{ab} = \sqrt[n]{a} \cdot \sqrt[n]{b}.$$
> $\left(\sqrt[n]{a} \text{ and } \sqrt[n]{b} \text{ must both be real numbers.}\right)$

To illustrate, suppose we wish to simplify $\sqrt{20}$. Since this is a *square* root, we check to see if there is a factor of 20 that is a perfect square. There is one, 4, so we express 20 as $4 \cdot 5$ and use the product rule:

$\sqrt{20} = \sqrt{4 \cdot 5}$ Factoring the radicand (4 is a perfect square)

$\quad = \sqrt{4} \cdot \sqrt{5}$ Factoring into two radicals

$\quad = 2\sqrt{5}$.   Finding the square root of 4

> **To Simplify a Radical Expression with Index n by Factoring**
> **1.** Express the radicand as a product in which one factor is the largest perfect nth power possible.
> **2.** Rewrite the expression as the nth root of each factor.
> **3.** Simplify the expression containing the perfect nth power.
> **4.** Simplification is complete when no radicand has a factor that is a perfect nth power.

It is often safe to assume that a radicand does not represent a negative number raised to an even power. We will henceforth make this assumption—unless functions are involved—and discontinue use of absolute-value notation when taking even roots.

EXAMPLE **2** Simplify by factoring: **(a)** $\sqrt{200}$; **(b)** $\sqrt{18x^2y}$; **(c)** $\sqrt[3]{-72}$; **(d)** $\sqrt[4]{162x^6}$.

SOLUTION

a) $\sqrt{200} = \sqrt{100 \cdot 2}$ 100 is the largest perfect-square factor of 200.

$\quad = \sqrt{100} \cdot \sqrt{2} = 10\sqrt{2}$

Express the radicand as a product.   **b)** $\sqrt{18x^2y} = \sqrt{9 \cdot 2 \cdot x^2 \cdot y}$ $9x^2$ is the largest perfect-square factor of $18x^2y$.

Rewrite as the nth root of each factor. $= \sqrt{9x^2} \cdot \sqrt{2y}$ Factoring into two radicals

Simplify. $= 3x\sqrt{2y}$ Taking the square root of $9x^2$

c) $\sqrt[3]{-72} = \sqrt[3]{-8 \cdot 9}$ -8 is a perfect-cube (third-power) factor of -72.

$= \sqrt[3]{-8} \cdot \sqrt[3]{9} = -2\sqrt[3]{9}$

d) $\sqrt[4]{162x^6} = \sqrt[4]{81 \cdot 2 \cdot x^4 \cdot x^2}$ $81 \cdot x^4$ is the largest perfect fourth-power factor of $162x^6$.

$= \sqrt[4]{81x^4} \cdot \sqrt[4]{2x^2}$ Factoring into two radicals

$= 3x\sqrt[4]{2x^2}$ Taking the fourth root of $81x^4$

Let's look at this example another way. We write a complete factorization and look for quadruples of factors. Each quadruple makes a perfect fourth power:

$$\sqrt[4]{162x^6} = \sqrt[4]{\boxed{3 \cdot 3 \cdot 3 \cdot 3} \cdot 2 \cdot \boxed{x \cdot x \cdot x \cdot x} \cdot x \cdot x}$$ $3 \cdot 3 \cdot 3 \cdot 3 = 3^4$
and
$x \cdot x \cdot x \cdot x = x^4$

$$= 3 \cdot x \cdot \sqrt[4]{2 \cdot x \cdot x}$$
$$= 3x\sqrt[4]{2x^2}.$$

> TRY EXERCISE 31

EXAMPLE 3   If $f(x) = \sqrt{3x^2 - 6x + 3}$, find a simplified form for $f(x)$. Because we are working with a function, assume that x can be any real number.

SOLUTION

$$f(x) = \sqrt{3x^2 - 6x + 3}$$
$$= \sqrt{3(x^2 - 2x + 1)}$$ Factoring the radicand; $x^2 - 2x + 1$ is a perfect square.
$$= \sqrt{(x-1)^2 \cdot 3}$$
$$= \sqrt{(x-1)^2} \cdot \sqrt{3}$$ Factoring into two radicals
$$= |x - 1|\sqrt{3}$$ Finding the square root of $(x-1)^2$

> TRY EXERCISE 43

TECHNOLOGY CONNECTION

To check Example 3, let $y_1 = \sqrt{\ }(3x^2 - 6x + 3)$, $y_2 = \text{abs}(x - 1)\sqrt{\ }(3)$, and $y_3 = (x - 1)\sqrt{\ }(3)$. Do the graphs all coincide? Why or why not?

EXAMPLE 4   Simplify: **(a)** $\sqrt{x^7y^{11}z^9}$; **(b)** $\sqrt[3]{16a^7b^{14}}$.

SOLUTION

a) There are many ways to factor $x^7y^{11}z^9$. Because of the square root (index of 2), we identify the largest exponents that are multiples of 2:

$$\sqrt{x^7y^{11}z^9} = \sqrt{x^6 \cdot x \cdot y^{10} \cdot y \cdot z^8 \cdot z}$$ The largest perfect-square factor is $x^6y^{10}z^8$.

$$= \sqrt{x^6y^{10}z^8} \sqrt{xyz}$$ Factoring into two radicals

$$= x^{6/2}y^{10/2}z^{8/2}\sqrt{xyz}$$ Converting to rational exponents. Try to do this mentally.

$$= x^3y^5z^4\sqrt{xyz}.$$ Simplifying

Check: $\left(x^3y^5z^4\sqrt{xyz}\right)^2 = (x^3)^2(y^5)^2(z^4)^2\left(\sqrt{xyz}\right)^2$
$$= x^6 \cdot y^{10} \cdot z^8 \cdot xyz = x^7y^{11}z^9.$$

Our check shows that $x^3y^5z^4\sqrt{xyz}$ is the square root of $x^7y^{11}z^9$.

b) There are many ways to factor $16a^7b^{14}$. Because of the cube root (index of 3), we identify factors with the largest exponents that are multiples of 3:

$$\sqrt[3]{16a^7b^{14}} = \sqrt[3]{8 \cdot 2 \cdot a^6 \cdot a \cdot b^{12} \cdot b^2}$$ The largest perfect-cube factor is $8a^6b^{12}$.

$$= \sqrt[3]{8a^6b^{12}}\sqrt[3]{2ab^2}$$ Rewriting as a product of cube roots

$$= 2a^2b^4\sqrt[3]{2ab^2}.$$ Simplifying the expression containing the perfect cube

As a check, let's redo the problem using a complete factorization of the radicand:

$$\sqrt[3]{16a^7b^{14}} = \sqrt[3]{2\cdot2\cdot2 \cdot 2 \cdot a\cdot a\cdot a \cdot a\cdot a\cdot a \cdot a \cdot b\cdot b\cdot b \cdot b\cdot b\cdot b \cdot b\cdot b\cdot b \cdot b\cdot b\cdot b \cdot b\cdot b}$$

Each triple of factors makes a cube.

$$= 2 \cdot a \cdot a \cdot b \cdot b \cdot b \cdot b \cdot \sqrt[3]{2 \cdot a \cdot b \cdot b}$$

$$= 2a^2b^4\sqrt[3]{2ab^2}.$$ Our answer checks.

TRY EXERCISE 51

> *Remember*: To simplify an nth root, identify factors in the radicand with exponents that are multiples of n.

Multiplying and Simplifying

We have used the product rule for radicals to find products and also to simplify radical expressions. For some radical expressions, it is possible to do both: First find a product and then simplify.

EXAMPLE 5 Multiply and simplify.

a) $\sqrt{15}\sqrt{6}$ **b)** $3\sqrt[3]{25} \cdot 2\sqrt[3]{5}$ **c)** $\sqrt[4]{8x^3y^5}\sqrt[4]{4x^2y^3}$

SOLUTION

a) $\sqrt{15}\sqrt{6} = \sqrt{15 \cdot 6}$ Multiplying radicands

$$= \sqrt{90} = \sqrt{9}\sqrt{10}$$ 9 is a perfect square.

$$= 3\sqrt{10}$$

b) $3\sqrt[3]{25} \cdot 2\sqrt[3]{5} = 3 \cdot 2 \cdot \sqrt[3]{25 \cdot 5}$ Using a commutative law; multiplying radicands

$$= 6 \cdot \sqrt[3]{125}$$ 125 is a perfect cube.

$$= 6 \cdot 5, \text{ or } 30$$

c) $\sqrt[4]{8x^3y^5}\sqrt[4]{4x^2y^3} = \sqrt[4]{32x^5y^8}$ Multiplying radicands

$$= \sqrt[4]{16x^4y^8 \cdot 2x}$$ Identifying the largest perfect fourth-power factor

$$= \sqrt[4]{16x^4y^8}\sqrt[4]{2x}$$ Factoring into radicals

$$= 2xy^2\sqrt[4]{2x}$$ Finding the fourth root; assume $x \geq 0$.

The checks are left to the student.

TRY EXERCISE 65

8.3 EXERCISE SET

For Extra Help

Concept Reinforcement *Classify each statement as either true or false.*

1. For any real numbers $\sqrt[n]{a}$ and $\sqrt[n]{b}$, $\sqrt[n]{a} \cdot \sqrt[n]{b} = \sqrt[n]{ab}$.

2. For any real numbers $\sqrt[n]{a}$ and $\sqrt[n]{b}$, $\sqrt[n]{a} + \sqrt[n]{b} = \sqrt[n]{a+b}$.

3. For any real numbers $\sqrt[n]{a}$ and $\sqrt[m]{b}$, $\sqrt[n]{a} \cdot \sqrt[m]{b} = \sqrt[nm]{ab}$.

4. For $x > 0$, $\sqrt{x^2 - 9} = x - 3$.

5. The expression $\sqrt[3]{X}$ is not simplified if X contains a factor that is a perfect cube.

6. It is often possible to simplify $\sqrt{A \cdot B}$ even though $\sqrt{A}$ and $\sqrt{B}$ cannot be simplified.

Multiply.

7. $\sqrt{3} \sqrt{10}$
8. $\sqrt{6} \sqrt{5}$
9. $\sqrt[3]{7} \sqrt[3]{5}$
10. $\sqrt[3]{2} \sqrt[3]{3}$
11. $\sqrt[4]{6} \sqrt[4]{9}$
12. $\sqrt[4]{4} \sqrt[4]{10}$
13. $\sqrt{2x} \sqrt{13y}$
14. $\sqrt{5a} \sqrt{6b}$
15. $\sqrt[5]{8y^3} \sqrt[5]{10y}$
16. $\sqrt[5]{9t^2} \sqrt[5]{2t}$
17. $\sqrt{y-b} \sqrt{y+b}$
18. $\sqrt{x-a} \sqrt{x+a}$
19. $\sqrt[3]{0.7y} \sqrt[3]{0.3y}$
20. $\sqrt[3]{0.5x} \sqrt[3]{0.2x}$
21. $\sqrt[5]{x-2} \sqrt[5]{(x-2)^2}$
22. $\sqrt[4]{x-1} \sqrt[4]{x^2+x+1}$
23. $\sqrt{\dfrac{2}{t}} \sqrt{\dfrac{3s}{11}}$
24. $\sqrt{\dfrac{7p}{6}} \sqrt{\dfrac{5}{q}}$
25. $\sqrt[7]{\dfrac{x-3}{4}} \sqrt[7]{\dfrac{5}{x+2}}$
26. $\sqrt[6]{\dfrac{a}{b-2}} \sqrt[6]{\dfrac{3}{b+2}}$

Simplify by factoring.

27. $\sqrt{12}$
28. $\sqrt{300}$
29. $\sqrt{45}$
30. $\sqrt{27}$
31. $\sqrt{8x^9}$
32. $\sqrt{75y^5}$
33. $\sqrt{120}$
34. $\sqrt{350}$
35. $\sqrt{36a^4b}$
36. $\sqrt{175y^8}$

37. $\sqrt[3]{8x^3y^2}$
38. $\sqrt[3]{27ab^6}$
39. $\sqrt[3]{-16x^6}$
40. $\sqrt[3]{-32a^6}$

Find a simplified form of $f(x)$. Assume that x can be any real number.

41. $f(x) = \sqrt[3]{40x^6}$
42. $f(x) = \sqrt[3]{27x^5}$
43. $f(x) = \sqrt{49(x-3)^2}$
44. $f(x) = \sqrt{81(x-1)^2}$
45. $f(x) = \sqrt{5x^2 - 10x + 5}$
46. $f(x) = \sqrt{2x^2 + 8x + 8}$

Simplify. Assume that no radicands were formed by raising negative numbers to even powers.

47. $\sqrt{a^{10}b^{11}}$
48. $\sqrt{x^8y^7}$
49. $\sqrt[3]{x^5y^6z^{10}}$
50. $\sqrt[3]{a^6b^7c^{13}}$
51. $\sqrt[4]{16x^5y^{11}}$
52. $\sqrt[5]{-32a^7b^{11}}$
53. $\sqrt[5]{x^{13}y^8z^{17}}$
54. $\sqrt[5]{a^6b^8c^9}$
55. $\sqrt[3]{-80a^{14}}$
56. $\sqrt[4]{810x^9}$

Multiply and simplify. Assume that no radicands were formed by raising negative numbers to even powers.

57. $\sqrt{5} \sqrt{10}$
58. $\sqrt{2} \sqrt{6}$
59. $\sqrt{6} \sqrt{33}$
60. $\sqrt{10} \sqrt{35}$
61. $\sqrt[3]{9} \sqrt[3]{3}$
62. $\sqrt[3]{2} \sqrt[3]{4}$

Aha! 63. $\sqrt{24y^5} \sqrt{24y^5}$
64. $\sqrt{120t^9} \sqrt{120t^9}$
65. $\sqrt[3]{5a^2} \sqrt[3]{2a}$
66. $\sqrt[3]{7x} \sqrt[3]{3x^2}$
67. $\sqrt{2x^5} \sqrt{10x^2}$
68. $\sqrt{5a^7} \sqrt{15a^3}$
69. $\sqrt[3]{s^2t^4} \sqrt[3]{s^4t^6}$
70. $\sqrt[3]{x^2y^4} \sqrt[3]{x^2y^6}$
71. $\sqrt[3]{(x-y)^2} \sqrt[3]{(x-y)^{10}}$
72. $\sqrt[3]{(t+4)^5} \sqrt[3]{(t+4)}$
73. $\sqrt[4]{20a^3b^7} \sqrt[4]{4a^2b^5}$
74. $\sqrt[4]{9x^7y^2} \sqrt[4]{9x^2y^9}$
75. $\sqrt[5]{x^3(y+z)^6} \sqrt[5]{x^3(y+z)^4}$
76. $\sqrt[5]{a^3(b-c)^4} \sqrt[5]{a^7(b-c)^4}$

77. Explain how you could convince a friend that $\sqrt{x^2 - 16} \neq \sqrt{x^2} - \sqrt{16}$.

78. Why is it incorrect to say that, in general, $\sqrt{x^2} = x$?

Skill Review

Review simplifying rational expressions (Sections 4.1–4.5).

Perform the indicated operation and, if possible, simplify.

79. $\dfrac{15a^2x}{8b} \cdot \dfrac{24b^2x}{5a}$ [4.2]

80. $\dfrac{x^2 - 1}{x^2 - 4} \div \dfrac{x^2 - x - 2}{x^2 + x - 2}$ [4.2]

81. $\dfrac{x - 3}{2x - 10} - \dfrac{3x - 5}{x^2 - 25}$ [4.4]

82. $\dfrac{6x}{25y^2} + \dfrac{3y}{10x}$ [4.4]

83. $\dfrac{a^{-1} + b^{-1}}{ab}$ [4.5]

84. $\dfrac{\dfrac{1}{x + 1} - \dfrac{2}{x}}{\dfrac{3}{x} + \dfrac{1}{x + 1}}$ [4.5]

Synthesis

85. Explain why it is true that $\sqrt[n]{ab} = \sqrt[n]{a} \cdot \sqrt[n]{b}$ for any real numbers $\sqrt[n]{a}$ and $\sqrt[n]{b}$.

86. Is the equation $\sqrt{(2x + 3)^8} = (2x + 3)^4$ always, sometimes, or never true? Why?

87. *Radar range.* The function given by

$$R(x) = \frac{1}{2}\sqrt[4]{\frac{x \cdot 3.0 \times 10^6}{\pi^2}}$$

can be used to determine the maximum range $R(x)$, in miles, of an ARSR-3 surveillance radar with a peak power of x watts. Determine the maximum radar range when the peak power is 5×10^4 watts.
Source: Introduction to RADAR Techniques, Federal Aviation Administration, 1988

88. *Speed of a skidding car.* Police can estimate the speed at which a car was traveling by measuring its skid marks. The function given by

$$r(L) = 2\sqrt{5L}$$

can be used, where L is the length of a skid mark, in feet, and $r(L)$ is the speed, in miles per hour. Find

the exact speed and an estimate (to the nearest tenth mile per hour) for the speed of a car that left skid marks **(a)** 20 ft long; **(b)** 70 ft long; **(c)** 90 ft long. See also Exercise 102.

89. *Wind chill temperature.* When the temperature is T degrees Celsius and the wind speed is v meters per second, the *wind chill temperature*, T_w, is the temperature (with no wind) that it feels like. Here is a formula for finding wind chill temperature:

$$T_w = 33 - \frac{(10.45 + 10\sqrt{v} - v)(33 - T)}{22}.$$

Estimate the wind chill temperature (to the nearest tenth of a degree) for the given actual temperatures and wind speeds.

a) $T = 7°C$, $v = 8$ m/sec
b) $T = 0°C$, $v = 12$ m/sec
c) $T = -5°C$, $v = 14$ m/sec
d) $T = -23°C$, $v = 15$ m/sec

Simplify. Assume that all variables are nonnegative.

90. $\left(\sqrt{r^3t}\right)^7$

91. $\left(\sqrt[3]{25x^4}\right)^4$

92. $\left(\sqrt[3]{a^2b^4}\right)^5$

93. $\left(\sqrt{a^3b^5}\right)^7$

Draw and compare the graphs of each group of equations.

94. $f(x) = \sqrt{x^2 - 2x + 1}$,
$g(x) = x - 1$,
$h(x) = |x - 1|$

95. $f(x) = \sqrt{x^2 + 2x + 1}$,
$g(x) = x + 1$,
$h(x) = |x + 1|$

96. If $f(t) = \sqrt{t^2 - 3t - 4}$, what is the domain of f?

97. What is the domain of g, if $g(x) = \sqrt{x^2 - 6x + 8}$?

Solve.

98. $\sqrt[3]{5x^{k+1}} \sqrt[3]{25x^k} = 5x^7$, for k

99. $\sqrt[5]{4a^{3k+2}} \sqrt[5]{8a^{6-k}} = 2a^4$, for k

100. Use a graphing calculator to check your answers to Exercises 21 and 41.

101. Blair is puzzled. When he uses a graphing calculator to graph $y = \sqrt{x} \cdot \sqrt{x}$, he gets the following screen. Explain why Blair did not get the complete line $y = x$.

102. Does a car traveling twice as fast as another car leave a skid mark that is twice as long? (See Exercise 88.) Why or why not?

8.4 Dividing Radical Expressions

Dividing and Simplifying ▪ Rationalizing Denominators or Numerators with One Term

Dividing and Simplifying

Just as the root of a product can be expressed as the product of two roots, the root of a quotient can be expressed as the quotient of two roots. For example,

$$\sqrt[3]{\frac{27}{8}} = \frac{3}{2} \quad \text{and} \quad \frac{\sqrt[3]{27}}{\sqrt[3]{8}} = \frac{3}{2}.$$

This example suggests the following.

> **The Quotient Rule for Radicals**
> For any real numbers $\sqrt[n]{a}$ and $\sqrt[n]{b}$, $b \neq 0$,
> $$\sqrt[n]{\frac{a}{b}} = \frac{\sqrt[n]{a}}{\sqrt[n]{b}}.$$

Remember that an nth root is simplified when its radicand has no factors that are perfect nth powers. Unless functions are involved, we assume that no radicands represent negative quantities raised to an even power.

EXAMPLE 1 Simplify by taking the roots of the numerator and the denominator.

a) $\sqrt[3]{\dfrac{27}{125}}$ 　　　　　　　　　　　　**b)** $\sqrt{\dfrac{25}{y^2}}$

SOLUTION

a) $\sqrt[3]{\dfrac{27}{125}} = \dfrac{\sqrt[3]{27}}{\sqrt[3]{125}} = \dfrac{3}{5}$ 　Taking the cube roots of the numerator and the denominator

b) $\sqrt{\dfrac{25}{y^2}} = \dfrac{\sqrt{25}}{\sqrt{y^2}} = \dfrac{5}{y}$ 　Taking the square roots of the numerator and the denominator. Assume $y > 0$.　　　**TRY EXERCISE** 9

Any radical expressions appearing in the answers should be simplified as much as possible.

EXAMPLE 2 Simplify: **(a)** $\sqrt{\dfrac{16x^3}{y^8}}$; **(b)** $\sqrt[3]{\dfrac{27y^{14}}{8x^3}}$.

SOLUTION

a) $\sqrt{\dfrac{16x^3}{y^8}} = \dfrac{\sqrt{16x^3}}{\sqrt{y^8}}$

$= \dfrac{\sqrt{16x^2 \cdot x}}{\sqrt{y^8}}$

$= \dfrac{4x\sqrt{x}}{y^4}$ 　　Simplifying the numerator and the denominator

b) $\sqrt[3]{\dfrac{27y^{14}}{8x^3}} = \dfrac{\sqrt[3]{27y^{14}}}{\sqrt[3]{8x^3}}$

$= \dfrac{\sqrt[3]{27y^{12}y^2}}{\sqrt[3]{8x^3}}$ y^{12} is the largest perfect-cube factor of y^{14}.

$= \dfrac{\sqrt[3]{27y^{12}}\,\sqrt[3]{y^2}}{\sqrt[3]{8x^3}}$

$= \dfrac{3y^4\sqrt[3]{y^2}}{2x}$ Simplifying the numerator and the denominator

TRY EXERCISE ▶ 17

If we read from right to left, the quotient rule tells us that to divide two radical expressions that have the same index, we can divide the radicands.

EXAMPLE 3   Divide and, if possible, simplify.

a) $\dfrac{\sqrt{80}}{\sqrt{5}}$

b) $\dfrac{5\sqrt[3]{32}}{\sqrt[3]{2}}$

c) $\dfrac{\sqrt{72xy}}{2\sqrt{2}}$

d) $\dfrac{\sqrt[4]{18a^9b^5}}{\sqrt[4]{3b}}$

SOLUTION

STUDENT NOTES ⎯⎯⎯⎯

When writing radical signs, pay careful attention to what is included as the radicand. Each of the following represents a *different* number:

$$\sqrt{\dfrac{5\cdot 2}{3}},\quad \dfrac{\sqrt{5\cdot 2}}{3},\quad \dfrac{\sqrt{5}\cdot 2}{3}.$$

a) $\dfrac{\sqrt{80}}{\sqrt{5}} = \sqrt{\dfrac{80}{5}} = \sqrt{16} = 4$

> Because the indices match, we can divide the radicands.

b) $\dfrac{5\sqrt[3]{32}}{\sqrt[3]{2}} = 5\sqrt[3]{\dfrac{32}{2}} = 5\sqrt[3]{16}$

$= 5\sqrt[3]{8\cdot 2}$ 8 is the largest perfect-cube factor of 16.

$= 5\sqrt[3]{8}\,\sqrt[3]{2} = 5\cdot 2\sqrt[3]{2}$

$= 10\sqrt[3]{2}$

c) $\dfrac{\sqrt{72xy}}{2\sqrt{2}} = \dfrac{1}{2}\sqrt{\dfrac{72xy}{2}}$

> Because the indices match, we can divide the radicands.

$= \dfrac{1}{2}\sqrt{36xy} = \dfrac{1}{2}\cdot 6\sqrt{xy}$

$= 3\sqrt{xy}$

d) $\dfrac{\sqrt[4]{18a^9b^5}}{\sqrt[4]{3b}} = \sqrt[4]{\dfrac{18a^9b^5}{3b}}$

$= \sqrt[4]{6a^9b^4} = \sqrt[4]{a^8b^4}\,\sqrt[4]{6a}$ Note that 8 is the largest power less than 9 that is a multiple of the index 4.

$= a^2b\sqrt[4]{6a}$ *Partial check:* $(a^2b)^4 = a^8b^4$

TRY EXERCISE ▶ 27

Rationalizing Denominators or Numerators with One Term*

The expressions

$$\frac{1}{\sqrt{2}} \quad \text{and} \quad \frac{\sqrt{2}}{2}$$

are equivalent, but the second expression does not have a radical expression in the denominator.[†] We can **rationalize the denominator** of a radical expression if we multiply by 1 in either of two ways.

One way is to multiply by 1 *under* the radical to make the denominator of the radicand a perfect power.

EXAMPLE 4 Rationalize each denominator.

a) $\sqrt{\dfrac{7}{3}}$
b) $\sqrt[3]{\dfrac{5}{16}}$

SOLUTION

a) We multiply by 1 under the radical, using $\frac{3}{3}$. We do this so that the denominator of the radicand will be a perfect square:

$$\sqrt{\frac{7}{3}} = \sqrt{\frac{7}{3} \cdot \frac{3}{3}} \qquad \text{Multiplying by 1 under the radical}$$

$$= \sqrt{\frac{21}{9}} \qquad \text{The denominator, 9, is now a perfect square.}$$

$$= \frac{\sqrt{21}}{\sqrt{9}} \qquad \text{Using the quotient rule for radicals}$$

$$= \frac{\sqrt{21}}{3}.$$

b) Note that $16 = 4^2$. Thus, to make the denominator a perfect cube, we multiply under the radical by $\frac{4}{4}$:

$$\sqrt[3]{\frac{5}{16}} = \sqrt[3]{\frac{5}{4 \cdot 4} \cdot \frac{4}{4}} \qquad \text{Since the index is 3, we need 3 identical factors in the denominator.}$$

$$= \sqrt[3]{\frac{20}{4^3}} \qquad \text{The denominator is now a perfect cube.}$$

$$= \frac{\sqrt[3]{20}}{\sqrt[3]{4^3}}$$

$$= \frac{\sqrt[3]{20}}{4}.$$

TRY EXERCISE 41

Another way to rationalize a denominator is to multiply by 1 *outside* the radical.

EXAMPLE 5 Rationalize each denominator.

a) $\sqrt{\dfrac{4}{5b}}$
b) $\dfrac{\sqrt[3]{a}}{\sqrt[3]{25bc^5}}$
c) $\dfrac{3x}{\sqrt[5]{2x^2y^3}}$

---

*Denominators and numerators with two terms are rationalized in Section 8.5.
[†]See Exercise 73 on p. 521.

SOLUTION

a) We rewrite the expression as a quotient of two radicals. Then we simplify and multiply by 1:

$$\sqrt{\frac{4}{5b}} = \frac{\sqrt{4}}{\sqrt{5b}} = \frac{2}{\sqrt{5b}} \qquad \text{We assume } b > 0.$$

$$= \frac{2}{\sqrt{5b}} \cdot \frac{\sqrt{5b}}{\sqrt{5b}} \qquad \text{Multiplying by 1}$$

$$= \frac{2\sqrt{5b}}{\left(\sqrt{5b}\right)^2} \qquad \text{Try to do this step mentally.}$$

$$= \frac{2\sqrt{5b}}{5b}.$$

b) Note that the radicand $25bc^5$ is $5 \cdot 5 \cdot b \cdot c \cdot c \cdot c \cdot c \cdot c$. In order for this to be a cube, we need another factor of 5, two more factors of b, and one more factor of c. Thus we multiply by 1, using $\sqrt[3]{5b^2c}/\sqrt[3]{5b^2c}$:

$$\frac{\sqrt[3]{a}}{\sqrt[3]{25bc^5}} = \frac{\sqrt[3]{a}}{\sqrt[3]{25bc^5}} \cdot \frac{\sqrt[3]{5b^2c}}{\sqrt[3]{5b^2c}} \qquad \text{Multiplying by 1}$$

$$= \frac{\sqrt[3]{5ab^2c}}{\sqrt[3]{125b^3c^6}} \longleftarrow \text{This radicand is now a perfect cube.}$$

$$= \frac{\sqrt[3]{5ab^2c}}{5bc^2}.$$

c) To change the radicand $2x^2y^3$ into a perfect fifth power, we need four more factors of 2, three more factors of x, and two more factors of y. Thus we multiply by 1, using $\sqrt[5]{2^4x^3y^2}/\sqrt[5]{2^4x^3y^2}$, or $\sqrt[5]{16x^3y^2}/\sqrt[5]{16x^3y^2}$:

$$\frac{3x}{\sqrt[5]{2x^2y^3}} = \frac{3x}{\sqrt[5]{2x^2y^3}} \cdot \frac{\sqrt[5]{16x^3y^2}}{\sqrt[5]{16x^3y^2}} \qquad \text{Multiplying by 1}$$

$$= \frac{3x\sqrt[5]{16x^3y^2}}{\sqrt[5]{32x^5y^5}} \longleftarrow \qquad \text{This radicand is now a perfect fifth power.}$$

$$= \frac{3x\sqrt[5]{16x^3y^2}}{2xy} = \frac{3\sqrt[5]{16x^3y^2}}{2y}. \qquad \text{Always simplify if possible.}$$

> TRY EXERCISE 47

Sometimes in calculus it is necessary to rationalize a numerator. To do so, we multiply by 1 to make the radicand in the *numerator* a perfect power.

EXAMPLE **6** Rationalize the numerator: $\dfrac{\sqrt[3]{4a^2}}{\sqrt[3]{5b}}$.

SOLUTION

$$\frac{\sqrt[3]{4a^2}}{\sqrt[3]{5b}} = \frac{\sqrt[3]{4a^2}}{\sqrt[3]{5b}} \cdot \frac{\sqrt[3]{2a}}{\sqrt[3]{2a}} \qquad \text{Multiplying by 1}$$

$$= \frac{\sqrt[3]{8a^3}}{\sqrt[3]{10ba}} \longleftarrow \text{This radicand is now a perfect cube.}$$

$$= \frac{2a}{\sqrt[3]{10ab}}$$

> TRY EXERCISE 59

In Section 8.5, we will discuss rationalizing denominators and numerators in which two terms appear.

8.4 EXERCISE SET

For Extra Help

Concept Reinforcement *In each of Exercises 1–8, match the expression with an equivalent expression from the column on the right. Assume $a, b > 0$.*

1. ___ $\sqrt[4]{\dfrac{16a^6}{a^2}}$
   a) $\dfrac{\sqrt[5]{a^2}\sqrt[5]{b^2}}{\sqrt[5]{b^5}}$

2. ___ $\dfrac{\sqrt[3]{a^6}}{\sqrt[3]{b^9}}$
   b) $\dfrac{a^2}{b^3}$

3. ___ $\sqrt[5]{\dfrac{a^6}{b^4}}$
   c) $\sqrt{\dfrac{a \cdot b}{b^3 \cdot b}}$

4. ___ $\sqrt{\dfrac{a}{b^3}}$
   d) $\sqrt{a}$

   e) $\dfrac{\sqrt[3]{a^2}}{b^2}$

5. ___ $\dfrac{\sqrt[5]{a^2}}{\sqrt[5]{b^2}}$
   f) $\sqrt[5]{\dfrac{a^6 b}{b^4 \cdot b}}$

6. ___ $\dfrac{\sqrt{5a^4}}{\sqrt{5a^3}}$
   g) $2a$

7. ___ $\dfrac{\sqrt[5]{a^2}}{\sqrt[5]{b^3}}$
   h) $\dfrac{\sqrt[5]{a^2 b^3}}{\sqrt[5]{b^5}}$

8. ___ $\sqrt[3]{\dfrac{a^2}{b^6}}$

Simplify by taking the roots of the numerator and the denominator. Assume all variables represent positive numbers.

9. $\sqrt{\dfrac{49}{100}}$
10. $\sqrt{\dfrac{81}{25}}$
11. $\sqrt[3]{\dfrac{125}{8}}$

12. $\sqrt[3]{\dfrac{1000}{27}}$
13. $\sqrt{\dfrac{121}{t^2}}$
14. $\sqrt{\dfrac{144}{p^2}}$

15. $\sqrt{\dfrac{36y^3}{x^4}}$
16. $\sqrt{\dfrac{25a^5}{b^6}}$
17. $\sqrt[3]{\dfrac{27a^4}{8b^3}}$

18. $\sqrt[3]{\dfrac{64x^7}{216y^6}}$
19. $\sqrt[4]{\dfrac{32a^4}{2b^4c^8}}$
20. $\sqrt[4]{\dfrac{81x^4}{y^8z^4}}$

21. $\sqrt[4]{\dfrac{a^5b^8}{c^{10}}}$
22. $\sqrt[4]{\dfrac{x^9y^{12}}{z^6}}$
23. $\sqrt[5]{\dfrac{32x^6}{y^{11}}}$

24. $\sqrt[5]{\dfrac{243a^9}{b^{13}}}$
25. $\sqrt[6]{\dfrac{x^6y^8}{z^{15}}}$
26. $\sqrt[6]{\dfrac{a^9b^{12}}{c^{13}}}$

Divide and, if possible, simplify. Assume all variables represent positive numbers.

27. $\dfrac{\sqrt{18y}}{\sqrt{2y}}$
28. $\dfrac{\sqrt{700x}}{\sqrt{7x}}$

29. $\dfrac{\sqrt[3]{26}}{\sqrt[3]{13}}$
30. $\dfrac{\sqrt[3]{35}}{\sqrt[3]{5}}$

31. $\dfrac{\sqrt{40xy^3}}{\sqrt{8x}}$
32. $\dfrac{\sqrt{56ab^3}}{\sqrt{7a}}$

33. $\dfrac{\sqrt[3]{96a^4b^2}}{\sqrt[3]{12a^2b}}$
34. $\dfrac{\sqrt[3]{189x^5y^7}}{\sqrt[3]{7x^2y^2}}$

35. $\dfrac{\sqrt{100ab}}{5\sqrt{2}}$
36. $\dfrac{\sqrt{75ab}}{3\sqrt{3}}$

37. $\dfrac{\sqrt[4]{48x^9y^{13}}}{\sqrt[4]{3xy^{-2}}}$
38. $\dfrac{\sqrt[5]{64a^{11}b^{28}}}{\sqrt[5]{2ab^{-2}}}$

39. $\dfrac{\sqrt[3]{x^3 - y^3}}{\sqrt[3]{x - y}}$
40. $\dfrac{\sqrt[3]{r^3 + s^3}}{\sqrt[3]{r + s}}$

Hint: Factor and then simplify.

Rationalize each denominator. Assume all variables represent positive numbers.

41. $\sqrt{\dfrac{2}{5}}$
42. $\sqrt{\dfrac{7}{2}}$
43. $\dfrac{2\sqrt{5}}{7\sqrt{3}}$

44. $\dfrac{3\sqrt{5}}{2\sqrt{7}}$
45. $\sqrt[3]{\dfrac{5}{4}}$
46. $\sqrt[3]{\dfrac{2}{9}}$

47. $\dfrac{\sqrt[3]{3a}}{\sqrt[3]{5c}}$
48. $\dfrac{\sqrt[3]{7x}}{\sqrt[3]{3y}}$
49. $\dfrac{\sqrt[4]{5y^6}}{\sqrt[4]{9x}}$

50. $\dfrac{\sqrt[5]{3a^4}}{\sqrt[5]{2b^7}}$
51. $\sqrt[3]{\dfrac{2}{x^2y}}$
52. $\sqrt[3]{\dfrac{5}{ab^2}}$

53. $\sqrt{\dfrac{7a}{18}}$
54. $\sqrt{\dfrac{3x}{20}}$
55. $\sqrt[5]{\dfrac{9}{32x^5y}}$

56. $\sqrt[4]{\dfrac{7}{64a^2b^4}}$
Aha! 57. $\sqrt{\dfrac{10ab^2}{72a^3b}}$
58. $\sqrt{\dfrac{21x^2y}{75xy^5}}$

Rationalize each numerator. Assume all variables represent positive numbers.

59. $\sqrt{\dfrac{5}{11}}$ **60.** $\sqrt{\dfrac{2}{3}}$ **61.** $\dfrac{2\sqrt{6}}{5\sqrt{7}}$

62. $\dfrac{3\sqrt{10}}{2\sqrt{3}}$ **63.** $\dfrac{\sqrt{8}}{2\sqrt{3x}}$ **64.** $\dfrac{\sqrt{12}}{\sqrt{5y}}$

65. $\dfrac{\sqrt[3]{7}}{\sqrt[3]{2}}$ **66.** $\dfrac{\sqrt[3]{5}}{\sqrt[3]{4}}$ **67.** $\sqrt{\dfrac{7x}{3y}}$

68. $\sqrt{\dfrac{7a}{6b}}$ **69.** $\sqrt[3]{\dfrac{2a^5}{5b}}$ **70.** $\sqrt[3]{\dfrac{2a^4}{7b}}$

71. $\sqrt{\dfrac{x^3y}{2}}$ **72.** $\sqrt{\dfrac{ab^5}{3}}$

73. Explain why it is easier to approximate

$$\dfrac{\sqrt{2}}{2} \quad \text{than} \quad \dfrac{1}{\sqrt{2}}$$

if no calculator is available and $\sqrt{2} \approx 1.414213562$.

74. A student *incorrectly* claims that

$$\dfrac{5 + \sqrt{2}}{\sqrt{18}} = \dfrac{5 + \sqrt{1}}{\sqrt{9}} = \dfrac{5 + 1}{3}.$$

How could you convince the student that a mistake has been made? How would you explain the correct way of rationalizing the denominator?

Skill Review

To prepare for Section 8.5, review factoring expressions and multiplying polynomials (Section 3.1).

Factor. [3.1]

75. $3x - 8xy + 2xz$ **76.** $4a^2c + 9ac - 3a^3c$

Multiply.

77. $(a + b)(a - b)$ **78.** $(a^2 - 2y)(a^2 + 2y)$

79. $(8 + 3x)(7 - 4x)$ **80.** $(2y - x)(3a - c)$

Synthesis

81. Is the quotient of two irrational numbers always an irrational number? Why or why not?

82. Is it possible to understand how to rationalize a denominator without knowing how to multiply rational expressions? Why or why not?

83. *Pendulums.* The *period* of a pendulum is the time it takes to complete one cycle, swinging to and fro. For a pendulum that is L centimeters long, the period T is given by the formula

$$T = 2\pi\sqrt{\dfrac{L}{980}},$$

where T is in seconds. Find, to the nearest hundredth of a second, the period of a pendulum of length **(a)** 65 cm; **(b)** 98 cm; **(c)** 120 cm. Use a calculator's $\boxed{\pi}$ key if possible.

Perform the indicated operations.

84. $\dfrac{7\sqrt{a^2b}\,\sqrt{25xy}}{5\sqrt{a^{-4}b^{-1}}\,\sqrt{49x^{-1}y^{-3}}}$ **85.** $\dfrac{\left(\sqrt[3]{81mn^2}\right)^2}{\left(\sqrt[3]{mn}\right)^2}$

86. $\dfrac{\sqrt{44x^2y^9z}\,\sqrt{22y^9z^6}}{\left(\sqrt{11xy^8z^2}\right)^2}$

87. $\sqrt{a^2 - 3} - \dfrac{a^2}{\sqrt{a^2 - 3}}$

88. $5\sqrt{\dfrac{x}{y}} + 4\sqrt{\dfrac{y}{x}} - \dfrac{3}{\sqrt{xy}}$

89. Provide a reason for each step in the following derivation of the quotient rule:

$$\sqrt[n]{\dfrac{a}{b}} = \left(\dfrac{a}{b}\right)^{1/n} \quad \underline{\hspace{2cm}}$$
$$= \dfrac{a^{1/n}}{b^{1/n}} \quad \underline{\hspace{2cm}}$$
$$= \dfrac{\sqrt[n]{a}}{\sqrt[n]{b}} \quad \underline{\hspace{2cm}}$$

90. Show that $\dfrac{\sqrt[n]{a}}{\sqrt[n]{b}}$ is the nth root of $\dfrac{a}{b}$ by raising it to the nth power and simplifying.

91. Let $f(x) = \sqrt{18x^3}$ and $g(x) = \sqrt{2x}$. Find $(f/g)(x)$ and specify the domain of f/g.

92. Let $f(t) = \sqrt{2t}$ and $g(t) = \sqrt{50t^3}$. Find $(f/g)(t)$ and specify the domain of f/g.

93. Let $f(x) = \sqrt{x^2 - 9}$ and $g(x) = \sqrt{x - 3}$. Find $(f/g)(x)$ and specify the domain of f/g.

8.5   Expressions Containing Several Radical Terms

Adding and Subtracting Radical Expressions   •   Products and Quotients of Two or More Radical Terms   •   Rationalizing Denominators or Numerators with Two Terms   •   Terms with Differing Indices

Radical expressions like $6\sqrt{7} + 4\sqrt{7}$ or $(\sqrt{a} + \sqrt{b})(\sqrt{a} - \sqrt{b})$ contain more than one *radical term* and can sometimes be simplified.

Adding and Subtracting Radical Expressions

When two radical expressions have the same indices and radicands, they are said to be **like radicals**. Like radicals can be combined (added or subtracted) in much the same way that we combine like terms.

EXAMPLE 1

Simplify by combining like radical terms.

a) $6\sqrt{7} + 4\sqrt{7}$

b) $\sqrt[3]{2} - 7x\sqrt[3]{2} + 5\sqrt[3]{2}$

c) $6\sqrt[5]{4x} + 3\sqrt[5]{4x} - \sqrt[3]{4x}$

SOLUTION

a) $6\sqrt{7} + 4\sqrt{7} = (6 + 4)\sqrt{7}$ Using the distributive law (factoring out $\sqrt{7}$)

$= 10\sqrt{7}$ You can think: 6 square roots of 7 plus 4 square roots of 7 is 10 square roots of 7.

b) $\sqrt[3]{2} - 7x\sqrt[3]{2} + 5\sqrt[3]{2} = (1 - 7x + 5)\sqrt[3]{2}$ Factoring out $\sqrt[3]{2}$

$= (6 - 7x)\sqrt[3]{2}$ These parentheses are important!

c) $6\sqrt[5]{4x} + 3\sqrt[5]{4x} - \sqrt[3]{4x} = (6 + 3)\sqrt[5]{4x} - \sqrt[3]{4x}$ Try to do this step mentally.

$= 9\sqrt[5]{4x} - \sqrt[3]{4x}$ The indices are different. We cannot combine these terms.

TRY EXERCISE   7

Our ability to simplify radical expressions can help us to find like radicals even when, at first, it may appear that there are none.

EXAMPLE 2

Simplify by combining like radical terms, if possible.

a) $3\sqrt{8} - 5\sqrt{2}$

b) $9\sqrt{5} - 4\sqrt{3}$

c) $\sqrt[3]{2x^6y^4} + 7\sqrt[3]{2y}$

SOLUTION

a) $3\sqrt{8} - 5\sqrt{2} = 3\sqrt{4 \cdot 2} - 5\sqrt{2}$

$= 3\sqrt{4} \cdot \sqrt{2} - 5\sqrt{2}$ Simplifying $\sqrt{8}$

$= 3 \cdot 2 \cdot \sqrt{2} - 5\sqrt{2}$

$= 6\sqrt{2} - 5\sqrt{2}$

$= \sqrt{2}$ Combining like radicals

b) $9\sqrt{5} - 4\sqrt{3}$ cannot be simplified.　　The radicands are different.

c) $\sqrt[3]{2x^6y^4} + 7\sqrt[3]{2y} = \sqrt[3]{x^6y^3 \cdot 2y} + 7\sqrt[3]{2y}$

$\qquad\qquad\qquad = \sqrt[3]{x^6y^3} \cdot \sqrt[3]{2y} + 7\sqrt[3]{2y}$　　Simplifying $\sqrt[3]{2x^6y^4}$

$\qquad\qquad\qquad = x^2y \cdot \sqrt[3]{2y} + 7\sqrt[3]{2y}$

$\qquad\qquad\qquad = (x^2y + 7)\sqrt[3]{2y}$　　Factoring to combine like radical terms

TRY EXERCISE　17

Products and Quotients of Two or More Radical Terms

Radical expressions often contain factors that have more than one term. Multiplying such expressions is similar to finding products of polynomials. Some products will yield like radical terms, which we can now combine.

EXAMPLE 3　　Multiply.

a) $\sqrt{3}(x - \sqrt{5})$

b) $\sqrt[3]{y}\left(\sqrt[3]{y^2} + \sqrt[3]{2}\right)$

c) $(4\sqrt{3} + \sqrt{2})(\sqrt{3} - 5\sqrt{2})$

d) $(\sqrt{a} + \sqrt{b})(\sqrt{a} - \sqrt{b})$

SOLUTION

a) $\sqrt{3}(x - \sqrt{5}) = \sqrt{3} \cdot x - \sqrt{3} \cdot \sqrt{5}$　　Using the distributive law

$\qquad\qquad\quad = x\sqrt{3} - \sqrt{15}$　　Multiplying radicals

b) $\sqrt[3]{y}\left(\sqrt[3]{y^2} + \sqrt[3]{2}\right) = \sqrt[3]{y} \cdot \sqrt[3]{y^2} + \sqrt[3]{y} \cdot \sqrt[3]{2}$　　Using the distributive law

$\qquad\qquad\qquad\quad = \sqrt[3]{y^3} + \sqrt[3]{2y}$　　Multiplying radicals

$\qquad\qquad\qquad\quad = y + \sqrt[3]{2y}$　　Simplifying $\sqrt[3]{y^3}$

$\qquad\qquad\qquad\qquad\qquad\qquad\quad$ F $\qquad$ O $\qquad$ I $\qquad$ L

c) $(4\sqrt{3} + \sqrt{2})(\sqrt{3} - 5\sqrt{2}) = 4(\sqrt{3})^2 - 20\sqrt{3} \cdot \sqrt{2} + \sqrt{2} \cdot \sqrt{3} - 5(\sqrt{2})^2$

$\qquad\qquad\qquad\qquad\qquad = 4 \cdot 3 - 20\sqrt{6} + \sqrt{6} - 5 \cdot 2$　　Multiplying radicals

$\qquad\qquad\qquad\qquad\qquad = 12 - 20\sqrt{6} + \sqrt{6} - 10$

$\qquad\qquad\qquad\qquad\qquad = 2 - 19\sqrt{6}$　　Combining like terms

d) $(\sqrt{a} + \sqrt{b})(\sqrt{a} - \sqrt{b}) = (\sqrt{a})^2 - \sqrt{a}\sqrt{b} + \sqrt{a}\sqrt{b} - (\sqrt{b})^2$　　Using FOIL

$\qquad\qquad\qquad\qquad\qquad = a - b$　　Combining like terms

TRY EXERCISE　41

In Example 3(d) above, you may have noticed that since the outer and inner products in FOIL are opposites, the result, $a - b$, is not itself a radical expression. Pairs of radical expressions like $\sqrt{a} + \sqrt{b}$ and $\sqrt{a} - \sqrt{b}$ are called **conjugates**.

Rationalizing Denominators or Numerators with Two Terms

The use of conjugates allows us to rationalize denominators or numerators that contain two terms.

EXAMPLE 4 Rationalize each denominator: **(a)** $\dfrac{4}{\sqrt{3} + x}$; **(b)** $\dfrac{4 + \sqrt{2}}{\sqrt{5} - \sqrt{2}}$.

SOLUTION

a) $\dfrac{4}{\sqrt{3} + x} = \dfrac{4}{\sqrt{3} + x} \cdot \dfrac{\sqrt{3} - x}{\sqrt{3} - x}$ Multiplying by 1, using the conjugate of $\sqrt{3} + x$, which is $\sqrt{3} - x$

$= \dfrac{4(\sqrt{3} - x)}{(\sqrt{3} + x)(\sqrt{3} - x)}$ Multiplying numerators and denominators

$= \dfrac{4(\sqrt{3} - x)}{(\sqrt{3})^2 - x^2}$ Using FOIL in the denominator

$= \dfrac{4\sqrt{3} - 4x}{3 - x^2}$ Simplifying. No radicals remain in the denominator.

b) $\dfrac{4 + \sqrt{2}}{\sqrt{5} - \sqrt{2}} = \dfrac{4 + \sqrt{2}}{\sqrt{5} - \sqrt{2}} \cdot \dfrac{\sqrt{5} + \sqrt{2}}{\sqrt{5} + \sqrt{2}}$ Multiplying by 1, using the conjugate of $\sqrt{5} - \sqrt{2}$, which is $\sqrt{5} + \sqrt{2}$

$= \dfrac{(4 + \sqrt{2})(\sqrt{5} + \sqrt{2})}{(\sqrt{5} - \sqrt{2})(\sqrt{5} + \sqrt{2})}$ Multiplying numerators and denominators

$= \dfrac{4\sqrt{5} + 4\sqrt{2} + \sqrt{2}\sqrt{5} + (\sqrt{2})^2}{(\sqrt{5})^2 - (\sqrt{2})^2}$ Using FOIL

$= \dfrac{4\sqrt{5} + 4\sqrt{2} + \sqrt{10} + 2}{5 - 2}$ Squaring in the denominator and the numerator

$= \dfrac{4\sqrt{5} + 4\sqrt{2} + \sqrt{10} + 2}{3}$ No radicals remain in the denominator.

TRY EXERCISE 61

To rationalize a numerator with two terms, we use the conjugate of the numerator.

EXAMPLE 5 Rationalize the numerator: $\dfrac{4 + \sqrt{2}}{\sqrt{5} - \sqrt{2}}$.

SOLUTION

$\dfrac{4 + \sqrt{2}}{\sqrt{5} - \sqrt{2}} = \dfrac{4 + \sqrt{2}}{\sqrt{5} - \sqrt{2}} \cdot \dfrac{4 - \sqrt{2}}{4 - \sqrt{2}}$ Multiplying by 1, using the conjugate of $4 + \sqrt{2}$, which is $4 - \sqrt{2}$

$= \dfrac{16 - (\sqrt{2})^2}{4\sqrt{5} - \sqrt{5}\sqrt{2} - 4\sqrt{2} + (\sqrt{2})^2}$

$= \dfrac{14}{4\sqrt{5} - \sqrt{10} - 4\sqrt{2} + 2}$

TRY EXERCISE 71

Terms with Differing Indices

To multiply or divide radical terms with identical radicands but different indices, we can convert to exponential notation, use the rules for exponents, and then convert back to radical notation.

EXAMPLE 6

Divide and, if possible, simplify: $\dfrac{\sqrt[4]{(x+y)^3}}{\sqrt{x+y}}$.

STUDENT NOTES

Expressions similar to the one in Example 6 are most easily simplified by rewriting the expression using exponents in place of radicals. After simplifying, remember to write your final result in radical notation. In general, if a problem is presented in one form, it is expected that the final result be presented in the same form.

SOLUTION

$$\frac{\sqrt[4]{(x+y)^3}}{\sqrt{x+y}} = \frac{(x+y)^{3/4}}{(x+y)^{1/2}}$$ Converting to exponential notation

$$= (x+y)^{3/4-1/2}$$ Since the bases are identical, we can subtract exponents: $\frac{3}{4} - \frac{1}{2} = \frac{3}{4} - \frac{2}{4} = \frac{1}{4}$.

$$= (x+y)^{1/4}$$

$$= \sqrt[4]{x+y}$$ Converting back to radical notation

TRY EXERCISE 95

The steps used in Example 6 can be used in a variety of situations.

To Simplify Products or Quotients with Differing Indices

1. Convert all radical expressions to exponential notation.
2. When the bases are identical, subtract exponents to divide and add exponents to multiply. This may require finding a common denominator.
3. Convert back to radical notation and, if possible, simplify.

EXAMPLE 7

Multiply and simplify: $\sqrt{x^3}\sqrt[3]{x}$.

SOLUTION

$$\sqrt{x^3}\sqrt[3]{x} = x^{3/2} \cdot x^{1/3}$$ Converting to exponential notation

$$= x^{11/6}$$ Adding exponents: $\frac{3}{2} + \frac{1}{3} = \frac{9}{6} + \frac{2}{6}$

$$= \sqrt[6]{x^{11}}$$ Converting back to radical notation

$$= \sqrt[6]{x^6}\sqrt[6]{x^5}$$

$$= x\sqrt[6]{x^5}$$ Simplifying

TRY EXERCISE 79

EXAMPLE 8

If $f(x) = \sqrt[3]{x^2}$ and $g(x) = \sqrt{x} + \sqrt[4]{x}$, find $(f \cdot g)(x)$.

SOLUTION Recall from Section 5.4 that $(f \cdot g)(x) = f(x) \cdot g(x)$. Thus,

$$(f \cdot g)(x) = \sqrt[3]{x^2}\left(\sqrt{x} + \sqrt[4]{x}\right)$$ x is assumed to be nonnegative.

$$= x^{2/3}(x^{1/2} + x^{1/4})$$ Converting to exponential notation

$$= x^{2/3} \cdot x^{1/2} + x^{2/3} \cdot x^{1/4}$$ Using the distributive law

$$= x^{2/3+1/2} + x^{2/3+1/4}$$ Adding exponents:

$$= x^{7/6} + x^{11/12}$$ $\frac{2}{3} + \frac{1}{2} = \frac{4}{6} + \frac{3}{6}, \frac{2}{3} + \frac{1}{4} = \frac{8}{12} + \frac{3}{12}$

$$= \sqrt[6]{x^7} + \sqrt[12]{x^{11}}$$ Converting back to radical notation

$$= \sqrt[6]{x^6}\sqrt[6]{x} + \sqrt[12]{x^{11}}$$

$$= x\sqrt[6]{x} + \sqrt[12]{x^{11}}.$$ Simplifying

TRY EXERCISE 103

We often can write the final result as a single radical expression by finding a common denominator in the exponents.

EXAMPLE 9   Divide and, if possible, simplify: $\dfrac{\sqrt[3]{a^2b^4}}{\sqrt{ab}}$.

SOLUTION

$$\frac{\sqrt[3]{a^2b^4}}{\sqrt{ab}} = \frac{(a^2b^4)^{1/3}}{(ab)^{1/2}} \qquad \text{Converting to exponential notation}$$

$$= \frac{a^{2/3}b^{4/3}}{a^{1/2}b^{1/2}} \qquad \text{Using the product and power rules}$$

$$= a^{2/3-1/2}b^{4/3-1/2} \qquad \text{Subtracting exponents}$$

$$= a^{1/6}b^{5/6}$$

$$= \sqrt[6]{a}\,\sqrt[6]{b^5} \qquad \text{Converting to radical notation}$$

$$= \sqrt[6]{ab^5} \qquad \text{Using the product rule for radicals}$$

TRY EXERCISE 91

8.5   EXERCISE SET

For Extra Help   **MyMathLab**   Math XL PRACTICE   WATCH   DOWNLOAD

Concept Reinforcement *For each of Exercises 1–6, fill in the blanks by selecting from the following words (which may be used more than once):*

radicand(s), indices, conjugate(s), base(s), denominator(s), numerator(s).

1. To add radical expressions, the _____ and the _____ must be the same.

2. To multiply radical expressions, the _____ must be the same.

3. To find a product by adding exponents, the _____ must be the same.

4. To add rational expressions, the _____ must be the same.

5. To rationalize the _____ of $\dfrac{\sqrt{c}-\sqrt{a}}{5}$, we multiply by a form of 1, using the _____ of $\sqrt{c}-\sqrt{a}$, or $\sqrt{c}+\sqrt{a}$, to write 1.

6. To find a quotient by subtracting exponents, the _____ must be the same.

Add or subtract. Simplify by combining like radical terms, if possible. Assume that all variables and radicands represent positive real numbers.

7. $4\sqrt{3} + 7\sqrt{3}$

8. $6\sqrt{5} + 2\sqrt{5}$

9. $7\sqrt[3]{4} - 5\sqrt[3]{4}$

10. $14\sqrt[5]{2} - 8\sqrt[5]{2}$

11. $\sqrt[3]{y} + 9\sqrt[3]{y}$

12. $4\sqrt[4]{t} - \sqrt[4]{t}$

13. $8\sqrt{2} - \sqrt{2} + 5\sqrt{2}$

14. $\sqrt{6} + 3\sqrt{6} - 8\sqrt{6}$

15. $9\sqrt[3]{7} - \sqrt{3} + 4\sqrt[3]{7} + 2\sqrt{3}$

16. $5\sqrt{7} - 8\sqrt[4]{11} + \sqrt{7} + 9\sqrt[4]{11}$

17. $4\sqrt{27} - 3\sqrt{3}$

18. $9\sqrt{50} - 4\sqrt{2}$

19. $3\sqrt{45} - 8\sqrt{20}$

20. $5\sqrt{12} + 16\sqrt{27}$

21. $3\sqrt[3]{16} + \sqrt[3]{54}$

22. $\sqrt[3]{27} - 5\sqrt[3]{8}$

23. $\sqrt{a} + 3\sqrt{16a^3}$

24. $2\sqrt{9x^3} - \sqrt{x}$

25. $\sqrt[3]{6x^4} - \sqrt[3]{48x}$

26. $\sqrt[3]{54x} - \sqrt[3]{2x^4}$

27. $\sqrt{4a-4} + \sqrt{a-1}$

28. $\sqrt{9y+27} + \sqrt{y+3}$

29. $\sqrt{x^3-x^2} + \sqrt{9x-9}$

30. $\sqrt{4x-4} - \sqrt{x^3-x^2}$

Multiply. Assume all variables represent nonnegative real numbers.

31. $\sqrt{2}(5 + \sqrt{2})$

32. $\sqrt{3}(6 - \sqrt{3})$

33. $3\sqrt{5}(\sqrt{6} - \sqrt{7})$

34. $4\sqrt{2}(\sqrt{3} + \sqrt{5})$

35. $\sqrt{2}(3\sqrt{10} - \sqrt{8})$

36. $\sqrt{3}(2\sqrt{15} - 3\sqrt{4})$

37. $\sqrt[3]{3}(\sqrt[3]{9} - 4\sqrt[3]{21})$

38. $\sqrt[3]{2}(\sqrt[3]{4} - 2\sqrt[3]{32})$

39. $\sqrt[3]{a}\left(\sqrt[3]{a^2} + \sqrt[3]{24a^2}\right)$

40. $\sqrt[3]{x}\left(\sqrt[3]{3x^2} - \sqrt[3]{81x^2}\right)$

41. $(2 + \sqrt{6})(5 - \sqrt{6})$

42. $(4 - \sqrt{5})(2 + \sqrt{5})$

43. $(\sqrt{2} + \sqrt{7})(\sqrt{3} - \sqrt{7})$

44. $(\sqrt{7} - \sqrt{2})(\sqrt{5} + \sqrt{2})$

45. $(2 - \sqrt{3})(2 + \sqrt{3})$

46. $(3 + \sqrt{11})(3 - \sqrt{11})$

47. $(\sqrt{10} - \sqrt{15})(\sqrt{10} + \sqrt{15})$

48. $(\sqrt{12} + \sqrt{5})(\sqrt{12} - \sqrt{5})$

49. $(3\sqrt{7} + 2\sqrt{5})(2\sqrt{7} - 4\sqrt{5})$

50. $(4\sqrt{5} - 3\sqrt{2})(2\sqrt{5} + 4\sqrt{2})$

51. $(4 + \sqrt{7})^2$ **52.** $(3 + \sqrt{10})^2$

53. $(\sqrt{3} - \sqrt{2})^2$ **54.** $(\sqrt{5} - \sqrt{3})^2$

55. $(\sqrt{2t} + \sqrt{5})^2$ **56.** $(\sqrt{3x} - \sqrt{2})^2$

57. $(3 - \sqrt{x + 5})^2$ **58.** $(4 + \sqrt{x - 3})^2$

59. $\left(2\sqrt[4]{7} - \sqrt[4]{6}\right)\left(3\sqrt[4]{9} + 2\sqrt[4]{5}\right)$

60. $\left(4\sqrt[3]{3} + \sqrt[3]{10}\right)\left(2\sqrt[3]{7} + 5\sqrt[3]{6}\right)$

Rationalize each denominator.

61. $\dfrac{6}{3 - \sqrt{2}}$ **62.** $\dfrac{5}{4 - \sqrt{5}}$

63. $\dfrac{2 + \sqrt{5}}{6 + \sqrt{3}}$ **64.** $\dfrac{1 + \sqrt{2}}{3 + \sqrt{5}}$

65. $\dfrac{\sqrt{a}}{\sqrt{a} + \sqrt{b}}$ **66.** $\dfrac{\sqrt{z}}{\sqrt{x} - \sqrt{z}}$

Aha! **67.** $\dfrac{\sqrt{7} - \sqrt{3}}{\sqrt{3} - \sqrt{7}}$ **68.** $\dfrac{\sqrt{7} + \sqrt{5}}{\sqrt{5} + \sqrt{2}}$

69. $\dfrac{3\sqrt{2} - \sqrt{7}}{4\sqrt{2} + 2\sqrt{5}}$ **70.** $\dfrac{5\sqrt{3} - \sqrt{11}}{2\sqrt{3} - 5\sqrt{2}}$

Rationalize each numerator. If possible, simplify your result.

71. $\dfrac{\sqrt{5} + 1}{4}$ **72.** $\dfrac{\sqrt{15} - 3}{6}$

73. $\dfrac{\sqrt{6} - 2}{\sqrt{3} + 7}$ **74.** $\dfrac{\sqrt{10} + 4}{\sqrt{2} - 3}$

75. $\dfrac{\sqrt{x} - \sqrt{y}}{\sqrt{x} + \sqrt{y}}$ **76.** $\dfrac{\sqrt{a} + \sqrt{b}}{\sqrt{a} - \sqrt{b}}$

77. $\dfrac{\sqrt{a + h} - \sqrt{a}}{h}$ **78.** $\dfrac{\sqrt{x - h} - \sqrt{x}}{h}$

Perform the indicated operation and simplify. Assume all variables represent positive real numbers.

79. $\sqrt[3]{a}\sqrt[6]{a}$ **80.** $\sqrt[10]{a}\sqrt[5]{a^2}$

81. $\sqrt{b^3}\sqrt[5]{b^4}$ **82.** $\sqrt[3]{b^4}\sqrt[4]{b^3}$

83. $\sqrt{xy^3}\ \sqrt[3]{x^2y}$ **84.** $\sqrt[5]{a^3b}\ \sqrt{ab}$

85. $\sqrt[4]{9ab^3}\sqrt{3a^4b}$ **86.** $\sqrt{2x^3y^3}\ \sqrt[3]{4xy^2}$

87. $\sqrt{a^4b^3c^4}\ \sqrt[3]{ab^2c}$ **88.** $\sqrt[3]{xy^2z}\sqrt{x^3yz^2}$

89. $\dfrac{\sqrt[3]{a^2}}{\sqrt[4]{a}}$ **90.** $\dfrac{\sqrt[3]{x^2}}{\sqrt[5]{x}}$

91. $\dfrac{\sqrt[4]{x^2y^3}}{\sqrt[3]{xy}}$ **92.** $\dfrac{\sqrt[5]{a^4b}}{\sqrt[3]{ab}}$

93. $\dfrac{\sqrt{ab^3}}{\sqrt[5]{a^2b^3}}$ **94.** $\dfrac{\sqrt[5]{x^3y^4}}{\sqrt{xy}}$

95. $\dfrac{\sqrt{(7 - y)^3}}{\sqrt[3]{(7 - y)^2}}$ **96.** $\dfrac{\sqrt[5]{(y - 9)^3}}{\sqrt{y - 9}}$

97. $\dfrac{\sqrt[4]{(5 + 3x)^3}}{\sqrt[3]{(5 + 3x)^2}}$ **98.** $\dfrac{\sqrt[3]{(2x + 1)^2}}{\sqrt[5]{(2x + 1)^2}}$

99. $\sqrt[3]{x^2y}\left(\sqrt{xy} - \sqrt[5]{xy^3}\right)$

100. $\sqrt[4]{a^2b}\left(\sqrt[3]{a^2b} - \sqrt[5]{a^2b^2}\right)$

101. $\left(m + \sqrt[3]{n^2}\right)\left(2m + \sqrt[4]{n}\right)$

102. $\left(r - \sqrt[4]{s^3}\right)\left(3r - \sqrt[5]{s}\right)$

In Exercises 103–106, $f(x)$ and $g(x)$ are as given. Find $(f \cdot g)(x)$. Assume all variables represent nonnegative real numbers.

103. $f(x) = \sqrt[4]{x}$, $g(x) = 2\sqrt{x} - \sqrt[3]{x^2}$

104. $f(x) = \sqrt[4]{2x} + 5\sqrt{2x}$, $g(x) = \sqrt[3]{2x}$

105. $f(x) = x + \sqrt{7}$, $g(x) = x - \sqrt{7}$

106. $f(x) = x - \sqrt{2}$, $g(x) = x + \sqrt{6}$

Let $f(x) = x^2$. Find each of the following.

107. $f(3 - \sqrt{2})$

108. $f(5 - \sqrt{3})$

109. $f(\sqrt{6} + \sqrt{21})$

110. $f(\sqrt{2} + \sqrt{10})$

111. In what way(s) is combining like radical terms similar to combining like terms that are monomials?

112. Why do we need to know how to multiply radical expressions before learning how to add them?

Skill Review

To prepare for Section 8.6, review solving equations (Sections 1.2, 3.7, and 4.6).

Solve.

113. $3x - 1 = 125$ [1.2]

114. $x + 5 - 2x = 3x + 6 - x$ [1.2]

115. $x^2 + 2x + 1 = 22 - 2x$ [3.7]

116. $9x^2 - 6x + 1 = 7 + 5x - x^2$ [3.7]

117. $\dfrac{1}{x} + \dfrac{1}{2} = \dfrac{1}{6}$ [4.6]

118. $\dfrac{x}{x - 4} + \dfrac{2}{x + 4} = \dfrac{x - 2}{x^2 - 16}$ [4.6]

Synthesis

119. Ramon *incorrectly* writes
$$\sqrt[5]{x^2} \cdot \sqrt{x^3} = x^{2/5} \cdot x^{3/2} = \sqrt[5]{x^3}.$$
What mistake do you suspect he is making?

120. After examining the expression $\sqrt[4]{25xy^3} \sqrt{5x^4y}$, Dyan (correctly) concludes that x and y are both nonnegative. Explain how she could reach this conclusion.

Find a simplified form for $f(x)$. Assume $x \geq 0$.

121. $f(x) = \sqrt{x^3 - x^2} + \sqrt{9x^3 - 9x^2} - \sqrt{4x^3 - 4x^2}$

122. $f(x) = \sqrt{20x^2 + 4x^3} - 3x\sqrt{45 + 9x} + \sqrt{5x^2 + x^3}$

123. $f(x) = \sqrt[4]{x^5 - x^4} + 3\sqrt[4]{x^9 - x^8}$

124. $f(x) = \sqrt[4]{16x^4 + 16x^5} - 2\sqrt[4]{x^8 + x^9}$

Simplify.

125. $7x\sqrt{(x + y)^3} - 5xy\sqrt{x + y} - 2y\sqrt{(x + y)^3}$

126. $\sqrt{27a^5(b + 1)} \sqrt[3]{81a(b + 1)^4}$

127. $\sqrt{8x(y + z)^5} \sqrt[3]{4x^2(y + z)^2}$

128. $\dfrac{1}{2}\sqrt{36a^5bc^4} - \dfrac{1}{2}\sqrt[3]{64a^4bc^6} + \dfrac{1}{6}\sqrt{144a^3bc^6}$

129. $\dfrac{\dfrac{1}{\sqrt{w}} - \sqrt{w}}{\dfrac{\sqrt{w} + 1}{\sqrt{w}}}$

130. $\dfrac{1}{4 + \sqrt{3}} + \dfrac{1}{\sqrt{3}} + \dfrac{1}{\sqrt{3} - 4}$

Express each of the following as the product of two radical expressions.

131. $x - 5$ **132.** $y - 7$

133. $x - a$

Multiply.

134. $\sqrt{9 + 3\sqrt{5}}\sqrt{9 - 3\sqrt{5}}$

135. $(\sqrt{x + 2} - \sqrt{x - 2})^2$

136. Use a graphing calculator to check your answers to Exercises 25, 39, and 81.

CONNECTING the CONCEPTS

Many radical expressions can be simplified. It is important to know under which conditions radical expressions can be multiplied and divided and radical terms can be combined.

Multiplication and division: The indices must be the same.

$$\frac{\sqrt{50t^5}}{\sqrt{2t^{11}}} = \sqrt{\frac{50t^5}{2t^{11}}} = \sqrt{\frac{25}{t^6}} = \frac{5}{t^3}; \qquad \sqrt[4]{8x^3} \cdot \sqrt[4]{2x} = \sqrt[4]{16x^4} = 2x$$

Combining like terms: The indices and the radicands must both be the same.

$$\sqrt{75x} + \sqrt{12x} - \sqrt{3x} = 5\sqrt{3x} + 2\sqrt{3x} - \sqrt{3x} = 6\sqrt{3x}$$

Radical expressions with differing indices can sometimes be simplified using rational exponents.

$$\sqrt[3]{x^2}\sqrt{x} = x^{2/3}x^{1/2} = x^{4/6}x^{3/6} = x^{7/6} = \sqrt[6]{x^7} = x\sqrt[6]{x}$$

MIXED REVIEW

Simplify. Assume that all variables represent non-negative numbers. Thus no absolute-value signs are needed in an answer.

1. $\sqrt{(t+5)^2}$

2. $\sqrt[3]{-27a^{12}}$

3. $\sqrt{6x}\sqrt{15x}$

4. $\dfrac{\sqrt{20y}}{\sqrt{45y}}$

5. $\sqrt{15t} + 4\sqrt{15t}$

6. $\sqrt[5]{a^5 b^{10} c^{11}}$

7. $\sqrt{6}(\sqrt{10} - \sqrt{33})$

8. $\dfrac{-\sqrt[4]{80a^2 b}}{\sqrt[4]{5a^{-1}b^{-6}}}$

9. $\dfrac{\sqrt{t}}{\sqrt[8]{t^3}}$

10. $\sqrt[5]{\dfrac{3a^{12}}{96a^2}}$

11. $2\sqrt{3} - 5\sqrt{12}$

12. $(\sqrt{5} + 3)(\sqrt{5} - 3)$

13. $(\sqrt{15} + \sqrt{10})^2$

14. $\sqrt{25x - 25} - \sqrt{9x - 9}$

15. $\sqrt{x^3 y}\sqrt[5]{xy^4}$

16. $\sqrt[3]{5000} + \sqrt[3]{625}$

17. $\sqrt{\sqrt[5]{x^2}}$

18. $\sqrt{3x^2 + 6x + 3}$

19. $\left(\sqrt[4]{a^2 b^3}\right)^2$

20. $\sqrt[3]{12x^2 y^5}\sqrt[3]{18x^7 y}$

8.6 Solving Radical Equations

The Principle of Powers ▪ Equations with Two Radical Terms

In Sections 8.1–8.5, we learned how to manipulate radical expressions as well as expressions containing rational exponents. We performed this work to find *equivalent expressions*.

Now that we know how to work with radicals and rational exponents, we can learn how to solve a new type of equation.

The Principle of Powers

A **radical equation** is an equation in which the variable appears in a radicand. Examples are

$$\sqrt[3]{2x} + 1 = 5, \qquad \sqrt{a - 2} = 7, \qquad \text{and} \qquad 4 - \sqrt{3x + 1} = \sqrt{6 - x}.$$

To solve such equations, we need a new principle. Suppose $a = b$ is true. If we square both sides, we get another true equation: $a^2 = b^2$. This can be generalized.

> **The Principle of Powers**
>
> If $a = b$, then $a^n = b^n$ for any exponent n.

Note that the principle of powers is an "if–then" statement. The statement obtained by interchanging the two parts of the sentence—"if $a^n = b^n$ for some exponent n, then $a = b$"—*is not always true*. For example, "if $x = 3$, then $x^2 = 9$" is true, but the statement "if $x^2 = 9$, then $x = 3$" is *not* true when x is replaced with -3. For this reason, when both sides of an equation are raised to an even exponent, it is essential to check the answer(s) in the *original* equation.

STUDY SKILLS ————

Plan Your Future

As you register for next semester's courses, be careful to consider your work and family commitments. Speak to faculty and other students to estimate how demanding each course is before signing up. If in doubt, it is usually better to take one fewer course than one too many.

EXAMPLE **1**   Solve: $\sqrt{x} - 3 = 4$.

SOLUTION   Before using the principle of powers, we need to isolate the radical term:

$$\sqrt{x} - 3 = 4$$
$$\sqrt{x} = 7 \qquad \text{Isolating the radical by adding 3 to both sides}$$
$$(\sqrt{x})^2 = 7^2 \qquad \text{Using the principle of powers}$$
$$x = 49.$$

Check:
$$\begin{array}{c|c} \sqrt{x} - 3 = 4 \\ \hline \sqrt{49} - 3 & 4 \\ 7 - 3 & \\ & 4 \stackrel{?}{=} 4 \quad \text{TRUE} \end{array}$$

The solution is 49.

TRY EXERCISE   7

EXAMPLE **2**   Solve: $\sqrt{x} + 5 = 3$.

SOLUTION

$$\sqrt{x} + 5 = 3$$
$$\sqrt{x} = -2 \qquad \text{Isolating the radical by adding } -5 \text{ to both sides}$$

> The equation $\sqrt{x} = -2$ has no solution because the principal square root of a number is never negative. We continue as in Example 1 for comparison.

$$(\sqrt{x})^2 = (-2)^2 \qquad \text{Using the principle of powers}$$
$$x = 4$$

Check:
$$\begin{array}{c|c} \sqrt{x} + 5 = 3 \\ \hline \sqrt{4} + 5 & 3 \\ 2 + 5 & \\ 7 \stackrel{?}{=} 3 & \text{FALSE} \end{array}$$

The number 4 does not check. Thus, $\sqrt{x} + 5 = 3$ has no solution.

TRY EXERCISE   27

> **CAUTION!**   Raising both sides of an equation to an even power may not produce an equivalent equation. In this case, a check is essential.

Note in Example 2 that $x = 4$ has the solution 4, but $\sqrt{x} + 5 = 3$ has *no* solution. Thus the equations $x = 4$ and $\sqrt{x} + 5 = 3$ are *not* equivalent.

> **To Solve an Equation with a Radical Term**
> 1. Isolate the radical term on one side of the equation.
> 2. Use the principle of powers and solve the resulting equation.
> 3. Check any possible solution in the original equation.

EXAMPLE 3

Solve: $x = \sqrt{x + 7} + 5$.

SOLUTION

$$x = \sqrt{x + 7} + 5$$
$$x - 5 = \sqrt{x + 7}$$

Isolating the radical by subtracting 5 from both sides

$$(x - 5)^2 = (\sqrt{x + 7})^2$$
$$x^2 - 10x + 25 = x + 7$$

Using the principle of powers; squaring both sides

$$x^2 - 11x + 18 = 0$$

Adding $-x - 7$ to both sides to write the quadratic equation in standard form

$$(x - 9)(x - 2) = 0$$

Factoring

$$x = 9 \quad or \quad x = 2$$

Using the principle of zero products

The possible solutions are 9 and 2. Let's check.

Check: For 9:

$$\frac{x = \sqrt{x + 7} + 5}{9 \ | \ \sqrt{9 + 7} + 5}$$
$$9 \overset{?}{=} 9 \qquad \text{TRUE}$$

For 2:

$$\frac{x = \sqrt{x + 7} + 5}{2 \ | \ \sqrt{2 + 7} + 5}$$
$$2 \overset{?}{=} 8 \qquad \text{FALSE}$$

Since 9 checks but 2 does not, the solution is 9.

TRY EXERCISE 39

It is important to isolate a radical term before using the principle of powers. Suppose in Example 3 that both sides of the equation were squared *before* isolating the radical. We then would have had the expression $(\sqrt{x + 7} + 5)^2$ or $x + 7 + 10\sqrt{x + 7} + 25$ on the right side, and the radical would have remained in the problem.

EXAMPLE 4

Solve: $(2x + 1)^{1/3} + 5 = 0$.

SOLUTION   We can use exponential notation to solve:

$$(2x + 1)^{1/3} + 5 = 0$$
$$(2x + 1)^{1/3} = -5$$

Subtracting 5 from both sides

$$[(2x + 1)^{1/3}]^3 = (-5)^3$$

Cubing both sides

$$(2x + 1)^1 = (-5)^3$$

Multiplying exponents. Try to do this mentally.

$$2x + 1 = -125$$
$$2x = -126$$

Subtracting 1 from both sides

$$x = -63.$$

Because both sides were raised to an *odd* power, a check is not *essential*. It is wise, however, for the student to confirm that -63 checks and is the solution.

TRY EXERCISE 25

Equations with Two Radical Terms

A strategy for solving equations with two or more radical terms is as follows.

> **To Solve an Equation with Two or More Radical Terms**
> 1. Isolate one of the radical terms.
> 2. Use the principle of powers.
> 3. If a radical remains, perform steps (1) and (2) again.
> 4. Solve the resulting equation.
> 5. Check possible solutions in the original equation.

EXAMPLE **5**   Solve: $\sqrt{2x - 5} = 1 + \sqrt{x - 3}$.

SOLUTION

$$\sqrt{2x - 5} = 1 + \sqrt{x - 3}$$

$(\sqrt{2x - 5})^2 = (1 + \sqrt{x - 3})^2$ One radical is already isolated. We square both sides.

> This is like squaring a binomial. We square 1, then find twice the product of 1 and $\sqrt{x - 3}$, and finally square $\sqrt{x - 3}$. Study this carefully.

$$2x - 5 = 1 + 2\sqrt{x - 3} + (\sqrt{x - 3})^2$$

$$2x - 5 = 1 + 2\sqrt{x - 3} + (x - 3)$$

$x - 3 = 2\sqrt{x - 3}$ Isolating the remaining radical term

$(x - 3)^2 = (2\sqrt{x - 3})^2$ Squaring both sides

$x^2 - 6x + 9 = 4(x - 3)$ Remember to square both the 2 and the $\sqrt{x - 3}$ on the right side.

$$x^2 - 6x + 9 = 4x - 12$$

$$x^2 - 10x + 21 = 0$$

$(x - 7)(x - 3) = 0$ Factoring

$x = 7 \ \ or \ \ x = 3$ Using the principle of zero products

We leave it to the student to show that 7 and 3 both check and are the solutions.

> TRY EXERCISE 41

> **CAUTION!**   A common error in solving equations like
> $$\sqrt{2x - 5} = 1 + \sqrt{x - 3}$$
> is to obtain $1 + (x - 3)$ as the square of the right side. This is wrong because $(A + B)^2 \neq A^2 + B^2$. For example,
> $$(1 + 2)^2 \neq 1^2 + 2^2$$
> $$3^2 \neq 1 + 4$$
> $$9 \neq 5.$$
>
> See Example 5 for the correct expansion of $(1 + \sqrt{x - 3})^2$.

EXAMPLE 6 Let $f(x) = \sqrt{x+5} - \sqrt{x-7}$. Find all x-values for which $f(x) = 2$.

SOLUTION We must have $f(x) = 2$, or

$$\sqrt{x+5} - \sqrt{x-7} = 2. \qquad \text{Substituting for } f(x)$$

To solve, we isolate one radical term and square both sides:

Isolate a radical term.	$\sqrt{x+5} = 2 + \sqrt{x-7}$	Adding $\sqrt{x-7}$ to both sides. This isolates one of the radical terms.
Raise both sides to the same power.	$(\sqrt{x+5})^2 = (2 + \sqrt{x-7})^2$	Using the principle of powers (squaring both sides)
	$x + 5 = 4 + 4\sqrt{x-7} + (x-7)$	Using $(A+B)^2 = A^2 + 2AB + B^2$
	$5 = 4\sqrt{x-7} - 3$	Adding $-x$ to both sides and combining like terms
Isolate a radical term.	$8 = 4\sqrt{x-7}$	Isolating the remaining radical term
	$2 = \sqrt{x-7}$	
Raise both sides to the same power.	$2^2 = (\sqrt{x-7})^2$	Squaring both sides
	$4 = x - 7$	
Solve.	$11 = x.$	

Check: $\quad f(11) = \sqrt{11+5} - \sqrt{11-7}$
$= \sqrt{16} - \sqrt{4}$
$= 4 - 2 = 2.$

We have $f(x) = 2$ when $x = 11$.

TRY EXERCISE 49

8.6 EXERCISE SET

For Extra Help

Concept Reinforcement *Classify each statement as either true or false.*

1. If $x^2 = 25$, then $x = 5$.
2. If $t = 7$, then $t^2 = 49$.
3. If $\sqrt{x} = 3$, then $(\sqrt{x})^2 = 3^2$.
4. If $x^2 = 36$, then $x = 6$.
5. $\sqrt{x} - 8 = 7$ is equivalent to $\sqrt{x} = 15$.
6. $\sqrt{t} + 5 = 8$ is equivalent to $\sqrt{t} = 3$.

Solve.

7. $\sqrt{5x+1} = 4$
8. $\sqrt{7x-3} = 5$
9. $\sqrt{3x} + 1 = 5$
10. $\sqrt{2x} - 1 = 2$

11. $\sqrt{y+5} - 4 = 1$
12. $\sqrt{x-2} - 7 = -4$
13. $\sqrt{8-x} + 7 = 10$
14. $\sqrt{y+4} + 6 = 7$
15. $\sqrt[3]{y+3} = 2$
16. $\sqrt[3]{x-2} = 3$
17. $\sqrt[4]{t-10} = 3$
18. $\sqrt[4]{t+5} = 2$
19. $6\sqrt{x} = x$
20. $7\sqrt{y} = y$
21. $2y^{1/2} - 13 = 7$
22. $3x^{1/2} + 12 = 9$
23. $\sqrt[3]{x} = -5$
24. $\sqrt[3]{y} = -4$
25. $z^{1/4} + 8 = 10$
26. $x^{1/4} - 2 = 1$
Aha! 27. $\sqrt{n} = -2$
28. $\sqrt{a} = -1$
29. $\sqrt[4]{3x+1} - 4 = -1$
30. $\sqrt[4]{2x+3} - 5 = -2$
31. $(21x+55)^{1/3} = 10$
32. $(5y+31)^{1/4} = 2$

33. $\sqrt[3]{3y + 6} + 7 = 8$

34. $\sqrt[3]{6x + 9} + 5 = 2$

35. $\sqrt{3t + 4} = \sqrt{4t + 3}$

36. $\sqrt{2t - 7} = \sqrt{3t - 12}$

37. $3(4 - t)^{1/4} = 6^{1/4}$

38. $2(1 - x)^{1/3} = 4^{1/3}$

39. $3 + \sqrt{5 - x} = x$

40. $x = \sqrt{x - 1} + 3$

41. $\sqrt{4x - 3} = 2 + \sqrt{2x - 5}$

42. $3 + \sqrt{z - 6} = \sqrt{z + 9}$

43. $\sqrt{20 - x} + 8 = \sqrt{9 - x} + 11$

44. $4 + \sqrt{10 - x} = 6 + \sqrt{4 - x}$

45. $\sqrt{x + 2} + \sqrt{3x + 4} = 2$

46. $\sqrt{6x + 7} - \sqrt{3x + 3} = 1$

47. If $f(x) = \sqrt{x} + \sqrt{x - 9}$, find any x for which $f(x) = 1$.

48. If $g(x) = \sqrt{x} + \sqrt{x - 5}$, find any x for which $g(x) = 5$.

49. If $f(t) = \sqrt{t - 2} - \sqrt{4t + 1}$, find any t for which $f(t) = -3$.

50. If $g(t) = \sqrt{2t + 7} - \sqrt{t + 15}$, find any t for which $g(t) = -1$.

51. If $f(x) = \sqrt{2x - 3}$ and $g(x) = \sqrt{x + 7} - 2$, find any x for which $f(x) = g(x)$.

52. If $f(x) = 2\sqrt{3x + 6}$ and $g(x) = 5 + \sqrt{4x + 9}$, find any x for which $f(x) = g(x)$.

53. If $f(t) = 4 - \sqrt{t - 3}$ and $g(t) = (t + 5)^{1/2}$, find any t for which $f(t) = g(t)$.

54. If $f(t) = 7 + \sqrt{2t - 5}$ and $g(t) = 3(t + 1)^{1/2}$, find any t for which $f(t) = g(t)$.

55. Explain in your own words why it is important to check your answers when using the principle of powers.

56. The principle of powers is an "if–then" statement that becomes false when the sentence parts are interchanged. Give an example of another such if–then statement from everyday life (answers will vary).

Skill Review

To prepare for Section 8.7, review finding dimensions of triangles and rectangles (Sections 1.5 and 3.8).

Solve.

57. *Sign dimensions.* The largest sign in the United States is a rectangle with a perimeter of 430 ft. The length of the rectangle is 5 ft longer than thirteen times the width. Find the dimensions of the sign. [1.5]
Source: Florida Center for Instructional Technology

58. *Sign dimensions.* The base of a triangular sign is 4 in. longer than twice the height. The area of the sign is 255 in². Find the dimensions of the sign. [3.8]

59. *Photograph dimensions.* A rectangular family photo is 4 in. longer than it is wide. The area of the photo is 140 in². Find the dimensions of the photograph. [3.8]

60. *Sidewalk length.* The length of a rectangular lawn between classroom buildings is 2 yd less than twice the width of the lawn. A path that is 34 yd long stretches diagonally across the area. What are the dimensions of the lawn? [3.8]

61. The sides of a right triangle are consecutive even integers. Find the length of each side. [3.8]

62. One leg of a right triangle is 5 cm long. The hypotenuse is 1 cm longer than the other leg. Find the length of the hypotenuse. [3.8]

Synthesis

63. Describe a procedure that could be used to create radical equations that have no solution.

64. Is checking essential when the principle of powers is used with an odd power n? Why or why not?

65. *Firefighting.* The velocity of water flow, in feet per second, from a nozzle is given by

$$v(p) = 12.1\sqrt{p},$$

where p is the nozzle pressure, in pounds per square inch (psi). Find the nozzle pressure if the water flow is 100 feet per second.
Source: Houston Fire Department Continuing Education

66. *Firefighting.* The velocity of water flow, in feet per second, from a water tank that is h feet high is given by

$$v(h) = 8\sqrt{h}.$$

Find the height of a water tank that provides a water flow of 60 feet per second.
Source: Houston Fire Department Continuing Education

67. *Music.*   The frequency of a violin string varies directly with the square root of the tension on the string. A violin string vibrates with a frequency of 260 Hz when the tension on the string is 28 N. What is the frequency when the tension is 32 N?

68. *Music.*   The frequency of a violin string varies inversely with the square root of the density of the string. A nylon violin string with a density of 1200 kg/m^3 vibrates with a frequency of 250 Hz. What is the frequency of a silk violin string with a density of 1300 kg/m^3?
Source: www.speech.kth.se

Steel manufacturing.   In the production of steel and other metals, the temperature of the molten metal is so great that conventional thermometers melt. Instead, sound is transmitted across the surface of the metal to a receiver on the far side and the speed of the sound is measured. The formula

$$S(t) = 1087.7\sqrt{\frac{9t + 2617}{2457}}$$

gives the speed of sound $S(t)$, in feet per second, at a temperature of t degrees Celsius.

69. Find the temperature of a blast furnace where sound travels 1880 ft/sec.

70. Find the temperature of a blast furnace where sound travels 1502.3 ft/sec.

71. Solve the above equation for t.

Automotive repair.   For an engine with a displacement of 2.8 L, the function given by

$$d(n) = 0.75\sqrt{2.8n}$$

can be used to determine the diameter size of the carburetor's opening, in millimeters. Here n is the number of rpm's at which the engine achieves peak performance.
Source: macdizzy.com

72. If the diameter of a carburetor's opening is 81 mm, for what number of rpm's will the engine produce peak power?

73. If a carburetor's opening is 84 mm, for what number of rpm's will the engine produce peak power?

Escape velocity.   A formula for the escape velocity v of a satellite is

$$v = \sqrt{2gr}\sqrt{\frac{h}{r + h}},$$

where g is the force of gravity, r is the planet or star's radius, and h is the height of the satellite above the planet or star's surface.

74. Solve for h.

75. Solve for r.

Solve.

76. $\left(\dfrac{z}{4} - 5\right)^{2/3} = \dfrac{1}{25}$

77. $\dfrac{x + \sqrt{x + 1}}{x - \sqrt{x + 1}} = \dfrac{5}{11}$

78. $\sqrt{\sqrt{\sqrt{y} + 49}} = 7$

79. $(z^2 + 17)^{3/4} = 27$

80. $x^2 - 5x - \sqrt{x^2 - 5x - 2} = 4$
(*Hint*: Let $u = x^2 - 5x - 2$.)

81. $\sqrt{8 - b} = b\sqrt{8 - b}$

Without graphing, determine the x-intercepts of the graphs given by each of the following.

82. $f(x) = \sqrt{x - 2} - \sqrt{x + 2} + 2$

83. $g(x) = 6x^{1/2} + 6x^{-1/2} - 37$

84. $f(x) = (x^2 + 30x)^{1/2} - x - (5x)^{1/2}$

85. Use a graphing calculator to check your answers to Exercises 9, 15, and 31.

86. Saul is trying to solve Exercise 73 using a graphing calculator. Without resorting to trial and error, how can he determine a suitable viewing window for finding the solution?

87. Use a graphing calculator to check your answers to Exercises 27, 35, and 41.

COLLABORATIVE CORNER

Tailgater Alert

Focus: Radical equations and problem solving

Time: 15–25 minutes

Group size: 2–3

Materials: Calculators or square-root tables

The faster a car is traveling, the more distance it needs to stop. Thus it is important for drivers to allow sufficient space between their vehicle and the vehicle in front of them. Police recommend that for each 10 mph of speed, a driver allow 1 car length. Thus a driver going 30 mph should have at least 3 car lengths between his or her vehicle and the one in front.

In Exercise Set 8.3, the function $r(L) = 2\sqrt{5L}$ was used to find the speed, in miles per hour, that a car was traveling when it left skid marks L feet long.

ACTIVITY

1. Each group member should estimate the length of a car in which he or she frequently travels. (Each should use a different length, if possible.)

2. Using a calculator as needed, each group member should complete the table below. Column 1 gives a car's speed s, and column 2

lists the minimum amount of space between cars traveling s miles per hour, as recommended by police. Column 3 is the speed that a vehicle *could* travel were it forced to stop in the distance listed in column 2, using the above function.

Column 1 s (in miles per hour)	Column 2 $L(s)$ (in feet)	Column 3 $r(L)$ (in miles per hour)
20		
30		
40		
50		
60		
70		

3. Determine whether there are any speeds at which the "1 car length per 10 mph" guideline might not suffice. On what reasoning do you base your answer? Compare tables to determine how car length affects the results. What recommendations would your group make to a new driver?

8.7 The Distance and Midpoint Formulas and Other Applications

Using the Pythagorean Theorem • Two Special Triangles • The Distance and Midpoint Formulas

Using the Pythagorean Theorem

There are many kinds of problems that involve powers and roots. Many also involve right triangles and the Pythagorean theorem, which we studied in Section 3.8 and restate here.

The Pythagorean Theorem*

In any right triangle, if a and b are the lengths of the legs and c is the length of the hypotenuse, then

$$a^2 + b^2 = c^2.$$

In using the Pythagorean theorem, we often make use of the following principle.

The Principle of Square Roots

For any nonnegative real number n,

If $x^2 = n$, then $x = \sqrt{n}$ or $x = -\sqrt{n}$.

For most real-world applications involving length or distance, $-\sqrt{n}$ is not needed.

EXAMPLE 1

Baseball.   A baseball diamond is actually a square 90 ft on a side. Suppose a catcher fields a ball while standing on the third-base line 10 ft from home plate, as shown in the figure. How far is the catcher's throw to first base? Give an exact answer and an approximation to three decimal places.

SOLUTION   We make a drawing and let d = the distance, in feet, to first base. Note that a right triangle is formed in which the leg from home plate to first base measures 90 ft and the leg from home plate to where the catcher fields the ball measures 10 ft.

We substitute these values into the Pythagorean theorem to find d:

$$d^2 = 90^2 + 10^2$$
$$d^2 = 8100 + 100$$
$$d^2 = 8200.$$

We now use the principle of square roots: If $d^2 = 8200$, then $d = \sqrt{8200}$ or $d = -\sqrt{8200}$. Since d represents a length, it follows that d is the positive square root of 8200:

$$d = \sqrt{8200} \text{ ft} \qquad \text{This is an exact answer.}$$
$$d \approx 90.554 \text{ ft.} \qquad \text{Using a calculator for an approximation}$$

TRY EXERCISE 19

---

*The converse of the Pythagorean theorem also holds. That is, if a, b, and c are the lengths of the sides of a triangle and $a^2 + b^2 = c^2$, then the triangle is a right triangle.

EXAMPLE **2** *Guy wires.* The base of a 40-ft long guy wire is located 15 ft from the telephone pole that it is anchoring. How high up the pole does the guy wire reach? Give an exact answer and an approximation to three decimal places.

SOLUTION We make a drawing and let $h = $ the height, in feet, to which the guy wire reaches. A right triangle is formed in which one leg measures 15 ft and the hypotenuse measures 40 ft. Using the Pythagorean theorem, we have

$$h^2 + 15^2 = 40^2$$
$$h^2 + 225 = 1600$$
$$h^2 = 1375$$
$$h = \sqrt{1375}.$$

Exact answer:

$h = \sqrt{1375}$ ft   Using the positive square root

Approximation:

$h \approx 37.081$ ft   Using a calculator

TRY EXERCISE 23

Two Special Triangles

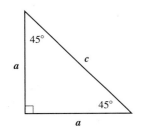

When both legs of a right triangle are the same size, as shown at left, we call the triangle an *isosceles right triangle*. If one leg of an isosceles right triangle has length a, we can find a formula for the length of the hypotenuse as follows:

$$c^2 = a^2 + b^2$$
$$c^2 = a^2 + a^2 \qquad \text{Because the triangle is isosceles, both legs are the same size: } a = b.$$
$$c^2 = 2a^2. \qquad \text{Combining like terms}$$

Next, we use the principle of square roots. Because a, b, and c are lengths, there is no need to consider negative square roots or absolute values. Thus,

$$c = \sqrt{2a^2} \qquad \text{Using the principle of square roots}$$
$$c = \sqrt{a^2 \cdot 2} = a\sqrt{2}.$$

EXAMPLE **3** One leg of an isosceles right triangle measures 7 cm. Find the length of the hypotenuse. Give an exact answer and an approximation to three decimal places.

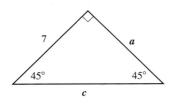

SOLUTION We substitute:

$$c = a\sqrt{2} \qquad \text{This equation is worth remembering.}$$
$$c = 7\sqrt{2}.$$

Exact answer: $c = 7\sqrt{2}$ cm

Approximation: $c \approx 9.899$ cm   Using a calculator

TRY EXERCISE 29

When the hypotenuse of an isosceles right triangle is known, the lengths of the legs can be found.

EXAMPLE 4

The hypotenuse of an isosceles right triangle is 5 ft long. Find the length of a leg. Give an exact answer and an approximation to three decimal places.

SOLUTION   We replace c with 5 and solve for a:

$$5 = a\sqrt{2} \qquad \text{Substituting 5 for } c \text{ in } c = a\sqrt{2}$$

$$\frac{5}{\sqrt{2}} = a \qquad \text{Dividing both sides by } \sqrt{2}$$

$$\frac{5\sqrt{2}}{2} = a. \qquad \text{Rationalize the denominator if desired.}$$

Exact answer: $a = \dfrac{5}{\sqrt{2}}$ ft, or $\dfrac{5\sqrt{2}}{2}$ ft

Approximation: $a \approx 3.536$ ft   Using a calculator

TRY EXERCISE 35

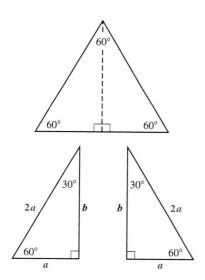

A second special triangle is known as a 30°–60°–90° triangle, so named because of the measures of its angles. Note that in an equilateral triangle, all sides have the same length and all angles are 60°. An altitude, drawn dashed in the figure, bisects, or splits in half, one angle and one side. Two 30°–60°–90° right triangles are thus formed.

If we let a represent the length of the shorter leg in a 30°–60°–90° triangle, then $2a$ represents the length of the hypotenuse. We have

$$a^2 + b^2 = (2a)^2 \qquad \text{Using the Pythagorean theorem}$$
$$a^2 + b^2 = 4a^2$$
$$b^2 = 3a^2 \qquad \text{Subtracting } a^2 \text{ from both sides}$$
$$b = \sqrt{3a^2} \qquad \text{Considering only the positive square root}$$
$$b = \sqrt{a^2 \cdot 3}$$
$$b = a\sqrt{3}.$$

EXAMPLE 5

The shorter leg of a 30°–60°–90° triangle measures 8 in. Find the lengths of the other sides. Give exact answers and, where appropriate, an approximation to three decimal places.

SOLUTION   The hypotenuse is twice as long as the shorter leg, so we have

$$c = 2a \qquad \text{This relationship is worth remembering.}$$
$$= 2 \cdot 8 = 16 \text{ in.} \qquad \text{This is the length of the hypotenuse.}$$

The length of the longer leg is the length of the shorter leg times $\sqrt{3}$. This gives us

$$b = a\sqrt{3} \qquad \text{This is also worth remembering.}$$
$$= 8\sqrt{3} \text{ in.} \qquad \text{This is the length of the longer leg.}$$

Exact answer: $c = 16$ in., $b = 8\sqrt{3}$ in.

Approximation: $b \approx 13.856$ in.

TRY EXERCISE 37

EXAMPLE　6

The length of the longer leg of a 30°–60°–90° triangle is 14 cm. Find the length of the hypotenuse. Give an exact answer and an approximation to three decimal places.

SOLUTION　The length of the hypotenuse is twice the length of the shorter leg. We first find a, the length of the shorter leg, by using the length of the longer leg:

$$14 = a\sqrt{3} \qquad \text{Substituting 14 for } b \text{ in } b = a\sqrt{3}$$

$$\frac{14}{\sqrt{3}} = a. \qquad \text{Dividing by } \sqrt{3}$$

Since the hypotenuse is twice as long as the shorter leg, we have

$$c = 2a$$
$$= 2 \cdot \frac{14}{\sqrt{3}} \qquad \text{Substituting}$$
$$= \frac{28}{\sqrt{3}} \text{ cm.}$$

Exact answer:　$c = \dfrac{28}{\sqrt{3}}$ cm, or $\dfrac{28\sqrt{3}}{3}$ cm if the denominator is rationalized.

Approximation:　$c \approx 16.166$ cm

TRY EXERCISE ▶ 33

STUDENT NOTES

Perhaps the easiest way to remember the important results listed in the adjacent box is to write out, on your own, the derivations shown on pp. 538 and 539.

Lengths Within Isosceles and 30°–60°–90° Right Triangles

The length of the hypotenuse in an isosceles right triangle is the length of a leg times $\sqrt{2}$.

The length of the longer leg in a 30°–60°–90° right triangle is the length of the shorter leg times $\sqrt{3}$. The hypotenuse is twice as long as the shorter leg.

The Distance and Midpoint Formulas

We can use the Pythagorean theorem to find the distance between two points on a plane.

To find the distance between two points on the number line, we subtract. Depending on the order in which we subtract, the difference may be positive or negative. However, if we take the absolute value of the difference, we always obtain a positive value for the distance:

$$|4 - (-3)| = |7| = 7$$
$$|-3 - 4| = |-7| = 7$$

If two points are on a horizontal line, they have the same second coordinate. We can find the distance between them by subtracting their first coordinates and taking the absolute value of that difference.

The distance between the points (x_1, y_1) and (x_2, y_1) on a horizontal line is thus $|x_2 - x_1|$. Similarly, the distance between the points (x_2, y_1) and (x_2, y_2) on a vertical line is $|y_2 - y_1|$.

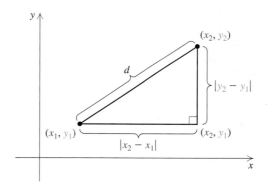

Now consider two points (x_1, y_1) and (x_2, y_2). If $x_1 \neq x_2$ and $y_1 \neq y_2$, these points, along with the point (x_2, y_1), describe a right triangle. The lengths of the legs are $|x_2 - x_1|$ and $|y_2 - y_1|$. We find d, the length of the hypotenuse, by using the Pythagorean theorem:

$$d^2 = |x_2 - x_1|^2 + |y_2 - y_1|^2.$$

Since the square of a number is the same as the square of its opposite, we can replace the absolute-value signs with parentheses:

$$d^2 = (x_2 - x_1)^2 + (y_2 - y_1)^2.$$

Taking the principal square root, we have a formula for distance.

> **The Distance Formula**
> The distance d between any two points (x_1, y_1) and (x_2, y_2) is given by
> $$d = \sqrt{(x_2 - x_1)^2 + (y_2 - y_1)^2}.$$

EXAMPLE 7

Find the distance between $(5, -1)$ and $(-4, 6)$. Find an exact answer and an approximation to three decimal places.

SOLUTION   We substitute into the distance formula:

$$d = \sqrt{(-4 - 5)^2 + [6 - (-1)]^2} \quad \text{Substituting. A drawing is optional.}$$
$$= \sqrt{(-9)^2 + 7^2}$$
$$= \sqrt{130} \quad \text{This is exact.}$$
$$\approx 11.402. \quad \text{Using a calculator for an approximation}$$

> TRY EXERCISE 51

The distance formula is needed to verify a formula for the coordinates of the *midpoint* of a segment connecting two points. We state the midpoint formula and leave its proof to the exercises.

STUDENT NOTES

To help remember the formulas correctly, note that the distance formula (a variation on the Pythagorean theorem) involves both subtraction and addition, whereas the midpoint formula does not include any subtraction.

> **The Midpoint Formula**
> If the endpoints of a segment are (x_1, y_1) and (x_2, y_2), then the coordinates of the midpoint are
> $$\left(\frac{x_1 + x_2}{2}, \frac{y_1 + y_2}{2} \right).$$
>
>
>
> (To locate the midpoint, average the x-coordinates and average the y-coordinates.)

EXAMPLE 8

Find the midpoint of the segment with endpoints $(-2, 3)$ and $(4, -6)$.

SOLUTION   Using the midpoint formula, we obtain

$$\left(\frac{-2 + 4}{2}, \frac{3 + (-6)}{2} \right), \quad \text{or} \quad \left(\frac{2}{2}, \frac{-3}{2} \right), \quad \text{or} \quad \left(1, -\frac{3}{2} \right).$$

> TRY EXERCISE 65

8.7 EXERCISE SET

For Extra Help

Concept Reinforcement *Complete each sentence with the best choice from the column on the right.*

1. In any _____ triangle, the square of the length of the hypotenuse is the sum of the squares of the lengths of the legs.

2. The shortest side of a right triangle is always one of the two _____.

3. The principle of _____ states that if $x^2 = n$, then $x = \sqrt{n}$ or $x = -\sqrt{n}$.

4. In a(n) _____ right triangle, both legs have the same length.

5. In a(n) _____ right triangle, the hypotenuse is twice as long as the shorter leg.

6. If both legs in a right triangle have measure a, then the _____ measures $a\sqrt{2}$.

a) Hypotenuse

b) Isosceles

c) Legs

d) Right

e) Square roots

f) $30°-60°-90°$

In a right triangle, find the length of the side not given. Give an exact answer and, where appropriate, an approximation to three decimal places.

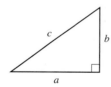

7. $a = 5, b = 3$

8. $a = 8, b = 10$

Aha! 9. $a = 9, b = 9$

10. $a = 10, b = 10$

11. $b = 15, c = 17$

12. $a = 7, c = 25$

In Exercises 13–18, give an exact answer and, where appropriate, an approximation to three decimal places.

13. A right triangle's hypotenuse is 8 m and one leg is $4\sqrt{3}$ m. Find the length of the other leg.

14. A right triangle's hypotenuse is 6 cm and one leg is $\sqrt{5}$ cm. Find the length of the other leg.

15. The hypotenuse of a right triangle is $\sqrt{20}$ in. and one leg measures 1 in. Find the length of the other leg.

16. The hypotenuse of a right triangle is $\sqrt{15}$ ft and one leg measures 2 ft. Find the length of the other leg.

Aha! 17. One leg in a right triangle is 1 m and the hypotenuse measures $\sqrt{2}$ m. Find the length of the other leg.

18. One leg of a right triangle is 1 yd and the hypotenuse measures 2 yd. Find the length of the other leg.

In Exercises 19–28, give an exact answer and, where appropriate, an approximation to three decimal places.

19. *Bicycling.* Clare routinely bicycles across a rectangular parking lot on her way to work. If the lot is 200 ft long and 150 ft wide, how far does Clare travel when she rides across the lot diagonally?

150 ft

200 ft

20. *Guy wire.*   How long is a guy wire if it reaches from the top of a 15-ft pole to a point on the ground 10 ft from the pole?

21. *Softball.*   A slow-pitch softball diamond is actually a square 65 ft on a side. How far is it from home plate to second base?

22. *Baseball.*   Suppose the catcher in Example 1 makes a throw to second base from the same location. How far is that throw?

23. *Television sets.*   What does it mean to refer to a 51-in. TV set? Such units refer to the diagonal of the screen. A 51-in. TV set has a width of 45 in. What is its height?

24. *Television sets.*   A 53-in. TV set has a screen with a height of 28 in. What is its width? (See Exercise 23.)

25. *Speaker placement.*   A stereo receiver is in a corner of a 12-ft by 14-ft room. Wire will run under a rug, diagonally, to a subwoofer in the far corner. If 4 ft of slack is required on each end, how long a piece of wire should be purchased?

26. *Distance over water.*   To determine the width of a pond, a surveyor locates two stakes at either end of the pond and uses instrumentation to place a third stake so that the distance across the pond is the length of a hypotenuse. If the third stake is 90 m from one stake and 70 m from the other, what is the distance across the pond?

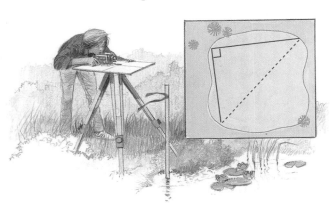

27. *Walking.*   Students at Pohlman Community College have worn a path that cuts diagonally across the campus "quad." If the quad is actually a rectangle that Marissa measured to be 70 paces long and 40 paces wide, how many paces will Marissa save by using the diagonal path?

28. *Crosswalks.*   The diagonal crosswalk at the intersection of State St. and Main St. is the hypotenuse of a triangle in which the crosswalks across State St. and Main St. are the legs. If State St. is 28 ft wide and Main St. is 40 ft wide, how much shorter is the distance traveled by pedestrians using the diagonal crosswalk?

For each triangle, find the missing length(s). Give an exact answer and, where appropriate, an approximation to three decimal places.

29.

30.

31.

32.

33.

34.

35.

36.

37.

14, ?, 30°, ?

38.

?, ?, 60°, 9

39.

10, ?, 10, 10

40.

6, ?, 6, 6

41.

7, 7, ?, 7

42.

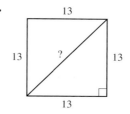

13, 13, ?, 13, 13

43.

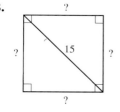

?, ?, 15, ?, ?

44.

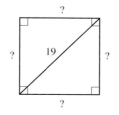

?, ?, 19, ?, ?

In Exercises 45–48, give an exact answer and, where appropriate, an approximation to three decimal places.

45. *Bridge expansion.* During the summer heat, a 2-mi bridge expands 2 ft in length. If we assume that the bulge occurs straight up the middle, how high is the bulge? (The answer may surprise you. Most bridges have expansion spaces to avoid such buckling.)

46. Triangle *ABC* has sides of lengths 25 ft, 25 ft, and 30 ft. Triangle *PQR* has sides of lengths 25 ft, 25 ft, and 40 ft. Which triangle, if either, has the greater area and by how much?

47. *Architecture.* The Rushton Triangular Lodge in Northamptonshire, England, was designed and constructed by Sir Thomas Tresham between 1593 and 1597. The building is in the shape of an equilateral triangle with walls of length 33 ft. How many square feet of land is covered by the lodge?

Source: The Internet Encyclopedia of Science

48. *Antenna length.* As part of an emergency radio communication station, Rik sets up an "Inverted-V" antenna. He stretches a copper wire from one point on the ground to a point on a tree and then back down to the ground, forming two 30°–60°–90° triangles. If the wire is fastened to the tree 34 ft above the ground, how long is the copper wire?

49. Find all points on the y-axis of a Cartesian coordinate system that are 5 units from the point $(3, 0)$.

50. Find all points on the x-axis of a Cartesian coordinate system that are 5 units from the point $(0, 4)$.

Find the distance between each pair of points. Where appropriate, find an approximation to three decimal places.

51. $(4, 5)$ and $(7, 1)$

52. $(0, 8)$ and $(6, 0)$

53. $(0, -5)$ and $(1, -2)$

54. $(-1, -4)$ and $(-3, -5)$

55. $(-4, 4)$ and $(6, -6)$

56. $(5, 21)$ and $(-3, 1)$

Aha! **57.** $(8.6, -3.4)$ and $(-9.2, -3.4)$

58. $(5.9, 2)$ and $(3.7, -7.7)$

59. $\left(\frac{1}{2}, \frac{1}{3}\right)$ and $\left(\frac{5}{6}, -\frac{1}{6}\right)$

60. $\left(\frac{5}{7}, \frac{1}{14}\right)$ and $\left(\frac{1}{7}, \frac{11}{14}\right)$

61. $(-\sqrt{6}, \sqrt{6})$ and $(0, 0)$

62. $(\sqrt{5}, -\sqrt{3})$ and $(0, 0)$

63. $(-1, -30)$ and $(-2, -40)$

64. $(0.5, 100)$ and $(1.5, -100)$

Find the midpoint of each segment with the given endpoints.

65. $(-2, 5)$ and $(8, 3)$

66. $(1, 4)$ and $(9, -6)$

67. $(2, -1)$ and $(5, 8)$

68. $(-1, 2)$ and $(1, -3)$

69. $(-8, -5)$ and $(6, -1)$

70. $(8, -2)$ and $(-3, 4)$

71. $(-3.4, 8.1)$ and $(4.8, -8.1)$

72. $(4.1, 6.9)$ and $(5.2, -8.9)$

73. $\left(\frac{1}{6}, -\frac{3}{4}\right)$ and $\left(-\frac{1}{3}, \frac{5}{6}\right)$

74. $\left(-\frac{4}{5}, -\frac{2}{3}\right)$ and $\left(\frac{1}{8}, \frac{3}{4}\right)$

75. $(\sqrt{2}, -1)$ and $(\sqrt{3}, 4)$

76. $(9, 2\sqrt{3})$ and $(-4, 5\sqrt{3})$

77. Are there any right triangles, other than those with sides measuring 3, 4, and 5, that have consecutive numbers for the lengths of the sides? Why or why not?

78. If a $30°-60°-90°$ triangle and an isosceles right triangle have the same perimeter, which will have the greater area? Why?

Skill Review

Review graphing (Sections 2.2, 2.3, 2.6, and 7.4).

Graph on a plane.

79. $y = 2x - 3$ [2.6]

80. $y < x$ [7.4]

81. $8x - 4y = 8$ [2.3]

82. $2y - 1 = 7$ [2.3]

83. $x \geq 1$ [7.4]

84. $x - 5 = 6 - 2y$ [2.2]

Synthesis

85. Describe a procedure that uses the distance formula to determine whether three points, (x_1, y_1), (x_2, y_2), and (x_3, y_3), are vertices of a right triangle.

86. Outline a procedure that uses the distance formula to determine whether three points, (x_1, y_1), (x_2, y_2), and (x_3, y_3), are collinear (lie on the same line).

87. The perimeter of a regular hexagon is 72 cm. Determine the area of the shaded region shown.

88. If the perimeter of a regular hexagon is 120 ft, what is its area? (*Hint*: See Exercise 87.)

89. Each side of a regular octagon has length s. Find a formula for the distance d between the parallel sides of the octagon.

90. *Roofing.* Kit's home, which is 24 ft wide and 32 ft long, needs a new roof. By counting clapboards that are 4 in. apart, Kit determines that the peak of the roof is 6 ft higher than the sides. A packet of shingles covers 100 ft². How many packets will the job require?

91. *Painting.* (Refer to Exercise 90.) A gallon of Benjamin Moore® exterior acrylic paint covers 450–500 ft². If Kit's house has dimensions as shown above, how many gallons of paint should be bought to paint the house? What assumption(s) is made in your answer?

92. *Contracting.* Oxford Builders has an extension cord on their generator that permits them to work, with electricity, anywhere in a circular area of 3850 ft². Find the dimensions of the largest square room they could work on without having to relocate the generator to reach each corner of the floor plan.

93. *Contracting.* Cleary Construction has a hose attached to their insulation blower that permits them to reach anywhere in a circular area of 6160 ft². Find the dimensions of the largest square room with 12-ft ceilings in which they could reach all corners with the hose while leaving the blower centrally located. Assume that the blower sits on the floor.

94. The length and the width of a rectangle are given by consecutive integers. The area of the rectangle is 90 cm². Find the length of a diagonal of the rectangle.

95. A cube measures 5 cm on each side. How long is the diagonal that connects two opposite corners of the cube? Give an exact answer.

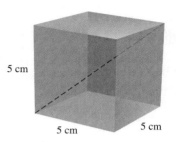

96. Prove the midpoint formula by showing that

i) the distance from (x_1, y_1) to
$$\left(\frac{x_1 + x_2}{2}, \frac{y_1 + y_2}{2} \right)$$
equals the distance from (x_2, y_2) to
$$\left(\frac{x_1 + x_2}{2}, \frac{y_1 + y_2}{2} \right);$$
and

ii) the points
$$(x_1, y_1), \left(\frac{x_1 + x_2}{2}, \frac{y_1 + y_2}{2} \right),$$
and
$$(x_2, y_2)$$
lie on the same line (see Exercise 86).

8.8 The Complex Numbers

Imaginary and Complex Numbers ▪ Addition and Subtraction ▪ Multiplication ▪ Conjugates and Division ▪ Powers of i

Imaginary and Complex Numbers

Negative numbers do not have square roots in the real-number system. However, a larger number system that contains the real-number system is designed so that negative numbers *do* have square roots. That system is called the **complex-number system**, and it will allow us to solve equations like $x^2 + 1 = 0$. The complex-number system makes use of i, a number that is, by definition, a square root of -1.

The Number i

i is the unique number for which $i = \sqrt{-1}$ and $i^2 = -1$.

We can now define the square root of a negative number as follows:

$$\sqrt{-p} = \sqrt{-1}\sqrt{p} = i\sqrt{p} \text{ or } \sqrt{p}i, \text{ for any positive number } p.$$

EXAMPLE 1 Express in terms of i: **(a)** $\sqrt{-7}$; **(b)** $\sqrt{-16}$; **(c)** $-\sqrt{-13}$; **(d)** $-\sqrt{-50}$.

SOLUTION

a) $\sqrt{-7} = \sqrt{-1 \cdot 7} = \sqrt{-1} \cdot \sqrt{7} = i\sqrt{7}, \text{ or } \sqrt{7}i$ i is *not* under the radical.

b) $\sqrt{-16} = \sqrt{-1 \cdot 16} = \sqrt{-1} \cdot \sqrt{16} = i \cdot 4 = 4i$

c) $-\sqrt{-13} = -\sqrt{-1 \cdot 13} = -\sqrt{-1} \cdot \sqrt{13} = -i\sqrt{13}, \text{ or } -\sqrt{13}i$

d) $-\sqrt{-50} = -\sqrt{-1} \cdot \sqrt{25} \cdot \sqrt{2} = -i \cdot 5 \cdot \sqrt{2} = -5i\sqrt{2}, \text{ or } -5\sqrt{2}i$

TRY EXERCISE 9

Imaginary Numbers

An *imaginary number* is a number that can be written in the form $a + bi$, where a and b are real numbers and $b \neq 0$.

Don't let the name "imaginary" fool you. Imaginary numbers appear in fields such as engineering and the physical sciences. The following are examples of imaginary numbers:

$5 + 4i,$ Here $a = 5, b = 4$.

$\sqrt{3} - \pi i,$ Here $a = \sqrt{3}, b = -\pi$.

$\sqrt{7}i$ Here $a = 0, b = \sqrt{7}$.

The union of the set of all imaginary numbers and the set of all real numbers is the set of all **complex numbers**.

> ### Complex Numbers
>
> A *complex number* is any number that can be written in the form $a + bi$, where a and b are real numbers. (Note that a and b both can be 0.)

The following are examples of complex numbers:

$7 + 3i$ (here $a \neq 0, b \neq 0$); $\qquad$ $4i$ (here $a = 0, b \neq 0$);

8 (here $a \neq 0, b = 0$); $\qquad$ 0 (here $a = 0, b = 0$).

Complex numbers like $17i$ or $4i$, in which $a = 0$ and $b \neq 0$, are called *pure imaginary numbers*.

For $b = 0$, we have $a + 0i = a$, so every real number is a complex number. The relationships among various real and complex numbers are shown below.

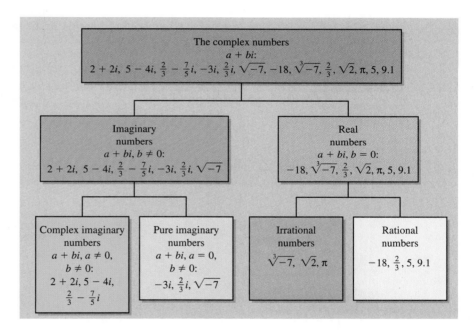

Note that although $\sqrt{-7}$ and $\sqrt[3]{-7}$ are both complex numbers, $\sqrt{-7}$ is imaginary whereas $\sqrt[3]{-7}$ is real.

Addition and Subtraction

The complex numbers obey the commutative, associative, and distributive laws. Thus we can add and subtract them as we do binomials.

EXAMPLE 2 Add or subtract and simplify.

a) $(8 + 6i) + (3 + 2i)$ $\qquad\qquad$ **b)** $(4 + 5i) - (6 - 3i)$

SOLUTION

a) $(8 + 6i) + (3 + 2i) = (8 + 3) + (6i + 2i)$ $\qquad$ Combining the real parts and the imaginary parts

$\qquad\qquad = 11 + (6 + 2)i = 11 + 8i$

b) $(4 + 5i) - (6 - 3i) = (4 - 6) + [5i - (-3i)]$ Note that the 6 and the $-3i$ are *both* being subtracted.

$$= -2 + 8i$$

TRY EXERCISE 27

STUDENT NOTES —————

The rule developed in Section 8.3, $\sqrt[n]{a} \cdot \sqrt[n]{b} = \sqrt[n]{a \cdot b}$, does *not* apply when n is 2 and either a or b is negative. Indeed this condition is stated on p. 510 when it is specified that $\sqrt[n]{a}$ and $\sqrt[n]{b}$ are both *real* numbers.

Multiplication

To multiply square roots of negative real numbers, we first express them in terms of i. For example,

$$\sqrt{-2} \cdot \sqrt{-5} = \sqrt{-1} \cdot \sqrt{2} \cdot \sqrt{-1} \cdot \sqrt{5}$$
$$= i \cdot \sqrt{2} \cdot i \cdot \sqrt{5}$$
$$= i^2 \cdot \sqrt{10}$$
$$= -1\sqrt{10} = -\sqrt{10} \text{ is correct!}$$

> *CAUTION!* With complex numbers, simply multiplying radicands is *incorrect* when both radicands are negative: $\sqrt{-2} \cdot \sqrt{-5} \neq \sqrt{10}$.

With this in mind, we can now multiply complex numbers.

EXAMPLE 3

Multiply and simplify. When possible, write answers in the form $a + bi$.

a) $\sqrt{-4}\sqrt{-25}$ **b)** $\sqrt{-5} \cdot \sqrt{-7}$ **c)** $-3i \cdot 8i$
d) $-4i(3 - 5i)$ **e)** $(1 + 2i)(4 + 3i)$

SOLUTION

a) $\sqrt{-4}\sqrt{-25} = \sqrt{-1} \cdot \sqrt{4} \cdot \sqrt{-1} \cdot \sqrt{25}$
$$= i \cdot 2 \cdot i \cdot 5$$
$$= i^2 \cdot 10$$
$$= -1 \cdot 10 \qquad i^2 = -1$$
$$= -10$$

b) $\sqrt{-5} \cdot \sqrt{-7} = \sqrt{-1} \cdot \sqrt{5} \cdot \sqrt{-1} \cdot \sqrt{7}$ Try to do this step mentally.
$$= i \cdot \sqrt{5} \cdot i \cdot \sqrt{7}$$
$$= i^2 \cdot \sqrt{35}$$
$$= -1 \cdot \sqrt{35} \qquad i^2 = -1$$
$$= -\sqrt{35}$$

c) $-3i \cdot 8i = -24 \cdot i^2$
$$= -24 \cdot (-1) \qquad i^2 = -1$$
$$= 24$$

d) $-4i(3 - 5i) = -4i \cdot 3 + (-4i)(-5i)$ Using the distributive law
$$= -12i + 20i^2$$
$$= -12i - 20 \qquad\qquad i^2 = -1$$
$$= -20 - 12i \qquad\qquad \text{Writing in the form } a + bi$$

e) $(1 + 2i)(4 + 3i) = 4 + 3i + 8i + 6i^2$ Multiplying each term of $4 + 3i$ by each term of $1 + 2i$ (FOIL)

$$= 4 + 3i + 8i - 6 \qquad i^2 = -1$$
$$= -2 + 11i \qquad\qquad \text{Combining like terms}$$

TRY EXERCISES 35 and 49

Conjugates and Division

Recall that the conjugate of $4 + \sqrt{2}$ is $4 - \sqrt{2}$.

Conjugates of complex numbers are defined in a similar manner.

> ### Conjugate of a Complex Number
> The *conjugate* of a complex number $a + bi$ is $a - bi$, and the *conjugate* of $a - bi$ is $a + bi$.

EXAMPLE 4   Find the conjugate of each number.

a) $-3 - 7i$ **b)** $4i$

SOLUTION

a) $-3 - 7i$ The conjugate is $-3 + 7i$.

b) $4i$ The conjugate is $-4i$. Note that $4i = 0 + 4i$.

The product of a complex number and its conjugate is a real number.

EXAMPLE 5   Multiply: $(5 + 7i)(5 - 7i)$.

SOLUTION

$$(5 + 7i)(5 - 7i) = 5^2 - (7i)^2 \qquad \text{Using } (A + B)(A - B) = A^2 - B^2$$
$$= 25 - 49i^2$$
$$= 25 - 49(-1) \qquad i^2 = -1$$
$$= 25 + 49 = 74$$

TRY EXERCISE 55

Conjugates are used when dividing complex numbers. The procedure is much like that used to rationalize denominators in Section 8.5.

EXAMPLE 6   Divide and simplify to the form $a + bi$.

a) $\dfrac{-2 + 9i}{1 - 3i}$ **b)** $\dfrac{7 + 4i}{5i}$

SOLUTION

a) To divide and simplify $(-2 + 9i)/(1 - 3i)$, we multiply by 1, using the conjugate of the denominator to form 1:

$$\frac{-2 + 9i}{1 - 3i} = \frac{-2 + 9i}{1 - 3i} \cdot \frac{1 + 3i}{1 + 3i} \qquad \begin{array}{l}\text{Multiplying by 1 using the conjugate of}\\\text{the denominator in the symbol for 1}\end{array}$$

$$= \frac{(-2 + 9i)(1 + 3i)}{(1 - 3i)(1 + 3i)} \qquad \begin{array}{l}\text{Multiplying numerators;}\\\text{multiplying denominators}\end{array}$$

$$= \frac{-2 - 6i + 9i + 27i^2}{1^2 - 9i^2} \qquad \text{Using FOIL}$$

$$= \frac{-2 + 3i + (-27)}{1 - (-9)} \qquad i^2 = -1$$

$$= \frac{-29 + 3i}{10}$$

$$= -\frac{29}{10} + \frac{3}{10}i. \qquad \begin{array}{l}\text{Writing in the form } a + bi;\\\text{note that } \dfrac{X + Y}{Z} = \dfrac{X}{Z} + \dfrac{Y}{Z}\end{array}$$

b) The conjugate of $5i$ is $-5i$, so we *could* multiply by $-5i/(-5i)$. However, when the denominator is a pure imaginary number, it is easiest if we multiply by i/i:

$$\frac{7 + 4i}{5i} = \frac{7 + 4i}{5i} \cdot \frac{i}{i} \qquad \text{Multiplying by 1 using } i/i. \text{ We can also use the conjugate of } 5i \text{ to write } -5i/(-5i).$$

$$= \frac{7i + 4i^2}{5i^2} \qquad \text{Multiplying}$$

$$= \frac{7i + 4(-1)}{5(-1)} \qquad i^2 = -1$$

$$= \frac{7i - 4}{-5} = \frac{-4}{-5} + \frac{7}{-5}\,i, \text{ or } \frac{4}{5} - \frac{7}{5}\,i. \qquad \text{Writing in the form } a + bi$$

> **TRY EXERCISE** 73

Powers of i

Answers to problems involving complex numbers are generally written in the form $a + bi$. In the following discussion, we show why there is no need to use powers of i (other than 1) when writing answers.

Recall that -1 raised to an *even* power is 1, and -1 raised to an *odd* power is -1. Simplifying powers of i can then be done by using the fact that $i^2 = -1$ and expressing the given power of i in terms of i^2. Consider the following:

$$i^2 = -1,$$
$$i^3 = i^2 \cdot i = (-1)i = -i,$$
$$i^4 = (i^2)^2 = (-1)^2 = 1,$$
$$i^5 = i^4 \cdot i = (i^2)^2 \cdot i = (-1)^2 \cdot i = i,$$
$$i^6 = (i^2)^3 = (-1)^3 = -1. \longleftarrow \text{The pattern is now repeating.}$$

The powers of i cycle themselves through the values i, -1, $-i$, and 1. Even powers of i are -1 or 1 whereas odd powers of i are i or $-i$.

EXAMPLE 7 Simplify: **(a)** i^{18}; **(b)** i^{24}.

SOLUTION

a) $i^{18} = (i^2)^9$ Using the power rule

$\qquad = (-1)^9 = -1$ Raising -1 to a power

b) $i^{24} = (i^2)^{12}$

$\qquad = (-1)^{12} = 1$

> **TRY EXERCISE** 83

To simplify i^n when n is odd, we rewrite i^n as $i^{n-1} \cdot i$.

EXAMPLE 8 Simplify: **(a)** i^{29}; **(b)** i^{75}.

SOLUTION

a) $i^{29} = i^{28}i^1$ Using the product rule. This is a key step when i is raised to an odd power.

$\qquad = (i^2)^{14}i$ Using the power rule

$\qquad = (-1)^{14}i$

$\qquad = 1 \cdot i = i$

b) $i^{75} = i^{74}i^1$ Using the product rule

$\qquad = (i^2)^{37}i$ Using the power rule

$\qquad = (-1)^{37}i$

$\qquad = -1 \cdot i = -i$

> **TRY EXERCISE** 85

8.8 EXERCISE SET

For Extra Help   PRACTICE WATCH DOWNLOAD

Concept Reinforcement *Classify each statement as either true or false.*

1. Imaginary numbers are so named because they have no real-world applications.

2. Every real number is imaginary, but not every imaginary number is real.

3. Every imaginary number is a complex number, but not every complex number is imaginary.

4. Every real number is a complex number, but not every complex number is real.

5. We add complex numbers by combining real parts and combining imaginary parts.

6. The product of a complex number and its conjugate is always a real number.

7. The square of a complex number is always a real number.

8. The quotient of two complex numbers is always a complex number.

Express in terms of i.

9. $\sqrt{-100}$

10. $\sqrt{-9}$

11. $\sqrt{-5}$

12. $\sqrt{-7}$

13. $\sqrt{-8}$

14. $\sqrt{-12}$

15. $-\sqrt{-11}$

16. $-\sqrt{-17}$

17. $-\sqrt{-49}$

18. $-\sqrt{-81}$

19. $-\sqrt{-300}$

20. $-\sqrt{-75}$

21. $6 - \sqrt{-84}$

22. $4 - \sqrt{-60}$

23. $-\sqrt{-76} + \sqrt{-125}$

24. $\sqrt{-4} + \sqrt{-12}$

25. $\sqrt{-18} - \sqrt{-64}$

26. $\sqrt{-72} - \sqrt{-25}$

Perform the indicated operation and simplify. Write each answer in the form $a + bi$.

27. $(3 + 4i) + (2 - 7i)$

28. $(5 - 6i) + (8 + 9i)$

29. $(9 + 5i) - (2 + 3i)$

30. $(8 + 7i) - (2 + 4i)$

31. $(7 - 4i) - (5 - 3i)$

32. $(5 - 3i) - (9 + 2i)$

33. $(-5 - i) - (7 + 4i)$

34. $(-2 + 6i) - (-7 + i)$

35. $5i \cdot 8i$

36. $3i \cdot 9i$

37. $(-4i)(-6i)$

38. $7i \cdot (-8i)$

39. $\sqrt{-36}\sqrt{-9}$

40. $\sqrt{-49}\sqrt{-16}$

41. $\sqrt{-3}\sqrt{-10}$

42. $\sqrt{-6}\sqrt{-7}$

43. $\sqrt{-6}\sqrt{-21}$

44. $\sqrt{-15}\sqrt{-10}$

45. $5i(2 + 6i)$

46. $2i(7 + 3i)$

47. $-7i(3 + 4i)$

48. $-4i(6 - 5i)$

49. $(1 + i)(3 + 2i)$

50. $(4 + i)(2 + 3i)$

51. $(6 - 5i)(3 + 4i)$

52. $(5 - 6i)(2 + 5i)$

53. $(7 - 2i)(2 - 6i)$

54. $(-4 + 5i)(3 - 4i)$

55. $(3 + 8i)(3 - 8i)$

56. $(1 + 2i)(1 - 2i)$

57. $(-7 + i)(-7 - i)$

58. $(-4 + 5i)(-4 - 5i)$

59. $(4 - 2i)^2$

60. $(1 - 2i)^2$

61. $(2 + 3i)^2$

62. $(3 + 2i)^2$

63. $(-2 + 3i)^2$

64. $(-5 - 2i)^2$

65. $\dfrac{10}{3 + i}$

66. $\dfrac{26}{5 + i}$

67. $\dfrac{2}{3 - 2i}$

68. $\dfrac{4}{2 - 3i}$

69. $\dfrac{2i}{5 + 3i}$

70. $\dfrac{3i}{4 + 2i}$

71. $\dfrac{5}{6i}$

72. $\dfrac{4}{7i}$

73. $\dfrac{5 - 3i}{4i}$

74. $\dfrac{2 + 7i}{5i}$

Aha! 75. $\dfrac{7i + 14}{7i}$

76. $\dfrac{6i + 3}{3i}$

77. $\dfrac{4 + 5i}{3 - 7i}$

78. $\dfrac{5 + 3i}{7 - 4i}$

79. $\dfrac{2 + 3i}{2 + 5i}$

80. $\dfrac{3 + 2i}{4 + 3i}$

81. $\dfrac{3 - 2i}{4 + 3i}$

82. $\dfrac{5 - 2i}{3 + 6i}$

Simplify.

83. i^{32}

84. i^{19}

85. i^{15}

86. i^{38}

87. i^{42}

88. i^{64}

89. i^9

90. $(-i)^{71}$

91. $(-i)^6$

92. $(-i)^4$

93. $(5i)^3$

94. $(-3i)^5$

95. $i^2 + i^4$

96. $5i^5 + 4i^3$

97. Is the product of two imaginary numbers always an imaginary number? Why or why not?

98. In what way(s) are conjugates of complex numbers similar to the conjugates used in Section 8.5?

Skill Review

To prepare for Section 9.1, review solving quadratic equations (Section 3.7).

Solve. [3.7]

99. $x^2 - x - 6 = 0$

100. $(x - 5)^2 = 0$

101. $t^2 = 100$

102. $2t^2 - 50 = 0$

103. $15x^2 = 14x + 8$

104. $6x^2 = 5x + 6$

Synthesis

105. Is the set of real numbers a subset of the set of complex numbers? Why or why not?

106. Is the union of the set of imaginary numbers and the set of real numbers the set of complex numbers? Why or why not?

Complex numbers are often graphed on a plane. The horizontal axis is the real axis and the vertical axis is the imaginary axis. A complex number such as $5 - 2i$ then corresponds to 5 on the real axis and -2 on the imaginary axis.

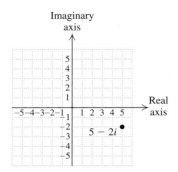

107. Graph each of the following.
   a) $3 + 2i$ b) $-1 + 4i$
   c) $3 - i$ d) $-5i$

108. Graph each of the following.
   a) $1 - 4i$ b) $-2 - 3i$
   c) i d) 4

The absolute value of a complex number $a + bi$ is its distance from the origin. Using the distance formula, we have $|a + bi| = \sqrt{a^2 + b^2}$. Find the absolute value of each complex number.

109. $|3 + 4i|$ 110. $|8 - 6i|$

111. $|-1 + i|$ 112. $|-3 - i|$

A function g is given by
$$g(z) = \frac{z^4 - z^2}{z - 1}.$$

113. Find $g(3i)$. 114. Find $g(1 + i)$.

115. Find $g(5i - 1)$. 116. Find $g(2 - 3i)$.

117. Evaluate
$$\frac{1}{w - w^2} \quad \text{for} \quad w = \frac{1 - i}{10}.$$

Simplify.

118. $\dfrac{i^5 + i^6 + i^7 + i^8}{(1 - i)^4}$ 119. $(1 - i)^3(1 + i)^3$

120. $\dfrac{5 - \sqrt{5}i}{\sqrt{5}i}$ 121. $\dfrac{6}{1 + \dfrac{3}{i}}$

122. $\left(\dfrac{1}{2} - \dfrac{1}{3}i\right)^2 - \left(\dfrac{1}{2} + \dfrac{1}{3}i\right)^2$

123. $\dfrac{i - i^{38}}{1 + i}$

Study Summary

KEY TERMS AND CONCEPTS	EXAMPLES

SECTION 8.1: RADICAL EXPRESSIONS AND FUNCTIONS

c is a **square root** of a if $c^2 = a$.

c is a **cube root** of a if $c^3 = a$.

$\sqrt{a}$ indicates the **principal** square root of a.

$\sqrt[n]{a}$ indicates the **nth root** of a.

index ——— $\sqrt[n]{a}$ ——— **radicand**

radical symbol

The square roots of 25 are -5 and 5.

The cube root of -8 is -2.

$\sqrt{25} = 5$

$\sqrt[3]{-8} = -2$

For all a,

$$\sqrt[n]{a^n} = |a| \text{ when } n \text{ is even;}$$
$$\sqrt[n]{a^n} = a \text{ when } n \text{ is odd.}$$

If a represents a nonnegative number,

$$\sqrt[n]{a^n} = a.$$

Assume that x can be any real number.
$$\sqrt{(3 + x)^2} = |3 + x|$$

Assume that x represents a nonnegative number.
$$\sqrt{(7x)^2} = 7x$$

SECTION 8.2: RATIONAL NUMBERS AS EXPONENTS

$a^{1/n}$ means $\sqrt[n]{a}$.

$a^{m/n}$ means $(\sqrt[n]{a})^m$ or $\sqrt[n]{a^m}$.

$a^{-m/n}$ means $\dfrac{1}{a^{m/n}}$.

$64^{1/2} = \sqrt{64} = 8$

$125^{2/3} = (\sqrt[3]{125})^2 = 5^2 = 25$

$8^{-1/3} = \dfrac{1}{8^{1/3}} = \dfrac{1}{2}$

SECTION 8.3: MULTIPLYING RADICAL EXPRESSIONS

The Product Rule for Radicals

For any real numbers $\sqrt[n]{a}$ and $\sqrt[n]{b}$,
$$\sqrt[n]{a} \cdot \sqrt[n]{b} = \sqrt[n]{a \cdot b}.$$

$$\sqrt[3]{4x} \cdot \sqrt[3]{5y} = \sqrt[3]{20xy}$$

Using the Product Rule to Simplify

For any real numbers $\sqrt[n]{a}$ and $\sqrt[n]{b}$,
$$\sqrt[n]{a \cdot b} = \sqrt[n]{a} \cdot \sqrt[n]{b}.$$

$$\begin{aligned}\sqrt{75x^8y^{11}} &= \sqrt{25 \cdot x^8 \cdot y^{10} \cdot 3 \cdot y}\\ &= \sqrt{25} \cdot \sqrt{x^8} \cdot \sqrt{y^{10}} \cdot \sqrt{3y}\\ &= 5x^4y^5\sqrt{3y} \qquad \text{Assuming } y \text{ is nonnegative}\end{aligned}$$

SECTION 8.4: DIVIDING RATIONAL EXPRESSIONS

The Quotient Rule for Radicals

For any real numbers $\sqrt[n]{a}$ and $\sqrt[n]{b}$, $b \neq 0$,
$$\sqrt[n]{\dfrac{a}{b}} = \dfrac{\sqrt[n]{a}}{\sqrt[n]{b}}.$$

$$\sqrt[3]{\dfrac{8y^4}{125}} = \dfrac{\sqrt[3]{8y^4}}{\sqrt[3]{125}} = \dfrac{2y\sqrt[3]{y}}{5}$$

$$\dfrac{\sqrt{18a^9}}{\sqrt{2a^3}} = \sqrt{\dfrac{18a^9}{2a^3}} = \sqrt{9a^6} = 3a^3 \qquad \text{Assuming } a \text{ is positive}$$

We can **rationalize a denominator** by multiplying by 1.	$\dfrac{\sqrt[3]{5}}{\sqrt[3]{4y}} = \dfrac{\sqrt[3]{5}}{\sqrt[3]{4y}} \cdot \dfrac{\sqrt[3]{2y^2}}{\sqrt[3]{2y^2}} = \dfrac{\sqrt[3]{10y^2}}{\sqrt[3]{8y^3}} = \dfrac{\sqrt[3]{10y^2}}{2y}$

SECTION 8.5: EXPRESSIONS CONTAINING SEVERAL RADICAL TERMS

Like radicals have the same indices and radicands and can be combined.	$\sqrt{12} + 5\sqrt{3} = \sqrt{4 \cdot 3} + 5\sqrt{3} = 2\sqrt{3} + 5\sqrt{3} = 7\sqrt{3}$
Radical expressions are multiplied in much the same way that polynomials are multiplied.	$(1 + 5\sqrt{6})(4 - \sqrt{6}) = 1 \cdot 4 - 1\sqrt{6} + 4 \cdot 5\sqrt{6} - 5\sqrt{6} \cdot \sqrt{6}$ $= 4 - \sqrt{6} + 20\sqrt{6} - 5 \cdot 6$ $= -26 + 19\sqrt{6}$
To rationalize a denominator containing two terms, we use the **conjugate** of the denominator to write a form of 1.	$\dfrac{2}{1 - \sqrt{3}} = \dfrac{2}{1 - \sqrt{3}} \cdot \dfrac{1 + \sqrt{3}}{1 + \sqrt{3}} \quad \begin{array}{l} 1 + \sqrt{3} \text{ is the} \\ \text{conjugate of } 1 - \sqrt{3}. \end{array}$ $= \dfrac{2(1 + \sqrt{3})}{-2} = -1 - \sqrt{3}$
When terms have different indices, we can often use rational exponents to simplify.	$\sqrt[3]{p} \cdot \sqrt[4]{q^3} = p^{1/3} \cdot q^{3/4}$ $= p^{4/12} \cdot q^{9/12} \qquad \text{Finding a common denominator}$ $= \sqrt[12]{p^4 q^9}$

SECTION 8.6: SOLVING RADICAL EQUATIONS

The Principle of Powers If $a = b$, then $a^n = b^n$. To solve a radical equation, use the principle of powers and the steps on pp. 530 and 532. Solutions found using the principle of powers must be checked in the original equation.	$\begin{aligned} x - 7 &= \sqrt{x - 5} \\ (x - 7)^2 &= (\sqrt{x - 5})^2 \\ x^2 - 14x + 49 &= x - 5 \\ x^2 - 15x + 54 &= 0 \\ (x - 6)(x - 9) &= 0 \\ x = 6 \ &or \ x = 9 \end{aligned}$ Only 9 checks and is the solution. $\qquad \begin{aligned} 2 + \sqrt{t} &= \sqrt{t + 8} \\ (2 + \sqrt{t})^2 &= (\sqrt{t + 8})^2 \\ 4 + 4\sqrt{t} + t &= t + 8 \\ 4\sqrt{t} &= 4 \\ \sqrt{t} &= 1 \\ (\sqrt{t})^2 &= (1)^2 \\ t &= 1 \end{aligned}$ 1 checks and is the solution.

SECTION 8.7: THE DISTANCE AND MIDPOINT FORMULAS AND OTHER APPLICATIONS

The Pythagorean Theorem In any right triangle, if a and b are the lengths of the legs and c is the length of the hypotenuse, then $$a^2 + b^2 = c^2.$$	*Find the length of the hypotenuse of a right triangle with legs of lengths 4 and 7. Give an exact answer in radical notation, as well as a decimal approximation to three decimal places.* $\begin{aligned} a^2 + b^2 &= c^2 \\ 4^2 + 7^2 &= c^2 \qquad \text{Substituting} \\ 16 + 49 &= c^2 \\ 65 &= c^2 \\ \sqrt{65} &= c \qquad \text{This is exact.} \\ 8.062 &\approx c \qquad \text{This is approximate.} \end{aligned}$

Special Triangles

The length of the hypotenuse in an isosceles right triangle is the length of a leg times $\sqrt{2}$.

Find the missing lengths. Give an exact answer and, where appropriate, an approximation to three decimal places.

$$a = 10; \quad c = a\sqrt{2}$$
$$c = 10\sqrt{2}$$
$$c \approx 14.142$$

The length of the longer leg in a $30°-60°-90°$ triangle is the length of the shorter leg times $\sqrt{3}$. The hypotenuse is twice as long as the shorter leg.

$$18 = a\sqrt{3} \qquad c = 2a$$
$$\frac{18}{\sqrt{3}} = a \qquad c = 2\left(\frac{18}{\sqrt{3}}\right)$$
$$10.392 \approx a; \qquad c = \frac{36}{\sqrt{3}}$$
$$c \approx 20.785$$

The Distance Formula

The distance d between any two points (x_1, y_1) and (x_2, y_2) is given by

$$d = \sqrt{(x_2 - x_1)^2 + (y_2 - y_1)^2}.$$

Find the distance between $(3, -5)$ and $(-1, -2)$.

$$d = \sqrt{(-1 - 3)^2 + (-2 - (-5))^2}$$
$$= \sqrt{(-4)^2 + (3)^2}$$
$$= \sqrt{16 + 9} = \sqrt{25} = 5$$

The Midpoint Formula

If the endpoints of a segment are (x_1, y_1) and (x_2, y_2), then the coordinates of the midpoint are

$$\left(\frac{x_1 + x_2}{2}, \frac{y_1 + y_2}{2}\right).$$

Find the midpoint of the segment with endpoints $(3, -5)$ and $(-1, -2)$.

$$\left(\frac{3 + (-1)}{2}, \frac{-5 + (-2)}{2}\right), \text{ or } \left(1, -\frac{7}{2}\right)$$

SECTION 8.8: THE COMPLEX NUMBERS

A **complex number** is any number that can be written in the form $a + bi$, where a and b are real numbers,

$$i = \sqrt{-1}, \quad \text{and} \quad i^2 = -1.$$

$$(3 + 2i) + (4 - 7i) = 7 - 5i$$

$$(8 + 6i) - (5 + 2i) = 3 + 4i$$

$$(2 + 3i)(4 - i) = 8 - 2i + 12i - 3i^2$$
$$= 8 + 10i - 3(-1) = 11 + 10i$$

$$\frac{1 - 4i}{3 - 2i} = \frac{1 - 4i}{3 - 2i} \cdot \frac{3 + 2i}{3 + 2i} \qquad \text{The conjugate of } 3 - 2i \text{ is } 3 + 2i.$$

$$= \frac{3 + 2i - 12i - 8i^2}{9 + 6i - 6i - 4i^2}$$

$$= \frac{3 - 10i - 8(-1)}{9 - 4(-1)} = \frac{11 - 10i}{13} = \frac{11}{13} - \frac{10}{13}i$$

Review Exercises: Chapter 8

🦢 **Concept Reinforcement** *Classify each statement as either true or false.*

1. $\sqrt{ab} = \sqrt{a} \cdot \sqrt{b}$ for any real numbers $\sqrt{a}$ and $\sqrt{b}$. [8.3]

2. $\sqrt{a + b} = \sqrt{a} + \sqrt{b}$ for any real numbers $\sqrt{a}$ and $\sqrt{b}$. [8.5]

3. $\sqrt{a^2} = a$, for any real number a. [8.1]

4. $\sqrt[3]{a^3} = a$, for any real number a. [8.1]

5. $x^{2/5}$ means $\sqrt[5]{x^2}$ and $\left(\sqrt[5]{x}\right)^2$. [8.2]

6. The hypotenuse of a right triangle is never shorter than either leg. [8.7]

7. Some radical equations have no solution. [8.6]

8. If $f(x) = \sqrt{x - 5}$, then the domain of f is the set of all nonnegative real numbers. [8.1]

Simplify. [8.1]

9. $\sqrt{\dfrac{100}{121}}$

10. $-\sqrt{0.36}$

Let $f(x) = \sqrt{x + 10}$. Find the following. [8.1]

11. $f(15)$

12. The domain of f

Simplify. Assume that each variable can represent any real number. [8.1]

13. $\sqrt{64t^2}$

14. $\sqrt{(c + 7)^2}$

15. $\sqrt{4x^2 + 4x + 1}$

16. $\sqrt[5]{-32}$

17. Write an equivalent expression using exponential notation: $\left(\sqrt[3]{5ab}\right)^4$. [8.2]

18. Write an equivalent expression using radical notation: $(16a^6)^{3/4}$. [8.2]

Use rational exponents to simplify. Assume $x, y \geq 0$. [8.2]

19. $\sqrt{x^6 y^{10}}$

20. $\left(\sqrt[6]{x^2 y}\right)^2$

Simplify. Do not use negative exponents in the answers. [8.2]

21. $(x^{-2/3})^{3/5}$

22. $\dfrac{7^{-1/3}}{7^{-1/2}}$

23. If $f(x) = \sqrt{25(x - 6)^2}$, find a simplified form for $f(x)$. [8.3]

Simplify. Write all answers using radical notation. Assume that all variables represent nonnegative numbers.

24. $\sqrt[4]{16x^{20}y^8}$ [8.3]

25. $\sqrt{250x^3y^2}$ [8.3]

26. $\sqrt{5a}\sqrt{7b}$ [8.3]

27. $\sqrt[3]{3x^4b}\sqrt[3]{9xb^2}$ [8.3]

28. $\sqrt[3]{-24x^{10}y^8} \, \sqrt[3]{18x^7y^4}$ [8.3]

29. $\sqrt[3]{-\dfrac{27y^{12}}{64}}$ [8.4]

30. $\dfrac{\sqrt[3]{60xy^3}}{\sqrt[3]{10x}}$ [8.4]

31. $\dfrac{\sqrt{75x}}{2\sqrt{3}}$ [8.4]

32. $\sqrt[4]{\dfrac{48a^{11}}{c^8}}$ [8.4]

33. $5\sqrt[3]{4y} + 2\sqrt[3]{4y}$ [8.5]

34. $2\sqrt{75} - 9\sqrt{3}$ [8.5]

35. $\sqrt[3]{8x^4} + \sqrt[3]{xy^6}$ [8.5]

36. $\sqrt{50} + 2\sqrt{18} + \sqrt{32}$ [8.5]

37. $(3 + \sqrt{10})(3 - \sqrt{10})$ [8.5]

38. $(\sqrt{3} - 3\sqrt{8})(\sqrt{5} + 2\sqrt{8})$ [8.5]

39. $\sqrt[4]{x}\sqrt{x}$ [8.5]

40. $\dfrac{\sqrt[3]{x^2}}{\sqrt[4]{x}}$ [8.5]

41. If $f(x) = x^2$, find $f(2 - \sqrt{a})$. [8.5]

42. Rationalize the denominator:
$$\dfrac{4\sqrt{5}}{\sqrt{2} + \sqrt{3}}. \quad [8.5]$$

43. Rationalize the numerator of the expression in Exercise 42. [8.5]

Solve. [8.6]

44. $\sqrt{y + 6} - 2 = 3$

45. $(x + 1)^{1/3} = -5$

46. $1 + \sqrt{x} = \sqrt{3x - 3}$

47. If $f(x) = \sqrt{x + 2} + x$, find a such that $f(a) = 4$. [8.6]

Solve. Give an exact answer and, where appropriate, an approximation to three decimal places. [8.7]

48. The diagonal of a square has length 10 cm. Find the length of a side of the square.

49. A skate-park jump has a ramp that is 6 ft long and is 2 ft high. How long is its base?

50. Find the missing lengths. Give exact answers and, where appropriate, an approximation to three decimal places.

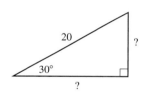

51. Find the distance between $(-6, 4)$ and $(-1, 5)$. Give an exact answer and an approximation to three decimal places. [8.7]

52. Find the midpoint of the segment with endpoints $(-7, -2)$ and $(3, -1)$. [8.7]

53. Express in terms of i and simplify: $\sqrt{-45}$. [8.8]

54. Add: $(-4 + 3i) + (2 - 12i)$. [8.8]

55. Subtract: $(9 - 7i) - (3 - 8i)$. [8.8]

Simplify. [8.8]

56. $(2 + 5i)(2 - 5i)$

57. i^{34}

58. $(6 - 3i)(2 - i)$

59. Divide. Write the answer in the form $a + b$.

$$\frac{7 - 2i}{3 + 4i} \quad [8.8]$$

Synthesis

60. What makes some complex numbers real and others imaginary? [8.8]

61. Explain why $\sqrt[n]{x^n} = |x|$ when n is even, but $\sqrt[n]{x^n} = x$ when n is odd. [8.1]

62. Write a quotient of two imaginary numbers that is a real number (answers may vary). [8.8]

63. Solve:
$$\sqrt{11x + \sqrt{6 + x}} = 6. \quad [8.6]$$

64. Simplify:
$$\frac{2}{1 - 3i} - \frac{3}{4 + 2i}. \quad [8.8]$$

65. Don's Discount Shoes has two locations. The sign at the original location is shaped like an isosceles right triangle. The sign at the newer location is shaped like a 30°–60°–90° triangle. The hypotenuse of each sign measures 6 ft. Which sign has the greater area and by how much? (Round to three decimal places.) [8.7]

Test: Chapter 8

CHAPTER **Test Prep** VIDEO CD *Step-by-step test solutions are found on the video CD in the front of this book.*

Simplify. Assume that variables can represent any real number.

1. $\sqrt{50}$

2. $\sqrt[3]{-\dfrac{8}{x^6}}$

3. $\sqrt{81a^2}$

4. $\sqrt{x^2 - 8x + 16}$

5. Write an equivalent expression using exponential notation: $\sqrt{7xy}$.

6. Write an equivalent expression using radical notation: $(4a^3b)^{5/6}$.

7. If $f(x) = \sqrt{2x - 10}$, determine the domain of f.

8. If $f(x) = x^2$, find $f(5 + \sqrt{2})$.

Simplify. Write all answers using radical notation. Assume that all variables represent positive numbers.

9. $\sqrt[5]{32x^{16}y^{10}}$

10. $\sqrt[3]{4w}\,\sqrt[3]{4v^2}$

11. $\sqrt{\dfrac{100a^4}{9b^6}}$

12. $\dfrac{\sqrt[5]{48x^6y^{10}}}{\sqrt[5]{16x^2y^9}}$

13. $\sqrt[4]{x^3}\,\sqrt{x}$

14. $\dfrac{\sqrt{y}}{\sqrt[10]{y}}$

15. $8\sqrt{2} - 2\sqrt{2}$

16. $\sqrt{x^4y} + \sqrt{9y^3}$

17. $(7 + \sqrt{x})(2 - 3\sqrt{x})$

18. Rationalize the denominator:
$$\dfrac{\sqrt{3}}{5 + \sqrt{2}}.$$

Solve.

19. $6 = \sqrt{x - 3} + 5$

20. $x = \sqrt{3x + 3} - 1$

21. $\sqrt{2x} = \sqrt{x + 1} + 1$

Solve. For Exercises 22–24, give exact answers and approximations to three decimal places.

22. A referee jogs diagonally from one corner of a 50-ft by 90-ft basketball court to the far corner. How far does she jog?

23. The hypotenuse of a 30°–60°–90° triangle is 10 cm long. Find the lengths of the legs.

24. Find the distance between the points $(3, 7)$ and $(-1, 8)$.

25. Find the midpoint of the segment with endpoints $(2, -5)$ and $(1, -7)$.

26. Express in terms of i and simplify: $\sqrt{-50}$.

27. Subtract: $(9 + 8i) - (-3 + 6i)$.

28. Multiply. Write the answer in the form $a + bi$.
$$(4 - i)^2$$

29. Divide. Write the answer in the form $a + bi$.
$$\dfrac{-2 + i}{3 - 5i}$$

30. Simplify: i^{37}.

Synthesis

31. Solve:
$$\sqrt{2x - 2} + \sqrt{7x + 4} = \sqrt{13x + 10}.$$

32. Simplify:
$$\dfrac{1 - 4i}{4i(1 + 4i)^{-1}}.$$

33. The function $D(h) = 1.2\sqrt{h}$ can be used to approximate the distance D, in miles, that a person can see to the horizon from a height h, in feet. How far above sea level must a pilot fly in order to see a horizon that is 180 mi away?

Cumulative Review: Chapters 1–8

Solve.

1. $2(x - 5) - 3 = 3(2x + 5)$ [1.2]

2. $x(x + 2) = 35$ [3.7]

3. $2y^2 = 50$ [3.7]

4. $\dfrac{1}{x} = \dfrac{2}{5}$ [4.6]

5. $\sqrt[3]{t} = -1$ [8.6]

6. $25x^2 - 10x + 1 = 0$ [3.7]

7. $|x - 2| \leq 5$ [7.3]

8. $2x + 5 > 6 \text{ or } x - 3 \leq 9$ [7.2]

9. $\dfrac{2x}{x - 1} + \dfrac{x}{x - 3} = 2$ [4.6]

10. $x = \sqrt{2x - 5} + 4$ [8.6]

11. $3x + y = 5,$
$\quad x - y = -5$ [6.2]

12. $2x - y + z = 1,$
$\quad x + 2y + z = -3,$
$\quad 5x - y + 3z = 0$ [6.4]

Graph on a plane.

13. $3y = -6$ [2.3]

14. $y = -x + 5$ [2.6]

15. $x + y \leq 2$ [7.4]

16. $2x = y$ [2.2]

17. Determine the slope and the y-intercept of the line given by $y = -6 - x$. [2.6]

18. Find an equation for the line parallel to the line given by $y = 7x$ and passing through the point $(0, -11)$. [2.6]

Perform the indicated operations and, if possible, simplify. For radical expressions, assume that all variables represent positive numbers.

19. $18 \div 3 \cdot 2 - 6^2 \div (2 + 4)$

20. $(x^2y - 3x^2 - 4xy^2) - (x^2y - 3x^2 + 4xy^2)$

21. $(2a - 5b)^2$

22. $(c^2 - 3d)(c^2 + 3d)$

23. $\dfrac{1}{x} + \dfrac{1}{x + 1}$ [4.4]

24. $\dfrac{x + 3}{x - 2} - \dfrac{x + 5}{x + 1}$ [4.4]

25. $\dfrac{a^2 - a - 6}{a^2 - 1} \div \dfrac{a^2 - 6a + 9}{2a^2 + 3a + 1}$ [4.2]

26. $\dfrac{\dfrac{1}{x} + \dfrac{1}{x + 1}}{\dfrac{x}{x + 1}}$ [4.5]

27. $\sqrt{200} - 5\sqrt{8}$ [8.5]

28. $(1 + \sqrt{5})(4 - \sqrt{5})$ [8.5]

29. $\sqrt{10a^2b} \cdot \sqrt{15ab^3}$ [8.3]

30. $\sqrt[3]{y}\sqrt[5]{y}$ [8.5]

Factor.

31. $x^2 - 5x - 14$ [3.2]

32. $4y^8 - 4y^5$ [3.5]

33. $100c^2 - 25d^2$ [3.4]

34. $3t^2 - 5t - 8$ [3.3]

35. $3x^2 - 6x - 21$ [3.1]

36. $yt - xt - yz^2 + xz^2$ [3.1]

Find the domain of each function.

37. $f(x) = \dfrac{2x - 3}{x^2 - 6x + 9}$ [5.2]

38. $f(x) = \sqrt{2x - 11}$ [7.1]

Find each of the following, if $f(x) = \sqrt{2x - 3}$ and $g(x) = x^2$.

39. $f(14)$ [8.1]

40. $g(1 - \sqrt{5})$ [8.5]

41. $(f + g)(x)$ [5.4]

Solve.

42. *Flood rescue.* A flood rescue team uses a boat that travels 10 mph in still water. To reach a stranded family, they travel 7 mi against the current and return 7 mi with the current in a total time of $1\frac{2}{3}$ hr. What is the speed of the current? [4.7]

43. *Emergency shelter.* The entrance to a tent used by a rescue team is the shape of an equilateral triangle. If the base of the tent is 4 ft wide, how tall is the tent? Give an exact answer and an approximation to three decimal places. [8.7]

44. *Age at marriage.* The median age at first marriage for U.S. men has grown from 25.1 in 2001 to 25.5 in 2006. Let $m(t)$ represent the median age of men at first marriage t years after 2000. [5.3]
Source: U.S. Census Bureau

a) Find a linear function that fits the data.
b) Use the function from part (a) to predict the median age of men at first marriage in 2020.
c) In what year will the median age of men at first marriage be 28?

45. *Salary.* Neil's annual salary is $38,849. This includes a 6% superior performance raise. What would Neil's salary have been without the performance raise? [1.5]

46. *Food service.* Melted Goodness mixes Swiss chocolate and whipping cream to make a dessert fondue. Swiss chocolate costs $1.20 per ounce and whipping cream costs $0.30 per ounce. How much of each does Melted Goodness use to make 65 oz of fondue at a cost of $60.00? [6.3]

47. *Food cost.* The average cost of a Thanksgiving dinner in the United States rose from $34.56 in 2002 to $42.26 in 2007. What was the rate of increase? [2.4]
Sources: Purdue University; American Farm Bureau Federation

48. *Landscaping.* A rectangular parking lot is 80 ft by 100 ft. Part of the asphalt is removed in order to install a landscaped border of uniform width around it. The area of the new parking lot is 6300 ft^2. How wide is the landscaped border? [3.8]

Synthesis

49. Give an equation in standard form for the line whose x-intercept is $(-3, 0)$ and whose y-intercept is $(0, 5)$. [2.6]

50. Solve by graphing:
$$y = x - 1,$$
$$y = x^2 - 1. \quad [6.1]$$

Solve.

51. $\dfrac{\dfrac{1}{x} + \dfrac{1}{x+1}}{\dfrac{1}{x} - 1} = 1$ [4.4], [4.5]

52. $3\sqrt{2x - 11} = 2 + \sqrt{5x - 1}$ [8.6]

Quadratic Functions and Equations

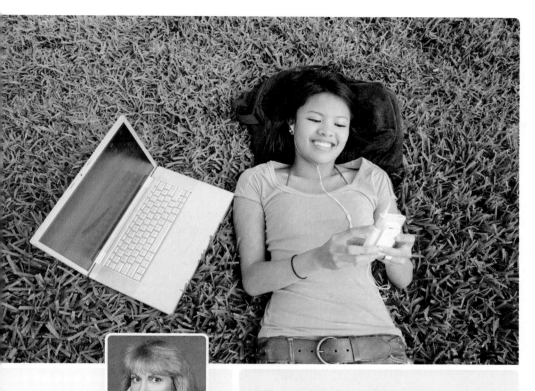

JANET FISHER
MUSIC PUBLISHER AND
RECORD LABEL OWNER
Los Angeles, California

As a music publisher and record label owner, I pay our songwriters and artists royalties based on sales and uses of their songs, both physical and digital. In the world of digital downloads, these royalties run from fractions of cents for a "streamed listen," to a set number of cents per download, depending on the site from which the purchase or stream is made. Varying advances are split between publishers and writers when a song is used in a film or TV show. When a writer has a combination of uses for his or her song, you can imagine how important math is in order to pay them properly.

AN APPLICATION

As more listeners download their music purchases, sales of compact discs are decreasing. According to Nielsen SoundScan, sales of music CDs increased from 500 million in 1997 to 700 million in 2001 and then decreased to 450 million in 2007. Find a quadratic function that fits the data, and use the function to estimate the sales of music CDs in 2009.

This problem appears as Example 3 in Section 9.8.

563

The mathematical translation of a problem is often a function or an equation containing a second-degree polynomial in one variable. Such functions or equations are said to be *quadratic*. In this chapter, we examine a variety of ways to solve quadratic equations and look at graphs and applications of quadratic functions.

9.1 Quadratic Equations

The Principle of Square Roots ● Completing the Square ● Problem Solving

The general form of a quadratic function is

$$f(x) = ax^2 + bx + c, \quad \text{with } a \neq 0.$$

The graph of a quadratic function is a *parabola*. Such graphs open up or down and can have 0, 1, or 2 x-intercepts. We learn to graph quadratic functions later in this chapter.

ALGEBRAIC–GRAPHICAL CONNECTION

The graphs of the quadratic function $f(x) = x^2 + 6x + 8$ and the linear function $g(x) = 0$ are shown below.

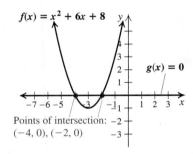

Note that $(-4, 0)$ and $(-2, 0)$ are the points of intersection of the graphs of $f(x) = x^2 + 6x + 8$ and $g(x) = 0$ (the x-axis). In Sections 9.6 and 9.7, we will develop efficient ways to graph quadratic functions. For now, the graphs help us visualize solutions.

In Chapter 3, we solved equations like $x^2 + 6x + 8 = 0$ by factoring:

$$x^2 + 6x + 8 = 0$$
$$(x + 4)(x + 2) = 0 \qquad \text{Factoring}$$
$$x + 4 = 0 \quad or \quad x + 2 = 0 \qquad \text{Using the principle of zero products}$$
$$x = -4 \quad or \qquad x = -2.$$

Note that -4 and -2 are the first coordinates of the points of intersection (or the x-intercepts) of the graph of $f(x)$ above.

In this section and the next, we develop algebraic methods for solving *any* quadratic equation, whether it is factorable or not.

EXAMPLE 1

Solve: $x^2 = 25$.

SOLUTION We have

$$x^2 = 25$$
$$x^2 - 25 = 0 \qquad \text{Writing in standard form}$$
$$(x - 5)(x + 5) = 0 \qquad \text{Factoring}$$
$$x - 5 = 0 \quad or \quad x + 5 = 0 \qquad \text{Using the principle of zero products}$$
$$x = 5 \quad or \quad x = -5.$$

The solutions are 5 and -5. A graph in which $f(x) = x^2$ represents the left side of the original equation and $g(x) = 25$ represents the right side provides a check (see the figure at left). Of course, we can also check by substituting 5 and -5 into the original equation.

TRY EXERCISE 7

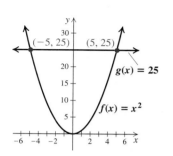

A visualization of Example 1

The Principle of Square Roots

Let's reconsider $x^2 = 25$. We know from Chapter 8 that the number 25 has two real-number square roots, 5 and -5, the solutions of the equation in Example 1. Thus we see that square roots provide quick solutions for equations of the type $x^2 = k$.

The Principle of Square Roots

For any real number k, if $x^2 = k$, then
$$x = \sqrt{k} \quad or \quad x = -\sqrt{k}.$$

EXAMPLE 2

Solve: $3x^2 = 6$. Give exact solutions and approximations to three decimal places.

SOLUTION We have

$$3x^2 = 6$$
$$x^2 = 2 \qquad \text{Isolating } x^2$$
$$x = \sqrt{2} \quad or \quad x = -\sqrt{2}. \qquad \text{Using the principle of square roots}$$

We can use the symbol $\pm\sqrt{2}$ to represent both of the solutions.

CAUTION! There are *two* solutions: $\sqrt{2}$ and $-\sqrt{2}$. Don't forget the second solution.

Check:

For $\sqrt{2}$:

$$\begin{array}{c|c} 3x^2 = 6 \\ \hline 3(\sqrt{2})^2 & 6 \\ 3 \cdot 2 & \\ 6 \stackrel{?}{=} 6 & \text{TRUE} \end{array}$$

For $-\sqrt{2}$:

$$\begin{array}{c|c} 3x^2 = 6 \\ \hline 3(-\sqrt{2})^2 & 6 \\ 3 \cdot 2 & \\ 6 \stackrel{?}{=} 6 & \text{TRUE} \end{array}$$

The solutions are $\sqrt{2}$ and $-\sqrt{2}$, or $\pm\sqrt{2}$, which round to 1.414 and -1.414.

TRY EXERCISE 11

A visualization of Example 2

EXAMPLE 3

A visualization of Example 3

Solve: $-5x^2 + 2 = 0$.

SOLUTION   We have

$$-5x^2 + 2 = 0$$
$$x^2 = \frac{2}{5} \qquad \text{Isolating } x^2$$
$$x = \sqrt{\frac{2}{5}} \quad or \quad x = -\sqrt{\frac{2}{5}}. \qquad \text{Using the principle of square roots}$$

The solutions are $\sqrt{\frac{2}{5}}$ and $-\sqrt{\frac{2}{5}}$, or simply $\pm\sqrt{\frac{2}{5}}$. If we rationalize the denominator, the solutions are written $\pm\frac{\sqrt{10}}{5}$. The checks are left to the student.

TRY EXERCISE 15

Sometimes we get solutions that are imaginary numbers.

EXAMPLE 4

Solve: $4x^2 + 9 = 0$.

SOLUTION   We have

$$4x^2 + 9 = 0$$
$$x^2 = -\frac{9}{4} \qquad \text{Isolating } x^2$$
$$x = \sqrt{-\frac{9}{4}} \quad or \quad x = -\sqrt{-\frac{9}{4}} \qquad \text{Using the principle of square roots}$$
$$x = \sqrt{\frac{9}{4}}\sqrt{-1} \quad or \quad x = -\sqrt{\frac{9}{4}}\sqrt{-1}$$
$$x = \frac{3}{2}i \quad or \quad x = -\frac{3}{2}i. \qquad \text{Recall that } \sqrt{-1} = i.$$

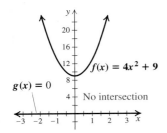

A visualization of Example 4

Check: For $\frac{3}{2}i$:

$$\begin{array}{rl} 4x^2 + 9 &= 0 \\ \hline 4\left(\frac{3}{2}i\right)^2 + 9 & \,\Big|\, 0 \\ 4 \cdot \frac{9}{4} \cdot i^2 + 9 & \\ 9(-1) + 9 & \\ & 0 \overset{?}{=} 0 \quad \text{TRUE} \end{array}$$

For $-\frac{3}{2}i$:

$$\begin{array}{rl} 4x^2 + 9 &= 0 \\ \hline 4\left(-\frac{3}{2}i\right)^2 + 9 & \,\Big|\, 0 \\ 4 \cdot \frac{9}{4} \cdot i^2 + 9 & \\ 9(-1) + 9 & \\ & 0 \overset{?}{=} 0 \quad \text{TRUE} \end{array}$$

The solutions are $\frac{3}{2}i$ and $-\frac{3}{2}i$, or $\pm\frac{3}{2}i$. The graph at left confirms that there are no real-number solutions.

TRY EXERCISE 19

The principle of square roots can be restated in a more general form for any equation in which some algebraic expression squared equals a constant.

> ## The Principle of Square Roots (Generalized Form)
> For any real number k and any algebraic expression X:
> $$\text{If } X^2 = k, \quad \text{then} \quad X = \sqrt{k} \quad or \quad X = -\sqrt{k}.$$

EXAMPLE 5

Let $f(x) = (x-2)^2$. Find all x-values for which $f(x) = 7$.

SOLUTION   We are asked to find all x-values for which

$$f(x) = 7,$$

or

$$(x - 2)^2 = 7. \qquad \text{Substituting } (x-2)^2 \text{ for } f(x)$$

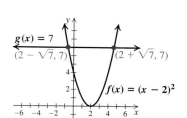

A visualization of Example 5

The generalized principle of square roots gives us

$$x - 2 = \sqrt{7} \quad \text{or} \quad x - 2 = -\sqrt{7} \qquad \text{Using the principle of square roots}$$

$$x = 2 + \sqrt{7} \quad \text{or} \qquad x = 2 - \sqrt{7}.$$

Check: $f(2 + \sqrt{7}) = (2 + \sqrt{7} - 2)^2 = (\sqrt{7})^2 = 7.$

Similarly,

$$f(2 - \sqrt{7}) = (2 - \sqrt{7} - 2)^2 = (-\sqrt{7})^2 = 7.$$

The solutions are $2 + \sqrt{7}$ and $2 - \sqrt{7}$, or simply $2 \pm \sqrt{7}$.

TRY EXERCISE 35

Example 5 is of the form $(x - a)^2 = c$, where a and c are constants. Sometimes we must factor in order to obtain this form.

EXAMPLE 6

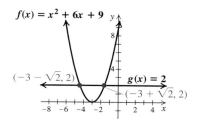

A visualization of Example 6

Solve: $x^2 + 6x + 9 = 2$.

SOLUTION We have

$$x^2 + 6x + 9 = 2 \qquad \text{The left side is the square of a binomial.}$$

$$(x + 3)^2 = 2 \qquad \text{Factoring}$$

$$x + 3 = \sqrt{2} \quad \text{or} \quad x + 3 = -\sqrt{2} \qquad \text{Using the principle of square roots}$$

$$x = -3 + \sqrt{2} \quad \text{or} \qquad x = -3 - \sqrt{2}. \qquad \text{Adding } -3 \text{ to both sides}$$

The solutions are $-3 + \sqrt{2}$ and $-3 - \sqrt{2}$, or $-3 \pm \sqrt{2}$. The checks are left to the student.

TRY EXERCISE 29

Completing the Square

Not all quadratic equations are in the form $X^2 = k$. By using a method called *completing the square*, we can use the principle of square roots to solve *any* quadratic equation by writing it in this form.

Suppose we want to solve the quadratic equation

$$x^2 + 6x + 4 = 0.$$

The trinomial $x^2 + 6x + 4$ is not a perfect square. We can, however, create an equivalent equation with a perfect-square trinomial on one side:

$$x^2 + 6x + 4 = 0$$

$$x^2 + 6x = -4 \qquad \text{Only variable terms are on the left side.}$$

$$x^2 + 6x + 9 = -4 + 9 \qquad \text{Adding 9 to both sides. We explain this shortly.}$$

$$(x + 3)^2 = 5. \qquad \text{We could now use the principle of square roots to solve.}$$

We chose to add 9 to both sides because it creates a perfect-square trinomial on the left side. The 9 was determined by taking half of the coefficient of x and squaring it—that is,

$$\left(\tfrac{1}{2} \cdot 6\right)^2 = 3^2, \quad \text{or} \quad 9.$$

To understand why this procedure works, examine the following drawings.

 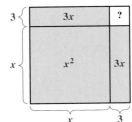

Note that the shaded areas in both figures represent the same area, $x^2 + 6x$. However, only the figure on the right, in which the $6x$ is halved, can be converted into a square with the addition of a constant term. The constant 9 is the "missing" piece that *completes* the square.

To complete the square for $x^2 + bx$, we add $(b/2)^2$.

Example 7, which follows, provides practice in finding numbers that complete the square. We will then use this skill to solve equations.

EXAMPLE 7

Replace the blanks in each equation with constants to form a true equation.

a) $x^2 + 14x + \underline{\quad} = (x + \underline{\quad})^2$

b) $x^2 - 5x + \underline{\quad} = (x - \underline{\quad})^2$

c) $x^2 + \frac{3}{4}x + \underline{\quad} = (x + \underline{\quad})^2$

SOLUTION We take half of the coefficient of x and square it.

a) Half of 14 is 7, and $7^2 = 49$. Thus, $x^2 + 14x + 49$ is a perfect-square trinomial and is equivalent to $(x + 7)^2$. We have

$$x^2 + 14x + 49 = (x + 7)^2.$$

b) Half of -5 is $-\frac{5}{2}$, and $\left(-\frac{5}{2}\right)^2 = \frac{25}{4}$. Thus, $x^2 - 5x + \frac{25}{4}$ is a perfect-square trinomial and is equivalent to $\left(x - \frac{5}{2}\right)^2$. We have

$$x^2 - 5x + \frac{25}{4} = \left(x - \frac{5}{2}\right)^2.$$

c) Half of $\frac{3}{4}$ is $\frac{3}{8}$, and $\left(\frac{3}{8}\right)^2 = \frac{9}{64}$. Thus, $x^2 + \frac{3}{4}x + \frac{9}{64}$ is a perfect-square trinomial and is equivalent to $\left(x + \frac{3}{8}\right)^2$. We have

$$x^2 + \frac{3}{4}x + \frac{9}{64} = \left(x + \frac{3}{8}\right)^2.$$

TRY EXERCISE 39

STUDENT NOTES

In problems like Examples 7(b) and (c), it is best to avoid decimal notation. Most students have an easier time recognizing $\frac{9}{64}$ as $\left(\frac{3}{8}\right)^2$ than seeing 0.140625 as 0.375^2.

We can now use the method of completing the square to solve equations.

EXAMPLE 8

Solve: $x^2 - 8x - 7 = 0$.

SOLUTION We begin by adding 7 to both sides:

$$x^2 - 8x - 7 = 0$$
$$x^2 - 8x = 7 \qquad \text{Adding 7 to both sides. We can now complete the square on the left side.}$$
$$x^2 - 8x + 16 = 7 + 16 \qquad \text{Adding 16 to both sides to complete the square: } \frac{1}{2}(-8) = -4, \text{ and } (-4)^2 = 16$$
$$(x - 4)^2 = 23 \qquad \text{Factoring and simplifying}$$
$$x - 4 = \pm\sqrt{23} \qquad \text{Using the principle of square roots}$$
$$x = 4 \pm \sqrt{23}. \qquad \text{Adding 4 to both sides}$$

TECHNOLOGY CONNECTION

One way to check Example 8 is to store $4 + \sqrt{23}$ as x using the (STO) key. We can then evaluate $x^2 - 8x - 7$ by entering $x^2 - 8x - 7$ and pressing (ENTER).

1. Check Example 8 using the method described above.

Check: For $4 + \sqrt{23}$:

$$\begin{array}{rl} x^2 - 8x - 7 = 0 & \\ \hline (4 + \sqrt{23})^2 - 8(4 + \sqrt{23}) - 7 & 0 \\ 16 + 8\sqrt{23} + 23 - 32 - 8\sqrt{23} - 7 & \\ 16 + 23 - 32 - 7 + 8\sqrt{23} - 8\sqrt{23} & \\ 0 \overset{?}{=} 0 & \text{TRUE} \end{array}$$

For $4 - \sqrt{23}$:

$$\begin{array}{rl} x^2 - 8x - 7 = 0 & \\ \hline (4 - \sqrt{23})^2 - 8(4 - \sqrt{23}) - 7 & 0 \\ 16 - 8\sqrt{23} + 23 - 32 + 8\sqrt{23} - 7 & \\ 16 + 23 - 32 - 7 - 8\sqrt{23} + 8\sqrt{23} & \\ 0 \overset{?}{=} 0 & \text{TRUE} \end{array}$$

The solutions are $4 + \sqrt{23}$ and $4 - \sqrt{23}$, or $4 \pm \sqrt{23}$.   **TRY EXERCISE** 53

Recall that the value of $f(x)$ must be 0 at any x-intercept of the graph of f. If $f(a) = 0$, then $(a, 0)$ is an x-intercept of the graph.

EXAMPLE 9   Find the x-intercepts of the graph of $f(x) = x^2 + 5x - 3$.

SOLUTION   We set $f(x)$ equal to 0 and solve:

$$f(x) = 0$$
$$x^2 + 5x - 3 = 0 \qquad \text{Substituting}$$
$$x^2 + 5x = 3 \qquad \text{Adding 3 to both sides}$$
$$x^2 + 5x + \frac{25}{4} = 3 + \frac{25}{4} \qquad \begin{array}{l}\text{Completing the square:} \\ \frac{1}{2} \cdot 5 = \frac{5}{2}, \text{ and } \left(\frac{5}{2}\right)^2 = \frac{25}{4}\end{array}$$
$$\left(x + \frac{5}{2}\right)^2 = \frac{37}{4} \qquad \text{Factoring and simplifying}$$
$$x + \frac{5}{2} = \pm\frac{\sqrt{37}}{2} \qquad \begin{array}{l}\text{Using the principle of square roots} \\ \text{and the quotient rule for radicals}\end{array}$$
$$x = -\frac{5}{2} \pm \frac{\sqrt{37}}{2}, \quad \text{or} \quad \frac{-5 \pm \sqrt{37}}{2}. \qquad \text{Adding } -\frac{5}{2} \text{ to both sides}$$

The x-intercepts are

$$\left(-\frac{5}{2} - \frac{\sqrt{37}}{2}, 0\right) \quad \text{and} \quad \left(-\frac{5}{2} + \frac{\sqrt{37}}{2}, 0\right), \quad \text{or}$$
$$\left(\frac{-5 - \sqrt{37}}{2}, 0\right) \quad \text{and} \quad \left(\frac{-5 + \sqrt{37}}{2}, 0\right).$$

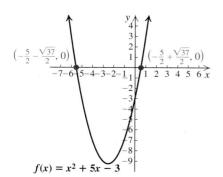

$f(x) = x^2 + 5x - 3$

A visualization of Example 9

The checks are left to the student.   **TRY EXERCISE** 59

Before we complete the square in a quadratic equation, the leading coefficient must be 1. When it is not 1, we divide both sides of the equation by whatever that coefficient may be.

To Solve a Quadratic Equation in x by Completing the Square

1. Isolate the terms with variables on one side of the equation, and arrange them in descending order.
2. Divide both sides by the coefficient of x^2 if that coefficient is not 1.
3. Complete the square by taking half of the coefficient of x and adding its square to both sides.
4. Express the trinomial as the square of a binomial (factor the trinomial) and simplify the other side.
5. Use the principle of square roots (find the square roots of both sides).
6. Solve for x by adding or subtracting on both sides.

EXAMPLE 10 Solve: $3x^2 + 7x - 2 = 0$.

SOLUTION We follow the steps listed above:

$$3x^2 + 7x - 2 = 0$$

Isolate the variable terms.

$$3x^2 + 7x = 2 \qquad \text{Adding 2 to both sides}$$

Divide both sides by the x^2-coefficient.

$$x^2 + \frac{7}{3}x = \frac{2}{3} \qquad \text{Dividing both sides by 3}$$

Complete the square.

$$x^2 + \frac{7}{3}x + \frac{49}{36} = \frac{2}{3} + \frac{49}{36} \qquad \text{Completing the square: } \left(\frac{1}{2} \cdot \frac{7}{3}\right)^2 = \frac{49}{36}$$

Factor the trinomial.

$$\left(x + \frac{7}{6}\right)^2 = \frac{73}{36} \qquad \text{Factoring and simplifying}$$

Use the principle of square roots.

$$x + \frac{7}{6} = \pm\frac{\sqrt{73}}{6} \qquad \text{Using the principle of square roots and the quotient rule for radicals}$$

Solve for x.

$$x = -\frac{7}{6} \pm \frac{\sqrt{73}}{6}, \text{ or } \frac{-7 \pm \sqrt{73}}{6}. \qquad \text{Adding } -\frac{7}{6} \text{ to both sides}$$

The checks are left to the student. The solutions are $-\frac{7}{6} \pm \frac{\sqrt{73}}{6}$, or $\frac{-7 \pm \sqrt{73}}{6}$.

This can be written as

$$-\frac{7}{6} + \frac{\sqrt{73}}{6} \text{ and } -\frac{7}{6} - \frac{\sqrt{73}}{6}, \text{ or } \frac{-7 + \sqrt{73}}{6} \text{ and } \frac{-7 - \sqrt{73}}{6}.$$

TRY EXERCISE 69

Any quadratic equation can be solved by completing the square. The procedure is also useful when graphing quadratic equations and will be used in the next section to develop a formula for solving quadratic equations.

Problem Solving

After one year, an amount of money P, invested at 4% per year, is worth 104% of P, or $P(1.04)$. If that amount continues to earn 4% interest per year, after the second year the investment will be worth 104% of $P(1.04)$, or $P(1.04)^2$. This is called **compounding interest** since after the first time period, interest is earned on both the initial investment *and* the interest from the first time period. Continuing the above pattern, we see that after the third year, the investment will be worth 104% of $P(1.04)^2$. Generalizing, we have the following.

> ## The Compound-Interest Formula
>
> If an amount of money P is invested at interest rate r, compounded annually, then in t years, it will grow to the amount A given by
>
> $$A = P(1 + r)^t. \qquad (r \text{ is written in decimal notation.})$$

We can use quadratic equations to solve certain interest problems.

EXAMPLE 11

Investment growth. Katia invested \$4000 at interest rate r, compounded annually. In 2 yr, it grew to \$4410. What was the interest rate?

SOLUTION

1. **Familiarize.** We are already familiar with the compound-interest formula. If we were not, we would need to consult an outside source.

2. **Translate.** The translation consists of substituting into the formula:

$$A = P(1 + r)^t$$
$$4410 = 4000(1 + r)^2. \qquad \text{Substituting}$$

3. **Carry out.** We solve for r:

$$4410 = 4000(1 + r)^2$$
$$\tfrac{4410}{4000} = (1 + r)^2 \qquad \text{Dividing both sides by 4000}$$
$$\tfrac{441}{400} = (1 + r)^2 \qquad \text{Simplifying}$$
$$\pm\sqrt{\tfrac{441}{400}} = 1 + r \qquad \text{Using the principle of square roots}$$
$$\pm\tfrac{21}{20} = 1 + r \qquad \text{Simplifying}$$
$$-\tfrac{20}{20} \pm \tfrac{21}{20} = r \qquad \text{Adding } -1, \text{ or } -\tfrac{20}{20}, \text{ to both sides}$$
$$\tfrac{1}{20} = r \quad \text{or} \quad -\tfrac{41}{20} = r.$$

4. **Check.** Since the interest rate cannot be negative, we need check only $\tfrac{1}{20}$, or 5%. If \$4000 were invested at 5% interest, compounded annually, then in 2 yr it would grow to $4000(1.05)^2$, or \$4410. The rate 5% checks.

5. **State.** The interest rate was 5%.

> TRY EXERCISE 75

EXAMPLE 12

Free-falling objects. The formula $s = 16t^2$ is used to approximate the distance s, in feet, that an object falls freely from rest in t seconds. The Grand Canyon Skywalk is 4000 ft above the Colorado River. How long will it take a stone to fall from the Skywalk to the river? Round to the nearest tenth of a second.

Source: www.grandcanyonskywalk.com

SOLUTION

1. **Familiarize.** We agree to disregard air resistance and use the given formula.

2. **Translate.** We substitute into the formula:

$$s = 16t^2$$
$$4000 = 16t^2.$$

3. Carry out. We solve for t:

$$4000 = 16t^2$$
$$250 = t^2$$
$$\sqrt{250} = t \qquad \text{Using the principle of square roots; rejecting the negative square root since } t \text{ cannot be negative in this problem}$$
$$15.8 \approx t. \qquad \text{Using a calculator and rounding to the nearest tenth}$$

4. Check. Since $16(15.8)^2 = 3994.24 \approx 4000$, our answer checks.

5. State. It takes about 15.8 sec for a stone to fall freely from the Grand Canyon Skywalk to the river.

TRY EXERCISE ▶ 79

TECHNOLOGY CONNECTION

As we saw in Section 3.7, a graphing calculator can be used to find approximate solutions of any quadratic equation that has real-number solutions.

To check Example 8, we graph $y = x^2 - 8x - 7$ and use the ZERO or ROOT option of the CALC menu. When asked for a Left and Right Bound, we enter cursor positions to the left of and to the right of the root. A Guess between the bounds is entered and a value for the root then appears.

$y = x^2 - 8x - 7$

Zero
X = −.7958315 Y = 0

Yscl = 5

1. Use a graphing calculator to check the second solution of Example 8.
2. Use a graphing calculator to confirm the solutions in Example 9.
3. Can a graphing calculator be used to find *exact* solutions in Example 10? Why or why not?
4. Use a graphing calculator to confirm that there are no real-number solutions of $x^2 - 6x + 11 = 0$.

9.1 EXERCISE SET

For Extra Help — MyMathLab — Math XL PRACTICE — WATCH — DOWNLOAD

Concept Reinforcement *Complete each of the following to form true statements.*

1. The principle of square roots states that if $x^2 = k$, then $x = $ ____ or $x = $ ____.

2. If $(x + 5)^2 = 49$, then $x + 5 = $ ____ or $x + 5 = $ ____.

3. If $t^2 + 6t + 9 = 17$, then $($ ____ $)^2 = 17$ and ____ $= \pm\sqrt{17}$.

4. The equations $x^2 + 8x + $ ____ $= 23$ and $x^2 + 8x = 7$ are equivalent.

5. The expressions $t^2 + 10t + $ ____ and $(t + $ ____ $)^2$ are equivalent.

6. The expressions $x^2 - 6x + $ ____ and $(x - $ ____ $)^2$ are equivalent.

Solve.

7. $x^2 = 100$

8. $t^2 = 144$

9. $p^2 - 50 = 0$

10. $c^2 - 8 = 0$

11. $5y^2 = 30$

12. $4y^2 = 12$

13. $9x^2 - 49 = 0$

14. $36a^2 - 25 = 0$

15. $6t^2 - 5 = 0$

16. $7x^2 - 5 = 0$

17. $a^2 + 1 = 0$

18. $t^2 + 4 = 0$

19. $4d^2 + 81 = 0$

20. $25y^2 + 16 = 0$

21. $(x - 3)^2 = 16$

22. $(x + 1)^2 = 100$

23. $(t + 5)^2 = 12$

24. $(y - 4)^2 = 18$

25. $(x + 1)^2 = -9$

26. $(x - 1)^2 = -49$

27. $\left(y + \frac{3}{4}\right)^2 = \frac{17}{16}$

28. $\left(t + \frac{3}{2}\right)^2 = \frac{7}{2}$

29. $x^2 - 10x + 25 = 64$ **30.** $x^2 - 6x + 9 = 100$

31. Let $f(x) = x^2$. Find x such that $f(x) = 19$.

32. Let $f(x) = x^2$. Find x such that $f(x) = 11$.

33. Let $f(x) = (x - 5)^2$. Find x such that $f(x) = 16$.

34. Let $g(x) = (x - 2)^2$. Find x such that $g(x) = 25$.

35. Let $F(t) = (t + 4)^2$. Find t such that $F(t) = 13$.

36. Let $f(t) = (t + 6)^2$. Find t such that $f(t) = 15$.

Aha! **37.** Let $g(x) = x^2 + 14x + 49$. Find x such that $g(x) = 49$.

38. Let $F(x) = x^2 + 8x + 16$. Find x such that $F(x) = 9$.

Replace the blanks in each equation with constants to complete the square and form a true equation.

39. $x^2 + 16x + \underline{\quad} = (x + \underline{\quad})^2$

40. $x^2 + 12x + \underline{\quad} = (x + \underline{\quad})^2$

41. $t^2 - 10t + \underline{\quad} = (t - \underline{\quad})^2$

42. $t^2 - 6t + \underline{\quad} = (t - \underline{\quad})^2$

43. $t^2 - 2t + \underline{\quad} = (t - \underline{\quad})^2$

44. $x^2 + 2x + \underline{\quad} = (x + \underline{\quad})^2$

45. $x^2 + 3x + \underline{\quad} = \left(x + \underline{\quad}\right)^2$

46. $t^2 - 9t + \underline{\quad} = \left(t - \underline{\quad}\right)^2$

47. $x^2 + \frac{2}{5}x + \underline{\quad} = \left(x + \underline{\quad}\right)^2$

48. $x^2 + \frac{2}{3}x + \underline{\quad} = \left(x + \underline{\quad}\right)^2$

49. $t^2 - \frac{5}{6}t + \underline{\quad} = \left(t - \underline{\quad}\right)^2$

50. $t^2 - \frac{5}{3}t + \underline{\quad} = \left(t - \underline{\quad}\right)^2$

Solve by completing the square. Show your work.

51. $x^2 + 6x = 7$

52. $x^2 + 8x = 9$

53. $t^2 - 10t = -23$

54. $t^2 - 4t = -1$

55. $x^2 + 12x + 32 = 0$

56. $x^2 + 16x + 15 = 0$

57. $t^2 + 8t - 3 = 0$

58. $t^2 + 6t - 5 = 0$

Complete the square to find the x-intercepts of each function given by the equation listed.

59. $f(x) = x^2 + 6x + 7$

60. $f(x) = x^2 + 10x - 2$

61. $g(x) = x^2 + 9x - 25$

62. $g(x) = x^2 + 5x + 2$

63. $f(x) = x^2 - 10x - 22$

64. $f(x) = x^2 - 8x - 10$

Solve by completing the square. Remember to first divide, as in Example 10, to make sure that the coefficient of x^2 is 1.

65. $9x^2 + 18x = -8$ **66.** $4x^2 + 8x = -3$

67. $3x^2 - 5x - 2 = 0$ **68.** $2x^2 - 5x - 3 = 0$

69. $5x^2 + 4x - 3 = 0$ **70.** $4x^2 + 3x - 5 = 0$

71. Find the x-intercepts of the function given by $f(x) = 4x^2 + 2x - 3$.

72. Find the x-intercepts of the function given by $f(x) = 3x^2 + x - 5$.

73. Find the x-intercepts of the function given by $g(x) = 2x^2 - 3x - 1$.

74. Find the x-intercepts of the function given by $g(x) = 3x^2 - 5x - 1$.

Interest. Use $A = P(1 + r)^t$ to find the interest rate in Exercises 75–78. Refer to Example 11.

75. $2000 grows to $2420 in 2 yr

76. $1000 grows to $1440 in 2 yr

77. $6250 grows to $6760 in 2 yr

78. $6250 grows to $7290 in 2 yr

Free-falling objects. Use $s = 16t^2$ for Exercises 79–82. Refer to Example 12 and neglect air resistance.

79. At a height of 290 ft, the Rainbow Bridge in Lake Powell National Monument, Utah, is the world's highest natural arch. How long would it take an object to fall freely from the bridge?
Source: *Guinness World Records* 2008

80. The Sears Tower in Chicago is 1454 ft tall. How long would it take an object to fall freely from the top?

81. At 2063 ft, the KVLY-TV tower in North Dakota is the tallest supported tower. How long would it take an object to fall freely from the top?
Source: North Dakota Tourism Division

82. El Capitan in Yosemite National Park is 3593 ft high. How long would it take a carabiner to fall freely from the top?
Source: *Guinness World Records* 2008

83. Explain in your own words a sequence of steps that can be used to solve any quadratic equation in the quickest way.

84. Write an interest-rate problem for a classmate to solve. Devise the problem so that the solution is "The loan was made at 7% interest."

Skill Review

To prepare for Section 9.2, review evaluating expressions and simplifying radical expressions (Sections 8.3, and 8.8).

Evaluate.

85. $b^2 - 4ac$, for $a = 3$, $b = 2$, and $c = -5$

86. $b^2 - 4ac$, for $a = 1$, $b = -1$, and $c = 4$

Simplify. [8.3], [8.8]

87. $\sqrt{200}$ **88.** $\sqrt{96}$

89. $\sqrt{-4}$ **90.** $\sqrt{-25}$

91. $\sqrt{-8}$ **92.** $\sqrt{-24}$

Synthesis

93. What would be better: to receive 3% interest every 6 months, or to receive 6% interest every 12 months? Why?

94. Write a problem involving a free-falling object for a classmate to solve (see Example 12). Devise the problem so that the solution is "The object takes about 4.5 sec to fall freely from the top of the structure."

Find b such that each trinomial is a square.

95. $x^2 + bx + 81$ **96.** $x^2 + bx + 49$

97. If $f(x) = 2x^5 - 9x^4 - 66x^3 + 45x^2 + 280x$ and $x^2 - 5$ is a factor of $f(x)$, find all a for which $f(a) = 0$.

98. If $f(x) = \left(x - \frac{1}{3}\right)(x^2 + 6)$ and $g(x) = \left(x - \frac{1}{3}\right)\left(x^2 - \frac{2}{3}\right)$, find all a for which $(f + g)(a) = 0$.

99. *Boating.* A barge and a fishing boat leave a dock at the same time, traveling at a right angle to each other. The barge travels 7 km/h slower than the fishing boat. After 4 hr, the boats are 68 km apart. Find the speed of each boat.

100. Find three consecutive integers such that the square of the first plus the product of the other two is 67.

101. Exercises 29, 33, and 53 can be solved on a graphing calculator without first rewriting in standard form. Simply let y_1 represent the left side of the equation and y_2 the right side. Then use a graphing calculator to determine the x-coordinate of any point of intersection. Use a graphing calculator to solve Exercises 29, 33, and 53 in this manner.

102. Use a graphing calculator to check your answers to Exercises 5, 13, 71, and 73.

103. Example 11 can be solved with a graphing calculator by graphing each side of
$$4410 = 4000(1 + r)^2.$$
How could you determine, from a reading of the problem, a suitable viewing window? What might that window be?

9.2 The Quadratic Formula

Solving Using the Quadratic Formula • Approximating Solutions

We can use the process of completing the square to develop a general formula for solving quadratic equations.

Solving Using the Quadratic Formula

Each time we solve by completing the square, the procedure is the same. When a procedure is repeated many times, we can often develop a formula to speed up our work.

We begin with a quadratic equation in standard form,

$$ax^2 + bx + c = 0,$$

with $a > 0$. For $a < 0$, a slightly different derivation is needed (see Exercise 60), but the result is the same. Let's solve by completing the square. As the steps are performed, compare them with Example 10 on p. 570.

$$ax^2 + bx = -c \qquad \text{Adding to both sides}$$

$$x^2 + \frac{b}{a}x = -\frac{c}{a} \qquad \text{Dividing both sides by } a$$

Half of $\dfrac{b}{a}$ is $\dfrac{b}{2a}$ and $\left(\dfrac{b}{2a}\right)^2$ is $\dfrac{b^2}{4a^2}$. We add $\dfrac{b^2}{4a^2}$ to both sides:

$$x^2 + \frac{b}{a}x + \frac{b^2}{4a^2} = -\frac{c}{a} + \frac{b^2}{4a^2} \qquad \text{Adding } \frac{b^2}{4a^2} \text{ to complete the square}$$

$$\left(x + \frac{b}{2a}\right)^2 = -\frac{4ac}{4a^2} + \frac{b^2}{4a^2} \qquad \text{Factoring on the left side; finding a common denominator on the right side}$$

$$\left(x + \frac{b}{2a}\right)^2 = \frac{b^2 - 4ac}{4a^2}$$

$$x + \frac{b}{2a} = \pm \frac{\sqrt{b^2 - 4ac}}{2a} \qquad \text{Using the principle of square roots and the quotient rule for radicals. Since } a > 0,\ \sqrt{4a^2} = 2a.$$

$$x = \frac{-b \pm \sqrt{b^2 - 4ac}}{2a}. \qquad \text{Adding } -\frac{b}{2a} \text{ to both sides}$$

It is important to remember the quadratic formula and know how to use it.

The Quadratic Formula

The solutions of $ax^2 + bx + c = 0$, $a \neq 0$, are given by

$$x = \frac{-b \pm \sqrt{b^2 - 4ac}}{2a}.$$

EXAMPLE 1   Solve $5x^2 + 8x = -3$ using the quadratic formula.

SOLUTION   We first find standard form and determine a, b, and c:

$$5x^2 + 8x + 3 = 0; \quad \text{Adding 3 to both sides to get 0 on one side}$$
$$a = 5, \quad b = 8, \quad c = 3.$$

Next, we use the quadratic formula:

$$x = \frac{-b \pm \sqrt{b^2 - 4ac}}{2a} \qquad \text{It is important to remember this formula.}$$

$$x = \frac{-8 \pm \sqrt{8^2 - 4 \cdot 5 \cdot 3}}{2 \cdot 5} \qquad \text{Substituting}$$

$$x = \frac{-8 \pm \sqrt{64 - 60}}{10}$$

Be sure to write the fraction bar all the way across.

$$x = \frac{-8 \pm \sqrt{4}}{10} = \frac{-8 \pm 2}{10}$$

$$x = \frac{-8 + 2}{10} \quad or \quad x = \frac{-8 - 2}{10} \qquad \text{The symbol } \pm \text{ indicates two solutions.}$$

$$x = \frac{-6}{10} \quad or \quad x = \frac{-10}{10}$$

$$x = -\frac{3}{5} \quad or \quad x = -1.$$

The solutions are $-\frac{3}{5}$ and -1. The checks are left to the student.

TRY EXERCISE 25

Because $5x^2 + 8x + 3$ can be factored, the quadratic formula may not have been the fastest way of solving Example 1. However, because the quadratic formula works for *any* quadratic equation, we need not spend too much time struggling to solve a quadratic equation by factoring.

STUDY SKILLS

Know It "By Heart"

When memorizing something like the quadratic formula, try to first understand and write out the derivation. Doing this two or three times will help you remember the formula.

To Solve a Quadratic Equation

1. If the equation can be easily written in the form $ax^2 = p$ or $(x + k)^2 = d$, use the principle of square roots as in Section 9.1.
2. If step (1) does not apply, write the equation in the form $ax^2 + bx + c = 0$.
3. Try factoring and using the principle of zero products.
4. If factoring seems difficult or impossible, use the quadratic formula. Completing the square can also be used.

The solutions of a quadratic equation can always be found using the quadratic formula. They cannot always be found by factoring.

Recall that a second-degree polynomial in one variable is said to be quadratic. Similarly, a second-degree polynomial function in one variable is said to be a **quadratic function**.

EXAMPLE 2

For the quadratic function given by $f(x) = 3x^2 - 6x - 4$, find all x for which $f(x) = 0$.

SOLUTION We substitute and solve for x:

$$f(x) = 0$$
$$3x^2 - 6x - 4 = 0. \quad \text{Substituting}$$

Since $3x^2 - 6x - 4$ does not factor, we use the quadratic formula with $a = 3$, $b = -6$, and $c = -4$:

$$x = \frac{-(-6) \pm \sqrt{(-6)^2 - 4 \cdot 3 \cdot (-4)}}{2 \cdot 3}$$

$$= \frac{6 \pm \sqrt{36 + 48}}{6} \quad (-6)^2 - 4 \cdot 3 \cdot (-4) = 36 - (-48) = 36 + 48$$

$$= \frac{6 \pm \sqrt{84}}{6} \quad \text{Note that 4 is a perfect-square factor of 84.}$$

$$= \frac{6}{6} \pm \frac{\sqrt{84}}{6} \quad \text{Writing as two fractions to simplify each separately}$$

$$= 1 \pm \frac{\sqrt{4}\sqrt{21}}{6} \quad 84 = 4 \cdot 21$$

$$= 1 \pm \frac{2\sqrt{21}}{2 \cdot 3}$$

$$= 1 \pm \frac{\sqrt{21}}{3}. \quad \left.\right\} \quad \text{Simplifying by removing a factor of 1: } \frac{2}{2} = 1$$

The solutions are $1 - \dfrac{\sqrt{21}}{3}$ and $1 + \dfrac{\sqrt{21}}{3}$. The checks are left to the student.

TRY EXERCISE 39

Some quadratic equations have solutions that are imaginary numbers.

EXAMPLE 3

Solve: $x(x + 5) = 2(2x - 1)$.

SOLUTION We first find standard form:

$$x^2 + 5x = 4x - 2 \quad \text{Multiplying}$$
$$x^2 + x + 2 = 0. \quad \text{Subtracting } 4x \text{ and adding 2 to both sides}$$

Since we cannot factor $x^2 + x + 2$, we use the quadratic formula with $a = 1$, $b = 1$, and $c = 2$:

$$x = \frac{-1 \pm \sqrt{1^2 - 4 \cdot 1 \cdot 2}}{2 \cdot 1} \quad \text{Substituting}$$

$$= \frac{-1 \pm \sqrt{1 - 8}}{2}$$

$$= \frac{-1 \pm \sqrt{-7}}{2}$$

$$= \frac{-1 \pm i\sqrt{7}}{2}, \text{ or } -\frac{1}{2} \pm \frac{\sqrt{7}}{2} i.$$

The solutions are $-\dfrac{1}{2} - \dfrac{\sqrt{7}}{2} i$ and $-\dfrac{1}{2} + \dfrac{\sqrt{7}}{2} i$. The checks are left to the student.

TRY EXERCISE 35

TECHNOLOGY CONNECTION

To check Example 2 by graphing $y_1 = 3x^2 - 6x - 4$, press TRACE and enter $1 + \sqrt{21}/3$. A rational approximation and the y-value 0 should appear.

$y = 3x^2 - 6x - 4$

X = 2.5275252 Y = 0

Use this approach to check the other solution of Example 2.

$g(x) = 2(2x - 1)$

No real-number solution exists.

$f(x) = x(x + 5)$

A visualization of Example 3

The quadratic formula can be used to solve certain rational equations.

EXAMPLE **4**

If $f(t) = 2 + \dfrac{7}{t}$ and $g(t) = \dfrac{4}{t^2}$, find all t for which $f(t) = g(t)$.

SOLUTION We set $f(t)$ equal to $g(t)$ and solve:

$$f(t) = g(t)$$
$$2 + \frac{7}{t} = \frac{4}{t^2}. \qquad \text{Substituting. Note that } t \neq 0.$$

This is a rational equation similar to those in Section 4.6. To solve, we multiply both sides by the LCD, t^2:

$$t^2\left(2 + \frac{7}{t}\right) = t^2 \cdot \frac{4}{t^2}$$
$$2t^2 + 7t = 4 \qquad \text{Simplifying}$$
$$2t^2 + 7t - 4 = 0. \qquad \text{Subtracting 4 from both sides}$$

We use the quadratic formula with $a = 2$, $b = 7$, and $c = -4$:

$$t = \frac{-7 \pm \sqrt{7^2 - 4 \cdot 2 \cdot (-4)}}{2 \cdot 2}$$
$$= \frac{-7 \pm \sqrt{49 + 32}}{4} \qquad 7^2 - 4 \cdot 2 \cdot (-4) = 49 - (-32) = 49 + 32$$
$$= \frac{-7 \pm \sqrt{81}}{4}$$
$$= \frac{-7 \pm 9}{4} \qquad \text{This means } \frac{-7 + 9}{4} \; or \; \frac{-7 - 9}{4}.$$
$$t = \frac{2}{4} = \frac{1}{2} \quad or \quad t = \frac{-16}{4} = -4. \qquad \begin{array}{l}\text{Both answers should check} \\ \text{since } t \neq 0.\end{array}$$

You can confirm that $f\left(\frac{1}{2}\right) = g\left(\frac{1}{2}\right)$ and $f(-4) = g(-4)$. The solutions are $\frac{1}{2}$ and -4.

TRY EXERCISE 41

Approximating Solutions

When the solution of an equation is irrational, a rational-number approximation is often useful. This is often the case in real-world applications similar to those found in Section 9.4.

EXAMPLE **5**

Use a calculator to approximate, to three decimal places, the solutions of Example 2.

SOLUTION On most calculators, one of the following sequences of keystrokes can be used to approximate $1 + \sqrt{21}/3$:

Similar keystrokes can be used to approximate $1 - \sqrt{21}/3$.

The solutions are approximately 2.527525232 and -0.5275252317. Rounded to three decimal places, the solutions are approximately 2.528 and -0.528.

TRY EXERCISE 45

TECHNOLOGY CONNECTION

We saw in Sections 3.7 and 9.1 how graphing calculators can solve quadratic equations. To determine whether quadratic equations are solved more quickly on a graphing calculator or by using the quadratic formula, solve Examples 2 and 4 both ways. Which method is faster? Which method is more precise? Why?

STUDENT NOTES ———

It is important that you understand both the rules for order of operations *and* the manner in which your calculator applies those rules.

Concept Reinforcement *Classify each statement as either true or false.*

1. The quadratic formula can be used to solve *any* quadratic equation.

2. The steps used to derive the quadratic formula are the same as those used when solving by completing the square.

3. The quadratic formula does not work if solutions are imaginary numbers.

4. Solving by factoring is always slower than using the quadratic formula.

5. A quadratic equation can have as many as four solutions.

6. It is possible for a quadratic equation to have no real-number solutions.

Solve.

7. $2x^2 + 3x - 5 = 0$

8. $3x^2 - 7x + 2 = 0$

9. $u^2 + 2u - 4 = 0$

10. $u^2 - 2u - 2 = 0$

11. $t^2 + 3 = 6t$

12. $t^2 + 4t = 1$

13. $x^2 = 3x + 5$

14. $x^2 + 5x + 3 = 0$

15. $3t(t + 2) = 1$

16. $2t(t + 2) = 1$

17. $\dfrac{1}{x^2} - 3 = \dfrac{8}{x}$

18. $\dfrac{9}{x} - 2 = \dfrac{5}{x^2}$

19. $t^2 + 10 = 6t$

20. $t^2 + 10t + 26 = 0$

21. $p^2 - p + 1 = 0$

22. $p^2 + p + 4 = 0$

23. $x^2 + 4x + 6 = 0$

24. $x^2 + 11 = 6x$

25. $12t^2 + 17t = 40$

26. $15t^2 + 7t = 2$

27. $25x^2 - 20x + 4 = 0$

28. $36x^2 + 84x + 49 = 0$

29. $7x(x + 2) + 5 = 3x(x + 1)$

30. $5x(x - 1) - 7 = 4x(x - 2)$

31. $14(x - 4) - (x + 2) = (x + 2)(x - 4)$

32. $11(x - 2) + (x - 5) = (x + 2)(x - 6)$

33. $51p = 2p^2 + 72$

34. $72 = 3p^2 + 50p$

35. $x(x - 3) = x - 9$

36. $x(x - 1) = 2x - 7$

37. $x^3 - 8 = 0$ (*Hint*: Factor the difference of cubes. Then use the quadratic formula.)

38. $x^3 + 1 = 0$

39. Let $f(x) = 6x^2 - 7x - 20$. Find x such that $f(x) = 0$.

40. Let $g(x) = 4x^2 - 2x - 3$. Find x such that $g(x) = 0$.

41. Let
$$f(x) = \frac{7}{x} + \frac{7}{x + 4}.$$
Find all x for which $f(x) = 1$.

42. Let
$$g(x) = \frac{2}{x} + \frac{2}{x + 3}.$$
Find all x for which $g(x) = 1$.

43. Let
$$F(x) = \frac{3 - x}{4} \quad \text{and} \quad G(x) = \frac{1}{4x}.$$
Find all x for which $F(x) = G(x)$.

44. Let
$$f(x) = x + 5 \quad \text{and} \quad g(x) = \frac{3}{x - 5}.$$
Find all x for which $f(x) = g(x)$.

Solve using the quadratic formula. Then use a calculator to approximate, to three decimal places, the solutions as rational numbers.

45. $x^2 + 4x - 7 = 0$

46. $x^2 + 6x + 4 = 0$

Aha! 47. $x^2 - 6x + 4 = 0$

48. $x^2 - 4x + 1 = 0$

49. $2x^2 - 3x - 7 = 0$

50. $3x^2 - 3x - 2 = 0$

51. Are there any equations that can be solved by the quadratic formula but not by completing the square? Why or why not?

52. Suppose you are solving a quadratic equation with no constant term ($c = 0$). Would you use factoring or the quadratic formula to solve? Why?

Skill Review

To prepare for Section 9.3, review multiplying and simplifying radical and complex-number expressions (Sections 8.5 and 8.8).

Multiply and simplify.

53. $(x - 2i)(x + 2i)$ [8.8]

54. $(x - 6\sqrt{5})(x + 6\sqrt{5})$ [8.5]

55. $(x - (2 - \sqrt{7}))(x - (2 + \sqrt{7}))$ [8.5]

56. $(x - (-3 + 5i))(x - (-3 - 5i))$ [8.8]

Simplify.

57. $\dfrac{-6 \pm \sqrt{(-4)^2 - 4(2)(2)}}{2(2)}$ [8.3]

58. $\dfrac{-(-1) \pm \sqrt{(6)^2 - 4(3)(5)}}{2(3)}$ [8.8]

Synthesis

59. Explain how you could use the quadratic formula to help factor a quadratic polynomial.

60. If $a < 0$ and $ax^2 + bx + c = 0$, then $-a$ is positive and the equivalent equation, $-ax^2 - bx - c = 0$, can be solved using the quadratic formula.
   a) Find this solution, replacing a, b, and c in the formula with $-a$, $-b$, and $-c$ from the equation.
   b) How does the result of part (a) indicate that the quadratic formula "works" regardless of the sign of a?

For Exercises 61–63, let

$$f(x) = \frac{x^2}{x - 2} + 1 \quad and \quad g(x) = \frac{4x - 2}{x - 2} + \frac{x + 4}{2}.$$

61. Find the x-intercepts of the graph of f.

62. Find the x-intercepts of the graph of g.

63. Find all x for which $f(x) = g(x)$.

Solve. Approximate the solutions to three decimal places.

64. $x^2 - 0.75x - 0.5 = 0$

65. $z^2 + 0.84z - 0.4 = 0$

Solve.

66. $(1 + \sqrt{3})x^2 - (3 + 2\sqrt{3})x + 3 = 0$

67. $\sqrt{2}x^2 + 5x + \sqrt{2} = 0$

68. $ix^2 - 2x + 1 = 0$

69. One solution of $kx^2 + 3x - k = 0$ is -2. Find the other.

70. Use a graphing calculator to solve Exercises 9, 27, and 43.

71. Use a graphing calculator to solve Exercises 11, 33, and 41. Use the method of graphing each side of the equation.

72. Can a graphing calculator be used to solve *any* quadratic equation? Why or why not?

9.3   Studying Solutions of Quadratic Equations

The Discriminant • Writing Equations from Solutions

The Discriminant

It is sometimes enough to know what *type* of number a solution will be, without actually solving the equation. Suppose we want to know if $4x^2 - 5x - 2 = 0$ has rational solutions (and thus can be solved by factoring). Using the quadratic formula, we would have

$$x = \frac{-b \pm \sqrt{b^2 - 4ac}}{2a}$$

$$= \frac{-(-5) \pm \sqrt{(-5)^2 - 4 \cdot 4(-2)}}{2 \cdot 4}.$$

Since $(-5)^2 - 4 \cdot 4 \cdot (-2) = 25 - 16(-2) = 25 + 32 = 57$ and since 57 is not a perfect square, the solutions of the equation are not rational numbers. This means that $4x^2 - 5x - 2 = 0$ *cannot* be solved by factoring. Note that the radicand, 57, determines what type of number the solutions will be.

The radicand $b^2 - 4ac$ is known as the **discriminant**. If a, b, and c are rational, then we have the following.

- When $b^2 - 4ac$ simplifies to 0, it doesn't matter if we use $+\sqrt{b^2 - 4ac}$ or $-\sqrt{b^2 - 4ac}$; we get the same solution twice. Thus, when the discriminant is 0, there is one *repeated* solution and it is rational.

  Example: $9x^2 + 6x + 1 = 0 \rightarrow b^2 - 4ac = 6^2 - 4 \cdot 9 \cdot 1 = 0$.
  Solving $9x^2 + 6x + 1 = 0$ gives the (repeated) solution $-\frac{1}{3}$.

- When $b^2 - 4ac$ is positive, there are two different real-number solutions: If $b^2 - 4ac$ is a perfect square, these solutions are rational numbers.

  Example: $6x^2 + 5x + 1 = 0 \rightarrow b^2 - 4ac = 5^2 - 4 \cdot 6 \cdot 1 = 1$.
  Solving $6x^2 + 5x + 1 = 0$ gives the solutions $-\frac{1}{3}$ and $-\frac{1}{2}$.

- When $b^2 - 4ac$ is positive but not a perfect square, there are two irrational solutions and they are conjugates of each other (see p. 523).

  Example: $x^2 + 4x + 2 = 0 \rightarrow b^2 - 4ac = 4^2 - 4 \cdot 1 \cdot 2 = 8$.
  Solving $x^2 + 4x + 2 = 0$ gives the solutions $-2 + \sqrt{2}$ and $-2 - \sqrt{2}$.

- When the discriminant is negative, there are two imaginary-number solutions and they are complex conjugates of each other.

  Example: $x^2 + 4x + 5 = 0 \rightarrow b^2 - 4ac = 4^2 - 4 \cdot 1 \cdot 5 = -4$.
  Solving $x^2 + 4x + 5 = 0$ gives the solutions $-2 + i$ and $-2 - i$.

Note that any equation for which $b^2 - 4ac$ is a perfect square can be solved by factoring.

Discriminant $b^2 - 4ac$	Nature of Solutions
0	One solution; a rational number

Positive
  Perfect square
  Not a perfect square
	Two different real-number solutions
	  Solutions are rational.
	  Solutions are irrational conjugates.

Negative	Two different imaginary-number solutions (complex conjugates)

EXAMPLE 1 For each equation, determine what type of number the solutions are and how many solutions exist.

a) $9x^2 - 12x + 4 = 0$ **b)** $x^2 + 5x + 8 = 0$ **c)** $2x^2 + 7x - 3 = 0$

SOLUTION

a) For $9x^2 - 12x + 4 = 0$, we have

$$a = 9, \quad b = -12, \quad c = 4.$$

We substitute and compute the discriminant:

$$b^2 - 4ac = (-12)^2 - 4 \cdot 9 \cdot 4$$
$$= 144 - 144 = 0.$$

There is exactly one solution, and it is rational. This indicates that $9x^2 - 12x + 4 = 0$ can be solved by factoring.

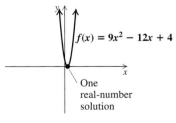

$f(x) = 9x^2 - 12x + 4$

One real-number solution

A visualization of part (a)

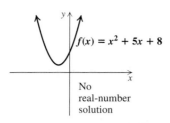

$f(x) = x^2 + 5x + 8$

No real-number solution

A visualization of part (b)

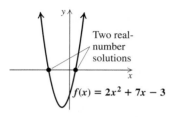

Two real-number solutions

$f(x) = 2x^2 + 7x - 3$

A visualization of part (c)

b) For $x^2 + 5x + 8 = 0$, we have

$$a = 1, \quad b = 5, \quad c = 8.$$

We substitute and compute the discriminant:

$$b^2 - 4ac = 5^2 - 4 \cdot 1 \cdot 8$$
$$= 25 - 32 = -7.$$

Since the discriminant is negative, there are two different imaginary-number solutions that are complex conjugates of each other.

c) For $2x^2 + 7x - 3 = 0$, we have

$$a = 2, \quad b = 7, \quad c = -3.$$

We substitute and compute the discriminant:

$$b^2 - 4ac = 7^2 - 4 \cdot 2(-3)$$
$$= 49 - (-24) = 73.$$

The discriminant is a positive number that is not a perfect square. Thus there are two different irrational solutions that are conjugates of each other.

> **TRY EXERCISE** 7

Discriminants can also be used to determine the number of x-intercepts of the graph of a quadratic function.

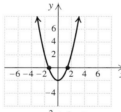

$y = ax^2 + bx + c$
$b^2 - 4ac > 0$
Two real solutions
of $ax^2 + bx + c = 0$
Two x-intercepts

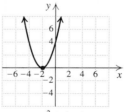

$y = ax^2 + bx + c$
$b^2 - 4ac = 0$
One real solution
of $ax^2 + bx + c = 0$
One x-intercept

$y = ax^2 + bx + c$
$b^2 - 4ac < 0$
No real solutions
of $ax^2 + bx + c = 0$
No x-intercept

Writing Equations from Solutions

We know by the principle of zero products that $(x - 2)(x + 3) = 0$ has solutions 2 and -3. If we wish for two given numbers to be solutions of an equation, we can create such an equation, using the principle in reverse.

EXAMPLE 2   Find an equation for which the given numbers are solutions.

a) 3 and $-\frac{2}{5}$ **b)** $2i$ and $-2i$

c) $5\sqrt{7}$ and $-5\sqrt{7}$ **d)** $-4, 0,$ and 1

SOLUTION

a)
$$x = 3 \quad or \quad x = -\tfrac{2}{5}$$
$$x - 3 = 0 \quad or \quad x + \tfrac{2}{5} = 0 \qquad \text{Getting 0's on one side}$$
$$(x - 3)\left(x + \tfrac{2}{5}\right) = 0 \qquad \text{Using the principle of zero products (multiplying)}$$
$$x^2 + \tfrac{2}{5}x - 3x - 3 \cdot \tfrac{2}{5} = 0 \qquad \text{Multiplying}$$
$$x^2 - \tfrac{13}{5}x - \tfrac{6}{5} = 0 \qquad \text{Combining like terms}$$
$$5x^2 - 13x - 6 = 0 \qquad \text{Multiplying both sides by 5 to clear fractions}$$

To check Example 2(a), we can let $y_1 = 5x^2 - 13x - 6$ and verify that the x-intercepts are 3 and $-\frac{2}{5}$. One way to do this is to press TRACE and then enter 3. The cursor then appears on the curve at $x = 3$. Since this is an x-intercept, we know that $5x^2 - 13x - 6 = 0$ is an equation that has 3 as a solution.

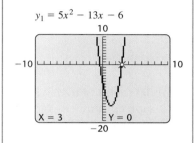

$y_1 = 5x^2 - 13x - 6$

1. Confirm that $5x^2 - 13x - 6 = 0$ also has $-\frac{2}{5}$ as a solution.
2. Check Example 2(c).
3. Check Example 2(d).

Note that multiplying both sides by the LCD, 5, clears the equation of fractions. Had we preferred, we could have multiplied $x + \frac{2}{5} = 0$ by 5, thus clearing fractions *before* using the principle of zero products.

b)
$$x = 2i \quad or \quad x = -2i$$
$$x - 2i = 0 \quad or \quad x + 2i = 0 \quad \text{Getting 0's on one side}$$
$$(x - 2i)(x + 2i) = 0 \quad \text{Using the principle of zero products (multiplying)}$$
$$x^2 - (2i)^2 = 0 \quad \text{Finding the product of a sum and a difference}$$
$$x^2 - 4i^2 = 0$$
$$x^2 + 4 = 0 \quad i^2 = -1$$

c)
$$x = 5\sqrt{7} \quad or \quad x = -5\sqrt{7}$$
$$x - 5\sqrt{7} = 0 \quad or \quad x + 5\sqrt{7} = 0 \quad \text{Getting 0's on one side}$$
$$(x - 5\sqrt{7})(x + 5\sqrt{7}) = 0 \quad \text{Using the principle of zero products}$$
$$x^2 - (5\sqrt{7})^2 = 0 \quad \text{Finding the product of a sum and a difference}$$
$$x^2 - 25 \cdot 7 = 0$$
$$x^2 - 175 = 0$$

d)
$$x = -4 \quad or \quad x = 0 \quad or \quad x = 1$$
$$x + 4 = 0 \quad or \quad x = 0 \quad or \quad x - 1 = 0 \quad \text{Getting 0's on one side}$$
$$(x + 4)x(x - 1) = 0 \quad \text{Using the principle of zero products}$$
$$x(x^2 + 3x - 4) = 0 \quad \text{Multiplying}$$
$$x^3 + 3x^2 - 4x = 0$$

TRY EXERCISE ▸ 29

To check any of these equations, we can simply substitute one or more of the given solutions. For example, in Example 2(d) above,

$$(-4)^3 + 3(-4)^2 - 4(-4) = -64 + 3 \cdot 16 + 16$$
$$= -64 + 48 + 16 = 0.$$

The other checks are left to the student.

9.3 EXERCISE SET

For Extra Help — **MyMathLab**

🪝 ***Concept Reinforcement*** *Match the nature of the solution(s) with each discriminant. Answers may be used more than once.*

1. ____ $b^2 - 4ac = 9$ **a)** One rational solution

2. ____ $b^2 - 4ac = 0$ **b)** Two different rational solutions

3. ____ $b^2 - 4ac = -1$

4. ____ $b^2 - 4ac = 1$ **c)** Two different irrational solutions

5. ____ $b^2 - 4ac = 8$ **d)** Two different imaginary-number solutions

6. ____ $b^2 - 4ac = 12$

For each equation, determine what type of number the solutions are and how many solutions exist.

7. $x^2 - 7x + 5 = 0$ **8.** $x^2 - 5x + 3 = 0$

9. $x^2 + 11 = 0$ **10.** $x^2 + 7 = 0$

11. $x^2 - 11 = 0$ **12.** $x^2 - 7 = 0$

13. $4x^2 + 8x - 5 = 0$ **14.** $4x^2 - 12x + 9 = 0$

15. $x^2 + 4x + 6 = 0$ **16.** $x^2 - 2x + 4 = 0$

17. $9t^2 - 48t + 64 = 0$ **18.** $10t^2 - t - 2 = 0$

Aha! **19.** $9t^2 + 3t = 0$ **20.** $4m^2 + 7m = 0$

21. $x^2 + 4x = 8$

22. $x^2 + 5x = 9$

23. $2a^2 - 3a = -5$

24. $3a^2 + 5 = -7a$

25. $7x^2 = 19x$

26. $5x^2 = 48x$

27. $y^2 + \frac{9}{4} = 4y$

28. $x^2 = \frac{1}{2}x - \frac{3}{5}$

Write a quadratic equation having the given numbers as solutions.

29. $-5, 4$

30. $-2, 8$

31. 3, only solution (*Hint*: It must be a repeated solution.)

32. -5, only solution

33. $-1, -3$

34. $-2, -5$

35. $5, \frac{3}{4}$

36. $4, \frac{2}{3}$

37. $-\frac{1}{4}, -\frac{1}{2}$

38. $\frac{1}{2}, \frac{1}{3}$

39. $2.4, -0.4$

40. $-0.6, 1.4$

41. $-\sqrt{3}, \sqrt{3}$

42. $-\sqrt{7}, \sqrt{7}$

43. $2\sqrt{5}, -2\sqrt{5}$

44. $3\sqrt{2}, -3\sqrt{2}$

45. $4i, -4i$

46. $3i, -3i$

47. $2 - 7i, 2 + 7i$

48. $5 - 2i, 5 + 2i$

49. $3 - \sqrt{14}, 3 + \sqrt{14}$

50. $2 - \sqrt{10}, 2 + \sqrt{10}$

51. $1 - \dfrac{\sqrt{21}}{3}, 1 + \dfrac{\sqrt{21}}{3}$

52. $\dfrac{5}{4} - \dfrac{\sqrt{33}}{4}, \dfrac{5}{4} + \dfrac{\sqrt{33}}{4}$

Write a third-degree equation having the given numbers as solutions.

53. $-2, 1, 5$

54. $-5, 0, 2$

55. $-1, 0, 3$

56. $-2, 2, 3$

57. Explain why there are not two different solutions when the discriminant is 0.

58. Describe a procedure that could be used to write an equation having the first 7 natural numbers as solutions.

Skill Review

To prepare for Section 9.4, review solving formulas and solving motion problems (Sections 4.7, 5.5, and 6.3).

Solve each formula for the specified variable. [5.5]

59. $\dfrac{c}{d} = c + d$, for c

60. $\dfrac{p}{q} = \dfrac{a + b}{b}$, for b

61. $x = \dfrac{3}{1 - y}$, for y

Solve.

62. *Boating.* Kiara's motorboat took 4 hr to make a trip downstream with a 2-mph current. The return trip against the same current took 6 hr. Find the speed of the boat in still water. [6.3]

63. *Walking.* Jamal walks 1.5 mph faster than Kade. In the time it takes Jamal to walk 7 mi, Kade walks 4 mi. Find the speed of each person. [4.7]

64. *Aviation.* Taryn's Cessna travels 120 mph in still air. She flies 140 mi into the wind and 140 mi with the wind in a total of 2.4 hr. Find the wind speed. [4.7]

Synthesis

65. If we assume that a quadratic equation has integers for coefficients, will the product of the solutions always be a real number? Why or why not?

66. Can a fourth-degree equation with rational coefficients have exactly three irrational solutions? Why or why not?

67. The graph of an equation of the form

$$y = ax^2 + bx + c$$

is a curve similar to the one shown below. Determine a, b, and c from the information given.

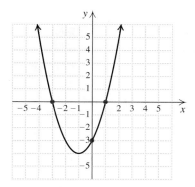

68. Show that the product of the solutions of $ax^2 + bx + c = 0$ is c/a.

*For each equation under the given condition, **(a)** find k and **(b)** find the other solution.*

69. $kx^2 - 2x + k = 0$; one solution is -3

70. $x^2 - kx + 2 = 0$; one solution is $1 + i$

71. $x^2 - (6 + 3i)x + k = 0$; one solution is 3

72. Show that the sum of the solutions of $ax^2 + bx + c = 0$ is $-b/a$.

73. Show that whenever there is just one solution of $ax^2 + bx + c = 0$, that solution is of the form $-b/(2a)$.

74. Find h and k, where $3x^2 - hx + 4k = 0$, the sum of the solutions is -12, and the product of the solutions is 20. (*Hint*: See Exercises 68 and 72.)

75. Suppose that $f(x) = ax^2 + bx + c$, with $f(-3) = 0$, $f\left(\frac{1}{2}\right) = 0$, and $f(0) = -12$. Find a, b, and c.

76. Find an equation for which $2 - \sqrt{3}$, $2 + \sqrt{3}$, $5 - 2i$, and $5 + 2i$ are solutions.

Aha! **77.** Write a quadratic equation with integer coefficients for which $-\sqrt{2}$ is one solution.

78. Write a quadratic equation with integer coefficients for which $10i$ is one solution.

79. Find an equation with integer coefficients for which $1 - \sqrt{5}$ and $3 + 2i$ are two of the solutions.

80. A discriminant that is a perfect square indicates that factoring can be used to solve the quadratic equation. Why?

81. While solving a quadratic equation of the form $ax^2 + bx + c = 0$ with a graphing calculator, Keisha gets the following screen. How could the sign of the discriminant help her check the graph?

9.4 Applications Involving Quadratic Equations

Solving Problems • Solving Formulas

Solving Problems

As we found in Section 4.7, some problems translate to rational equations. The solution of such rational equations can involve quadratic equations.

EXAMPLE 1 *Motorcycle travel.* Fiona rode her motorcycle 300 mi at a certain average speed. Had she traveled 10 mph faster, the trip would have taken 1 hr less. Find Fiona's average speed.

SOLUTION

1. **Familiarize.** We make a drawing, labeling it with the information provided. As in Section 4.7, we can create a table. We let r represent the rate, in miles per hour, and t the time, in hours, for Fiona's trip.

300 miles
Time t Speed r

300 miles
Time $t - 1$ Speed $r + 10$

Distance	Speed	Time
300	r	t
300	$r + 10$	$t - 1$

$$\longrightarrow r = \frac{300}{t}$$
$$\longrightarrow r + 10 = \frac{300}{t - 1}$$

Recall that the definition of speed, $r = d/t$, relates the three quantities.

2. **Translate.** From the table, we obtain

$$r = \frac{300}{t} \quad \text{and} \quad r + 10 = \frac{300}{t - 1}.$$

3. **Carry out.** A system of equations has been formed. We substitute for r from the first equation into the second and solve the resulting equation:

$$\frac{300}{t} + 10 = \frac{300}{t - 1}$$

Substituting $300/t$ for r

$$t(t - 1) \cdot \left[\frac{300}{t} + 10 \right] = t(t - 1) \cdot \frac{300}{t - 1}$$

Multiplying by the LCD to clear fractions

$$t(t - 1) \cdot \frac{300}{t} + t(t - 1) \cdot 10 = t(t - 1) \cdot \frac{300}{t - 1}$$

Using the distributive law

$$\frac{\cancel{t}(t - 1)}{1} \cdot \frac{300}{\cancel{t}} + t(t - 1) \cdot 10 = \frac{t\cancel{(t - 1)}}{1} \cdot \frac{300}{\cancel{t - 1}}$$

Removing factors that equal 1: $t/t = 1$ and $(t - 1)/(t - 1) = 1$

$$\left. \begin{aligned} 300(t - 1) + 10(t^2 - t) &= 300t \\ 300t - 300 + 10t^2 - 10t &= 300t \\ 10t^2 - 10t - 300 &= 0 \end{aligned} \right\}$$

Rewriting in standard form

$$t^2 - t - 30 = 0$$

Multiplying by $\frac{1}{10}$ or dividing by 10

$$(t - 6)(t + 5) = 0$$

Factoring

$$t = 6 \quad or \quad t = -5.$$

Principle of zero products

4. **Check.** Note that we have solved for t, not r as required. Since negative time has no meaning here, we disregard the -5 and use 6 hr to find r:

$$r = \frac{300\text{ mi}}{6\text{ hr}} = 50\text{ mph}.$$

> **CAUTION!** Always make sure that you find the quantity asked for in the problem.

To see if 50 mph checks, we increase the speed 10 mph to 60 mph and see how long the trip would have taken at that speed:

$$t = \frac{d}{r} = \frac{300\text{ mi}}{60\text{ mph}} = 5\text{ hr.}$$

Note that $\text{mi/mph} = \text{mi} \div \frac{\text{mi}}{\text{hr}} = \cancel{\text{mi}} \cdot \frac{\text{hr}}{\cancel{\text{mi}}} = \text{hr.}$

This is 1 hr less than the trip actually took, so the answer checks.

5. **State.** Fiona traveled at an average speed of 50 mph. **TRY EXERCISE** 1

Solving Formulas

Recall that to solve a formula for a certain letter, we use the principles for solving equations to get that letter alone on one side.

EXAMPLE 2

Period of a pendulum. The time T required for a pendulum of length l to swing back and forth (complete one period) is given by the formula $T = 2\pi\sqrt{l/g}$, where g is the earth's gravitational constant. Solve for l.

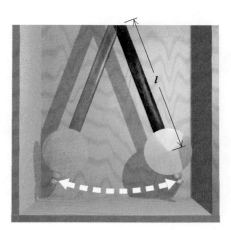

SOLUTION We have

$$T = 2\pi\sqrt{\frac{l}{g}} \qquad \text{This is a radical equation (see Section 8.6).}$$

$$T^2 = \left(2\pi\sqrt{\frac{l}{g}}\right)^2 \qquad \text{Squaring both sides}$$

$$T^2 = 2^2\pi^2\frac{l}{g}$$

$$gT^2 = 4\pi^2 l \qquad \text{Multiplying both sides by } g \text{ to clear fractions}$$

$$\frac{gT^2}{4\pi^2} = l. \qquad \text{Dividing both sides by } 4\pi^2$$

We now have l alone on one side and l does not appear on the other side, so the formula is solved for l. **TRY EXERCISE** 21

In formulas for which variables represent only nonnegative numbers, there is no need for absolute-value signs when taking square roots.

EXAMPLE 3

*Hang time.** An athlete's *hang time* is the amount of time that the athlete can remain airborne when jumping. A formula relating an athlete's vertical leap V, in inches, to hang time T, in seconds, is $V = 48T^2$. Solve for T.

SOLUTION We have

$$48T^2 = V$$

$$T^2 = \frac{V}{48} \qquad \text{Dividing by 48 to isolate } T^2$$

$$T = \frac{\sqrt{V}}{\sqrt{48}} \qquad \begin{array}{l}\text{Using the principle of square roots}\\ \text{and the quotient rule for radicals.}\\ \text{We assume } V, T \geq 0.\end{array}$$

$$= \frac{\sqrt{V}}{\sqrt{16}\sqrt{3}}$$

$$= \frac{\sqrt{V}}{4\sqrt{3}}$$

$$\left.\begin{array}{l}= \frac{\sqrt{V}}{4\sqrt{3}} \cdot \frac{\sqrt{3}}{\sqrt{3}}\\[2mm] = \frac{\sqrt{3V}}{12}.\end{array}\right\} \quad \text{Rationalizing the denominator}$$

TRY EXERCISE 15

EXAMPLE 4

Falling distance. An object tossed downward with an initial speed (velocity) of v_0 will travel a distance of s meters, where $s = 4.9t^2 + v_0 t$ and t is measured in seconds. Solve for t.

SOLUTION Since t is squared in one term and raised to the first power in the other term, the equation is quadratic in t.

$$4.9t^2 + v_0 t = s$$

$$4.9t^2 + v_0 t - s = 0 \qquad \text{Writing standard form}$$

$$a = 4.9, \quad b = v_0, \quad c = -s$$

$$t = \frac{-v_0 \pm \sqrt{(v_0)^2 - 4(4.9)(-s)}}{2(4.9)} \qquad \text{Using the quadratic formula}$$

Since the negative square root would yield a negative value for t, we use only the positive root:

$$t = \frac{-v_0 + \sqrt{(v_0)^2 + 19.6s}}{9.8}.$$

TRY EXERCISE 25

STUDENT NOTES ────────

After identifying which numbers to use as a, b, and c, be careful to replace only the *letters* in the quadratic formula.

───────────────

*This formula is taken from an article by Peter Brancazio, "The Mechanics of a Slam Dunk," *Popular Mechanics,* November 1991. Courtesy of Professor Peter Brancazio, Brooklyn College.

The following list of steps should help you when solving formulas for a given letter. Try to remember that when solving a formula, you use the same approach that you would to solve an equation.

To Solve a Formula for a Letter—Say, h

1. Clear fractions and use the principle of powers, as needed. Perform these steps until radicals containing h are gone and h is not in any denominator.
2. Combine all like terms.
3. If the only power of h is h^1, the equation can be solved as in Sections 1.3 and 5.5. (See Example 2.)
4. If h^2 appears but h does not, solve for h^2 and use the principle of square roots to solve for h. (See Example 3.)
5. If there are terms containing both h and h^2, put the equation in standard form and use the quadratic formula. (See Example 4.)

9.4 EXERCISE SET

For Extra Help **MyMathLab** Math XL PRACTICE WATCH DOWNLOAD

Solve.

1. *Car trips.* During the first part of a trip, Tara's Honda traveled 120 mi at a certain speed. Tara then drove another 100 mi at a speed that was 10 mph slower. If the total time of Tara's trip was 4 hr, what was her speed on each part of the trip?

2. *Canoeing.* During the first part of a canoe trip, Ken covered 60 km at a certain speed. He then traveled 24 km at a speed that was 4 km/h slower. If the total time for the trip was 8 hr, what was the speed on each part of the trip?

3. *Car trips.* Diane's Dodge travels 200 mi averaging a certain speed. If the car had gone 10 mph faster, the trip would have taken 1 hr less. Find Diane's average speed.

4. *Car trips.* Stuart's Subaru travels 280 mi averaging a certain speed. If the car had gone 5 mph faster, the trip would have taken 1 hr less. Find Stuart's average speed.

5. *Air travel.* A Cessna flies 600 mi at a certain speed. A Beechcraft flies 1000 mi at a speed that is 50 mph faster, but takes 1 hr longer. Find the speed of each plane.

6. *Air travel.* A turbo-jet flies 50 mph faster than a super-prop plane. If a turbo-jet goes 2000 mi in 3 hr less time than it takes the super-prop to go 2800 mi, find the speed of each plane.

7. *Bicycling.* Naoki bikes the 36 mi to Hillsboro averaging a certain speed. The return trip is made at a speed 3 mph slower. Total time for the round trip is 7 hr. Find Naoki's average speed on each part of the trip.

8. *Car speed.* On a sales trip, Mark drives the 600 mi to Richmond averaging a certain speed. The return trip is made at an average speed that is 10 mph slower. Total time for the round trip is 22 hr. Find Mark's average speed on each part of the trip.

9. *Navigation.* The Hudson River flows at a rate of 3 mph. A patrol boat travels 60 mi upriver and returns in a total time of 9 hr. What is the speed of the boat in still water?

10. *Navigation.* The current in a typical Mississippi River shipping route flows at a rate of 4 mph. In order for a barge to travel 24 mi upriver and then return in a total of 5 hr, approximately how fast must the barge be able to travel in still water?

11. *Filling a pool.* A well and a spring are filling a swimming pool. Together, they can fill the pool in 3 hr. The well, working alone, can fill the pool in 8 hr less time than the spring. How long would the spring take, working alone, to fill the pool?

12. *Filling a tank.* Two pipes are connected to the same tank. Working together, they can fill the tank in 4 hr. The larger pipe, working alone, can fill the tank in 6 hr less time than the smaller one. How long would the smaller one take, working alone, to fill the tank?

13. *Paddleboats.* Kofi paddles 1 mi upstream and 1 mi back in a total time of 1 hr. The speed of the river is 2 mph. Find the speed of Kofi's paddleboat in still water.

14. *Rowing.* Abby rows 10 km upstream and 10 km back in a total time of 3 hr. The speed of the river is 5 km/h. Find Abby's speed in still water.

Solve each formula for the indicated letter. Assume that all variables represent nonnegative numbers.

15. $A = 4\pi r^2$, for r
(Surface area of a sphere of radius r)

16. $A = 6s^2$, for s
(Surface area of a cube with sides of length s)

17. $A = 2\pi r^2 + 2\pi rh$, for r
(Surface area of a right cylindrical solid with radius r and height h)

18. $N = \dfrac{k^2 - 3k}{2}$, for k
(Number of diagonals of a polygon with k sides)

19. $F = \dfrac{Gm_1 m_2}{r^2}$, for r
(Law of gravity)

20. $N = \dfrac{kQ_1 Q_2}{s^2}$, for s
(Number of phone calls between two cities)

21. $c = \sqrt{gH}$, for H
(Velocity of ocean wave)

22. $V = 3.5\sqrt{h}$, for h
(Distance to horizon from a height)

23. $a^2 + b^2 = c^2$, for b
(Pythagorean formula in two dimensions)

24. $a^2 + b^2 + c^2 = d^2$, for c
(Pythagorean formula in three dimensions)

25. $s = v_0 t + \dfrac{gt^2}{2}$, for t
(A motion formula)

26. $A = \pi r^2 + \pi rs$, for r
(Surface area of a cone)

27. $N = \frac{1}{2}(n^2 - n)$, for n
(Number of games if n teams play each other once)

28. $A = A_0(1 - r)^2$, for r
(A business formula)

29. $T = 2\pi\sqrt{\dfrac{l}{g}}$, for g
(A pendulum formula)

30. $W = \sqrt{\dfrac{1}{LC}}$, for L
(An electricity formula)

Aha! 31. $at^2 + bt + c = 0$, for t
(An algebraic formula)

32. $A = P_1(1 + r)^2 + P_2(1 + r)$, for r
(Amount in an account when P_1 is invested for 2 yr and P_2 for 1 yr at interest rate r)

Solve.

33. *Falling distance.* (Use $4.9t^2 + v_0 t = s$.)
   a) A bolt falls off an airplane at an altitude of 500 m. Approximately how long does it take the bolt to reach the ground?
   b) A ball is thrown downward at a speed of 30 m/sec from an altitude of 500 m. Approximately how long does it take the ball to reach the ground?
   c) Approximately how far will an object fall in 5 sec, when thrown downward at an initial velocity of 30 m/sec from a plane?

34. *Falling distance.* (Use $4.9t^2 + v_0 t = s$.)
   a) A ring is dropped from a helicopter at an altitude of 75 m. Approximately how long does it take the ring to reach the ground?
   b) A coin is tossed downward with an initial velocity of 30 m/sec from an altitude of 75 m. Approximately how long does it take the coin to reach the ground?
   c) Approximately how far will an object fall in 2 sec, if thrown downward at an initial velocity of 20 m/sec from a helicopter?

35. *Bungee jumping.* Chad is tied to one end of a 40-m elasticized (bungee) cord. The other end of the cord is tied to the middle of a bridge. If Chad jumps off the bridge, for how long will he fall before the cord begins to stretch? (Use $4.9t^2 = s$.)

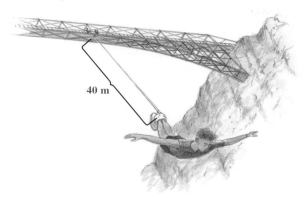

40 m

36. *Bungee jumping.* Chika is tied to a bungee cord (see Exercise 35) and falls for 2.5 sec before her cord begins to stretch. How long is the bungee cord?

37. *Hang time.* The NBA's Dwight Howard has a vertical leap of 38 in. What is his hang time? (Use $V = 48T^2$.)
Source: www.dwighthoward.com

38. *League schedules.* In a bowling league, each team plays each of the other teams once. If a total of 66 games is played, how many teams are in the league? (See Exercise 27.)

For Exercises 39 and 40, use $4.9t^2 + v_0t = s$.

39. *Downward speed.* A stone thrown downward from a 100-m cliff travels 51.6 m in 3 sec. What was the initial velocity of the object?

40. *Downward speed.* A pebble thrown downward from a 200-m cliff travels 91.2 m in 4 sec. What was the initial velocity of the object?

For Exercises 41 and 42, use $A = P_1(1 + r)^2 + P_2(1 + r)$. (See Exercise 32.)

41. *Compound interest.* A firm invests $3200 in a savings account for 2 yr. At the beginning of the second

year, an additional $1800 is invested. If a total of $5375.48 is in the account at the end of the second year, what is the annual interest rate?

42. *Compound interest.* A business invests $10,000 in a savings account for 2 yr. At the beginning of the second year, an additional $3500 is invested. If a total of $14,822.75 is in the account at the end of the second year, what is the annual interest rate?

43. Marti is tied to a bungee cord that is twice as long as the cord tied to Rafe's. Will Marti's fall take twice as long as Rafe's before their cords begin to stretch? Why or why not? (See Exercises 35 and 36.)

44. Under what circumstances would a negative value for t, time, have meaning?

Skill Review

To prepare for Section 9.5, review raising a power to a power and solving rational equations and radical equations (Sections 4.6, and 8.6).

Simplify.

45. $(m^{-1})^2$

46. $(t^{1/3})^2$ [8.2]

47. $(y^{1/6})^2$ [8.2]

48. $(z^{1/4})^2$ [8.2]

Solve.

49. $t^{-1} = \dfrac{1}{2}$ [4.6], [8.6]

50. $x^{1/4} = 3$ [8.6]

Synthesis

51. Write a problem for a classmate to solve. Devise the problem so that **(a)** the solution is found after solving a rational equation and **(b)** the solution is "The express train travels 90 mph."

52. In what ways do the motion problems of this section (like Example 1) differ from the motion problems in Section 4.7?

53. *Biochemistry.* The equation

$$A = 6.5 - \frac{20.4t}{t^2 + 36}$$

is used to calculate the acid level A in a person's blood t minutes after sugar is consumed. Solve for t.

54. *Special relativity.* Einstein found that an object with initial mass m_0 and traveling velocity v has mass

$$m = \frac{m_0}{\sqrt{1 - \dfrac{v^2}{c^2}}},$$

where c is the speed of light. Solve the formula for c.

55. Find a number for which the reciprocal of 1 less than the number is the same as 1 more than the number.

56. *Purchasing.* A discount store bought a quantity of potted plants for $250 and sold all but 15 at a profit of $3.50 per plant. With the total amount received, the manager could buy 4 more than twice as many as were bought before. Find the cost per plant.

57. *Art and aesthetics.* For over 2000 yr, artists, sculptors, and architects have regarded the proportions of a "golden" rectangle as visually appealing. A rectangle of width w and length l is considered "golden" if

$$\frac{w}{l} = \frac{l}{w + l}.$$

Solve for l.

58. *Diagonal of a cube.* Find a formula that expresses the length of the three-dimensional diagonal of a cube as a function of the cube's surface area.

59. Solve for n:
$$mn^4 - r^2pm^3 - r^2n^2 + p = 0.$$

60. *Surface area.* Find a formula that expresses the diameter of a right cylindrical solid as a function of its surface area and its height. (See Exercise 17.)

61. A sphere is inscribed in a cube as shown in the figure below. Express the surface area of the sphere as a function of the surface area S of the cube. (See Exercise 15.)

9.5 Equations Reducible to Quadratic

Recognizing Equations in Quadratic Form • Radical Equations and Rational Equations

STUDY SKILLS ———————

Use Your Words

When a new word or phrase (such as *reducible to quadratic*) arises, try to use it in conversation with classmates, your instructor, or a study partner. Although it may seem awkward at first, doing so will help you in your reading, deepen your level of understanding, and increase your confidence.

Recognizing Equations in Quadratic Form

Certain equations that are not really quadratic can be thought of in such a way that they can be solved as quadratic. For example, because the square of x^2 is x^4, the equation $x^4 - 9x^2 + 8 = 0$ is said to be "quadratic in x^2":

$$x^4 - 9x^2 + 8 = 0$$

$$(x^2)^2 - 9(x^2) + 8 = 0 \qquad \text{Thinking of } x^4 \text{ as } (x^2)^2$$

$$u^2 - 9u + 8 = 0. \qquad \text{To make this clearer, write } u \text{ instead of } x^2.$$

The equation $u^2 - 9u + 8 = 0$ can be solved for u by factoring or by the quadratic formula. Then, remembering that $u = x^2$, we can solve for x. Equations that can be solved like this are *reducible to quadratic* and are said to be *in quadratic form*.

EXAMPLE 1

Solve: $x^4 - 9x^2 + 8 = 0$.

SOLUTION   We begin by letting $u = x^2$ and finding u^2:

$$u = x^2$$
$$u^2 = (x^2)^2 = x^4.$$

Then we solve by substituting u^2 for x^4 and u for x^2:

$$u^2 - 9u + 8 = 0$$
$$(u - 8)(u - 1) = 0 \qquad \text{Factoring}$$
$$u - 8 = 0 \quad or \quad u - 1 = 0 \qquad \text{Principle of zero products}$$
$$u = 8 \quad or \qquad u = 1.$$

STUDENT NOTES

To identify an equation in quadratic form, look for two variable expressions in the equation. The exponent in one expression is twice the exponent in the other expression.

We replace u with x^2 and solve these equations:

$$x^2 = 8 \qquad or \quad x^2 = 1$$
$$x = \pm\sqrt{8} \quad or \qquad x = \pm 1 \qquad \boxed{\text{We are solving for } x.}$$
$$x = \pm 2\sqrt{2} \quad or \qquad x = \pm 1.$$

To check, note that for both $x = 2\sqrt{2}$ and $-2\sqrt{2}$, we have $x^2 = 8$ and $x^4 = 64$. Similarly, for both $x = 1$ and -1, we have $x^2 = 1$ and $x^4 = 1$. Thus instead of making four checks, we need make only two.

Check: For $\pm 2\sqrt{2}$:

$$\frac{x^4 - 9x^2 + 8 = 0}{(\pm 2\sqrt{2})^4 - 9(\pm 2\sqrt{2})^2 + 8 \ \Big|\ 0}$$
$$64 - 9 \cdot 8 + 8 \ \Big|$$
$$0 \overset{?}{=} 0 \quad \text{TRUE}$$

For ± 1:

$$\frac{x^4 - 9x^2 + 8 = 0}{(\pm 1)^4 - 9(\pm 1)^2 + 8 \ \Big|\ 0}$$
$$1 - 9 + 8 \ \Big|$$
$$0 \overset{?}{=} 0 \quad \text{TRUE}$$

The solutions are $1, -1, 2\sqrt{2},$ and $-2\sqrt{2}$.

TRY EXERCISE 17

> *CAUTION!*   A common error when working on problems like Example 1 is to solve for u but forget to solve for x. Remember to solve for the *original* variable!

Equations like those in Example 1 can be solved directly by factoring:

$$x^4 - 9x^2 + 8 = 0$$
$$(x^2 - 1)(x^2 - 8) = 0$$
$$x^2 - 1 = 0 \quad or \quad x^2 - 8 = 0$$
$$x^2 = 1 \quad or \qquad x^2 = 8$$
$$x = \pm 1 \quad or \qquad x = \pm 2\sqrt{2}.$$

However, it often becomes difficult to solve the equation without first making a substitution.

To recognize an equation in quadratic form, inspect all the variable expressions in the equation. For an equation to be written in the form $au^2 + bu + c = 0$, it is necessary to identify one variable expression as u and a second variable expression as u^2.

EXAMPLE 2 Find the x-intercepts of the graph of $f(x) = (x^2 - 1)^2 - (x^2 - 1) - 2$.

SOLUTION The x-intercepts occur where $f(x) = 0$ so we must have

$$(x^2 - 1)^2 - (x^2 - 1) - 2 = 0. \quad \text{Setting } f(x) \text{ equal to } 0$$

If we identify $x^2 - 1$ as u, the equation can be written in quadratic form:

$$u = x^2 - 1$$
$$u^2 = (x^2 - 1)^2.$$

Substituting, we have

$$u^2 - u - 2 = 0 \qquad \text{Substituting in}$$
$$\qquad\qquad\qquad (x^2 - 1)^2 - (x^2 - 1) - 2 = 0$$
$$(u - 2)(u + 1) = 0$$
$$u = 2 \quad or \quad u = -1. \quad \text{Using the principle of zero products}$$

Next, we replace u with $x^2 - 1$ and solve these equations:

$$x^2 - 1 = 2 \qquad or \quad x^2 - 1 = -1$$
$$x^2 = 3 \qquad or \qquad x^2 = 0 \quad \text{Adding 1 to both sides}$$
$$x = \pm\sqrt{3} \quad or \qquad x = 0. \quad \text{Using the principle of square roots}$$

The x-intercepts occur at $(-\sqrt{3}, 0)$, $(0, 0)$, and $(\sqrt{3}, 0)$. **TRY EXERCISE** 49

Radical Equations and Rational Equations

Sometimes rational equations, radical equations, or equations containing exponents that are fractions are reducible to quadratic. It is especially important that answers to these equations be checked in the original equation.

EXAMPLE 3 Solve: $x - 3\sqrt{x} - 4 = 0$.

SOLUTION This radical equation could be solved using the method discussed in Section 8.6. However, if we note that the square of $\sqrt{x}$ is x, we can regard the equation as "quadratic in $\sqrt{x}$."

We determine u and u^2:

$$u = \sqrt{x}$$
$$u^2 = x.$$

Substituting, we have

$$x - 3\sqrt{x} - 4 = 0$$
$$u^2 - 3u - 4 = 0$$
$$(u - 4)(u + 1) = 0$$
$$u = 4 \quad or \quad u = -1. \quad \text{Using the principle of zero products}$$

Next, we replace u with $\sqrt{x}$ and solve these equations:

$$\sqrt{x} = 4 \quad or \quad \sqrt{x} = -1.$$

Squaring gives us $x = 16$ or $x = 1$ and also makes checking essential.

TECHNOLOGY CONNECTION

Check Example 3 with a graphing calculator. Use the ZERO, ROOT, or INTERSECT option, if possible.

Check: For 16:

$$\begin{array}{c|c} x - 3\sqrt{x} - 4 = 0 & \\ \hline 16 - 3\sqrt{16} - 4 & 0 \\ 16 - 3 \cdot 4 - 4 & \\ & 0 \overset{?}{=} 0 \quad \text{TRUE} \end{array}$$

For 1:

$$\begin{array}{c|c} x - 3\sqrt{x} - 4 = 0 & \\ \hline 1 - 3\sqrt{1} - 4 & 0 \\ 1 - 3 \cdot 1 - 4 & \\ & -6 \overset{?}{=} 0 \quad \text{FALSE} \end{array}$$

The number 16 checks, but 1 does not. Had we noticed that $\sqrt{x} = -1$ has no solution (since principal square roots are never negative), we could have solved only the equation $\sqrt{x} = 4$. The solution is 16.

TRY EXERCISE ▶ 21

The following tips may prove useful.

> **To Solve an Equation That Is Reducible to Quadratic**
> 1. Look for two variable expressions in the equation. One expression should be the square of the other.
> 2. Write down any substitutions that you are making.
> 3. Remember to solve for the variable that is used in the original equation.
> 4. Check possible answers in the original equation.

EXAMPLE 4

Solve: $2m^{-2} + m^{-1} - 15 = 0$.

SOLUTION Note that the square of m^{-1} is $(m^{-1})^2$, or m^{-2}. We let $u = m^{-1}$:

Determine u and u^2.

$$u = m^{-1}$$
$$u^2 = m^{-2}.$$

Substituting, we have

Substitute.

$$2u^2 + u - 15 = 0 \qquad \text{Substituting in } 2m^{-2} + m^{-1} - 15 = 0$$

$$(2u - 5)(u + 3) = 0$$

$$2u - 5 = 0 \quad or \quad u + 3 = 0 \qquad \text{Using the principle of zero products}$$

$$2u = 5 \quad or \qquad u = -3$$

Solve for u.

$$u = \frac{5}{2} \quad or \qquad u = -3.$$

Now we replace u with m^{-1} and solve:

$$m^{-1} = \frac{5}{2} \quad or \quad m^{-1} = -3$$

$$\frac{1}{m} = \frac{5}{2} \quad or \quad \frac{1}{m} = -3 \qquad \text{Recall that } m^{-1} = \frac{1}{m}.$$

$$1 = \frac{5}{2}m \quad or \qquad 1 = -3m \qquad \text{Multiplying both sides by } m$$

Solve for the original variable.

$$\frac{2}{5} = m \quad or \quad -\frac{1}{3} = m. \qquad \text{Solving for } m$$

Check.

Check:

For $\frac{2}{5}$:

$$\begin{array}{rcl}
2m^{-2} + m^{-1} - 15 = 0 \\
\hline
2\left(\frac{2}{5}\right)^{-2} + \left(\frac{2}{5}\right)^{-1} - 15 & \bigg| & 0 \\
2\left(\frac{5}{2}\right)^2 + \left(\frac{5}{2}\right) - 15 & \bigg| \\
2\left(\frac{25}{4}\right) + \frac{5}{2} - 15 & \bigg| \\
\frac{25}{2} + \frac{5}{2} - 15 & \bigg| \\
\frac{30}{2} - 15 & \bigg|
\end{array}$$
$$0 \overset{?}{=} 0 \quad \text{TRUE}$$

For $-\frac{1}{3}$:

$$\begin{array}{rcl}
2m^{-2} + m^{-1} - 15 = 0 \\
\hline
2\left(-\frac{1}{3}\right)^{-2} + \left(-\frac{1}{3}\right)^{-1} - 15 & \bigg| & 0 \\
2\left(-\frac{3}{1}\right)^2 + \left(-\frac{3}{1}\right) - 15 & \bigg| \\
2(9) + (-3) - 15 & \bigg| \\
18 - 3 - 15 & \bigg|
\end{array}$$
$$0 \overset{?}{=} 0 \quad \text{TRUE}$$

Both numbers check. The solutions are $-\frac{1}{3}$ and $\frac{2}{5}$.

> **TRY EXERCISE** 29

Note that Example 4 can also be written

$$\frac{2}{m^2} + \frac{1}{m} - 15 = 0.$$

It can then be solved by letting $u = 1/m$ and $u^2 = 1/m^2$ or by clearing fractions as in Section 4.6.

EXAMPLE 5

Solve: $t^{2/5} - t^{1/5} - 2 = 0$.

SOLUTION Note that the square of $t^{1/5}$ is $(t^{1/5})^2$, or $t^{2/5}$. The equation is therefore quadratic in $t^{1/5}$, so we let $u = t^{1/5}$:

$$u = t^{1/5}$$
$$u^2 = t^{2/5}.$$

Substituting, we have

$$u^2 - u - 2 = 0 \qquad \text{Substituting in } t^{2/5} - t^{1/5} - 2 = 0$$
$$(u - 2)(u + 1) = 0$$
$$u = 2 \quad or \quad u = -1. \qquad \text{Using the principle of zero products}$$

Now we replace u with $t^{1/5}$ and solve:

$$t^{1/5} = 2 \quad or \quad t^{1/5} = -1$$
$$t = 32 \quad or \qquad t = -1. \qquad \begin{array}{l}\text{Principle of powers; raising both sides to} \\ \text{the 5th power}\end{array}$$

Check:

For 32:

$$\begin{array}{rcl}
t^{2/5} - t^{1/5} - 2 = 0 \\
\hline
32^{2/5} - 32^{1/5} - 2 & \bigg| & 0 \\
(32^{1/5})^2 - 32^{1/5} - 2 & \bigg| \\
2^2 - 2 - 2 & \bigg|
\end{array}$$
$$0 \overset{?}{=} 0 \quad \text{TRUE}$$

For -1:

$$\begin{array}{rcl}
t^{2/5} - t^{1/5} - 2 = 0 \\
\hline
(-1)^{2/5} - (-1)^{1/5} - 2 & \bigg| & 0 \\
[(-1)^{1/5}]^2 - (-1)^{1/5} - 2 & \bigg| \\
(-1)^2 - (-1) - 2 & \bigg|
\end{array}$$
$$0 \overset{?}{=} 0 \quad \text{TRUE}$$

Both numbers check. The solutions are 32 and -1.

> **TRY EXERCISE** 33

EXAMPLE 6

Solve: $(5 + \sqrt{r})^2 + 6(5 + \sqrt{r}) + 2 = 0$.

SOLUTION We determine u and u^2:

$$u = 5 + \sqrt{r}$$
$$u^2 = (5 + \sqrt{r})^2.$$

Substituting, we have

$$u^2 + 6u + 2 = 0$$

$$u = \frac{-6 \pm \sqrt{6^2 - 4 \cdot 1 \cdot 2}}{2 \cdot 1} \quad \text{Using the quadratic formula}$$

$$= \frac{-6 \pm \sqrt{28}}{2}$$

$$= \frac{-6}{2} \pm \frac{2\sqrt{7}}{2} \quad \text{Simplifying; } \sqrt{28} = \sqrt{4}\sqrt{7}$$

$$= -3 \pm \sqrt{7}.$$

Now we replace u with $5 + \sqrt{r}$ and solve for r:

$$5 + \sqrt{r} = -3 + \sqrt{7} \quad or \quad 5 + \sqrt{r} = -3 - \sqrt{7} \qquad u = -3 + \sqrt{7}$$
$$\sqrt{r} = -8 + \sqrt{7} \quad or \qquad \sqrt{r} = -8 - \sqrt{7}. \qquad or \; u = -3 - \sqrt{7}$$

We could now solve for r and check possible solutions, but first let's examine $-8 + \sqrt{7}$ and $-8 - \sqrt{7}$. Since $\sqrt{7} \approx 2.6$, both $-8 + \sqrt{7}$ and $-8 - \sqrt{7}$ are negative. Since the principal square root of r is never negative, both values of $\sqrt{r}$ must be rejected. Note too that in the original equation, $(5 + \sqrt{r})^2$, $6(5 + \sqrt{r})$, and 2 are all positive. Thus it is impossible for their sum to be 0.

The original equation has no solution.

TRY EXERCISE 25

9.5 EXERCISE SET

For Extra Help
MyMathLab | Math XL PRACTICE | WATCH | DOWNLOAD

Concept Reinforcement *In each of Exercises 1–8, match the equation with a substitution from the column on the right that could be used to reduce the equation to quadratic form.*

1. ____ $4x^6 - 2x^3 + 1 = 0$ a) $u = x^{-1/3}$

2. ____ $3x^4 + 4x^2 - 7 = 0$ b) $u = x^{1/3}$

3. ____ $5x^8 + 2x^4 - 3 = 0$ c) $u = x^{-2}$

4. ____ $2x^{2/3} - 5x^{1/3} + 4 = 0$ d) $u = x^2$

5. ____ $3x^{4/3} + 4x^{2/3} - 7 = 0$ e) $u = x^{-2/3}$

6. ____ $2x^{-2/3} + x^{-1/3} + 6 = 0$ f) $u = x^3$

7. ____ $4x^{-4/3} - 2x^{-2/3} + 3 = 0$ g) $u = x^{2/3}$

8. ____ $3x^{-4} + 4x^{-2} - 2 = 0$ h) $u = x^4$

Write the substitution that could be used to make each equation quadratic in u.

9. For $3p - 4\sqrt{p} + 6 = 0$, use $u =$ _____.

10. For $x^{1/2} - x^{1/4} - 2 = 0$, use $u =$ _____.

11. For $(x^2 + 3)^2 + (x^2 + 3) - 7 = 0$, use $u =$ _____.

12. For $t^{-6} + 5t^{-3} - 6 = 0$, use $u =$ _____.

13. For $(1 + t)^4 + (1 + t)^2 + 4 = 0$, use $u =$ _____.

14. For $w^{1/3} - 3w^{1/6} + 8 = 0$, use $w =$ _____.

Solve.

15. $x^4 - 13x^2 + 36 = 0$ 16. $x^4 - 17x^2 + 16 = 0$

17. $t^4 - 7t^2 + 12 = 0$ 18. $t^4 - 11t^2 + 18 = 0$

19. $4x^4 - 9x^2 + 5 = 0$

20. $9x^4 - 38x^2 + 8 = 0$

21. $w + 4\sqrt{w} - 12 = 0$

22. $s + 3\sqrt{s} - 40 = 0$

23. $(x^2 - 7)^2 - 3(x^2 - 7) + 2 = 0$

24. $(x^2 - 2)^2 - 12(x^2 - 2) + 20 = 0$

25. $r - 2\sqrt{r} - 6 = 0$

26. $s - 4\sqrt{s} - 1 = 0$

27. $(1 + \sqrt{x})^2 + 5(1 + \sqrt{x}) + 6 = 0$

28. $(3 + \sqrt{x})^2 + 3(3 + \sqrt{x}) - 10 = 0$

29. $x^{-2} - x^{-1} - 6 = 0$

30. $2x^{-2} - x^{-1} - 1 = 0$

31. $4t^{-2} - 3t^{-1} - 1 = 0$

32. $2m^{-2} + 7m^{-1} - 15 = 0$

33. $t^{2/3} + t^{1/3} - 6 = 0$

34. $w^{2/3} - 2w^{1/3} - 8 = 0$

35. $y^{1/3} - y^{1/6} - 6 = 0$

36. $t^{1/2} + 3t^{1/4} + 2 = 0$

37. $t^{1/3} + 2t^{1/6} = 3$

38. $m^{1/2} + 6 = 5m^{1/4}$

39. $(3 - \sqrt{x})^2 - 10(3 - \sqrt{x}) + 23 = 0$

40. $(5 + \sqrt{x})^2 - 12(5 + \sqrt{x}) + 33 = 0$

41. $16\left(\dfrac{x - 1}{x - 8}\right)^2 + 8\left(\dfrac{x - 1}{x - 8}\right) + 1 = 0$

42. $9\left(\dfrac{x + 2}{x + 3}\right)^2 - 6\left(\dfrac{x + 2}{x + 3}\right) + 1 = 0$

43. $x^4 + 5x^2 - 36 = 0$

44. $x^4 + 5x^2 + 4 = 0$

45. $(n^2 + 6)^2 - 7(n^2 + 6) + 10 = 0$

46. $(m^2 + 7)^2 - 6(m^2 + 7) - 16 = 0$

Find all x-intercepts of the given function f. If none exists, state this.

47. $f(x) = 5x + 13\sqrt{x} - 6$

48. $f(x) = 3x + 10\sqrt{x} - 8$

49. $f(x) = (x^2 - 3x)^2 - 10(x^2 - 3x) + 24$

50. $f(x) = (x^2 - 6x)^2 - 2(x^2 - 6x) - 35$

51. $f(x) = x^{2/5} + x^{1/5} - 6$

52. $f(x) = x^{1/2} - x^{1/4} - 6$

Aha! 53. $f(x) = \left(\dfrac{x^2 + 2}{x}\right)^4 + 7\left(\dfrac{x^2 + 2}{x}\right)^2 + 5$

54. $f(x) = \left(\dfrac{x^2 + 1}{x}\right)^4 + 4\left(\dfrac{x^2 + 1}{x}\right)^2 + 12$

55. To solve $25x^6 - 10x^3 + 1 = 0$, Jose lets $u = 5x^3$ and Robin lets $u = x^3$. Can they both be correct? Why or why not?

56. Jenn writes that the solutions of $x^4 - 5x^2 + 6 = 0$ are 2 and 3. What mistake is she making?

Skill Review

To prepare for Section 9.6, review graphing functions (Section 5.3).

Graph. [5.3]

57. $f(x) = x$

58. $g(x) = x + 2$

59. $h(x) = x - 2$

60. $f(x) = x^2$

61. $g(x) = x^2 + 2$

62. $h(x) = x^2 - 2$

Synthesis

63. Describe a procedure that could be used to solve any equation of the form $ax^4 + bx^2 + c = 0$.

64. Describe a procedure that could be used to write an equation that is quadratic in $3x^2 - 1$. Then explain how the procedure could be adjusted to write equations that are quadratic in $3x^2 - 1$ and have no real-number solution.

Solve.

65. $3x^4 + 5x^2 - 1 = 0$

66. $5x^4 - 7x^2 + 1 = 0$

67. $(x^2 - 5x - 1)^2 - 18(x^2 - 5x - 1) + 65 = 0$

68. $(x^2 - 4x - 2)^2 - 13(x^2 - 4x - 2) + 30 = 0$

69. $\dfrac{x}{x - 1} - 6\sqrt{\dfrac{x}{x - 1}} - 40 = 0$

70. $\left(\sqrt{\dfrac{x}{x - 3}}\right)^2 - 24 = 10\sqrt{\dfrac{x}{x - 3}}$

71. $a^5(a^2 - 25) + 13a^3(25 - a^2) + 36a(a^2 - 25) = 0$

72. $a^3 - 26a^{3/2} - 27 = 0$

73. $x^6 - 28x^3 + 27 = 0$

74. $x^6 + 7x^3 - 8 = 0$

75. Use a graphing calculator to check your answers to Exercises 15, 17, 41, and 53.

76. Use a graphing calculator to solve
$$x^4 - x^3 - 13x^2 + x + 12 = 0.$$

77. While trying to solve $0.05x^4 - 0.8 = 0$ with a graphing calculator, Salam gets the screen at right. Can Salam solve this equation with a graphing calculator? Why or why not?

$y_1 = .05x^4 - .8$

CONNECTING the CONCEPTS

We have studied four different ways of solving quadratic equations. Each method has advantages and disadvantages, as outlined below. Note that although the quadratic formula can be used to solve *any* quadratic equation, the other methods are sometimes faster and easier to use. Also note that any of these methods can be used when solving equations that are reducible to quadratic.

Method	Advantages	Disadvantages	Example
Factoring	Can be very fast.	Can be used only on certain equations. Many equations are difficult or impossible to solve by factoring.	$x^2 - x - 6 = 0$ $(x - 3)(x + 2) = 0$ $x = 3$ *or* $x = -2$
The principle of square roots	Fastest way to solve equations of the form $X^2 = k$. Can be used to solve *any* quadratic equation.	Can be slow when original equation is not written in the form $X^2 = k$.	$(x - 5)^2 = 2$ $x - 5 = \pm\sqrt{2}$ $x = 5 \pm \sqrt{2}$
Completing the square	Works well on equations of the form $x^2 + bx = -c$, when b is even. Can be used to solve *any* quadratic equation.	Can be complicated when $a \neq 1$ or when b is not even in $x^2 + bx = -c$.	$x^2 + 14x = -2$ $x^2 + 14x + 49 = -2 + 49$ $(x + 7)^2 = 47$ $x + 7 = \pm\sqrt{47}$ $x = -7 \pm \sqrt{47}$
The quadratic formula	Can be used to solve *any* quadratic equation.	Can be slower than factoring or the principle of square roots for certain equations.	$x^2 - 2x - 5 = 0$ $x = \dfrac{-(-2) \pm \sqrt{(-2)^2 - 4(1)(-5)}}{2 \cdot 1}$ $= \dfrac{2 \pm \sqrt{24}}{2}$ $= \dfrac{2}{2} \pm \dfrac{2\sqrt{6}}{2} = 1 \pm \sqrt{6}$

MIXED REVIEW

Solve. Examine each exercise carefully, and try to solve using the easiest method.

1. $x^2 - 3x - 10 = 0$ −2
2. $x^2 = 121$
3. $x^2 + 6x = 10$
4. $x^2 + x - 3 = 0$
5. $(x + 1)^2 = 2$
6. $x^2 - 10x + 25 = 0$
7. $x^2 - x - 1 = 0$
8. $x^2 - 2x = 6$
9. $4t^2 = 11$

(continued)

10. $2t^2 + 1 = 3t$

11. $c^2 + c + 1 = 0$

12. $16c^2 = 7c$

13. $6y^2 - 7y - 10 = 0$

14. $y^2 - 2y + 8 = 0$

15. $x^4 - 10x^2 + 9 = 0$

16. $x^4 - 8x^2 - 9 = 0$

17. $t(t - 3) = 2t(t + 1)$

18. $(t + 4)(t - 3) = 18$

19. $(m^2 + 3)^2 - 4(m^2 + 3) - 5 = 0$

20. $m^{-4} - 5m^{-2} + 6 = 0$

9.6 Quadratic Functions and Their Graphs

The Graph of $f(x) = ax^2$ ▪ The Graph of $f(x) = a(x - h)^2$ ▪ The Graph of $f(x) = a(x - h)^2 + k$

We have seen that the graph of any linear function $f(x) = mx + b$ is a straight line. In this section and the next, we will see that the graph of any quadratic function $f(x) = ax^2 + bx + c$ is a *parabola*. We examine the shape of such graphs by first looking at quadratic functions with $b = 0$ and $c = 0$.

The Graph of $f(x) = ax^2$

The most basic quadratic function is $f(x) = x^2$.

EXAMPLE 1

Graph: $f(x) = x^2$.

SOLUTION   We choose some values for x and compute $f(x)$ for each. Then we plot the ordered pairs and connect them with a smooth curve.

x	$f(x) = x^2$	$(x, f(x))$
-3	9	$(-3, 9)$
-2	4	$(-2, 4)$
-1	1	$(-1, 1)$
0	0	$(0, 0)$
1	1	$(1, 1)$
2	4	$(2, 4)$
3	9	$(3, 9)$

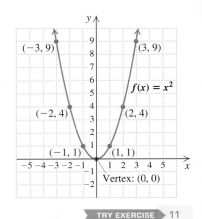

TRY EXERCISE 11

All quadratic functions have graphs similar to the one in Example 1. Such curves are called **parabolas**. They are U-shaped and can open upward, as in Example 1, or downward. The "turning point" of the graph is called the **vertex** of the parabola. The vertex of the graph in Example 1 is (0, 0).

A parabola is symmetric with respect to a line that goes through the center of the parabola and the vertex. This line is known as the parabola's **axis of symmetry**. In Example 1, the y-axis (the vertical line $x = 0$) is the axis of symmetry. Were the paper folded on this line, the two halves of the curve would match.

STUDENT NOTES

By paying attention to the symmetry of each parabola and the location of the vertex, you save yourself considerable work. Note too that when we are graphing ax^2, the x-values 1 unit to the right or left of the vertex are paired with the y-value a units above the vertex. Thus the graph of $y = \frac{3}{2}x^2$ includes the points $\left(-1, \frac{3}{2}\right)$ and $\left(1, \frac{3}{2}\right)$.

TECHNOLOGY CONNECTION

To explore the effect of a on the graph of $y = ax^2$, let $y_1 = x^2$, $y_2 = 3x^2$, and $y_3 = \frac{1}{3}x^2$. Graph the equations and use TRACE to see how the y-values compare, using ⌃ or ⌄ to hop the cursor from one curve to the next.

Many graphing calculators include a Transfrm application. If you run that application and let $y_1 = Ax^2$, the graph becomes interactive. A value for A can be entered while viewing the graph, or the values can be stepped up or down by pressing ◁ or ▷.

1. Compare the graphs of $y_1 = \frac{1}{5}x^2$, $y_2 = x^2$, $y_3 = \frac{5}{2}x^2$, $y_4 = -\frac{1}{5}x^2$, $y_5 = -x^2$, and $y_6 = -\frac{5}{2}x^2$.
2. Describe the effect that A has on each graph.

The graph of any function of the form $y = ax^2$ has a vertex of $(0, 0)$ and an axis of symmetry $x = 0$. By plotting points, we can compare the graphs of $g(x) = \frac{1}{2}x^2$ and $h(x) = 2x^2$ with the graph of $f(x) = x^2$.

x	$g(x) = \frac{1}{2}x^2$
-3	$\frac{9}{2}$
-2	2
-1	$\frac{1}{2}$
0	0
1	$\frac{1}{2}$
2	2
3	$\frac{9}{2}$

x	$h(x) = 2x^2$
-3	18
-2	8
-1	2
0	0
1	2
2	8
3	18

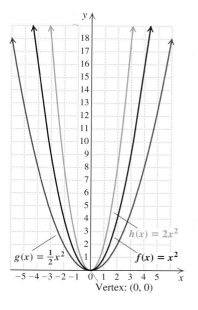

Note that the graph of $g(x) = \frac{1}{2}x^2$ is "wider" than the graph of $f(x) = x^2$, and the graph of $h(x) = 2x^2$ is "narrower." The vertex and the axis of symmetry, however, remain $(0, 0)$ and the line $x = 0$, respectively.

When we consider the graph of $k(x) = -\frac{1}{2}x^2$, we see that the parabola is the same shape as the graph of $g(x) = \frac{1}{2}x^2$, but opens downward. We say that the graphs of k and g are *reflections* of each other across the x-axis.

x	$k(x) = -\frac{1}{2}x^2$
-3	$-\frac{9}{2}$
-2	-2
-1	$-\frac{1}{2}$
0	0
1	$-\frac{1}{2}$
2	-2
3	$-\frac{9}{2}$

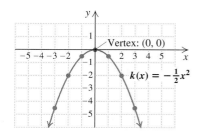

> **Graphing $f(x) = ax^2$**
>
> The graph of $f(x) = ax^2$ is a parabola with $x = 0$ as its axis of symmetry. Its vertex is the origin.
>
> For $a > 0$, the parabola opens upward. For $a < 0$, the parabola opens downward.
>
> If $|a|$ is greater than 1, the parabola is narrower than $y = x^2$.
>
> If $|a|$ is between 0 and 1, the parabola is wider than $y = x^2$.

The width of a parabola and whether it opens upward or downward are determined by the coefficient a in $f(x) = ax^2 + bx + c$. In the remainder of this section, we graph quadratic functions that are written in a form from which the vertex can be read directly.

The Graph of $f(x) = a(x - h)^2$

EXAMPLE 2

Graph: $f(x) = (x - 3)^2$.

SOLUTION We choose some values for x and compute $f(x)$. Since $(x - 3)^2 = 1 \cdot (x - 3)^2$, $a = 1$, and the graph opens upward. It is important to note that when an input here is 3 more than an input for Example 1, the outputs match. We plot the points and draw the curve.

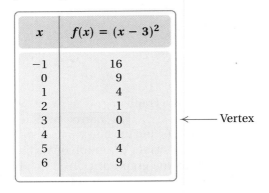

x	$f(x) = (x - 3)^2$
-1	16
0	9
1	4
2	1
3	0 ← Vertex
4	1
5	4
6	9

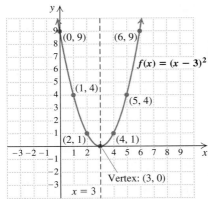

Note that $f(x)$ is smallest when $x - 3$ is 0, that is, for $x = 3$. Thus the line $x = 3$ is now the axis of symmetry and the point $(3, 0)$ is the vertex. Had we recognized earlier that $x = 3$ is the axis of symmetry, we could have computed some values on one side, such as $(4, 1)$, $(5, 4)$, and $(6, 9)$, and then used symmetry to get their mirror images $(2, 1)$, $(1, 4)$, and $(0, 9)$ without further computation.

TRY EXERCISE 19

The result of Example 2 can be generalized:

The vertex of the graph of $f(x) = a(x - h)^2$ is $(h, 0)$.

EXAMPLE 3

Graph: $g(x) = -2(x + 4)^2$.

SOLUTION We choose some values for x and compute $g(x)$. Since $a = -2$, the graph will open downward. Note that $g(x)$ is greatest when $x + 4$ is 0, that is, for $x = -4$. Thus the line given by $x = -4$ is the axis of symmetry and the point $(-4, 0)$ is the vertex. We plot some points and draw the curve.

TECHNOLOGY CONNECTION

To explore the effect of h on the graph of $f(x) = a(x - h)^2$, let $y_1 = 7x^2$ and $y_2 = 7(x - 1)^2$. Graph both y_1 and y_2 and compare y-values, beginning at $x = 1$ and increasing x by one unit at a time. The G-T or HORIZ **MODE** can be used to view a split screen showing both the graph and a table.

Next, let $y_3 = 7(x - 2)^2$ and compare its graph and y-values with those of y_1 and y_2. Then let $y_4 = 7(x + 1)^2$ and $y_5 = 7(x + 2)^2$.

1. Compare graphs and y-values and describe the effect of h on the graph of $f(x) = a(x - h)^2$.
2. If the Transfrm application is available, let $y_1 = A(x - B)^2$ and describe the effect that A and B have on each graph.

x	$g(x) = -2(x + 4)^2$
-6	-8
-5	-2
-4	0
-3	-2
-2	-8

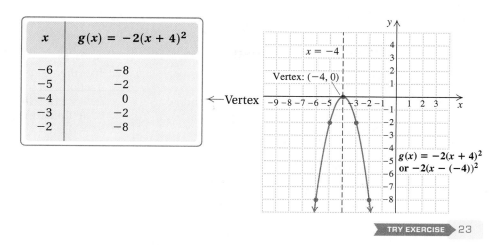

TRY EXERCISE 23

In Example 2, the graph of $f(x) = (x - 3)^2$ looks just like the graph of $y = x^2$, except that it is moved, or *translated*, 3 units to the right. In Example 3, the graph of $g(x) = -2(x + 4)^2$ looks like the graph of $y = -2x^2$, except that it is shifted 4 units to the left. These results are generalized as follows.

Graphing $f(x) = a(x - h)^2$

The graph of $f(x) = a(x - h)^2$ has the same shape as the graph of $y = ax^2$.

- If h is positive, the graph of $y = ax^2$ is shifted h units to the right.
- If h is negative, the graph of $y = ax^2$ is shifted $|h|$ units to the left.
- The vertex is $(h, 0)$ and the axis of symmetry is $x = h$.

The Graph of $f(x) = a(x - h)^2 + k$

Given a graph of $f(x) = a(x - h)^2$, what happens if we add a constant k? Suppose that we add 2. This increases $f(x)$ by 2, so the curve is moved up. If k is negative, the curve is moved down. The axis of symmetry for the parabola remains $x = h$, but the vertex will be at (h, k), or, equivalently, $(h, f(h))$.

Because of the shape of their graphs, quadratic functions have either a *minimum* value or a *maximum* value. Many real-world applications involve finding that value. For example, a business owner is concerned with minimizing cost and maximizing profit. If a parabola opens upward $(a > 0)$, the function value, or y-value, at the vertex is a least, or minimum, value. That is, it is less than the y-value at any other point on the graph. If the parabola opens downward $(a < 0)$, the function value at the vertex is a greatest, or maximum, value.

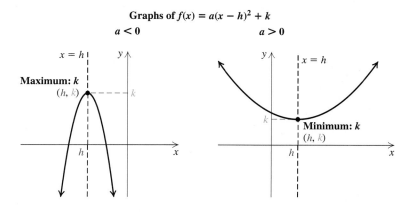

Graphs of $f(x) = a(x - h)^2 + k$

TECHNOLOGY CONNECTION

To study the effect of k on the graph of $f(x) = a(x - h)^2 + k$, let $y_1 = 7(x - 1)^2$ and $y_2 = 7(x - 1)^2 + 2$. Graph both y_1 and y_2 in the window $[-5, 5, -5, 5]$ and use TRACE or a TABLE to compare the y-values for any given x-value.

1. Let $y_3 = 7(x - 1)^2 - 4$ and compare its graph and y-values with those of y_1 and y_2.

2. Try other values of k, including decimals and fractions. Describe the effect of k on the graph of $f(x) = a(x - h)^2$.

3. If the Transfrm application is available, let $y_1 = A(x - B)^2 + C$ and describe the effect that A, B, and C have on each graph.

Graphing $f(x) = a(x - h)^2 + k$

The graph of $f(x) = a(x - h)^2 + k$ has the same shape as the graph of $y = a(x - h)^2$.

- If k is positive, the graph of $y = a(x - h)^2$ is shifted k units up.
- If k is negative, the graph of $y = a(x - h)^2$ is shifted $|k|$ units down.
- The vertex is (h, k), and the axis of symmetry is $x = h$.
- For $a > 0$, the minimum function value is k. For $a < 0$, the maximum function value is k.

EXAMPLE **4** Graph $g(x) = (x - 3)^2 - 5$, and find the minimum function value.

SOLUTION The graph will look like that of $f(x) = (x - 3)^2$ (see Example 2) but shifted 5 units down. You can confirm this by plotting some points. For instance, $g(4) = (4 - 3)^2 - 5 = -4$, whereas in Example 2, $f(4) = (4 - 3)^2 = 1$.

The vertex is now $(3, -5)$, and the minimum function value is -5.

x	$g(x) = (x - 3)^2 - 5$	
0	4	
1	-1	
2	-4	
3	-5	← Vertex
4	-4	
5	-1	
6	4	

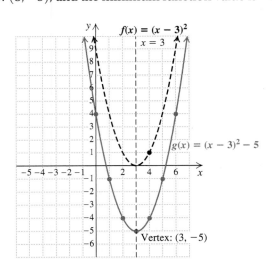

TRY EXERCISE 39

EXAMPLE 5 Graph $h(x) = \frac{1}{2}(x - 3)^2 + 6$, and find the minimum function value.

SOLUTION The graph looks just like that of $f(x) = \frac{1}{2}x^2$ but moved 3 units to the right and 6 units up. The vertex is $(3, 6)$, and the axis of symmetry is $x = 3$. We draw $f(x) = \frac{1}{2}x^2$ and then shift the curve over and up. The minimum function value is 6. By plotting some points, we have a check.

x	$h(x) = \frac{1}{2}(x - 3)^2 + 6$
0	$10\frac{1}{2}$
1	8
3	6
5	8
6	$10\frac{1}{2}$

← Vertex

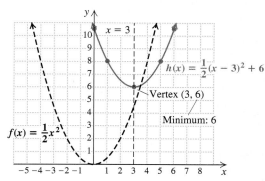

TRY EXERCISE 43

EXAMPLE 6 Graph $y = -2(x + 3)^2 + 5$. Find the vertex, the axis of symmetry, and the maximum or minimum value.

SOLUTION We first express the equation in the equivalent form

$$y = -2[x - (-3)]^2 + 5. \qquad \text{This is in the form } y = a(x - h)^2 + k.$$

The graph looks like that of $y = -2x^2$ translated 3 units to the left and 5 units up. The vertex is $(-3, 5)$, and the axis of symmetry is $x = -3$. Since -2 is negative, the graph opens downward, and we know that 5, the second coordinate of the vertex, is the maximum y-value.

We compute a few points as needed, selecting convenient x-values on either side of the vertex. The graph is shown here.

x	$y = -2(x + 3)^2 + 5$
-4	3
-3	5
-2	3

← Vertex

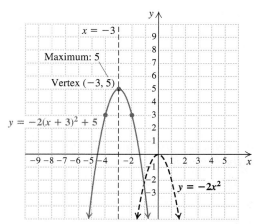

TRY EXERCISE 45

9.6   EXERCISE SET

For Extra Help MyMathLab Math XL PRACTICE WATCH DOWNLOAD

Concept Reinforcement *In each of Exercises 1–8, match the equation with the corresponding graph from those shown.*

1. ____ $f(x) = 2(x - 1)^2 + 3$

2. ____ $f(x) = -2(x - 1)^2 + 3$

3. ____ $f(x) = 2(x + 1)^2 + 3$

4. ____ $f(x) = 2(x - 1)^2 - 3$

5. ____ $f(x) = -2(x + 1)^2 + 3$

6. ____ $f(x) = -2(x + 1)^2 - 3$

7. ____ $f(x) = 2(x + 1)^2 - 3$

8. ____ $f(x) = -2(x - 1)^2 - 3$

c)

d)

e)

f)

a)

b)

g)

h)

Graph.

9. $f(x) = x^2$

10. $f(x) = -x^2$

11. $f(x) = -2x^2$

12. $f(x) = -3x^2$

13. $g(x) = \frac{1}{3}x^2$

14. $g(x) = \frac{1}{4}x^2$

Aha! 15. $h(x) = -\frac{1}{3}x^2$

16. $h(x) = -\frac{1}{4}x^2$

17. $f(x) = \frac{5}{2}x^2$

18. $f(x) = \frac{3}{2}x^2$

For each of the following, graph the function, label the vertex, and draw the axis of symmetry.

19. $g(x) = (x + 1)^2$

20. $g(x) = (x + 4)^2$

21. $f(x) = (x - 2)^2$

22. $f(x) = (x - 1)^2$

23. $f(x) = -(x + 1)^2$

24. $f(x) = -(x - 1)^2$

25. $g(x) = -(x - 2)^2$

26. $g(x) = -(x + 4)^2$

27. $f(x) = 2(x + 1)^2$

28. $f(x) = 2(x + 4)^2$

29. $g(x) = 3(x - 4)^2$

30. $g(x) = 3(x - 5)^2$

31. $h(x) = -\frac{1}{2}(x - 4)^2$

32. $h(x) = -\frac{3}{2}(x - 2)^2$

33. $f(x) = \frac{1}{2}(x - 1)^2$

34. $f(x) = \frac{1}{3}(x + 2)^2$

35. $f(x) = -2(x + 5)^2$

36. $f(x) = -3(x + 7)^2$

37. $h(x) = -3\left(x - \frac{1}{2}\right)^2$

38. $h(x) = -2\left(x + \frac{1}{2}\right)^2$

For each of the following, graph the function and find the vertex, the axis of symmetry, and the maximum value or the minimum value.

39. $f(x) = (x - 5)^2 + 2$

40. $f(x) = (x + 3)^2 - 2$

41. $f(x) = (x + 1)^2 - 3$

42. $f(x) = (x - 1)^2 + 2$

43. $g(x) = \frac{1}{2}(x + 4)^2 + 1$

44. $g(x) = -(x - 2)^2 - 4$

45. $h(x) = -2(x - 1)^2 - 3$

46. $h(x) = -2(x + 1)^2 + 4$

47. $f(x) = 2(x + 3)^2 + 1$

48. $f(x) = 2(x - 5)^2 - 3$

49. $g(x) = -\frac{3}{2}(x - 2)^2 + 4$

50. $g(x) = \frac{3}{2}(x + 2)^2 - 1$

Without graphing, find the vertex, the axis of symmetry, and the maximum value or the minimum value.

51. $f(x) = 5(x - 3)^2 + 9$

52. $f(x) = 2(x - 1)^2 - 10$

53. $f(x) = -\frac{3}{7}(x + 8)^2 + 2$

54. $f(x) = -\frac{1}{4}(x + 4)^2 - 12$

55. $f(x) = \left(x - \frac{7}{2}\right)^2 - \frac{29}{4}$

56. $f(x) = -\left(x + \frac{3}{4}\right)^2 + \frac{17}{16}$

57. $f(x) = -\sqrt{2}(x + 2.25)^2 - \pi$

58. $f(x) = 2\pi(x - 0.01)^2 + \sqrt{15}$

59. Explain, without plotting points, why the graph of $y = x^2 - 4$ looks like the graph of $y = x^2$ translated 4 units down.

60. Explain, without plotting points, why the graph of $y = (x + 2)^2$ looks like the graph of $y = x^2$ translated 2 units to the left.

Skill Review

To prepare for Section 9.7, review finding intercepts and completing the square (Sections 2.3, 3.7, and 7.1).

Find the x-intercept and the y-intercept. [2.3]

61. $8x - 6y = 24$

62. $3x + 4y = 8$

Find the x-intercepts. [3.7]

63. $y = x^2 + 8x + 15$

64. $y = 2x^2 - x - 3$

Replace the blanks with constants to form a true equation. [9.1]

65. $x^2 - 14x +$ ___ $= (x -$ ___ $)^2$

66. $x^2 + 7x +$ ___ $= \left(x +$ ___ $\right)^2$

Synthesis

67. Before graphing a quadratic function, Martha always plots five points. First, she calculates and plots the coordinates of the vertex. Then she plots *four* more points after calculating *two* more ordered pairs. How is this possible?

68. If the graphs of $f(x) = a_1(x - h_1)^2 + k_1$ and $g(x) = a_2(x - h_2)^2 + k_2$ have the same shape, what, if anything, can you conclude about the a's, the h's, and the k's? Why?

Write an equation for a function having a graph with the same shape as the graph of $f(x) = \frac{3}{5}x^2$, but with the given point as the vertex.

69. $(1, 3)$

70. $(2, 8)$

71. $(4, -7)$

72. $(9, -6)$

73. $(-2, -5)$

74. $(-4, -2)$

For each of the following, write the equation of the parabola that has the shape of $f(x) = 2x^2$ or $g(x) = -2x^2$ and has a maximum value or a minimum value at the specified point.

75. Minimum: $(2, 0)$

76. Minimum: $(-4, 0)$

77. Maximum: $(0, -5)$

78. Maximum: $(3, 8)$

Use the following graph of $f(x) = a(x - h)^2 + k$ for Exercises 79–82.

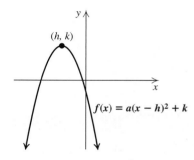

79. Describe what will happen to the graph if h is increased.

80. Describe what will happen to the graph if k is decreased.

81. Describe what will happen to the graph if a is replaced with $-a$.

82. Describe what will happen to the graph if $(x - h)$ is replaced with $(x + h)$.

Find an equation for the quadratic function F that satisfies the following conditions.

83. The graph of F is the same shape as the graph of f, where $f(x) = 3(x + 2)^2 + 7$, and $F(x)$ is a minimum at the same point that $g(x) = -2(x - 5)^2 + 1$ is a maximum.

84. The graph of F is the same shape as the graph of f, where $f(x) = -\frac{1}{3}(x - 2)^2 + 7$, and $F(x)$ is a maximum at the same point that $g(x) = 2(x + 4)^2 - 6$ is a minimum.

Functions other than parabolas can be translated. When calculating $f(x)$, if we replace x with $x - h$, where h is a constant, the graph will be moved horizontally. If we replace $f(x)$ with $f(x) + k$, the graph will be moved vertically. Use the graph below for Exercises 85–90.

Draw a graph of each of the following.

85. $y = f(x - 1)$ **86.** $y = f(x + 2)$

87. $y = f(x) + 2$ **88.** $y = f(x) - 3$

89. $y = f(x + 3) - 2$ **90.** $y = f(x - 3) + 1$

91. Use the TRACE and/or TABLE features of a graphing calculator to confirm the maximum and minimum values given as answers to Exercises 51, 53, and 55. Be sure to adjust the window appropriately. On many graphing calculators, a maximum or minimum option may be available by using a CALC key.

92. Use a graphing calculator to check your graphs for Exercises 18, 28, and 48.

93. While trying to graph $y = -\frac{1}{2}x^2 + 3x + 1$, Yusef gets the following screen. How can Yusef tell at a glance that a mistake has been made?

COLLABORATIVE CORNER

Match the Graph

Focus: Graphing quadratic functions

Time: 15–20 minutes

Group size: 6

Materials: Index cards

ACTIVITY

1. On each of six index cards, write one of the following equations:

$y = \frac{1}{2}(x - 3)^2 + 1$; $y = \frac{1}{2}(x - 1)^2 + 3$;
$y = \frac{1}{2}(x + 1)^2 - 3$; $y = \frac{1}{2}(x + 3)^2 + 1$;
$y = \frac{1}{2}(x + 3)^2 - 1$; $y = \frac{1}{2}(x + 1)^2 + 3$.

2. Fold each index card and mix up the six cards in a hat or bag. Then, one by one, each group member should select one of the equations. Do not let anyone see your equation.

3. Each group member should carefully graph the equation selected. Make the graph large enough so that when it is finished, it can be easily viewed by the rest of the group. Be sure to scale the axes and label the vertex, but **do not label the graph with the equation used**.

4. When all group members have drawn a graph, place the graphs in a pile. The group should then match and agree on the correct equation for each graph *with no help from the person who drew the graph*. If a mistake has been made and a graph has no match, determine what its equation *should* be.

5. Compare your group's labeled graphs with those of other groups to reach consensus within the class on the correct label for each graph.

9.7 More About Graphing Quadratic Functions

Completing the Square ■ Finding Intercepts

Completing the Square

By *completing the square* (see Section 9.1), we can rewrite any polynomial $ax^2 + bx + c$ in the form $a(x - h)^2 + k$. Once that has been done, the procedures discussed in Section 9.6 will enable us to graph any quadratic function.

EXAMPLE 1 Graph: $g(x) = x^2 - 6x + 4$. Label the vertex and the axis of symmetry.

SOLUTION We have

$$g(x) = x^2 - 6x + 4$$
$$= (x^2 - 6x) + 4.$$

To complete the square inside the parentheses, we take half the x-coefficient, $\frac{1}{2} \cdot (-6) = -3$, and square it to get $(-3)^2 = 9$. Then we add $9 - 9$ inside the parentheses:

$$g(x) = (x^2 - 6x + 9 - 9) + 4 \qquad \text{The effect is of adding 0.}$$
$$= (x^2 - 6x + 9) + (-9 + 4) \qquad \text{Using the associative law of addition to regroup}$$
$$= (x - 3)^2 - 5. \qquad \text{Factoring and simplifying}$$

This equation appeared as Example 4 of Section 9.6. The graph is that of $f(x) = x^2$ translated 3 units right and 5 units down. The vertex is $(3, -5)$, and the axis of symmetry is $x = 3$.

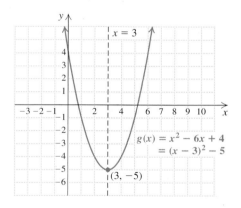

TRY EXERCISE 19

When the leading coefficient is not 1, we factor out that number from the first two terms. Then we complete the square and use the distributive law.

EXAMPLE 2 Graph: $f(x) = 3x^2 + 12x + 13$. Label the vertex and the axis of symmetry.

SOLUTION Since the coefficient of x^2 is not 1, we need to factor out that number—in this case, 3—from the first two terms. Remember that we want the form $f(x) = a(x - h)^2 + k$:

$$f(x) = 3x^2 + 12x + 13$$
$$= 3(x^2 + 4x) + 13.$$

STUDY SKILLS

Use What You Know

An excellent and common strategy for solving any new type of problem is to rewrite the problem in an equivalent form that we already know how to solve. Although this is not always feasible, when it is—as in most of the problems in this section—it can make a new topic much easier to learn.

STUDENT NOTES ————

In this section, we add and subtract the same number when completing the square instead of adding the same number to both sides of the equation. We do this because we are using function notation. The effect is the same with both approaches: An equivalent equation is formed.

Now we complete the square as before. We take half of the x-coefficient, $\frac{1}{2} \cdot 4 = 2$, and square it: $2^2 = 4$. Then we add $4 - 4$ inside the parentheses:

$$f(x) = 3(x^2 + 4x + 4 - 4) + 13. \qquad \text{Adding } 4 - 4, \text{ or } 0, \text{ inside the parentheses}$$

The distributive law allows us to separate the -4 from the perfect-square trinomial so long as it is multiplied by 3. *This step is critical*:

$$f(x) = 3(x^2 + 4x + 4) + 3(-4) + 13 \qquad \begin{array}{l}\text{This leaves a perfect-square} \\ \text{trinomial inside the} \\ \text{parentheses.}\end{array}$$

$$= 3(x + 2)^2 + 1. \qquad \text{Factoring and simplifying}$$

The vertex is $(-2, 1)$, and the axis of symmetry is $x = -2$. The coefficient of x^2 is 3, so the graph is narrow and opens upward. We choose a few x-values on either side of the vertex, compute y-values, and then graph the parabola.

x	$f(x) = 3(x + 2)^2 + 1$
-2	1
-3	4
-1	4

←——— Vertex

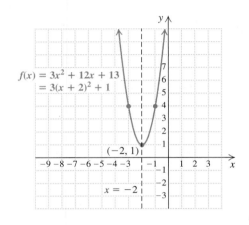

$$f(x) = 3x^2 + 12x + 13 = 3(x + 2)^2 + 1$$

TRY EXERCISE ▸ 23

EXAMPLE 3 Graph $f(x) = -2x^2 + 10x - 7$, and find the maximum or minimum function value.

SOLUTION We first find the vertex by completing the square. To do so, we factor out -2 from the first two terms of the expression. This makes the coefficient of x^2 inside the parentheses 1:

$$f(x) = -2x^2 + 10x - 7$$
$$= -2(x^2 - 5x) - 7.$$

Now we complete the square as before. We take half of the x-coefficient and square it to get $\frac{25}{4}$. Then we add $\frac{25}{4} - \frac{25}{4}$ inside the parentheses:

$$f(x) = -2\left(x^2 - 5x + \frac{25}{4} - \frac{25}{4}\right) - 7$$
$$= -2\left(x^2 - 5x + \frac{25}{4}\right) + (-2)\left(-\frac{25}{4}\right) - 7 \qquad \begin{array}{l}\text{Multiplying by } -2, \\ \text{using the distributive} \\ \text{law, and regrouping}\end{array}$$
$$= -2\left(x - \frac{5}{2}\right)^2 + \frac{11}{2}. \qquad \begin{array}{l}\text{Factoring and} \\ \text{simplifying}\end{array}$$

The vertex is $\left(\frac{5}{2}, \frac{11}{2}\right)$, and the axis of symmetry is $x = \frac{5}{2}$. The coefficient of x^2, -2, is negative, so the graph opens downward and the second coordinate of the vertex, $\frac{11}{2}$, is the maximum function value.

We plot a few points on either side of the vertex, including the y-intercept, $f(0)$, and graph the parabola.

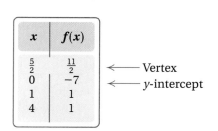

$\leftarrow$ Vertex
$\leftarrow$ y-intercept

TRY EXERCISE 39

The method used in Examples 1–3 can be generalized to find a formula for locating the vertex. We complete the square as follows:

$$f(x) = ax^2 + bx + c$$
$$= a\left(x^2 + \frac{b}{a}x\right) + c. \qquad \text{Factoring } a \text{ out of the first two terms.}$$
$$\text{Check by multiplying.}$$

Half of the x-coefficient, $\frac{b}{a}$, is $\frac{b}{2a}$. We square it to get $\frac{b^2}{4a^2}$ and add $\frac{b^2}{4a^2} - \frac{b^2}{4a^2}$ inside the parentheses. Then we distribute the a and regroup terms:

$$f(x) = a\left(x^2 + \frac{b}{a}x + \frac{b^2}{4a^2} - \frac{b^2}{4a^2}\right) + c$$
$$= a\left(x^2 + \frac{b}{a}x + \frac{b^2}{4a^2}\right) + a\left(-\frac{b^2}{4a^2}\right) + c \qquad \text{Using the distributive law}$$
$$= a\left(x + \frac{b}{2a}\right)^2 + \frac{-b^2}{4a} + \frac{4ac}{4a} \qquad \text{Factoring and finding a common denominator}$$
$$= a\left[x - \left(-\frac{b}{2a}\right)\right]^2 + \frac{4ac - b^2}{4a}.$$

Thus we have the following.

STUDENT NOTES ——————

It is easier to remember a formula when you understand its derivation. Check with your instructor to determine what formulas you will be expected to remember.

The Vertex of a Parabola

The vertex of the parabola given by $f(x) = ax^2 + bx + c$ is
$$\left(-\frac{b}{2a}, f\left(-\frac{b}{2a}\right)\right), \quad \text{or} \quad \left(-\frac{b}{2a}, \frac{4ac - b^2}{4a}\right).$$

- The x-coordinate of the vertex is $-b/(2a)$.
- The axis of symmetry is $x = -b/(2a)$.
- The second coordinate of the vertex is most commonly found by computing $f\left(-\frac{b}{2a}\right)$.

Let's reexamine Example 3 to see how we could have found the vertex directly. From the formula above,

$$\text{the } x\text{-coordinate of the vertex is } -\frac{b}{2a} = -\frac{10}{2(-2)} = \frac{5}{2}.$$

Substituting $\frac{5}{2}$ into $f(x) = -2x^2 + 10x - 7$, we find the second coordinate of the vertex:

$$\begin{aligned} f\left(\tfrac{5}{2}\right) &= -2\left(\tfrac{5}{2}\right)^2 + 10\left(\tfrac{5}{2}\right) - 7 \\ &= -2\left(\tfrac{25}{4}\right) + 25 - 7 \\ &= -\tfrac{25}{2} + 18 \\ &= -\tfrac{25}{2} + \tfrac{36}{2} = \tfrac{11}{2}. \end{aligned}$$

The vertex is $\left(\frac{5}{2}, \frac{11}{2}\right)$. The axis of symmetry is $x = \frac{5}{2}$.

We have actually developed two methods for finding the vertex. One is by completing the square and the other is by using a formula. You should check to see if your instructor prefers one method over the other or wants you to use both.

Finding Intercepts

All quadratic functions have a y-intercept and 0, 1, or 2 x-intercepts. For $f(x) = ax^2 + bx + c$, the y-intercept is $(0, f(0))$, or $(0, c)$. To find x-intercepts, if any exist, we look for points where $y = 0$ or $f(x) = 0$. Thus, for $f(x) = ax^2 + bx + c$, the x-intercepts occur at those x-values for which

$$ax^2 + bx + c = 0.$$

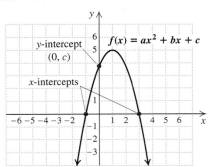

EXAMPLE 4 Find any x-intercepts and the y-intercept of the graph of $f(x) = x^2 - 2x - 2$.

SOLUTION The y-intercept is simply $(0, f(0))$, or $(0, -2)$. To find any x-intercepts, we solve

$$0 = x^2 - 2x - 2.$$

We are unable to factor $x^2 - 2x - 2$, so we use the quadratic formula and get $x = 1 \pm \sqrt{3}$. Thus the x-intercepts are $(1 - \sqrt{3}, 0)$ and $(1 + \sqrt{3}, 0)$.

If graphing, we would approximate, to get $(-0.7, 0)$ and $(2.7, 0)$.

TRY EXERCISE 43

If the solutions of $f(x) = 0$ are imaginary, the graph of f has no x-intercepts.

Visualizing for Success

A

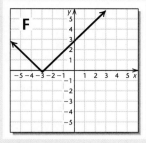

F

Match each function with its graph.

1. $f(x) = 3x^2$

2. $f(x) = x^2 - 4$

3. $f(x) = (x - 4)^2$

4. $f(x) = x - 4$

5. $f(x) = -2x^2$

6. $f(x) = x + 3$

7. $f(x) = |x + 3|$

8. $f(x) = (x + 3)^2$

9. $f(x) = \sqrt{x + 3}$

10. $f(x) = (x + 3)^2 - 4$

B

G

C

H

D

I

E

J

Answers on page A-40.

An additional, animated version of this activity appears in MyMathLab. To use MyMathLab, you need a course ID and a student access code. Contact your instructor for more information.

9.7 EXERCISE SET

For Extra Help MyMathLab   PRACTICE WATCH DOWNLOAD

Concept Reinforcement *Classify each statement as either true or false.*

1. The graph of $f(x) = 3x^2 - x + 6$ opens upward.

2. The function given by $g(x) = -x^2 + 3x + 1$ has a minimum value.

3. The graph of $f(x) = -2(x - 3)^2 + 7$ has its vertex at $(3, 7)$.

4. The graph of $g(x) = 4(x + 6)^2 - 2$ has its vertex at $(-6, -2)$.

5. The graph of $g(x) = \frac{1}{2}(x - \frac{3}{2})^2 + \frac{1}{4}$ has $x = \frac{1}{4}$ as its axis of symmetry.

6. The function given by $f(x) = (x - 2)^2 - 5$ has a minimum value of -5.

7. The y-intercept of the graph of $f(x) = 2x^2 - 6x + 7$ is $(7, 0)$.

8. If the graph of a quadratic function f opens upward and has a vertex of $(1, 5)$, then the graph has no x-intercepts.

Complete the square to write each function in the form $f(x) = a(x - h)^2 + k.$

9. $f(x) = x^2 - 8x + 2$

10. $f(x) = x^2 - 6x - 1$

11. $f(x) = x^2 + 3x - 5$

12. $f(x) = x^2 + 5x + 3$

13. $f(x) = 3x^2 + 6x - 2$

14. $f(x) = 2x^2 - 20x - 3$

15. $f(x) = -x^2 - 4x - 7$

16. $f(x) = -2x^2 - 8x + 4$

17. $f(x) = 2x^2 - 5x + 10$

18. $f(x) = 3x^2 + 7x - 3$

For each quadratic function, **(a)** *find the vertex and the axis of symmetry and* **(b)** *graph the function.*

19. $f(x) = x^2 + 4x + 5$

20. $f(x) = x^2 + 2x - 5$

21. $f(x) = x^2 + 8x + 20$

22. $f(x) = x^2 - 10x + 21$

23. $h(x) = 2x^2 - 16x + 25$

24. $h(x) = 2x^2 + 16x + 23$

25. $f(x) = -x^2 + 2x + 5$

26. $f(x) = -x^2 - 2x + 7$

27. $g(x) = x^2 + 3x - 10$

28. $g(x) = x^2 + 5x + 4$

29. $h(x) = x^2 + 7x$

30. $h(x) = x^2 - 5x$

31. $f(x) = -2x^2 - 4x - 6$

32. $f(x) = -3x^2 + 6x + 2$

For each quadratic function, **(a)** *find the vertex, the axis of symmetry, and the maximum or minimum function value and* **(b)** *graph the function.*

33. $g(x) = x^2 - 6x + 13$

34. $g(x) = x^2 - 4x + 5$

35. $g(x) = 2x^2 - 8x + 3$

36. $g(x) = 2x^2 + 5x - 1$

37. $f(x) = 3x^2 - 24x + 50$

38. $f(x) = 4x^2 + 16x + 13$

39. $f(x) = -3x^2 + 5x - 2$

40. $f(x) = -3x^2 - 7x + 2$

41. $h(x) = \frac{1}{2}x^2 + 4x + \frac{19}{3}$

42. $h(x) = \frac{1}{2}x^2 - 3x + 2$

Find any x-intercepts and the y-intercept. If no x-intercepts exist, state this.

43. $f(x) = x^2 - 6x + 3$

44. $f(x) = x^2 + 5x + 4$

45. $g(x) = -x^2 + 2x + 3$

46. $g(x) = x^2 - 6x + 9$

Aha! 47. $f(x) = x^2 - 9x$

48. $f(x) = x^2 - 7x$

49. $h(x) = -x^2 + 4x - 4$

50. $h(x) = -2x^2 - 20x - 50$

51. $g(x) = x^2 + x - 5$

52. $g(x) = 2x^2 + 3x - 1$

53. $f(x) = 2x^2 - 4x + 6$

54. $f(x) = x^2 - x + 2$

55. The graph of a quadratic function f opens downward and has no x-intercepts. In what quadrant(s) must the vertex lie? Explain your reasoning.

56. Is it possible for the graph of a quadratic function to have only one x-intercept if the vertex is off the x-axis? Why or why not?

Skill Review

To prepare for Section 9.8, review solving systems of three equations in three unknowns (Section 6.4).

Solve. [6.4]

57. $x + y + z = 3,$
   $x - y + z = 1,$
   $-x - y + z = -1$

58. $x - y + z = -6,$
   $2x + y + z = 2,$
   $3x + y + z = 0$

59. $z = 8,$
   $x + y + z = 23,$
   $2x + y - z = 17$

60. $z = -5,$
   $2x - y + 3z = -27,$
   $x + 2y + 7z = -26$

61. $1.5 = c,$
   $52.5 = 25a + 5b + c,$
   $7.5 = 4a + 2b + c$

62. $\frac{1}{2} = c,$
   $5 = 9a + 6b + 2c,$
   $29 = 81a + 9b + c$

Synthesis

63. If the graphs of two quadratic functions have the same x-intercepts, will they also have the same vertex? Why or why not?

64. Suppose that the graph of $f(x) = ax^2 + bx + c$ has $(x_1, 0)$ and $(x_2, 0)$ as x-intercepts. Explain why the graph of $g(x) = -ax^2 - bx - c$ will also have $(x_1, 0)$ and $(x_2, 0)$ as x-intercepts.

For each quadratic function, find **(a)** *the maximum or minimum value and* **(b)** *any x-intercepts and the y-intercept.*

65. $f(x) = 2.31x^2 - 3.135x - 5.89$

66. $f(x) = -18.8x^2 + 7.92x + 6.18$

67. Graph the function
$$f(x) = x^2 - x - 6.$$
Then use the graph to approximate solutions to each of the following equations.

a) $x^2 - x - 6 = 2$
b) $x^2 - x - 6 = -3$

68. Graph the function
$$f(x) = \frac{x^2}{2} + x - \frac{3}{2}.$$
Then use the graph to approximate solutions to each of the following equations.

a) $\dfrac{x^2}{2} + x - \dfrac{3}{2} = 0$

b) $\dfrac{x^2}{2} + x - \dfrac{3}{2} = 1$

c) $\dfrac{x^2}{2} + x - \dfrac{3}{2} = 2$

Find an equivalent equation of the type
$$f(x) = a(x - h)^2 + k.$$

69. $f(x) = mx^2 - nx + p$

70. $f(x) = 3x^2 + mx + m^2$

71. A quadratic function has $(-1, 0)$ as one of its intercepts and $(3, -5)$ as its vertex. Find an equation for the function.

72. A quadratic function has $(4, 0)$ as one of its intercepts and $(-1, 7)$ as its vertex. Find an equation for the function.

Graph.

73. $f(x) = |x^2 - 1|$

74. $f(x) = |x^2 - 3x - 4|$

75. $f(x) = |2(x - 3)^2 - 5|$

76. Use a graphing calculator to check your answers to Exercises 25, 41, 53, 65, and 67.

9.8 Problem Solving and Quadratic Functions

Maximum and Minimum Problems ▪ Fitting Quadratic Functions to Data

Let's look now at some of the many situations in which quadratic functions are used for problem solving.

Maximum and Minimum Problems

We have seen that for any quadratic function f, the value of $f(x)$ at the vertex is either a maximum or a minimum. Thus problems in which a quantity must be maximized or minimized can be solved by finding the coordinates of a vertex, assuming the problem can be modeled with a quadratic function.

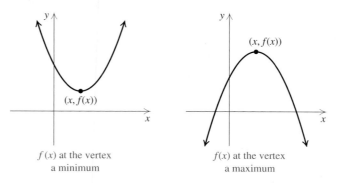

$f(x)$ at the vertex
a minimum

$f(x)$ at the vertex
a maximum

EXAMPLE 1

Museum attendance. After the admission fee was dropped, attendance at the Indianapolis Museum of Art began to rise after several years of decline. The number of museum admissions, in thousands, t years after 2000 can be approximated by $m(t)$, where $m(t) = 32t^2 - 320t + 975$. In what year was the museum attendance the lowest, and how many people went to the museum that year?

Source: Based on information in the *Indianapolis Star*, 9/9/07

SOLUTION

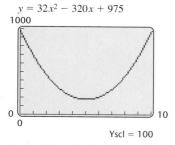

$y = 32x^2 - 320x + 975$

Yscl = 100

A visualization for Example 1

1., 2. Familiarize and **Translate.** We are given the function for museum attendance. Note that it is a quadratic function of the number of years since 2000. The coefficient of the squared term is positive, so the graph opens upward and there is a minimum value. The calculator-generated graph at left confirms this.

3. Carry out. We can either complete the square or use the formula for the vertex. Completing the square, we have

$$m(t) = 32t^2 - 320t + 975$$
$$= 32(t^2 - 10t) + 975$$
$$= 32(t^2 - 10t + 25 - 25) + 975 \quad \text{Completing the square}$$
$$= 32(t^2 - 10t + 25) - (32)(25) + 975$$
$$= 32(t - 5)^2 + 175. \quad \text{Factoring and simplifying}$$

There is a minimum value of 175 when $t = 5$.

4. **Check.** Using the formula, we have $-b/(2a) = -(-320)/64 = 5$. Then

$$m(5) = 32(5)^2 - 320(5) + 975 = 175.$$

Both approaches give the same minimum, and that minimum is also confirmed by the graph. The answer checks.

5. **State.** The minimum attendance was 175,000. It occurred 5 yr after 2000, or in 2005.

TRY EXERCISE ▸ 7

EXAMPLE 2

Swimming area. A lifeguard has 100 m of roped-together flotation devices with which to cordon off a rectangular swimming area at North Beach. If the shoreline forms one side of the rectangle, what dimensions will maximize the size of the area for swimming?

SOLUTION

1. **Familiarize.** We make a drawing and label it, letting w = the width of the rectangle, in meters, and l = the length of the rectangle, in meters.

   Recall that Area = $l \cdot w$ and Perimeter = $2w + 2l$. Since the beach forms one length of the rectangle, the flotation devices comprise three sides. Thus

   $$2w + l = 100.$$

   To get a better feel for the problem, we can look at some possible dimensions for a rectangular area that can be enclosed with 100 m of flotation devices. All possibilities are chosen so that $2w + l = 100$.

> **TECHNOLOGY CONNECTION**
>
> To generate a table of values for Example 2, let x represent the width of the swimming area, in meters. If l represents the length, in meters, we must have $100 = 2x + l$. Next, solve for l and use that expression for y_1. Then let $y_2 = x \cdot y_1$ (to enter y_1, press **VARS** and select Y-VARS and then FUNCTION and then 1) so that y_2 represents the area. Scroll through the resulting table, adjusting the settings as needed, to determine at what point the area is maximized.

l	w	Rope Length	Area	
40 m	30 m	100 m	1200 m²	What choice of l and
30 m	35 m	100 m	1050 m²	w will maximize A?
20 m	40 m	100 m	800 m²	
⋮	⋮	⋮	⋮	

2. **Translate.** We have two equations: One guarantees that all 100 m of flotation devices are used; the other expresses area in terms of length and width.

$$2w + l = 100,$$
$$A = l \cdot w$$

3. **Carry out.** We need to express A as a function of l or w but not both. To do so, we solve for l in the first equation to obtain $l = 100 - 2w$. Substituting for l in the second equation, we get a quadratic function:

$A = (100 - 2w)w$ Substituting for l

$\quad = 100w - 2w^2.$ This represents a parabola opening downward, so a maximum exists.

Factoring and completing the square, we get

$A = -2(w^2 - 50w + 625 - 625)$ We could also use the vertex formula.

$\quad = -2(w - 25)^2 + 1250.$

There is a maximum value of 1250 when $w = 25$.

4. **Check.** If $w = 25$ m, then $l = 100 - 2 \cdot 25 = 50$ m. These dimensions give an area of 1250 m^2. Note that 1250 m^2 is greater than any of the values for A found in the *Familiarize* step. To be more certain, we could check values other than those used in that step. For example, if $w = 26$ m, then $l = 48$ m, and $A = 26 \cdot 48 = 1248$ m^2. Since 1250 m^2 is greater than 1248 m^2, it appears that we have a maximum.

5. **State.** The largest rectangular area for swimming that can be enclosed is 25 m by 50 m.

> TRY EXERCISE ▶ 11

Fitting Quadratic Functions to Data

Whenever a certain quadratic function fits a situation, that function can be determined if three inputs and their outputs are known. Each of the given ordered pairs is called a *data point*.

EXAMPLE **3**

Music CDs. As more listeners download their music purchases, sales of compact discs are decreasing. According to Nielsen SoundScan, sales of music CDs increased from 500 million in 1997 to 700 million in 2001 and then decreased to 450 million in 2007. As the graph suggests, sales of music CDs can be modeled by a quadratic function.

Years After 1997	Number of Music CDs Sold in the United States (in millions)
0	500
4	700
10	450

Source: Nielsen SoundScan

Sliding sales

a) Let t represent the number of years since 1997 and $S(t)$ the total number of CDs sold, in millions. Use the data points (0, 500), (4, 700), and (10, 450) to find a quadratic function that fits the data.

b) Use the function from part (a) to estimate the sales of music CDs in 2009.

SOLUTION

a) We are looking for a function of the form $S(t) = at^2 + bt + c$ given that $S(0) = 500$, $S(4) = 700$, and $S(10) = 450$. Thus,

$$500 = a \cdot 0^2 + b \cdot 0 + c, \qquad \text{Using the data point (0, 500)}$$
$$700 = a \cdot 4^2 + b \cdot 4 + c, \qquad \text{Using the data point (4, 700)}$$
$$450 = a \cdot 10^2 + b \cdot 10 + c. \qquad \text{Using the data point (10, 450)}$$

After simplifying, we see that we need to solve the system

$$500 = c, \qquad\qquad\qquad (1)$$
$$700 = 16a + 4b + c, \qquad (2)$$
$$450 = 100a + 10b + c. \qquad (3)$$

STUDENT NOTES ———————

Try to keep the "big picture" in mind on problems like Example 3. Solving a system of three equations is but one part of the solution.

TECHNOLOGY CONNECTION

To use a graphing calculator to fit a quadratic function to the data in Example 3, we first select EDIT in the **STAT** menu and enter the given data.

L1	L2	L3 2
0	500	------
4	700	
10	450	

L2(4) =

To fit a quadratic function to the data, we press **STAT** ▷ **5** **VARS** ▷ **1** **1** **ENTER**. The first three keystrokes select QuadReg from the STAT CALC menu. The keystrokes **VARS** ▷ **1** **1** copy the regression equation to the equation-editor screen as y_1.

QuadReg
y=ax²+bx+c
a=−9.166666667
b=86.66666667
c=500

We see that the regression equation is $y = -9.166666667x^2 + 86.66666667x + 500$. We press **Y=** ^ **ENTER** to turn on the PLOT feature and **ZOOM** **9** to see the regression equation graphed with the data points.

To check Example 3(b), we set Indpnt to Ask in the Table Setup and enter $X = 12$ in the table. A Y_1-value of 220 confirms our answer.

1. Use the above approach to estimate the sales of music CDs in 2005.

We know from equation (1) that $c = 500$. Substituting that value into equations (2) and (3), we have

$$700 = 16a + 4b + 500,$$
$$450 = 100a + 10b + 500.$$

Subtracting 500 from both sides of each equation, we have

$$200 = 16a + 4b, \quad \textbf{(4)}$$
$$-50 = 100a + 10b. \quad \textbf{(5)}$$

To solve, we multiply equation (4) by 5 and equation (5) by -2. We then add to eliminate b:

$$1000 = 80a + 20b$$
$$\underline{100 = -200a - 20b}$$
$$1100 = -120a$$

$$-\frac{1100}{120} = a, \quad \text{or} \quad a = -\frac{55}{6}. \qquad \text{Simplifying}$$

Next, we solve for b, using equation (5) above:

$$-50 = 100\left(-\frac{55}{6}\right) + 10b$$

$$-50 = -\frac{2750}{3} + 10b$$

$$\frac{2600}{3} = 10b \qquad \text{Adding } \tfrac{2750}{3} \text{ to both sides and simplifying}$$

$$\frac{2600}{30} = b, \quad \text{or} \quad b = \frac{260}{3}. \qquad \text{Dividing both sides by 10 and simplifying}$$

We can now write $S(t) = at^2 + bt + c$ as

$$S(t) = -\frac{55}{6}t^2 + \frac{260}{3}t + 500.$$

b) To find the sales of CDs in 2009, we evaluate the function. Note that 2009 is 12 yr after 1997. Thus,

$$S(12) = -\frac{55}{6} \cdot 12^2 + \frac{260}{3} \cdot 12 + 500$$
$$= 220.$$

In 2009, an estimated 220 million music CDs will be sold.

TRY EXERCISE 35

9.8 EXERCISE SET

For Extra Help — MyMathLab — Math XL PRACTICE — WATCH — DOWNLOAD

Concept Reinforcement *In each of Exercises 1–6, match the description with the graph that displays that characteristic.*

1. ____ A minimum value of $f(x)$ exists.

2. ____ A maximum value of $f(x)$ exists.

3. ____ No maximum or minimum value of $f(x)$ exists.

4. ____ The data points appear to suggest a linear model for g.

5. ____ The data points appear to suggest that g is a quadratic function with a maximum.

6. ____ The data points appear to suggest that g is a quadratic function with a minimum.

a)

b)

c)

d)

e)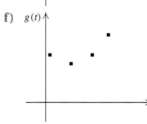

f)

Solve.

7. *Newborn calves.* The number of pounds of milk per day recommended for a calf that is x weeks old can be approximated by $p(x)$, where

$$p(x) = -0.2x^2 + 1.3x + 6.2.$$

When is a calf's milk consumption greatest and how much milk does it consume at that time?
Source: C. Chaloux, University of Vermont, 1998

8. *Stock prices.* The value of a share of I. J. Solar can be represented by $V(x) = x^2 - 6x + 13$, where x is the number of months after January 2009. What is the lowest value $V(x)$ will reach, and when did that occur?

9. *Minimizing cost.* Sweet Harmony Crafts has determined that when x hundred dulcimers are built, the average cost per dulcimer can be estimated by

$$C(x) = 0.1x^2 - 0.7x + 2.425,$$

where $C(x)$ is in hundreds of dollars. What is the minimum average cost per dulcimer and how many dulcimers should be built in order to achieve that minimum?

10. *Maximizing profit.* Recall that total profit P is the difference between total revenue R and total cost C. Given $R(x) = 1000x - x^2$ and $C(x) = 3000 + 20x$, find the total profit, the maximum value of the total profit, and the value of x at which it occurs.

11. *Architecture.* An architect is designing an atrium for a hotel. The atrium is to be rectangular with a perimeter of 720 ft of brass piping. What dimensions will maximize the area of the atrium?

12. *Furniture design.* A furniture builder is designing a rectangular end table with a perimeter of 128 in. What dimensions will yield the maximum area?

13. *Patio design.* A stone mason has enough stones to enclose a rectangular patio with 60 ft of perimeter, assuming that the attached house forms one side of the rectangle. What is the maximum area that the mason can enclose? What should the dimensions of the patio be in order to yield this area?

14. *Garden design.* Ginger is fencing in a rectangular garden, using the side of her house as one side of the rectangle. What is the maximum area that she can enclose with 40 ft of fence? What should the dimensions of the garden be in order to yield this area?

15. *Molding plastics.* Economite Plastics plans to produce a one-compartment vertical file by bending the long side of an 8-in. by 14-in. sheet of plastic along two lines to form a U shape. How tall should the file be in order to maximize the volume that the file can hold?

16. *Composting.* A rectangular compost container is to be formed in a corner of a fenced yard, with 8 ft of chicken wire completing the other two sides of the rectangle. If the chicken wire is 3 ft high, what dimensions of the base will maximize the container's volume?

17. What is the maximum product of two numbers that add to 18? What numbers yield this product?

18. What is the maximum product of two numbers that add to 26? What numbers yield this product?

19. What is the minimum product of two numbers that differ by 8? What are the numbers?

20. What is the minimum product of two numbers that differ by 7? What are the numbers?

Aha! **21.** What is the maximum product of two numbers that add to −10? What numbers yield this product?

22. What is the maximum product of two numbers that add to −12? What numbers yield this product?

Choosing models. *For the scatterplots and graphs in Exercises 23–34, determine which, if any, of the following functions might be used as a model for the data: Linear, with $f(x) = mx + b$; quadratic, with $f(x) = ax^2 + bx + c$, $a > 0$; quadratic, with $f(x) = ax^2 + bx + c$, $a < 0$; neither quadratic nor linear.*

23. **Sonoma Sunshine**

Source: www.city-data.com

24. **Sonoma Precipitation**

Source: www.city-data.com

25. **Safe sight distance to the left**

Source: Institute of Traffic Engineers

26. **Safe sight distance to the right**

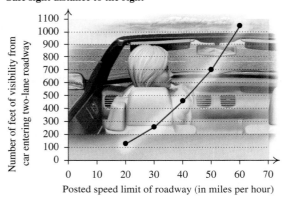

Source: Institute of Traffic Engineers

27. **Winter Olympic volunteers**

28. **U.S. senior population**

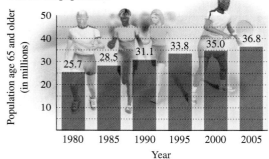

Source: U.S. Bureau of Labor Statistics

29. **Changing work force**

Source: U.S. Department of Labor, Bureau of Labor Statistics

30. **Airline bumping rate**

Source: U.S. Department of Transportation

31. **Hybrid vehicles**

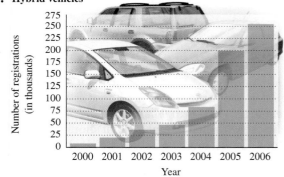

Source: R.L. Polk & Co.

32.

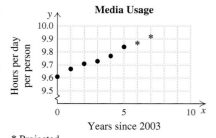

Media Usage

* Projected

Source: Statistical Abstract of the United States

33. **Employee contribution to health insurance premium**

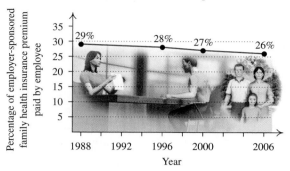

Source: Based on data from Kaiser

34. **Average number of live births per 1000 women, 2005**

Source: U.S. Centers for Disease Control

Find a quadratic function that fits the set of data points.

35. $(1, 4), (-1, -2), (2, 13)$

36. $(1, 4), (-1, 6), (-2, 16)$

37. $(2, 0), (4, 3), (12, -5)$

38. $(-3, -30), (3, 0), (6, 6)$

39. a) Find a quadratic function that fits the following data.

Travel Speed (in kilometers per hour)	Number of Nighttime Accidents (for every 200 million kilometers driven)
60	400
80	250
100	250

b) Use the function to estimate the number of nighttime accidents that occur at 50 km/h.

40. a) Find a quadratic function that fits the following data.

Travel Speed (in kilometers per hour)	Number of Daytime Accidents (for every 200 million kilometers driven)
60	100
80	130
100	200

b) Use the function to estimate the number of daytime accidents that occur at 50 km/h.

41. *Archery.* The Olympic flame tower at the 1992 Summer Olympics was lit at a height of about 27 m by a flaming arrow that was launched about 63 m from the base of the tower. If the arrow landed about 63 m beyond the tower, find a quadratic function that expresses the height h of the arrow as a function of the distance d that it traveled horizontally.

42. *Outsourcing.* The revenue, in billions of dollars, from India's outsourcing industry is shown in the following table.

Year	Outsourcing Revenue (in billions of dollars)
2001	$12
2004	21
2007	48

Source: Nasscom

a) Let t represent the number of years since 2000 and $r(t)$ the revenue, in billions of dollars. Find a quadratic function that fits the data.

b) Use the function to estimate India's outsourcing revenue in 2012.

43. Does every nonlinear function have a minimum or a maximum value? Why or why not?

44. Explain how the leading coefficient of a quadratic function can be used to determine if a maximum or a minimum function value exists.

Skill Review

To prepare for Section 9.9, review solving inequalities and rational expressions and equations (Chapters 4 and 7).

Solve.

45. $2x - 3 > 5$ [7.1]

46. $4 - x \leq 7$ [7.1]

47. $|9 - x| \geq 2$ [7.3]

48. $|4x + 1| < 11$ [7.3]

Subtract. [4.4]

49. $\dfrac{x - 3}{x + 4} - 5$

50. $\dfrac{x}{x - 1} - 1$

Solve. [4.6]

51. $\dfrac{x - 3}{x + 4} = 5$

52. $\dfrac{x}{x - 1} = 1$

53. $\dfrac{x}{(x - 3)(x + 7)} = 0$

54. $\dfrac{(x + 6)(x - 9)}{x + 5} = 0$

Synthesis

The following graphs can be used to compare the baseball statistics of pitcher Roger Clemens with the 31 other pitchers since 1968 who started at least 10 games in at least 15 seasons and pitched at least 3000 innings. Use the graphs to answer questions 55 and 56.

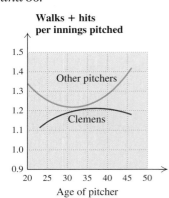

Source: *The New York Times,* February 10, 2008;
Eric Bradlow, Shane Jensen, Justin Wolfers and Adi Wyner

55. The earned run average describes how many runs a pitcher has allowed per game. The lower the earned run average, the better a pitcher. Compare, in terms of maximums or minimums, the earned run average of Roger Clemens with that of other pitchers. Is there any reason to suspect that the aging process was unusual for Clemens? Explain.

56. The statistic "Walks + hits per innings pitched" is related to how often a pitcher allows a batter to reach a base. The lower this statistic, the better. Compare, in terms of maximums or minimums, the "walks + hits" statistic of Roger Clemens with that of other pitchers.

57. *Bridge design.* The cables supporting a straight-line suspension bridge are nearly parabolic in shape. Suppose that a suspension bridge is being designed with concrete supports 160 ft apart and with vertical cables 30 ft above road level at the midpoint of the bridge and 80 ft above road level at a point 50 ft from the midpoint of the bridge. How long are the longest vertical cables?

58. *Trajectory of a launched object.* The height above the ground of a launched object is a quadratic function of the time that it is in the air. Suppose that a flare is launched from a cliff 64 ft above sea level. If 3 sec after being launched the flare is again level with the cliff, and if 2 sec after that it lands in the sea, what is the maximum height that the flare will reach?

59. *Cover charges.* When the owner of Sweet Sounds charges a $10 cover charge, an average of 80 people will attend a show. For each 25¢ increase in admission price, the average number attending decreases by 1. What should the owner charge in order to make the most money?

60. *Crop yield.* An orange grower finds that she gets an average yield of 40 bushels (bu) per tree when she plants 20 trees on an acre of ground. Each time she adds one tree per acre, the yield per tree decreases by 1 bu, due to congestion. How many trees per acre should she plant for maximum yield?

61. *Norman window.* A *Norman window* is a rectangle with a semicircle on top. Big Sky Windows is designing a Norman window that will require 24 ft of trim. What dimensions will allow the maximum amount of light to enter a house?

62. *Minimizing area.* A 36-in. piece of string is cut into two pieces. One piece is used to form a circle while the other is used to form a square. How should the string be cut so that the sum of the areas is a minimum?

Regression can be used to find the "best"-fitting quadratic function when more than three data points are provided. In Exercises 63 and 64, six data points are given, but the approach used in the Technology Connection on p. 619 still applies.

63. *Hybrid vehicles.* The number of hybrid vehicles in the United States during several years is shown in the table below.

Year	Number of Vehicles
2001	19,963
2002	35,934
2003	45,943
2004	83,153
2005	199,148
2006	254,545

Source: R. L. Polk & Co.

a) Use regression to find a quadratic function that can be used to estimate the number of hybrid vehicles $h(x)$ in the United States x years after 2000.

b) Use the function found in part (a) to predict the number of hybrid vehicles in the United States in 2010.

64. *Hydrology.* The drawing below shows the cross section of a river. Typically rivers are deepest in the middle, with the depth decreasing to 0 at the edges. A hydrologist measures the depths D, in feet, of a river at distances x, in feet, from one bank. The results are listed in the table below.

Distance x, from the Left Bank (in feet)	Depth, D, of the River (in feet)
0	0
15	10.2
25	17
50	20
90	7.2
100	0

a) Use regression to find a quadratic function that fits the data.

b) Use the function to estimate the depth of the river 70 ft from the left bank.

COLLABORATIVE CORNER

Parabolic Pizza

Focus: Modeling

Time: 20–30 minutes

Group size: 3

Materials: Graphing calculators are optional.

College Pizza on Chestnut Street in Philadelphia, PA, sells a 10-in.-diameter cheese pizza for $5.00, a 14-in. cheese pizza for $7.50, and an 18-in. cheese pizza for $11.00. Which models better the price of the pizza: a linear function or a quadratic function of the diameter?

Source: Campusfood.com

ACTIVITY

1. As a group, carefully graph the ordered pairs from the data above in the form (diameter, price). Do the data appear to be quadratic or linear?

2. Each group member should choose one of the following to fit a model to the data, where $p(x)$ is the price, in dollars, of an x-inch-diameter pizza. Then, using a different color for each graph, that member should graph the function on the same graph as the ordered pairs.

   a) Linear function $p(x) = mx + b$, using the points (10, 5) and (14, 7.5)
   b) Linear function $p(x) = mx + b$, using the points (10, 5) and (18, 11)
   c) Quadratic function $p(x) = ax^2 + bx + c$, using all three points

3. As a group, determine which function from part (1) appears to be the best fit.

4. One way to tell whether a function is a good fit is to see how well it predicts another known value. College Pizza also sells a 16-in. cheese pizza for $9.00. Each group member should use the function from part (2) to predict the price of a 16-in. cheese pizza. Which function came the closest to predicting the actual value?

5. If a graphing calculator is available, use the LINREG and QUADREG options to fit and graph linear and quadratic functions for the four data points (three pairs from part (1) and one pair from part (4)). Which function appears to give the best fit?

6. Because the area of a circle is given by $A = \pi r^2$, would you expect the price of a cheese pizza to be quadratic or linear?

9.9 Polynomial and Rational Inequalities

Quadratic and Other Polynomial Inequalities • Rational Inequalities

Quadratic and Other Polynomial Inequalities

Inequalities like the following are called *polynomial inequalities*:

$$x^3 - 5x > x^2 + 7, \qquad 4x - 3 < 9, \qquad 5x^2 - 3x + 2 \geq 0.$$

Second-degree polynomial inequalities in one variable are called *quadratic inequalities*. To solve polynomial inequalities, we often focus attention on where the outputs of a polynomial function are positive and where they are negative.

EXAMPLE 1 Solve: $x^2 + 3x - 10 > 0$.

SOLUTION Consider the "related" function $f(x) = x^2 + 3x - 10$. We are looking for those x-values for which $f(x) > 0$. Graphically, function values are positive when the graph is above the x-axis.

The graph of f opens upward since the leading coefficient is positive. Thus y-values are positive *outside* the interval formed by the x-intercepts. To find the intercepts, we set the polynomial equal to 0 and solve:

$$x^2 + 3x - 10 = 0$$
$$(x + 5)(x - 2) = 0$$
$$x + 5 = 0 \quad or \quad x - 2 = 0$$
$$x = -5 \quad or \quad x = 2. \qquad \text{The } x\text{-intercepts are } (-5, 0) \text{ and } (2, 0).$$

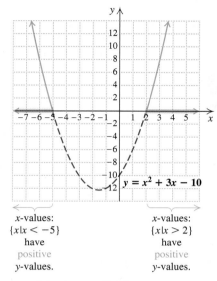

Thus the solution set of the inequality is

$$(-\infty, -5) \cup (2, \infty), \text{ or } \{x | x < -5 \, or \, x > 2\}.$$

TRY EXERCISE 13

Any inequality with 0 on one side can be solved by considering a graph of the related function and finding intercepts as in Example 1. Sometimes the quadratic formula is needed to find the intercepts.

EXAMPLE 2

Solve: $x^2 - 2x \leq 2$.

SOLUTION We first write the quadratic inequality in standard form, with 0 on one side:

$$x^2 - 2x - 2 \leq 0. \qquad \text{This is equivalent to the original inequality.}$$

The graph of $f(x) = x^2 - 2x - 2$ is a parabola opening upward. Values of $f(x)$ are negative for x-values between the x-intercepts. We find the x-intercepts by solving $f(x) = 0$:

$$x = \frac{-b \pm \sqrt{b^2 - 4ac}}{2a}$$
$$= \frac{-(-2) \pm \sqrt{(-2)^2 - 4 \cdot 1 (-2)}}{2 \cdot 1}$$
$$= \frac{2 \pm \sqrt{12}}{2} = \frac{2}{2} \pm \frac{2\sqrt{3}}{2} = 1 \pm \sqrt{3}.$$

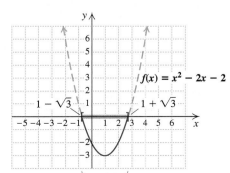

At the x-intercepts, $1 - \sqrt{3}$ and $1 + \sqrt{3}$, the value of $f(x)$ is 0. Since the inequality symbol is $\leq$, the solution set will include all values of x for which $f(x)$ is negative *or* $f(x)$ is 0. Thus the solution set of the inequality is

$$[1 - \sqrt{3}, 1 + \sqrt{3}], \quad \text{or} \quad \{x \mid 1 - \sqrt{3} \leq x \leq 1 + \sqrt{3}\}.$$

> **TRY EXERCISE** 21

In Example 2, it was not essential to draw the graph. The important information came from finding the x-intercepts and the sign of $f(x)$ on each side of those intercepts. We now solve a third-degree polynomial inequality, without graphing, by locating the x-intercepts, or **zeros**, of f and then using *test points* to determine the sign of $f(x)$ over each interval of the x-axis.

EXAMPLE 3

For $f(x) = 5x^3 + 10x^2 - 15x$, find all x-values for which $f(x) > 0$.

SOLUTION We first solve the related equation:

$$f(x) = 0$$
$$5x^3 + 10x^2 - 15x = 0 \quad \text{Substituting}$$
$$5x(x^2 + 2x - 3) = 0$$
$$5x(x + 3)(x - 1) = 0$$
$$5x = 0 \quad or \quad x + 3 = 0 \quad or \quad x - 1 = 0$$
$$x = 0 \quad or \quad x = -3 \quad or \quad x = 1.$$

The zeros of f are $-3, 0$, and 1. These zeros divide the number line, or x-axis, into four intervals: A, B, C, and D.

Next, selecting one convenient test value from each interval, we determine the sign of $f(x)$ for that interval. We know that, within each interval, the sign of $f(x)$ cannot change. If it did, there would need to be another zero in that interval. Using the factored form of $f(x)$ eases the computations:

$$f(x) = 5x(x + 3)(x - 1).$$

For interval A,

$$f(-4) = \underbrace{5(-4)}\underbrace{((-4) + 3)}\underbrace{((-4) - 1)}$$

-4 is a convenient value in interval A.

$$\underbrace{\text{Negative} \cdot \text{Negative} \cdot \text{Negative}}$$
$$\text{Negative}$$

Only the sign is important. The product of three negative numbers is negative, so $f(-4)$ is negative.

For interval B,

$$f(-1) = \underbrace{5(-1)}\underbrace{((-1) + 3)}\underbrace{((-1) - 1)}$$

-1 is a convenient value in interval B.

$$\underbrace{\text{Negative} \cdot \text{Positive} \cdot \text{Negative}}$$
$$\text{Positive}$$

$f(-1)$ is positive.

STUDENT NOTES ————

When we are evaluating test values, there is often no need to do lengthy computations since all we need to determine is the sign of the result.

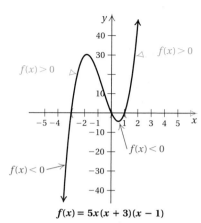

$f(x) = 5x(x + 3)(x - 1)$

A visualization of Example 3

For interval C,

$$f\left(\tfrac{1}{2}\right) = \underbrace{5 \cdot \tfrac{1}{2}} \cdot \underbrace{\left(\tfrac{1}{2} + 3\right)} \cdot \underbrace{\left(\tfrac{1}{2} - 1\right)}. \qquad \tfrac{1}{2} \text{ is a convenient value in interval C.}$$

$$\underbrace{\text{Positive} \cdot \text{Positive} \cdot \text{Negative}}$$

$$\text{Negative} \qquad f\left(\tfrac{1}{2}\right) \text{ is negative.}$$

For interval D,

$$f(2) = \underbrace{5 \cdot 2} \cdot \underbrace{(2 + 3)} \cdot \underbrace{(2 - 1)}. \qquad 2 \text{ is a convenient value in interval D.}$$

$$\underbrace{\text{Positive} \cdot \text{Positive} \cdot \text{Positive}} \qquad f(2) \text{ is positive.}$$

Recall that we are looking for all x for which $5x^3 + 10x^2 - 15x > 0$. The calculations above indicate that $f(x)$ is positive for any number in intervals B and D. The solution set of the original inequality is

$$(-3, 0) \cup (1, \infty), \quad \text{or} \quad \{x \mid -3 < x < 0 \, or \, x > 1\}.$$

The calculations in Example 3 were made simpler by using a factored form of the polynomial and by focusing on only the *sign* of $f(x)$. By looking at how many positive or negative factors are multiplied, we are able to determine the sign of the polynomial function.

To Solve a Polynomial Inequality Using Factors

1. Add or subtract to get 0 on one side and solve the related polynomial equation by factoring.
2. Use the numbers found in step (1) to divide the number line into intervals.
3. Using a test value from each interval, determine the sign of the function over each interval. First find the sign of each factor, and then determine the sign of the product of the factors. Remember that the product of an odd number of negative numbers is negative.
4. Select the interval(s) for which the inequality is satisfied and write interval notation or set-builder notation for the solution set. Include endpoints of intervals when $\leq$ or $\geq$ is used.

EXAMPLE 4

For $f(x) = 4x^3 - 4x$, find all x-values for which $f(x) \leq 0$.

SOLUTION   We first solve the related equation:

Solve $f(x) = 0$.

$$f(x) = 0$$
$$4x^3 - 4x = 0$$
$$4x(x^2 - 1) = 0$$
$$4x(x + 1)(x - 1) = 0$$
$$4x = 0 \quad or \quad x + 1 = 0 \quad or \quad x - 1 = 0$$
$$x = 0 \quad or \quad x = -1 \quad or \quad x = 1.$$

Divide the number line into intervals.

The function f has zeros at $-1, 0$, and 1, so we divide the number line into four intervals:

The product $4x(x + 1)(x - 1)$ is positive or negative, depending on the signs of $4x$, $x + 1$, and $x - 1$. This can be determined by making a chart.

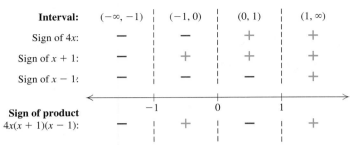

Determine the sign of the function over each interval.

A product is negative when it has an odd number of negative factors. Since the $\leq$ sign allows for equality, the endpoints -1, 0, and 1 are solutions. From the chart, we see that the solution set is

Select the interval(s) for which the inequality is satisfied.

$$(-\infty, -1] \cup [0, 1], \quad \text{or} \quad \{x \mid x \leq -1 \text{ or } 0 \leq x \leq 1\}.$$

TRY EXERCISE 31

TECHNOLOGY CONNECTION

To solve $2.3x^2 \leq 9.11 - 2.94x$, we write the inequality in the form $2.3x^2 + 2.94x - 9.11 \leq 0$ and graph the function $f(x) = 2.3x^2 + 2.94x - 9.11$.

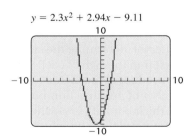

$y = 2.3x^2 + 2.94x - 9.11$

The region in which the graph lies *on or below* the x-axis begins somewhere between -3 and -2, and

continues to somewhere between 1 and 2. Using the ZERO option of CALC and rounding, we find that the endpoints are -2.73 and 1.45. The solution set is approximately $\{x \mid -2.73 \leq x \leq 1.45\}$.

Had the inequality been $2.3x^2 > 9.11 - 2.94x$, we would look for portions of the graph that lie *above* the x-axis. An approximate solution set of this inequality is $\{x \mid x < -2.73 \text{ or } x > 1.45\}$.

Use a graphing calculator to solve each inequality. Round the values of the endpoints to the nearest hundredth.

1. $4.32x^2 - 3.54x - 5.34 \leq 0$
2. $7.34x^2 - 16.55x - 3.89 \geq 0$
3. $10.85x^2 + 4.28x + 4.44$
   $> 7.91x^2 + 7.43x + 13.03$
4. $5.79x^3 - 5.68x^2 + 10.68x$
   $> 2.11x^3 + 16.90x - 11.69$

Rational Inequalities

Inequalities involving rational expressions are called **rational inequalities**. Like polynomial inequalities, rational inequalities can be solved using test values. Unlike polynomials, however, rational expressions often have values for which the expression is undefined. These values must be used when dividing the number line into intervals.

EXAMPLE 5   Solve: $\dfrac{x - 3}{x + 4} \geq 2$.

SOLUTION   We write the related equation by changing the $\geq$ symbol to $=$:

$$\frac{x - 3}{x + 4} = 2. \qquad \text{Note that } x \neq -4.$$

Next, we solve this related equation:

$$(x + 4) \cdot \frac{x - 3}{x + 4} = (x + 4) \cdot 2 \qquad \text{Multiplying both sides by the LCD, } x + 4$$

$$x - 3 = 2x + 8$$

$$-11 = x. \qquad \text{Solving for } x$$

Since -11 is a solution of the related equation, we use -11 when dividing the number line into intervals. Since the rational expression is undefined for $x = -4$, we also use -4:

We test a number from each interval to see where the original inequality is satisfied:

$$\frac{x - 3}{x + 4} \geq 2.$$

For Interval A,

$$\text{Test } -15, \quad \frac{-15 - 3}{-15 + 4} = \frac{-18}{-11}$$

$$= \frac{18}{11} \not\geq 2. \qquad -15 \text{ } is \text{ } not \text{ a solution, so interval A is not part of the solution set.}$$

For Interval B,

$$\text{Test } -8, \quad \frac{-8 - 3}{-8 + 4} = \frac{-11}{-4}$$

$$= \frac{11}{4} \geq 2. \qquad -8 \text{ } is \text{ a solution, so interval B is part of the solution set.}$$

For Interval C,

$$\text{Test } 1, \quad \frac{1 - 3}{1 + 4} = \frac{-2}{5}$$

$$= -\frac{2}{5} \not\geq 2. \qquad 1 \text{ } is \text{ } not \text{ a solution, so interval C is not part of the solution set.}$$

The solution set includes interval B. The endpoint -11 is included because the inequality symbol is $\geq$ and -11 is a solution of the related equation. The number -4 is *not* included because $(x - 3)/(x + 4)$ is undefined for $x = -4$. Thus the solution set of the original inequality is

$$[-11, -4), \quad \text{or} \quad \{x \mid -11 \leq x < -4\}.$$

TRY EXERCISE ▶ 37

ALGEBRAIC–GRAPHICAL CONNECTION

To compare the algebraic solution of Example 5 with a graphical solution, we graph $f(x) = (x - 3)/(x + 4)$ and the line $y = 2$. The solutions of $(x - 3)/(x + 4) \geq 2$ are found by locating all x-values for which $f(x) \geq 2$.

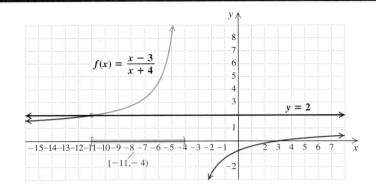

To Solve a Rational Inequality

1. Find any replacements for which any rational expression is undefined.
2. Change the inequality symbol to an equals sign and solve the related equation.
3. Use the numbers found in steps (1) and (2) to divide the number line into intervals.
4. Substitute a test value from each interval into the inequality. If the number is a solution, then the interval to which it belongs is part of the solution set.
5. Select the interval(s) and any endpoints for which the inequality is satisfied and use interval notation or set-builder notation for the solution set. If the inequality symbol is $\leq$ or $\geq$, then the solutions from step (2) are also included in the solution set. All numbers found in step (1) must be excluded from the solution set, even if they are solutions from step (2).

9.9　EXERCISE SET

For Extra Help　MyMathLab　　　　

Concept Reinforcement　*Classify each statement as either true or false.*

1. The solution of $(x - 3)(x + 2) \leq 0$ is $[-2, 3]$.

2. The solution of $(x + 5)(x - 4) \geq 0$ is $[-5, 4]$.

3. The solution of $(x - 1)(x - 6) > 0$ is $\{x | x < 1 \ or \ x > 6\}$.

4. The solution of $(x + 4)(x + 2) < 0$ is $(-4, -2)$.

5. To solve $\dfrac{x + 2}{x - 3} < 0$ using intervals, we divide the number line into the intervals $(-\infty, -2)$ and $(-2, \infty)$.

6. To solve $\dfrac{x - 5}{x + 4} \geq 0$ using intervals, we divide the number line into the intervals $(-\infty, -4), (-4, 5)$, and $(5, \infty)$.

Solve each inequality using the graph provided.

7. $p(x) \leq 0$

8. $p(x) < 0$

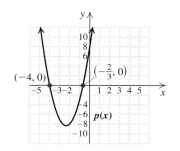

9. $x^4 + 12x > 3x^3 + 4x^2$

10. $x^4 + x^3 \geq 6x^2$

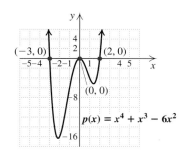

11. $\dfrac{x - 1}{x + 2} < 3$

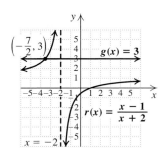

12. $\dfrac{2x - 1}{x - 5} \geq 1$

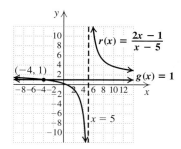

Solve.

13. $(x - 6)(x - 5) < 0$

14. $(x + 8)(x + 10) > 0$

15. $(x + 7)(x - 2) \geq 0$

16. $(x - 1)(x + 4) \leq 0$

17. $x^2 - x - 2 > 0$

18. $x^2 + x - 2 < 0$

Aha! **19.** $x^2 + 4x + 4 < 0$

20. $x^2 + 6x + 9 < 0$

21. $x^2 - 4x \leq 3$

22. $x^2 + 6x \geq 2$

23. $3x(x + 2)(x - 2) < 0$

24. $5x(x + 1)(x - 1) > 0$

25. $(x - 1)(x + 2)(x - 4) \geq 0$

26. $(x + 3)(x + 2)(x - 1) < 0$

27. For $f(x) = 7 - x^2$, find all x-values for which $f(x) \geq 3$.

28. For $f(x) = 14 - x^2$, find all x-values for which $f(x) > 5$.

29. For $g(x) = (x - 2)(x - 3)(x + 1)$, find all x-values for which $g(x) > 0$.

30. For $g(x) = (x + 3)(x - 2)(x + 1)$, find all x-values for which $g(x) < 0$.

31. For $F(x) = x^3 - 7x^2 + 10x$, find all x-values for which $F(x) \leq 0$.

32. For $G(x) = x^3 - 8x^2 + 12x$, find all x-values for which $G(x) \geq 0$.

Solve.

33. $\dfrac{1}{x - 5} < 0$

34. $\dfrac{1}{x + 4} > 0$

35. $\dfrac{x + 1}{x - 3} \geq 0$

36. $\dfrac{x - 2}{x + 4} \leq 0$

37. $\dfrac{x + 1}{x + 6} \geq 1$

38. $\dfrac{x - 1}{x - 2} \leq 1$

39. $\dfrac{(x - 2)(x + 1)}{x - 5} \leq 0$

40. $\dfrac{(x + 4)(x - 1)}{x + 3} \geq 0$

41. $\dfrac{x}{x + 3} \geq 0$

42. $\dfrac{x - 2}{x} \leq 0$

43. $\dfrac{x - 5}{x} < 1$

44. $\dfrac{x}{x - 1} > 2$

45. $\dfrac{x - 1}{(x - 3)(x + 4)} \leq 0$

46. $\dfrac{x + 2}{(x - 2)(x + 7)} \geq 0$

47. For $f(x) = \dfrac{5 - 2x}{4x + 3}$, find all x-values for which $f(x) \geq 0$.

48. For $g(x) = \dfrac{2 + 3x}{2x - 4}$, find all x-values for which $g(x) \geq 0$.

49. For $G(x) = \dfrac{1}{x - 2}$, find all x-values for which $G(x) \leq 1$.

50. For $F(x) = \dfrac{1}{x - 3}$, find all x-values for which $F(x) \leq 2$.

51. Explain how any quadratic inequality can be solved by examining a parabola.

52. Describe a method for creating a quadratic inequality for which there is no solution.

Skill Review

Review function notation from Chapter 5.

Graph each function. [5.3]

53. $f(x) = x^3 - 2$

54. $g(x) = \dfrac{2}{x}$

55. If $f(x) = x + 7$, find $f\left(\dfrac{1}{a^2}\right)$. [5.1]

56. If $g(x) = x^2 - 3$, find $g(\sqrt{a - 5})$. [5.1], [8.1]

57. If $g(x) = x^2 + 2$, find $g(2a + 5)$. [5.1]

58. If $f(x) = \sqrt{4x + 1}$, find $g(3a - 5)$. [5.1]

Synthesis

59. Step (5) on p. 632 states that even when the inequality symbol is $\leq$ or $\geq$, the solutions from step (2) may not be part of the solution set. Why?

60. Describe a method that could be used to create a quadratic inequality that has $(-\infty, a] \cup [b, \infty)$ as the solution set. Assume $a < b$.

Find each solution set.

61. $x^2 + 2x < 5$

62. $x^4 + 2x^2 \geq 0$

63. $x^4 + 3x^2 \leq 0$

64. $\left|\dfrac{x + 2}{x - 1}\right| \leq 3$

65. *Total profit.* Derex, Inc., determines that its total-profit function is given by

$$P(x) = -3x^2 + 630x - 6000.$$

a) Find all values of x for which Derex makes a profit.

b) Find all values of x for which Derex loses money.

66. *Height of a thrown object.* The function

$$S(t) = -16t^2 + 32t + 1920$$

gives the height S, in feet, of an object thrown from a cliff that is 1920 ft high. Here t is the time, in seconds, that the object is in the air.

a) For what times does the height exceed 1920 ft?

b) For what times is the height less than 640 ft?

67. *Number of handshakes.* There are n people in a room. The number N of possible handshakes by the people is given by the function

$$N(n) = \dfrac{n(n - 1)}{2}.$$

For what number of people n is $66 \leq N \leq 300$?

68. *Number of diagonals.* A polygon with n sides has D diagonals, where D is given by the function

$$D(n) = \dfrac{n(n - 3)}{2}.$$

Find the number of sides n if

$$27 \leq D \leq 230.$$

Use a graphing calculator to graph each function and find solutions of $f(x) = 0$. Then solve the inequalities $f(x) < 0$ and $f(x) > 0$.

69. $f(x) = x^3 - 2x^2 - 5x + 6$

70. $f(x) = \dfrac{1}{3}x^3 - x + \dfrac{2}{3}$

71. $f(x) = x + \dfrac{1}{x}$

72. $f(x) = x - \sqrt{x}, x \geq 0$

73. $f(x) = \dfrac{x^3 - x^2 - 2x}{x^2 + x - 6}$

74. $f(x) = x^4 - 4x^3 - x^2 + 16x - 12$

Find the domain of each function

75. $f(x) = \sqrt{x^2 - 4x - 45}$

76. $f(x) = \sqrt{9 - x^2}$

77. $f(x) = \sqrt{x^2 + 8x}$

78. $f(x) = \sqrt{x^2 + 2x + 1}$

79. Describe a method that could be used to create a rational inequality that has $(-\infty, a] \cup (b, \infty)$ as the solution set. Assume $a < b$.

80. Use a graphing calculator to solve Exercises 43 and 49 by drawing two curves, one for each side of the inequality.

Study Summary

KEY TERMS AND CONCEPTS	EXAMPLES
SECTION 9.1: QUADRATIC EQUATIONS	
A **quadratic equation in standard form** is written $ax^2 + bx + c = 0$, with $a, b,$ and c constant and $a \neq 0$. Some quadratic equations can be solved by factoring.	$x^2 - 3x - 10 = 0$ $(x + 2)(x - 5) = 0$ $x + 2 = 0 \quad or \quad x - 5 = 0$ $x = -2 \quad or \quad x = 5$
The Principle of Square Roots For any real number k, if $X^2 = k$, then $X = \sqrt{k} \quad or \quad X = -\sqrt{k}.$	$x^2 - 8x + 16 = 25$ $(x - 4)^2 = 25$ $x - 4 = -5 \quad or \quad x - 4 = 5$ $x = -1 \quad or \quad x = 9$
Any quadratic equation can be solved by **completing the square**.	$x^2 + 6x = 1$ $x^2 + 6x + \left(\frac{6}{2}\right)^2 = 1 + \left(\frac{6}{2}\right)^2$ $x^2 + 6x + 9 = 1 + 9$ $(x + 3)^2 = 10$ $x + 3 = \pm\sqrt{10}$ $x = -3 \pm \sqrt{10}$

SECTION 9.2: THE QUADRATIC FORMULA

The Quadratic Formula
The solutions of $ax^2 + bx + c = 0$ are given by
$$x = \frac{-b \pm \sqrt{b^2 - 4ac}}{2a}.$$

$3x^2 - 2x - 5 = 0 \qquad a = 3, b = -2, c = -5$
$$x = \frac{-(-2) \pm \sqrt{(-2)^2 - 4 \cdot 3(-5)}}{2 \cdot 3}$$
$$x = \frac{2 \pm \sqrt{4 + 60}}{6}$$
$$x = \frac{2 \pm \sqrt{64}}{6}$$
$$x = \frac{2 \pm 8}{6}$$
$$x = \frac{10}{6} = \frac{5}{3} \quad or \quad x = \frac{-6}{6} = -1$$

SECTION 9.3: STUDYING SOLUTIONS OF QUADRATIC EQUATIONS

The **discriminant** of the quadratic formula is $b^2 - 4ac$.

$b^2 - 4ac = 0 \rightarrow$ One solution; a rational number

For $4x^2 - 12x + 9 = 0$, $b^2 - 4ac = (-12)^2 - 4(4)(9)$
$$= 144 - 144 = 0. \qquad \text{The discriminant is zero.}$$
Thus, $4x^2 - 12x + 9 = 0$ has one rational solution.

$b^2 - 4ac > 0 \rightarrow$ Two real solutions; both are rational if $b^2 - 4ac$ is a perfect square.

For $x^2 + 6x - 2 = 0$, $b^2 - 4ac = (6)^2 - 4(1)(-2)$
$$= 36 + 8 = 44. \qquad \text{The discriminant is not a perfect square.}$$
Thus, $x^2 + 6x - 2 = 0$ has two irrational real-number solutions.

$b^2 - 4ac < 0 \rightarrow$ Two imaginary-number solutions

For $2x^2 - 3x + 5 = 0$, $b^2 - 4ac = (-3)^2 - 4(2)(5)$
$$= 9 - 40 = -31. \qquad \text{The discriminant is negative.}$$
Thus, $2x^2 - 3x + 5 = 0$ has two imaginary-number solutions.

SECTION 9.4: APPLICATIONS INVOLVING QUADRATIC EQUATIONS

To solve a formula for a letter, use the same principles used to solve equations.

Solve $y = pn^2 + dn$ for n.
$pn^2 + dn - y = 0$ Writing standard form of a quadratic equation
$$n = \frac{-d \pm \sqrt{d^2 - 4p(-y)}}{2 \cdot p}$$ Using the quadratic formula; $a = p, b = d, c = -y$
$$n = \frac{-d \pm \sqrt{d^2 + 4py}}{2p}$$

SECTION 9.5: EQUATIONS REDUCIBLE TO QUADRATIC

Equations that are **reducible to quadratic** or in **quadratic form** can be solved by making an appropriate substitution.

$x^4 - 10x^2 + 9 = 0$ Let $u = x^2$. Then $u^2 = x^4$.
$u^2 - 10u + 9 = 0$ Substituting
$(u - 9)(u - 1) = 0$
$u - 9 = 0 \quad or \quad u - 1 = 0$
$\quad u = 9 \quad or \qquad u = 1$ Solving for u
$\quad x^2 = 9 \quad or \qquad x^2 = 1$
$\quad x = \pm 3 \quad or \qquad x = \pm 1$ Solving for x

SECTION 9.6: QUADRATIC FUNCTIONS AND THEIR GRAPHS
SECTION 9.7: MORE ABOUT GRAPHING QUADRATIC FUNCTIONS

The graph of a quadratic function

$$f(x) = ax^2 + bx + c = a(x - h)^2 + k$$

is a **parabola**. The graph opens upward for $a > 0$ and downward for $a < 0$.

The **vertex** is (h, k) and the **axis of symmetry** is $x = h$.

If $a > 0$, the function has a **minimum** value of k, and if $a < 0$, the function has a **maximum** value of k.

The vertex and the axis of symmetry

occur at $x = -\dfrac{b}{2a}$.

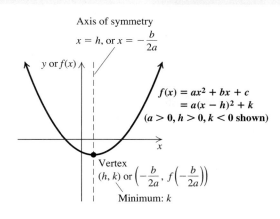

SECTION 9.8: PROBLEM SOLVING AND QUADRATIC FUNCTIONS

Some problem situations can be **modeled** using quadratic functions. For those problems, a quantity can often be **maximized** or **minimized** by finding the coordinates of a vertex.

A lifeguard has 100 m of roped-together flotation devices with which to cordon off a rectangular swimming area at North Beach. If the shoreline forms one side of the rectangle, what dimensions will maximize the size of the area for swimming?

This problem and its solution appear as Example 2 on pp. 617–618.

SECTION 9.9: POLYNOMIAL AND RATIONAL INEQUALITIES

The x-intercepts, or **zeros**, of a function are used to divide the x-axis into intervals when solving a **polynomial inequality**. (See p. 629.)

Solve: $x^2 - 2x - 15 > 0$.

$$x^2 - 2x - 15 = 0 \qquad \text{Solving the related equation}$$
$$(x - 5)(x + 3) = 0$$
$$x = 5 \quad or \quad x = -3 \qquad \text{-3 and 5 divide the number line into three intervals.}$$

The solutions of a rational equation and any replacements that make a denominator zero are both used to divide the x-axis into intervals when solving a **rational inequality**. (See p. 632.)

Since $f(x) = x^2 - 2x - 15 = (x - 5)(x + 3)$,

$\quad f(x)$ is positive for $x < -3$;
$\quad f(x)$ is negative for $-3 < x < 5$;
$\quad f(x)$ is positive for $x > 5$.

Thus, $x^2 - 2x - 15 > 0$ for $(-\infty, -3) \cup (5, \infty)$, or $\{x \mid x < -3 \ or \ x > 5\}$.

Review Exercises: Chapter 9

Concept Reinforcement *Classify each statement as either true or false.*

1. Every quadratic equation has two different solutions. [9.3]

2. Every quadratic equation has at least one solution. [9.3]

3. If an equation cannot be solved by completing the square, it cannot be solved by the quadratic formula. [9.2]

4. A negative discriminant indicates two imaginary-number solutions of a quadratic equation. [9.3]

5. The graph of $f(x) = 2(x + 3)^2 - 4$ has its vertex at $(3, -4)$. [9.6]

6. The graph of $g(x) = 5x^2$ has $x = 0$ as its axis of symmetry. [9.6]

7. The graph of $f(x) = -2x^2 + 1$ has no minimum value. [9.6]

8. The zeros of $g(x) = x^2 - 9$ are -3 and 3. [9.6]

9. If a quadratic function has two different imaginary-number zeros, the graph of the function has two x-intercepts. [9.7]

10. To solve a polynomial inequality, we often must solve a polynomial equation. [9.9]

Solve.

11. $9x^2 - 2 = 0$ [9.1]

12. $8x^2 + 6x = 0$ [9.1]

13. $x^2 - 12x + 36 = 9$ [9.1]

14. $x^2 - 4x + 8 = 0$ [9.2]

15. $x(3x + 4) = 4x(x - 1) + 15$ [9.2]

16. $x^2 + 9x = 1$ [9.2]

17. $x^2 - 5x - 2 = 0$. Use a calculator to approximate, to three decimal places, the solutions with rational numbers. [9.2]

18. Let $f(x) = 4x^2 - 3x - 1$. Find x such that $f(x) = 0$. [9.2]

Replace the blanks with constants to form a true equation. [9.1]

19. $x^2 - 18x + \underline{\quad} = (x - \underline{\quad})^2$

20. $x^2 + \frac{3}{5}x + \underline{\quad} = \left(x + \underline{\quad}\right)^2$

21. Solve by completing the square. Show your work.
$$x^2 - 6x + 1 = 0 \quad [9.1]$$

22. \$2500 grows to \$2704 in 2 yr. Use the formula $A = P(1 + r)^t$ to find the interest rate. [9.1]

23. The U.S. Bank Tower in Los Angeles, California, is 1018 ft tall. Use $s = 16t^2$ to approximate how long it would take an object to fall from the top. [9.1]

For each equation, determine whether the solutions are real or imaginary. If they are real, specify whether they are rational or irrational. [9.3]

24. $x^2 + 3x - 6 = 0$

25. $x^2 + 2x + 5 = 0$

26. Write a quadratic equation having the solutions $3i$ and $-3i$. [9.3]

27. Write a quadratic equation having -5 as its only solution. [9.3]

Solve. [9.4]

28. Horizons has a manufacturing plant located 300 mi from company headquarters. Their corporate pilot must fly from headquarters to the plant and back in 4 hr. If there is a 20-mph headwind going and a 20-mph tailwind returning, how fast must the plane be able to travel in still air?

29. Working together, Dani and Cheri can reply to a day's worth of customer-service e-mails in 4 hr. Working alone, Dani takes 6 hr longer than Cheri. How long would it take Cheri to reply to the e-mails alone?

30. Find all x-intercepts of the graph of $f(x) = x^4 - 13x^2 + 36$. [9.5]

Solve. [9.5]

31. $15x^{-2} - 2x^{-1} - 1 = 0$

32. $(x^2 - 4)^2 - (x^2 - 4) - 6 = 0$

33. a) Graph: $f(x) = -3(x + 2)^2 + 4$. [9.6]
    b) Label the vertex.
    c) Draw the axis of symmetry.
    d) Find the maximum or the minimum value.

34. For the function given by $f(x) = 2x^2 - 12x + 23$: [9.7]
    a) find the vertex and the axis of symmetry;
    b) graph the function.

35. Find any x-intercepts and the y-intercept of the graph of
$$f(x) = x^2 - 9x + 14. \quad [9.7]$$

36. Solve $N = 3\pi\sqrt{\dfrac{1}{p}}$ for p. [9.4]

37. Solve $2A + T = 3T^2$ for T. [9.4]

State whether each graph appears to represent a quadratic function or a linear function. [9.8]

38. Increase in health insurance premiums

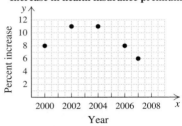

Source: Kaiser/HRET

39. Health benefits in small firms

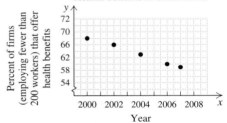

Source: Kaiser/HRET

40. Eastgate Consignments wants to build a rectangular area in a corner for children to play in while their parents shop. They have 30 ft of low fencing. What is the maximum area they can enclose? What dimensions will yield this area? [9.8]

41. The following table lists the percent increase in health insurance premiums x years after 2000. (See Exercise 38.) [9.8]

Years Since 2000	Percent Increase in Health Insurance Premiums
0	8
2	11
6	8

  a) Find the quadratic function that fits the data.
  b) Use the function to estimate the percent increase in health insurance premiums in 2005.

Solve. [9.9]

42. $x^3 - 3x > 2x^2$

43. $\dfrac{x - 5}{x + 3} \le 0$

Synthesis

44. Explain how the x-intercepts of a quadratic function can be used to help find the maximum or minimum value of the function. [9.7], [9.8]

45. Suppose that the quadratic formula is used to solve a quadratic equation. If the discriminant is a perfect square, could factoring have been used to solve the equation? Why or why not? [9.2], [9.3]

46. What is the greatest number of solutions that an equation of the form $ax^4 + bx^2 + c = 0$ can have? Why? [9.5]

47. Discuss two ways in which completing the square was used in this chapter. [9.1], [9.2], [9.7]

48. A quadratic function has x-intercepts at -3 and 5. If the y-intercept is at -7, find an equation for the function. [9.7]

49. Find h and k if, for $3x^2 - hx + 4k = 0$, the sum of the solutions is 20 and the product of the solutions is 80. [9.3]

50. The average of two positive integers is 171. One of the numbers is the square root of the other. Find the integers. [9.5]

Test: Chapter 9

Solve.

1. $25x^2 - 7 = 0$

2. $4x(x - 2) - 3x(x + 1) = -18$

3. $x^2 + 2x + 3 = 0$

4. $2x + 5 = x^2$

5. $x^{-2} - x^{-1} = \frac{3}{4}$

6. $x^2 + 3x = 5$. Use a calculator to approximate, to three decimal places, the solutions with rational numbers.

7. Let $f(x) = 12x^2 - 19x - 21$. Find x such that $f(x) = 0$.

Replace the blanks with constants to form a true equation.

8. $x^2 - 20x + \underline{\quad} = (x - \underline{\quad})^2$

9. $x^2 + \frac{2}{7}x + \underline{\quad} = (x + \underline{\quad})^2$

10. Solve by completing the square. Show your work.
$$x^2 + 10x + 15 = 0$$

11. Determine the type of number that the solutions of $x^2 + 2x + 5 = 0$ will be.

12. Write a quadratic equation having solutions $\sqrt{11}$ and $-\sqrt{11}$.

Solve.

13. The Connecticut River flows at a rate of 4 km/h for the length of a popular scenic route. In order for a cruiser to travel 60 km upriver and then return in a total of 8 hr, how fast must the boat be able to travel in still water?

14. Dal and Kim can assemble a swing set in $1\frac{1}{2}$ hr. Working alone, it takes Kim 4 hr longer than Dal to assemble the swing set. How long would it take Dal, working alone, to assemble the swing set?

15. Find all x-intercepts of the graph of
$$f(x) = x^4 - 15x^2 - 16.$$

16. a) Graph: $f(x) = 4(x - 3)^2 + 5$.
   b) Label the vertex.
   c) Draw the axis of symmetry.
   d) Find the maximum or the minimum function value.

17. For the function $f(x) = 2x^2 + 4x - 6$:
   a) find the vertex and the axis of symmetry;
   b) graph the function.

18. Find the x- and y-intercepts of
$$f(x) = x^2 - x - 6.$$

19. Solve $V = \frac{1}{3}\pi(R^2 + r^2)$ for r. Assume all variables are positive.

20. State whether the graph appears to represent a linear function, a quadratic function, or neither.

Average price of electricity

Source: Energy Information Administration, U.S. Department of Energy

21. Jay's Metals has determined that when x hundred storage cabinets are built, the average cost per cabinet is given by
$$C(x) = 0.2x^2 - 1.3x + 3.4025,$$
where $C(x)$ is in hundreds of dollars. What is the minimum cost per cabinet and how many cabinets should be built to achieve that minimum?

22. Find the quadratic function that fits the data points $(0, 0)$, $(3, 0)$, and $(5, 2)$.

Solve.

23. $x^2 + 5x < 6$

24. $x - \dfrac{1}{x} \geq 0$

Synthesis

25. One solution of $kx^2 + 3x - k = 0$ is -2. Find the other solution.

26. Find a fourth-degree polynomial equation, with integer coefficients, for which $-\sqrt{3}$ and $2i$ are solutions.

27. Solve: $x^4 - 4x^2 - 1 = 0$.

Cumulative Review: Chapters 1–9

Simplify.

1. $-3 \cdot 8 \div (-2)^3 \cdot 4 - 6(5 - 7)$

2. $\dfrac{18a^5bc^{10}}{24a^{-5}bc^3}$

3. $(5x^2y - 8xy - 6xy^2) - (2xy - 9x^2y + 3xy^2)$

4. $(9p^2q + 8t)(9p^2q - 8t)$

5. $\dfrac{t^2 - 25}{9t^2 + 24t + 16} \div \dfrac{3t^2 - 11t - 20}{t^2 + t}$ [4.2]

6. $\dfrac{1}{4 - x} + \dfrac{8}{x^2 - 16} - \dfrac{2}{x + 4}$ [4.4]

7. $\sqrt[3]{18x^4y} \cdot \sqrt[3]{6x^2y}$ [8.3]

8. $(3\sqrt{2} + i)(2\sqrt{2} - i)$ [8.8]

Factor.

9. $12x^4 - 75y^4$ [3.4]

10. $x^3 - 24x^2 + 80x$ [3.2]

11. $100m^6 - 100$ [3.5]

12. $6t^2 + 35t + 36$ [3.3]

Solve.

13. $2(5x - 3) - 8x = 4 - (3 - x)$ [1.2]

14. $2(5x - 3) - 8x < 4 - (3 - x)$ [1.6]

15. $\begin{aligned} 2x - 6y &= 3, \\ -3x + 8y &= -5 \end{aligned}$ [6.2]

16. $x(x - 5) = 66$ [3.7]

17. $\dfrac{2}{t} + \dfrac{1}{t - 1} = 2$ [4.6]

18. $\sqrt{x} = 1 + \sqrt{2x - 7}$ [8.6]

19. $m^2 + 10m + 25 = 2$ [9.1]

20. $3x^2 + 1 = x$ [9.2]

Graph.

21. $9x - 2y = 18$ [2.3]

22. $x < \frac{1}{2}y$ [7.4]

23. $y = 2(x - 3)^2 + 1$ [9.6]

24. $f(x) = x^2 + 4x + 3$ [9.7]

25. Find an equation in slope–intercept form whose graph has slope -5 and y-intercept $\left(0, \frac{1}{2}\right)$. [2.6]

26. Find the slope of the line containing $(8, 3)$ and $(-2, 10)$. [2.5]

27. For the function described by $f(x) = 3x^2 - 8x - 7$, find $f(-2)$. [5.1]

Find the domain of each function.

28. $f(x) = \sqrt{10 - x}$ [7.1]

29. $f(x) = \dfrac{x + 3}{x - 4}$ [7.2]

Solve each formula for the specified letter.

30. $b = \dfrac{a + c}{2a}$, for a [5.5]

31. $p = 2\sqrt{\dfrac{r}{3t}}$, for t [9.4]

Solve.

32. *Mobile ad spending.* The amount spent worldwide in advertising on mobile devices can be estimated by $f(x) = 0.4x^2 + 0.01x + 0.9$, where x is the number of years after 2005 and $f(x)$ is in billions of dollars.
Source: Based on data from eMarketer

   a) How much was spent worldwide for mobile ads in 2008? [5.1]

   b) When will worldwide mobile ad spending reach $41 billion? [9.4]

33. *Wi-fi hotspots.* The number of Wi-fi hotspots worldwide grew from 19,000 in 2002 to 118,000 in 2005. Let $h(t)$ represent the number of hotspots, in thousands, t years after 2000. [5.1]
Source: IDC

   a) Find a linear function that fits the data.

   b) Use the function from part (a) to predict the number of Wi-fi hotspots in 2010.

   c) In what year will there be 500,000 Wi-fi hotspots?

34. *Gold prices.* Annette is selling some of her gold jewelry. She has 4 bracelets and 1 necklace that weigh a total of 3 oz. [1.5]

  a) Annette's jewelry is 58% gold. How many ounces of gold does her jewelry contain?
  b) A gold dealer offers Annette $1044 for the jewelry. How much per ounce of gold was she offered?
  c) The price of gold at the time of Annette's sale was $800 an ounce. What percent of the gold price was she offered for her jewelry?

35. *Education.* Sven ordered number tiles at $9 per set and alphabet tiles at $15 per set for his classroom. He ordered a total of 36 sets for $384. How many sets of each did he order? [6.3]

36. *Minimizing cost.* Dormitory Furnishings has determined that when x bunk beds are built, the average cost, in dollars, per bunk bed can be estimated by $c(x) = 0.004375x^2 - 3.5x + 825$. What is the minimum average cost per bunk bed and how many bunk beds should be built to achieve that minimum? [9.8]

37. *Volunteer work.* It takes Deanna twice as long to set up a fundraising auction as it takes Donna. Together they can set up for the auction in 4 hr. How long would it take each of them to do the job alone? [4.7]

38. *Canoeing.* Kent paddled for 2 hr with a 5-km/h current to reach a campsite. The return trip against the same current took 7 hr. Find the speed of Kent's canoe in still water. [6.3]

39. *Truck rentals.* Josh and Lindsay plan to rent a moving truck. The truck costs $70 plus 40¢ per mile. They have budgeted $90 for the truck rental. For what mileages will they not exceed their budget? [1.7]

Synthesis

Solve.

40. $\dfrac{\dfrac{1}{x}}{2 + \dfrac{1}{x-1}} = 3$ [4.5], [9.2]

41. $x^4 + 5x^2 \le 0$ [9.9]

42. The graph of the function $f(x) = mx + b$ contains the point $(2, 3)$ and is perpendicular to the line containing the points $(-1, 4)$ and $(-2, 5)$. Find the equation of the function. [2.7]

43. Find the points of intersection of the graphs of $f(x) = x^2 + 8x + 1$ and $g(x) = 10x + 6$. [9.2]

Photo Credits

Appendixes

A Mean, Median, and Mode

Mean • Median • Mode

One way to analyze data is to look for a single representative number, called a **center point** or **measure of central tendency**. Those most often used are the **mean** (or **average**), the **median**, and the **mode**.

Mean

Let's first consider the *mean*, or *average*.

> **Mean, or Average**
>
> The *mean*, or *average*, of a set of numbers is the sum of the numbers divided by the number of addends.

EXAMPLE 1

Consider the following data on revenue, in billions of dollars, for Starbucks Corporation in five recent years:

$$\$2.2, \quad \$2.6, \quad \$3.3, \quad \$4.1, \quad \$5.3.$$

What is the mean of the numbers?

SOLUTION   First, we add the numbers:

$$2.2 + 2.6 + 3.3 + 4.1 + 5.3 = 17.5.$$

Then we divide by the number of addends, 5:

$$\frac{(2.2 + 2.6 + 3.3 + 4.1 + 5.3)}{5} = \frac{17.5}{5} = 3.5.$$

The mean, or average, revenue of Starbucks for those five years is $3.5 billion.

Note that $3.5 + 3.5 + 3.5 + 3.5 + 3.5 = 17.5$. If we use this center point, 3.5, repeatedly as the addend, we get the same sum that we do when adding individual data numbers.

Median

The *median* is useful when we wish to de-emphasize extreme scores. For example, suppose five workers in a technology company manufactured the following number of computers during one day's work:

Sarah:	88
Matt:	92
Pat:	66
Jen:	94
Mark:	91

Let's first list the scores in order from smallest to largest:

66   88   91   92   94.

↑

Middle number

The middle number—in this case, 91—is the **median**.

> ### Median
> Once a set of data has been arranged from smallest to largest, the *median* of the set of data is the middle number if there is an odd number of data numbers. If there is an even number of data numbers, then there are two middle numbers and the median is the *average* of the two middle numbers.

EXAMPLE 2 Find the median of the following set of household incomes:

$76,000, $58,000, $87,000, $32,500, $64,800, $62,500.

SOLUTION   We first rearrange the numbers in order from smallest to largest.

$32,500, $58,000, $62,500, $64,800, $76,000, $87,000

↑

Median

There is an even number of numbers. We look for the middle two, which are $62,500 and $64,800. The median is the average of $62,500 and $64,800:

$$\frac{\$62,500 + \$64,800}{2} = \$63,650.$$

Mode

The last center point we consider is called the *mode*. A number that occurs most often in a set of data is sometimes considered a representative number or center point.

> ### Mode
> The *mode* of a set of data is the number or numbers that occur most often. If each number occurs the same number of times, then there is *no* mode.

EXAMPLE 3   Find the mode of the following data:

23, 24, 27, 18, 19, 27.

SOLUTION   The number that occurs most often is 27. Thus the mode is 27.

It is easier to find the mode of a set of data if the data are ordered.

EXAMPLE 4   Find the mode of the following data:

83, 84, 84, 84, 85, 86, 87, 87, 87, 88, 89, 90.

SOLUTION   There are two numbers that occur most often, 84 and 87. Thus the modes are 84 and 87.

EXAMPLE 5   Find the mode of the following data:

115, 117, 211, 213, 219.

SOLUTION   Each number occurs the same number of times. The set of data has *no* mode.

A   EXERCISE SET

For each set of numbers, find the mean (average), the median, and any modes that exist.

1. 13, 21, 18, 13, 20

2. 5, 2, 8, 10, 7, 1, 9

3. 3, 8, 20, 3, 20, 10

4. 19, 19, 8, 16, 8, 7

5. 4.7, 2.3, 4.6, 4.9, 3.8

6. 13.4, 13.4, 12.6, 42.9

7. 234, 228, 234, 228, 234, 278

8. $29.95, $28.79, $30.95, $29.95

9. *Hurricanes.*   The following bar graph shows the number of hurricanes that struck the United States by month from 1851 to 2006. What is the average number for the 8 months given? the median? the mode?

Atlantic Storms and Hurricanes

Source: Atlantic Oceanographic and Meteorological Laboratory

10. *iPod prices.*   A price comparison showed the following online prices for an Apple iPod Nano:

$199, $197.97, $249.99, $179, $197.97.

What was the average price? the median price? the mode?

11. *NBA tall men.* The following lists the heights, in inches, of the tallest men in the NBA in a recent year. Find the mean, the median, and the mode.

Zydrunas Ilgauskas	87
Yao Ming	90
Dikembe Mutombo	86
Kosta Perovic	86

Source: National Basketball Association

12. *Coffee consumption.* The following lists the annual coffee consumption, in number of cups per person, for various countries. Find the mean, the median, and the mode.

Germany	1113
United States	610
Switzerland	1215
France	798
Italy	750

Source: Beverage Marketing Corporation

13. *PBA scores.* Kelly Kulick rolled scores of 254, 202, 184, 269, 151, 223, 258, 222, and 202 in a recent tour trial for the Professional Bowlers Association. What was her average? her median? her mode?

Source: Professional Bowlers Association

14. *Salmon prices.* The following prices per pound of Atlantic salmon were found at six fish markets:

$8.99, $8.49, $8.99, $9.99, $9.49, $7.99.

What was the average price per pound? the median price? the mode?

Synthesis

15. *Hank Aaron.* Hank Aaron averaged $34\frac{7}{22}$ home runs per year over a 22-yr career. After 21 yr, Aaron had averaged $35\frac{10}{21}$ home runs per year. How many home runs did Aaron hit in his final year?

16. *Length of pregnancy.* Marta was pregnant 270 days, 259 days, and 272 days for her first three pregnancies. In order for Marta's average length of pregnancy to equal the worldwide average of 266 days, how long must her fourth pregnancy last?
Source: David Crystal (ed.), *The Cambridge Factfinder.* Cambridge CB2 1RP: Cambridge University Press, 1993, p. 84.

17. The ordered set of data 18, 21, 24, a, 36, 37, b has a median of 30 and an average of 32. Find a and b.

18. *Male height.* Jason's brothers are 174 cm, 180 cm, 179 cm, and 172 cm tall. The average male is 176.5 cm tall. How tall is Jason if he and his brothers have an average height of 176.5 cm?

B   Sets

Naming Sets ▪ Membership ▪ Subsets ▪ Intersections ▪ Unions

A **set** is a collection of objects. In mathematics the objects, or **elements**, of a set are generally numbers. This section provides an introduction to sets and how to combine them.

Naming Sets

To name the set of whole numbers less than 6, we can use *roster notation*, as follows:

$$\{0, 1, 2, 3, 4, 5\}.$$

The set of real numbers x for which x is less than 6 cannot be named by listing all its members because there is an infinite number of them. We name such a set using *set-builder notation*, as follows:

$$\{x \mid x < 6\}.$$

This is read

"The set of all x such that x is less than 6."

See Section 1.6 for more on this notation.

Membership

The symbol $\in$ means *is a member of* or *belongs to*, or *is an element of*. Thus,

$$x \in A$$

means

x is a member of A,   or x belongs to A,   or x is an element of A.

EXAMPLE 1   Classify each of the following as true or false.

a) $1 \in \{1, 2, 3\}$

b) $1 \in \{2, 3\}$

c) $4 \in \{x \mid x \text{ is an even whole number}\}$

d) $5 \in \{x \mid x \text{ is an even whole number}\}$

SOLUTION

a) Since 1 is listed as a member of the set, $1 \in \{1, 2, 3\}$ is true.

b) Since 1 is *not* a member of $\{2, 3\}$, the statement $1 \in \{2, 3\}$ is false.

c) Since 4 is an even whole number, $4 \in \{x \mid x \text{ is an even whole number}\}$ is true.

d) Since 5 is *not* even, $5 \in \{x \mid x \text{ is an even whole number}\}$ is false.

TRY EXERCISE 7

Set membership can be illustrated with a diagram, as shown below.

$x \in A$

Subsets

If every element of A is also an element of B, then A is a *subset* of B. This is denoted $A \subseteq B$.

The set of whole numbers is a subset of the set of integers. The set of rational numbers is a subset of the set of real numbers.

EXAMPLE 2

Classify each of the following as true or false.

a) $\{1, 2\} \subseteq \{1, 2, 3, 4\}$

b) $\{p, q, r, w\} \subseteq \{a, p, r, z\}$

c) $\{x \mid x < 6\} \subseteq \{x \mid x \leq 11\}$

SOLUTION

a) Since every element of $\{1, 2\}$ is in the set $\{1, 2, 3, 4\}$, it follows that $\{1, 2\} \subseteq \{1, 2, 3, 4\}$ is true.

b) Since $q \in \{p, q, r, w\}$, but $q \notin \{a, p, r, z\}$, it follows that $\{p, q, r, w\} \subseteq \{a, p, r, z\}$ is false.

c) Since every number that is less than 6 is also less than 11, the statement $\{x \mid x < 6\} \subseteq \{x \mid x \leq 11\}$ is true.

TRY EXERCISE 15

Intersections

The *intersection* of sets A and B, denoted $A \cap B$, is the set of members common to both sets.

EXAMPLE 3

Find each intersection.

a) $\{0, 1, 3, 5, 25\} \cap \{2, 3, 4, 5, 6, 7, 9\}$

b) $\{a, p, q, w\} \cap \{p, q, t\}$

SOLUTION

a) $\{0, 1, 3, 5, 25\} \cap \{2, 3, 4, 5, 6, 7, 9\} = \{3, 5\}$

b) $\{a, p, q, w\} \cap \{p, q, t\} = \{p, q\}$

TRY EXERCISE 19

Set intersection can be illustrated with a diagram, as shown below.

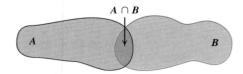

The set without members is known as the *empty set*, and is written $\varnothing$ and sometimes $\{\ \}$. Each of the following is a description of the empty set:

The set of all 12-ft–tall people;

$\{2, 3\} \cap \{5, 6, 7\}$;

$\{x \mid x$ is an even natural number$\} \cap \{x \mid x$ is an odd natural number$\}$.

Unions

Two sets A and B can be combined to form a set that contains the members of both A and B. The new set is called the *union* of A and B, denoted $A \cup B$.

EXAMPLE 4

Find each union.

a) $\{0, 5, 7, 13, 27\} \cup \{0, 2, 3, 4, 5\}$

b) $\{a, c, e, g\} \cup \{b, d, f\}$

SOLUTION

a) $\{0, 5, 7, 13, 27\} \cup \{0, 2, 3, 4, 5\} = \{0, 2, 3, 4, 5, 7, 13, 27\}$

Note that the 0 and the 5 are *not* listed twice in the solution.

b) $\{a, c, e, g\} \cup \{b, d, f\} = \{a, b, c, d, e, f, g\}$

TRY EXERCISE ▸ 25

Set union can be illustrated with a diagram, as shown below.

$A \cup B$ **is shaded.**

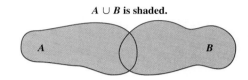

B   EXERCISE SET

Name each set using the roster method.

1. The set of whole numbers 8 through 11

2. The set of whole numbers 83 through 89

3. The set of odd numbers between 40 and 50

4. The set of multiples of 5 between 10 and 40

5. $\{x \mid$ the square of x is 9$\}$

6. $\{x \mid x$ is the cube of $\frac{1}{2}\}$

Classify each statement as either true or false.

7. $5 \in \{x \mid x$ is an odd number$\}$

8. $8 \in \{x \mid x$ is an odd number$\}$

9. Skiing $\in$ The set of all sports

10. Pharmacist $\in$ The set of all professions requiring a college degree

11. $3 \in \{-4, -3, 0, 1\}$

12. $0 \in \{-4, -3\} \subseteq \{-3, -2, -1, 1, 2, 3\}$

13. $\frac{2}{3} \in \{x \mid x$ is a rational number$\}$

14. $\frac{2}{3} \in \{x \mid x$ is a real number$\}$

15. $\{-1, 0, 1\} \subseteq \{-3, -2, -1, 1, 2, 3\}$

16. The set of vowels $\subseteq$ The set of consonants

17. The set of integers $\subseteq$ The set of rational numbers

18. $\{2, 4, 6\} \subseteq \{1, 2, 3, 4, 5, 6, 7\}$

Find each intersection.

19. $\{a, b, c, d, e\} \cap \{c, d, e, f, g\}$

20. $\{a, e, i, o, u\} \cap \{q, u, i, c, k\}$

21. $\{1, 2, 3, 4, 6, 12\} \cap \{1, 2, 3, 6, 9, 18\}$

22. $\{1, 2, 3, 4, 6, 12\} \cap \{1, 5, 7, 35\}$

23. $\{2, 4, 6, 8\} \cap \{1, 3, 5, 7\}$

24. $\{a, e, i, o, u\} \cap \{m, n, f, g, h\}$

Find each union.

25. $\{a, e, i, o, u\} \cup \{q, u, i, c, k\}$

26. $\{a, b, c, d, e\} \cup \{c, d, e, f, g\}$

27. $\{1, 2, 3, 4, 6, 12\} \cup \{1, 2, 3, 6, 9, 18\}$

28. $\{1, 2, 3, 4, 6, 12\} \cup \{1, 5, 7, 35\}$

29. $\{2, 4, 6, 8\} \cup \{1, 3, 5, 7\}$

30. $\{a, e, i, o, u\} \cup \{m, n, f, g, h\}$

31. What advantage(s) does set-builder notation have over roster notation?

32. What advantage(s) does roster notation have over set-builder notation?

Synthesis

33. Find the union of the set of integers and the set of whole numbers.

34. Find the intersection of the set of odd integers and the set of even integers.

35. Find the union of the set of rational numbers and the set of irrational numbers.

36. Find the intersection of the set of even integers and the set of positive rational numbers.

37. Find the intersection of the set of rational numbers and the set of irrational numbers.

38. Find the union of the set of negative integers, the set of positive integers, and the set containing 0.

39. For a set A, find each of the following.
   a) $A \cup \varnothing$
   b) $A \cup A$
   c) $A \cap A$
   d) $A \cap \varnothing$

Classify each statement as either true or false.

40. The empty set can be written $\varnothing$, { }, or {0}.

41. For any set A, $\varnothing \subseteq A$.

42. For any set A, $A \subseteq A$.

43. For any sets A and B, $A \cap B \subseteq A$.

44. A set is *closed* under an operation if, when the operation is performed on its members, the result is in the set. For example, the set of real numbers is closed under the operation of addition since the sum of any two real numbers is a real number.
   a) Is the set of even numbers closed under addition?
   b) Is the set of odd numbers closed under addition?
   c) Is the set {0, 1} closed under addition?
   d) Is the set {0, 1} closed under multiplication?
   e) Is the set of real numbers closed under multiplication?
   f) Is the set of integers closed under division?

45. Experiment with sets of various types and determine whether the following distributive law for sets is true:
$$A \cap (B \cup C) = (A \cap B) \cup (A \cap C).$$

C Synthetic Division

Streamlining Long Division • The Remainder Theorem

Streamlining Long Division

To divide a polynomial by a binomial of the type $x - a$, we can streamline the usual procedure to develop a process called *synthetic division*.

Compare the following. In each stage, we attempt to write less than in the previous stage, while retaining enough essentials to solve the problem.

STAGE 1

When a polynomial is written in descending order, the coefficients provide the essential information:

$$
\begin{array}{r}
4x^2 + 5x + 11 \\
x - 2\,\overline{)\,4x^3 - 3x^2 + x + 7} \\
\underline{4x^3 - 8x^2} \\
5x^2 + x \\
\underline{5x^2 - 10x} \\
11x + 7 \\
\underline{11x - 22} \\
29
\end{array}
\qquad
\begin{array}{r}
4 + 5 + 11 \\
1 - 2\,\overline{)\,4 - 3 + 1 + 7} \\
\underline{4 - 8} \\
5 + 1 \\
\underline{5 - 10} \\
11 + 7 \\
\underline{11 - 22} \\
29
\end{array}
$$

Because the leading coefficient in $x - 2$ is 1, each time we multiply it by a term in the answer, the leading coefficient of that product duplicates a coefficient in the answer. In the next stage, rather than duplicate these numbers we focus on where -2 is used and drop the 1 from the divisor.

STAGE 2

$$x - 2 \overline{)\begin{array}{l} 4x^2 + 5x + 11 \\ 4x^3 - 3x^2 + x + 7 \end{array}}$$

$$\begin{array}{r} 4x^3 - 8x^2 \\ \hline 5x^2 + x \\ 5x^2 - 10x \\ \hline 11x + 7 \\ 11x - 22 \\ \hline 29 \end{array}$$

$$-2 \overline{)\,4 - 3 + 1 + 7\,}$$

$-8 \longleftarrow$ Multiply: $-2 \cdot 4 = -8$.

$\overline{5 + 1}$ Subtract: $-3 - (-8) = 5$.

$-10 \longleftarrow$ Multiply: $-2 \cdot 5 = -10$.

$\overline{11 + 7}$ Subtract: $1 - (-10) = 11$.

$-22 \longleftarrow$ Multiply: $-2 \cdot 11 = -22$.

$\overline{29} \longleftarrow$ Subtract: $7 - (-22) = 29$.

To simplify further, we now reverse the sign of the -2 in the divisor and, in exchange, *add* at each step in the long division.

STAGE 3

$$x - 2 \overline{)\begin{array}{l} 4x^2 + 5x + 11 \\ 4x^3 - 3x^2 + x + 7 \end{array}}$$

$$\begin{array}{r} 4x^3 - 8x^2 \\ \hline 5x^2 + x \\ 5x^2 - 10x \\ \hline 11x + 7 \\ 11x - 22 \\ \hline 29 \end{array}$$

$$2 \overline{)\,4 - 3 + 1 + 7\,}$$ Replace the -2 with 2.

$8 \longleftarrow$ Multiply: $2 \cdot 4 = 8$.

$\overline{5 + 1}$ Add: $-3 + 8 = 5$.

$10 \longleftarrow$ Multiply: $2 \cdot 5 = 10$.

$\overline{11 + 7}$ Add: $1 + 10 = 11$.

$22 \longleftarrow$ Multiply: $2 \cdot 11 = 22$.

$\overline{29} \longleftarrow$ Add: $7 + 22 = 29$.

The blue numbers can be eliminated if we look at the red numbers instead.

STAGE 4

$$x - 2 \overline{)\begin{array}{l} 4x^2 + 5x + 11 \\ 4x^3 - 3x^2 + x + 7 \end{array}}$$

$$\begin{array}{r} 4x^3 - 8x^2 \\ \hline 5x^2 + x \\ 5x^2 - 10x \\ \hline 11x + 7 \\ 11x - 22 \\ \hline 29 \end{array}$$

$$2 \overline{)\begin{array}{rrrr} 4 & 5 & 11 & \\ 4 & -3 & 1 & 7 \\ & 8 & 10 & 22 \\ \hline & 5 & 11 & 29 \end{array}}$$

Note that the 5 and the 11 preceding the remainder 29 coincide with the 5 and the 11 following the 4 on the top line. By writing a 4 to the left of 5 on the bottom line, we can eliminate the top line in stage 4 and read our answer from the bottom line. This final stage is commonly called **synthetic division**.

STAGE 5

$$2 \overline{)\begin{array}{rrr} 4 & 5 & 11 \\ 4 & -3 & 1 \quad 7 \\ & 8 & 10 \quad 22 \\ \hline & 5 & 11 \quad 29 \end{array}}$$

$$\underline{2} \; | \begin{array}{rrrr} 4 & -3 & 1 & 7 \\ & 8 & 10 & 22 \\ \hline 4 & 5 & 11 & | \; 29 \end{array}$$

$\longleftarrow$ This is the remainder.

This is the zero-degree coefficient.

This is the first-degree coefficient.

This is the second-degree coefficient.

The quotient is $4x^2 + 5x + 11$ with a remainder of 29.

> Remember that for this method to work, the divisor must be of the form $x - a$, that is, a variable minus a constant.

EXAMPLE 1 Use synthetic division to divide: $(x^3 + 6x^2 - x - 30) \div (x - 2)$.

SOLUTION

$$
\begin{array}{r|rrrr}
2 & 1 & 6 & -1 & -30 \\
\hline
 & 1
\end{array}
$$
Write the 2 of $x - 2$ and the coefficients of the dividend.

Bring down the first coefficient.

$$
\begin{array}{r|rrrr}
2 & 1 & 6 & -1 & -30 \\
 & & 2 \\
\hline
 & 1 & 8
\end{array}
$$
Multiply 1 by 2 to get 2.

Add 6 and 2.

$$
\begin{array}{r|rrrr}
2 & 1 & 6 & -1 & -30 \\
 & & 2 & 16 \\
\hline
 & 1 & 8 & 15
\end{array}
$$
Multiply 8 by 2.

Add -1 and 16.

$$
\begin{array}{r|rrrr}
2 & 1 & 6 & -1 & -30 \\
 & & 2 & 16 & 30 \\
\hline
 & 1 & 8 & 15 & 0
\end{array}
$$
Multiply 15 by 2 and add.

The answer is $x^2 + 8x + 15$ with R 0, or just $x^2 + 8x + 15$.

> TRY EXERCISE 7

EXAMPLE 2 Use synthetic division to divide.

a) $(2x^3 + 7x^2 - 5) \div (x + 3)$

b) $(10x^2 - 13x + 3x^3 - 20) \div (4 + x)$

SOLUTION

a) $(2x^3 + 7x^2 - 5) \div (x + 3)$

The dividend has no x-term, so we need to write 0 as the coefficient of x. Note that $x + 3 = x - (-3)$, so we write -3 inside the ⌐.

$$
\begin{array}{r|rrrr}
-3 & 2 & 7 & 0 & -5 \\
 & & -6 & -3 & 9 \\
\hline
 & 2 & 1 & -3 & 4
\end{array}
$$

The answer is $2x^2 + x - 3$, with R 4, or $2x^2 + x - 3 + \dfrac{4}{x + 3}$.

b) We first rewrite $(10x^2 - 13x + 3x^3 - 20) \div (4 + x)$ in descending order:

$$(3x^3 + 10x^2 - 13x - 20) \div (x + 4).$$

Next, we use synthetic division. Note that $x + 4 = x - (-4)$.

$$
\begin{array}{r|rrrr}
-4 & 3 & 10 & -13 & -20 \\
 & & -12 & 8 & 20 \\
\hline
 & 3 & -2 & -5 & 0
\end{array}
$$

The answer is $3x^2 - 2x - 5$.

> TRY EXERCISE 15

The Remainder Theorem

TECHNOLOGY CONNECTION

In Example 1, the division by $x - 2$ gave a remainder of 0. The remainder theorem tells us that this means that when $x = 2$, the value of $x^3 + 6x^2 - x - 30$ is 0. Check this both graphically and algebraically (by substitution). Then perform a similar check for Example 2(b).

Because the remainder is 0, Example 1 shows that $x - 2$ is a factor of $x^3 + 6x^2 - x - 30$ and that $x^3 + 6x^2 - x - 30 = (x - 2)(x^2 + 8x + 15)$. Thus if $f(x) = x^3 + 6x^2 - x - 30$, then $f(2) = 0$ (since $x - 2$ is a factor of $f(x)$). Similarly, from Example 2(b), we know that if $g(x) = 10x^2 - 13x + 3x^3 - 20$, then $x + 4$ is a factor of $g(x)$ and $g(-4) = 0$. In both examples, the remainder from the division, 0, can serve as a function value. Remarkably, this pattern extends to nonzero remainders. For example, the remainder in Example 2(a) is 4, and if $f(x) = 2x^3 + 7x^2 - 5$, then $f(-3)$ is also 4 (you should check this). The fact that the remainder and the function value coincide is predicted by the remainder theorem.

> **The Remainder Theorem**
>
> The remainder obtained by dividing $P(x)$ by $x - r$ is $P(r)$.

A proof of this result is outlined in Exercise 31.

EXAMPLE 3   Let $f(x) = 8x^5 - 6x^3 + x - 8$. Use synthetic division to find $f(2)$.

SOLUTION   The remainder theorem tells us that $f(2)$ is the remainder when $f(x)$ is divided by $x - 2$. We use synthetic division to find that remainder:

$$
\begin{array}{r|rrrrrr}
2 & 8 & 0 & -6 & 0 & 1 & -8 \\
  &   & 16 & 32 & 52 & 104 & 210 \\
\hline
  & 8 & 16 & 26 & 52 & 105 & 202
\end{array}
$$

Although the bottom line can be used to find the quotient for the division $(8x^5 - 6x^3 + x - 8) \div (x - 2)$, what we are really interested in is the remainder. It tells us that $f(2) = 202$.

TRY EXERCISE ▶ 21

The remainder theorem is often used to check division. Thus Example 2(a) can be checked by computing $P(-3) = 2(-3)^3 + 7(-3)^2 - 5$. Since $P(-3) = 4$ and the remainder in Example 2(a) is also 4, our division was probably correct.

C   EXERCISE SET

For Extra Help

🖐 ***Concept Reinforcement***   *Classify each statement as either true or false.*

1. If $x - 2$ is a factor of some polynomial $P(x)$, then $P(2) = 0$.

2. If $p(3) = 0$ for some polynomial $p(x)$, then $x - 3$ is a factor of $p(x)$.

3. If $P(-5) = 39$ and $P(x) = x^3 + 7x^2 + 3x + 4$, then

$$
\begin{array}{r|rrrr}
-5 & 1 & 7 & 3 & 4 \\
   &   & -5 & -10 & 35 \\
\hline
   & 1 & 2 & -7 & 39
\end{array}
$$

4. In order for $f(x)/g(x)$ to exist, $g(x)$ must be 0.

5. In order to use synthetic division, we must be sure that the divisor is of the form $x - a$.

6. Synthetic division can be used in problems in which long division could not be used.

Use synthetic division to divide.

7. $(x^3 - 4x^2 - 2x + 5) \div (x - 1)$

8. $(x^3 - 4x^2 + 5x - 6) \div (x - 3)$

9. $(a^2 + 8a + 11) \div (a + 3)$

10. $(a^2 + 8a + 11) \div (a + 5)$

11. $(2x^3 - x^2 - 7x + 14) \div (x + 2)$

12. $(3x^3 - 10x^2 - 9x + 15) \div (x - 4)$

13. $(a^3 - 10a + 12) \div (a - 2)$

14. $(a^3 - 14a + 15) \div (a - 3)$

15. $(3y^3 - 7y^2 - 20) \div (y - 3)$

16. $(2x^3 - 3x^2 + 8) \div (x + 2)$

17. $(x^5 - 32) \div (x - 2)$

18. $(y^5 - 1) \div (y - 1)$

19. $(3x^3 + 1 - x + 7x^2) \div (x + \frac{1}{3})$

20. $(8x^3 - 1 + 7x - 6x^2) \div (x - \frac{1}{2})$

Use synthetic division to find the indicated function value.

21. $f(x) = 5x^4 + 12x^3 + 28x + 9$; $f(-3)$

22. $g(x) = 3x^4 - 25x^2 - 18$; $g(3)$

23. $P(x) = 2x^4 - x^3 - 7x^2 + x + 2$; $P(-3)$

24. $F(x) = 3x^4 + 8x^3 + 2x^2 - 7x - 4$; $F(-2)$

25. $f(x) = x^4 - 6x^3 + 11x^2 - 17x + 20$; $f(4)$

26. $p(x) = x^4 + 7x^3 + 11x^2 - 7x - 12$; $p(2)$

27. Why is it that we *add* when performing synthetic division, but *subtract* when performing long division?

28. Explain how synthetic division could be useful when attempting to factor a polynomial.

Synthesis

29. Let $Q(x)$ be a polynomial function with $p(x)$ a factor of $Q(x)$. If $p(3) = 0$, does it follow that $Q(3) = 0$? Why or why not? If $Q(3) = 0$, does it follow that $p(3) = 0$? Why or why not?

30. What adjustments must be made if synthetic division is to be used to divide a polynomial by a binomial of the form $ax + b$, with $a > 1$?

31. To prove the remainder theorem, note that any polynomial $P(x)$ can be rewritten as $(x - r) \cdot Q(x) + R$, where $Q(x)$ is the quotient polynomial that arises when $P(x)$ is divided by $x - r$, and R is some constant (the remainder).

  a) How do we know that R must be a constant?
  b) Show that $P(r) = R$ (this says that $P(r)$ is the remainder when $P(x)$ is divided by $x - r$).

32. Let $f(x) = 6x^3 - 13x^2 - 79x + 140$. Find $f(4)$ and then solve the equation $f(x) = 0$.

33. Let $f(x) = 4x^3 + 16x^2 - 3x - 45$. Find $f(-3)$ and then solve the equation $f(x) = 0$.

34. Use the TRACE feature on a graphing calculator to check your answer to Exercise 32.

35. Use the TRACE feature on a graphing calculator to check your answer to Exercise 33.

Nested evaluation. *One way to evaluate a polynomial function like $P(x) = 3x^4 - 5x^3 + 4x^2 - 1$ is to successively factor out x as shown:*

$$P(x) = x(x(x(3x - 5) + 4) + 0) - 1.$$

Computations are then performed using this "nested" form of $P(x)$.

36. Use nested evaluation to find $f(4)$ in Exercise 32. Note the similarities to the calculations performed with synthetic division.

37. Use nested evaluation to find $f(-3)$ in Exercise 33. Note the similarities to the calculations performed with synthetic division.

Tables

TABLE 1   Fraction and Decimal Equivalents

Fraction Notation	$\frac{1}{10}$	$\frac{1}{8}$	$\frac{1}{6}$	$\frac{1}{5}$	$\frac{1}{4}$	$\frac{3}{10}$	$\frac{1}{3}$	$\frac{3}{8}$	$\frac{2}{5}$	$\frac{1}{2}$
Decimal Notation	0.1	0.125	$0.16\overline{6}$	0.2	0.25	0.3	$0.333\overline{3}$	0.375	0.4	0.5
Percent Notation	10%	12.5%, or $12\frac{1}{2}\%$	$16.6\overline{6}\%$, or $16\frac{2}{3}\%$	20%	25%	30%	$33.3\overline{3}\%$, or $33\frac{1}{3}\%$	37.5%, or $37\frac{1}{2}\%$	40%	50%
Fraction Notation	$\frac{3}{5}$	$\frac{5}{8}$	$\frac{2}{3}$	$\frac{7}{10}$	$\frac{3}{4}$	$\frac{4}{5}$	$\frac{5}{6}$	$\frac{7}{8}$	$\frac{9}{10}$	$\frac{1}{1}$
Decimal Notation	0.6	0.625	$0.666\overline{6}$	0.7	0.75	0.8	$0.83\overline{3}$	0.875	0.9	1
Percent Notation	60%	62.5%, or $62\frac{1}{2}\%$	$66.6\overline{6}\%$, or $66\frac{2}{3}\%$	70%	75%	80%	$83.3\overline{3}\%$, or $83\frac{1}{3}\%$	87.5%, or $87\frac{1}{2}\%$	90%	100%

TABLE 2   Squares and Square Roots with Approximations to Three Decimal Places

N	$\sqrt{N}$	N^2	N	$\sqrt{N}$	N^2	N	$\sqrt{N}$	N^2	N	$\sqrt{N}$	N^2
1	1	1	26	5.099	676	51	7.141	2601	76	8.718	5776
2	1.414	4	27	5.196	729	52	7.211	2704	77	8.775	5929
3	1.732	9	28	5.292	784	53	7.280	2809	78	8.832	6084
4	2	16	29	5.385	841	54	7.348	2916	79	8.888	6241
5	2.236	25	30	5.477	900	55	7.416	3025	80	8.944	6400
6	2.449	36	31	5.568	961	56	7.483	3136	81	9	6561
7	2.646	49	32	5.657	1024	57	7.550	3249	82	9.055	6724
8	2.828	64	33	5.745	1089	58	7.616	3364	83	9.110	6889
9	3	81	34	5.831	1156	59	7.681	3481	84	9.165	7056
10	3.162	100	35	5.916	1225	60	7.746	3600	85	9.220	7225
11	3.317	121	36	6	1296	61	7.810	3721	86	9.274	7396
12	3.464	144	37	6.083	1369	62	7.874	3844	87	9.327	7569
13	3.606	169	38	6.164	1444	63	7.937	3969	88	9.381	7744
14	3.742	196	39	6.245	1521	64	8	4096	89	9.434	7921
15	3.873	225	40	6.325	1600	65	8.062	4225	90	9.487	8100
16	4	256	41	6.403	1681	66	8.124	4356	91	9.539	8281
17	4.123	289	42	6.481	1764	67	8.185	4489	92	9.592	8464
18	4.243	324	43	6.557	1849	68	8.246	4624	93	9.644	8649
19	4.359	361	44	6.633	1936	69	8.307	4761	94	9.695	8836
20	4.472	400	45	6.708	2025	70	8.367	4900	95	9.747	9025
21	4.583	441	46	6.782	2116	71	8.426	5041	96	9.798	9216
22	4.690	484	47	6.856	2209	72	8.485	5184	97	9.849	9409
23	4.796	529	48	6.928	2304	73	8.544	5329	98	9.899	9604
24	4.899	576	49	7	2401	74	8.602	5476	99	9.950	9801
25	5	625	50	7.071	2500	75	8.660	5625	100	10	10,000

Answers

The complete step-by-step solutions for the exercises listed below can be found in the *Student's Solutions Manual*, ISBN 0-558-76673-0/978-0-558-76673-3, which can be purchased online or at your bookstore.

CHAPTER 1
Exercise Set 1.1, pp. 7–9

1. (c) **2.** (b) **3.** (f) **4.** (a) **5.** (d) **6.** (e) **7.** (d)
8. (b) **9.** (c) **10.** (a) **11.** 11 **13.** -25 **15.** -31
17. 41 **19.** 19 **21.** -6 **23.** $\frac{7}{3}$ **25.** $-\frac{1}{10}$ **27.** $\frac{41}{24}$
29. $-\frac{1}{20}$ **31.** 9.1 **33.** -5 **35.** 7 **37.** 12 **39.** -38
41. 8 **43.** -7 **45.** 8 **47.** 88 **49.** 20 **51.** -54
53. $-\frac{5}{9}$ **55.** 1 **57.** $\frac{9}{2}$ **59.** -7.6 **61.** -2.5 **63.** -15
65. -5 **67.** $-\frac{7}{6}$ **69.** -128 **71.** $-\frac{1}{2}$ **73.** -15 **75.** 9
77. 310.756 **79.** ✍ **81.** -6 **82.** 2 **83.** 1
84. -16 **85.** ✍ **87.** 11.6 **89.** 2 **91.** $-23, 23$
93. 9000 **95.** 250

Technology Connection, p. 12

1.   **2.**

3. 4; not reliable because, depending on the choice of ΔTbl, it is easy to scroll past a solution without realizing it.

Exercise Set 1.2, pp. 15–16

1. (c) **2.** (e) **3.** (a) **4.** (f) **5.** (b) **6.** (d) **7.** 8
9. 7 **11.** 5 **13.** $\frac{10}{3}$ **15.** -7 **17.** -5 **19.** -4
21. 19 **23.** -2.8 **25.** 3 **27.** 15 **29.** -6 **31.** $-\frac{25}{2}$
33. All real numbers; identity **35.** -3 **37.** -6 **39.** 2
41. 0 **43.** 6 **45.** No solution; contradiction **47.** $-\frac{1}{2}$
49. 0 **51.** 10 **53.** 4 **55.** 0 **57.** No solution;
contradiction **59.** $\frac{5}{2}$ **61.** -8 **63.** $\frac{1}{6}$
65. All real numbers; identity **67.** 2 **69.** $\frac{16}{3}$ **71.** $\frac{2}{5}$
73. 1 **75.** -4 **77.** $1.\overline{6}$ **79.** $-\frac{60}{37}$ **81.** 11 **83.** 8
85. $\frac{16}{15}$ **87.** $-\frac{1}{31}$ **89.** 2 **91.** ✍ **93.** -7 **94.** 15
95. -15 **96.** -28 **97.** ✍ **99.** $\frac{1136}{909}$, or $1.\overline{2497}$
101. No solution; contradiction **103.** $\frac{2}{3}$ **105.** 0
107. $\frac{52}{45}$ **109.** All real numbers; identity

Technology Connection, p. 18

1. 800

Exercise Set 1.3, pp. 21–24

1. 309.6 m **3.** 1423 students **5.** 8.4734 **7.** 255 mg
9. $b = \frac{A}{h}$ **11.** $r = \frac{d}{t}$ **13.** $P = \frac{I}{rt}$ **15.** $m = 65 - H$
17. $l = \frac{P - 2w}{2}$, or $l = \frac{P}{2} - w$ **19.** $\pi = \frac{A}{r^2}$
21. $h = \frac{2A}{b}$ **23.** $c^2 = \frac{E}{m}$ **25.** $d = 2Q - c$
27. $b = 3A - a - c$ **29.** $r = wf$ **31.** $C = \frac{5}{9}(F - 32)$
33. $y = 2x - 1$ **35.** $y = -\frac{2}{5}x + 2$ **37.** $y = \frac{4}{3}x - 2$
39. $y = -\frac{9}{8}x + \frac{1}{2}$ **41.** $y = \frac{3}{5}x - \frac{8}{5}$
43. $x = \frac{z - 13}{2} - y$, or $x = \frac{z - 13 - 2y}{2}$
45. $l = 4(t - 27) + w$ **47.** $t = \frac{A}{a + b}$ **49.** $h = \frac{2A}{a + b}$
51. $L = W - \frac{N(R - r)}{400}$, or $L = \frac{400W - NR + Nr}{400}$
53. ✍ **55.** -10 **56.** -196 **57.** 0 **58.** -32
59. -13 **60.** 65 **61.** ✍ **63.** 40 yr **65.** 27 in³
67. $a = \frac{w}{c} \cdot d$ **69.** $c = \frac{d}{a - b}$ **71.** $a = \frac{c}{3 + b + d}$
73. $K = 9.632w + 19.685h - 10.54a + 102.3$

Exercise Set 1.4, pp. 28–33

1. (d) **2.** (c) **3.** (e) **4.** (b) **5.** (c) **6.** (d) **7.** (f)
8. (a) **9.** (b) **10.** (e) **11.** 0.49 **13.** 0.01
15. 0.041 **17.** 0.2 **19.** 0.0625 **21.** 0.002 **23.** 1.75
25. 38% **27.** 3.9% **29.** 45% **31.** 70% **33.** 0.09%
35. 106% **37.** 180% **39.** 60% **41.** 32% **43.** 25%
45. 26% **47.** $46\frac{2}{3}$, or $\frac{140}{3}$ **49.** 2.5 **51.** 10,000
53. 125% **55.** 0.8 **57.** 50% **59.** $33.\overline{3}$%, or $33\frac{1}{3}$%
61. 2.85 million Americans **63.** 23.37 million Americans
65. 75 credits **67.** 595 at bats **69.** (a) 16%; (b) $29
71. $33.\overline{3}$%, or $33\frac{1}{3}$%; $66.\overline{6}$%, or $66\frac{2}{3}$% **73.** $168
75. 285 women **77.** $19.20 an hour **79.** The actual
cost was 43.7% more than the estimate. **81.** $45
83. $148.50 **84.** $1225 **85.** $955 **86.** $890
87. $230 **88.** $72 **89.** $4300 **90.** 124 **91.** $68
92. $130.50 **93.** $1820.80 **94.** $18.90 **95.** $37.50
96. $3.50 **97.** $0.75 **98.** $280 **99.** $273.68
101. About 31.5 lb **103.** About 2.45 billion pieces of mail
105. About 165 calories **107.** ✍ **109.** Let l represent the
length and w represent the width; $2l + 2w$ **110.** $0.05 \cdot 180$

111. Let p represent the number of points Tino scored; $p - 5$
112. $15 + 1.5x$ **113.** $10\left(\frac{1}{2}a\right)$ **114.** Let n represent the
number; $3n + 10$ **115.** Let l represent the length and w
represent the width; $w = l - 2$ **116.** Let x represent the
first number and y represent the second number; $x = 4y$
117. ✍   **119.** 18,500 people   **121.** About 6 ft 7 in.
123. About 27%   **125.** ✍

Exercise Set 1.5, pp. 40–45

1. 11   **3.** $\frac{11}{2}$ **5.** \$150   **7.** \$130   **9.** About 78.4 mi
11. 160 mi   **13.** 1204 and 1205   **15.** 285 and 287
17. 32, 33, 34   **19.** Man: 103 yr; woman: 101 yr
21. Non-spam: 25 billion messages; spam: 100 billion
messages   **23.** 140 and 141   **25.** Width: 100 ft; length:
160 ft; area: 16,000 ft^2 **27.** Width: 21 m; length: 25 m
29. $1\frac{3}{4}$ in. by $3\frac{1}{2}$ in.   **31.** 30°, 90°, 60°   **33.** 70°
35. Bottom: 144 ft; middle: 72 ft; top: 24 ft   **37.** 8.75 mi,
or $8\frac{3}{4}$ mi   **39.** $128\frac{1}{3}$ mi   **41.** 65°, 25°   **43.** 140°, 40°
45. Length: 27.9 cm; width: 21.6 cm   **47.** \$6600
49. 830 points   **51.** \$125,000   **53.** 160 chirps per
minute   **55.** ✍   **57.** <   **58.** >   **59.** >   **60.** <
61. $-4 \le x$ **62.** $5 > x$ **63.** $y < 5$ **64.** $t \ge -10$
65. ✍   **67.** \$37   **69.** 20   **71.** Half-dollars: 5;
quarters: 10; dimes: 20; nickels: 60   **73.** \$95.99
75. 5 DVDs   **77.** 6 mi   **79.** ✍   **81.** Width: 23.31 cm;
length: 27.56 cm

Exercise Set 1.6, pp. 52–54

1. $\ge$ **2.** $\le$ **3.** <   **4.** >   **5.** Equivalent
6. Equivalent   **7.** Equivalent   **8.** Not equivalent
9. (a) Yes; (b) no; (c) no   **11.** (a) Yes; (b) no; (c) yes
13. (a) Yes; (b) yes; (c) yes   **15.** (a) No; (b) yes; (c) no
17. $y < 2$
19. $x \ge -1$
21. $0 \le t$
23. $-5 \le x < 2$
25. $-4 < x < 0$
27. $\{y|y < 6\}, (-\infty, 6)$
29. $\{x|x \ge -4\}, [-4, \infty)$
31. $\{t|t > -3\}, (-3, \infty)$
33. $\{x|x \le -7\}, (-\infty, -7]$
35. $\{x|x > -4\}, (-4, \infty)$ **37.** $\{x|x \le 2\}, (-\infty, 2]$
39. $\{x|x < -1\}, (-\infty, -1)$ **41.** $\{x|x \ge 0\}, [0, \infty)$
43. $\{y|y > 3\}, (3, \infty)$
45. $\{n|n < 17\}, (-\infty, 17)$,
47. $\{x|x \le -9\}, (-\infty, -9]$,
49. $\{y|y \le \frac{1}{2}\}, \left(-\infty, \frac{1}{2}\right]$,

51. $\{t|t > \frac{5}{8}\}, \left(\frac{5}{8}, \infty\right)$,
53. $\{x|x < 0\}, (-\infty, 0)$,
55. $\{t|t < 23\}, (-\infty, 23)$
57. $\{y|y \ge 22\}, [22, \infty)$,
59. $\{x|x < 7\}, (-\infty, 7)$
61. $\{t|t < -3\}, (-\infty, -3)$,
63. $\{n|n \ge -1.5\}, [-1.5, \infty)$,
65. $\{y|y \ge -\frac{1}{10}\}, \left[-\frac{1}{10}, \infty\right)$
67. $\{x|x < -\frac{4}{5}\}, \left(-\infty, -\frac{4}{5}\right)$

69. $\{x|x < 6\}$, or $(-\infty, 6)$ **71.** $\{t|t \le 7\}$, or $(-\infty, 7]$
73. $\{x|x > -4\}$, or $(-4, \infty)$ **75.** $\{y|y < -\frac{10}{3}\}$, or
$\left(-\infty, -\frac{10}{3}\right)$ **77.** $\{x|x > -10\}$, or $(-10, \infty)$
79. $\{y|y < 0\}$, or $(-\infty, 0)$ **81.** $\{y|y \ge \frac{3}{2}\}$, or $\left[\frac{3}{2}, \infty\right)$
83. $\{x|x > -4\}$, or $(-4, \infty)$ **85.** $\{t|t > 1\}$, or $(1, \infty)$
87. $\{x|x \le -9\}$, or $(-\infty, -9]$ **89.** $\{t|t < 14\}$, or
$(-\infty, 14)$ **91.** $\{y|y \le -4\}$, or $(-\infty, -4]$
93. $\{t|t < -\frac{5}{3}\}$, or $\left(-\infty, -\frac{5}{3}\right)$ **95.** $\{r|r > -3\}$, or $(-3, \infty)$
97. $\{x|x \le 7\}$, or $(-\infty, 7]$ **99.** $\{x|x > -\frac{5}{32}\}$, or $\left(-\frac{5}{32}, \infty\right)$
101. ✍   **103.** $17x - 6$ **104.** $2m - 16n$
105. $7x - 8y - 46$ **106.** $-47t + 1$
107. $35a - 20b - 17$ **108.** $-21x + 32$ **109.** ✍
111. $\{x|x$ is a real number$\}$, or $(-\infty, \infty)$
113. $\{x|x \le \frac{5}{6}\}$, or $\left(-\infty, \frac{5}{6}\right]$
115. $\{x|x \le -4a\}$, or $(-\infty, -4a]$
117. $\left\{x|x > \dfrac{y - b}{a}\right\}$, or $\left(\dfrac{y - b}{a}, \infty\right)$
119. $\{x|x$ is a real number$\}$, or $(-\infty, \infty)$

Connecting the Concepts, pp. 54–55

1. 21   **2.** $\{x|x \le 21\}$, or $(-\infty, 21]$ **3.** -6
4. $\{x|x > -6\}$, or $(-6, \infty)$ **5.** $\{x|x < 6\}$, or $(-\infty, 6)$
6. 3   **7.** $-\frac{1}{3}$ **8.** $\{y|y < 3\}$, or $(-\infty, 3)$
9. $\{t|t \le -16\}$, or $(-\infty, -16]$ **10.** $\frac{11}{2}$
11. $\{a|a < -1\}$, or $(-\infty, -1)$ **12.** $\{x|x < 10.75\}$, or
$(-\infty, 10.75)$ **13.** $\{x|x \ge -11\}$, or $[-11, \infty)$
14. 105   **15.** -4.24 **16.** 15   **17.** $\{y|y \ge 3\}$, or $[3, \infty)$
18. $\frac{14}{3}$ **19.** $\{x|x > \frac{22}{5}\}$, or $\left(\frac{22}{5}, \infty\right)$
20. $\{a|a \ge 0\}$, or $[0, \infty)$

Translating for Success, p. 58

1. F   **2.** I   **3.** C   **4.** E   **5.** D   **6.** J   **7.** O   **8.** M
9. B   **10.** L

Exercise Set 1.7, pp. 59–62

1. $b \leq a$ **2.** $b < a$ **3.** $a \leq b$ **4.** $a < b$ **5.** $b \leq a$
6. $a \leq b$ **7.** $b < a$ **8.** $a < b$ **9.** Let n represent the number; $n < 10$ **11.** Let t represent the temperature; $t \leq -3$ **13.** Let d represent the number of years of driving experience; $d \geq 5$ **15.** Let a represent the age of the altar; $a > 1200$ **17.** Let h represent Tania's hourly wage; $12 < h < 15$ **19.** Let w represent the wind speed; $w > 50$ **21.** Let c represent the cost of a room; $c \leq 120$ **23.** More than 2.375 hr   **25.** At least 2.25   **27.** Scores greater than or equal to 97   **29.** 8 credits or more
31. At least 3 plate appearances   **33.** Lengths greater than 6 cm   **35.** Depths less than 437.5 ft   **37.** Blue-book value is greater than or equal to $10,625   **39.** Lengths less than 55 in.   **41.** Temperatures greater than 37°C
43. No more than 3 ft tall   **45.** A serving contains at least 16 g of fat.   **47.** Dates after September 16   **49.** No more than 134 text messages   **51.** Years after 2012
53. Mileages less than or equal to 225   **55.** 🖩   **57.** -14
58. $-\frac{2}{3}$ **59.** -60 **60.** -11.1 **61.** 0   **62.** 5
63. -2 **64.** -1 **65.** 🖩   **67.** Temperatures between $-15°C$ and $-9\frac{4}{9}°C$ **69.** Lengths less than or equal to 8 cm
71. They contain at least 7.5 g of fat per serving.
73. At least $42   **75.** 🖩

Review Exercises: Chapter 1, pp. 66–67

1. True   **2.** False   **3.** True   **4.** True   **5.** True
6. False   **7.** True   **8.** True   **9.** -25 **10.** 7
11. -65 **12.** 3   **13.** -20 **14.** 1.11   **15.** $\frac{1}{2}$ **16.** $-\frac{3}{2}$
17. -8 **18.** -4 **19.** $-\frac{1}{3}$ **20.** 4   **21.** No solution; contradiction   **22.** 4   **23.** 16   **24.** 1   **25.** $-\frac{7}{5}$ **26.** 0

27. All real numbers; identity   **28.** $d = \frac{C}{\pi}$ **29.** $B = \frac{3V}{h}$

30. $y = \frac{5}{2}x - 5$ **31.** $x = \frac{b}{t - a}$ **32.** 0.012   **33.** 44%

34. 70%   **35.** 140   **36.** No   **37.** Yes   **38.** No
39. $5x - 6 < 2x + 3$
$\xleftarrow{\;\;\;} -5\,-4\,-3\,-2\,-1\;\;0\;\;1\;\;2\;\;3\;\;4\;\;5 \xrightarrow{\;\;\;}$
40. $-2 < x \leq 5$
$\xleftarrow{\;\;\;} -5\,-4\,-3\,-2\,-1\;\;0\;\;1\;\;2\;\;3\;\;4\;\;5 \xrightarrow{\;\;\;}$
41. $t > 0$
$\xleftarrow{\;\;\;} -5\,-4\,-3\,-2\,-1\;\;0\;\;1\;\;2\;\;3\;\;4\;\;5 \xrightarrow{\;\;\;}$ **42.** $\left\{t \mid t \geq -\frac{1}{2}\right\}$, or $\left[-\frac{1}{2}, \infty\right)$
43. $\{x \mid x \geq 7\}$, or $[7, \infty)$ **44.** $\{y \mid y > 3\}$, or $(3, \infty)$
45. $\{y \mid y \leq -4\}$, or $(-\infty, -4]$
46. $\{x \mid x < -11\}$, or $(-\infty, -11)$ **47.** $\{y \mid y > -7\}$, or $(-7, \infty)$ **48.** $\{x \mid x > -6\}$, or $(-6, \infty)$
49. $\left\{x \mid x > -\frac{9}{11}\right\}$, or $\left(-\frac{9}{11}, \infty\right)$ **50.** $\{t \mid t \leq -12\}$, or $(-\infty, -12]$ **51.** $\{x \mid x \leq -8\}$, or $(-\infty, -8]$
52. About 48%   **53.** 8 ft, 10 ft   **54.** Japanese students: 41,000; Chinese students: 62,000   **55.** 57, 59
56. Width: 11 cm; length: 17 cm   **57.** $160   **58.** About 109 million subscribers   **59.** 35°, 85°, 60°   **60.** No more than 55 g of fat   **61.** 14 or fewer copies   **62.** 🖩 Multiplying both sides of an equation by *any* nonzero number results in

an equivalent equation. When multiplying on both sides of an inequality, the sign of the number being multiplied by must be considered. If the number is positive, the direction of the inequality symbol remains unchanged; if the number is negative, the direction of the inequality symbol must be reversed to produce an equivalent inequality.   **63.** 🖩 The solutions of an equation can usually each be checked. The solutions of an inequality are normally too numerous to check. Checking a few numbers from the solution set found cannot guarantee that the answer is correct, although if any number does not check, the answer found is incorrect.   **64.** About 1 hr 36 min   **65.** Nile: 4160 mi; Amazon: 4225 mi   **66.** $16   **67.** $-23, 23$ **68.** $-20, 20$

69. $a = \dfrac{y - 3}{2 - b}$ **70.** $F = \dfrac{0.3(12w)}{9}$, or $F = 0.4w$

Test: Chapter 1, p. 68

1. [1.1] 9   **2.** [1.1] 15   **3.** [1.1] -3 **4.** [1.1] 49
5. [1.1] -12 **6.** [1.2] 2   **7.** [1.1] -8 **8.** [1.2] $-\frac{23}{67}$
9. [1.2] 7   **10.** [1.2] $\frac{23}{3}$ **11.** [1.2] All real numbers; identity
12. [1.6] $\{x \mid x > -5\}$, or $(-5, \infty)$
13. [1.6] $\{x \mid x > -13\}$, or $(-13, \infty)$
14. [1.6] $\{y \mid y \leq -13\}$, or $(-\infty, -13]$
15. [1.6] $\left\{y \mid y \leq -\frac{15}{2}\right\}$, or $\left(-\infty, -\frac{15}{2}\right]$
16. [1.6] $\{n \mid n < -5\}$, or $(-\infty, -5)$
17. [1.6] $\{x \mid x < -7\}$, or $(-\infty, -7)$
18. [1.6] $\{t \mid t \geq -1\}$, or $[-1, \infty)$
19. [1.6] $\{x \mid x \leq -1\}$, or $(-\infty, -1]$

20. [1.3] $r = \dfrac{A}{2\pi h}$ **21.** [1.3] $l = 2w - P$ **22.** [1.4] 2.3

23. [1.4] 0.3%   **24.** [1.4] 14.8   **25.** [1.4] 44%
26. [1.6]
$y < 4$
$\xleftarrow{\;\;\;} -10\,-8\,-6\,-4\,-2\;\;0\;\;2\;\;4\;\;6\;\;8\;\;10 \xrightarrow{\;\;\;}$
27. [1.6]
$-2 \leq x \leq 2$
$\xleftarrow{\;\;\;} -5\,-4\,-3\,-2\,-1\;\;0\;\;1\;\;2\;\;3\;\;4\;\;5 \xrightarrow{\;\;\;}$
28. [1.5] Width: 7 cm; length: 11 cm   **29.** [1.5] 525 mi from Springer Mountain and 1575 mi from Mt. Katahdin
30. [1.5] 81 mm, 83 mm, 85 mm   **31.** [1.4] $65
32. [1.7] More than 36 one-way trips per month

33. [1.3] $d = \dfrac{a}{3}$ **34.** [1.2] $-15, 15$ **35.** [1.7] Let

$h =$ the number of hours of sun each day; $4 \leq h \leq 6$
36. [1.5] 60 tickets

Cumulative Review: Chapter 1, pp. 69–70

1. -12 **2.** $\frac{3}{4}$ **3.** -4.2 **4.** 10   **5.** 134   **6.** 149
7. $2x + 1$ **8.** $-10t + 12$ **9.** $-21n + 36$
10.
$-\frac{5}{2}$
$\xleftarrow{\;\;\;} -5\,-4\,-3\,-2\,-1\;\;0\;\;1\;\;2\;\;3\;\;4\;\;5 \xrightarrow{\;\;\;}$ **11.** 27
12. $6(2x + 3y + 5z)$ **13.** -6 **14.** 16   **15.** 9

16. $\frac{13}{18}$ **17.** 1   **18.** $-\frac{7}{2}$ **19.** $z = \dfrac{x}{4y}$ **20.** $y = \frac{4}{9}x - \frac{1}{9}$

21. $n = \dfrac{p}{a + r}$ **22.** 1.83   **23.** 37.5%

24.

25. $\{t \mid t \le -2\}$, or $(-\infty, -2]$

26. $\{t \mid t < 3\}$, or $(-\infty, 3)$ **27.** $\{x \mid x < 30\}$, or $(-\infty, 30)$
28. $\{n \mid n \ge 2\}$, or $[2, \infty)$ **29.** 48 million **30.** 3.2 hr
31. $14\frac{1}{3}$ m **32.** 9 ft, 15 ft **33.** No more than \$52
34. About 194% **35.** 105° **36.** For widths greater than
27 cm **37.** $4t$ **38.** $-5, 5$ **39.** \$1025

CHAPTER 2

Exercise Set 2.1, pp. 78–81

1. (a) **2.** (c) **3.** (b) **4.** (d) **5.** 2 drinks
7. The person weighs more than 140 lb. **9.** About \$5156
11. \$231,856,000 **13.** About 29.2 million tons **15.** About
3.2 million tons **17.** About \$12 billion **19.** 2001
21.

23.

25.

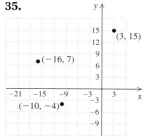

27. $A(-4, 5); B(-3, -3); C(0, 4); D(3, 4); E(3, -4)$
29. $A(4, 1); B(0, -5); C(-4, 0); D(-3, -2); E(3, 0)$
31.

33.

35.

37.

39.

41. IV **43.** III **45.** I
47. II **49.** I and IV
51. I and III **53.** ▨

55. $y = \dfrac{2x}{5}$, or $y = \frac{2}{5}x$

56. $y = \dfrac{-3x}{2}$, or $y = -\frac{3}{2}x$

57. $y = x - 8$
58. $y = -\frac{2}{5}x + 2$
59. $y = -\frac{2}{3}x + \frac{5}{3}$

60. $y = \frac{5}{8}x - \frac{1}{8}$ **61.** ▨ **63.** II or IV **65.** $(-1, -5)$

67.

69. $\frac{65}{2}$ sq units
71. Latitude 27° North;
longitude 81° West

73. ▨

Technology Connection, p. 88

1. $y = -5x + 6.5$

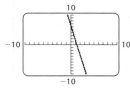

2. $y = 3x + 4.5$

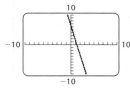

3. $7y - 4x = 22$, or $y = \frac{4}{7}x + \frac{22}{7}$

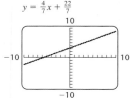

4. $5y + 11x = -20$, or $y = -\frac{11}{5}x - 4$

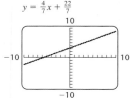

5. $2y - x^2 = 0$, or $y = 0.5x^2$

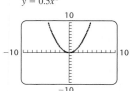

6. $y + x^2 = 8$, or $y = -x^2 + 8$

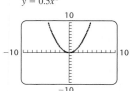

Exercise Set 2.2, pp. 89–91

1. False **2.** True **3.** True **4.** True **5.** True
6. False **7.** Yes **9.** No **11.** No
13.

$y = x + 3$
$\begin{array}{c|c} 2 & -1 + 3 \end{array}$
$2 \overset{?}{=} 2$ True

$y = x + 3$
$\begin{array}{c|c} 7 & 4 + 3 \end{array}$
$7 \overset{?}{=} 7$ True

$(2, 5)$; answers may vary

15. $y = \frac{1}{2}x + 3$

$5 \;\big|\; \frac{1}{2} \cdot 4 + 3$
$\quad\;\; 2 + 3$

$5 \stackrel{?}{=} 5$ True

$(0, 3)$; answers may vary

$y = \frac{1}{2}x + 3$

$2 \;\big|\; \frac{1}{2}(-2) + 3$
$\quad\;\; -1 + 3$

$2 \stackrel{?}{=} 2$ True

17. $y + 3x = 7$

$1 + 3 \cdot 2 \;\big|\; 7$
$\quad\; 1 + 6$

$\qquad 7 \stackrel{?}{=} 7$ True

$(1, 4)$; answers may vary

$y + 3x = 7$

$-5 + 3 \cdot 4 \;\big|\; 7$
$\quad\; -5 + 12$

$\qquad 7 \stackrel{?}{=} 7$ True

19. $4x - 2y = 10$

$4 \cdot 0 - 2(-5) \;\big|\; 10$
$\qquad 0 + 10$

$\qquad\qquad 10 \stackrel{?}{=} 10$ True

$(2, -1)$; answers may vary

$4x - 2y = 10$

$4 \cdot 4 - 2 \cdot 3 \;\big|\; 10$
$\qquad 16 - 6$

$\qquad\qquad 10 \stackrel{?}{=} 10$ True

21.

23.

25.

27.

29.

31.

33.

35.

37.

39.

41.

43.

45.

47.

49. About \$3800

51. About \$49

53. About \$96

55. About 33 gal

57. About $1700

59. ✍ **61.** $\frac{12}{5}$ **62.** $-\frac{3}{4}$
63. 3 **64.** $-\frac{21}{5}$
65. $Q = 2A - T$
66. $p = \dfrac{w}{q + 1}$
67. $y = \dfrac{C - Ax}{B}$
68. $y = m(x - h) + k$
69. ✍

Technology Connection, p. 95

1. $y = -0.72x - 15$

Xscl = 5, Yscl = 5

2. $y - 2.13x = 27$, or $y = 2.13x + 27$

Xscl = 5, Yscl = 5

71.

73. $x + y = 5$, or $y = -x + 5$
75. $y = x + 2$

3. $5x + 6y = 84$, or $y = -\frac{5}{6}x + 14$

Xscl = 5, Yscl = 5

4. $2x - 7y = 150$, or $y = \frac{2}{7}x - \frac{150}{7}$

Xscl = 10, Yscl = 5

77.

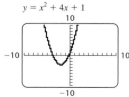

$25d + 5l = 225$

Answers may vary.
1 dinner, 40 lunches;
5 dinners, 20 lunches;
8 dinners, 5 lunches

5. $19x - 17y = 200$, or $y = \frac{19}{17}x - \frac{200}{17}$

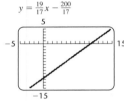

6. $6x + 5y = 159$, or $y = -\frac{6}{5}x + \frac{159}{5}$

Xscl = 5, Yscl = 5

Exercise Set 2.3, pp. 97–99

1. (f) **2.** (e) **3.** (d) **4.** (c) **5.** (b) **6.** (a)
7. (a) $(0, 5)$; **(b)** $(2, 0)$ **9. (a)** $(0, -4)$; **(b)** $(3, 0)$
11. (a) $(0, -2)$; **(b)** $(-3, 0), (3, 0)$ **13. (a)** $(0, 0)$;
(b) $(-2, 0), (0, 0), (5, 0)$ **15. (a)** $(0, 3)$; **(b)** $(5, 0)$
17. (a) $(0, -18)$; **(b)** $(4, 0)$ **19. (a)** $(0, 16)$; **(b)** $(-20, 0)$
21. (a) None; **(b)** $(12, 0)$ **23. (a)** $(0, -9)$; **(b)** none

79.

$y = -|x|$

81.

$y = x^2$

25.

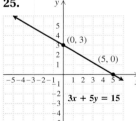

$3x + 5y = 15$

27.

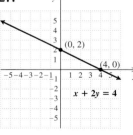

$x + 2y = 4$

83. $y = -2.8x + 3.5$

85. $y = 2.8x - 3.5$

87. $y = x^2 + 4x + 1$

89. $56.62; 16.2 gal

29.

$-x + 2y = 8$

31.

$3x + y = 9$

33.

35.

57.

59.

37.

39.

61.

63.

41.

43.

65.

67.

45.

47.

69.

71. $y = -1$ **73.** $x = 4$
75. $x = 0$ **77.** ✍
79. $d - 7$
80. $w + 5$, or $5 + w$
81. Let n represent the number; $7 + 4n$
82. Let n represent the number; $3n$
83. Let x and y represent the numbers; $2(x + y)$
84. Let a and b represent the numbers; $\frac{1}{2}(a + b)$
85. ✍   **87.** $y = 0$ **89.** $x = -2$ **91.** $(-3, 4)$
93. $-5x + 3y = 15$, or $y = \frac{5}{3}x + 5$ **95.** -24
97. $\left(\frac{C - D}{A}, 0\right)$ **99.** $\left(0, -\frac{80}{7}\right)$, or $(0, -11.\overline{428571})$; $(40, 0)$
101. $(0, -9)$; $(45, 0)$ **103.** $\left(0, \frac{1}{25}\right)$, or $(0, 0.04)$; $\left(\frac{1}{50}, 0\right)$, or $(0.02, 0)$

49.

51.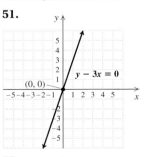

Exercise Set 2.4, pp. 103–108

1. Miles per hour, or $\dfrac{\text{miles}}{\text{hour}}$

2. Hours per chapter, or $\dfrac{\text{hours}}{\text{chapter}}$

3. Dollars per mile, or $\dfrac{\text{dollars}}{\text{mile}}$

53.

55.

4. Petunias per foot, or $\dfrac{\text{petunias}}{\text{foot}}$

5. Minutes per errand, or $\dfrac{\text{minutes}}{\text{errand}}$

6. Cups of flour per cake, or $\dfrac{\text{cups of flour}}{\text{cake}}$

7. (a) 30 mpg; **(b)** \$39.33/day; **(c)** 130 mi/day; **(d)** 30¢/mi
9. (a) 7 mph; **(b)** \$7.50/hr; **(c)** \$1.07/mi
11. (a) \$22/hr; **(b)** 20.6 pages/hr; **(c)** \$1.07/page
13. \$568.4 billion/yr **15. (a)** 14.5 floors/min;
(b) 4.14 sec/floor **17. (a)** 23.42 ft/min; **(b)** 0.04 min/ft

19. **21.**

23.

25.

27.

29. 20 calls/hr **31.** 75 mi/hr **33.** 12¢/min
35. −2000 people/yr **37.** 0.02 gal/mi **39.** (e) **41.** (d)
43. (b) **45.** 🖉 **47.** 5 **48.** −6 **49.** −1 **50.** $-\frac{4}{3}$
51. $-\frac{4}{3}$ **52.** 1 **53.** 0 **54.** Undefined **55.** 🖉

57. **59.**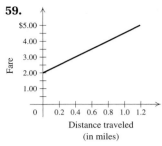

61. 0.45 min/mi **63.** About 41.6 min **65.** 3.6 bu/hr

Exercise Set 2.5, pp. 114–120

1. Positive **2.** Negative **3.** Negative **4.** Positive
5. Positive **6.** Negative **7.** Zero **8.** Positive
9. Negative **10.** Zero **11.** \$60/blog **13.** −\$6/month
15. 1 point/\$1000 income **17.** About −2.1°/min **19.** $\frac{4}{3}$
21. $\frac{3}{2}$ **23.** 2 **25.** −1 **27.** 0 **29.** $-\frac{1}{3}$
31. Undefined **33.** $-\frac{3}{4}$ **35.** $\frac{1}{4}$ **37.** 0 **39.** $\frac{5}{4}$
41. $-\frac{4}{5}$ **43.** $\frac{2}{3}$ **45.** −1 **47.** $-\frac{1}{2}$ **49.** 0
51. 1 **53.** Undefined **55.** 0 **57.** Undefined
59. Undefined **61.** 0 **63.** 15% **65.** 35%
67. $\frac{29}{98}$, or about 30% **69.** About 5.1%; yes **71.** 🖉
73. $y = \dfrac{c - ax}{b}$ **74.** $r = \dfrac{p + mn}{x}$ **75.** $y = \dfrac{ax - c}{b}$
76. $t = \dfrac{q - rs}{n}$

77. **78.**

79. 🖉 **81.** 0.364, or 36.4% **83.** $\{m \,|\, m \geq \frac{5}{2}\}$ **85.** $\frac{1}{2}$

Technology Connection, p. 125

1.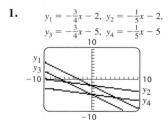
$$y_1 = -\tfrac{3}{4}x - 2, \ y_2 = -\tfrac{1}{5}x - 2,$$
$$y_3 = -\tfrac{3}{4}x - 5, \ y_4 = -\tfrac{1}{5}x - 5$$

Exercise Set 2.6, pp. 127–129

1. (f)   **2.** (b)   **3.** (d)   **4.** (c)   **5.** (e)   **6.** (a)

7.

9.

11.

13.

15.

17.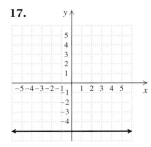

19. $-\frac{2}{7}; (0, 5)$ **21.** $\frac{1}{3}; (0, 7)$ **23.** $\frac{9}{5}; (0, -4)$ **25.** $3; (0, 7)$
27. $-2; (0, 4)$ **29.** $0; (0, 3)$ **31.** $\frac{2}{5}; \left(0, \frac{8}{5}\right)$ **33.** $\frac{9}{8}; (0, 0)$
35. $y = 5x + 7$ **37.** $y = \frac{7}{8}x - 1$ **39.** $y = -\frac{5}{3}x - 8$
41. $y = \frac{1}{3}$ **43.** $y = \frac{3}{2}x + 17$, where y is the number
of gallons per person and x is the number of years since
2000   **45.** $y = \frac{2}{5}x + 15$, where y is the number of jobs, in
millions, and x is the number of years since 2000

47.

49.

51.

53.

55.

57.

59.

61.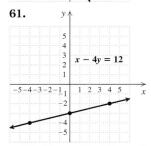

63. Yes   **65.** No   **67.** Yes   **69.** Yes   **71.** No   **73.** Yes
75. $y = 5x + 11$ **77.** $y = \frac{1}{2}x$ **79.** $y = x + 3$
81. $y = x - 4$ **83.** 📝   **85.** $y = m(x - h) + k$
86. $y = -2(x + 4) + 9$ **87.** -7 **88.** 13   **89.** -9
90. -11 **91.** 📝   **93.** When $x = 0, y = b$, so $(0, b)$ is
on the line. When $x = 1, y = m + b$, so $(1, m + b)$ is on the
line. Then

$$\text{slope} = \frac{(m + b) - b}{1 - 0} = m.$$

95. $y = \frac{1}{3}x + 3$ **97.** $y = -\frac{5}{3}x + 3$ **99.** $y = -\frac{2}{3}x$

Connecting the Concepts, p. 130

1. (a) Yes;
(b)

2. (a) Yes;
(b)

3. (a) Yes;
(b)

4. (a) Yes;
(b)

5. (a) Yes;
(b)

6. (a) Yes;
(b)

7. (a) No
8. (a) Yes;
(b)

9. (a) Yes;
(b)

10. (a) No
11. (a) Yes;
(b)

12. (a) Yes;
(b)

13. (a) Yes;
(b)

14. (a) Yes;
(b)

15. (a) Yes; **(b)**

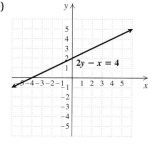

16. (a) No

17. (a) Yes;
(b)

18. (a) Yes;
(b)

19. (a) Yes;
(b)

20. (a) Yes;
(b)

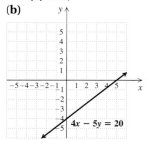

Technology Connection, p. 132

1. $y_1 = \frac{3}{4}x + 2$; $y_2 = -\frac{4}{3}x - 1$

2. $y_1 = -\frac{2}{5}x - 4$; $y_2 = \frac{5}{2}x + 3$

3. $y_1 = \frac{31}{40}x + 2$; $y_2 = -\frac{40}{30}x - 1$ No: $-\dfrac{40}{30} \neq -\dfrac{1}{\frac{31}{40}}$

Although the lines appear to be perpendicular, they are not, because the product of their slopes is not -1:

$$\frac{31}{40}\left(-\frac{40}{30}\right) = -\frac{1240}{1200} \neq -1.$$

Visualizing for Success, p. 136

1. C   **2.** G   **3.** F   **4.** B   **5.** D   **6.** A   **7.** I
8. H   **9.** J   **10.** E

Exercise Set 2.7, pp. 137–140

1. (g)   **2.** (b)   **3.** (d)   **4.** (h)   **5.** (e)   **6.** (a)
7. (f)   **8.** (c)   **9.** (c)   **10.** (b)   **11.** (d)   **12.** (a)
13. $y - 6 = 3(x - 1)$ **15.** $y - 8 = \frac{3}{5}(x - 2)$
17. $y - 1 = -4(x - 3)$ **19.** $y - (-4) = \frac{3}{2}(x - 5)$
21. $y - 6 = -\frac{5}{4}(x - (-2))$

23. $y - (-1) = -2(x - (-4))$
25. $y - 8 = 1(x - (-2))$ **27.** $y = 4x - 7$
29. $y = \frac{7}{4}x - 9$ **31.** $y = -2x + 1$ **33.** $y = -4x - 9$
35. $y = \frac{2}{3}x + \frac{8}{3}$ **37.** $y = -\frac{5}{6}x + 4$ **39.** $y = \frac{1}{2}x + 4$
41. $y = 4x - 5$ **43.** $y = -\frac{2}{3}x - \frac{13}{3}$ **45.** $x = 5$
47. $y = -\frac{3}{2}x + \frac{11}{2}$ **49.** $y = x + 6$ **51.** $y = -\frac{1}{2}x + 6$
53. $x = -3$

55.

57.

59.

61.

63.

65.

67.

69.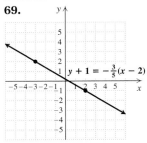

71. (a) 51.6 births per 1000 females; **(b)** 39.8 births per 1000 females   **73. (a)** About 13.1%; **(b)** 4%
75. (a) 16.47 million students; **(b)** 18.95 million students
77. (a) 33.65 million residents; **(b)** about 38.6 million residents
79. $y = -x + 5$ **81.** $y = \frac{2}{3}x + 3$ **83.** $y = \frac{2}{5}x - 2$
85. $y = 2x + 7$ **87.** 📄   **89.** -125 **90.** 64   **91.** -64
92. 8   **93.** 28   **94.** -4 **95.** 📄

97.

99. $y = 2x - 9$
101. $y = -\frac{4}{3}x + \frac{23}{3}$
103. $y = -4x + 7$
105. $y = \frac{10}{3}x + \frac{25}{3}$
107. $(2, 0), (0, 5)$

109. $-\dfrac{x}{4} + \dfrac{y}{3} = 1; (-4, 0), (0, 3)$ **111.** 📄

Connecting the Concepts, pp. 140–141

1. Slope–intercept form   **2.** Standard form
3. None of these   **4.** Standard form
5. Point–slope form   **6.** None of these
7. $2x - 5y = 10$ **8.** $x - y = 2$
9. $-2x + y = 7$, or $2x - y = -7$ **10.** $\frac{1}{2}x + y = 3$
11. $3x - y = -23$, or $-3x + y = 23$ **12.** $x + 0y = 18$
13. $y = \frac{2}{7}x - \frac{8}{7}$ **14.** $y = -x - 8$ **15.** $y = 8x - 3$
16. $y = -\frac{3}{5}x + 3$ **17.** $y = -\frac{8}{9}x + \frac{5}{9}$ **18.** $y = -x$
19. $y = -\frac{1}{2}$ **20.** $y = \frac{1}{2}x$

Review Exercises: Chapter 2, pp. 144–146

1. True   **2.** True   **3.** False   **4.** False   **5.** True
6. True   **7.** True   **8.** False   **9.** True   **10.** True
11. About 1.3 billion searches   **12.** About 1137 searches

13.–15.

16. III   **17.** IV   **18.** II
19. $(-5, -1)$ **20.** $(-2, 5)$
21. $(3, 0)$

22.

23. (a) No; **(b)** yes

24.

$$\frac{2x - y = 3}{\begin{array}{c} 2 \cdot 0 - (-3) \\ 0 + 3 \end{array} \,\Big|\, 3}$$

$$3 \overset{?}{=} 3 \quad \text{True}$$

$$\frac{2x - y = 3}{\begin{array}{c} 2 \cdot 2 - 1 \\ 4 - 1 \end{array} \,\Big|\, 3}$$

$$3 \overset{?}{=} 3 \quad \text{True}$$

$(-1, -5)$; answers may vary

25. $y = x - 5$

26. $y = -\frac{1}{4}x$

27. $y = -x + 4$

28. $4x + y = 3$

29. $4x + 5 = 3$

30. $5x - 2y = 10$

31. About 7 million viewers

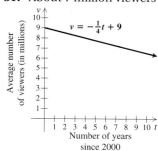
$v = -\frac{1}{4}t + 9$

32. (a) $\frac{2}{15}$ mi/min; **(b)** 7.5 min/mi

33. 12 mpg **34.** 0

35. $\frac{7}{3}$ **36.** $-\frac{3}{7}$ **37.** $-\frac{6}{5}$

38. 0 **39.** Undefined

40. 2 **41.** $8.\overline{3}\%$

42. $(16, 0), (0, -10)$

43. $-\frac{3}{5}; (0, 9)$

44. Perpendicular

45. Parallel

46. $y = \frac{3}{8}x + 7$ **47.** $y - 9 = -\frac{1}{3}(x - (-2))$

48. (a) \$1725; **(b)** \$2701 **49.** $y = 5x - 25$

50. $y = -\frac{5}{3}x - \frac{5}{3}$

51. $y = \frac{2}{3}x - 5$

52. $2x + y = 4$

53. $y = 6$

54. $x = -2$

55. $y + 2 = -\frac{1}{2}(x - 3)$

56. ✍ Two perpendicular lines share the same y-intercept if their point of intersection is on the y-axis.

57. ✍ The graph of a vertical line has only an x-intercept. The graph of a horizontal line has only a y-intercept. The graph of a nonvertical, non-horizontal line will have only one intercept if it passes through the origin: $(0, 0)$ is both the x-intercept and the y-intercept. **58.** -1

59. 19 **60.** Area: 45 sq units; perimeter: 28 units

61. $(0, 4), (1, 3), (-1, 3)$; answers may vary

Test: Chapter 2, pp. 146–147

1. [2.1] About 95 students **2.** [2.1] About 137 students

3. [2.1] III **4.** [2.1] II **5.** [2.1] $(3, 4)$ **6.** [2.1] $(0, -4)$

7. [2.1] $(-5, 2)$

8. [2.2] 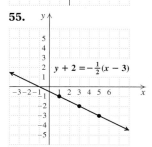 $y = 2x - 1$

9. [2.3] 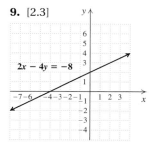 $2x - 4y = -8$

10. [2.3] 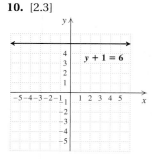 $y + 1 = 6$

11. [2.2] 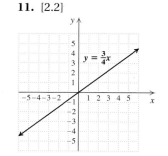 $y = \frac{3}{4}x$

12. [2.2]

13. [2.3]

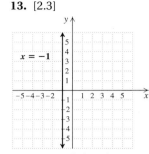

14. [2.5] 5   **15.** [2.5] $-\frac{9}{4}$ **16.** [2.5] Undefined

17. [2.4] $\frac{1}{3}$ km/min   **18.** [2.5] 31.5%

19. [2.3] $(6, 0)$, $(0, -30)$ **20.** [2.6] 8; $(0, 10)$

21. [2.6] $y = -\frac{1}{3}x - 11$ **22.** [2.6] Parallel

23. [2.6] Perpendicular   **24.** [2.7] $y = -\frac{5}{2}x - \frac{11}{2}$

25. [2.7] **(a)**   **(b)** 138 beats per minute

26. [2.6]

27. [2.7]

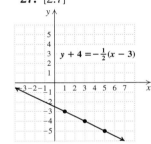

28. [2.6] $y = \frac{2}{5}x + 9$ **29.** [2.1] Area: 25 sq units; perimeter: 20 units   **30.** [2.2], [2.7] $(0, 12)$, $(-3, 15)$, $(5, 7)$

Cumulative Review: Chapters 1–2, pp. 148–149

1. 7   **2.** $12a - 6b + 18$ **3.** $4(2x - y + 1)$ **4.** $2 \cdot 3^3$
5. -0.15 **6.** 37   **7.** $\frac{1}{10}$ **8.** -10 **9.** 0.367   **10.** $\frac{11}{60}$
11. 2.6   **12.** 7.28   **13.** $-\frac{5}{12}$ **14.** -3 **15.** 27
16. $-2y - 7$ **17.** $5x + 11$ **18.** -2.6 **19.** -27
20. 16   **21.** -6 **22.** 2   **23.** $\frac{7}{9}$ **24.** -17 **25.** 2
26. $\{x \mid x < 16\}$, or $(-\infty, 16)$ **27.** $\{x \mid x \le -\frac{11}{8}\}$, or $(-\infty, -\frac{11}{8}]$ **28.** $h = \dfrac{A - \pi r^2}{2\pi r}$ **29.** IV

30.

31.

32.

33.

34.

35.

36.

37.

38. $\left(\frac{21}{2}, 0\right)$, $(0, -3)$

39. $\left(-\frac{5}{4}, 0\right)$, $(0, 5)$

40. 3; $(0, -2)$ **41.** $-\frac{1}{3}$

42. $y = \frac{2}{7}x - 4$

43. $y - 4 = -\frac{3}{8}(x - (-6))$

44. $y = -\frac{3}{8}x + \frac{7}{4}$

45. $y = 2x + 1$

46. 0.5 million bicycles per year

47. (a)   **(b)** about 353 calories per hour

48. $210 billion   **49.** $54,533   **50.** 21 million Americans
51. $120   **52.** 50 m, 53 m, 40 m   **53.** 4 hr
54. $25,000   **55.** $-4, 4$ **56.** 2   **57.** -5 **58.** 3
59. No solution   **60.** $Q = \dfrac{2 - pm}{p}$
61. $y = -\frac{7}{3}x + 7$; $y = -\frac{7}{3}x - 7$; $y = \frac{7}{3}x - 7$; $y = \frac{7}{3}x + 7$

CHAPTER 3

Technology Connection, p. 158

1. Correct   **2.** Correct   **3.** Not correct
4. Not correct   **5.** Not correct   **6.** Correct
7. Not correct   **8.** Correct

Exercise Set 3.1, pp. 158–159

1. (h)   **2.** (f)   **3.** (b)   **4.** (e)   **5.** (c)   **6.** (g)
7. (d)   **8.** (a)   **9.** Answers may vary. $(14x)(x^2)$,
$(7x^2)(2x), (-2)(-7x^3)$ **11.** Answers may vary. $(-15)(a^4)$,
$(-5a)(3a^3), (-3a^2)(5a^2)$ **13.** Answers may vary.
$(5t^2)(5t^3), (25t)(t^4), (-5t)(-5t^4)$
15. $8(x + 3)$ **17.** $6(x - 5)$ **19.** $2(x^2 + x - 4)$
21. $t(3t + 1)$ **23.** $-5y(y + 2)$ **25.** $x^2(x + 6)$
27. $8a^2(2a^2 - 3)$ **29.** $-t^2(6t^4 - 9t^2 + 4)$
31. $6x^2(x^6 + 2x^4 - 4x^2 + 5)$
33. $x^2y^2(x^3y^3 + x^2y + xy - 1)$
35. $-5a^2b^2(7ab^2 - 2b + 3a)$ **37.** $(n - 6)(n + 3)$
39. $(x + 3)(x^2 - 7)$ **41.** $(2y - 9)(y^2 + 1)$
43. $(x + 2)(x^2 + 5)$ **45.** $(a + 3)(5a^2 + 2)$
47. $(3n - 2)(3n^2 + 1)$ **49.** $(t - 5)(4t^2 + 3)$
51. $(7x + 5)(x^2 - 3)$ **53.** $(6a + 7)(a^2 + 1)$
55. $(x + 6)(2x^2 - 5)$ **57.** Not factorable by grouping
59. $(y + 8)(y^2 - 2)$ **61.** $(x - 4)(2x^2 - 9)$ **63.** ⟡
65. $x^2 + 9x + 14$ **66.** $x^2 - 9x + 14$ **67.** $x^2 - 5x - 14$
68. $x^2 + 5x - 14$ **69.** $a^2 - 4a + 3$ **70.** $t^2 + 8t + 15$
71. $t^2 + 5t - 50$ **72.** $a^2 - 2a - 24$ **73.** ⟡
75. $(2x^3 + 3)(2x^2 + 3)$ **77.** $2x(x + 1)(x^2 - 2)$
79. $(x - 1)(5x^4 + x^2 + 3)$ **81.** Answers may vary.
$8x^4y^3 - 24x^2y^4 + 16x^3y^4$

Exercise Set 3.2, pp. 165–166

1. Positive; positive   **2.** Negative; negative
3. Negative; positive   **4.** Positive; positive
5. Positive   **6.** Negative   **7.** $(x + 4)(x + 4)$
9. $(x + 1)(x + 10)$ **11.** $(x + 3)(x + 7)$
13. $(t - 2)(t - 7)$ **15.** $(b - 4)(b - 1)$
17. $(a - 3)(a - 4)$ **19.** $(d - 2)(d - 5)$
21. $(x - 5)(x + 3)$ **23.** $(x + 5)(x - 3)$
25. $2(x + 2)(x - 9)$ **27.** $-x(x + 2)(x - 8)$
29. $(y - 5)(y + 9)$ **31.** $(x - 6)(x + 12)$
33. $-5(b - 3)(b + 10)$ **35.** $x^3(x - 2)(x + 1)$
37. Prime   **39.** $(t + 4)(t + 8)$ **41.** $(x + 9)(x + 11)$
43. $3x(x - 25)(x + 4)$ **45.** $-2(x - 24)(x + 3)$
47. $(y - 12)(y - 8)$ **49.** $-a^4(a - 6)(a + 15)$
51. $\left(t + \frac{1}{3}\right)^2$ **53.** Prime   **55.** $(p - 5q)(p - 2q)$
57. Prime   **59.** $(s - 6t)(s + 2t)$ **61.** $6a^8(a - 2)(a + 7)$
63. ⟡   **65.** $6x^2 + 17x + 12$ **66.** $6x^2 + x - 12$
67. $6x^2 - x - 12$ **68.** $6x^2 - 17x + 12$
69. $5x^2 - 36x + 7$ **70.** $3x^2 + 13x - 30$
71. ⟡   **73.** $-5, 5, -23, 23, -49, 49$
75. $(y + 0.2)(y - 0.4)$ **77.** $-\frac{1}{3}a(a - 3)(a + 2)$
79. $(x^m + 4)(x^m + 7)$ **81.** $(a + 1)(x + 2)(x + 1)$
83. $(x + 3)^3$, or $(x^3 + 9x^2 + 27x + 27)$ cubic meters
85. $x^2\left(\frac{3}{4}\pi + 2\right)$, or $\frac{1}{4}x^2(3\pi + 8)$ **87.** $x^2\left(9 - \frac{1}{2}\pi\right)$
89. $(x + 4)(x + 5)$

Exercise Set 3.3, pp. 175–176

1. (c)   **2.** (a)   **3.** (d)   **4.** (b)   **5.** $(2x - 1)(x + 4)$
7. $(3x + 1)(x - 6)$ **9.** $(2t + 1)(2t + 5)$
11. $(5a - 3)(3a - 1)$ **13.** $(3x + 4)(2x + 3)$
15. $2(3x + 1)(x - 2)$ **17.** $t(7t + 1)(t + 2)$
19. $(4x - 5)(3x - 2)$ **21.** $-1(7x + 4)(5x + 2)$, or
$-(7x + 4)(5x + 2)$ **23.** Prime   **25.** $(5x + 4)^2$
27. $(20y - 1)(y + 3)$ **29.** $(7x + 5)(2x + 9)$
31. $-1(x - 3)(2x + 5)$, or $-(x - 3)(2x + 5)$
33. $-3(2x + 1)(x + 5)$ **35.** $2(a + 1)(5a - 9)$
37. $4(3x - 1)(x + 6)$ **39.** $(3x + 1)(x + 1)$
41. $(x + 3)(x - 2)$ **43.** $(4t - 3)(2t - 7)$
45. $(3x + 2)(2x + 5)$ **47.** $(y + 4)(2y - 1)$
49. $(3a - 4)(2a - 1)$ **51.** $(16t + 7)(t + 1)$
53. $-1(3x + 1)(3x + 5)$, or $-(3x + 1)(3x + 5)$
55. $10(x^2 + 3x - 7)$ **57.** $3x(3x - 1)(2x + 3)$
59. $(x + 1)(25x + 64)$ **61.** $3x(7x + 1)(8x + 1)$
63. $-t^2(2t - 3)(7t + 1)$ **65.** $2(2y + 9)(8y - 3)$
67. $(2a - b)(a - 2b)$ **69.** $2(s + t)(4s + 7t)$
71. $3(3x - 4y)^2$ **73.** $-2(3a - 2b)(4a - 3b)$
75. $x^2(2x + 3)(7x - 1)$ **77.** $a^6(3a + 4)(3a + 2)$
79. ⟡   **81.** $x^2 - 4x + 4$ **82.** $x^2 + 4x + 4$
83. $x^2 - 4$ **84.** $25t^2 - 30t + 9$ **85.** $16a^2 + 8a + 1$
86. $4n^2 - 49$ **87.** $9c^2 - 60c + 100$
88. $1 - 10a + 25a^2$ **89.** $64n^2 - 9$ **90.** $81 - y^2$
91. ⟡   **93.** $(3xy + 2)(6xy - 5)$ **95.** Prime
97. $(4t^5 - 1)^2$ **99.** $-1(5x^m - 2)(3x^m - 4)$, or
$-(5x^m - 2)(3x^m - 4)$ **101.** $(3a^{3n} + 1)(a^{3n} - 1)$
103. $[7(t - 3)^n - 2][(t - 3)^n + 1]$

Connecting the Concepts, pp. 176–177

1. $6x^2(x^3 - 3)$ **2.** $(x + 2)(x + 8)$ **3.** $(x + 7)(2x - 1)$
4. $(x + 3)(x^2 + 2)$ **5.** $5(x - 2)(x + 10)$ **6.** Prime
7. $7y(x - 4)(x + 1)$ **8.** $3a^2(5a^2 - 9b^2 + 7b)$
9. $(b - 7)^2$ **10.** $(3x - 1)(4x + 1)$
11. $(c + 1)(c + 2)(c - 2)$ **12.** $2(x - 5)(x + 20)$
13. Prime   **14.** $15(d^2 - 2d + 5)$
15. $(3p + 2q)(5p + 2q)$ **16.** $-2t(t + 2)(t + 3)$
17. $(x + 11)(x - 7)$ **18.** $10(c + 1)^2$
19. $-1(2x - 5)(x + 1)$ **20.** $2n(m - 5)(m^2 - 3)$

Exercise Set 3.4, pp. 182–183

1. Prime polynomial   **2.** Difference of squares
3. Difference of squares   **4.** None of these
5. Perfect-square trinomial   **6.** Perfect-square trinomial
7. None of these   **8.** Prime polynomial
9. Difference of squares   **10.** Perfect-square trinomial
11. Yes   **13.** No   **15.** No   **17.** Yes   **19.** $(x + 8)^2$
21. $(x - 5)^2$ **23.** $5(p + 2)^2$ **25.** $(1 - t)^2$, or $(t - 1)^2$
27. $2(3x + 1)^2$ **29.** $(7 - 4y)^2$, or $(4y - 7)^2$
31. $-x^3(x - 9)^2$ **33.** $2n(n + 10)^2$ **35.** $5(2x + 5)^2$
37. $(7 - 3x)^2$, or $(3x - 7)^2$ **39.** $(4x + 3)^2$
41. $2(1 + 5x)^2$, or $2(5x + 1)^2$ **43.** $(3p + 2q)^2$
45. Prime   **47.** $-1(8m + n)^2$, or $-(8m + n)^2$
49. $-2(4s - 5t)^2$ **51.** Yes   **53.** No   **55.** Yes
57. $(x + 5)(x - 5)$ **59.** $(p + 3)(p - 3)$

61. $(7 + t)(-7 + t)$, or $(t + 7)(t - 7)$
63. $6(a + 2)(a - 2)$ **65.** $(7x - 1)^2$
67. $2(10 + t)(10 - t)$ **69.** $-5(4a + 3)(4a - 3)$
71. $5(t + 4)(t - 4)$ **73.** $2(2x + 9)(2x - 9)$
75. $x(6 + 7x)(6 - 7x)$ **77.** Prime
79. $(t^2 + 1)(t + 1)(t - 1)$ **81.** $-3x(x - 4)^2$
83. $3t(5t + 3)(5t - 3)$ **85.** $a^6(a - 1)^2$
87. $10(a + b)(a - b)$ **89.** $(4x^2 + y^2)(2x + y)(2x - y)$
91. $2(3t + 2s)(3t - 2s)$ **93.** 🔳   **95.** $8x^6y^{12}$
96. $-125x^6y^3$ **97.** $x^3 + 3x^2 + 3x + 1$
98. $x^3 - 3x^2 + 3x - 1$ **99.** $p^3 + 3p^2q + 3pq^2 + q^3$
100. $p^3 - 3p^2q + 3pq^2 - q^3$ **101.** 🔳
103. $(x^4 + 2^4)(x^2 + 2^2)(x + 2)(x - 2)$, or
$(x^4 + 16)(x^2 + 4)(x + 2)(x - 2)$
105. $2x\left(3x - \frac{2}{5}\right)\left(3x + \frac{2}{5}\right)$
107. $[(y - 5)^2 + z^4][(y - 5) + z^2][(y - 5) - z^2]$, or
$(y^2 - 10y + 25 + z^4)(y - 5 + z^2)(y - 5 - z^2)$
109. $-1(x^2 + 1)(x + 3)(x - 3)$, or $-(x^2 + 1)(x + 3)(x - 3)$
111. $(y + 4)^2$ **113.** $(3p + 5)(3p - 5)^2$
115. $(9 + b^{2k})(3 + b^k)(3 - b^k)$ **117.** $2x^3 - x^2 - 1$
119. $(y + x + 7)(y - x - 1)$ **121.** 16
123. $(x + 1)^2 - x^2 = [(x + 1) + x][(x + 1) - x] =$
$2x + 1 = (x + 1) + x$

Exercise Set 3.5, p. 187

1. Difference of cubes   **2.** Sum of cubes   **3.** Difference
of squares   **4.** None of these   **5.** Sum of cubes
6. Difference of cubes   **7.** None of these   **8.** Difference
of squares   **9.** Difference of cubes   **10.** None of these
11. $(x - 4)(x^2 + 4x + 16)$ **13.** $(z + 1)(z^2 - z + 1)$
15. $(t - 10)(t^2 + 10t + 100)$
17. $(3x + 1)(9x^2 - 3x + 1)$
19. $(4 - 5x)(16 + 20x + 25x^2)$
21. $(x - y)(x^2 + xy + y^2)$ **23.** $\left(a + \frac{1}{2}\right)\left(a^2 - \frac{1}{2}a + \frac{1}{4}\right)$
25. $8(t - 1)(t^2 + t + 1)$ **27.** $2(3x + 1)(9x^2 - 3x + 1)$
29. $rs(s + 4)(s^2 - 4s + 16)$
31. $5(x - 2z)(x^2 + 2xz + 4z^2)$
33. $\left(y - \frac{1}{10}\right)\left(y^2 + \frac{1}{10}y + \frac{1}{100}\right)$
35. $(x + 0.1)(x^2 - 0.1x + 0.01)$
37. $8(2x^2 - t^2)(4x^4 + 2x^2t^2 + t^4)$
39. $2y(3y - 4)(9y^2 + 12y + 16)$
41. $(z + 1)(z^2 - z + 1)(z - 1)(z^2 + z + 1)$
43. $(t^2 + 4y^2)(t^4 - 4t^2y^2 + 16y^4)$
45. $(x^4 - yz^4)(x^8 + x^4yz^4 + y^2z^8)$ **47.** 🔳
49. $-\frac{1}{5}$ **50.** $\frac{1}{4}$
51.

$2x - 5y = 10$

52.

$-5x = 10$

53.

$y = \frac{2}{3}x - 1$

54.

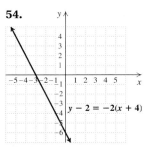

$y - 2 = -2(x + 4)$

55. 🔳   **57.** $(x^{2a} - y^b)(x^{4a} + x^{2a}y^b + y^{2b})$
59. $2x(x^2 + 75)$ **61.** $5\left(xy^2 - \frac{1}{2}\right)\left(x^2y^4 + \frac{1}{2}xy^2 + \frac{1}{4}\right)$
63. $-(3x^{4a} + 3x^{2a} + 1)$ **65.** $(t - 8)(t - 1)(t^2 + t + 1)$

Exercise Set 3.6, pp. 191–193

1. Common factor   **2.** Perfect-square trinomial
3. Grouping   **4.** Multiplying   **5.** $5(a + 5)(a - 5)$
7. $(y - 7)^2$ **9.** $(3t + 7)(t + 3)$ **11.** $x(x + 9)^2$
13. $(x - 5)^2(x + 5)$ **15.** $3t(3t + 1)(3t - 1)$
17. $3x(3x - 5)(x + 3)$ **19.** Prime   **21.** $6(y - 5)(y + 8)$
23. $-2a^4(a - 2)^2$ **25.** $5x(x^2 + 4)(x + 2)(x - 2)$
27. $(t^2 + 3)(t^2 - 3)$ **29.** $-x^4(x^2 - 2x + 7)$
31. $(x - y)(x^2 + xy + y^2)$ **33.** $a(x^2 + y^2)$
35. $2\pi r(h + r)$ **37.** $(a + b)(5a + 3b)$
39. $(x + 1)(x + y)$ **41.** $(a - 2)(a - y)$
43. $(3x - 2y)(x + 5y)$ **45.** $8mn(m^2 - 4mn + 3)$
47. $(a - 2b)^2$ **49.** $(4x + 3y)^2$ **51.** Prime
53. $(a^2b^2 + 4)(ab + 2)(ab - 2)$ **55.** $4c(4d - c)(5d - c)$
57. $(2t + 1)(4t^2 - 2t + 1)(2t - 1)(4t^2 + 2t + 1)$
59. $-1(xy + 2)(xy + 6)$, or $-(xy + 2)(xy + 6)$
61. $5(pq + 6)(pq - 1)$
63. $2a(3a + 2b)(9a^2 - 6ab + 4b^2)$
65. $x^4(x + 2y)(x - y)$ **67.** $\left(6a - \frac{5}{4}\right)^2$ **69.** $\left(\frac{1}{9}x - \frac{4}{3}\right)^2$
71. $(1 + 4x^6y^6)(1 + 2x^3y^3)(1 - 2x^3y^3)$ **73.** $(2ab + 3)^2$
75. $z(z + 6)(z^2 - 6)$ **77.** 🔳   **79.** $\frac{9}{8}$ **80.** $-\frac{5}{3}$
81. $-\frac{7}{2}$ **82.** $\frac{1}{4}$ **83.** 3   **84.** 11   **85.** -1 **86.** 3
87. 🔳   **89.** $-x(x^2 + 9)(x^2 - 2)$
91. $-1(x^2 + 2)(x + 3)(x - 3)$, or
$-(x^2 + 2)(x + 3)(x - 3)$ **93.** $(y + 1)(y - 7)(y + 3)$
95. $(y + 4 + x)^2$ **97.** $(a + 3)^2(2a + b + 4)(a - b + 5)$
99. $(7x^2 + 1 + 5x^3)(7x^2 + 1 - 5x^3)$ **100.** $\left(\frac{3}{4} + y\right)\left(\frac{3}{4} - y\right)$
101. $\left(\frac{1}{6}a + m\right)\left(\frac{1}{6}a - m\right)$ **102.** $\left(\frac{1}{3}x + 9\right)^2$ **103.** $\left(\frac{4}{5}x - \frac{1}{10}\right)^2$
104. $y(x^2 + 9)(x + 3)(x - 3)$
105. $13(n^2 + 1)(n + 1)(n - 1)$
106. $10a^2(4m^2 + 1)(2m + 1)(2m - 1)$
107. $2(4t^2 + 9y^2)(2t + 3y)(2t - 3y)$
108. $2(10 + 9n)(10 - 9n)$ **109.** $10(3 + 2x)(3 - 2x)$
110. $10(5 - 3x)(2 + 3x)$ **111.** $2(9 + 2t)(5 - 3t)$
112. $(2x - 3)(5x + 2)$ **113.** $(3x - 7)(8x + 3)$
114. $(3x - 2)(4x - 3)$ **115.** $(5x - 3)(4x - 5)$
116. $(9m + 2)(2m + 3)$ **117.** $(4n + 3)(5n + 2)$
118. $(4t - 3)(2t + 5)$ **119.** $(6y - 5)(2y + 3)$
120. $(8y - 3)(2y - 3)$ **121.** $(6m - 5)(4m - 3)$
122. $(x + 5)(x + 1)(x - 1)$ **123.** $(x + 3)(x + 4)(x - 4)$

124. $(a - 2)(a + 3)(a - 3)$ **125.** $(y - 1)(y + 5)(y - 5)$
126. $(x + 3)(3x + 2)(3x - 2)$
127. $(x + 5)(2x + 1)(2x - 1)$
128. $(2y - 5)(y + 2)(y - 2)$
129. $(3m - 4)(m + 3)(m - 3)$
130. $(6 - x + a)(6 - x - a)$
131. $(10 - t + 2y)(10 - t - 2y)$
132. $(3 - 2y + 7x)(3 - 2y - 7x)$
133. $(1 - 5m + t)(1 - 5m - t)$

Technology Connection, p. 199

1. $-4.65, 0.65$ **2.** $-0.37, 5.37$ **3.** $-8.98, -4.56$
4. No solution **5.** $0, 2.76$

Exercise Set 3.7, pp. 200–202

1. (c) **2.** (a) **3.** (d) **4.** (b) **5.** $-9, -2$ **7.** $-6, \frac{3}{2}$
9. $\frac{1}{7}, \frac{3}{10}$ **11.** $0, 7$ **13.** $\frac{1}{21}, \frac{18}{11}$ **15.** $-\frac{8}{3}, 0$ **17.** $50, 70$
19. $-5, \frac{2}{3}, 1$ **21.** $1, 6$ **23.** $-7, 3$ **25.** $-9, -2$ **27.** $0, 10$
29. $-6, 0$ **31.** $-6, 6$ **33.** $-\frac{7}{2}, \frac{7}{2}$ **35.** -5 **37.** 8
39. $0, 2$ **41.** $-\frac{5}{4}, 3$ **43.** 3 **45.** $0, \frac{4}{3}$ **47.** $-\frac{7}{6}, \frac{7}{6}$
49. $-4, -\frac{2}{3}$ **51.** $-3, 1$ **53.** $-1, 0, \frac{3}{2}$ **55.** $-7, -\frac{8}{3}, \frac{5}{2}$
57. $-1, 4$ **59.** $-3, 2$ **61.** $(-2, 0), (3, 0)$ **63.** $(-4, 0),$
$(2, 0)$ **65.** $(-3, 0), \left(\frac{3}{2}, 0\right)$ **67.** ✍ **69.** Let m and n
represent the numbers; $(m + n)^2$ **70.** Let m and n repre-
sent the numbers; $m^2 + n^2$ **71.** Let x represent the first
integer; then $x + 1$ represents the second integer; $x(x + 1)$
72. Mother's Day: \$13.8 billion; Father's Day: \$9 billion
73. $140°, 35°, 5°$ **74.** Length: 64 in.; width: 32 in.
75. ✍ **77.** (a) $x^2 - x - 20 = 0$; (b) $x^2 - 6x - 7 = 0$;
(c) $4x^2 - 13x + 3 = 0$; (d) $6x^2 - 5x + 1 = 0$;
(e) $12x^2 - 17x + 6 = 0$; (f) $x^3 - 4x^2 + x + 6 = 0$
79. $-5, 4$ **81.** $-\frac{3}{5}, \frac{3}{5}$ **83.** $-4, 2$
85. (a) $2x^2 + 20x - 4 = 0$; (b) $x^2 - 3x - 18 = 0$;
(c) $(x + 1)(5x - 5) = 0$; (d) $(2x + 8)(2x - 5) = 0$;
(e) $4x^2 + 8x + 36 = 0$; (f) $9x^2 - 12x + 24 = 0$
87. ✍ **89.** $2.33, 6.77$ **91.** $-9.15, -4.59$ **93.** $-3.76, 0$
95. $-10, 10$ **96.** $-\frac{3}{10}, \frac{3}{10}$ **97.** $0, \frac{2}{5}$ **98.** $0, 8$ **99.** $-\frac{1}{4}, 0$
100. $0, \frac{3}{2}$ **101.** $-\frac{2}{3}, \frac{2}{3}$ **102.** $-\frac{2}{5}, \frac{2}{5}$ **103.** $\frac{1}{6}, \frac{5}{2}$ **104.** $-\frac{1}{2}, \frac{4}{3}$
105. $-\frac{3}{5}, \frac{5}{4}$ **106.** $-\frac{3}{8}, \frac{5}{2}$ **107.** $-4, -3, 3$ **108.** $-1, 1, 5$
109. $-2, \frac{1}{5}, 2$ **110.** $-3, -\frac{1}{4}, 3$

Connecting the Concepts, p. 203

1. Expression **2.** Equation **3.** Equation
4. Expression **5.** Expression **6.** Equation
7. $2x^3 + x^2 - 8x$ **8.** $-2x^2 - 11$ **9.** $-10, 10$
10. $6a^2 - 19a + 10$ **11.** $(n - 1)(n - 9)$ **12.** $2, 8$
13. $-\frac{5}{2}$ **14.** $7x^3 + 2x - 7$ **15.** $(4x + 9)(4x - 9)$
16. $-3, 8$ **17.** $-4a^2 - a - 11$
18. $2x^2(9x^2 - 12x + 10)$ **19.** $-1, -\frac{2}{3}$
20. $8x^5 - 20x^4 + 12x^2$

Translating for Success, p. 210

1. O **2.** M **3.** K **4.** I **5.** G **6.** E **7.** C
8. A **9.** H **10.** B

Exercise Set 3.8, pp. 211–216

1. $-2, 3$ **3.** 6 m, 8 m, 10 m **5.** 11, 12
7. -14 and -12; 12 and 14 **9.** Length: 30 ft; width: 6 ft
11. Length: 6 cm; width: 4 cm **13.** Base: 12 in.; height: 9 in.
15. Foot: 7 ft; height: 12 ft **17.** 1 min, 3 min **19.** In 2008
21. 16 teams **23.** 66 handshakes **25.** 12 players
27. 9 ft **29.** 32 ft **31.** 300 ft by 400 ft by 500 ft
33. Dining room: 12 ft by 12 ft; kitchen: 12 ft by 10 ft
35. 20 ft **37.** 1 sec, 2 sec **39.** ✍ **41.** $-\frac{12}{35}$ **42.** $-\frac{21}{20}$
43. -1 **44.** $-\frac{7}{4}$ **45.** $\frac{1}{4}$ **46.** $\frac{4}{5}$ **47.** $\frac{53}{168}$ **48.** $\frac{19}{18}$
49. ✍ **51.** \$180 **53.** 39 cm **55.** 4 in., 6 in.
57. 35 ft **59.** 2 hr, 4.2 hr **61.** 3 hr **62.** 60 ft; 65 ft
63. Tower height: 16 m; distance from base of tower to wire:
12 m **64.** 41 ft **65.** 24 ft **66.** 8 in. **67.** 24 m; 25 m
68. 15 cm; 17 cm **69.** 12 ft; 35 ft; 37 ft **70.** 11 yd; 60 yd;
61 yd **71.** 9 m; 12 m **72.** 5 cm **73.** 13 ft **74.** 15 ft by
20 ft **75.** 30 cm by 40 cm **76.** 4.5 m by 6 m **77.** 3.5 in.
by 24 in. **78.** Base: 8 ft; height: 15 ft **79.** Base: 14 m;
height: 4 m

Exercise Set 3.9, pp. 220–221

1. $8x^6 - 5x^3$ **3.** $1 - 2u + u^6$ **5.** $6t^2 - 8t + 2$
7. $7x^3 - 6x + \frac{3}{2}$ **9.** $-4t^2 - 2t + 1$ **11.** $4x - 5 + \frac{1}{2x}$
13. $x + 2x^3y + 3$ **15.** $-3rs - r + 2s$ **17.** $x - 6$
19. $t - 5 + \frac{-45}{t - 5}$ **21.** $2x - 1 + \frac{1}{x + 6}$
23. $t^2 - 3t + 9$ **25.** $a + 5 + \frac{4}{a - 5}$
27. $x - 3 - \frac{3}{5x - 1}$ **29.** $3a + 1 + \frac{3}{2a + 5}$
31. $t^2 - 3t + 1$ **33.** $x^2 + 1$ **35.** $t^2 - 1 + \frac{3t - 1}{t^2 + 5}$
37. $3x^2 - 3 + \frac{x - 1}{2x^2 + 1}$ **39.** ✍

41. **42.**

43. **44.**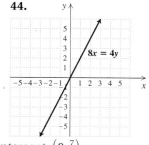

45. $-\frac{3}{10}$ **46.** Slope: 4; y-intercept: $\left(0, \frac{7}{2}\right)$
47. $y = -5x - 10$ **48.** $y = \frac{5}{4}x - \frac{9}{2}$ **49.** ✍
51. $5x^{6k} - 16x^{3k} + 14$ **53.** $3t^{2h} + 2t^h - 5$

55. $a + 3 + \dfrac{5}{5a^2 - 7a - 2}$ **57.** $2x^2 + x - 3$
59. 3   **61.** -1

Review Exercises: Chapter 3, pp. 224–226

1. False   **2.** True   **3.** True   **4.** False   **5.** False
6. True   **7.** True   **8.** False   **9.** Answers may vary.
$(4x)(5x^2), (-2x^2)(-10x), (x^3)(20)$
10. Answers may vary. $(-3x^2)(6x^3), (2x^4)(-9x),$
$(-18x)(x^4)$ **11.** $6x^3(2x - 3)$ **12.** $4a(2a - 3)$
13. $(10t + 1)(10t - 1)$ **14.** $(x + 4)(x - 3)$
15. $(x + 7)^2$ **16.** $3x(2x + 1)^2$ **17.** $(2x + 3)(3x^2 + 1)$
18. $(6a - 5)(a + 1)$ **19.** $(5t - 3)^2$
20. $2(24t^2 - 14t + 3)$ **21.** $(9a^2 + 1)(3a + 1)(3a - 1)$
22. $3x(3x - 5)(x + 3)$ **23.** $2(x - 5)(x^2 + 5x + 25)$
24. $(x + 4)(x^3 - 2)$ **25.** $(ab^2 + 8)(ab^2 - 8)$
26. $-4x^4(2x^2 - 8x + 1)$ **27.** $3(2x - 5)^2$
28. Prime   **29.** $-t(t + 6)(t - 7)$ **30.** $(2x + 5)(2x - 5)$
31. $(n + 6)(n - 10)$ **32.** $5(z^2 - 6z + 2)$
33. $(4t + 5)(t + 2)$ **34.** $(2t + 1)(t - 4)$
35. $7x(x + 1)(x + 4)$ **36.** $(2y + 3x^2)(4y^2 - 6x^2y + 9x^4)$
37. $5(2x - 1)^2$ **38.** $-6x(x + 5)(x - 5)$
39. $(5 - x)(3 - x)$ **40.** Prime   **41.** $(xy + 8)(xy - 2)$
42. $3(2a + 7b)^2$ **43.** $(m + 5)(m + t)$
44. $32(x^2 + 2y^2z^2)(x^2 - 2y^2z^2)$ **45.** $(2m + n)(3m + n)$
46. $(3r + 5s)(2r - 3s)$ **47.** $-11, 9$ **48.** $-7, 5$
49. $-\frac{3}{4}, \frac{3}{4}$ **50.** $\frac{2}{3}, 1$ **51.** $-\frac{5}{2}, 6$ **52.** $-2, 3$ **53.** $0, \frac{3}{5}$
54. 1   **55.** $-3, 4$ **56.** 10 teams   **57.** $(-1, 0), \left(\frac{5}{2}, 0\right)$
58. Height: 14 ft; base: 14 ft   **59.** 10 holes
60. ✍ Answers may vary. Because Celia did not first factor out the largest common factor, 4, her factorization will not be "complete" until she removes a common factor of 2 from each binomial. The answer should be $4(x - 5)(x + 5)$. Awarding 3 to 7 points would seem reasonable.   **61.** ✍ The equations solved in this chapter have an x^2-term (are quadratic), whereas those solved previously have no x^2-term (are linear). The principle of zero products is used to solve quadratic equations and is not used to solve linear equations.   **62.** 2.5 cm   **63.** 0, 2   **64.** Length: 12 cm; width: 6 cm   **65.** 100 cm^2, 225 cm^2 **66.** $-3, 2, \frac{5}{2}$
67. No real solution

Test: Chapter 3, pp. 226–227

1. [3.1] Answers may vary. $(3x^2)(4x^2), (-2x)(-6x^3),$
$(12x^3)(x)$ **2.** [3.2] $(x - 4)(x - 9)$ **3.** [3.4] $(x - 5)^2$
4. [3.1] $2y^2(2y^2 - 4y + 3)$ **5.** [3.1] $(x + 1)(x^2 + 2)$
6. [3.1] $t^5(t^2 - 3)$ **7.** [3.2] $a(a + 4)(a - 1)$
8. [3.3] $2(5x - 6)(x + 4)$ **9.** [3.4] $(2t + 5)(2t - 5)$
10. [3.2] $(x + 2)(x - 3)$ **11.** [3.3] $-3m(2m + 1)(m + 1)$
12. [3.5] $3(r - 1)(r^2 + r + 1)$ **13.** [3.4] $5(3r + 2)^2$
14. [3.4] $3(x^2 + 4)(x + 2)(x - 2)$ **15.** [3.4] $(7t + 6)^2$
16. [3.1] $(x + 2)(x^3 - 3)$ **17.** [3.2] Prime
18. [3.3] $(2x + 3)(2x - 5)$ **19.** [3.3] $3t(2t + 5)(t - 1)$

20. [3.3] $3(m - 5n)(m + 2n)$ **21.** [3.7] 1, 5
22. [3.7] $-\frac{3}{2}, 5$ **23.** [3.7] $0, \frac{2}{5}$ **24.** [3.7] $-\frac{1}{5}, \frac{1}{5}$
25. [3.7] $-4, 5$ **26.** [3.7] $(-1, 0), \left(\frac{8}{3}, 0\right)$
27. [3.8] Length: 10 m; width: 4 m   **28.** [3.8] 10 people
29. [3.8] 5 ft   **30.** [3.8] 15 cm by 30 cm
31. [3.2] $(a - 4)(a + 8)$ **32.** [3.7] $-\frac{8}{3}, 0, \frac{2}{5}$

Cumulative Review: Chapters 1–3, pp. 227–228

1. $\frac{1}{2}$ **2.** $\frac{9}{32}$ **3.** $\frac{9}{8}$ **4.** 29   **5.** $\dfrac{1}{9x^4y^6}$ **6.** t^{10}
7. $3x^4 + 5x^3 + x - 10$ **8.** $-3a^2b - ab^2 + 2b^3$
9. $\dfrac{t^8}{4s^2}$ **10.** $-\dfrac{8x^6y^3}{27z^{12}}$ **11.** 8   **12.** -8 **13.** $-x^4$
14. $2x^3 - 5x^2 + \frac{1}{2}x - 1$ **15.** $-4t^{11} + 8t^9 + 20t^8$
16. $9x^2 - 30x + 25$ **17.** $100x^{10} - y^2$
18. $x^3 - 2x^2 + 1$ **19.** $(c + 1)(c - 1)$
20. $5(x + y)(1 + 2x)$ **21.** $(2r - t)^2$
22. $(2x - 5)(3x - 2)$ **23.** $10(y^2 + 4)$
24. $y(x - 1)(x - 2)$ **25.** $(3x - 2y)(4x + y)$
26. $(5a + 4b)(25a^2 - 20ab + 16b^2)$ **27.** $\frac{1}{12}$
28. 1   **29.** $-\frac{9}{4}$ **30.** $\{x | x \geq 1\}$, or $[1, \infty)$ **31.** $-3, 1$
32. $-4, 3$ **33.** $-2, 2$ **34.** $0, 4$ **35.** $c = \dfrac{a}{b + d}$ **36.** 0
37. $-2; (0, 5)$ **38.** $y = 5x - \frac{1}{3}$ **39.** $y = 5x + \frac{5}{3}$

40.

41.

42.

43.

44.
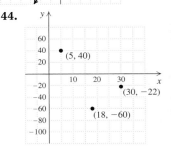

45. 372 min
46. 11,616,000 subscribers per year   **47.** 60,000,000 users   **48.** 101,180 people
49. Bottom of ladder to building: 5 ft; top of ladder to ground: 12 ft
50. Length: 12 ft; width: 2 ft
51. Scores that are 9 and higher

52. (a)

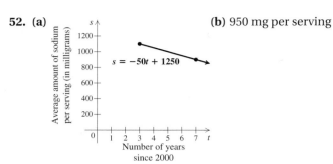

(b) 950 mg per serving

53. $b = \dfrac{2}{a+1}$ **54.** $y = -8$

55. (a) $9y^2 + 12y + 4 - x^2$; **(b)** $(3y + 2 + x)(3y + 2 - x)$
56. $-1, 0, \frac{1}{3}$

CHAPTER 4

Technology Connection, p. 233

1. Correct   **2.** Correct   **3.** Not correct   **4.** Not correct

Exercise Set 4.1, pp. 235–237

1. (e)   **2.** (a)   **3.** (d)   **4.** (b)   **5.** (c)   **6.** (f)

7. 0   **9.** -5 **11.** 5   **13.** $-4, 7$ **15.** $-6, \frac{1}{2}$ **17.** $\dfrac{5a}{4b^2}$

19. $\dfrac{t+2}{t-3}$ **21.** $\frac{7}{8}$ **23.** $\dfrac{a-3}{a+1}$ **25.** $-\dfrac{2x^3}{3}$ **27.** $\dfrac{y-3}{4y}$

29. $\dfrac{t-4}{t-5}$ **31.** $\dfrac{a+4}{2(a-4)}$ **33.** $\dfrac{x-4}{x+4}$ **35.** $\dfrac{1}{n^2+2n+4}$

37. $t - 1$ **39.** $\dfrac{y^2+4}{y+2}$ **41.** $\frac{1}{2}$ **43.** $\dfrac{y}{2y+1}$

45. $\dfrac{2x-3}{5x+2}$ **47.** -1 **49.** -7 **51.** $-\frac{1}{4}$ **53.** $-\frac{3}{2}$

55. -1 **57.** ✏️   **59.** $-\frac{4}{21}$ **60.** $-\frac{5}{3}$ **61.** $-\frac{15}{4}$

62. $-\frac{21}{16}$ **63.** $\frac{13}{63}$ **64.** $\frac{5}{48}$ **65.** ✏️   **67.** $-(2y + x)$

69. $\dfrac{x^3+4}{(x^3+2)(x^2+2)}$ **71.** $\dfrac{(t-1)(t-9)^2}{(t+1)(t^2+9)}$

73. $\dfrac{(x-y)^3}{(x+y)^2(x-5y)}$ **75.** ✏️   **76.** $x + 3$ **77.** $x + 2$

78. $\dfrac{2}{x-6}$ **79.** $\dfrac{x+2}{(x+5)(x-5)}$ **80.** $\dfrac{(x-1)(x-3)}{(x+1)}$

81. $\dfrac{x-4}{x-1}$ **82.** $\dfrac{a+1}{a^2+a+1}$ **83.** $\dfrac{t^2-t+1}{t-1}$

84. $\dfrac{x^2-xy+y^2}{2(x-y)}$ **85.** $\dfrac{x+y}{x^2+xy+y^2}$ **86.** $\dfrac{2x-3}{3x-1}$

87. $\dfrac{2x-3}{2x+3}$ **88.** $\dfrac{x(2x+5)}{6x-5}$ **89.** $\dfrac{2(3x-5)}{4x-1}$

90. $\dfrac{2(10a-3)}{x(2a+5)}$ **91.** $\dfrac{w(8p+3)}{10(4p+7)}$

Technology Connection, p. 240

1. Let $y_1 = ((x^2 + 3x + 2)/(x^2 + 4))/(5x^2 + 10x)$ and $y_2 = (x + 1)/((x^2 + 4)(5x))$. With the tables set in AUTO mode, note that the values in the Y1- and Y2-columns match except for $x = -2$.   **2.** ERROR messages occur when division by 0 is attempted. Since the simplified expression has no factor of $x + 5$ or $x + 1$ in a denominator, no ERROR message occurs in Y2 for $x = -5$ or -1.

Exercise Set 4.2, pp. 240–243

1. $\dfrac{3x(x+2)}{8(5x-1)}$ **3.** $\dfrac{(a-4)(a+2)}{(a+6)^2}$ **5.** $\dfrac{(2x+3)(x+1)}{4(x-5)}$

7. $\dfrac{(n-4)(n+4)}{(n^2+4)(n^2-4)}$ **9.** $\dfrac{(y+6)(y-3)}{(1+y)(y+3)}$ **11.** $\dfrac{6t}{5}$

13. $\dfrac{4}{c^2 d}$ **15.** $\dfrac{(x-5)(x+2)}{x-2}$ **17.** $\dfrac{(n-5)(n-1)(n-6)}{(n+6)(n^2+36)}$

19. $\dfrac{7(a+3)}{a(a+4)}$ **21.** $\dfrac{3v}{v-2}$ **23.** $\dfrac{t-5}{t+5}$ **25.** $\dfrac{9(y-5)}{10(y-1)}$

27. 1   **29.** $\dfrac{(t-2)(t+5)}{(t-5)(t-5)}$ **31.** $(2x-1)^2$ **33.** $c(c-2)$

35. $\dfrac{9}{2x}$ **37.** $\dfrac{1}{a^4+3a}$ **39.** $\frac{20}{27}$ **41.** $\dfrac{x^2}{20}$ **43.** $\dfrac{a^3}{b^3}$

45. $\dfrac{4(t-3)}{3(t+1)}$ **47.** $4(y-2)$ **49.** $-\dfrac{a}{b}$

51. $\dfrac{(n+3)(n+3)}{n-2}$ **53.** $\frac{15}{16}$ **55.** $\dfrac{-x^2-4}{x+2}$

57. $\dfrac{a-5}{3(a-1)}$ **59.** $\dfrac{(2x-1)(2x+1)}{x-5}$

61. $\dfrac{(w-7)(w-8)}{(2w-7)(3w+1)}$ **63.** $\dfrac{1}{(c-5)(5c-3)}$

65. $\dfrac{(x-4y)(x-y)}{(x+y)^3}$ **67.** $\dfrac{x^2+4x+16}{(x+4)^2}$ **69.** $\dfrac{(2a+b)^2}{2(a+b)}$

71. ✏️   **73.** $\frac{19}{12}$ **74.** $\frac{41}{24}$ **75.** $\frac{1}{18}$ **76.** $-\frac{1}{6}$ **77.** $x^2 + 3$

78. $-2x^2 - 4x + 1$ **79.** ✏️   **81.** $\dfrac{3}{7x}$ **83.** 1

85. $\dfrac{1}{(x+y)^3(3x+y)}$ **87.** $\dfrac{a^2-2b}{a^2+3b}$ **89.** $\dfrac{(z+4)^3}{3(z-4)^2}$

91. $\dfrac{a-3b}{c}$ **93.** 〰️   **94.** $\dfrac{(7x+5)(3x+4)}{8}$

95. $\dfrac{(3t+2)^2}{2}$ **96.** $\dfrac{2x+5y}{x^2 y}$ **97.** $\dfrac{x(2x-y)(3x-4y)}{y(2x+y)(4x+3y)}$

98. $\dfrac{(2x-3y)^2}{2x+3y}$ **99.** $\dfrac{2x-3}{3x(3x+5)}$ **100.** 1   **101.** $2x$

102. $\dfrac{(3n+2)(2n-1)}{(2n+1)(3n-2)}$ **103.** $\dfrac{(p-2)^2}{(4p+5)^2}$ **104.** $\dfrac{(x+1)^2}{(x-1)^2}$

105. $b^2 + 1$ **106.** $\dfrac{8}{a}$ **107.** $\dfrac{2y}{3}$ **108.** 1   **109.** $\dfrac{x+2}{x+4}$

Exercise Set 4.3, pp. 250–252

1. Numerators; denominator   2. Term   3. Least common denominator; LCD   4. Factorizations; denominators   5. $\frac{8}{t}$ 7. $\frac{3x + 5}{12}$ 9. $\frac{9}{a + 3}$

11. $\frac{8}{4x - 7}$ 13. $\frac{2y + 7}{2y}$ 15. 6   17. $\frac{4(x - 1)}{x + 3}$

19. $a + 5$ 21. $y - 7$ 23. 0   25. $\frac{1}{x + 2}$ 27. $\frac{t - 4}{t + 3}$

29. $\frac{y + 2}{y - 4}$ 31. $-\frac{5}{x - 4}$, or $\frac{5}{4 - x}$ 33. $-\frac{1}{x - 1}$, or $\frac{1}{1 - x}$

35. 180   37. 72   39. 60   41. $18t^5$ 43. $30a^4b^8$

45. $6(y - 3)$ 47. $(x - 5)(x + 3)(x - 3)$

49. $t(t - 4)(t + 2)^2$ 51. $120x^2y^3z^2$

53. $(a + 1)(a - 1)^2$ 55. $(2n - 1)(n + 1)(n + 2)$

57. $12x^3(x - 5)(x - 3)(x - 1)$

59. $2(x + 1)(x - 1)(x^2 + x + 1)$ 61. $\frac{15}{18t^4}, \frac{st^2}{18t^4}$

63. $\frac{21y}{9x^4y^3}, \frac{4x^3}{9x^4y^3}$ 65. $\frac{2x(x + 3)}{(x - 2)(x + 2)(x + 3)}$,

$\frac{4x(x - 2)}{(x - 2)(x + 2)(x + 3)}$ 67. 🔄   69. $\frac{-5}{8}, \frac{5}{-8}$

70. $\frac{-4}{11}, -\frac{4}{11}$ 71. $-x + y$, or $y - x$ 72. $-3 + a$, or $a - 3$

73. $-2x + 7$, or $7 - 2x$ 74. $-a + b$, or $b - a$ 75. 🔄

77. $\frac{18x + 5}{x - 1}$ 79. $\frac{x}{3x + 1}$ 81. 30 strands

83. 60 strands   85. $(2x + 5)(2x - 5)(3x + 4)^4$

87. 30 sec   89. 7:55 A.M.   91. 🔄

Exercise Set 4.4, pp. 257–260

1. LCD   2. Missing; denominator   3. Numerators; LCD

4. Simplify   5. $\frac{3 + 5x}{x^2}$ 7. $-\frac{5}{24r}$ 9. $\frac{3u^2 + 4v}{u^3v^2}$

11. $\frac{-2(xy + 9)}{3x^2y^3}$ 13. $\frac{7x + 1}{24}$ 15. $\frac{-x - 4}{6}$

17. $\frac{a^2 + 13a - 5}{15a^2}$ 19. $\frac{7z - 12}{12z}$ 21. $\frac{(3c - d)(c + d)}{c^2d^2}$

23. $\frac{4x^2 - 13xt + 9t^2}{3x^2t^2}$ 25. $\frac{6x}{(x + 2)(x - 2)}$

27. $\frac{(t - 3)(t + 1)}{(t - 1)(t + 3)}$ 29. $\frac{11x + 2}{3x(x + 1)}$ 31. $\frac{-5t + 3}{2t(t - 1)}$

33. $\frac{a^2}{(a - 3)(a + 3)}$ 35. $\frac{16}{3(z + 4)}$ 37. $\frac{5q - 3}{(q - 1)^2}$

39. $\frac{1}{t^2 + t + 1}$ 41. $\frac{9a}{4(a - 5)}$ 43. 0

45. $\frac{10}{(a - 3)(a + 2)}$ 47. $\frac{x - 5}{(x + 5)(x + 3)}$

49. $\frac{3z^2 + 19z - 20}{(z - 2)^2(z + 3)}$ 51. $\frac{-7}{x^2 + 25x + 24}$ 53. $\frac{3x - 1}{2}$

55. $y + 3$ 57. 0   59. $\frac{p^2 + 7p + 1}{(p - 5)(p + 5)}$

61. $\frac{(x + 1)(x + 3)}{(x - 4)(x + 4)}$ 63. $\frac{-a - 2}{(a + 1)(a - 1)}$, or $\frac{a + 2}{(1 + a)(1 - a)}$ 65. $\frac{2(5x + 3y)}{(x - y)(x + y)}$ 67. $\frac{2x - 3}{2 - x}$

69. 3   71. 0   73. 🔄   75. $-\frac{3}{22}$ 76. $\frac{7}{9}$ 77. $\frac{9}{10}$

78. $\frac{16}{27}$ 79. $\frac{2}{3}$ 80. $\frac{(x - 3)(x + 2)}{(x - 2)(x + 3)}$ 81. 🔄

83. Perimeter: $\frac{2(5x - 7)}{(x - 5)(x + 4)}$; area: $\frac{6}{(x - 5)(x + 4)}$

85. $\frac{x}{3x + 1}$ 87. $\frac{x^4 + 4x^3 - 5x^2 - 126x - 441}{(x + 2)^2(x + 7)^2}$

89. $\frac{5(a^2 + 2ab - b^2)}{(a - b)(3a + b)(3a - b)}$ 91. $\frac{a}{a - b} + \frac{3b}{b - a}$;

answers may vary.   93. 🔄, 📊   94. $\frac{2}{(x + 3)(x + 4)}$

95. $\frac{1}{(x - 1)(x + 2)}$ 96. $\frac{1}{(x + 1)(x + 2)}$

97. $\frac{2}{(x + 4)(x + 5)}$ 98. $\frac{-29}{(x - 3)(x + 1)}$

99. $\frac{11}{(x + 1)(x + 3)}$ 100. $\frac{3}{(x - 1)(x + 1)}$

101. $\frac{11}{(x - 2)(x + 2)}$ 102. $\frac{6x + 7}{2x + 1}$ 103. $\frac{11 - 2x}{5 - x}$

104. $\frac{10 - 3x}{4 - x}$ 105. $\frac{12x + 5}{3x + 2}$

Connecting the Concepts, pp. 259–260

1. Addition; $\frac{3x + 10}{5x^2}$ 2. Multiplication; $\frac{6}{5x^3}$

3. Division; $\frac{3x}{10}$ 4. Subtraction; $\frac{3x - 10}{5x^2}$

5. Multiplication; $\frac{x - 3}{15(x - 2)}$ 6. Multiplication; $\frac{6}{(x + 3)(x + 4)}$ 7. Division; $\frac{1}{3}$ 8. Subtraction; $\frac{x^2 - 2x - 2}{(x - 1)(x + 2)}$ 9. Addition; $\frac{5x + 17}{(x + 3)(x + 4)}$

10. Addition; -5 11. Subtraction; $\frac{5}{x - 4}$ 12. Division; $\frac{(2x + 3)(x + 3)}{(x + 1)^2}$ 13. Subtraction; $\frac{1}{6}$ 14. Multiplication; $\frac{x(x + 4)}{(x - 1)^2}$ 15. Addition; $\frac{x + 7}{(x - 5)(x + 1)}$

16. Division; $\frac{9(u - 1)}{16}$ 17. Addition; $\frac{7t + 8}{30}$

18. Multiplication; $(t + 5)^2$ **19.** Division; $\dfrac{a - 1}{(a + 2)(a - 2)^2}$ **20.** Subtraction; $\dfrac{-3x^2 + 9x - 14}{2x}$

Technology Connection, p. 264

1. $(1 - 1/x)/(1 - 1/x^2)$ **2.** Parentheses are needed to group separate terms into factors. When a fraction bar is replaced with a division sign, we need parentheses to preserve the groupings that had been created by the fraction bar. This holds for denominators and numerators alike.

Exercise Set 4.5, pp. 265–267

1. (d)   **2.** (a)   **3.** (b)   **4.** (c)   **5.** $\frac{5}{11}$ **7.** 10
9. $\dfrac{5x^2}{4(x^2 + 4)}$ **11.** $\dfrac{-10t}{5t - 2}$ **13.** $\dfrac{2(2a - 5)}{a - 7}$
15. $\dfrac{x^2 - 18}{2(x + 3)}$ **17.** $-\frac{1}{5}$ **19.** $\dfrac{1 + t^2}{t(1 - t)}$ **21.** $\dfrac{x}{x - y}$
23. $c(4c \not\subseteq$ **25.** $\dfrac{15(4 - a^3)}{14a^2(9 + 2a)}$ **27.** 1
29. $\dfrac{3a^2 + 4b^3}{b^3(5 - 3a^2)}$ **31.** $\dfrac{(t - 3)(t + 3)}{t^2 + 4}$ **33.** $\dfrac{a^2b^2}{b^2 - ab + a^2}$
35. $\dfrac{a(3ab^3 + 4)}{b^2(3 + a)}$ **37.** $\dfrac{t^2 + 5t + 3}{(t + 1)^2}$ **39.** $\dfrac{x^2 - 2x - 1}{x^2 - 5x - 4}$
41. ✍   **43.** -4 **44.** -4 **45.** $\frac{19}{3}$ **46.** $-\frac{14}{27}$ **47.** 3, 4
48. $-15, 2$ **49.** ✍   **51.** 6, 7, 8   **53.** $-3, -\frac{4}{5}, 3$
55. $\dfrac{A}{B} \div \dfrac{C}{D} = \dfrac{\frac{A}{B}}{\frac{C}{D}} = \dfrac{\frac{A}{B}}{\frac{C}{D}} \cdot \dfrac{BD}{BD} = \dfrac{AD}{BC} = \dfrac{A}{B} \cdot \dfrac{D}{C}$
57. $\dfrac{x^2 + 5x + 15}{-x^2 + 10}$ **59.** 0   **61.** $\dfrac{2z(5z - 2)}{(z + 2)(13z - 6)}$
63. ✍   **65.** $\dfrac{x - 5}{x - 3}$ **66.** $\dfrac{3x - 2}{x - 1}$ **67.** $\dfrac{2t + 1}{2t + 3}$
68. $\dfrac{3t + 2}{3t + 1}$ **69.** $\dfrac{4a^2 - 2a + 1}{a(a - 3)}$ **70.** $\dfrac{9a^2 + 12a + 16}{a(a + 1)}$
71. $\dfrac{y}{y + 1}$ **72.** $\dfrac{2y - 1}{y}$ **73.** $\dfrac{5a + 1}{a}$ **74.** $\dfrac{a}{a - 3}$

Exercise Set 4.6, pp. 273–274

1. False   **2.** True   **3.** True   **4.** True   **5.** $-\frac{2}{5}$ **7.** $\frac{6}{7}$
9. $\frac{24}{5}$ **11.** $-4, -1$ **13.** $-6, 6$ **15.** 12   **17.** $\frac{14}{3}$
19. -10 **21.** $-4, -3$ **23.** $\frac{23}{2}$ **25.** $\frac{5}{2}$ **27.** -1
29. No solution   **31.** -10 **33.** $-\frac{7}{3}$ **35.** $-2, \frac{7}{3}$
37. $-3, 13$ **39.** 2   **41.** -8 **43.** No solution
45. $-6, 6$ **47.** ✍   **49.** 137, 139   **50.** 14 yd

51. Base: 9 cm; height: 12 cm   **52.** $-8, -6; 6, 8$
53. 0.06 cm per day   **54.** 0.28 in. per day   **55.** ✍
57. -2 **59.** 3   **61.** 4   **63.** 4   **65.** -2 **67.** 📐
68. $\varnothing$ (3 does not check)   **69.** $\varnothing$ (-4 does not check)
70. 1 (2 does not check)   **71.** -1 (5 does not check)
72. -1 (3 does not check)   **73.** 4 (1 does not check)
74. $\varnothing$ (1 does not check)   **75.** $\varnothing$ (-2 does not check)

Connecting the Concepts, pp. 274–275

1. Expression; $\dfrac{x - 2}{x + 1}$ **2.** Expression; $\dfrac{19n - 2}{5n(2n - 1)}$
3. Equation; 8   **4.** Expression; $\dfrac{(z + 1)^2(z - 1)}{z}$
5. Equation; $-\frac{1}{2}$ **6.** Expression; $\dfrac{8(t + 1)}{(t - 1)(2t - 1)}$
7. Expression; $\dfrac{2a}{a - 1}$ **8.** Equation; $-5, 3$
9. Expression; $\dfrac{3x}{10}$ **10.** Equation; $-10, 10$

Translating for Success, p. 285

1. K   **2.** E   **3.** C   **4.** N   **5.** D   **6.** O   **7.** F   **8.** H
9. B   **10.** A

Exercise Set 4.7, pp. 286–291

1. $\frac{1}{2}$ cake per hour   **2.** $\frac{1}{3}$ cake per hour   **3.** $\frac{5}{6}$ cake per hour
4. 1 lawn per hour   **5.** $\frac{1}{3}$ lawn per hour   **6.** $\frac{2}{3}$ lawn per hour
7. $3\frac{3}{7}$ hr   **9.** $\frac{42}{13}$ min, or $3\frac{3}{13}$ min   **11.** $19\frac{1}{11}$ min
13. H470: 135 min; K5400: $67\frac{1}{2}$ min   **15.** Austin: 15 min; Airgle: 30 min   **17.** 300 min, or 5 hr
19.

	Distance (in km)	Speed (in km/h)	Time (in hours)
B & M	330	$r - 14$	$\dfrac{330}{r - 14}$
AMTRAK	400	r	$\dfrac{400}{r}$

AMTRAK: 80 km/h; B & M: 66 km/h
21. 7 mph   **23.** 5.2 ft/sec   **25.** 3 hr   **27.** 9 km/h
29. 2 km/h   **31.** 20 mph   **33.** 10.5   **35.** $\frac{8}{3}$ **37.** $3\frac{3}{4}$ in.
39. 20 ft   **41.** 15 ft   **43.** 12.6   **45.** 1440 messages
47. About 231,000 people   **49.** 18 gal   **51.** $26\frac{2}{3}$ cm
53. 52 bulbs   **55.** $7\frac{1}{2}$ oz   **57.** 90 whales
59. (a) 1.92 T; (b) 28.8 lb   **61.** ✍

63.

$y = 2x - 6$

64.

$y = -2x + 6$

65.
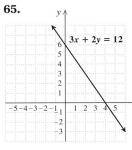
$3x + 2y = 12$

66.

$x - 3y = 6$

67.

$y = -\frac{3}{4}x + 2$

68.

$y = \frac{2}{5}x - 4$

69. ✍   **71.** $49\frac{1}{2}$ hr   **73.** 2250 people per hour
75. $14\frac{7}{8}$ mi   **77.** About 57%   **79.** Page 278
81. $\frac{B}{A} = \frac{D}{C}; \frac{A}{C} = \frac{B}{D}; \frac{C}{A} = \frac{D}{B}$ **83.** $51\frac{3}{7}$ mph   **85.** ✍

Review Exercises: Chapter 4, pp. 295–296

1. False   **2.** True   **3.** False   **4.** True   **5.** True
6. False   **7.** False   **8.** False   **9.** 0   **10.** −5
11. −6, 6   **12.** −6, 5   **13.** −2   **14.** $\frac{x - 3}{x + 5}$ **15.** $\frac{7x + 3}{x - 3}$
16. $\frac{3(y - 3)}{2(y + 3)}$ **17.** $-5(x + 2y)$ **18.** $\frac{a - 6}{5}$
19. $\frac{3(y - 2)^2}{4(2y - 1)(y - 1)}$ **20.** $-32t$ **21.** $\frac{2x(x - 1)}{x + 1}$
22. $\frac{(x^2 + 1)(2x + 1)}{(x - 2)(x + 1)}$ **23.** $\frac{(t + 4)^2}{t + 1}$ **24.** $60a^5b^8$
25. $x^4(x - 1)(x + 1)$ **26.** $(y - 2)(y + 2)(y + 1)$
27. $\frac{15 - 3x}{x + 3}$ **28.** $\frac{4}{x - 4}$ **29.** $\frac{x + 5}{2x}$
30. $\frac{2a^2 - 21ab + 15b^2}{5a^2b^2}$ **31.** $y - 4$ **32.** $\frac{t(t - 2)}{(t - 1)(t + 1)}$
33. $d + 2$ **34.** $\frac{-x^2 + x + 26}{(x + 1)(x - 5)(x + 5)}$ **35.** $\frac{2(x - 2)}{x + 2}$
36. $\frac{3(7t + 2)}{4t(3t + 2)}$ **37.** $\frac{z}{1 - z}$ **38.** $\frac{10x}{3x^2 + 16}$ **39.** $c - d$

40. 4   **41.** $\frac{7}{2}$ **42.** −6, −1   **43.** $5\frac{1}{7}$ hr   **44.** Core 2
Duo: 45 sec; Core 2 Quad: 30 sec   **45.** Car: 105 km/h;
train: 90 km/h   **46.** 24 mph   **47.** 55 seals
48. 6   **49.** ✍ The LCM of denominators is used to clear
fractions when simplifying a complex rational expression
using the method of multiplying by the LCD, and when
solving rational equations.   **50.** ✍ Although multiplying
the denominators of the expressions being added results in a
common denominator, it is often not the *least* common
denominator. Using a common denominator other than the
LCD makes the expressions more complicated, requires
additional simplifying after the addition has been performed,
and leaves more room for error.   **51.** $\frac{5(a + 3)^2}{a}$
52. $\frac{10a}{(a - b)(b - c)}$ **53.** 0

Test: Chapter 4, pp. 296–297

1. [4.1] 0   **2.** [4.1] −8   **3.** [4.1] −1, 1   **4.** [4.1] 1, 2
5. [4.1] $\frac{3x + 7}{x + 3}$ **6.** [4.2] $\frac{2t(t + 3)}{3(t - 1)}$
7. [4.2] $\frac{(5y + 1)(y + 1)}{3y(y + 2)}$ **8.** [4.2] $\frac{(2a + 1)(4a^2 + 1)}{4a^2(2a - 1)}$
9. [4.2] $(x + 3)(x - 3)$ **10.** [4.3] $(y - 3)(y + 3)(y + 7)$
11. [4.3] $\frac{-3x + 9}{x^3}$ **12.** [4.3] $\frac{-2t + 8}{t^2 + 1}$ **13.** [4.4] 1
14. [4.4] $\frac{3x - 5}{x - 3}$ **15.** [4.4] $\frac{11t - 8}{t(t - 2)}$
16. [4.4] $\frac{y^2 + 3}{(y - 1)(y + 3)^2}$ **17.** [4.4] $\frac{x^2 + 2x - 7}{(x + 1)(x - 1)^2}$
18. [4.5] $\frac{3y + 1}{y}$ **19.** [4.5] $x - 8$ **20.** [4.6] $\frac{8}{3}$
21. [4.6] −3, 5   **22.** [4.7] 12 min   **23.** [4.7] $1\frac{1}{4}$ mi
24. [4.7] Ryan: 65 km/h; Alicia: 45 km/h   **25.** [4.7] Rema:
4 hr; Pe'rez: 10 hr   **26.** [4.5] a **27.** [4.7] −1

Cumulative Review: Chapters 1–4, pp. 297–298

1. $a + cb$ **2.** −25   **3.** 25   **4.** $-3x + 33$ **5.** 10
6. −7, 7   **7.** $-\frac{5}{3}$ **8.** $\frac{8}{5}$ **9.** 4   **10.** −10, −1   **11.** −8
12. 1, 4   **13.** $\{y \mid y \leq -\frac{2}{3}\}$ **14.** −17   **15.** −4, $\frac{1}{2}$
16. $\{x \mid x > 43\}$ **17.** 5   **18.** $-\frac{7}{2}$, 5   **19.** −13
20. $b = 3a - c + 9$ **21.** $y = \frac{4z - 3x}{6}$

22.

$y = \frac{3}{4}x + 5$

23.
$x = -3$

24. **25.**

59. 19 watts; 30 watts

26. -2 **27.** Slope: $\frac{1}{2}$; y-intercept: $\left(0, -\frac{1}{4}\right)$

28. $y = -\frac{5}{8}x - 4$ **29.** $\frac{1}{x^2}$ **30.** y^{-7}, or $\frac{1}{y^7}$

31. $-4a^4 b^{14}$ **32.** $-y^3 - 2y^2 - 2y + 7$

33. $-15a + 10b - 5c$ **34.** $2x^5 + x^3 - 6x^2 - x + 3$

35. $36x^2 - 60xy + 25y^2$ **36.** $3n^2 - 13n - 10$

37. $4x^6 - 1$ **38.** $2x(3 - x - 12x^3)$

39. $(4x + 9)(4x - 9)$ **40.** $10(t + 1)(t^2 - t + 1)$

41. $(4x + 3)(2x + 1)$ **42.** $2(3x - 2)(x - 4)$

43. $(5t + 4)^2$ **44.** $(xy - 5)(xy + 4)$

45. $(x + 2)(x^3 - 3)$ **46.** $\frac{4}{t + 4}$ **47.** 1

61. 3.5 drinks; 6 drinks

48. $\frac{a^2 + 7ab + b^2}{(a + b)(a - b)}$ **49.** $\frac{2x + 5}{4 - x}$ **50.** $\frac{x}{x - 2}$

51. $\frac{y(3y^2 + 2)}{y^3 - 3}$ **52.** $6x^2 - 5x + 2 + \frac{4}{x} + \frac{1}{x^2}$

53. $15x^3 - 57x^2 + 177x - 529 + \frac{1605}{x + 3}$ **54.** 15 books

55. About 340.8 billion admissions **56.** 33,339,507 and 33,339,508 **57.** 12 ft **58.** $\frac{75}{4}$ min, or $18\frac{3}{4}$ min

59. 90 antelope **60.** 150 calories **61.** $-144, 144$

62. $16y^6 - y^4 + 6y^2 - 9$ **63.** $-7, 4, 12$ **64.** 18

63. $257,000; $306,000

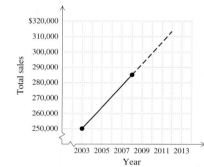

65. ⬚ **67.** 6
68. $-6, 6$ **69.** $-\frac{1}{2}$
70. $-1, 1$
71. $-4, 3$ **72.** $\frac{9}{32}$
73. $\frac{1}{7}$ **74.** $-4, 8$
75. ⬚ **77.** 26; 99
79. Worm
81. About 2 min 50 sec
83. 1 every 3 min

CHAPTER 5

Exercise Set 5.1, pp. 306–311

1. Correspondence **2.** Exactly **3.** Domain
4. Range **5.** Horizontal **6.** Vertical **7.** "f of 3," "f at 3," or "the value of f at 3" **8.** Vertical **9.** Yes **11.** Yes
13. No **15.** Yes **17.** Function **19.** Function
21. (a) -1; (b) -3 **23.** (a) 3; (b) 3 **25.** (a) 3; (b) 0
27. (a) 3; (b) -3 **29.** (a) 1; (b) 3 **31.** (a) 4; (b) $-1, 3$
33. (a) 2; (b) $\{x | 0 < x \le 2\}$, or $(0, 2]$ **35.** Yes **37.** Yes
39. No **41.** (a) 5; (b) -3; (c) -9; (d) 21;
(e) $2a + 9$; (f) $2a + 7$ **43.** (a) 0; (b) 1; (c) 57;
(d) $5t^2 + 4t$; (e) $20a^2 + 8a$; (f) 48 **45.** (a) $\frac{3}{5}$; (b) $\frac{1}{3}$; (c) $\frac{4}{7}$;
(d) 0; (e) $\frac{x - 1}{2x - 1}$; (f) $\frac{a + h - 3}{2a + 2h - 5}$

47. $4\sqrt{3}$ cm$^2 \approx 6.93$ cm^2 **49.** 36π in$^2 \approx 113.10$ in^2

51. 164.98 cm **53.** 23°F

55. 75 heart attacks per 10,000 men **57.** 500 movies

85.

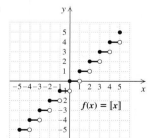

Exercise Set 5.2, pp. 317–319

1. (c) **2.** (d) **3.** (d) **4.** (b) **5.** (c) **6.** (b)
7. Domain: $\{2, 9, -2, -4\}$; range: $\{8, 3, 10, 4\}$
9. Domain: $\{0, 4, -5, -1\}$; range: $\{0, -2\}$
11. Domain: $\{-4, -2, 0, 2, 4\}$; range: $\{-2, -1, 0, 1, 2\}$
13. Domain: $\{-5, -3, -1, 0, 2, 4\}$; range: $\{-1, 1\}$

15. Domain: $\{x | -4 \le x \le 3\}$, or $[-4, 3]$; range: $\{y | -3 \le y \le 4\}$, or $[-3, 4]$ **17.** Domain: $\{x | -4 \le x \le 5\}$, or $[-4, 5]$; range: $\{y | -2 \le y \le 4\}$, or $[-2, 4]$ **19.** Domain: $\{x | -4 \le x \le 4\}$, or $[-4, 4]$; range: $\{-3, -1, 1\}$ **21.** Domain: $\mathbb{R}$; range: $\mathbb{R}$
23. Domain: $\mathbb{R}$; range: $\{4\}$ **25.** Domain: $\mathbb{R}$; range: $\{y | y \ge 1\}$, or $[1, \infty)$ **27.** Domain: $\{x | x$ is a real number *and* $x \ne -2\}$; range: $\{y | y$ is a real number *and* $y \ne -4\}$
29. Domain: $\{x | x \ge 0\}$, or $[0, \infty)$; range: $\{y | y \ge 0\}$, or $[0, \infty)$ **31.** $\{x | x$ is a real number *and* $x \ne 3\}$
33. $\{x | x$ is a real number *and* $x \ne \frac{1}{2}\}$ **35.** $\mathbb{R}$ **37.** $\mathbb{R}$
39. $\{x | x$ is a real number *and* $x \ne 3$ *and* $x \ne -3\}$ **41.** $\mathbb{R}$
43. $\{x | x$ is a real number *and* $x \ne -1$ *and* $x \ne -7\}$
45. $\{t | 0 \le t < 624\}$, or $[0, 624)$
47. $\{p | \$0 \le p \le \$10.60\}$, or $[0, 10.60]$ **49.** $\{d | d \ge 0\}$, or $[0, \infty)$ **51.** $\{t | 0 \le t \le 5\}$, or $[0, 5]$ **53. (a)** -5;
(b) 1; **(c)** 21   **55. (a)** 0; **(b)** 2; **(c)** 7   **57. (a)** 100;
(b) 100; **(c)** 131   **59.** ✍

61.

62.

63. Slope: $\frac{2}{3}$; y-intercept: $(0, -4)$
64. Slope: $-\frac{1}{4}$; y-intercept: $(0, 6)$
65. Slope: $\frac{4}{3}$; y-intercept: $(0, 0)$
66. Slope: -5; y-intercept: $(0, 0)$ **67.** ✍

69.

71.

73. Domain: $\{x | x$ is a real number *and* $x \ne 0\}$; range: $\{y | y$ is a real number *and* $y \ne 0\}$
75. Domain: $\{x | x < -2$ *or* $x > 0\}$; range: $\{y | y < -2$ *or* $y > 3\}$ **77.** Domain: $\mathbb{R}$; range: $\{y | y \ge 0\}$, or $[0, \infty)$ **79.** Domain: $\{x | x$ is a real number *and* $x \ne 2\}$; range: $\{y | y$ is a real number *and* $y \ne 0\}$
81. $\{h | 0 \le h \le 144\}$, or $[0, 144]$

83.

85.

87.

89.

Visualizing for Success, p. 325

1. D   **2.** J   **3.** A   **4.** E   **5.** B   **6.** C   **7.** I   **8.** F
9. G   **10.** H

Exercise Set 5.3, pp. 326–329

1. False   **2.** True   **3.** False   **4.** True
5. True   **6.** True

7.

9.

11.

13.

15.

17.

19.

21.

23.

25. $C(d) = 0.75d + 30$; 60 miles
27. $L(t) = \frac{1}{2}t + 5$; 20 months after the haircut
29. $A(t) = 849t + 5960$; 5 years after 2006, or 2011
31. (a) $a(t) = 0.9t + 12.7$; **(b)** 24.4 million cars; **(c)** about 2014
33. (a) $E(t) = 0.14t + 78.44$; **(b)** 81.52 yr
35. (a) $A(t) = 22.525t + 236.95$; **(b)** \$462.2 million
37. (a) $N(t) = 9.4t + 16$; **(b)** 110 million Americans; **(c)** 2015 **39. (a)** $A(t) = \frac{41}{110}t + \frac{1615}{22}$; **(b)** about 80.9 million acres **41.** Linear function; $\mathbb{R}$
43. Quadratic function; $\mathbb{R}$ **45.** Rational function; $\{t \mid t \text{ is a real number } and \, t \neq -\frac{4}{3}\}$ **47.** Polynomial function; $\mathbb{R}$
49. Rational function; $\{x \mid x \text{ is a real number } and \, x \neq \frac{5}{2}\}$
51. Rational function; $\{n \mid n \text{ is a real number } and \, n \neq -1$ $and \, n \neq -2\}$ **53.** Linear function; $\mathbb{R}$ **55.** $\{y \mid y \geq 0\}$, or $[0, \infty)$ **57.** $\mathbb{R}$ **59.** $\{y \mid y \leq 0\}$, or $(-\infty, 0]$

61.

63.

Domain: $\mathbb{R}$; range: $\mathbb{R}$ Domain: $\mathbb{R}$; range: $\{-1\}$

65.

67.

Domain: $\mathbb{R}$; range: $\{y \mid y \geq 1\}$, or $[1, \infty)$ Domain: $\mathbb{R}$; range: $\{y \mid y \geq 0\}$, or $[0, \infty)$

69. ⊠ **71.** $4x^2 + 2x - 1$ **72.** $2x^3 - x^2 - x + 7$
73. $2x^2 - 13x - 7$ **74.** $x^2 + x - 12$
75. $x^3 - 2x^2 - 3x + 5$ **76.** $x^3 + 2x^2 + x + 4$
77. ⊠ **79.** False **81.** False **83.** 21.1°C **85.** \$60
87. (a) $g(x) = x - 8$; **(b)** -10; **(c)** 83

Connecting the Concepts, p. 330

1. $\{-1, 0, 3, 4\}$ **2.** $\{-2, 0, 6, 8\}$ **3.** -2
4.

5. $\mathbb{R}$

6. $\{x \mid x \text{ is a real number } and \, x \neq 0\}$ **7.** $\frac{1}{5}$ **8.** 2 **9.** 3
10. $\{x \mid x \text{ is a real number } and \, x \neq 0 \, and \, x \neq 1\}$
11. Linear function **12.** Rational function
13. Range: $\mathbb{R}$

14. Yes **15.** -4
16. $\{x \mid x \geq -3\}$, or $[-3, \infty)$
17. $\{y \mid y \geq -4\}$, or $[-4, \infty)$
18. 4 **19.** 10 **20.** 13

Exercise Set 5.4, pp. 336–339

1. Sum **2.** Subtract **3.** Evaluate **4.** Domains
5. Excluding **6.** Sum **7.** 1 **9.** 5 **11.** -7 **13.** 1
15. -5 **17.** $x^2 - 2x - 2$ **19.** $x^2 - x + 3$ **21.** 5
23. $-a^3 + 5a^2 + 2a - 10$ **25.** $\frac{x^2 - 2}{5 - x}, x \neq 5$ **27.** $\frac{7}{2}$
29. -2 **31.** $1.2 + 2.9 = 4.1$ million **33.** 4%
35. About 95 million; the number of tons of municipal solid waste that was composted or recycled in 2005 **37.** About 215 million; the number of tons of municipal solid waste in 1996 **39.** About 230 million; the number of tons of municipal solid waste that was not composted in 2004
41. $\mathbb{R}$ **43.** $\{x \mid x \text{ is a real number } and \, x \neq -5\}$
45. $\{x \mid x \text{ is a real number } and \, x \neq 0\}$
47. $\{x \mid x \text{ is a real number } and \, x \neq 1\}$
49. $\{x \mid x \text{ is a real number } and \, x \neq -\frac{9}{2} \, and \, x \neq 1\}$
51. $\{x \mid x \text{ is a real number } and \, x \neq 3\}$
53. $\{x \mid x \text{ is a real number } and \, x \neq -4\}$
55. $\{x \mid x \text{ is a real number } and \, x \neq 4 \, and \, x \neq 5\}$
57. $\{x \mid x \text{ is a real number } and \, x \neq -1 \, and \, x \neq -\frac{5}{2}\}$
59. 4; 3 **61.** 5; -1 **63.** $\{x \mid 0 \leq x \leq 9\}$; $\{x \mid 3 \leq x \leq 10\}$; $\{x \mid 3 \leq x \leq 9\}$; $\{x \mid 3 \leq x \leq 9\}$

65.

67. 🖎   **69.** $c = \dfrac{b}{a}$

70. $w = \dfrac{x - y}{z}$

71. $q = \dfrac{st}{p - r}$

72. $b = \dfrac{d}{a + c}$

73. $b = \dfrac{cd + d}{a - 3}$

74. $d = \dfrac{ab - 3b}{c + 1}$

75. 🖎   **77.** $\{x \,|\, x \text{ is a real number } and \ x \neq 4 \ and \ x \neq 3 \ and \ x \neq 2 \ and \ x \neq -2\}$

79. Answers may vary.

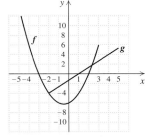

81. $\{x \,|\, x \text{ is a real number } and \ -1 < x < 5 \ and \ x \neq \frac{3}{2}\}$

83. Answers may vary. $f(x) = \dfrac{1}{x + 2}, g(x) = \dfrac{1}{x - 5}$

85. 〰

Exercise Set 5.5, pp. 346-353

1. (d)   **2.** (f)   **3.** (e)   **4.** (b)   **5.** (a)   **6.** (c)
7. Inverse   **8.** Direct   **9.** Direct   **10.** Inverse

11. Inverse   **12.** Direct   **13.** $d = \dfrac{L}{f}$

15. $v_1 = \dfrac{2s}{t} - v_2,$ or $\dfrac{2s - tv_2}{t}$ **17.** $b = \dfrac{at}{a - t}$

19. $g = \dfrac{Rs}{s - R}$ **21.** $n = \dfrac{IR}{E - Ir}$ **23.** $q = \dfrac{pf}{p - f}$

25. $t_1 = \dfrac{H}{Sm} + t_2,$ or $\dfrac{H + Smt_2}{Sm}$ **27.** $r = \dfrac{Re}{E - e}$

29. $r = 1 - \dfrac{a}{S},$ or $\dfrac{S - a}{S}$ **31.** $a + b = \dfrac{f}{c^2}$

33. $r = \dfrac{A}{P} - 1,$ or $\dfrac{A - P}{P}$

35. $t_1 = t_2 - \dfrac{d_2 - d_1}{v},$ or $\dfrac{vt_2 - d_2 + d_1}{v}$ **37.** $t = \dfrac{ab}{b + a}$

39. $Q = \dfrac{2Tt - 2AT}{A - q}$ **41.** $w = \dfrac{4.15c - 98.42}{p + 0.082}$

43. $k = 6; y = 6x$ **45.** $k = 1.7; y = 1.7x$

47. $k = 10; y = 10x$ **49.** $k = 100; y = \dfrac{100}{x}$

51. $k = 44; y = \dfrac{44}{x}$ **53.** $k = 9; y = \dfrac{9}{x}$ **55.** $33\frac{1}{3}$ cm

57. 3.5 hr   **59.** 56 in.   **61.** 32 kg   **63.** 286 Hz
65. About 21 min   **67.** About 110,000,000 tons

69. $y = \frac{1}{2}x^2$ **71.** $y = \dfrac{5000}{x^2}$ **73.** $y = 1.5xz$

75. $y = \dfrac{4wx^2}{z}$ **77.** 61.3 ft   **79.** 308 cm^3

81. About 57 mph   **83.** 🖎   **85.** $y = \frac{1}{6}x - \frac{1}{2}$
86. $y = \frac{3}{8}x - \frac{5}{8}$ **87.** $y = -\frac{5}{2}x - \frac{3}{2}$ **88.** $y = -\frac{1}{8}x + \frac{1}{2}$
89. Let n represent the number; $2n + 5 = 49$ **90.** Let x represent the number; $\frac{1}{2}x - 3 = 57$ **91.** Let x represent the number; $x + (x + 1) = 145$ **92.** Let n represent the number; $n - (-n) = 20$ **93.** 🖎   **95.** 567 mi

97. Ratio is $\dfrac{a + 12}{a + 6}$; percent increase is $\dfrac{6}{a + 6} \cdot 100\%$, or

$\dfrac{600}{a + 6}\%$ **99.** $t_1 = t_2 + \dfrac{(d_2 - d_1)(t_4 - t_3)}{a(t_4 - t_2)(t_4 - t_3) + d_3 - d_4}$
101. The intensity is halved.   **103.** About 1.7 m

105. $d(s) = \dfrac{28}{s}; 70$ yd   **106.** $x = \dfrac{9}{b - a}$ **107.** $x = \dfrac{2}{c - b}$

108. $y = \dfrac{24}{a + d}$ **109.** $y = \dfrac{19}{c + d}$ **110.** $m = \dfrac{h + k}{a - c}$

111. $n = \dfrac{d - c}{b - a},$ or $n = \dfrac{c - d}{a - b}$ **112.** $x = \dfrac{ab - b}{c + d}$

113. $x = \dfrac{uv + v}{b + d}$ **114.** $y = -4x + 8$ **115.** $y = 2x - 6$

116. $y = \frac{6}{5}x - 12$ **117.** $y = -\frac{2}{5}x - 4$ **118.** $y = \frac{3}{5}x + 3$

119. $y = -2x - 4$ **120.** $y = \frac{3}{10}x + 24$ **121.** $y = \frac{5}{4}x - 50$

122. $y = \dfrac{3x^2}{wz}$ **123.** $y = \dfrac{4xz}{w^2}$ **124.** $y = \dfrac{xw^3}{3z}$

125. $y = \dfrac{x}{10w^3z}$ **126.** $y = \dfrac{2.1\,wzp}{x^2}$ **127.** $y = \dfrac{1.6z^2p}{wx}$

128. 1.6 m^2 **129.** 2.25 lb   **130.** 5760 N   **131.** 432 cm^2
132. 9   **133.** 150   **134.** 108   **135.** 0.48   **136.** 4
137. 8   **138.** 0.2   **139.** $\frac{1}{12}$ **140.** 50   **141.** 2000
142. $\frac{5}{4}$ **143.** $\frac{3}{4}$ **144.** $\frac{24}{25}$ **145.** 5   **146.** 150
147. 2500   **148.** $\frac{64}{25}$ **149.** 0.4   **150.** $\frac{1}{27}$ **151.** 0.075

Review Exercises: Chapter 5, pp. 356-358

1. True   **2.** True   **3.** False   **4.** True   **5.** False
6. True   **7.** True   **8.** True   **9.** True   **10.** False
11. (a) 3; **(b)** $\{x \,|\, -2 \leq x \leq 4\}$, or $[-2, 4]$; **(c)** -1;
(d) $\{y \,|\, 1 \leq y \leq 5\}$, or $[1, 5]$ **12.** $\frac{3}{2}$ **13.** $4a^2 + 4a - 3$
14. 10.53 yr   **15.** About $9.30;

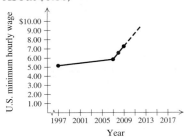

16. (a) Yes; **(b)** Domain: $\mathbb{R}$; range: $\{y|y \geq 0\}$, or $[0, \infty)$
17. (a) No   **18. (a)** No   **19. (a)** Yes; **(b)** Domain: $\mathbb{R}$;
range: $\{-2\}$ **20.** $\mathbb{R}$
21. $\{x|x$ is a real number $and\ x \neq 1\}$
22. $\{t|t$ is a real number $and\ t \neq -1\ and\ t \neq -4\}$
23. $\{t|0 \leq t \leq 60\}$, or $[0, 60]$ **24. (a)** 5; **(b)** 4;
(c) 16; **(d)** 35   **25.** $C(t) = 30t + 90$; 7 months
26. (a) $R(t) = -\frac{43}{2400}t + \frac{15,843}{800}$; **(b)** about 19.21 sec; about
19.09 sec   **27.** Absolute-value function   **28.** Polynomial
function   **29.** Quadratic function   **30.** Linear function
31. Rational function
32.

33.

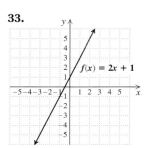

Domain: $\mathbb{R}$; range: $\{3\}$ Domain: $\mathbb{R}$; range: $\mathbb{R}$
34.

35. 102   **36.** -17
37. $-\frac{9}{2}$ **38.** $\mathbb{R}$

Domain: $\mathbb{R}$; range: $\{y|y \geq 0\}$,
or $[0, \infty)$

39. $\{x|x$ is a real number $and\ x \neq 2\}$ **40.** $r = \dfrac{2V - IR}{2I}$,
or $\dfrac{V}{I} - \dfrac{R}{2}$ **41.** $m = \dfrac{H}{S(t_1 - t_2)}$ **42.** $c = \dfrac{b + 3a}{2}$
43. $t_1 = \dfrac{-A}{vT} + t_2$, or $\dfrac{-A + vTt_2}{vT}$ **44.** $y = \frac{15}{2}x$
45. $y = \dfrac{\frac{3}{4}}{x}$ **46.** $y = \dfrac{1}{2}\dfrac{xw^2}{z}$ **47.** 15 min
48. 22.5 lb   **49.** About 2.9 sec   **50.** ✍ Two functions
that have the same domain and range are not necessarily
identical. For example, the functions $f: \{(-2, 1), (-3, 2)\}$
and $g: \{(-2, 2), (-3, 1)\}$ have the same domain and range
but are different functions.   **51.** ✍ Jenna is not correct.
Any value of the variable that makes a denominator 0
is not in the domain; 0 itself may or may not make a
denominator 0.   **52.** $f(x) = 10.94x + 20$ **53.** Domain:
$\{x|x \geq -4\ and\ x \neq 2\}$; range: $\{y|y \geq 0\ and\ y \neq 3\}$

Test: Chapter 5, pp. 359–360

1. [5.1], [5.2] **(a)** 1; **(b)** $\{x|-3 \leq x \leq 4\}$, or $[-3, 4]$; **(c)** 3;
(d) $\{y|-1 \leq y \leq 2\}$, or $[-1, 2]$ **2.** [5.1] About 49 million
international visitors   **3. (a)** [5.1] Yes; **(b)** [5.2] domain: $\mathbb{R}$;

range: $\mathbb{R}$ **4. (a)** [5.1] Yes; **(b)** [5.2] domain: $\mathbb{R}$;
range: $\{y|y \geq 1\}$, or $[1, \infty)$ **5. (a)** [5.1] No
6. [5.2] $\{t|0 \leq t \leq 4\}$, or $[0, 4]$ **7.** [5.2] **(a)** -5; **(b)** 10
8. [5.3] $C(t) = 55t + 180$; 12 months
9. [5.3] **(a)** $C(m) = 0.3m + 25$; **(b)** \$175
10. [5.3] Linear function; $\mathbb{R}$ **11.** [5.3] Rational function;
$\{x|x$ is a real number $and\ x \neq -4\ and\ x \neq 4\}$
12. [5.3] Quadratic function; $\mathbb{R}$
13. [5.3]   **14.** [5.3]

Domain: $\mathbb{R}$; range: $\mathbb{R}$ Domain: $\mathbb{R}$; range: $\{y|y \geq -1\}$,
or $[-1, \infty)$

15. [5.3]

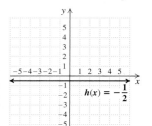

16. [5.1] -1
17. [5.1] $10a + 1$
18. [5.4] $\frac{1}{x} + 2x + 1$

Domain: $\mathbb{R}$; range: $\{-\frac{1}{2}\}$
19. [5.1] $\{x|x$ is a real number $and\ x \neq 0\}$
20. [5.4] $\{x|x$ is a real number $and\ x \neq 0\}$
21. [5.4] $\{x|x$ is a real number $and\ x \neq 0\ and\ x \neq -\frac{1}{2}\}$
22. [5.5] $s = \dfrac{Rg}{g - R}$ **23.** [5.5] $y = \frac{1}{2}x$ **24.** [5.5] 30 workers
25. [5.5] 637 in^2 **26.** [5.3] **(a)** 30 mi; **(b)** 15 mph
27. [5.4] $h(x) = 7x - 2$

Cumulative Review: Chapters 1–5, pp. 360–362

1. 10   **2.** 3.91×10^8 **3.** Slope: $\frac{7}{4}$; y-intercept: $(0, -3)$
4. $y = -2x + 5$ **5. (a)** 0; **(b)** $\{x|x$ is a real number and
$x \neq 5\ and\ x \neq 6\}$
6.

7.

8.   **9.**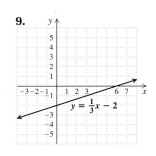

10. $-24x^4y^4$ **11.** $15x^4 - x^3 - 9x^2 + 5x - 2$
12. $9x^4 + 6x^2y + y^2$ **13.** $4x^4 - 81$

14. $-m^3n^2 - m^2n^2 - 5mn^3$ **15.** $\dfrac{y-6}{2}$ **16.** $x-1$

17. $\dfrac{a^2 + 7ab + b^2}{(a-b)(a+b)}$ **18.** $\dfrac{-m^2 + 5m - 6}{(m+1)(m-5)}$ **19.** $\dfrac{3y^2 - 2}{3y}$

20. $\dfrac{y-x}{xy(x+y)}$ **21.** $4x(x^2 + 100)$ **22.** $(x-6)(x+14)$
23. $(4y-5)(4y+5)$ **24.** $8(2x+1)(4x^2 - 2x + 1)$
25. $(t-8)^2$ **26.** $x^2(x-1)(x+1)(x^2+1)$
27. $\left(\frac{1}{2}b - c\right)\left(\frac{1}{4}b^2 + \frac{1}{2}bc + c^2\right)$ **28.** $(3t-4)(t+7)$
29. $(x^2 - y)(x^3 + y)$ **30.** $\frac{1}{4}$ **31.** $-12, 12$
32. $\{x \mid x \geq -1\}$, or $[-1, \infty)$ **33.** $\frac{3}{5}$ **34.** -1

35. No solution   **36.** $a = \dfrac{Pb}{4-P}$ **37.** -5 **38.** 8

39. 0   **40.** $y = -x + 3$ **41.** 99   **42.** $\dfrac{x^2 - 1}{x+5}$

43. $\{x \mid x$ is a real number $and\; x \neq -6\}$
44. Domain: $\{x \mid -4 \leq x \leq 3\}$; or $[-4, 3]$;
range: $\{y \mid -3 \leq y \leq 0\; or\; y = 2\}$
45. (a) $r(t) = 45.95t + 20$; **(b)** $1076.85 million; **(c)** in
2016–2017   **46.** 34 performances per month, or 408 performances per year   **47.** 72 in.   **48.** IQAir HealthPro:
10 min; Austin Healthmate: 15 min   **49.** 12 billion hr
50. $22\frac{1}{2}$ min   **51.** $1.09 billion
52. $x^3 - 12x^2 + 48x - 64$ **53.** $-3, 3, -5, 5$
54. All real numbers except 9 and -5 **55.** $-\frac{1}{4}, 0, \frac{1}{4}$
56. $C(x) = \begin{cases} 12, & \text{if } x \leq 20, \\ 12 + 0.75(x-20), & \text{if } x > 20 \end{cases}$

CHAPTER 6

Technology Connection, p. 368

1. $(1.53, 2.58)$ **2.** $(-0.26, 57.06)$ **3.** $(2.23, 1.14)$
4. $(0.87, -0.32)$

Visualizing for Success, p. 370

1. C   **2.** H   **3.** J   **4.** G   **5.** D   **6.** I   **7.** A   **8.** F
9. E   **10.** B

Exercise Set 6.1, pp. 371–373

1. False   **2.** True   **3.** True   **4.** True   **5.** True
6. False   **7.** False   **8.** True   **9.** Yes   **11.** No
13. Yes   **15.** Yes   **17.** $(3, 2)$ **19.** $(2, -1)$ **21.** $(1, 4)$
23. $(-3, -2)$ **25.** $(3, -1)$ **27.** $(3, -7)$ **29.** $(7, 2)$
31. $(4, 0)$ **33.** No solution   **35.** $\{(x, y) \mid y = 3 - x\}$
37. All except Exercise 33   **39.** Exercise 35
41. Let x represent the first number and y the second number; $x + y = 10, x = \frac{2}{3}y$ **43.** Let p represent the number
of personal e-mails and b the number of business e-mails;
$p + b = 578, b = p + 30$ **45.** Let x and y represent the
angles; $x + y = 180, x = 2y - 3$ **47.** Let x represent the
number of two-point shots and y the number of foul shots;
$x + y = 64, 2x + y = 100$ **49.** Let x represent the
number of hats sold and y the number of tee shirts sold;
$x + y = 45, 14.50x + 19.50y = 697.50$ **51.** Let h represent the number of vials of Humalog sold and n the number
of vials of Lantus; $h + n = 50, 83.29h + 76.76n = 3981.66$
53. Let l represent the length, in yards, and w the width, in
yards; $2l + 2w = 340; l = w + 50$ **55.** ✍   **57.** $\frac{8}{13}$
58. -1 **59.** $-\frac{1}{10}$ **60.** 11   **61.** $y = 3x - 4$
62. $x = \frac{5}{2}y - \frac{7}{2}$ **63.** ✍   **65.** Answers may vary.
(a) $x + y = 6, x - y = 4$; **(b)** $x + y = 1, 2x + 2y = 3$;
(c) $x + y = 1, 2x + 2y = 2$ **67.** $A = -\frac{17}{4}, B = -\frac{12}{5}$
69. Let x and y represent the number of years that Dell
and Juanita have taught at the university, respectively;
$x + y = 46, x - 2 = 2.5(y - 2)$ **71.** Let s and v represent
the number of ounces of baking soda and vinegar needed,
respectively; $s = 4v, s + v = 16$ **73.** Mineral oil: 12 oz;
vinegar: 4 oz   **75.** $(0, 0), (1, 1)$ **77.** $(0.07, -7.95)$
79. $(0.00, 1.25)$

Exercise Set 6.2, pp. 379–381

1. (d)   **2.** (e)   **3.** (a)   **4.** (f)   **5.** (c)   **6.** (b)
7. $(2, -1)$ **9.** $(-4, 3)$ **11.** $(2, -2)$
13. $\{(x, y) \mid 2x - 3 = y\}$ **15.** $(-2, 1)$ **17.** $\left(\frac{1}{2}, \frac{1}{2}\right)$
19. $(2, 0)$ **21.** No solution   **23.** $(1, 2)$ **25.** $(7, -2)$
27. $(-1, 2)$ **29.** $\left(\frac{49}{11}, -\frac{12}{11}\right)$ **31.** $(6, 2)$ **33.** No solution
35. $(20, 0)$ **37.** $(3, -1)$ **39.** $\{(x, y) \mid -4x + 2y = 5\}$
41. $\left(2, -\frac{3}{2}\right)$ **43.** $(-2, -9)$ **45.** $(30, 6)$
47. $\{(x, y) \mid 4x - 2y = 2\}$ **49.** No solution
51. $(140, 60)$ **53.** $\left(\frac{1}{3}, -\frac{2}{3}\right)$ **55.** ✍   **57.** Toaster oven:
3 kWh; convection oven: 12 kWh   **58.** 90   **59.** $105,000
60. 290 mi   **61.** First: 30 in.; second: 60 in.; third: 6 in.
62. 165 min   **63.** ✍   **65.** $m = -\frac{1}{2}, b = \frac{5}{2}$
67. $a = 5, b = 2$ **69.** $\left(-\frac{32}{17}, \frac{38}{17}\right)$ **71.** $\left(-\frac{1}{5}, \frac{1}{10}\right)$ **73.** ✍
74. $(6, 10)$ **75.** $(-8, -12)$ **76.** $(12, -9)$ **77.** $(-15, 10)$
78. $(-4, -9)$ **79.** $(6, 5)$ **80.** $(-3, 4)$ **81.** $(5, -2)$
82. $(-8, -10)$ **83.** $(3, 6)$ **84.** $(9, 2)$ **85.** $(-1, -3)$
86. $(9, -10)$ **87.** $(-1, 2)$ **88.** $(5, 8)$ **89.** $(-3, -4)$

Connecting the Concepts, p. 382

1. $(1, 1)$ **2.** $(9, 1)$ **3.** $(4, 3)$ **4.** $(5, 7)$ **5.** $(5, 10)$
6. $\left(2, \frac{2}{5}\right)$ **7.** No solution **8.** $\{(x, y) \mid x = 2 - y\}$
9. $(1, 1)$ **10.** $(0, 0)$ **11.** $(6, -1)$ **12.** No solution
13. $(3, 1)$ **14.** $\left(\frac{95}{71}, -\frac{1}{142}\right)$ **15.** $(1, 1)$ **16.** $(11, -3)$
17. $\{(x, y) \mid x - 2y = 5\}$ **18.** $\left(1, -\frac{1}{19}\right)$ **19.** $\left(\frac{201}{23}, -\frac{18}{23}\right)$
20. $\left(\frac{40}{9}, \frac{10}{3}\right)$

Exercise Set 6.3, pp. 392–396

1. $4, 6$ **3.** Personal e-mails: 274; business e-mails: 304
5. $119°, 61°$ **7.** Two-point shots: 36; foul shots: 28
9. Hats: 36; tee shirts: 9 **11.** Humalog vials: 22; Lantus
vials: 28 **13.** Length: 110 yd; width: 60 yd **15.** Regular
paper: 32 reams; recycled paper: 84 reams **17.** 13-watt
bulbs: 60; 18-watt bulbs: 140 **19.** HP C7115A cartridges:
180; M3908GA cartridges: 270 **21.** Mexican: 14 lb;
Peruvian: 14 lb **23.** Custom-printed M&Ms: 64 oz; bulk
M&Ms: 256 oz **25.** 50%-chocolate: 7.5 lb;10%-chocolate:
12.5 lb **27.** Deep Thought: 12 lb; Oat Dream: 8 lb
29. $7500 at 6.5%; $4500 at 7.2% **31.** $3600 at 4%; $6400
at 5.5% **32.** $8100 at 7.5%; $900 at 8.4% **33.** $3150 at
6%; $1575 at 8% **34.** $320 at 7.5%; $640 at 5% **35.** $5200
at 3%; $3200 at 4.5% **36.** $2400 at 2.4%; $9600 at 5.65%
37. City Bank: 3.25%; Farm Bank: 1.25% **38.** First Bank:
2.75%; Second Bank: 3.75% **39.** $1200 at 6.8%; $8500 at
3.4% **40.** $4800 at 2.5%; $3000 at 5% **41.** $4500 at 8%;
$20,500 at 7.2% **42.** $5500 at 4.35%; $2500 at 2.8%
43. $1800 at 5%; $4200 at 6% **44.** $3400 at 3%; $3600
at 8% **45.** Steady State: 12.5 L; Even Flow: 7.5 L
47. 87-octane: 2.5 gal; 95-octane: 7.5 gal **49.** Whole
milk: $169\frac{3}{13}$ lb; cream: $30\frac{10}{13}$ lb **51.** 375 km **53.** 14 km/h
55. About 1489 mi **57.** Length: 265 ft; width: 165 ft
59. Wii game machines: 3.63 million; PlayStation 3 consoles: 1.21 million **61.** $8.99 plans: 182; $4.99 plans: 68
63. Quarters: 17; fifty-cent pieces: 13 **65.** ⟑ **67.** 1
68. $\frac{1}{2}$ **69.** -13 **70.** 17 **71.** 7 **72.** $\frac{13}{4}$ **73.** ⟑
75. 0%: 20 reams; 30%: 40 reams **77.** $10\frac{2}{3}$ oz
79. 12 sets **81.** Brown: 0.8 gal; neutral: 0.2 gal **83.** City:
261 mi; highway: 204 mi **85.** $P(x) = \dfrac{0.1 + x}{1.5}$ (This
expresses the percent as a decimal quantity.)

Exercise Set 6.4, pp. 403–404

1. True **2.** False **3.** False **4.** True **5.** True
6. False **7.** Yes **9.** $(3, 1, 2)$ **11.** $(1, -2, 2)$
13. $(2, -5, -6)$ **15.** No solution **17.** $(-2, 0, 5)$
19. $(21, -14, -2)$ **21.** The equations are dependent.
23. $\left(3, \frac{1}{2}, -4\right)$ **25.** $\left(\frac{1}{2}, \frac{1}{3}, \frac{1}{6}\right)$ **27.** $\left(\frac{1}{2}, \frac{2}{3}, -\frac{5}{6}\right)$
29. $(15, 33, 9)$ **31.** $(3, 4, -1)$ **33.** $(10, 23, 50)$
35. No solution **37.** The equations are dependent.
39. ⟑ **41.** Let x and y represent the numbers: $x = \frac{1}{2}y$
42. Let x and y represent the numbers; $x - y = 2x$
43. Let x represent the first number;
$x + (x + 1) + (x + 2) = 100$

44. Let $x, y,$ and z represent the numbers; $x + y + z = 100$
45. Let $x, y,$ and z represent the numbers; $xy = 5z$
46. Let x and y represent the numbers; $xy = 2(x + y)$
47. ⟑ **49.** $(1, -1, 2)$ **51.** $(1, -2, 4, -1)$
53. $\left(-1, \frac{1}{5}, -\frac{1}{2}\right)$ **55.** 14 **57.** $z = 8 - 2x - 4y$ **59.** ⟑

Exercise Set 6.5, pp. 408–411

1. $8, 15, 62$ **3.** $8, 21, -3$ **5.** $32°, 96°, 52°$
7. Reading: 502; mathematics: 515; writing: 494
9. Bran muffin: 1.5 g; banana: 3 g; 1 cup of Wheaties: 3 g
11. Basic price: $30,610; tow package: $205; camera: $750
13. 12-oz cups: 17; 16-oz cups: 25; 20-oz cups: 13
15. Bank loan: $15,000; small-business loan: $35,000;
mortgage: $70,000
17. Gold: $30/g; silver: $3/g; copper: $0.02/g
19. Roast beef: 2 servings; baked potato: 1 serving;
broccoli: 2 servings
21. First mezzanine: 8 tickets; main floor: 12 tickets;
second mezzanine: 20 tickets
23. Asia: 5.5 billion; Africa: 2.0 billion; rest of the world:
1.9 billion **25.** ⟑ **27.** $-4x + 6y$ **28.** $-x + 6y$
29. $7y$ **30.** $11a$ **31.** $-2a + b + 6c$
32. $-50a - 30b + 10c$ **33.** $-12x + 5y - 8z$
34. $23x - 13z$ **35.** ⟑ **37.** Applicant: $87; spouse: $87;
first child: $47; second child: $42 **39.** 20 yr **41.** 35 tickets

Exercise Set 6.6, pp. 415–416

1. Matrix **2.** Horizontal; columns **3.** Entry
4. Matrices **5.** Rows **6.** First **7.** $(3, 4)$ **9.** $(-2, 5)$
11. $\left(\frac{3}{2}, \frac{5}{2}\right)$ **13.** $\left(2, \frac{1}{2}, -2\right)$ **15.** $(2, -2, 1)$ **17.** $\left(4, \frac{1}{2}, -\frac{1}{2}\right)$
19. $(1, -3, -2, -1)$ **21.** Dimes: 18; nickels: 24
23. Dried fruit: 9 lb; macadamia nuts: 6 lb
25. $400 at 7%; $500 at 8%; $1600 at 9% **27.** ⟑
29. 17 **30.** -19 **31.** 37 **32.** 422 **33.** ⟑ **35.** 1324

Exercise Set 6.7, pp. 420–421

1. True **2.** True **3.** True **4.** False **5.** False
6. False **7.** 4 **9.** -50 **11.** 27 **13.** -3 **15.** -5
17. $(-3, 2)$ **19.** $\left(\frac{9}{19}, \frac{51}{38}\right)$ **21.** $\left(-1, -\frac{6}{7}, \frac{11}{7}\right)$
23. $(2, -1, 4)$ **25.** $(1, 2, 3)$ **27.** ⟑ **29.** 9700
30. $70x - 2500$ **31.** -1800 **32.** 4500 **33.** $\frac{250}{7}$
34. $\frac{250}{7}$ **35.** ⟑ **37.** 12 **39.** 10

Exercise Set 6.8, pp. 425–427

1. (b) **2.** (f) **3.** (h) **4.** (a) **5.** (e) **6.** (d)
7. (c) **8.** (g)
9. (a) $P(x) = 20x - 200,000;$ (b) $(10,000$ units, $550,000)$
11. (a) $P(x) = 25x - 3100;$ (b) $(124$ units, $4960)$
13. (a) $P(x) = 45x - 22,500;$ (b) $(500$ units, $42,500)$
15. (a) $P(x) = 16x - 50,000;$ (b) $(3125$ units, $125,000)$

17. (a) $P(x) = 50x - 100,000$; **(b)** (2000 units, \$250,000)
19. (\$60, 1100)   **21.** (\$22, 474)   **23.** (\$50, 6250)
25. (\$10, 1070)   **27. (a)** $C(x) = 45,000 + 40x$;
(b) $R(x) = 130x$;   **(c)** $P(x) = 90x - 45,000$;
(d) \$225,000 profit, \$9000 loss   **(e)** (500 phones, \$65,000)
29. (a) $C(x) = 10,000 + 30x$; **(b)** $R(x) = 80x$;
(c) $P(x) = 50x - 10,000$; **(d)** \$90,000 profit, \$7500 loss;
(e) (200 seats, \$16,000)   **31.** ✍   **33.** 6   **34.** -2
35. $-\frac{11}{9}$ **36.** $\frac{3}{4}$ **37.** -6 **38.** -5 **39.** ✍
41. (\$5, 300 yo-yo's)   **43. (a)** \$8.74; **(b)** 24,509 units

Review Exercises: Chapter 6, pp. 431–432

1. Substitution   **2.** Elimination   **3.** Graphical
4. Dependent   **5.** Inconsistent   **6.** Contradiction
7. Parallel   **8.** Square   **9.** Determinant   **10.** Zero
11. (4, 1)   **12.** (3, −2)   **13.** $\left(\frac{8}{3}, \frac{14}{3}\right)$ **14.** No solution
15. $\left(-\frac{4}{5}, \frac{2}{5}\right)$ **16.** $\left(\frac{9}{4}, \frac{7}{10}\right)$ **17.** $\left(\frac{76}{17}, -\frac{2}{119}\right)$ **18.** (−2, −3)
19. $\{(x, y) \mid 3x + 4y = 6\}$
20. Melon: \$2.49; pineapple: \$3.98   **21.** 4 hr
22. 8% juice: 10 L; 15% juice: 4 L   **23.** (4, −8, 10)
24. The equations are dependent.   **25.** (2, 0, 4)
26. $\left(\frac{8}{9}, -\frac{2}{3}, \frac{10}{9}\right)$ **27.** A: 90°; B: 67.5°; C: 22.5°
28. Oil: $21\frac{1}{3}$ oz; lemon juice: $10\frac{2}{3}$ oz
29. Man: 1.4; woman: 5.3; one-year-old child: 50
30. $\left(55, -\frac{89}{2}\right)$ **31.** (−1, 1, 3)   **32.** −5   **33.** 9
34. (6, −2)   **35.** (−3, 0, 4)   **36.** (\$3, 81)
37. (a) $C(x) = 4.75x + 54,000$; **(b)** $R(x) = 9.25x$;
(c) $P(x) = 4.5x - 54,000$; **(d)** \$31,500 loss, \$13,500 profit;
(e) (12,000 pints of honey, \$111,000)
38. ✍ To solve a problem involving four variables, go through the *Familiarize* and *Translate* steps as usual. The resulting system of equations can be solved using the elimination method just as for three variables but likely with more steps.   **39.** ✍ A system of equations can be both dependent and inconsistent if it is equivalent to a system with fewer equations that has no solution. An example is a system of three equations in three unknowns in which two of the equations represent the same plane, and the third represents a parallel plane.   **40.** 20,000 pints
41. Round Stic: 15 packs; Matic Grip: 9 packs
42. (0, 2), (1, 3)   **43.** $a = -\frac{2}{3}, b = -\frac{4}{3}, c = 3$;
$f(x) = -\frac{2}{3}x^2 - \frac{4}{3}x + 3$

Test: Chapter 6, pp. 432–433

1. [6.1] (2, 4)   **2.** [6.2] $\left(3, -\frac{11}{3}\right)$
3. [6.2] $\{(x, y) \mid x = 2y - 3\}$ **4.** [6.2] (2, −1)
5. [6.2] No solution   **6.** [6.2] $\left(-\frac{3}{2}, -\frac{3}{2}\right)$
7. [6.3] Length: 94 ft; width: 50 ft
8. [6.3] Pepperidge Farm Goldfish: 120 g;
Rold Gold Pretzels: 500 g   **9.** [6.3] 5.5 hr   **10.** [6.4] The equations are dependent.   **11.** [6.4] $\left(2, -\frac{1}{2}, -1\right)$
12. [6.4] No solution   **13.** [6.4] (0, 1, 0)
14. [6.6] $\left(\frac{22}{5}, -\frac{28}{5}\right)$ **15.** [6.6] (3, 1, −2)   **16.** [6.7] −14
17. [6.7] −59   **18.** [6.7] $\left(\frac{7}{13}, -\frac{17}{26}\right)$ **19.** [6.5] Electrician: 3.5 hr; carpenter: 8 hr; plumber: 10 hr   **20.** [6.8] (\$3, 55)

21. [6.8] **(a)** $C(x) = 25x + 44,000$; **(b)** $R(x) = 80x$;
(c) $P(x) = 55x - 44,000$; **(d)** \$27,500 loss, \$5500 profit;
(e) (800 hammocks, \$64,000)
22. [5.3], [6.3] $m = 7, b = 10$ **23.** [6.3] $\frac{120}{7}$ lb

Cumulative Review: Chapters 1–6, pp. 434–435

1. 24   **2.** $\frac{1}{10}$ **3.** −10   **4.** $13x^2 - y$ **5.** −24
6. 2   **7.** x^{11} **8.** $-\frac{9x^4}{2y^6}$ **9.** $-\frac{2a^{11}}{5b^{33}}$ **10.** $\frac{81x^{36}}{256y^8}$
11. 1.87×10^6 **12.** 4×10^6 **13.** $\frac{9}{7}$ **14.** −3, −2
15. 2, 3   **16.** $\frac{1}{9}$ **17.** $\left\{y \mid y \geq -\frac{2}{3}\right\}$, or $\left[-\frac{2}{3}, \infty\right)$
18. −10, 10   **19.** (1, 2)   **20.** −11   **21.** $-\frac{1}{2}, \frac{2}{3}$
22. (7, 3)   **23.** (−3, 2, −4)   **24.** (0, −1, 2)
25. $p = \frac{3t}{q}$ **26.** $s = 2A - r$ **27.** $3a^3 + 8a^2 - 14$
28. $\frac{m(m + 2n)}{(m - n)(2m + n)}$ **29.** $-3a^3 + 8a^2 - 12a$
30. $\frac{2x + 4}{x - 2}$ **31.** $25a^4 - b^2$
32. $-15x^5 + 18x^4 + 6x^3 - 3x^2$ **33.** $4n^2 + 20n + 25$
34. $8t^5 + 5t^3 + 32t^2 + 20$ **35.** $\frac{(x - 1)(x + 2)}{(x - 2)^2}$
36. $2x + 1$ **37.** $\frac{x}{2(x + 1)(x + 2)}$ **38.** $(x + 1)(x^2 + 2)$
39. $(m^2 + 1)(m + 1)(m - 1)$ **40.** $2x(x + 4)(x + 5)$
41. $(x^2 - 3)^2$ **42.** $2(2x^2 - x - 5)$
43. $(2x - 5)(5x - 2)$

44.

45.

46.

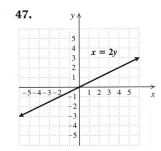

47.

48. x-intercept: (6, 0); y-intercept: (0, −4)
49. $y = -2x + \frac{4}{7}$ **50.** $y = -\frac{1}{10}x + \frac{12}{5}$ **51.** Parallel
52. $y = -2x + 5$ **53.** {−5, −3, −1, 1, 3}; {−3, −2, 1, 4, 5}; −2; 3   **54.** {$x \mid x$ is a real number and $x \neq -10$}   **55.** −31   **56.** 3   **57.** $2a^2 + 4a - 4$
58. 14   **59.** \$1260   **60.** Dog sled: 12 mph; snowmobile: 52 mph   **61.** At least 35 patients   **62.** 11 and 13
63. 100 min   **64.** 32.5°, 65°, 82.5°   **65.** 42 hr

66. $x = \dfrac{t}{p - q}$ **67.** $y = 2x + 7$ **68.** $\dfrac{3t^2(2t^2 - t + 1)}{4(t - 1)}$
69. $m = -\frac{5}{9}, b = -\frac{2}{9}$ **70.** Length: 6 in.; width: $4\frac{1}{4}$ in

CHAPTER 7

Exercise Set 7.1, pp. 443–446

1. Equivalent equations **2.** Equivalent expressions
3. Equivalent inequalities **4.** Not equivalent
5. Not equivalent **6.** Equivalent equations
7. Equivalent expressions **8.** Not equivalent
9. Not equivalent **10.** Equivalent inequalities
11. $\{x \mid x < 2\}$, or $(-\infty, 2)$ **13.** $\{x \mid x \le -9\}$, or $(-\infty, -9]$
15. $\{x \mid x < -26\}$, or $(-\infty, -26)$
17. $\left\{t \mid t \ge -\frac{13}{3}\right\}$, or $\left[-\frac{13}{3}, \infty\right)$ **19.** $\left\{y \mid y \le -\frac{3}{2}\right\}$, or $\left(-\infty, -\frac{3}{2}\right]$
21. $\left\{t \mid t < \frac{29}{5}\right\}$, or $\left(-\infty, \frac{29}{5}\right)$ **23.** $\left\{m \mid m > \frac{7}{3}\right\}$, or $\left(\frac{7}{3}, \infty\right)$
25. $\{x \mid x \ge 2\}$, or $[2, \infty)$ **27.** $\{x \mid x > 0\}$, or $(0, \infty)$
29. $\{x \mid x < 7\}$, or $(-\infty, 7)$ **31.** $\{x \mid x \ge 2\}$, or $[2, \infty)$
33. $\{x \mid x < 8\}$, or $(-\infty, 8)$ **35.** $\{x \mid x \le 2\}$, or $(-\infty, 2]$
37. $\{x \mid x \ge 2\}$, or $[2, \infty)$ **39.** $\left\{x \mid x > \frac{2}{3}\right\}$, or $\left(\frac{2}{3}, \infty\right)$
41. $\{x \mid x \ge 10\}$, or $[10, \infty)$ **43.** $\{x \mid x \le 3\}$, or $(-\infty, 3]$
45. $\left\{x \mid x \ge -\frac{7}{2}\right\}$, or $\left[-\frac{7}{2}, \infty\right)$ **47.** $\{x \mid x \le 4\}$, or $(-\infty, 4]$
49. $\{x \mid x \ge -15\}$, or $[-15, \infty)$ **51.** $\{x \mid x \ge 5\}$, or $[5, \infty)$
53. Lengths of time less than $7\frac{1}{2}$ hr **55.** At least 56 questions correct **57.** Years after 2010 **59.** Gross sales greater than $7000 **61.** For more than $6000
63. (a) Body densities less than $\frac{99}{95}$ kg/L, or about 1.04 kg/L; (b) body densities less than $\frac{495}{482}$ kg/L, or about 1.03 kg/L
65. (a) $\left\{x \mid x < 3913\frac{1}{23}\right\}$, or $\{x \mid x \le 3913\}$;
(b) $\left\{x \mid x > 3913\frac{1}{23}\right\}$, or $\{x \mid x \ge 3914\}$ **67.** 🖩
69. $\{x \mid x \text{ is a real number } and \, x \ne 0\}$
70. $\{x \mid x \text{ is a real number } and \, x \ne 6\}$
71. $\left\{x \mid x \text{ is a real number } and \, x \ne -\frac{1}{2}\right\}$
72. $\left\{x \mid x \text{ is a real number } and \, x \ne \frac{7}{5}\right\}$
73. $\mathbb{R}$ **74.** $\{x \mid x \text{ is a real number } and \, x \ne 0\}$ **75.** 🖩
77. $\left\{x \mid x \le \dfrac{2}{a - 1}\right\}$ **79.** $\left\{y \mid y \ge \dfrac{2a + 5b}{b(a - 2)}\right\}$
81. $\left\{x \mid x > \dfrac{4m - 2c}{d - (5c + 2m)}\right\}$ **83.** False; $2 < 3$ and $4 < 5$, but $2 - 4 = 3 - 5$. **85.** 🖩
87. $\mathbb{R}$ ⟵———|———⟶
                          0
89. $\{x \mid x \text{ is a real number } and \, x \ne 0\}$
⟵———✕———⟶
        0
91. $\{x \mid x \le 6\}$, or $(-\infty, 6]$ **93.** (a) $\{x \mid x < 4\}$, or $(-\infty, 4)$;
(b) $\{x \mid x \ge 2\}$, or $[2, \infty)$; (c) $\{x \mid x \ge 3.2\}$, or $[3.2, \infty)$
95. ◰

Exercise Set 7.2, pp. 453–456

1. (h) **2.** (j) **3.** (f) **4.** (a) **5.** (e) **6.** (d)
7. (b) **8.** (g) **9.** (c) **10.** (i) **11.** $\{4, 16\}$

13. $\{0, 5, 10, 15, 20\}$ **15.** $\{b, d, f\}$ **17.** $\{u, v, x, y, z\}$
19. $\varnothing$ **21.** $\{1, 3, 5\}$
23. ⟵|+|(——)|+|+|+|+|⟶ $(1, 3)$
        -2 -1 0 1 2 3 4 5 6 7 8
25. ⟵|+|[———]|+|+|+|⟶ $[-6, 0]$
        -8 -7 -6 -5 -4 -3 -2 -1 0 1 2
27. ⟵——)|+|+|+|(———⟶ $(-\infty, -1) \cup (4, \infty)$
        -3 -2 -1 0 1 2 3 4 5 6 7
29. ⟵———]|+|(———⟶ $(-\infty, -2] \cup (1, \infty)$
        -5 -4 -3 -2 -1 0 1 2 3 4 5
31. ⟵|+|(———]|+|⟶ $(-2, 4]$
        -5 -4 -3 -2 -1 0 1 2 3 4 5
33. ⟵|+|(———)|+|⟶ $(-2, 4)$
        -5 -4 -3 -2 -1 0 1 2 3 4 5
35. ⟵———)|+|(———⟶ $(-\infty, 5) \cup (7, \infty)$
        -1 0 1 2 3 4 5 6 7 8 9
37. ⟵———]|+|[———⟶ $(-\infty, -4] \cup [5, \infty)$
        -5 -4 -3 -2 -1 0 1 2 3 4 5
39. ⟵|[———)|+|⟶ $[-3, 7)$
        -3 -2 -1 0 1 2 3 4 5 6 7
41. ⟵|+|(———]|+|⟶ $(-7, 0]$
        -8 -7 -6 -5 -4 -3 -2 -1 0 1 2
43. ⟵———)|+|⟶ $(-\infty, 5)$
        -4 -3 -2 -1 0 1 2 3 4 5 6
45. $\{x \mid -5 \le x < 7\}$, or $[-5, 7)$ ⟵[———)⟶
                                                    -5 0 7
47. $\{t \mid 4 < t \le 8\}$, or $(4, 8]$ ⟵(———]⟶
                                              0 4 8
49. $\{a \mid -2 \le a < 2\}$, or $[-2, 2)$ ⟵[———)⟶
                                                  -2 0 2
51. $\mathbb{R}$, or $(-\infty, \infty)$ ⟵————⟶
                                                0
53. $\{x \mid -3 \le x \le 2\}$, or $[-3, 2]$ ⟵[———]⟶
                                                  -3 0 2
55. $\{x \mid 7 < x < 23\}$, or $(7, 23)$ ⟵(———)⟶
                                              0 7 23
57. $\{x \mid -32 \le x \le 8\}$, or $[-32, 8]$
⟵[————]⟶
  -32 0 8
59. $\{x \mid 1 \le x \le 3\}$, or $[1, 3]$ ⟵[—]⟶
                                              0 1 3
61. $\left\{x \mid -\frac{7}{2} < x \le 7\right\}$, or $\left(-\frac{7}{2}, 7\right]$ ⟵(———]⟶
                                                                      $-\frac{7}{2}$ 0 7
63. $\{t \mid t < 0 \, or \, t > 1\}$, or $(-\infty, 0) \cup (1, \infty)$
⟵—)|(—⟶
    0 1
65. $\left\{a \mid a < \frac{7}{2}\right\}$, or $\left(-\infty, \frac{7}{2}\right)$ ⟵———)⟶
                                                              0 $\frac{7}{2}$
67. $\{a \mid a < -5\}$, or $(-\infty, -5)$ ⟵———)⟶
                                              -5 0
69. $\varnothing$
71. $\{t \mid t \le 6\}$, or $(-\infty, 6]$ ⟵———]⟶
                                              0 6
73. $(-\infty, -6) \cup (-6, \infty)$ **75.** $(-\infty, 0) \cup (0, \infty)$
77. $(-\infty, 4) \cup (4, \infty)$ **79.** 🖩
81.

$g(x) = 2x$
82.
$f(x) = 4$

83.

$g(x) = -3$

84.
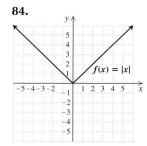
$f(x) = |x|$

85. -1 **86.** -4 **87.** ▨   **89.** $(-1, 6)$
91. Between 2003 and 2009   **93.** Sizes between 6 and 13
95. Densities between 1.03 kg/L and 1.04 kg/L
97. More than 12 and fewer than 125 trips
99. $\left\{m \mid m < \frac{6}{5}\right\}$, or $\left(-\infty, \frac{6}{5}\right)$

101. $\left\{x \mid -\frac{1}{8} < x < \frac{1}{2}\right\}$, or $\left(-\frac{1}{8}, \frac{1}{2}\right)$

103. False   **105.** True
107. $(-\infty, -7) \cup \left(-7, \frac{3}{4}\right]$ **109.** ▨   **111.** ▨

Technology Connection, p. 462

1. The x-values on the graph of $y_1 = |4x + 2|$ that are *below* the line $y = 6$ solve the inequality $|4x + 2| < 6$.
2. The x-values on the graph of $y_1 = |3x - 2|$ that are below the line $y = 4$ are in the interval $\left(-\frac{2}{3}, 2\right)$.
3. The graphs of $y_1 = \text{abs}(4x + 2)$ and $y_2 = -6$ do not intersect.

Exercise Set 7.3, pp. 463–465

1. True   **2.** False   **3.** True   **4.** True   **5.** True
6. True   **7.** False   **8.** False   **9.** (g)   **10.** (h)   **11.** (d)
12. (a)   **13.** (a)   **14.** (b)   **15.** $\{-10, 10\}$ **17.** $\varnothing$
19. $\{0\}$ **21.** $\left\{-\frac{1}{2}, \frac{7}{2}\right\}$ **23.** $\varnothing$ **25.** $\{-4, 8\}$
27. $\{6, 8\}$ **29.** $\{-5.5, 5.5\}$ **31.** $\{-8, 8\}$ **33.** $\{-1, 1\}$
35. $\left\{-\frac{11}{2}, \frac{13}{2}\right\}$ **37.** $\{-2, 12\}$ **39.** $\left\{-\frac{1}{3}, 3\right\}$ **41.** $\{-7, 1\}$
43. $\{-8.7, 8.7\}$ **45.** $\left\{-\frac{9}{2}, \frac{11}{2}\right\}$ **47.** $\{-8, 2\}$ **49.** $\left\{-\frac{1}{2}\right\}$
51. $\left\{-\frac{3}{5}, 5\right\}$ **53.** $\mathbb{R}$ **55.** $\left\{\frac{1}{4}\right\}$
57. $\{a \mid -3 \leq a \leq 3\}$, or $[-3, 3]$
59. $\{t \mid t < 0 \text{ or } t > 0\}$, or $(-\infty, 0) \cup (0, \infty)$

61. $\{x \mid -3 < x < 5\}$, or $(-3, 5)$

63. $\{n \mid -8 \leq n \leq 4\}$, or $[-8, 4]$

65. $\{x \mid x < -2 \text{ or } x > 8\}$, or $(-\infty, -2) \cup (8, \infty)$

67. $\mathbb{R}$, or $(-\infty, \infty)$

69. $\left\{a \mid a \leq -\frac{10}{3} \text{ or } a \geq \frac{2}{3}\right\}$, or $\left(-\infty, -\frac{10}{3}\right] \cup \left[\frac{2}{3}, \infty\right)$

71. $\{y \mid -9 < y < 15\}$, or $(-9, 15)$

73. $\{x \mid x \leq -8 \text{ or } x \geq 0\}$, or $(-\infty, -8] \cup [0, \infty)$

75. $\left\{x \mid x < -\frac{1}{2} \text{ or } x > \frac{7}{2}\right\}$, or $\left(-\infty, -\frac{1}{2}\right) \cup \left(\frac{7}{2}, \infty\right)$

77. $\varnothing$
79. $\left\{x \mid x < -\frac{43}{24} \text{ or } x > \frac{9}{8}\right\}$, or $\left(-\infty, -\frac{43}{24}\right) \cup \left(\frac{9}{8}, \infty\right)$

81. $\{m \mid -9 \leq m \leq 3\}$, or $[-9, 3]$

83. $\{a \mid -6 < a < 0\}$, or $(-6, 0)$

85. $\left\{x \mid -\frac{1}{2} \leq x \leq \frac{7}{2}\right\}$, or $\left[-\frac{1}{2}, \frac{7}{2}\right]$

87. $\left\{x \mid x \leq -\frac{7}{3} \text{ or } x \geq 5\right\}$, or $\left(-\infty, -\frac{7}{3}\right] \cup [5, \infty)$

89. $\{x \mid -4 < x < 5\}$, or $(-4, 5)$
91. ▨
93.

$3x - y = 6$

94.
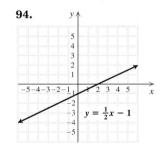
$y = \frac{1}{2}x - 1$

95.

$x = -2$

96.

$y = 4$

97. $\left(4, -\frac{4}{3}\right)$ **98.** $(5, 1)$ **99.** $\left(\frac{5}{7}, -\frac{18}{7}\right)$ **100.** $(-2, -5)$
101. ▨   **103.** $\left\{t \mid t \geq \frac{5}{3}\right\}$, or $\left[\frac{5}{3}, \infty\right)$
105. $\mathbb{R}$, or $(-\infty, \infty)$ **107.** $\left\{-\frac{1}{7}, \frac{7}{3}\right\}$ **109.** $|x| < 3$
111. $|x| \geq 6$ **113.** $|x + 3| > 5$
115. $|x - 7| < 2$, or $|7 - x| < 2$ **117.** $|x - 3| \leq 4$
119. $|x + 4| < 3$ **121.** Between 80 ft and 100 ft
123. $\{x \mid 1 \leq x \leq 5\}$, or $[1, 5]$ **125.** ▨, ▨

Connecting the Concepts, pp. 465–466

1. 2   **2.** $\{x \mid x > 3\}$, or $(3, \infty)$ **3.** $\frac{9}{2}$ **4.** $\{-4, 3\}$
5. $\{x \mid x \geq -6\}$, or $[-6, \infty)$ **6.** $\{t \mid -4 < t < 4\}$, or

$(-4, 4)$ **7.** $-\frac{11}{8}$ **8.** $\frac{62}{3}$ **9.** $\left\{-\frac{8}{3}, \frac{8}{3}\right\}$
10. $\{x \mid -7 \le x \le 13\}$, or $[-7, 13]$ **11.** 31 **12.** $\varnothing$
13. $\left\{x \mid x \le -\frac{17}{2} \text{ or } x \ge \frac{7}{2}\right\}$, or $\left(-\infty, -\frac{17}{2}\right] \cup \left[\frac{7}{2}, \infty\right)$
14. $\varnothing$ **15.** $\{m \mid -24 < m < 12\}$, or $(-24, 12)$
16. $\{-42, 38\}$ **17.** $\{t \mid t \le 4 \text{ or } t \ge 10\}$, or
$(-\infty, 4] \cup [10, \infty)$ **18.** $\frac{7}{2}$ **19.** $\{a \mid -7 < a < -5\}$, or
$(-7, -5)$ **20.** $\mathbb{R}$, or $(-\infty, \infty)$

Technology Connection, p. 470

1. $y > x + 3.5$

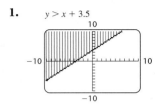

2. $7y \le 2x + 5$

3. $8x - 2y < 11$

4. $11x + 13y + 4 \ge 0$

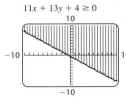

Technology Connection, p. 472

1. $y_1 \le 4 - x, \ y_2 > x - 4$

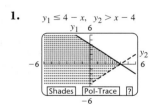

Visualizing for Success, p. 473

1. B **2.** F **3.** J **4.** A **5.** E **6.** G **7.** C **8.** D
9. I **10.** H

Exercise Set 7.4, pp. 474–476

1. (e) **2.** (c) **3.** (d) **4.** (a) **5.** (b) **6.** (f)
7. No **9.** Yes

11. $y \ge \frac{1}{2}x$

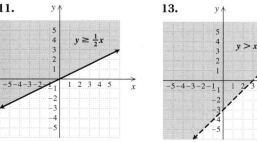

13. $y > x - 3$

15. $y \le x + 2$

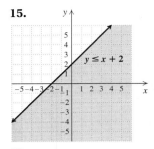

17. $x - y \le 4$

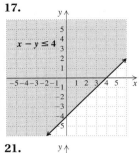

19. $2x + 3y < 6$

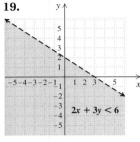

21. $2y - x \le 4$

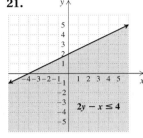

23. $2x - 2y \ge 8 + 2y$

25. $x > -2$

27. $y \le 6$

29. $-2 < y < 7$

31. $-5 \le x < 4$

33. $0 \le y \le 3$

35.

37.

55.

39.

41.

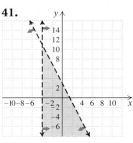

57. ✍　**59.** 3.25%　**60.** $228
61. 3%: $3600; 5%: $6400　**62.** Carrots: 12 lb; broccoli: 8 lb　**63.** Student tickets: 62; adult tickets: 108
64. Corn: 240 acres; soybeans: 160 acres　**65.** ✍

67.

69.

43.

45.

47.

49.

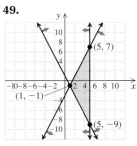

71.
$$w > 0,$$
$$h > 0,$$
$$w + h + 30 \leq 62, \text{ or}$$
$$w + h \leq 32,$$
$$2w + 2h + 30 \leq 130, \text{ or}$$
$$w + h \leq 50$$

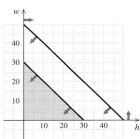

73.
$$q + v \geq 1150,$$
$$q \geq 700,$$
$$q \leq 800,$$
$$v \geq 400,$$
$$v \leq 800$$

51.

53.

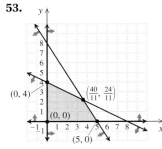

75.
$$35c + 75a > 1000,$$
$$c \geq 0,$$
$$a \geq 0$$

77. $h < 2w$,
$w \leq 1.5h$,
$h \leq 3200$,
$h \geq 0$,
$w \geq 0$

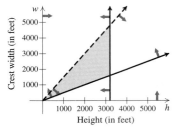

79. (a) $3x + 6y > 2$

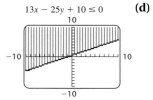

(b) $x - 5y \leq 10$

(c) $13x - 25y + 10 \leq 0$

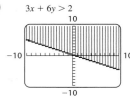

(d) $2x + 5y > 0$

Connecting the Concepts, pp. 477–478

1. (point at 5, open to right)

2. (open at 5, ray right)

3. (segment 0 to 5, open at 5)

4. (point at 13)

5. (open at −1, ray left)

6. (open at −2, ray right)

7. $x + y = 2$

8. $x + y < 2$

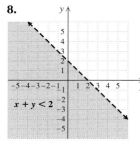

9. $x + y \geq 2$

10. $y = 3x - 3$

11. $x = 4$

12. $2x - 5y = -10$

13. $(1, 0)$

14.

15. $2x + y < 6$

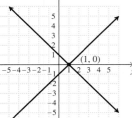

16. $x > 6y - 6$

17. $4x = 3y$

18. $\left(\frac{8}{5}, \frac{1}{5}\right)$

19.

20. $3y = 8$

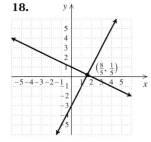

Exercise Set 7.5, pp. 482–484

1. Objective **2.** Constraints **3.** Corner
4. Feasible **5.** Vertices **6.** Vertex **7.** Maximum
84 when $x = 0$, $y = 6$; minimum 0 when $x = 0$, $y = 0$

9. Maximum 76 when $x = 7, y = 0$; minimum 16 when $x = 0, y = 4$ **11.** Maximum 5 when $x = 3, y = 7$; minimum -15 when $x = 3, y = -3$ **13.** Gumbo: 40 orders; sandwiches: 50 orders   **15.** 4-photo pages: 5; 6-photo pages: 15; 110 photos   **17.** Corporate bonds: \$22,000; municipal bonds: \$18,000; maximum: \$3110
19. Short-answer questions: 12; essay questions: 4
21. Merlot: 80 acres; Cabernet: 160 acres
23. 2.5 servings of each   **25.** 🔄   **27.** $4a - 7 + h$
28. $4a + 4h - 7$ **29.** $\{x | x \text{ is a real number } and \ x \neq -\frac{1}{2}\}$, or $\left(-\infty, -\frac{1}{2}\right) \cup \left(-\frac{1}{2}, \infty\right)$ **30.** $\mathbb{R}$
31. $\{x | x \geq -4\}$, or $[-4, \infty)$
32. $\{x | x \text{ is a real number } and \ x \neq -1 \ and \ x \neq 1\}$, or $(-\infty, -1) \cup (-1, 1) \cup (1, \infty)$ **33.** 🔄
35. T3's: 30; S5's:10   **37.** Chairs: 25; sofas: 9

Review Exercises: Chapter 7, pp. 487–488

1. True   **2.** False   **3.** True   **4.** False   **5.** True
6. True   **7.** True   **8.** False   **9.** False   **10.** False
11. $\{x | x > -\frac{3}{2}\}$, or $\left(-\frac{3}{2}, \infty\right)$ **12.** $\{x | x < -3\}$, or $(-\infty, -3)$ **13.** $\{y | y > -\frac{220}{23}\}$, or $\left(-\frac{220}{23}, \infty\right)$
14. $\{x | x \leq -\frac{5}{2}\}$, or $\left(-\infty, -\frac{5}{2}\right]$ **15.** $\{x | x < 5\}$, or $(-\infty, 5)$
16. $\{x | x < 1\}$, or $(-\infty, 1)$ **17.** $\{x | x \geq -4\}$, or $[-4, \infty)$
18. $\{x | x \geq 6\}$, or $[6, \infty)$ **19.** $\{x | x \leq 2\}$, or $(-\infty, 2]$
20. More than 125 hr   **21.** \$3000   **22.** $\{a, c\}$
23. $\{a, b, c, d, e, f, g\}$
24. <number line> $(-3, 2]$
25. <number line> $(-\infty, \infty)$
26. $\{x | -8 < x \leq 0\}$, or $(-8, 0]$ <number line>
27. $\{x | -\frac{5}{4} < x < \frac{5}{2}\}$, or $\left(-\frac{5}{4}, \frac{5}{2}\right)$ <number line>
28. $\{x | x < -3 \ or \ x > 1\}$, or $(-\infty, -3) \cup (1, \infty)$ <number line>
29. $\{x | x < -11 \ or \ x \geq -6\}$, or $(-\infty, -11) \cup [-6, \infty)$ <number line>
30. $\{x | x \leq -6 \ or \ x \geq 8\}$, or $(-\infty, -6] \cup [8, \infty)$ <number line>
31. $\{x | x < -\frac{2}{5} \ or \ x > \frac{8}{5}\}$, or $\left(-\infty, -\frac{2}{5}\right) \cup \left(\frac{8}{5}, \infty\right)$ <number line>
32. $(-\infty, -3) \cup (-3, \infty)$ **33.** $[2, \infty)$ **34.** $\left(-\infty, \frac{1}{4}\right]$
35. $\{-11, 11\}$ **36.** $\{t | t \leq -21 \ or \ t \geq 21\}$, or $(-\infty, -21] \cup [21, \infty)$ **37.** $\{5, 11\}$
38. $\{a | -\frac{7}{2} < a < 2\}$, or $\left(-\frac{7}{2}, 2\right)$
39. $\{x | x \leq -\frac{11}{3} \ or \ x \geq \frac{19}{3}\}$, or $\left(-\infty, -\frac{11}{3}\right] \cup \left[\frac{19}{3}, \infty\right)$
40. $\left\{-14, \frac{4}{3}\right\}$ **41.** $\varnothing$ **42.** $\{x | -16 \leq x \leq 8\}$, or $[-16, 8]$
43. $\{x | x < 0 \ or \ x > 10\}$, or $(-\infty, 0) \cup (10, \infty)$
44. $\{x | -6 \leq x \geq 4\}$, or $[-6, 4]$ **45.** $\varnothing$

46.   **47.**

48.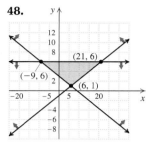

49. Maximum 40 when $x = 7, y = 15$; minimum 10 when $x = 1, y = 3$ **50.** Ohio plant: 120 computers; Oregon plant: 40 computers   **51.** 🔄 The equation $|X| = p$ has two solutions when p is positive because X can be either p or $-p$. The same equation has no solution when p is negative because no number has a negative absolute value.
52. 🔄 The solution set of a system of inequalities is all ordered pairs that make *all* the individual inequalities true. This consists of ordered pairs that are common to all the individual solution sets, or the intersection of the graphs.
53. $\{x | -\frac{8}{3} \leq x \leq -2\}$, or $\left[-\frac{8}{3}, -2\right]$ **54.** False: $-4 < 3$ is true, but $(-4)^2 < 9$ is false.   **55.** $|d - 2.5| \leq 0.003$

Test: Chapter 7, p. 489

1. [7.1] $\{y | y \leq -2\}$, or $(-\infty, -2]$ **2.** [7.1] $\{x | x > \frac{16}{5}\}$, or $\left(\frac{16}{5}, \infty\right)$ **3.** [7.1] $\{x | x \leq \frac{9}{16}\}$, or $\left(-\infty, \frac{9}{16}\right]$
4. [7.1] $\{x | x > 1\}$, or $(1, \infty)$ **5.** [7.1] $\{x | x \geq 4\}$, or $[4, \infty)$
6. [7.1] $\{x | x > 1\}$, or $(1, \infty)$ **7.** [7.1] More than $187\frac{1}{2}$ mi
8. [7.1] Less than or equal to 2.5 hr   **9.** [7.2] $\{a, e\}$
10. [7.2] $\{a, b, c, d, e, i, o, u\}$ **11.** [7.1] $(-\infty, 2]$
12. [7.2] $(-\infty, 7) \cup (7, \infty)$
13. [7.2] $\{x | -\frac{3}{2} < x \leq \frac{1}{2}\}$, or $\left(-\frac{3}{2}, \frac{1}{2}\right]$ <number line>
14. [7.2] $\{x | x < 3 \ or \ x > 6\}$, or $(-\infty, 3) \cup (6, \infty)$ <number line>
15. [7.2] $\{x | x < -4 \ or \ x \geq -\frac{5}{2}\}$, or $(-\infty, -4) \cup \left[-\frac{5}{2}, \infty\right)$ <number line>
16. [7.2] $\{x | -3 \leq x \leq 1\}$, or $[-3, 1]$ <number line>

17. [7.3] $\{-15, 15\}$

18. [7.3] $\{a \mid a < -5 \text{ or } a > 5\}$, or $(-\infty, -5) \cup (5, \infty)$

19. [7.3] $\left\{x \mid -2 < x < \frac{8}{3}\right\}$, or $\left(-2, \frac{8}{3}\right)$

20. [7.3] $\left\{t \mid t \le -\frac{13}{5} \text{ or } t \ge \frac{7}{5}\right\}$, or $\left(-\infty, -\frac{13}{5}\right] \cup \left[\frac{7}{5}, \infty\right)$

21. [7.3] $\varnothing$

22. [7.2] $\left\{x \mid x < \frac{1}{2} \text{ or } x > \frac{7}{2}\right\}$, or $\left(-\infty, \frac{1}{2}\right) \cup \left(\frac{7}{2}, \infty\right)$

23. [7.3] $\left\{-\frac{3}{2}\right\}$

24. [7.4]

25. [7.4]

26. [7.4]

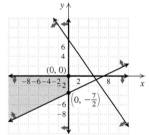

27. [7.5] Maximum 57 when $x = 6$, $y = 9$; minimum 5 when $x = 1$, $y = 0$ **28.** [7.5] Manicures: 35; haircuts: 15; maximum: \$690   **29.** [7.3] $[-1, 0] \cup [4, 6]$
30. [7.2] $\left(\frac{1}{5}, \frac{4}{5}\right)$ **31.** [7.3] $|x + 3| \le 5$

Cumulative Review: Chapters 1–7, pp. 490–491

1. 22   **2.** $c - 6$ **3.** $-\frac{1}{100}$ **4.** $-\frac{6x^4}{y^3}$ **5.** $\frac{9a^6}{4b^4}$

6. $\frac{2}{x^2 + 5x + 25}$ **7.** $x^2 - 25$ **8.** $15n^2 + 11n - 14$

9. $\frac{-10}{(x + 5)(x - 5)}$ **10.** $\frac{(x - 3)^2}{x^2(2x - 3)}$ **11.** $25(x - 1)^2$

12. $(4m + 7)(2n - 3)$ **13.** $8(t^2 + 100)$ **14.** 5
15. $\mathbb{R}$ **16.** $-2, 4$ **17.** $-4, 3$ **18.** No solution
19. $(5, 1)$ **20.** $\left\{-\frac{7}{2}, \frac{9}{2}\right\}$ **21.** $\left\{x \mid x < \frac{13}{2}\right\}$, or $\left(-\infty, \frac{13}{2}\right)$
22. $\{t \mid t < -3 \text{ or } t > 3\}$, or $(-\infty, -3) \cup (3, \infty)$
23. $\left\{x \mid -2 \le x \le \frac{10}{3}\right\}$, or $\left[-2, \frac{10}{3}\right]$

24.

25.

26.

27.

28.

29.

30. Slope: $\frac{4}{9}$; y-intercept: $(0, -2)$ **31.** $y = -7x - 25$
32. $y = \frac{2}{3}x + 4$ **33.** Domain: $\mathbb{R}$; range: $\{y \mid y \ge -2\}$, or $[-2, \infty)$ **34.** $\left\{x \mid x \text{ is a real number } and x \ne -\frac{5}{2}\right\}$, or $\left(-\infty, -\frac{5}{2}\right) \cup \left(-\frac{5}{2}, \infty\right)$ **35.** 22   **36.** $x^2 + 6x - 9$
37.

38. $\left\{x \mid x \text{ is a real number } and x \ne 0 and x \ne \frac{1}{3}\right\}$

39. $t = \dfrac{c}{a - d}$ **40.** 183 cannons   **41.** Beef: 9300 gal;
wheat: 2300 gal   **42.** (a) $b(t) = \frac{34}{15}t + 34.6$; (b) \$55 billion;
(c) 2008   **43.** (a) More than \$40; (b) costs greater than \$30
44. Length: 10 cm; width: 6 cm   **45.** \$640
46. \$50 billion   **47.** Vegetarian dinners: 12; steak
dinners: 16   **48.** $m = \frac{1}{3}$, $b = \frac{16}{3}$ **49.** $\frac{64}{3}$
50. $[-4, 0) \cup (0, \infty)$ **51.** 2^{11a-16}

CHAPTER 8

Technology Connection, p. 496

1. False   **2.** True   **3.** False

Visualizing for Success, p. 500

1. B   **2.** H   **3.** C   **4.** I   **5.** D   **6.** A   **7.** F   **8.** J
9. G   **10.** E

Exercise Set 8.1, pp. 501–502

1. Two   **2.** Negative   **3.** Positive   **4.** Negative
5. Irrational   **6.** Real   **7.** Nonnegative   **8.** Negative
9. $8, -8$ **11.** $10, -10$ **13.** $20, -20$ **15.** $25, -25$
17. 7 **19.** -4 **21.** $\frac{6}{7}$ **23.** -13 **25.** $-\frac{4}{9}$ **27.** 0.2
29. 0.09 **31.** $p^2 + 4; 2$ **33.** $\frac{x}{y+4}; 5$ **35.** $\sqrt{5}; 0;$
does not exist; does not exist   **37.** -7; does not exist; -1;
does not exist   **39.** $1; \sqrt{2}; \sqrt{101}$ **41.** $10|x|$
43. $|8 - t|$ **45.** $|y + 8|$ **47.** $|2x + 7|$ **49.** -4
51. -1 **53.** $\frac{2}{3}$ **55.** $|x|$ **57.** t **59.** $6|a|$ **61.** 6
63. $|a + b|$ **65.** $|a^{11}|$ **67.** Cannot be simplified
69. $4x$ **71.** $-3t$ **73.** $5b$ **75.** $a + 1$ **77.** 3 **79.** $2x$
81. $x - 1$ **83.** $5y$ **85.** t^9 **87.** $(x - 2)^4$
89. $2; 3; -2; -4$ **91.** 2; does not exist; does not exist; 3
93. $\{x|x \geq 6\}$, or $[6, \infty)$ **95.** $\{t|t \geq -8\}$, or $[-8, \infty)$
97. $\{x|x \leq 5\}$, or $(-\infty, 5]$ **99.** $\mathbb{R}$ **101.** $\left\{z|z \geq -\frac{2}{5}\right\}$, or
$\left[-\frac{2}{5}, \infty\right)$ **103.** $\mathbb{R}$ **105.**   **107.** a^6b^2 **108.** $15x^3y^9$
109. $\frac{125x^6}{y^9}$ **110.** $\frac{a^3}{8b^6c^3}$ **111.** $\frac{x^3}{2y^6}$ **112.** $\frac{y^4z^8}{16x^4}$
113.   **115.** About 1404 species
117. $\{x|x \geq -5\}$, or $[-5, \infty)$
119. $\{x|x \geq 0\}$, or $[0, \infty)$

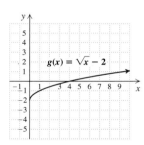

121. $\{x|-3 \leq x < 2\}$, or $[-3, 2)$
123. $\{x|x < -1 \text{ or } x > 6\}$, or $(-\infty, -1) \cup (6, \infty)$
125.

Technology Connection, p. 504

1. Without parentheses, the expression entered would be $\frac{7^2}{3}$.

2. For $x = 0$ or $x = 1$, $y_1 = y_2 = y_3$; on $(0, 1)$, $y_1 > y_2 > y_3$;
on $(1, \infty)$, $y_1 < y_2 < y_3$.

Technology Connection, p. 506

1. Many graphing calculators do not have keys for radicals
of index 3 or higher. On those graphing calculators that offer
$\sqrt[x]{}$ in a MATH menu, rational exponents still require fewer
keystrokes.

Exercise Set 8.2, pp. 507–509

1. (g)   **2.** (c)   **3.** (e)   **4.** (h)   **5.** (a)   **6.** (d)   **7.** (b)
8. (f)   **9.** $\sqrt[3]{y}$ **11.** 6 **13.** 2 **15.** 8 **17.** $\sqrt{xyz}$
19. $\sqrt[5]{a^2b^2}$ **21.** $\sqrt[6]{t^5}$ **23.** 8 **25.** 625 **27.** $27\sqrt[4]{x^3}$
29. $125x^6$ **31.** $18^{1/3}$ **33.** $30^{1/2}$ **35.** $x^{7/2}$ **37.** $m^{2/5}$

39. $(pq)^{1/4}$ **41.** $(xy^2z)^{1/5}$ **43.** $(3mn)^{3/2}$
45. $(8x^2y)^{5/7}$ **47.** $\frac{2x}{z^{2/3}}$ **49.** $\frac{1}{a^{1/4}}$ **51.** $\frac{1}{(2rs)^{3/4}}$
53. 8 **55.** $8a^{3/5}c$ **57.** $\frac{2a^{3/4}c^{2/3}}{b^{1/2}}$ **59.** $\frac{a^3}{3^{5/2}b^{7/3}}$
61. $\left(\frac{3c}{2ab}\right)^{5/6}$ **63.** $\frac{6a}{b^{1/4}}$ **65.** $11^{5/6}$ **67.** $3^{3/4}$
69. $4.3^{1/2}$ **71.** $10^{6/25}$ **73.** $a^{23/12}$ **75.** 64 **77.** $\frac{m^{1/3}}{n^{1/8}}$
79. $\sqrt[3]{x}$ **81.** y^5 **83.** $\sqrt{a}$ **85.** x^2y^2 **87.** $\sqrt{7a}$
89. $\sqrt[4]{8x^3}$ **91.** $\sqrt[10]{m}$ **93.** x^3y^3 **95.** a^6b^{12}
97. $\sqrt[12]{xy}$ **99.**   **101.** $x^2 - 25$ **102.** $x^3 - 8$
103. $(2x + 5)^2$ **104.** $(3a - 4)^2$ **105.** $5(t - 1)^2$
106. $3(n + 2)^2$ **107.**   **109.** $\sqrt[6]{x^5}$
111. $\sqrt[7]{c - d}, c \geq d$ **113.** $2^{7/12} \approx 1.498 \approx 1.5$
115. (a) 1.8 m; (b) 3.1 m; (c) 1.5 m; (d) 5.3 m
117. 338 cubic feet   **119.**

Technology Connection, p. 511

1. The graphs differ in appearance because the domain of
y_1 is the intersection of $[-3, \infty)$ and $[3, \infty)$, or $[3, \infty)$. The
domain of y_2 is $(-\infty, -3] \cup [3, \infty)$.

Exercise Set 8.3, pp. 514–515

1. True   **2.** False   **3.** False   **4.** False   **5.** True
6. True   **7.** $\sqrt{30}$ **9.** $\sqrt[3]{35}$ **11.** $\sqrt[4]{54}$ **13.** $\sqrt{26xy}$
15. $\sqrt[5]{80y^4}$ **17.** $\sqrt{y^2 - b^2}$ **19.** $\sqrt[3]{0.21y^2}$
21. $\sqrt[5]{(x - 2)^3}$ **23.** $\sqrt{\frac{6s}{11t}}$ **25.** $\sqrt[7]{\frac{5x - 15}{4x + 8}}$ **27.** $2\sqrt{3}$
29. $3\sqrt{5}$ **31.** $2x^4\sqrt{2x}$ **33.** $2\sqrt{30}$ **35.** $6a^2\sqrt{b}$
37. $2x\sqrt[3]{y^2}$ **39.** $-2x^2\sqrt[3]{2}$ **41.** $f(x) = 2x^2\sqrt[3]{5}$
43. $f(x) = |7(x - 3)|$, or $7|x - 3|$
45. $f(x) = |x - 1|\sqrt{5}$ **47.** $a^5b^5\sqrt{b}$ **49.** $xy^2z^3\sqrt[3]{x^2z}$
51. $2xy^2\sqrt[4]{xy^3}$ **53.** $x^2yz^3\sqrt[5]{x^3y^3z^2}$ **55.** $-2a^4\sqrt[3]{10a^2}$
57. $5\sqrt{2}$ **59.** $3\sqrt{22}$ **61.** 3 **63.** $24y^5$ **65.** $a\sqrt[4]{10}$
67. $2x^3\sqrt{5x}$ **69.** $s^2t^3\sqrt[3]{t}$ **71.** $(x - y)^4$
73. $2ab^3\sqrt[4]{5a}$ **75.** $x(y + z)^2\sqrt[5]{x}$ **77.**   **79.** $9abx^2$
80. $\frac{(x - 1)^2}{(x - 2)^2}$ **81.** $\frac{x + 1}{2(x + 5)}$ **82.** $\frac{3(4x^2 + 5y^3)}{50xy^2}$
83. $\frac{b + a}{a^2b^2}$ **84.** $\frac{-x - 2}{4x + 3}$ **85.**   **87.** 175.6 mi
89. (a) $-3.3°C$; (b) $-16.6°C$; (c) $-25.5°C$; (d) $-54.0°C$
91. $25x^5\sqrt[3]{25x}$ **93.** $a^{10}b^{17}\sqrt{ab}$
95. $f(x) = h(x); f(x) \neq g(x)$

97. $\{x|x \leq 2 \text{ or } x \geq 4\}$, or $(-\infty, 2] \cup [4, \infty)$ **99.** 6
101. ,

Exercise Set 8.4, pp. 520–521

1. (g)　**2.** (b)　**3.** (f)　**4.** (c)　**5.** (h)　**6.** (d)　**7.** (a)

8. (e)　**9.** $\frac{7}{10}$　**11.** $\frac{5}{2}$　**13.** $\frac{11}{t}$　**15.** $\frac{6y\sqrt{y}}{x^2}$　**17.** $\frac{3a\sqrt[3]{a}}{2b}$

19. $\frac{2a}{bc^2}$　**21.** $\frac{ab^2}{c^2}\sqrt[4]{\frac{a}{c^2}}$　**23.** $\frac{2x}{y^2}\sqrt[5]{\frac{x}{y}}$　**25.** $\frac{xy}{z^2}\sqrt[6]{\frac{y^2}{z^3}}$

27. 3　**29.** $\sqrt[3]{2}$　**31.** $y\sqrt{5y}$　**33.** $2\sqrt[3]{a^2b}$　**35.** $\sqrt{2ab}$

37. $2x^2y^3\sqrt[4]{y^3}$　**39.** $\sqrt[3]{x^2 + xy + y^2}$　**41.** $\frac{\sqrt{10}}{5}$

43. $\frac{2\sqrt{15}}{21}$　**45.** $\frac{\sqrt[3]{10}}{2}$　**47.** $\frac{\sqrt[3]{75ac^2}}{5c}$　**49.** $\frac{y\sqrt[4]{45y^2x^3}}{3x}$

51. $\frac{\sqrt[3]{2xy^2}}{xy}$　**53.** $\frac{\sqrt{14a}}{6}$　**55.** $\frac{\sqrt[5]{9y^4}}{2xy}$　**57.** $\frac{\sqrt{5b}}{6a}$

59. $\frac{5}{\sqrt{55}}$　**61.** $\frac{12}{5\sqrt{42}}$　**63.** $\frac{2}{\sqrt{6x}}$　**65.** $\frac{7}{\sqrt[3]{98}}$

67. $\frac{7x}{\sqrt{21xy}}$　**69.** $\frac{2a^2}{\sqrt[3]{20ab}}$　**71.** $\frac{x^2y}{\sqrt{2xy}}$　**73.** 📓

75. $x(3 - 8y + 2z)$　**76.** $ac(4a + 9 - 3a^2)$

77. $a^2 - b^2$　**78.** $a^4 - 4y^2$　**79.** $56 - 11x - 12x^2$

80. $6ay - 2cy - 3ax + cx$　**81.** 📓　**83.** (a) 1.62 sec;

(b) 1.99 sec; **(c)** 2.20 sec　**85.** $9\sqrt[3]{9n^2}$　**87.** $\frac{-3\sqrt{a^2 - 3}}{a^2 - 3}$,

or $\frac{-3}{\sqrt{a^2 - 3}}$　**89.** Step 1: $\sqrt[n]{a} = a^{1/n}$, by definition;

Step 2: $\left(\frac{a}{b}\right)^n = \frac{a^n}{b^n}$, raising a quotient to a power;

Step 3: $a^{1/n} = \sqrt[n]{a}$, by definition　**91.** $(f/g)(x) = 3x$, where x is a real number and $x > 0$

93. $(f/g)(x) = \sqrt{x + 3}$, where x is a real number and $x > 3$

Exercise Set 8.5, pp. 526–528

1. Radicands; indices　**2.** Indices　**3.** Bases

4. Denominators　**5.** Numerator; conjugate　**6.** Bases

7. $11\sqrt{3}$　**9.** $2\sqrt[3]{4}$　**11.** $10\sqrt[3]{y}$　**13.** $12\sqrt{2}$

15. $13\sqrt[3]{7} + \sqrt{3}$　**17.** $9\sqrt{3}$　**19.** $-7\sqrt{5}$　**21.** $9\sqrt[3]{2}$

23. $(1 + 12a)\sqrt{a}$　**25.** $(x - 2)\sqrt[3]{6x}$　**27.** $3\sqrt{a - 1}$

29. $(x + 3)\sqrt{x - 1}$　**31.** $5\sqrt{2} + 2$　**33.** $3\sqrt{30} - 3\sqrt{35}$

35. $6\sqrt{5} - 4$　**37.** $3 - 4\sqrt[3]{63}$　**39.** $a + 2a\sqrt[3]{3}$

41. $4 + 3\sqrt{6}$　**43.** $\sqrt{6} - \sqrt{14} + \sqrt{21} - 7$　**45.** 1

47. -5　**49.** $2 - 8\sqrt{35}$　**51.** $23 + 8\sqrt{7}$　**53.** $5 - 2\sqrt{6}$

55. $2t + 5 + 2\sqrt{10t}$　**57.** $14 + x - 6\sqrt{x + 5}$

59. $6\sqrt[4]{63} + 4\sqrt[4]{35} - 3\sqrt[4]{54} - 2\sqrt[4]{30}$　**61.** $\frac{18 + 6\sqrt{2}}{7}$

63. $\frac{12 - 2\sqrt{3} + 6\sqrt{5} - \sqrt{15}}{33}$　**65.** $\frac{a - \sqrt{ab}}{a - b}$　**67.** -1

69. $\frac{12 - 3\sqrt{10} - 2\sqrt{14} + \sqrt{35}}{6}$　**71.** $\frac{1}{\sqrt{5} - 1}$

73. $\frac{2}{14 + 2\sqrt{3} + 3\sqrt{2} + 7\sqrt{6}}$　**75.** $\frac{x - y}{x + 2\sqrt{xy} + y}$

77. $\frac{1}{\sqrt{a + h} + \sqrt{a}}$　**79.** $\sqrt{a}$　**81.** $b^2\sqrt[10]{b^3}$

83. $xy\sqrt[6]{xy^5}$　**85.** $3a^2b\sqrt[4]{ab}$　**87.** $a^2b^2c^2\sqrt[6]{a^2bc^2}$

89. $\sqrt[12]{a^5}$　**91.** $\sqrt[12]{x^2y^5}$　**93.** $\sqrt[10]{ab^9}$　**95.** $\sqrt[6]{(7 - y)^5}$

97. $\sqrt[12]{5} + 3x$　**99.** $x\sqrt[6]{xy^5} - \sqrt[15]{x^{13}y^{14}}$

101. $2m^2 + m\sqrt[4]{n} + 2m\sqrt[3]{n^2} + \sqrt[12]{n^{11}}$

103. $2\sqrt[4]{x^3} - \sqrt[12]{x^{11}}$　**105.** $x^2 - 7$　**107.** $11 - 6\sqrt{2}$

109. $27 + 6\sqrt{14}$　**111.** 📓　**113.** 42　**114.** $-\frac{1}{3}$

115. $-7, 3$　**116.** $-\frac{2}{5}, \frac{3}{2}$　**117.** -3　**118.** $-6, 1$

119. 📓　**121.** $f(x) = 2x\sqrt{x - 1}$

123. $f(x) = (x + 3x^2)\sqrt[4]{x - 1}$　**125.** $(7x^2 - 2y^2)\sqrt{x + y}$

127. $4x(y + z)^3\sqrt[6]{2x(y + z)}$　**129.** $1 - \sqrt{w}$

131. $(\sqrt{x} + \sqrt{5})(\sqrt{x} - \sqrt{5})$

133. $(\sqrt{x} + \sqrt{a})(\sqrt{x} - \sqrt{a})$　**135.** $2x - 2\sqrt{x^2 - 4}$

Connecting the Concepts, pp. 528–529

1. $t + 5$　**2.** $-3a^4$　**3.** $3x\sqrt{10}$　**4.** $\frac{2}{3}$　**5.** $5\sqrt{15t}$

6. $ab^2c^2\sqrt[5]{c}$　**7.** $2\sqrt{15} - 3\sqrt{22}$　**8.** $-2b\sqrt[4]{a^3b^3}$

9. $\sqrt[8]{t}$　**10.** $\frac{a^2}{2}$　**11.** $-8\sqrt{3}$　**12.** -4　**13.** $25 + 10\sqrt{6}$

14. $2\sqrt{x - 1}$　**15.** $xy\sqrt[10]{x^7y^3}$　**16.** $15\sqrt[3]{5}$　**17.** $\sqrt[5]{x}$

18. $(x + 1)\sqrt{3}$　**19.** $ab\sqrt{b}$　**20.** $6x^3y^2$

Technology Connection, p. 531

1. The x-coordinates of the points of intersection should approximate the solutions of the examples.

Exercise Set 8.6, pp. 533–535

1. False　**2.** True　**3.** True　**4.** False　**5.** True

6. True　**7.** 3　**9.** $\frac{16}{3}$　**11.** 20　**13.** -1　**15.** 5

17. 91　**19.** 0, 36　**21.** 100　**23.** -125　**25.** 16

27. No solution　**29.** $\frac{80}{3}$　**31.** 45　**33.** $-\frac{5}{3}$　**35.** 1

37. $\frac{106}{27}$　**39.** 4　**41.** 3, 7　**43.** $\frac{80}{9}$　**45.** -1

47. No solution　**49.** 2, 6　**51.** 2　**53.** 4　**55.** 📓

57. Length: 200 ft; width: 15 ft　**58.** Base: 34 in.; height: 15 in.

59. Length: 14 in.; width: 10 in.

60. Length: 30 yd; width: 16 yd　**61.** 6, 8, 10　**62.** 13 cm

63. 📓　**65.** About 68 psi　**67.** About 278 Hz

69. 524.8°C　**71.** $t = \frac{1}{9}\left(\frac{S^2 \cdot 2457}{1087.7^2} - 2617\right)$

73. 4480 rpm　**75.** $r = \frac{v^2h}{2gh - v^2}$　**77.** $-\frac{8}{9}$　**79.** $-8, 8$

81. 1, 8　**83.** $\left(\frac{1}{36}, 0\right), (36, 0)$　**85.** 📈　**87.** 📈

Exercise Set 8.7, pp. 543–547

1. (d)　**2.** (c)　**3.** (e)　**4.** (b)　**5.** (f)　**6.** (a)

7. $\sqrt{34}$; 5.831　**9.** $9\sqrt{2}$; 12.728　**11.** 8　**13.** 4 m

15. $\sqrt{19}$ in.; 4.359 in.　**17.** 1 m　**19.** 250 ft

21. $\sqrt{8450}$, or $65\sqrt{2}$ ft; 91.924 ft　**23.** 24 in.

25. $(\sqrt{340} + 8)$ ft; 26.439 ft

27. $(110 - \sqrt{6500})$ paces; 29.377 paces

29. Leg = 5; hypotenuse = $5\sqrt{2} \approx 7.071$

31. Shorter leg = 7; longer leg = $7\sqrt{3} \approx 12.124$

33. Leg = $5\sqrt{3} \approx 8.660$; hypotenuse = $10\sqrt{3} \approx 17.321$

35. Both legs = $\frac{13\sqrt{2}}{2} \approx 9.192$

37. Leg = $14\sqrt{3} \approx 24.249$; hypotenuse = 28

39. $5\sqrt{3} \approx 8.660$　**41.** $7\sqrt{2} \approx 9.899$

43. $\frac{15\sqrt{2}}{2} \approx 10.607$ **45.** $\sqrt{10{,}561}$ ft ≈ 102.767 ft

47. $\frac{1089}{4}\sqrt{3}$ ft$^2 \approx 471.551$ ft^2 **49.** $(0, -4), (0, 4)$

51. 5   **53.** $\sqrt{10} \approx 3.162$ **55.** $\sqrt{200} \approx 14.142$

57. 17.8   **59.** $\frac{\sqrt{13}}{6} \approx 0.601$ **61.** $\sqrt{12} \approx 3.464$

63. $\sqrt{101} \approx 10.050$ **65.** $(3, 4)$ **67.** $\left(\frac{7}{2}, \frac{7}{2}\right)$

69. $(-1, -3)$ **71.** $(0.7, 0)$ **73.** $\left(-\frac{1}{12}, \frac{1}{24}\right)$

75. $\left(\frac{\sqrt{2} + \sqrt{3}}{2}, \frac{3}{2}\right)$ **77.** 📝

79.

80.

81.

82.

83.

84.

85. 📝   **87.** $36\sqrt{3}$ cm^2; 62.354 cm^2 **89.** $d = s + s\sqrt{2}$
91. 5 gal. The total area of the doors and windows is 134 ft^2 or more.   **93.** 60.28 ft by 60.28 ft   **95.** $\sqrt{75}$ cm

Exercise Set 8.8, pp. 553–554

1. False   **2.** False   **3.** True   **4.** True   **5.** True
6. True   **7.** False   **8.** True   **9.** $10i$ **11.** $i\sqrt{5}$, or $\sqrt{5}i$
13. $2i\sqrt{2}$, or $2\sqrt{2}i$ **15.** $-i\sqrt{11}$, or $-\sqrt{11}i$ **17.** $-7i$
19. $-10i\sqrt{3}$, or $-10\sqrt{3}i$ **21.** $6 - 2i\sqrt{21}$, or $6 - 2\sqrt{21}i$
23. $(-2\sqrt{19} + 5\sqrt{5})i$ **25.** $(3\sqrt{2} - 8)i$ **27.** $5 - 3i$
29. $7 + 2i$ **31.** $2 - i$ **33.** $-12 - 5i$ **35.** -40
37. -24 **39.** -18 **41.** $-\sqrt{30}$ **43.** $-3\sqrt{14}$
45. $-30 + 10i$ **47.** $28 - 21i$ **49.** $1 + 5i$ **51.** $38 + 9i$
53. $2 - 46i$ **55.** 73 **57.** 50 **59.** $12 - 16i$
61. $-5 + 12i$ **63.** $-5 - 12i$ **65.** $3 - i$ **67.** $\frac{6}{13} + \frac{4}{13}i$
69. $\frac{3}{17} + \frac{5}{17}i$ **71.** $-\frac{5}{6}i$ **73.** $-\frac{3}{4} - \frac{5}{4}i$ **75.** $1 - 2i$
77. $-\frac{23}{58} + \frac{43}{58}i$ **79.** $\frac{19}{29} - \frac{4}{29}i$ **81.** $\frac{6}{25} - \frac{17}{25}i$ **83.** 1

85. $-i$ **87.** -1 **89.** i **91.** -1 **93.** $-125i$
95. 0 **97.** 📝   **99.** $-2, 3$ **100.** 5 **101.** $-10, 10$
102. $-5, 5$ **103.** $-\frac{2}{5}, \frac{4}{3}$ **104.** $-\frac{2}{3}, \frac{3}{2}$ **105.** 📝
107.

113. $-9 - 27i$ **115.** $50 - 120i$ **117.** $\frac{250}{41} + \frac{200}{41}i$
119. 8 **121.** $\frac{3}{5} + \frac{9}{5}i$ **123.** 1

Review Exercises: Chapter 8, pp. 558–559

1. True   **2.** False   **3.** False   **4.** True   **5.** True
6. True   **7.** True   **8.** False   **9.** $\frac{10}{11}$ **10.** -0.6
11. 5 **12.** $\{x \mid x \geq -10\}$, or $[-10, \infty)$ **13.** $8|t|$
14. $|c + 7|$ **15.** $|2x + 1|$ **16.** -2 **17.** $(5ab)^{4/3}$
18. $8a^4\sqrt{a}$ **19.** x^3y^5 **20.** $\sqrt[3]{x^2y}$ **21.** $\frac{1}{x^{2/5}}$
22. $7^{1/6}$ **23.** $f(x) = 5|x - 6|$ **24.** $2x^5y^2$
25. $5xy\sqrt{10x}$ **26.** $\sqrt{35ab}$ **27.** $3xb\sqrt[3]{x^2}$
28. $-6x^5y^4\sqrt[3]{2x^2}$ **29.** $-\frac{3y^4}{4}$ **30.** $y\sqrt[3]{6}$ **31.** $\frac{5\sqrt{x}}{2}$
32. $\frac{2a^2\sqrt[4]{3a^3}}{c^2}$ **33.** $7\sqrt[3]{4y}$ **34.** $\sqrt{3}$ **35.** $(2x + y^2)\sqrt[3]{x}$
36. $15\sqrt{2}$ **37.** -1 **38.** $\sqrt{15} + 4\sqrt{6} - 6\sqrt{10} - 48$
39. $\sqrt[4]{x^3}$ **40.** $\sqrt[12]{x^5}$ **41.** $4 - 4\sqrt{a} + a$
42. $-4\sqrt{10} + 4\sqrt{15}$ **43.** $\frac{20}{\sqrt{10} + \sqrt{15}}$ **44.** 19
45. -126 **46.** 4 **47.** 2 **48.** $5\sqrt{2}$ cm; 7.071 cm
49. $\sqrt{32}$ ft; 5.657 ft
50. Short leg $= 10$; long leg $= 10\sqrt{3} \approx 17.321$
51. $\sqrt{26} \approx 5.099$ **52.** $\left(-2, -\frac{3}{2}\right)$ **53.** $3i\sqrt{5}$, or $3\sqrt{5}i$
54. $-2 - 9i$ **55.** $6 + i$ **56.** 29 **57.** -1 **58.** $9 - 12i$
59. $\frac{13}{25} - \frac{34}{25}i$ **60.** 📝 A complex number $a + bi$ is real
when $b = 0$. It is imaginary when $b \neq 0$.   **61.** 📝 An
absolute-value sign must be used to simplify $\sqrt[n]{x^n}$ when n
is even, since x may be negative. If x is negative while n is
even, the radical expression cannot be simplified to x, since
$\sqrt[n]{x^n}$ represents the principal, or nonnegative, root. When n
is odd, there is only one root, and it will be positive or negative depending on the sign of x. Thus there is no absolute-
value sign when n is odd.   **62.** $\frac{2i}{3i}$; answers may vary

63. 3 **64.** $-\frac{2}{5} + \frac{9}{10}i$ **65.** The isosceles right triangle is
larger by about 1.206 ft^2.

Test: Chapter 8, p. 560

1. [8.3] $5\sqrt{2}$ **2.** [8.4] $-\frac{2}{x^2}$ **3.** [8.1] $9|a|$

4. [8.1] $|x - 4|$ **5.** [8.2] $(7xy)^{1/2}$ **6.** [8.2] $\sqrt[6]{(4a^3b)^5}$

7. [8.1] $\{x|x \geq 5\}$, or $[5, \infty)$ **8.** [8.5] $27 + 10\sqrt{2}$

9. [8.3] $2x^3y^2\sqrt[5]{x}$ **10.** [8.3] $2\sqrt[3]{2wv^2}$ **11.** [8.4] $\dfrac{10a^2}{3b^3}$

12. [8.4] $\sqrt[5]{3x^4y}$ **13.** [8.5] $x\sqrt[4]{x}$ **14.** [8.5] $\sqrt[5]{y^2}$

15. [8.5] $6\sqrt{2}$ **16.** [8.5] $(x^2 + 3y)\sqrt{y}$

17. [8.5] $14 - 19\sqrt{x} - 3x$ **18.** [8.5] $\dfrac{5\sqrt{3} - \sqrt{6}}{23}$

19. [8.6] 4 **20.** [8.6] $-1, 2$ **21.** [8.6] 8
22. [8.7] $\sqrt{10,600}$ ft ≈ 102.956 ft **23.** [8.7] 5 cm;
$5\sqrt{3}$ cm ≈ 8.660 cm **24.** [8.7] $\sqrt{17} \approx 4.123$
25. [8.7] $\left(\frac{3}{2}, -6\right)$ **26.** [8.8] $5i\sqrt{2}$, or $5\sqrt{2}i$
27. [8.8] $12 + 2i$ **28.** [8.8] $15 - 8i$ **29.** [8.8] $-\frac{11}{34} - \frac{7}{34}i$
30. [8.8] i **31.** [8.6] 3 **32.** [8.8] $-\frac{17}{4}i$ **33.** [8.6] 22,500 ft

Cumulative Review: Chapters 1–8, pp. 561–562

1. -7 **2.** $-7, 5$ **3.** $-5, 5$ **4.** $\frac{5}{2}$ **5.** -1 **6.** $\frac{1}{5}$
7. $\{x|-3 \leq x \leq 7\}$, or $[-3, 7]$ **8.** $\mathbb{R}$, or $(-\infty, \infty)$
9. $-3, 2$ **10.** 7 **11.** $(0, 5)$ **12.** $(1, -1, -2)$

13.

14.

15.

16.
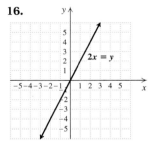

17. Slope: -1; y-intercept: $(0, -6)$
18. $y = 7x - 11$ **19.** 6 **20.** $-8xy^2$

21. $4a^2 - 20ab + 25b^2$ **22.** $c^4 - 9d^2$ **23.** $\dfrac{2x + 1}{x(x + 1)}$

24. $\dfrac{x + 13}{(x - 2)(x + 1)}$ **25.** $\dfrac{(a + 2)(2a + 1)}{(a - 3)(a - 1)}$ **26.** $\dfrac{2x + 1}{x^2}$

27. 0 **28.** $-1 + 3\sqrt{5}$ **29.** $5ab^2\sqrt{6a}$ **30.** $\sqrt[15]{y^8}$
31. $(x - 7)(x + 2)$ **32.** $4y^5(y - 1)(y^2 + y + 1)$
33. $25(2c + d)(2c - d)$ **34.** $(3t - 8)(t + 1)$
35. $3(x^2 - 2x - 7)$ **36.** $(y - x)(t - z^2)$
37. $\{x|x$ is a real number and $x \neq 3\}$, or $(-\infty, 3) \cup (3, \infty)$
38. $\left\{x|x \geq \frac{11}{2}\right\}$, or $\left[\frac{11}{2}, \infty\right)$ **39.** 5 **40.** $6 - 2\sqrt{5}$
41. $(f + g)(x) = x^2 + \sqrt{2x - 3}$ **42.** 4 mph
43. $2\sqrt{3}$ ft ≈ 3.464 ft **44.** (a) $m(t) = 0.08t + 25.02$;
(b) 26.62; (c) 2037 **45.** \$36,650 **46.** Swiss chocolate:
45 oz; whipping cream: 20 oz **47.** 4×10^5 programs
48. \$1.54 per year **49.** 5 ft **50.** $5x - 3y = -15$
51. $(0, -1), (1, 0)$ **52.** -2 **53.** 10

CHAPTER 9

Technology Connection, p. 572

1. The right-hand x-intercept should be an approximation
of $4 + \sqrt{23}$. **2.** x-intercepts should be approximations of
$(-5 + \sqrt{37})/2$ and $(-5 - \sqrt{37})/2$.
3. Most graphing calculators can give only rational-number
approximations of the two irrational solutions. An *exact* solution cannot be found with a graphing calculator.
4. The graph of $y = x^2 - 6x + 11$ has no x-intercepts.

Exercise Set 9.1, pp. 572–574

1. $\sqrt{k}; -\sqrt{k}$ **2.** $7; -7$ **3.** $t + 3; t + 3$ **4.** 16
5. $25; 5$ **6.** $9; 3$ **7.** ± 10 **9.** $\pm 5\sqrt{2}$ **11.** $\pm\sqrt{6}$

13. $\pm\frac{7}{3}$ **15.** $\pm\sqrt{\dfrac{5}{6}}$, or $\pm\dfrac{\sqrt{30}}{6}$ **17.** $\pm i$ **19.** $\pm\frac{9}{2}i$

21. $-1, 7$ **23.** $-5 \pm 2\sqrt{3}$ **25.** $-1 \pm 3i$

27. $-\dfrac{3}{4} \pm \dfrac{\sqrt{17}}{4}$, or $\dfrac{-3 \pm \sqrt{17}}{4}$ **29.** $-3, 13$ **31.** $\pm\sqrt{19}$

33. $1, 9$ **35.** $-4 \pm \sqrt{13}$ **37.** $-14, 0$
39. $x^2 + 16x + 64 = (x + 8)^2$
41. $t^2 - 10t + 25 = (t - 5)^2$
43. $t^2 - 2t + 1 = (t - 1)^2$ **45.** $x^2 + 3x + \frac{9}{4} = \left(x + \frac{3}{2}\right)^2$
47. $x^2 + \frac{2}{5}x + \frac{1}{25} = \left(x + \frac{1}{5}\right)^2$
49. $t^2 - \frac{5}{6}t + \frac{25}{144} = \left(t - \frac{5}{12}\right)^2$ **51.** $-7, 1$ **53.** $5 \pm \sqrt{2}$
55. $-8, -4$ **57.** $-4 \pm \sqrt{19}$
59. $(-3 - \sqrt{2}, 0), (-3 + \sqrt{2}, 0)$

61. $\left(-\dfrac{9}{2} - \dfrac{\sqrt{181}}{2}, 0\right), \left(-\dfrac{9}{2} + \dfrac{\sqrt{181}}{2}, 0\right)$, or
$\left(\dfrac{-9 - \sqrt{181}}{2}, 0\right), \left(\dfrac{-9 + \sqrt{181}}{2}, 0\right)$

63. $(5 - \sqrt{47}, 0), (5 + \sqrt{47}, 0)$ **65.** $-\frac{4}{3}, -\frac{2}{3}$

67. $-\frac{1}{3}, 2$ **69.** $-\dfrac{2}{5} \pm \dfrac{\sqrt{19}}{5}$, or $\dfrac{-2 \pm \sqrt{19}}{5}$

71. $\left(-\dfrac{1}{4} - \dfrac{\sqrt{13}}{4}, 0\right), \left(-\dfrac{1}{4} + \dfrac{\sqrt{13}}{4}, 0\right)$, or $\left(\dfrac{-1 - \sqrt{13}}{4}, 0\right),$
$\left(\dfrac{-1 + \sqrt{13}}{4}, 0\right)$ **73.** $\left(\dfrac{3}{4} - \dfrac{\sqrt{17}}{4}, 0\right), \left(\dfrac{3}{4} + \dfrac{\sqrt{17}}{4}, 0\right),$
or $\left(\dfrac{3 - \sqrt{17}}{4}, 0\right), \left(\dfrac{3 + \sqrt{17}}{4}, 0\right)$ **75.** 10% **77.** 4%

79. About 4.3 sec **81.** About 11.4 sec **83.** ⬛
85. 64 **86.** -15 **87.** $10\sqrt{2}$ **88.** $4\sqrt{6}$ **89.** $2i$
90. $5i$ **91.** $2i\sqrt{2}$, or $2\sqrt{2}i$ **92.** $2i\sqrt{6}$ or $2\sqrt{6}i$
93. ⬛ **95.** ± 18 **97.** $-\frac{7}{2}, -\sqrt{5}, 0, \sqrt{5}, 8$
99. Barge: 8 km/h; fishing boat: 15 km/h **101.** ⬜
103. ⬛, ⬜

Exercise Set 9.2, pp. 579–580

1. True **2.** True **3.** False **4.** False **5.** False
6. True **7.** $-\frac{5}{2}, 1$ **9.** $-1 \pm \sqrt{5}$ **11.** $3 \pm \sqrt{6}$

13. $\dfrac{3}{2} \pm \dfrac{\sqrt{29}}{2}$ **15.** $-1 \pm \dfrac{2\sqrt{3}}{3}$ **17.** $-\dfrac{4}{3} \pm \dfrac{\sqrt{19}}{3}$

19. $3 \pm i$ **21.** $\dfrac{1}{2} \pm \dfrac{\sqrt{3}}{2}i$ **23.** $-2 \pm \sqrt{2}i$ **25.** $-\frac{8}{3}, \frac{5}{4}$

27. $\frac{2}{5}$ **29.** $-\frac{11}{8} \pm \frac{\sqrt{41}}{8}$ **31.** 5, 10   **33.** $\frac{3}{2}$, 24

35. $2 \pm \sqrt{5}i$ **37.** 2, $-1 \pm \sqrt{3}i$

39. $-\frac{4}{3}, \frac{5}{2}$ **41.** $5 \pm \sqrt{53}$ **43.** $\frac{3}{2} \pm \frac{\sqrt{5}}{2}$

45. $-5.317, 1.317$ **47.** $0.764, 5.236$ **49.** $-1.266, 2.766$

51. 📊   **53.** $x^2 + 4$ **54.** $x^2 - 180$ **55.** $x^2 - 4x - 3$

56. $x^2 + 6x + 34$ **57.** $-\frac{3}{2}$ **58.** $\frac{1}{6} \pm \frac{\sqrt{6}}{3}i$ **59.** 📊

61. $(-2, 0), (1, 0)$ **63.** $4 - 2\sqrt{2}, 4 + 2\sqrt{2}$

65. $-1.179, 0.339$ **67.** $\frac{-5\sqrt{2} \pm \sqrt{34}}{4}$ **69.** $\frac{1}{2}$ **71.**

Technology Connection, p. 583

1. $(-0.4, 0)$ is the other x-intercept of $y = 5x^2 - 13x - 6$.
2. The x-intercepts of $y = x^2 - 175$ are $(-13.22875656, 0)$ and $(13.22875656, 0)$, or $(-5\sqrt{7}, 0)$ and $(5\sqrt{7}, 0)$.
3. The x-intercepts of $y = x^3 + 3x^2 - 4x$ are $(-4, 0), (0, 0)$, and $(1, 0)$.

Exercise Set 9.3, pp. 583–585

1. (b)   **2.** (a)   **3.** (d)   **4.** (b)   **5.** (c)   **6.** (c)
7. Two irrational   **9.** Two imaginary   **11.** Two irrational
13. Two rational   **15.** Two imaginary   **17.** One rational
19. Two rational   **21.** Two irrational
23. Two imaginary   **25.** Two rational
27. Two irrational   **29.** $x^2 + x - 20 = 0$
31. $x^2 - 6x + 9 = 0$ **33.** $x^2 + 4x + 3 = 0$
35. $4x^2 - 23x + 15 = 0$ **37.** $8x^2 + 6x + 1 = 0$
39. $x^2 - 2x - 0.96 = 0$ **41.** $x^2 - 3 = 0$
43. $x^2 - 20 = 0$ **45.** $x^2 + 16 = 0$
47. $x^2 - 4x + 53 = 0$ **49.** $x^2 - 6x - 5 = 0$
51. $3x^2 - 6x - 4 = 0$ **53.** $x^3 - 4x^2 - 7x + 10 = 0$
55. $x^3 - 2x^2 - 3x = 0$ **57.** 📊   **59.** $c = \frac{d^2}{1 - d}$

60. $b = \frac{aq}{p - q}$ **61.** $y = \frac{x - 3}{x}$, or $1 - \frac{3}{x}$
62. 10 mph   **63.** Jamal: 3.5 mph; Kade: 2 mph
64. 20 mph   **65.** 📊   **67.** $a = 1, b = 2, c = -3$
69. (a) $-\frac{3}{5}$; (b) $-\frac{1}{3}$ **71.** (a) $9 + 9i$; (b) $3 + 3i$
73. The solutions of $ax^2 + bx + c = 0$ are
$x = \frac{-b \pm \sqrt{b^2 - 4ac}}{2a}$. When there is just one solution,
$b^2 - 4ac$ must be 0, so $x = \frac{-b \pm 0}{2a} = \frac{-b}{2a}$.
75. $a = 8, b = 20, c = -12$ **77.** $x^2 - 2 = 0$
79. $x^4 - 8x^3 + 21x^2 - 2x - 52 = 0$ **81.** 📊,

Exercise Set 9.4, pp. 589–592

1. First part: 60 mph; second part: 50 mph   **3.** 40 mph
5. Cessna: 150 mph, Beechcraft: 200 mph; or Cessna:
200 mph, Beechcraft: 250 mph   **7.** To Hillsboro: 12 mph;
return trip: 9 mph   **9.** About 14 mph   **11.** 12 hr

13. About 3.24 mph   **15.** $r = \frac{1}{2}\sqrt{\frac{A}{\pi}}$

17. $r = \frac{-\pi h + \sqrt{\pi^2 h^2 + 2\pi A}}{2\pi}$ **19.** $r = \frac{\sqrt{Gm_1 m_2}}{F}$

21. $H = \frac{c^2}{g}$ **23.** $b = \sqrt{c^2 - a^2}$

25. $t = \frac{-v_0 + \sqrt{(v_0)^2 + 2gs}}{g}$ **27.** $n = \frac{1 + \sqrt{1 + 8N}}{2}$

29. $g = \frac{4\pi^2 l}{T^2}$ **31.** $t = \frac{-b \pm \sqrt{b^2 - 4ac}}{2a}$

33. (a) 10.1 sec; (b) 7.49 sec; (c) 272.5 m   **35.** 2.9 sec
37. 0.890 sec   **39.** 2.5 m/sec   **41.** 4.5%   **43.** 📊
45. m^{-2}, or $\frac{1}{m^2}$ **46.** $t^{2/3}$ **47.** $y^{1/3}$ **48.** $z^{1/2}$ **49.** 2
50. 81   **51.** 📊
53. $t = \frac{-10.2 + 6\sqrt{-A^2 + 13A - 39.36}}{A - 6.5}$ **55.** $\pm\sqrt{2}$

57. $l = \frac{w + w\sqrt{5}}{2}$

59. $n = \pm\sqrt{\frac{r^2 \pm \sqrt{r^4 + 4m^4 r^2 p - 4mp}}{2m}}$

61. $A(S) = \frac{\pi S}{6}$

Exercise Set 9.5, pp. 597–598

1. (f)   **2.** (d)   **3.** (h)   **4.** (b)   **5.** (g)   **6.** (a)
7. (e)   **8.** (c)   **9.** $\sqrt{p}$ **10.** $x^{1/4}$ **11.** $x^2 + 3$ **12.** t^{-3}
13. $(1 + t)^2$ **14.** $w^{1/6}$ **15.** $\pm 2, \pm 3$ **17.** $\pm\sqrt{3}, \pm 2$
19. $\pm\frac{\sqrt{5}}{2}, \pm 1$ **21.** 4   **23.** $\pm 2\sqrt{2}, \pm 3$
25. $8 + 2\sqrt{7}$ **27.** No solution   **29.** $-\frac{1}{2}, \frac{1}{3}$ **31.** $-4, 1$
33. $-27, 8$ **35.** 729   **37.** 1   **39.** No solution   **41.** $\frac{12}{5}$
43. $\pm 2, \pm 3i$ **45.** $\pm i, \pm 2i$ **47.** $\left(\frac{4}{25}, 0\right)$
49. $\left(\frac{3}{2} + \frac{\sqrt{33}}{2}, 0\right), \left(\frac{3}{2} - \frac{\sqrt{33}}{2}, 0\right), (4, 0), (-1, 0)$
51. $(-243, 0), (32, 0)$ **53.** No x-intercepts   **55.** 📊
57.

58.

59.

60.

61.

62.

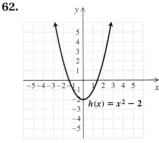

63. ⌼   **65.** $\pm\sqrt{\dfrac{-5 \pm \sqrt{37}}{6}}$ **67.** $-2, -1, 6, 7$

69. $\dfrac{100}{99}$ **71.** $-5, -3, -2, 0, 2, 3, 5$ **73.** $1, 3, -\dfrac{1}{2} + \dfrac{\sqrt{3}}{2}i,$

$-\dfrac{1}{2} - \dfrac{\sqrt{3}}{2}i, -\dfrac{3}{2} + \dfrac{3\sqrt{3}}{2}i, -\dfrac{3}{2} - \dfrac{3\sqrt{3}}{2}i$ **75.** ⌁

77. ⌼, ⌁

Connecting the Concepts, pp. 599–600

1. $-2, 5$ **2.** ± 11 **3.** $-3 \pm \sqrt{19}$ **4.** $-\dfrac{1}{2} \pm \dfrac{\sqrt{13}}{2}$

5. $-1 \pm \sqrt{2}$ **6.** 5 **7.** $\dfrac{1}{2} \pm \dfrac{\sqrt{5}}{2}$ **8.** $1 \pm \sqrt{7}$

9. $\pm\dfrac{\sqrt{11}}{2}$ **10.** $\dfrac{1}{2}, 1$ **11.** $-\dfrac{1}{2} \pm \dfrac{\sqrt{3}}{2}i$ **12.** $0, \dfrac{7}{16}$

13. $-\dfrac{5}{6}, 2$ **14.** $1 \pm \sqrt{7}i$ **15.** $\pm 1, \pm 3$ **16.** $\pm 3, \pm i$

17. $-5, 0$ **18.** $-6, 5$ **19.** $\pm\sqrt{2}, \pm 2i$

20. $\pm\dfrac{\sqrt{3}}{3}, \pm\dfrac{\sqrt{2}}{2}$

Technology Connection, p. 601

1. The graphs of y_1, y_2, and y_3 open upward. The graphs of y_4, y_5, and y_6 open downward. The graph of y_1 is wider than the graph of y_2. The graph of y_3 is narrower than the graph of y_2. Similarly, the graph of y_4 is wider than the graph of y_5, and the graph of y_6 is narrower than the graph of y_5.
2. If A is positive, the graph opens upward. If A is negative, the graph opens downward. Compared with the graph of $y = x^2$, the graph of $y = Ax^2$ is wider if $|A| < 1$ and narrower if $|A| > 1$.

Technology Connection, p. 603

1. Compared with the graph of $y = ax^2$, the graph of $y = a(x - h)^2$ is shifted left or right. It is shifted left if h is negative and right if h is positive.   **2.** The value of A makes the graph wider or narrower, and makes the graph open downward if A is negative. The value of B shifts the graph left or right.

Technology Connection, p. 604

1. The graph of y_2 looks like the graph of y_1 shifted up 2 units, and the graph of y_3 looks like the graph of y_1 shifted down 4 units.   **2.** Compared with the graph of $y = a(x - h)^2$,

the graph of $y = a(x - h)^2 + k$ is shifted up or down. It is shifted down if k is negative and up if k is positive.
3. The value of A makes the graph wider or narrower, and makes the graph open downward if A is negative. The value of B shifts the graph left or right. The value of C shifts the graph up or down.

Exercise Set 9.6, pp. 606–608

1. (h)   **2.** (g)   **3.** (f)   **4.** (d)   **5.** (b)   **6.** (c)
7. (e)   **8.** (a)

9.

11.

13.

15.

17.

19. Vertex: $(-1, 0)$; axis of symmetry: $x = -1$

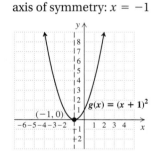

21. Vertex $(2, 0)$; axis of symmetry: $x = 2$

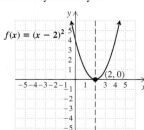

23. Vertex: $(-1, 0)$; axis of symmetry: $x = -1$

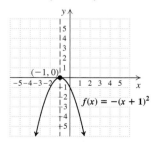

25. Vertex: $(2, 0)$;
axis of symmetry: $x = 2$

$g(x) = -(x-2)^2$

27. Vertex: $(-1, 0)$;
axis of symmetry: $x = -1$

$f(x) = 2(x+1)^2$

41. Vertex: $(-1, -3)$;
axis of symmetry: $x = -1$;
minimum: -3

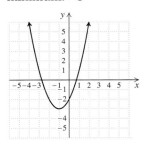

$f(x) = (x+1)^2 - 3$

43. Vertex: $(-4, 1)$;
axis of symmetry: $x = -4$;
minimum: 1

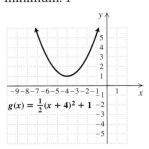

$g(x) = \frac{1}{2}(x+4)^2 + 1$

29. Vertex: $(4, 0)$;
axis of symmetry: $x = 4$

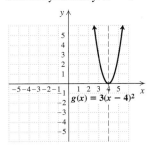

$g(x) = 3(x-4)^2$

31. Vertex: $(4, 0)$;
axis of symmetry: $x = 4$

$h(x) = -\frac{1}{2}(x-4)^2$

45. Vertex: $(1, -3)$;
axis of symmetry: $x = 1$;
maximum: -3

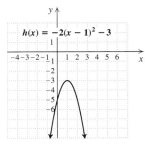

$h(x) = -2(x-1)^2 - 3$

47. Vertex: $(-3, 1)$;
axis of symmetry: $x = -3$
minimum: 1

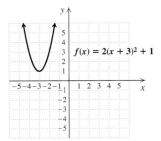

$f(x) = 2(x+3)^2 + 1$

33. Vertex: $(1, 0)$;
axis of symmetry: $x = 1$

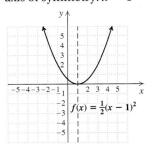

$f(x) = \frac{1}{2}(x-1)^2$

35. Vertex: $(-5, 0)$;
axis of symmetry: $x = -5$

$f(x) = -2(x+5)^2$

49. Vertex: $(2, 4)$;
axis of symmetry: $x = 2$;
maximum: 4

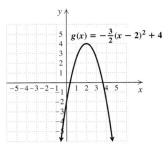

$g(x) = -\frac{3}{2}(x-2)^2 + 4$

37. Vertex: $\left(\frac{1}{2}, 0\right)$;
axis of symmetry: $x = \frac{1}{2}$

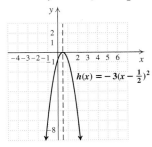

$h(x) = -3\left(x - \frac{1}{2}\right)^2$

39. Vertex: $(5, 2)$;
axis of symmetry: $x = 5$;
minimum: 2

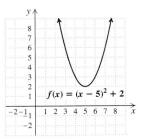

$f(x) = (x-5)^2 + 2$

51. Vertex: $(3, 9)$; axis of symmetry: $x = 3$; minimum: 9
53. Vertex: $(-8, 2)$; axis of symmetry: $x = -8$; maximum: 2
55. Vertex: $\left(\frac{7}{2}, -\frac{29}{4}\right)$; axis of symmetry: $x = \frac{7}{2}$;
minimum: $-\frac{29}{4}$ **57.** Vertex: $(-2.25, -\pi)$; axis of
symmetry: $x = -2.25$; maximum: $-\pi$ **59.** ✍
61. x-intercept: $(3, 0)$; y-intercept: $(0, -4)$
62. x-intercept: $\left(\frac{8}{3}, 0\right)$; y-intercept: $(0, 2)$
63. $(-5, 0), (-3, 0)$ **64.** $(-1, 0), \left(\frac{3}{2}, 0\right)$
65. $x^2 - 14x + 49 = (x-7)^2$

66. $x^2 + 7x + \frac{49}{4} = \left(x + \frac{7}{2}\right)^2$ **67.** ◲
69. $f(x) = \frac{3}{5}(x - 1)^2 + 3$ **71.** $f(x) = \frac{3}{5}(x - 4)^2 - 7$
73. $f(x) = \frac{3}{5}(x + 2)^2 - 5$ **75.** $f(x) = 2(x - 2)^2$
77. $g(x) = -2x^2 - 5$ **79.** The graph will move to the
right. **81.** The graph will be reflected across the x-axis.
83. $F(x) = 3(x - 5)^2 + 1$
85.

$y = f(x - 1)$

87.

$y = f(x) + 2$

89.

$y = f(x + 3) - 2$

91. ◺ **93.** ◲, ◺

Visualizing for Success, p. 613

1. B **2.** E **3.** A **4.** H **5.** C **6.** J **7.** F
8. G **9.** I **10.** D

Exercise Set 9.7, pp. 614–615

1. True **2.** False **3.** True **4.** True **5.** False
6. True **7.** False **8.** True
9. $f(x) = (x - 4)^2 + (-14)$
11. $f(x) = \left(x - \left(-\frac{3}{2}\right)\right)^2 + \left(-\frac{29}{4}\right)$
13. $f(x) = 3(x - (-1))^2 + (-5)$
15. $f(x) = -(x - (-2))^2 + (-3)$
17. $f(x) = 2\left(x - \frac{5}{4}\right)^2 + \frac{55}{8}$
19. (a) Vertex: $(-2, 1)$; **21. (a)** Vertex: $(-4, 4)$;
axis of symmetry: $x = -2$; axis of symmetry: $x = -4$;
(b)

$f(x) = x^2 + 4x + 5$

(b)

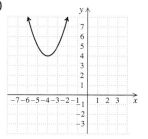

$f(x) = x^2 + 8x + 20$

23. (a) Vertex: $(4, -7)$;
axis of symmetry: $x = 4$;
(b)

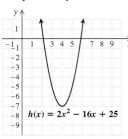

$h(x) = 2x^2 - 16x + 25$

25. (a) Vertex: $(1, 6)$;
axis of symmetry: $x = 1$;
(b)

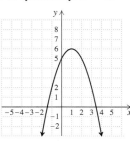

$f(x) = -x^2 + 2x + 5$

27. (a) Vertex: $\left(-\frac{3}{2}, -\frac{49}{4}\right)$;
axis of symmetry: $x = -\frac{3}{2}$;
(b)

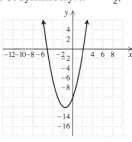

$g(x) = x^2 + 3x - 10$

29. (a) Vertex: $\left(-\frac{7}{2}, -\frac{49}{4}\right)$;
axis of symmetry: $x = -\frac{7}{2}$;
(b)

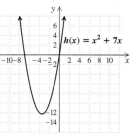

$h(x) = x^2 + 7x$

31. (a) Vertex: $(-1, -4)$;
axis of symmetry: $x = -1$;
(b)

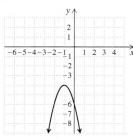

$f(x) = -2x^2 - 4x - 6$

33. (a) Vertex: $(3, 4)$;
axis of symmetry: $x = 3$;
minimum: 4;
(b)

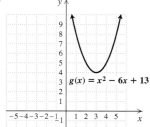

$g(x) = x^2 - 6x + 13$

35. (a) Vertex: $(2, -5)$;
axis of symmetry: $x = 2$;
minimum: -5;
(b)

$g(x) = 2x^2 - 8x + 3$

37. (a) Vertex: $(4, 2)$;
axis of symmetry: $x = 4$;
minimum: 2;
(b)

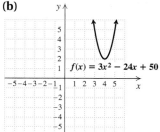

$f(x) = 3x^2 - 24x + 50$

39. (a) Vertex: $\left(\frac{5}{6}, \frac{1}{12}\right)$;
axis of symmetry: $x = \frac{5}{6}$;
maximum: $\frac{1}{12}$;
(b)

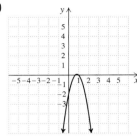

$$f(x) = -3x^2 + 5x - 2$$

41. (a) Vertex: $\left(-4, -\frac{5}{3}\right)$;
axis of symmetry: $x = -4$;
minimum: $-\frac{5}{3}$;
(b)

$$h(x) = \tfrac{1}{2}x^2 + 4x + \tfrac{19}{3}$$

43. $(3 - \sqrt{6}, 0), (3 + \sqrt{6}, 0); (0, 3)$ **45.** $(-1, 0), (3, 0);$
$(0, 3)$ **47.** $(0, 0), (9, 0); (0, 0)$ **49.** $(2, 0); (0, -4)$
51. $\left(-\frac{1}{2} - \frac{\sqrt{21}}{2}, 0\right), \left(-\frac{1}{2} + \frac{\sqrt{21}}{2}, 0\right); (0, -5)]$
53. No x-intercept; $(0, 6)$ **55.** ✍   **57.** $(1, 1, 1)$
58. $(-2, 5, 1)$ **59.** $(10, 5, 8)$ **60.** $(-3, 6, -5)$
61. $(2.4, -1.8, 1.5)$ **62.** $\left(\frac{1}{3}, \frac{1}{6}, \frac{1}{2}\right)$ **63.** ✍
65. (a) Minimum: -6.953660714; **(b)** $(-1.056433682, 0)$,
$(2.413576539, 0); (0, -5.89)$ **67. (a)** $-2.4, 3.4$;
(b) $-1.3, 2.3$ **69.** $f(x) = m\left(x - \dfrac{n}{2m}\right)^2 + \dfrac{4mp - n^2}{4m}$
71. $f(x) = \frac{5}{16}x^2 - \frac{15}{8}x - \frac{35}{16}$, or $f(x) = \frac{5}{16}(x - 3)^2 - 5$
73.

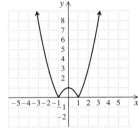

$$f(x) = |x^2 - 1|$$

75.

$$f(x) = |2(x - 3)^2 - 5|$$

Technology Connection, p. 619

1. About 607 million CDs

Exercise Set 9.8, pp. 620–625

1. (e)   **2. (b)**   **3. (c)**   **4. (a)**   **5. (d)**   **6. (f)**
7. $3\frac{1}{4}$ weeks; 8.3 lb of milk per day   **9.** $120/dulcimer;
350 dulcimers   **11.** 180 ft by 180 ft   **13.** 450 ft^2; 15 ft by 30 ft
(The house serves as a 30-ft side.)   **15.** 3.5 in.
17. 81; 9 and 9   **19.** -16; 4 and -4 **21.** 25; -5 and -5
23. $f(x) = ax^2 + bx + c, a < 0$ **25.** $f(x) = mx + b$
27. Neither quadratic nor linear
29. $f(x) = ax^2 + bx + c, a > 0$
31. $f(x) = ax^2 + bx + c, a > 0$ **33.** $f(x) = mx + b$
35. $f(x) = 2x^2 + 3x - 1$ **37.** $f(x) = -\frac{1}{4}x^2 + 3x - 5$
39. (a) $A(s) = \frac{3}{16}s^2 - \frac{135}{4}s + 1750$; **(b)** about 531 accidents

41. $h(d) = -0.0068d^2 + 0.8571d$ **43.** ✍
45. $\{x | x > 4\}$, or $(4, \infty)$ **46.** $\{x | x \geq -3\}$, or $[-3, \infty)$
47. $\{x | x \leq 7 \ or \ x \geq 11\}$, or $(-\infty, 7] \cup [11, \infty)$
48. $\left\{x \middle| -3 < x < \frac{5}{2}\right\}$, or $\left(-3, \frac{5}{2}\right)$
49. $\dfrac{-4x - 23}{x + 4}$ **50.** $\dfrac{1}{x - 1}$ **51.** $-\frac{23}{4}$ **52.** No solution
53. 0   **54.** $-6, 9$ **55.** ✍   **57.** 158 ft   **59.** $15
61. The radius of the circular portion of the window and
the height of the rectangular portion should each be $\dfrac{24}{\pi + 4}$ ft.
63. (a) $h(x) = 11,090.60714x^2 - 29,069.62143x + 39,983.8$;
(b) 858,348 vehicles

Technology Connection, p. 630

1. $\{x | -0.78 \leq x \leq 1.59\}$, or $[-0.78, 1.59]$
2. $\{x | x \leq -0.21 \ or \ x \geq 2.47\}$, or $(-\infty, -0.21] \cup [2.47, \infty)$
3. $\{x | x < -1.26 \ or \ x > 2.33\}$, or $(-\infty, -1.26) \cup (2.33, \infty)$
4. $\{x | x > -1.37\}$, or $(-1.37, \infty)$

Exercise Set 9.9, pp. 632–635

1. True   **2.** False   **3.** True   **4.** True   **5.** False
6. True   **7.** $\left[-4, \frac{3}{2}\right]$, or $\left\{x | -4 \leq x \leq \frac{3}{2}\right\}$
9. $(-\infty, -2) \cup (0, 2) \cup (3, \infty)$, or
$\{x | x < -2 \ or \ 0 < x < 2 \ or \ x > 3\}$
11. $\left(-\infty, -\frac{7}{2}\right) \cup (-2, \infty)$, or $\left\{x | x < -\frac{7}{2} \ or \ x > -2\right\}$
13. $(5, 6)$, or $\{x | 5 < x < 6\}$
15. $(-\infty, -7] \cup [2, \infty)$, or $\{x | x \leq -7 \ or \ x \geq 2\}$
17. $(-\infty, -1) \cup (2, \infty)$, or $\{x | x < -1 \ or \ x > 2\}$
19. $\varnothing$ **21.** $[2 - \sqrt{7}, 2 + \sqrt{7}]$, or
$\{x | 2 - \sqrt{7} \leq x \leq 2 + \sqrt{7}\}$ **23.** $(-\infty, -2) \cup (0, 2)$, or
$\{x | x < -2 \ or \ 0 < x < 2\}$ **25.** $[-2, 1] \cup [4, \infty)$, or
$\{x | -2 \leq x \leq 1 \ or \ x \geq 4\}$ **27.** $[-2, 2]$, or
$\{x | -2 \leq x \leq 2\}$ **29.** $(-1, 2) \cup (3, \infty)$, or
$\{x | -1 < x < 2 \ or \ x > 3\}$ **31.** $(-\infty, 0] \cup [2, 5]$, or
$\{x | x \leq 0 \ or \ 2 \leq x \leq 5\}$ **33.** $(-\infty, 5)$, or $\{x | x < 5\}$
35. $(-\infty, -1] \cup (3, \infty)$, or $\{x | x \leq -1 \ or \ x > 3\}$
37. $(-\infty, -6)$, or $\{x | x < -6\}$ **39.** $(-\infty, -1] \cup [2, 5)$, or
$\{x | x \leq -1 \ or \ 2 \leq x < 5\}$ **41.** $(-\infty, -3) \cup [0, \infty)$, or
$\{x | x < -3 \ or \ x \geq 0\}$ **43.** $(0, \infty)$, or $\{x | x > 0\}$
45. $(-\infty, -4) \cup [1, 3)$, or $\{x | x < -4 \ or \ 1 \leq x < 3\}$
47. $\left(-\frac{3}{4}, \frac{5}{2}\right]$, or $\left\{x | -\frac{3}{4} < x \leq \frac{5}{2}\right\}$ **49.** $(-\infty, 2) \cup [3, \infty)$, or
$\{x | x < 2 \ or \ x \geq 3\}$ **51.** ✍
53.

$$f(x) = x^3 - 2$$

54.

$$g(x) = \frac{2}{x}$$

55. $\dfrac{1}{a^2} + 7$ **56.** $a - 8$ **57.** $4a^2 + 20a + 27$

58. $\sqrt{12a - 19}$ **59.** ✍   **61.** $(-1 - \sqrt{6}, -1 + \sqrt{6})$, or $\{x | -1 - \sqrt{6} < x < -1 + \sqrt{6}\}$ **63.** $\{0\}$
65. (a) $(10, 200)$, or $\{x | 10 < x < 200\}$;
(b) $[0, 10) \cup (200, \infty)$, or $\{x | 0 \le x < 10 \, or \, x > 200\}$
67. $\{n | n \text{ is an integer } and \, 12 \le n \le 25\}$
69. $f(x) = 0$ for $x = -2, 1, 3$; $f(x) < 0$ for
$(-\infty, -2) \cup (1, 3)$, or $\{x | x < -2 \, or \, 1 < x < 3\}$; $f(x) > 0$
for $(-2, 1) \cup (3, \infty)$, or $\{x | -2 < x < 1 \, or \, x > 3\}$
71. $f(x)$ has no zeros; $f(x) < 0$ for $(-\infty, 0)$, or $\{x | x < 0\}$;
$f(x) > 0$ for $(0, \infty)$, or $\{x | x > 0\}$ **73.** $f(x) = 0$ for
$x = -1, 0$; $f(x) < 0$ for $(-\infty, -3) \cup (-1, 0)$, or
$\{x | x < -3 \, or -1 < x < 0\}$; $f(x) > 0$ for
$(-3, -1) \cup (0, 2) \cup (2, \infty)$, or
$\{x | -3 < x < -1 \, or \, 0 < x < 2 \, or \, x > 2\}$
75. $(-\infty, -5] \cup [9, \infty)$, or $\{x | x \le -5 \, or \, x \ge 9\}$
77. $(-\infty, -8] \cup [0, \infty)$, or $\{x | x \le -8 \, or \, x \ge 0\}$
79. ✍

Review Exercises: Chapter 9, pp. 638-639

1. False   **2.** True   **3.** True   **4.** True   **5.** False
6. True   **7.** True   **8.** True   **9.** False   **10.** True
11. $\pm \dfrac{\sqrt{2}}{3}$ **12.** $0, -\frac{3}{4}$ **13.** $3, 9$ **14.** $2 \pm 2i$ **15.** $3, 5$
16. $-\dfrac{9}{2} \pm \dfrac{\sqrt{85}}{2}$ **17.** $-0.372, 5.372$ **18.** $-\frac{1}{4}, 1$
19. $x^2 - 18x + 81 = (x - 9)^2$
20. $x^2 + \frac{3}{5}x + \frac{9}{100} = \left(x + \frac{3}{10}\right)^2$ **21.** $3 \pm 2\sqrt{2}$
22. 4%   **23.** 8.0 sec   **24.** Two irrational real numbers
25. Two imaginary numbers   **26.** $x^2 + 9 = 0$
27. $x^2 + 10x + 25 = 0$ **28.** About 153 mph   **29.** 6 hr
30. $(-3, 0), (-2, 0), (2, 0), (3, 0)$ **31.** $-5, 3$
32. $\pm\sqrt{2}, \pm\sqrt{7}$
33.

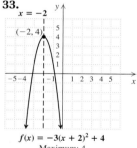

$f(x) = -3(x + 2)^2 + 4$
Maximum: 4

34. (a) Vertex: $(3, 5)$; axis of symmetry: $x = 3$;
(b)

35. $(2, 0), (7, 0)$; $(0, 14)$ **36.** $p = \dfrac{9\pi^2}{N^2}$

37. $T = \dfrac{1 \pm \sqrt{1 + 24A}}{6}$ **38.** Quadratic   **39.** Linear
40. 225 ft²; 15 ft by 15 ft   **41. (a)** $f(x) = -\frac{3}{8}x^2 + \frac{9}{4}x + 8$;
(b) about 10%   **42.** $(-1, 0) \cup (3, \infty)$, or
$\{x | -1 < x < 0 \, or \, x > 3\}$ **43.** $(-3, 5]$, or
$\{x | -3 < x \le 5\}$ **44.** ✍ The x-coordinate of the maximum or minimum point lies halfway between the
x-coordinates of the x-intercepts.   **45.** ✍ Yes; if the discriminant is a perfect square, then the solutions are rational
numbers, p/q and r/s. (Note that if the discriminant is 0,
then $p/q = r/s$.) Then the equation can be written in
factored form, $(qx - p)(sx - r) = 0$.   **46.** ✍ Four; let
$u = x^2$. Then $au^2 + bu + c = 0$ has at most two solutions,
$u = m$ and $u = n$. Now substitute x^2 for u and obtain
$x^2 = m$ or $x^2 = n$. These equations yield the solutions
$x = \pm\sqrt{m}$ and $x = \pm\sqrt{n}$. When $m \ne n$, the maximum
number of solutions, four, occurs.   **47.** ✍ Completing
the square was used to solve quadratic equations and to
graph quadratic functions by rewriting the function in the
form $f(x) = a(x - h)^2 + k$.   **48.** $f(x) = \frac{7}{15}x^2 - \frac{14}{15}x - 7$
49. $h = 60, k = 60$ **50.** $18, 324$

Test: Chapter 9, p. 640

1. [9.1] $\pm \dfrac{\sqrt{7}}{5}$ **2.** [9.1] $2, 9$ **3.** [9.2] $-1 \pm \sqrt{2}i$
4. [9.2] $1 \pm \sqrt{6}$ **5.** [9.5] $-2, \frac{2}{3}$ **6.** [9.2] $-4.193, 1.193$
7. [9.2] $-\frac{3}{4}, \frac{7}{3}$ **8.** [9.1] $x^2 - 20x + 100 = (x - 10)^2$
9. [9.1] $x^2 + \frac{2}{7}x + \frac{1}{49} = \left(x + \frac{1}{7}\right)^2$ **10.** [9.1] $-5 \pm \sqrt{10}$
11. [9.3] Two imaginary numbers   **12.** [9.3] $x^2 - 11 = 0$
13. [9.4] 16 km/h   **14.** [9.4] 2 hr   **15.** [9.5] $(-4, 0), (4, 0)$
16. [9.6]   **17.** [9.7] **(a)** $(-1, -8), x = -1$;
(b)

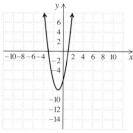

$f(x) = 4(x - 3)^2 + 5$
Minimum: 5

$f(x) = 2x^2 + 4x - 6$

18. [9.7] $(-2, 0), (3, 0)$; $(0, -6)$ **19.** [9.4] $r = \sqrt{\dfrac{3V}{\pi} - R^2}$
20. [9.8] Quadratic   **21.** [9.8] Minimum: \$129/cabinet
when 325 cabinets are built   **22.** [9.8] $f(x) = \frac{1}{5}x^2 - \frac{3}{5}x$
23. [9.9] $(-6, 1)$, or $\{x | -6 < x < 1\}$
24. [9.9] $[-1, 0) \cup [1, \infty)$, or $\{x | -1 \le x < 0 \, or \, x \ge 1\}$
25. [9.3] $\frac{1}{2}$ **26.** [11.3] $x^4 + x^2 - 12 = 0$; answers may vary
27. [9.5] $\pm\sqrt{\sqrt{5} + 2}, \pm\sqrt{\sqrt{5} - 2}i$

Cumulative Review: Chapters 1-9, pp. 641-642

1. 24   **2.** $\dfrac{3a^{10}c^7}{4}$ **3.** $14x^2y - 10xy - 9xy^2$
4. $81p^4q^2 - 64t^2$ **5.** $\dfrac{t(t + 1)(t + 5)}{(3t + 4)^3}$ **6.** $-\dfrac{3}{x + 4}$

7. $3x^2\sqrt[3]{4y^2}$ **8.** $13 - \sqrt{2}i$
9. $3(2x^2 + 5y^2)(2x^2 - 5y^2)$ **10.** $x(x - 20)(x - 4)$
11. $100(m + 1)(m^2 - m + 1)(m - 1)(m^2 + m + 1)$
12. $(2t + 9)(3t + 4)$ **13.** 7 **14.** $\{x|x < 7\}$, or $(-\infty, 7)$
15. $\left(3, \frac{1}{2}\right)$ **16.** $-6, 11$ **17.** $\frac{1}{2}, 2$ **18.** 4 **19.** $-5 \pm \sqrt{2}$
20. $\frac{1}{6} \pm \frac{\sqrt{11}}{6}i$

21.

22.

23.

24.

25. $y = -5x + \frac{1}{2}$ **26.** $-\frac{7}{10}$ **27.** 21
28. $(-\infty, 10]$, or $\{x|x \leq 10\}$
29. $\{x | x \text{ is a real number } and x \neq 4\}$, or $(-\infty, 4) \cup (4, \infty)$
30. $a = \frac{c}{2b - 1}$ **31.** $t = \frac{4r}{3p^2}$ **32.** **(a)** \$4.53 billion;
(b) 2015 **33.** **(a)** $h(t) = 33t - 47$; **(b)** 283,000 hotspots;
(c) about 2017 **34.** **(a)** 1.74 oz; **(b)** \$600 per ounce;
(c) 75% **35.** Number tiles: 26 sets; alphabet tiles: 10 sets
36. \$125/bunk bed; 400 bunk beds
37. Deanna: 12 hr; Donna: 6 hr
38. 9 km/h **39.** Mileages no greater than 50 mi
40. $\frac{1}{3} \pm \frac{\sqrt{2}}{6}i$ **41.** $\{0\}$ **42.** $f(x) = x + 1$
43. $(1 - \sqrt{6}, 16 - 10\sqrt{6}), (1 + \sqrt{6}, 16 + 10\sqrt{6})$

APPENDIXES

Exercise Set A, pp. 647–648

1. Mean: 17; median: 18; mode: 13 **3.** Mean: $10.\overline{6}$;
median: 9; mode: 3, 20 **5.** Mean: 4.06; median: 4.6;
mode: none **7.** Mean: $239.\overline{3}$; median: 234; mode: 234
9. Average: 34.875; median: 22; mode: 0 **11.** Mean: 87.25;
median: 86.5; mode: 86 **13.** Average: $218.\overline{3}$; median: 222;
mode: 202 **15.** 10 home runs **17.** $a = 30, b = 58$

Exercise Set B, pp. 651–652

1. $\{8, 9, 10, 11\}$ **3.** $\{41, 43, 45, 47, 49\}$ **5.** $\{-3, 3\}$
7. True **9.** True **11.** False **13.** True **15.** False
17. True **19.** $\{c, d, e\}$ **21.** $\{1, 2, 3, 6\}$ **23.** $\varnothing$
25. $\{a, e, i, o, u, q, c, k\}$ **27.** $\{1, 2, 3, 4, 6, 9, 12, 18\}$
29. $\{1, 2, 3, 4, 5, 6, 7, 8\}$ **31.** **33.** The set of integers
35. The set of real numbers **37.** $\varnothing$ **39.** **(a)** A; **(b)** A;
(c) A; **(d)** $\varnothing$ **41.** True **43.** True **45.** True

Exercise Set C, pp. 655–656

1. True **2.** True **3.** True **4.** False **5.** True
6. False **7.** $x^2 - 3x - 5$ **9.** $a + 5 + \frac{-4}{a + 3}$
11. $2x^2 - 5x + 3 + \frac{8}{x + 2}$ **13.** $a^2 + 2a - 6$
15. $3y^2 + 2y + 6 + \frac{-2}{y - 3}$
17. $x^4 + 2x^3 + 4x^2 + 8x + 16$
19. $3x^2 + 6x - 3 + \frac{2}{x + \frac{1}{3}}$ **21.** 6 **23.** 125 **25.** 0
27. **29.**
31. **(a)** The degree of R must be less than 1, the degree of
$x - r$; **(b)** Let $x = r$. Then
$$P(r) = (r - r) \cdot Q(r) + R$$
$$= 0 \cdot Q(r) + R$$
$$= R.$$
33. $0; -3, -\frac{5}{2}, \frac{3}{2}$ **35.** **37.** 0

Glossary

A

Absolute value The distance that a number is from 0 on the number line.

Additive inverse A number's opposite. Two numbers are additive inverses of each other if their sum is zero.

Algebraic expression A collection of numerals and/or variables on which the operations $+$, $-$, $\cdot$, $\div$, $(\ )^n$, or $\sqrt[n]{(\ )}$ are performed.

Arithmetic sequence A sequence in which the difference between any two successive terms is constant.

Arithmetic series A series for which the associated sequence is arithmetic.

Ascending order A polynomial written with the terms arranged according to degree of one variable, from least to greatest.

Associative law of addition The statement that when three numbers are added, regrouping the addends gives the same sum.

Associative law of multiplication The statement that when three numbers are multiplied, regrouping the factors gives the same product.

Asymptote A line that a graph approaches more and more closely as x increases or as x decreases.

Average [1.7] Most commonly, the mean of a set of numbers found by adding the numbers and dividing by the number of addends.

Axes (singular, axis) [2.1] Two perpendicular number lines used to identify points in a plane.

Axis of symmetry [9.6] A line that can be drawn through a graph such that the part of the graph on one side of the line is an exact reflection of the part on the opposite side.

B

Bar graph [2.1] A graphic display of data using bars proportional in length to the numbers represented.

Base In exponential notation, the number or expression being raised to a power. In expressions of the form a^n, a is the base.

Binomial A polynomial composed of two terms.

Branches The two curves that comprise a hyperbola.

Break-even point [6.8] In business, the point of intersection of the revenue function and the cost function.

C

Circle A set of points in a plane that are a fixed distance r, called the radius, from a fixed point (h, k), called the center.

Circle graph [2.1] A graphic display of data using sectors of a circle to represent percents.

Circumference [1.3] The distance around a circle.

Closed interval [a, b] [1.6] The set of all numbers x for which $a \leq x \leq b$. Thus, $[a, b] = \{x | a \leq x \leq b\}$.

Coefficient [1.1] The numerical multiplier of a variable or variables.

Combined variation [5.5] A mathematical relationship in which a variable varies directly and/or inversely, at the same time, with more than one other variable.

Common logarithm A logarithm with base 10.

Commutative law of addition The statement that when two numbers are added, changing the order in which the numbers are added does not affect the sum.

Commutative law of multiplication The statement that when two numbers are multiplied, changing the order in which the numbers are multiplied does not affect the product.

Complementary angles [1.5] A pair of angles, the sum of whose measures is 90°.

Completing the square [9.1] The procedure in which one adds a particular constant to an expression so that the resulting sum is a perfect square.

Complex number [8.8] Any number that can be written as $a + bi$, where a and b are real numbers and $i = \sqrt{-1}$.

Complex rational expression [4.5] A rational expression that has one or more rational expressions within its numerator and/or denominator.

Complex-number system [8.8] A number system that contains the real-number system and is designed so that negative numbers have defined square roots.

Composite function A function in which a quantity depends on a variable that, in turn, depends on another variable.

Composite number A natural number, other than 1, that is not prime.

Compound inequality [7.2] A statement in which two or more inequalities are combined using the word *and* or the word *or.*

Compound interest [9.1]   Interest computed on the sum of an original principal and the interest previously accrued by that principal.

Conditional equation [1.2]   An equation that is true for some replacements of a variable(s) and false for others.

Conic section   A curve formed by the intersection of a plane and a cone.

Conjugates [8.5], [8.8]   Pairs of radical expressions, like $a\sqrt{b} + c\sqrt{d}$ and $a\sqrt{b} - c\sqrt{d}$, for which the product does not have a radical term or pairs of imaginary numbers, like $a + bi$ and $a - bi$, for which the product is real.

Conjunction [7.2]   A sentence in which two statements are joined by the word *and*.

Consecutive numbers [1.5]   Integers that are one unit apart.

Consistent system of equations [6.1], [6.4]   A system of equations that has at least one solution.

Constant   A known number.

Constant function [5.3]   A function given by an equation of the form $f(x) = b$, where b is a real number.

Constant of proportionality [5.5]   The constant in an equation of variation.

Constraint [7.5]   A requirement imposed on a problem.

Contradiction [1.2]   An equation that is never true.

Coordinates [2.1]   The numbers in an ordered pair.

Cube root [8.1]   The number c is called the cube root of a if $c^3 = a$.

D

Data point [9.8]   A given ordered pair of a function, usually found experimentally.

Degree of a polynomial   The degree of the term of highest degree in a polynomial.

Degree of a term   The number of variable factors in a term.

Demand function [6.8]   A function modeling the relationship between the price of a good and the quantity of that good demanded.

Denominator [4.1]   The number below the fraction bar in a fraction or the expression below the fraction bar in a rational expression.

Dependent equations [6.1]   Equations in a system from which one equation can be removed without changing the solution set.

Descending order   A polynomial written with the terms arranged according to degree of one variable, from greatest to least.

Determinant [6.7]   A descriptor of a square matrix. The determinant of a two-by-two matrix $\begin{bmatrix} a & c \\ b & d \end{bmatrix}$ is denoted $\begin{vmatrix} a & c \\ b & d \end{vmatrix}$ and represents $ad - bc$.

Difference of squares [3.4]   An expression that can be written in the form $A^2 - B^2$.

Direct variation [5.5]   A situation that translates to an equation of the form $y = kx$, with k a nonzero constant.

Discriminant [9.3]   The expression $b^2 - 4ac$ from the quadratic formula.

Disjunction [7.2]   A sentence in which two statements are joined by the word *or*.

Distributive law   The statement that multiplying a factor by the sum of two addends gives the same result as multiplying the factor by each of the two addends and then adding.

Domain [5.2]   The set of all first coordinates of the ordered pairs in a function.

Doubling time   The time necessary for a population to double in size.

E

e   An irrational number that is approximately 2.7182818284, which is used in many applications.

Element [6.6]   An entry in a matrix.

Elimination method [6.2]   An algebraic method that uses the addition principle to solve a system of equations.

Ellipse   The set of all points in a plane for which the sum of the distances from two fixed points F_1 and F_2, called foci, is constant.

Equation   A number sentence with the verb $=$.

Equation of variation [5.5]   An equation used to represent direct, inverse, or combined variation.

Equilibrium point [6.8]   The point of intersection between the demand function and the supply function.

Equivalent equations [1.1]   Equations with the same solutions.

Equivalent expressions   Expressions that have the same value for all allowable replacements.

Equivalent inequalities [1.6]   Inequalities that have the same solution set.

Evaluate   To substitute a value for each occurrence of a variable in an expression and calculate the result.

Exponent   The power to which a base is raised. In expressions of the form a^n, the number n is an exponent. For n a natural number, a^n represents n factors of a.

Exponential decay   A decrease in quantity over time that can be modeled by an exponential equation of the form $P(t) = P_0 e^{-kt}, k > 0$.

Exponential equation   An equation in which a variable appears in an exponent.

Exponential function   A function that can be described by an exponential equation.

Exponential growth   An increase in quantity over time that can be modeled by an exponential function of the form $P(t) = P_0 e^{kt}, k > 0$.

Exponential notation   A representation of a number using a base raised to a power.

Extrapolation [2.7]   The process of predicting a future value on the basis of given data.

F

Factor   *Verb*: to write an equivalent expression that is a product. *Noun*: a multiplier.

Finite sequence   A function having for its domain a set of natural numbers: $\{1, 2, 3, 4, 5, \ldots, n\}$, for some natural number n.

Fixed costs [6.8]   In business, costs that are incurred regardless of how many items are produced.

Focus (plural, foci)   One of two fixed points that determine the points of an ellipse or a hyperbola.

FOIL   An acronym for a procedure for multiplying two binomials by multiplying the First terms, the Outer terms, the Inner terms, and the Last terms, and then adding the results.

Formula [1.3]   An equation that uses numbers and/or letters to represent a relationship between two or more quantities.

Fraction notation   A number written using a numerator and a denominator.

Function [5.1]   A correspondence that assigns to each member of a set called the domain exactly one member of a set called the range.

G

General term of a sequence   The nth term, denoted a_n.

Geometric sequence   A sequence in which the ratio of every pair of successive terms is constant.

Geometric series   A series for which the associated sequence is geometric.

Grade [2.5]   The ratio of the vertical distance a road rises over the horizontal distance it runs, expressed as a percent.

Graph [2.1]   A picture or diagram of the data in a table, or a line, a curve, a plane, or collection of points, etc., that represents all the solutions of an equation or an inequality.

H

Half-life   The amount of time necessary for half of a quantity to decay.

Half-open interval [1.6]   An interval that includes exactly one endpoint.

Horizontal-line test   The statement that if it is impossible to draw a horizontal line that intersects the graph of a function more than once, then that function is one-to-one.

Hyperbola   The set of all points P in the plane such that the difference of the distance from P to two fixed points is constant.

Hypotenuse [3.8]   In a right triangle, the side opposite the right angle.

I

i [8.8]   The square root of -1. That is, $i = \sqrt{-1}$ and $i^2 = -1$.

Identity [1.2]   An equation that is always true.

Identity property of 0   The statement that the sum of a number and 0 is always the original number.

Identity property of 1   The statement that the product of a number and 1 is always the original number.

Imaginary number [8.8]   A number that can be written in the form $a + bi$, where a and b are real numbers and $b \neq 0$ and $i = \sqrt{-1}$.

Inconsistent system of equations [6.1]   A system of equations for which there is no solution.

Independent equations [6.1]   Equations that are not dependent.

Index (plural, indices) [8.1]   In the radical $\sqrt[n]{a}$, the number n is called the index.

Inequality   A mathematical sentence using $<, >, \leq, \geq$, or $\neq$.

Infinite geometric series   The sum of the terms of an infinite geometric sequence.

Infinite sequence   A function having for its domain the set of natural numbers: $\{1, 2, 3, 4, 5, \ldots\}$.

Input [5.1]   A member of the domain of a function.

Integers   The whole numbers and their opposites.

Interpolation [2.7]   The process of estimating a value between given values.

Intersection of two sets [7.2]   The set of all elements that are common to both sets.

Interval notation [1.6]   The use of a pair of numbers inside parentheses and/or brackets to represent the set of all numbers between those two numbers. *See also* Closed, Open, and Half-open intervals.

Inverse relation   The relation formed by interchanging the members of the domain and the range of a relation.

Inverse variation [5.5]   A situation that translates to an equation of the form $y = k/x$, with k a nonzero constant.

Irrational number   A real number that cannot be named as a ratio of two integers. In decimal notation, irrational numbers neither terminate nor repeat.

Isosceles right triangle [8.7]   A right triangle in which both legs have the same length.

J

Joint variation [5.5]   A situation that translates to an equation of the form $y = kxz$, with k a nonzero constant.

L

Largest common factor [3.1]   The common factor of the terms of a polynomial with the largest possible coefficient and the largest possible exponent(s).

Leading coefficient   The coefficient of the term of highest degree in a polynomial.

Leading term   The term of highest degree in a polynomial.

Least common denominator (LCD) [4.3]   The least common multiple of the denominators of two or more rational expressions.

Least common multiple (LCM) [4.3] The multiple of all expressions under consideration that has the smallest positive coefficient and the least possible degree.

Legs [3.8] In a right triangle, the two sides that form the right angle.

Like radicals [8.5] Radical expressions that have identical indices and radicands.

Like terms Terms that have exactly the same variable factors.

Line graph [2.1] A graph in which quantities are represented as points connected by straight-line segments.

Linear equation [2.2], [6.4] In two variables, any equation that can be written in the form $y = mx + b$, or $Ax + By = C$, where x and y are variables and m, b, A, B, and C are constants and A and B are not both 0. In three variables, an equation that is equivalent to one of the form $Ax + By + Cz = D$, where x, y, and z are variables, and A, B, and C are constants that are not all 0.

Linear function [5.3] A function that can be described by an equation of the form $f(x) = mx + b$, where m and b are constants.

Linear inequality [7.4] An inequality whose related equation is a linear equation.

Linear programming [7.5] A branch of mathematics involving graphs of inequalities and their constraints.

Logarithmic equation An equation containing a logarithmic expression.

Logarithmic function, base a The inverse of an exponential function with base a.

M

Matrix (plural, matrices) [6.6] A rectangular array of numbers.

Maximum value [9.6] The greatest function value (output) achieved by a function.

Mean [1.7] The sum of a set of numbers divided by the number of addends.

Minimum value [9.6] The least function value (output) achieved by a function.

Monomial A constant, a variable, or a product of a constant and one or more variables.

Motion problem [4.7] A problem that deals with distance, speed, and time.

Multiplicative inverses Reciprocals; two numbers whose product is 1.

Multiplicative property of zero The statement that the product of 0 and any real number is 0.

N

Natural logarithm A logarithm with base e.

Natural numbers The counting numbers: 1, 2, 3, 4, 5, ...

Nonlinear function [5.3] A function whose graph is not a straight line.

Numerator [4.1] The number above the fraction bar in a fraction or the expression above the fraction bar in a rational expression.

O

Objective function [7.5] In linear programming, the function in which the expression being maximized or minimized appears.

One-to-one function A function for which all different inputs have different outputs.

Open interval (a, b) [1.6] The set of all numbers x for which $a < x < b$. Thus, $(a, b) = \{x | a < x < b\}$.

Opposite The additive inverse of a number. Opposites are the same distance from 0 on the number line but on different sides of 0.

Ordered pair [2.1] A pair of numbers of the form (h, k) for which the order in which the numbers are listed is important.

Origin [2.1] The point on a graph in a coordinate plane where the two axes intersect.

Output [5.1] A member of the range of a function.

P

Parabola [9.6] A graph of a second degree polynomial equation in one variable.

Parallel lines [2.6] Lines that extend indefinitely without intersecting.

Pascal's triangle A triangular array of coefficients of the expansion $(a + b)^n$ for $n = 0, 1, 2, \ldots$.

Perfect square [8.1] A rational number for which there exists a number a for which $a^2 = p$.

Perfect-square trinomial [3.4] A trinomial that is the square of a binomial.

Perpendicular lines [2.6] Lines that intersect at a right angle.

Piecewise function [5.2] A function that is defined by different equations for various parts of its domain.

Point–slope equation [2.7] An equation of the type $y - y_1 = m(x - x_1)$, where x and y are variables, and m is the slope of the line and (x_1, y_1) is a point on the line.

Polynomial A monomial or a sum of monomials.

Polynomial equation [3.7] An equation in which two polynomials are set equal to each other.

Polynomial inequality [9.9] An inequality that is equivalent to an inequality with a polynomial as one side and 0 as the other.

Price [6.8] The amount a purchaser pays for an item.

Prime factorization The factorization of a natural number into a product of its prime factors.

Prime number A natural number that has exactly two different natural number factors: the number itself and 1.

Principal square root [8.1]   The nonnegative square root of a number.

Proportion [4.7]   An equation stating that two ratios are equal.

Pure imaginary number [8.8]   A complex number of the form $a + bi$, with $a = 0$ and $b \neq 0$.

Pythagorean theorem [3.8]   The theorem that states that in any right triangle, if a and b are the lengths of the legs and c is the length of the hypotenuse, then $a^2 + b^2 = c^2$.

Q

Quadrants [2.1]   The four regions into which the axes divide a plane.

Quadratic equation [3.7]   An equation equivalent to one of the form $ax^2 + bx + c = 0$, where $a \neq 0$.

Quadratic formula [9.2] $x = \dfrac{-b \pm \sqrt{b^2 - 4ac}}{2a}$, which gives the solutions of $ax^2 + bx + c = 0$, where $a \neq 0$.

Quadratic function [9.1]   A second-degree polynomial function in one variable.

Quadratic inequality [9.9]   A second-degree polynomial inequality in one variable.

R

Radical equation [8.6]   An equation in which a variable appears in a radicand.

Radical expression [8.1]   An algebraic expression in which a radical sign appears.

Radical sign [8.1]   The symbol $\sqrt{}$ or $\sqrt[n]{}$, where $n > 2$.

Radical term [8.5]   A term in which a radical sign appears.

Radicand [8.1]   The expression under a radical sign.

Radius (plural, radii)   The distance from the center of a circle to a point on the circle. Also, a segment connecting the center to a point on the circle.

Range [5.2]   The set of all second coordinates of the ordered pairs in a function.

Rate [2.4]   A ratio that indicates how two quantities change with respect to each other.

Ratio [4.7]   The quotient of two quantities. The ratio of a to b is a/b, also written $a:b$.

Rational equation [4.6]   An equation containing one or more rational expressions.

Rational expression [4.1]   A quotient of two polynomials.

Rational inequality [9.9]   An inequality containing a rational expression.

Rational number   A number that can be written in the form $\dfrac{a}{b}$, where a and b are integers and $b \neq 0$. In decimal notation, a rational number repeats or terminates.

Rationalizing the denominator [8.4], [8.5]   A procedure for finding an equivalent expression without a radical in its denominator.

Rationalizing the numerator [8.4], [8.5]   A procedure for finding an equivalent expression without a radical in its numerator.

Real number   Any number that is either rational or irrational.

Reciprocal   A multiplicative inverse. Two numbers are reciprocals if their product is 1.

Reflection [9.6]   The mirror image of a graph.

Relation [5.1]   A correspondence between two sets, called the domain and the range, such that each member of the domain corresponds to at least one member of the range.

Repeating decimal   A decimal in which a block of digits repeats indefinitely.

Right triangle [3.8]   A triangle that includes a right angle.

Row-equivalent operations [6.6]   Operations used to produce equivalent systems of equations.

S

Scientific notation   A number written in the form $N \times 10^m$, where m is an integer, $1 \leq N < 10$, and N is expressed in decimal notation.

Sequence   A function for which the domain is a set of consecutive natural numbers beginning with 1.

Series   The sum of specified terms in a sequence.

Set   A collection of objects.

Set-builder notation [1.6]   The naming of a set by describing basic characteristics of the elements in the set.

Sigma notation   The naming of a sum using the Greek letter Σ (sigma) as part of an abbreviated form.

Similar triangles [8.7]   Triangles in which corresponding sides are proportional and corresponding angles have the same measure.

Simplify   To rewrite an expression in an equivalent, abbreviated, form.

Slope [2.5]   The ratio of the rise to the run for any two points on a line.

Slope–intercept equation [2.6]   An equation of the form $y = mx + b$, where x and y are variables, m is the slope of the line, and $(0, b)$ is its y-intercept.

Solution [1.1], [1.6], [6.1]   A replacement or substitution that makes an equation, an inequality, or a system of equations or inequalities true.

Solution set [1.1], [1.6], [6.1]   The set of all solutions of an equation, an inequality, or a system of equations or inequalities.

Solve [1.1], [1.6], [6.1]   To find all solutions of an equation, an inequality, or a system of equations or inequalities; to find the solution(s) of a problem.

Speed [4.7]   The ratio of distance traveled to the time required to travel that distance.

Square matrix [6.7]   A matrix with the same number of rows and columns.

Square root [8.1]   The number c is a square root of a if $c^2 = a$.

Substitute   To replace a variable with a number or an expression that represents a number.

Substitution method [6.2]   An algebraic method for solving systems of equations.

Supplementary angles [1.5]   A pair of angles, the sum of whose measure is 180°.

Supply function [6.8]   A function modeling the relationship between the price of a good and the quantity of that good supplied.

System of equations [6.1]   A set of two or more equations that are to be solved simultaneously.

T

Term   A number, a variable, or a product or a quotient of numbers and/or variables.

Terminating decimal   A number in decimal notation that can be written using a finite number of decimal places.

Total cost [6.8]   The amount spent to produce a product.

Total profit [6.8]   The amount taken in less the amount spent, or total revenue minus total cost.

Total revenue [6.8]   The amount taken in from the sale of a product.

Trinomial   A polynomial that is composed of three terms.

U

Undefined   An expression that has no meaning attached to it.

Union of A and B [7.2]   The set of all elements belonging to either A or B or both.

V

Value   The numerical result after a number has been substituted into an expression.

Variable   A letter that represents an unknown number.

Variable costs [6.8]   In business, costs that vary according to the amount produced.

Variable expression   An expression containing a variable.

Vertex (plural, vertices) [9.6]   The point at which the graph of a parabola, an ellipse, or a hyperbola crosses its axis of symmetry.

Vertical-line test [5.1]   The statement that a graph represents a function if it is impossible to draw a vertical line that intersects the graph more than once.

W

Whole numbers   The natural numbers and 0: 0, 1, 2, 3, . . .

X

x-intercept [2.3]   A point at which a graph crosses the x-axis.

Y

y-intercept [2.3]   A point at which a graph crosses the y-axis.

Z

Zeros [9.9]   The x-values for which $f(x)$ is 0, for any function f.

Index

Index of Applications

Geometric Formulas

Plane Geometry

Rectangle
Area: $A = lw$
Perimeter: $P = 2l + 2w$

Square
Area: $A = s^2$
Perimeter: $P = 4s$

Triangle
Area: $A = \frac{1}{2}bh$

Triangle
Sum of Angle Measures:
$A + B + C = 180°$

Right Triangle
Pythagorean Theorem
(Equation):
$a^2 + b^2 = c^2$

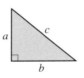

Parallelogram
Area: $A = bh$

Trapezoid
Area: $A = \frac{1}{2}h(b_1 + b_2)$

Circle
Area: $A = \pi r^2$
Circumference:
$C = \pi d = 2\pi r$
$\left(\frac{22}{7} \text{ and } 3.14 \text{ are different}\right.$
approximations for $\pi$$\left.\right)$

Solid Geometry

Rectangular Solid
Volume: $V = lwh$

Cube
Volume: $V = s^3$

Right Circular Cylinder
Volume: $V = \pi r^2 h$
Total Surface Area:
$S = 2\pi rh + 2\pi r^2$

Right Circular Cone
Volume: $V = \frac{1}{3}\pi r^2 h$
Total Surface Area:
$S = \pi r^2 + \pi rs$
Slant Height:
$s = \sqrt{r^2 + h^2}$

Sphere
Volume: $V = \frac{4}{3}\pi r^3$
Surface Area: $S = 4\pi r^2$

Selected Keys of the Scientific Calculator

This secondary function takes the square root of number displayed.

Squares number displayed.

Activates secondary functions printed above certain keys. Also denoted INV or 2nd.

Used when entering numbers in scientific notation. Also denoted EXP.

Finds reciprocal of number displayed.

Used to raise any base to a power. Also denoted y^x, a^x, or $\wedge$.

Stores number displayed in memory. Also denoted MIN or M.

Recalls number stored in memory. Also denoted MR.

This secondary function raises 10 to any power entered.

Clears all preceding numbers and operations. Also used to turn calculator on.

Used as an approximation for pi.

Used to perform indicated operation.

Used to control order in which certain operations are performed.

Clears last number displayed but not preceding operations.

Used when entering decimal notation.

Used to change sign of number displayed.